D0895287

Manual of
Steel Construction

Manual of

STEEL CONSTRUCTION

SEVENTH EDITION

First Revised Printing

American Institute of Steel Construction, Inc.

1221 Avenue of the Americas

New York, N.Y. 10020

First Revised Printing, Tenth Impression (4/79)

Printed in the United States of America

FOREWORD

The American Institute of Steel Construction, founded in 1921, is the non-profit technical specifying and trade organization for the fabricated structural steel industry in the United States.   Executive and engineering headquarters of AISC are maintained in New York City.   Regional offices are located throughout the country.

The Institute is supported by three classes of membership: Active Members totaling 325 companies engaged in the fabrication and erection of structural steel, Associate Members who are allied product manufacturers, and Professional Members who are individuals or firms engaged in the practice of architecture or engineering.   Professional Members also include architectural and engineering educators.   The continuing financial support and active participation of Active Members in the engineering, research and development activities of the Institute make possible the publishing of this *Manual of Steel Construction*.

The Institute's objectives are to improve and advance the use of fabricated structural steel through research and engineering studies to develop the most efficient and economical design of structures.   It also conducts programs to improve and control product quality.

To accomplish these objectives the Institute publishes manuals, textbooks, specifications, and technical booklets.   Best known and most widely used is the *Manual of Steel Construction* which holds a unique position in engineering literature.   Outstanding among AISC standards are the *Specification for the Design, Fabrication and Erection of Structural Steel for Buildings* and the *Code of Standard Practice for Steel Buildings and Bridges*.

The Institute also assists designers, contractors, educators, and others by publishing technical information and timely articles on structural applications through two quarterly publications: *Engineering Journal* and *Modern Steel Construction*.   In addition, public appreciation of aesthetically designed structures is encouraged through its annual award programs, Prize Bridges, Architectural Awards of Excellence, and student Fellowship Awards.

Recognizing the merits of personal contact in presenting the most advanced engineering information available to the technical professions, the Institute conducts a continuing program of seminars, educational lectures, and individual calls to render competent advisory services, without cost, to those interested or engaged in steel construction.

The Institute does not prepare engineering plans.   While every precaution is taken to insure that all data and information furnished are as accurate as possible, and while our engineers endeavor to supplement these data by conference and advice, the Institute cannot assume responsibility for errors or oversights in the use of such information or in the preparation of engineering plans.

PREFACE TO FIRST REVISED PRINTING

In Part 1, Table 3 (listing the principal producers of structural steel shapes and the range of sizes available) has been updated.

In Part 4, the discussion on Moment Connections has been modified.

In Part 5, Supplement Nos. 1 and 2 to the AISC Specification have been added and the current editions of the Code of Standard Practice, Specification for Structural Joints Using ASTM A325 or A490 Bolts, and the Standard Specifications and Load Tables for Steel Joists have been included. The Summary of ASTM Specifications and the Excerpts from ANSI A58.1 Minimum Design Loads have been revised to agree with the latest editions.

American Institute of Steel Construction

June 1973

PREFACE TO SEVENTH EDITION

The first AISC *Steel Construction Manual* was published in 1926; since then several editions have been issued. While only seven years have elapsed since the first printing of the Sixth Edition in 1963, the rapid technological progress and improvement in both steel manufacturing and fabrication practices culminated in a revision of the AISC *Specification for the Design, Fabrication and Erection of Structural Steel for Buildings*, dated February 12, 1969. These developments created the need for a new edition of the Manual — the Seventh.

Historically, this seven-year interval of elapsed time was marked by the withdrawal of the common grade of structural steel, ASTM A7, a material specification that has been fundamental to steel construction since the beginning of this century. ASTM A36 structural steel, with greater yield strength and improved qualities for modern fabrication, has become the commonly used grade of steel, but not exclusively.

Newer grades of high strength steels, with yield strengths ranging up to 100 kips per square inch, have been approved for use in construction as contrasted to the 50 kips per square inch limitation found in the Sixth Edition Manual. This advance in strength levels required inclusion of additional design and detailing information on new higher strength fasteners and welding electrodes in the Seventh Edition.

A new system of designations of structural shapes has been adopted by the steel industry, and the tables of dimensions and properties of rolled shapes have been adjusted. Although these changes are not drastic, they nevertheless will have a significant influence on design, detailing, and ordering as a complete transition to the new industry standards is attained. As a matter of explanation, the change in nomenclature reflects the requirements for efficient computerization of many operations through standardization, and the change in dimensions and properties is based on a recent survey and standardization achieved by the several structural rolling mills.

To satisfy the demand for listing of many additional useful design constants, the tables "Properties for designing" have been extended across two pages. The accompanying tables "Dimensions for detailing" appear separately in an adjoining section.

To cite the many changes made to introduce new material and design aids, and to enumerate the deletion of data no longer conforming to current design and fabrication practices, would be impractical. Suffice to state that many pages have been added and over two-thirds of the pages of the former Sixth Edition have been revised.

The Seventh Edition Manual was produced under the guidance of the AISC Manual Committee made up of experienced and knowledgeable engineers of member fabricator companies. The actual work extending over many months was performed by 20 engineers on the AISC staff. The valuable assistance furnished by the principal mill producers in assembling data and in generating many of the load tables by electronic computers is gratefully acknowledged.

American Institute of Steel Construction

June 1973

GENERAL NOMENCLATURE

A Cross-sectional area (sq. in.).

Area of beam or column base plate (sq. in.).

A_b Nominal body area of a fastener (sq. in.).

A_c Actual area of effective concrete flange in composite design (sq. in.).

A_{bc} Planar area of web at beam-to-column connection (sq. in.).

A_f Area of compression flange (sq. in.).

A_s Total area of steel section including cover plate in composite design (sq. in.).

A_{sr} Area of reinforcing steel providing composite action at point of negative moment (sq. in.).

A_{st} Cross-sectional area of stiffener or pair of stiffeners (sq. in.).

A_w Area of girder web (sq. in.).

B The bending factor for determining the equivalent axial load in square and circular shaped columns; equals A/S.

Width of beam or column base plate (in.).

B_x Bending factor with respect to the X-X axis and Y-Y axis, respec-
B_y tively, for determining the equivalent axial load in columns subjected to combined loading conditions; equal to A/S_x and A/S_y, respectively.

C Ratio of bolt tensile strength to tensile strength of connected part.

Coefficient for determining permissible loads in kips for eccentrically loaded connections.

C_a Coefficient used in Table 1-A of AISC Specification, Appendix A.

C_b Bending coefficient dependent upon moment gradient; equal to

$$1.75 + 1.05 \left(\frac{M_1}{M_2}\right) + 0.3 \left(\frac{M_1}{M_2}\right)^2$$

C_c Column slenderness ratio dividing elastic and inelastic buckling; equal to

$$\sqrt{\frac{2\pi^2 E}{F_y}}, \quad \text{except in Appendix C}$$

C_c' Column slenderness ratio dividing elastic and inelastic buckling, modified to account for effective width of wide compression elements; equal to

$$C_c \frac{1}{\sqrt{Q_a}} \quad \text{or} \quad C_c \frac{1}{\sqrt{Q_s}} \quad \text{or} \quad C_c \frac{1}{\sqrt{Q_a Q_s}}$$

C_m Coefficient applied to bending term in interaction formula and dependent upon column curvature caused by applied moments.

C_p Stiffness factor for primary member in a flat roof.

C_s Stiffness factor of secondary member in a flat roof.

C_v Ratio of "critical" web stress, according to the linear buckling theory, to the shear yield stress of web material; equal to

$$\frac{\pi^2 E k \sqrt{3}}{12(1 - \nu^2)(h/t)^2 F_y} \quad \text{or} \quad \frac{190}{h/t} \sqrt{\frac{k}{F_y}}$$

AMERICAN INSTITUTE OF STEEL CONSTRUCTION

C_W Warping constant for a section (in.^{6}).

C_1 Ratio of beam yield stress to column yield stress.

Coefficient for adjusting electrode capacities in Tables XIV, XV, XVI, XVII, XVIII, XIX, XX, XXI.

C_2 Ratio of column yield stress to stiffener yield stress.

D Factor depending upon type of transverse stiffeners.

Number of $\frac{1}{16}$-inches in weld size.

E Modulus of elasticity of steel (29,000 kips per square inch).

E_c Modulus of elasticity of concrete (kips per square inch).

E_0 Distance from the center of the web to the shear center of a channel section (in.).

F Load factor in plastic design.

Externally applied load per fastener in end plate and hanger type connections (kips).

F_a Axial stress permitted in the absence of bending moment (ksi).

F_{as} Axial compressive stress, permitted in the absence of bending moment, for bracing and other secondary members (ksi).

F_b Bending stress permitted in the absence of axial force (ksi).

F'_b Allowable bending stress in compression flange of plate girders as reduced for hybrid girders or because of large web depth-to-thickness ratio (ksi).

F'_e Euler stress divided by factor of safety; equal to

$$\frac{12\pi^2 E}{23(Kl_b/r_b)^2} \text{ (ksi)}$$

F_p Allowable bearing stress (ksi).

Allowable bearing pressure on support (ksi).

F_{sr} Stress range (ksi).

F_t Allowable tensile stress (ksi).

F_v Allowable shear stress (ksi).

F_{vp} Allowable shear stress in plate (ksi).

F_{vw} Allowable shear stress in welds (ksi).

F_y Specified minimum yield stress of the type of steel being used (ksi). As used in AISC Specification, "yield stress" denotes either the specified minimum yield point (for those steels that have a yield point) or specified minimum yield strength (for those steels that do not have a yield point).

F_y' The theoretical maximum yield stress (ksi) based on the width-thickness ratio of one-half the unstiffened compression flange, beyond which a particular shape is not "compact." See AISC Specification Sect. 1.5.1.4.1, subparagraph b.

$$= \left[\frac{52.2}{b_f/2t_f} \right]^2$$

F_y'' The theoretical maximum yield stress (ksi) based on the depth-thickness ratio of the web, beyond which a particular shape is not "compact." AISC Specification Sect. 1.5.1.4.1, subparagraph d. It is only applicable for cases of pure bending; i.e., $f_a = 0$.

$$= \left[\frac{412}{d/t_w} \right]^2$$

F_y''' The theoretical maximum yield stress (ksi) based on the depth-thickness ratio of the web below which a particular shape may be considered "compact" for any condition of combined bending and axial stresses. AISC Specification Sect. 1.5.1.4.1, subparagraph d.

$$= \left[\frac{257}{d/t_w} \right]^2$$

F_{yr} Minimum yield stress of longitudinal reinforcing steel providing composite action at point of negative moment (ksi).

G Nomograph designation of end condition used in column design to determine the effective length. See Specification Commentary, Fig. C1.8.2.

I Moment of inertia of a section (in.^{4}).

I_c Moment of inertia of a column (in.^{4}).

I_d Moment of inertia of steel deck on a flat roof (in.^{4} per ft.).

I_g Moment of inertia of a girder or beam (in.^{4}).

I_p Moment of inertia of primary member in flat roof framing (in.^{4}).
Polar moment of inertia (in.^{4}).

I_s Moment of inertia of secondary member in flat roof framing (in.^{4}).

I_{tr} Moment of inertia of transformed composite section (in.^{4}).

J Torsional constant of a cross-section (in.^{4}).

K Effective length factor.
Theoretical cover plate length factor in composite design.

L Span length (ft.).
Length of connection angles (in.).
Unbraced length of column (ft.).

L_b Unbraced length of compression flange (ft.).

L_c Maximum unbraced length of the compression flange at which the allowable bending stress may be taken at 0.66 F_y or as determined by AISC Specification Formula 1.5-5, when applicable (ft.).

L_p Length of primary member in a flat roof (ft.).

L_s Length of secondary member in a flat roof (ft.).

L_u Maximum unbraced length of the compression flange at which the allowable bending stress may be taken at 0.6 F_y (ft.).

M Moment (kip-ft.).

M_1 Smaller moment at end of unbraced length of beam-column (kip-ft.).

M_2 Larger moment at end of unbraced length of beam-column (kip-ft.).

M_D Moment produced by dead load (kip-ft.).

M_L Moment produced by live load (kip-ft.).

M_m Critical moment that can be resisted by a plastically designed member in absence of axial load (kip-ft.).

M_o Reduced plastic moment (kip-ft.).

M_p Plastic moment (kip-ft.).

M_R Beam resisting moment (kip-ft.).

N Length of bearing of applied load (in.).

N_e Length at end bearing to develop maximum web shear (in.).

N_1 Number of shear connectors equal to V_h/q or V'_h/q, as applicable.

N_2 Number of shear connectors required where closer spacing is needed adjacent to point of zero moment.

P Applied load (kips).

P' Equivalent axial load due to bending component in members subject to axial compression and bending (kips).

P_{cr} $= 1.70\ AF_a$

P_e $= 1.92\ AF_e'$

P_y Plastic axial load; equal to profile area times specified minimum yield stress (kips).

Q Statical moment of cover plate area about neutral axis of transformed section, or cover-plated section (in.^{3}).

Prying force per fastener (kips).

Q_a Ratio of effective profile area of an axially loaded member to its total profile area.

Q_s Axial stress reduction factor where width-thickness ratio of unstiffened elements exceeds limiting value given in Sect. 1.9.1.2.

R Reaction or concentrated transverse load applied to beam or girder (kips).

Maximum end reaction permitted without intermediate stiffeners for welded plate girders (kips).

Maximum end reaction for $3\frac{1}{2}$ in. of bearing (kips).

R_i Increase in reaction (R) in kips for each additional inch of bearing.

S Elastic section modulus (in.^{3}).

Spacing of secondary members in a flat roof (ft.).

S' Additional section modulus corresponding to $\frac{1}{16}$-inch increase in web thickness for welded plate girders (in.^{3}).

S_{eff} Effective section modulus corresponding to partial composite action (in.^{3}).

S_j Section modulus of transformed composite cross-section, referred to the top of steel beam (in.^{3}).

S_s Section modulus of steel beam used in composite design, referred to the bottom flange (in.^{3}).

S_t Section modulus of transformed composite cross-section, referred to the top of concrete (in.^{3}).

S_{tr} Section modulus of transformed composite cross-section, referred to the bottom flange (in.^{3}).

S_{ts} Section modulus of steel beam used in composite design, referred to the top flange (in.^{3}).

T Horizontal force in flanges of a beam to form a couple equal to beam end moment (kips).

T_b Specified pretension of a high strength bolt (kips).

V Statical shear on beam (kips).

Maximum permissible web shear (kips).

V_h Total horizontal shear to be resisted by connectors under full composite action (kips).

V'_h Total horizontal shear to be resisted by connectors in providing partial composite action (kips).

V_u Statical shear produced by "ultimate" load in plastic design (kips).

Y Ratio of yield stress of web steel to yield stress of stiffener steel.

Z Plastic section modulus (in.^{3}).

Z_x Plastic section modulus with respect to the major $(X\text{-}X)$ axis (in.^{3}).

Z_y Plastic section modulus with respect to the minor $(Y\text{-}Y)$ axis (in.^{3}).

a Clear distance between transverse stiffeners (in.).

Component of amplification factor for solving modified Formula (1.6-1a) when bending is about centroid of a square or circular section; equal to $0.149\ Ar^2 \times 10^6$.

Distance from bolt line to application of prying force Q (in.).

a' Distance required at ends of welded partial length cover plate to develop stress (in.).

a_x Component of amplification factor for solving modified Formula (1.6-1a) when bending is about the X-X axis; equal to $0.149\ Ar_x{}^2 \times 10^6$.

a_y Component of amplification factor for solving modified Formula (1.6-1a) when bending is about the Y-Y axis; equal to $0.149\ Ar_y{}^2 \times 10^6$.

b Effective width of the concrete flange in composite design (in.).
Width of cover plate (in.).
Actual width of stiffened and unstiffened compression elements (in.).
Fastener spacing vertically (in.).
Distance from bolt line to flange or web minus $\frac{1}{16}$ in. (in.).

b_e Effective width of stiffened compression element (in.).

b_f Flange width of rolled beam or plate girder (in.).

c Distance from neutral axis to extreme fiber of beams (in.).

d Depth of beam or girder (in.).
Diameter of roller or rocker bearing (in.).
Depth of bracket plate (in.).
Nominal bolt diameter (in.).

d_c Column web depth clear of fillets (in.).

d_s Total depth of steel section including cover plate in composite design (in.).

e Horizontal displacement, in the direction of the span, between top and bottom of simply supported beam at its ends (in.).

f Axial compression load on member divided by effective area (ksi).

f_a Computed axial stress (ksi).

f_b Computed bending stress (ksi).

f_c Concrete working stress (ksi).

f'_c Specified compression strength of concrete at 28 days (ksi).

f_p Actual bearing pressure on support (ksi).

f_t Computed tensile stress (ksi).

f_v Computed shear stress (ksi).

f_{vs} Shear between girder web and transverse stiffeners (kips per linear inch of single stiffener or pair of stiffeners).

f_1 Force on weld due to uniform distribution of load over total weld length (kips per linear in.).

f_2 Vertical force on a weld at a specified location due to moment (kips per linear in.).

f_3 Horizontal force on a weld at a specified location due to moment (kips per lineal in.).

g Transverse spacing between fastener gage lines (in.).

h Clear distance between flanges of a beam or girder (in.).

k Coefficient relating linear buckling strength of a plate to its dimensions and condition of edge support.
Distance from outer face of flange to web toe of fillet of rolled shape or equivalent distance on welded section (in.).
Ratio of length of horizontal weld to length of vertical weld.

l Actual unbraced length (in.).
Length of vertical weld (in.).
Length of each weld (in.).

l_b Actual unbraced length in plane of bending (in.).

l_{cr} Critical unbraced length adjacent to plastic hinge (in.).

n Modular ratio; equal to E/E_c.

Number of fasteners in one vertical row.

q Allowable horizontal shear to be resisted by a shear connector (kips).

r Governing radius of gyration (in.).

r_b Radius of gyration about axis of concurrent bending (in.).

r_T Radius of gyration of a section comprising the compression flange plus one-third of the compression web area, taken about an axis in the plane of the web (in.).

r_v Allowable shear or bearing value for one fastener (kips).

r_x Radius of gyration with respect to the X - X axis (in.).

r_y Radius of gyration with respect to the Y - Y axis (in.).

r_z Least radius of gyration with respect to the principal axis (in.).

s Spacing (pitch) between successive holes in line of stress (in.).

Distance between backs of pairs of angles (in.).

t Girder, beam, or column web thickness (in.).

Angle thickness (in.).

Thickness of concrete slab in composite design (in.).

t_f Flange thickness (in.).

t_p Thickness of plate (in.).

t_t Thickness of thinner part joined by partial penetration groove weld (in.).

t_w Web thickness (in.).

w Length of channel shear connectors (in.).

Length of flange tributary to each bolt (in.).

$\bar{x}$ Distance from the outside of the web to the minor (Y-Y) axis of a channel section (in.).

x Distance from minor axis (Y–Y) to outside surface of shape (in.).

y Distance from major axis (X–X) to outside surface of shape (in.).

Distance from the back of the flange to the major (X-X) axis of a tee section (in.).

α Ratio of hybrid girder web yield stress to flange yield stress.

β Ratio S_{tr}/S_s or S_{eff}/S_s.

ν Poisson's ratio, may be taken as 0.3 for steel.

Δ Beam deflection (in.).

kip   1000 pounds.

ksi   Expression of stress in kips per square inch.

PART 1
Dimensions and Properties

STRUCTURAL STEELS

PRODUCT AVAILABILITY

Section 1.4.1 of the AISC *Specification for the Design, Fabrication and Erection of Structural Steel for Buildings* lists thirteen ASTM specifications for structural steel approved for use in building construction.

Seven of these steels are available in hot-rolled structural shapes, plates, and bars. One steel, ASTM A514, is only available in plates. Table 1 shows five groups of shapes and nine ranges of thicknesses of plates and bars available in the various minimum yield stress* levels afforded by the eight steels. A listing of the shape sizes included in each of the five groups follows in Table 2, corresponding to the groupings given in Table A of ASTM A6.

Five additional grades of steel, other than those covering hot-rolled shapes, plates, and bars, are listed in Section 1.4.1 of the 1969 AISC Specification for the first time.** Each of these steels is occasionally used in building construction and has proven entirely satisfactory when used in accordance with the provisions of the Specification. They are ASTM A53 Grade B pipe, ASTM A375 sheet and strip, ASTM A500 cold-formed tubing, ASTM A501 hot-formed tubing, and ASTM A570 Grades D and E sheet and strip.

The principal producers of shapes listed in Part 1 of this Manual are shown in Table 3. For additional information on availability and classification of structural steel plates and bars, refer to the separate discussion beginning on page 1 - 108.

Space does not permit inclusion in Table 3, or in the listing of shapes and plates in Part 1 of this Manual, of all rolled shapes, or plates of greater thickness that are occasionally used in construction. For such products, reference should be made to the various producers' catalogs.

A summary of the scope and principal tensile properties of the thirteen steels listed in Section 1.4.1 of the AISC Specification appears in Part 5 of this Manual. For complete information on each steel, reference should be made to the appropriate ASTM Specification.

SELECTION OF THE APPROPRIATE STRUCTURAL STEEL

ASTM A36 has supplanted the earlier and now obsolete A7 and A373 steels as an all-purpose carbon grade steel widely used in building and bridge construction.

ASTM A529 structural carbon steel, ASTM A440 high-strength structural steel, ASTM A441 and A572 high-strength low-alloy structural steels, ASTM A242 and A588 corrosion-resistant high-strength low-alloy structural steels, and ASTM A514 quenched and tempered alloy structural steel plate may each have certain advantages over ASTM A36 structural carbon steel, depending on the application. These steels have proven to be economical choices where lighter members, resulting from use of higher allowable stresses, are not penalized because of instability, local buckling, deflection, or

---

* As used in the AISC Specification, "yield stress" denotes either the specified minimum yield point (for those steels that have a yield point) or specified minimum yield strength (for those steels that do not have a yield point).

** Also see Section 1.4.1 of Supplement Nos. 1 and 2 to the 1969 AISC Specification for other permitted steels.

other similar reasons. They are frequently used in tension members, beams in continuous and composite construction where deflections can be minimized, and columns having low slenderness ratios. The reduction of dead load, and associated savings in shipping costs, can be significant factors. However, higher strength steels are not to be used indiscriminately. Effective use of all steels depends on thorough cost and engineering analysis.

All steels listed in the AISC Specification are suitable for welded fabrication, with the exception of ASTM A440 steel which is not recommended for welding by AISC.

ASTM A242 and A588 corrosion-resistant high-strength low-alloy steels are more expensive than the high-strength low-alloy steels. They are suitable for use in the bare (uncoated) condition, where exposure to normal atmosphere causes a tightly adherent oxide to form on the surface protecting the steel from further oxidation. The reduction or elimination of maintenance resulting from use of these steels often offsets their higher initial cost. Designers should consult the steel producers on the corrosion-resistant properties of these steels prior to use in the bare (uncoated) condition, to determine how to use them to best advantage in a finished structure.

When either A242 or A588 steel is exposed to a more corrosive environment, its use in the coated condition provides longer coating life than with other structural steels. It should be noted that A588 steel, in addition to its ability to resist corrosion, offers the advantage of being the only listed "as-rolled" structural steel available at 50 ksi minimum specified yield strength in thicknesses up to 4 inches inclusive.

STRUCTURAL SHAPES — DESIGNATIONS, DIMENSIONS AND PROPERTIES

The designations for structural shapes listed in Part 1 of this Manual are related to the profiles of the shapes, and are different from the designations used for the same shapes in previous editions of the Manual. Furthermore, in many instances the values in the tables "Dimensions for Detailing" and "Properties for Designing" are slightly different from those published in previous editions of the Manual. The development of the new designations, the changes in dimensions, and the recalculation of the design properties are the result of joint activities of committees of the AISC and AISI.

The new designations are standard for the steel producing and fabricating industries, and should be used in all references to shapes including design, detailing, and ordering. Examples of the new designations for structural shapes, plates, and bars, as well as designations for pipe and structural tubing, are given in Table 4. The former designations used in previous editions of the Manual are included in the table for reference only.

W shapes have essentially parallel flange surfaces. The profile of a W shape of a given nominal depth and weight available from different producers is essentially the same except for the size of fillets between the web and flange. The "Properties for Designing" for W shapes are based on the smallest theoretical size fillets produced, and the tables of "Dimensions for Detailing" are adjusted for the largest theoretical size fillets produced.

HP bearing pile shapes have essentially parallel flange surfaces and equal web and flange thicknesses. The profile of an HP shape of a given nominal depth and weight available from different producers is essentially the same.

S shapes and American Standard channels (C) have a slope of approximately 16⅔% (2 in 12 inches) on their inner flange surfaces. The profiles of S and C shapes of a given nominal depth and weight available from different producers are essentially the same.

The letter M designates shapes that cannot be classified as W, HP, or S shapes. Similarly, MC designates channels that cannot be classified as American Standard channels. Because many of the M and MC shapes are only available from a limited number of producers, or are infrequently rolled, their availability should be checked prior to specifying these shapes. They have various slopes on their inner flange surfaces, dimensions for which may be obtained from the respective producing mills.

The flange thickness given in the tables for S and M shapes is the average flange thickness.

The theoretical properties and dimensions of the shapes given in the tables are either exact or slightly conservative for all producers who offer them, except as noted in the footnotes to Table 3.

Equal leg and unequal leg angle (L) shapes of the same nominal size available from different producers have profiles which are essentially the same, except for the size of fillet between the legs and the shape of the ends of the legs. The *k* distance given in the tables for each angle is based on the largest theoretical size fillet available.

In calculating the theoretical weights and properties of shapes listed in Part 1 of this Manual, fillets and roundings have been included for all shapes except angles.

AVAILABILITY OF SHAPES, PLATES AND BARS ACCORDING TO ASTM STRUCTURAL STEEL SPECIFICATIONS
TABLE 1

Steel Type	ASTM Designation	F_y Minimum Yield Stress (ksi)	Shapes Group per ASTM A6					Plates and Bars								
			a1	2	3	4	5	To ½" Incl.	Over ½" to ¾" Incl.	Over ¾" to 1" Incl.	Over 1" to 1½" Incl.	Over 1½" to 2½" Incl.	Over 2½" to 4" Incl.	Over 4" to 5" Incl.	Over 5" to 8" Incl.	Over 8"
Carbon	A36	32														▨
		36	▨	▨	▨	▨	▨	▨	▨	▨	▨	▨	▨	▨	▨	
	A529	42	▨	▨				▨								
High-Strength	A440	42				▨	▨					▨	▨			
		46			▨	▨					▨	▨				
		50	▨	▨				▨	▨							
High-Strength Low-Alloy	A441	40												▨	▨	
		42			▨	▨							▨	▨		
		46			▨	▨					▨	▨				
		50	▨	▨				▨	▨	▨						
	A572 (b) Gr. 42	42	▨	▨	▨	▨	▨	▨	▨	▨	▨	▨	▨			
	Gr. 45	45	▨	▨	▨	▨	▨	▨	▨	▨	▨	▨				
	Gr. 50	50	▨	▨	▨	▨	▨	▨	▨	▨	▨					
	Gr. 55	55	▨	▨	▨	▨		▨	▨	▨	▨					
	Gr. 60	60	▨	▨				▨	▨	▨						
	Gr. 65	65	▨					▨	▨							
Corrosion-Resistant High-Strength Low-Alloy	A242	42				▨	▨				▨	▨				
		46			▨	▨					▨					
		50	▨	▨	▨			▨	▨	▨						
	A588	42													▨	
		46				▨								▨		
		50	▨	▨	▨	▨		▨	▨	▨	▨	▨		▨	▨	
Quenched & Tempered Alloy	A514	90														
		100						▨	▨	▨	▨	▨	▨			

a Includes bar size shapes.
b To W 14 × 426 only.
▨ Available.
☐ Not available.

STRUCTURAL SHAPE SIZE GROUPINGS
FOR TENSILE PROPERTY CLASSIFICATION
TABLE 2

Structural Shape	Group 1	Group 2	Group 3	Group 4	Group 5
W Shapes	W 24 × 55, 61 W 21 × 44, 49 W 18 × 45 to 60 incl W 18 × 35, 40 W 16 × 26 to 50 incl W 14 × 22 to 53 incl W 12 × 14 to 58 incl W 10 × 11.5 to 45 incl W 8 × 10 to 48 incl W 6 × 8.5 to 25 incl W 5 × 16 to 18.5 incl W 4 × 13	W 36 × 135 to 194 incl W 33 × 118 to 152 incl W 30 × 99 to 210 incl W 27 × 84 to 177 incl W 24 × 68 to 160 incl W 21 × 55 to 142 incl W 18 × 64 to 114 incl W 16 × 58 to 96 incl W 14 × 61 to 136 incl W 12 × 65 to 106 incl W 10 × 49 to 112 incl W 8 × 58 to 67 incl	W 36 × 230 to 300 incl W 33 × 200 to 240 incl W 14 × 142 to 211 incl W 12 × 120 to 190 incl	W 14 × 219 to 550 incl	W 14 × 605 to 730 incl
M Shapes	to 35 lb/ft incl	over 35 lb/ft			
S Shapes	to 35 lb/ft incl	over 35 lb/ft			
HP Shapes		to 102 lb/ft incl	over 102 lb/ft		
American Standard Channels (C)	to 20 lb/ft incl	over 20 lb/ft			
Miscellaneous Channels (MC)	to 28.5 lb/ft incl	over 28.5 lb/ft			
Angles (L), Structural & Bar-Size	to ½ in. incl	over ½ to ¾ in. incl	over ¾ in.		

Note: Structural tees from W, M and S shapes fall in the same group as the structural shape from which they are cut.

PRINCIPAL PRODUCERS OF STRUCTURAL SHAPES
TABLE 3

A.	Armco Steel Corp.	K.	Kaiser Steel Corp.
B.	Bethlehem Steel Corp.	N.	Northwestern Steel & Wire Co.
C.	C F & I Steel Corp.	P.	Phoenix Steel Corp.
I.	Inland Steel Co.	U.	United States Steel Corp.
J.	Jones & Laughlin Steel Corp.	W.	Weirton Steel Div., National Steel Corp.

Section & Wt. per Ft.	Producer Code	Section & Wt. per Ft.	Producer Code
W 36—All	B, U	W 8 × 40	A, B, C, I, N, U
W 33—All	B, U	W 8 × 35–31	A, B, C, I, N, U, W
W 30—All	B, U	W 8 × 28–10	A, B, C, I, N, U
W 27—All	B, U	W 6 × 25–15.5	A, B, C, I, N, U
W 24 × 160–130	B, U	W 6 × 16–8.5	A, B, I, N, U
W 24 × 120–55	A, B, I, U	W5 × 18.5–16	A, B, C, U
W 21 × 142–112	B, U	W 4 × 13	B, N
W 21 × 96–44	A, B, I, U		
W 18 × 114–96	A, B, U	HP 14 × 117–73	B, U
W 18 × 85–77	A, B, I, U	HP 12 × 74–53	A, B, I, U
W18 × 70–35	A, B, I, N, U	HP 10 × 57–42	A, B, I, N, U
W 16 × 96–88	A, B, U	HP 8 × 36	A, B, C, I, N, U
W 16 × 78–71	A, B, I, U		
W 16 × 64–58	A, B, I, N, U	S 24 × 120–79.9	A, B, U
W 16 × 50–36	A, B, C, I, N, U, W	S 20 × 95–85	A, B, U
W 16 × 31–26	A, B, C, I, N, U	S 20 × 75–65.4	A, B, K, U
W 14 × 730–87	B, U	S 18 × 70–54.7	A, B, K, U, W
W 14 × 84–61	A, B, I, U	S 15 × 50–42.9	A, B, C, K, P, U, W
W 14 × 53–43	A, B, C, I, U, W	S 12 × 50–40.8	A, B, C, I, P, U, W
W 14 × 38–30	A, B, C, I, N, U, W	S 12 × 35–31.8	A, B, C, I, K, P, U, W
W 14 × 26–22	A, B, C, I, N, U	S 10 × 35	B, C, I, K, P, U, W
W 12 × 190–53	A, B, I, U	S 10 × 25.4	A, B, C, I, K, P, U, W
W 12 × 50–40	A, B, C, I, U, W	S 8 × 23–18.4	A, B, C, I, K, P, U, W
W 12 × 36–27	A, B, C, I, N, U, W	S 7 × 20	B, C, I, U
W 12 × 22–14	A, B, C, I, N, U	S 7 × 15.3	A, B, C, I, U
W 10 × 112–60	A, B, I, U	S 6 × 17.25–12.5	A, B, C, I, K, P, U, W
W 10 × 54–49	A, B, I, N, U	S 5 × 14.75	B, I, K, P, U
W 10 × 45–21	A, B, C, I, N, U, W	S 5 × 10	A, B, C, I, K, P, U
W 10 × 19–11.5	A, B, C, I, N, U	S 4 × 9.5–7.7	A, B, C, I, K, P, U
W 8 × 67–48	A, B, C, I, U	S 3 × 7.5–5.7	A, B, C, I, U

Angles (L) from 9 × 4 through 1 × 1, in various thicknesses, are rolled by one or more of the following producers: A, B, C, I, J, K, N, P, U, W.

The W shapes offered by producer W have a 3° taper of the inner flange surfaces, and have design properties about the Y-Y axis somewhat less than those tabulated. The M 14 × 17.2 shape offered by producer N, the M 6 × 25 shape offered by producer W, the M 6 × 22.5 shape offered by producer K, the M 6 × 20 shapes offered by producers K and W, and the M 4 × 13 shapes offered by producers A, C, and I have different profiles than listed in the tables. Catalogs of these producers should be consulted for exact information.

Maximum lengths of shapes obtainable vary widely with producers, but a conservative range for all mills is from 60 to 90 feet. Some mills will accept orders for lengths up to 120 feet, but only for certain shapes and subject to special arrangement. Consult the producers for unusual length requirements.

PRINCIPAL PRODUCERS OF STRUCTURAL SHAPES
TABLE 3

A. Armco Steel Corp.
B. Bethlehem Steel Corp.
C. C F & I Steel Corp.
I. Inland Steel Co.
J. Jones & Laughlin Steel Corp.

K. Kaiser Steel Corp.
N. Northwestern Steel & Wire Co.
P. Phoenix Steel Corp.
U. United States Steel Corp.
W. Weirton Steel Div., National Steel Corp.

Section & Wt. per Ft.	Producer Code	Section & Wt. per Ft.	Producer Code
M 14 × 17.2	N	MC 18 × 58–42.7	B, K, U, W
M 12 × 11.8	J	MC 13 × 50–31.8	B, I, P, U
M 10 × 29.1–22.9	K	MC 12 × 50–35	B, I, P, U, W
M 10 × 9	J, N	MC 12 × 37–30.9	B, P, U
M 8 × 40	K	MC 12 × 10.6	J
M 8 × 34.3–32.6	K	MC 10 × 41.1	B, U
M 8 × 22.5–18.5	K	MC 10 × 33.6–28.5	B, K, U
M 8 × 6.5	J, N	MC 10 × 28.3	B, P, U
M 7 × 5.5	J	MC 10 × 25.3	B, I, P, U
M 6 × 25	W	MC 10 × 24.9	B, P, U
M 6 × 22.5	C, K	MC 10 × 21.9	B, I, P, U
M 6 × 20	C, K, U, W	MC 10 × 8.4–6.5	J
M 6 × 4.4	J	MC 9 × 25.4–23.9	B, P, U
M 5 × 18.9	A, B, C, K, U	MC 8 × 22.8–18.7	B, P, U
M 4 × 13.8	C, K	MC 8 × 8.5	J
M 4 × 13	A, C, I, K, U	MC 7 × 22.7–17.6	B, I, P, U
		MC 6 × 18	B, U
C 15 × 50–33.9	B, C, I, K, N, P, U, W	MC 6 × 15.3	B, I, P, U
C 12 × 30–20.7	B, C, I, K, N, P, U, W	MC 6 × 16.3–15.1	B, U
C 10 × 30	B, I, N, P, U, W	MC 6 × 12	B, U
C 10 × 25–15.3	A, B, C, I, K, N, P, U, W	MC 4 × 13.8	U
C 9 × 20–13.4	A, B, C, I, K, P, U, W	MC 3 × 9	B, U
C 8 × 18.75–11.5	A, B, C, I, J, K, N, P, U, W	MC 3 × 7.1	B, I, U
C 7 × 14.75	A, B, C, I, K, P, U		
C 7 × 12.25–9.8	A, B, C, I, K, N, U		
C 6 × 13	A, B, C, I, J, N, P, U, W		
C 6 × 10.5–8.2	A, B, C, I, J, K, N, P, U, W		
C 5 × 9–6.7	A, B, C, I, J, K, N, P, U		
C 4 × 7.25–5.4	A, B, C, I, J, K, N, P, U		
C 3 × 6	A, B, C, I, J, N, U		
C 3 × 5–4.1	A, B, C, I, J, K, N, U		

Angles (L) from 9 × 4 through 1 × 1, in various thicknesses, are rolled by one or more of the following producers: A, B, C, I, J, K, N, P, U, W.

The W shapes offered by producer W have a 3° taper of the inner flange surfaces, and have design properties about the Y-Y axis somewhat less than those tabulated. The M 14 × 17.2 shape offered by producer N, the M 6 × 25 shape offered by producer W, the M 6 × 22.5 shape offered by producer K, the M 6 × 20 shapes offered by producers K and W, and the M 4 × 13 shapes offered by producers A, C, and I have different profiles than listed in the tables. Catalogs of these producers should be consulted for exact information.

Maximum lengths of shapes obtainable vary widely with producers, but a conservative range for all mills is from 60 to 90 feet. Some mills will accept orders for lengths up to 120 feet, but only for certain shapes and subject to special arrangement. Consult the producers for unusual length requirements.

HOT-ROLLED STRUCTURAL STEEL DESIGNATIONS
TABLE 4

New Designation	Type of Shape	Old Designation
W 24 × 76 W 14 × 26	W shape	24 WF 76 14 B 26
S 24 × 100	S shape	24 I 100
M 8 × 18.5 M 10 × 9 M 8 × 34.3	M shape	8 M 18.5 10 JR 9.0 8 × 8 M 34.3
C 12 × 20.7	American Standard Channel	12 C 20.7
MC 12 × 45 MC 12 × 10.6	Miscellaneous Channel	12 × 4 C 45.0 12 JR C 10.6
HP 14 × 73	HP shape	14 BP 73
L 6 × 6 × ¾ L 6 × 4 × ⅝	Equal Leg Angle Unequal Leg Angle	∠ 6 × 6 × ¾ ∠ 6 × 4 × ⅝
WT 12 × 38 WT 7 × 13	Structural Tee cut from W shape	ST 12 WF 38 ST 7 B 13
ST 12 × 50	Structural Tee cut from S shape	ST 12 I 50
MT 4 × 9.25 MT 5 × 4.5 MT 4 × 17.15	Structural Tee cut from M shape	ST 4 M 9.25 ST 5 JR 4.5 ST 4 M 17.15
PL ½ × 18	Plate	PL 18 × ½
Bar 1 �□ Bar 1¼ φ Bar 2½ × ½	Square Bar Round Bar Flat Bar	Bar 1 �□ Bar 1¼ φ Bar 2½ × ½
Pipe 4 Std. Pipe 4 X - Strong Pipe 4 XX - Strong	Pipe	Pipe 4 Std. Pipe 4 X-Strong Pipe 4 XX-Strong
TS 4 × 4 × .375 TS 5 × 3 × .375 TS 3 OD × .250	Structural Tubing: Square Structural Tubing: Rectangular Structural Tubing: Circular	Tube 4 × 4 × .375 Tube 5 × 3 × .375 Tube 3 OD × .250

DIMENSIONS FOR DETAILING

W Shapes
M Shapes
S Shapes
HP Shapes
American Standard Channels (C)
Miscellaneous Channels (MC)

W SHAPES
Dimensions for detailing

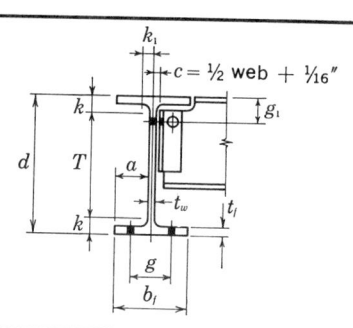

$$c = \tfrac{1}{2}\,web + \tfrac{1}{16}''$$

Designation	Depth d	Flange		Web Thick-ness t_w	$\dfrac{t_w}{2}$	Distance						Usual Gage g
		Width b_f	Thick-ness t_f			a	T	k	k_1	g_1	c	
	In.	In.	In.	In.	In.	In.	In.	In.	In.	In.	In.	In.
W 36×300	36¾	16⅝	1¹¹⁄₁₆	¹⁵⁄₁₆	½	7⅞	31⅛	2¹³⁄₁₆	1½	3¾	⁹⁄₁₆	5½
×280	36½	16⅝	1⁹⁄₁₆	⅞	⁷⁄₁₆	7⅞	31⅛	2¹¹⁄₁₆	1½	3¾	½	5½
×260	36¼	16½	1⁷⁄₁₆	¹³⁄₁₆	⁷⁄₁₆	7⅞	31⅛	2⁹⁄₁₆	1½	3½	½	5½
×245	36	16½	1⅜	¹³⁄₁₆	⅜	7⅞	31⅛	2⁷⁄₁₆	1⁷⁄₁₆	3½	⁷⁄₁₆	5½
×230	35⅞	16½	1¼	¾	⅜	7⅞	31⅛	2⅜	1⁷⁄₁₆	3½	⁷⁄₁₆	5½
W 36×194	36½	12⅛	1¼	¾	⅜	5⅝	32⅛	2³⁄₁₆	1³⁄₁₆	3½	⁷⁄₁₆	5½
×182	36⅜	12⅛	1³⁄₁₆	¾	⅜	5⅝	32⅛	2⅛	1³⁄₁₆	3¼	⁷⁄₁₆	5½
×170	36⅛	12	1⅛	¹¹⁄₁₆	⁵⁄₁₆	5⅝	32⅛	2	1³⁄₁₆	3¼	⅜	5½
×160	36	12	1	⅝	⁵⁄₁₆	5⅝	32⅛	1¹⁵⁄₁₆	1³⁄₁₆	3¼	⅜	5½
×150	35⅞	12	¹⁵⁄₁₆	⅝	⁵⁄₁₆	5⅝	32⅛	1⅞	1⅛	3	⅜	5½
×135	35½	12	¹³⁄₁₆	⅝	⁵⁄₁₆	5⅝	32⅛	1¹¹⁄₁₆	1⅛	3	⅜	5½
W 33×240	33½	15⅞	1⅜	¹³⁄₁₆	⁷⁄₁₆	7½	28⅝	2⁷⁄₁₆	1⅜	3½	½	5½
×220	33¼	15¾	1¼	¾	⅜	7½	28⅝	2⁵⁄₁₆	1⅜	3½	⁷⁄₁₆	5½
×200	33	15¾	1⅛	¹¹⁄₁₆	⅜	7½	28⅝	2³⁄₁₆	1⅜	3¼	⁷⁄₁₆	5½
W 33×152	33½	11⅝	1¹⁄₁₆	⅝	⁵⁄₁₆	5½	29¾	1⅞	1⅛	3¼	⅜	5½
×141	33¼	11½	¹⁵⁄₁₆	⅝	⁵⁄₁₆	5½	29¾	1¾	1¹⁄₁₆	3	⅜	5½
×130	33⅛	11½	⅞	⁹⁄₁₆	⁵⁄₁₆	5½	29¾	1¹¹⁄₁₆	1¹⁄₁₆	3	⅜	5½
×118	32⅞	11½	¾	⁹⁄₁₆	¼	5½	29¾	1⁹⁄₁₆	1¹⁄₁₆	2¾	⁵⁄₁₆	5½
W 30×210	30⅜	15⅛	1⁵⁄₁₆	¾	⅜	7⅛	25¾	2⁵⁄₁₆	1⁵⁄₁₆	3½	⁷⁄₁₆	5½
×190	30⅛	15	1³⁄₁₆	¹¹⁄₁₆	⅜	7⅛	25¾	2³⁄₁₆	1⁵⁄₁₆	3¼	⁷⁄₁₆	5½
×172	29⅞	15	1¹⁄₁₆	⅝	⁵⁄₁₆	7⅛	25¾	2¹⁄₁₆	1¼	3¼	⅜	5½
W 30×132	30¼	10½	1	⅝	⁵⁄₁₆	5	26¾	1¾	1¹⁄₁₆	3	⅜	5½
×124	30⅛	10½	¹⁵⁄₁₆	⁹⁄₁₆	⁵⁄₁₆	5	26¾	1¹¹⁄₁₆	1	3	⅜	5½
×116	30	10½	⅞	⁹⁄₁₆	⁵⁄₁₆	5	26¾	1⅝	1	3	⅜	5½
×108	29⅞	10½	¾	⁹⁄₁₆	¼	5	26¾	1⁹⁄₁₆	1	3	⁵⁄₁₆	5½
× 99	29⅝	10½	¹¹⁄₁₆	½	¼	5	26¾	1⁷⁄₁₆	1	2¾	⁵⁄₁₆	5½

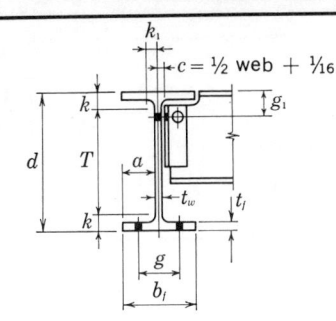

W SHAPES
Dimensions for detailing

Designation	Depth d	Flange Width b_f	Flange Thickness t_f	Web Thickness t_w	$\dfrac{t_w}{2}$	a	T	k	k_1	g_1	c	Usual Gage g
	In.	In.	In.	In.	In.	In.	In.	In.	In.	In.	In.	In.
W 27×177	27¼	14⅛	1³⁄₁₆	¾	⅜	6⅝	23	2⅛	1¼	3¼	⁷⁄₁₆	5½
×160	27⅛	14	1¹⁄₁₆	¹¹⁄₁₆	⁵⁄₁₆	6⅝	23	2¹⁄₁₆	1¼	3¼	⅜	5½
×145	26⅞	14	1	⅝	⁵⁄₁₆	6⅝	23	1¹⁵⁄₁₆	1³⁄₁₆	3	⅜	5½
W 27×114	27¼	10⅛	¹⁵⁄₁₆	⁹⁄₁₆	⁵⁄₁₆	4¾	23⅞	1¹¹⁄₁₆	¹⁵⁄₁₆	3	⅜	5½
×102	27⅛	10	¹³⁄₁₆	½	¼	4¾	23⅞	1⅝	¹⁵⁄₁₆	3	⁵⁄₁₆	5½
× 94	26⅞	10	¾	½	¼	4¾	23⅞	1½	¹⁵⁄₁₆	2¾	⁵⁄₁₆	5½
× 84	26¾	10	⅝	⁷⁄₁₆	¼	4¾	23⅞	1⁷⁄₁₆	¹⁵⁄₁₆	2¾	⁵⁄₁₆	5½
W 24×160	24¾	14⅛	1⅛	⅝	⁵⁄₁₆	6¾	20⅞	1¹⁵⁄₁₆	1¹⁄₁₆	3¼	⅜	5½
×145	24½	14	1	⅝	⁵⁄₁₆	6¾	20⅞	1¹³⁄₁₆	1¹⁄₁₆	3¼	⅜	5½
×130	24¼	14	⅞	⁹⁄₁₆	⁵⁄₁₆	6¾	20⅞	1¹¹⁄₁₆	1	3	⅜	5½
W 24×120	24¼	12⅛	¹⁵⁄₁₆	⁹⁄₁₆	¼	5¾	20⅞	1¹¹⁄₁₆	1	3	⁵⁄₁₆	5½
×110	24⅛	12	⅞	½	¼	5¾	20⅞	1⅝	1	3	⁵⁄₁₆	5½
×100	24	12	¾	⁷⁄₁₆	¼	5¾	20⅞	1⁹⁄₁₆	¹⁵⁄₁₆	3	⁵⁄₁₆	5½
W 24× 94	24¼	9	⅞	½	¼	4¼	21	1⅝	1	3	⁵⁄₁₆	5½
× 84	24⅛	9	¾	½	¼	4¼	21	1⁹⁄₁₆	¹⁵⁄₁₆	3	⁵⁄₁₆	5½
× 76	23⅞	9	¹¹⁄₁₆	⁷⁄₁₆	¼	4¼	21	1⁷⁄₁₆	¹⁵⁄₁₆	2¾	⁵⁄₁₆	5½
× 68	23¾	9	⁹⁄₁₆	⁷⁄₁₆	³⁄₁₆	4¼	21	1⅜	¹⁵⁄₁₆	2¾	¼	5½
W 24× 61	23¾	7	⁹⁄₁₆	⁷⁄₁₆	³⁄₁₆	3¼	21	1⅜	¹⁵⁄₁₆	2¾	¼	3½
× 55	23½	7	½	⅜	³⁄₁₆	3¼	21	1¼	¹⁵⁄₁₆	2¾	¼	3½
W 21×142	21½	13⅛	1⅛	¹¹⁄₁₆	⁵⁄₁₆	6¼	17¾	1⅞	1	3	⅜	5½
×127	21¼	13	1	⁹⁄₁₆	⁵⁄₁₆	6¼	17¾	1¾	1	3	⅜	5½
×112	21	13	⅞	½	¼	6¼	17¾	1⅝	¹⁵⁄₁₆	2¾	⁵⁄₁₆	5½
W 21× 96	21⅛	9	¹⁵⁄₁₆	⁹⁄₁₆	⁵⁄₁₆	4¼	17¾	1¹¹⁄₁₆	¹⁵⁄₁₆	3	⅜	5½
× 82	20⅞	9	¹³⁄₁₆	½	¼	4¼	17¾	1⁹⁄₁₆	¹⁵⁄₁₆	2¾	⁵⁄₁₆	5½
W 21× 73	21¼	8¼	¾	⁷⁄₁₆	¼	3⅞	18½	1⅜	¹³⁄₁₆	2¾	⁵⁄₁₆	5½
× 68	21⅛	8¼	¹¹⁄₁₆	⁷⁄₁₆	³⁄₁₆	3⅞	18½	1⁵⁄₁₆	¹³⁄₁₆	2¾	¼	5½
× 62	21	8¼	⅝	⅜	³⁄₁₆	3⅞	18½	1¼	¾	2½	¼	5½
× 55	20¾	8¼	½	⅜	³⁄₁₆	3⅞	18½	1⅛	¾	2½	¼	5½
W 21× 49	20⅞	6½	⁹⁄₁₆	⅜	³⁄₁₆	3⅛	18½	1³⁄₁₆	¾	2½	¼	3½
× 44	20⅝	6½	⁷⁄₁₆	⅜	³⁄₁₆	3⅛	18½	1¹⁄₁₆	¾	2½	¼	3½

W SHAPES
Dimensions for detailing

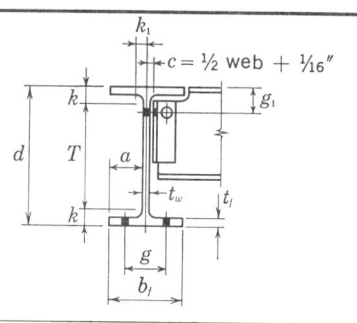

Designation	Depth d In.	Flange Width b_f In.	Flange Thickness t_f In.	Web Thickness t_w In.	$\dfrac{t_w}{2}$ In.	a In.	T In.	k In.	k_1 In.	g_1 In.	c In.	Usual Gage g In.
W 18×114	18½	11⅞	1	⅝	5/16	5⅝	15⅛	1 11/16	15/16	3	⅜	5½
×105	18⅜	11¾	15/16	9/16	¼	5⅝	15⅛	1⅝	15/16	3	5/16	5½
× 96	18⅛	11¾	13/16	½	¼	5⅝	15⅛	1½	⅞	2¾	5/16	5½
W 18× 85	18⅜	8⅞	15/16	½	¼	4⅛	15⅛	1⅝	⅞	3	5/16	5½
× 77	18⅛	8¾	13/16	½	¼	4⅛	15⅛	1½	⅞	2¾	5/16	5½
× 70	18	8¾	¾	7/16	¼	4⅛	15⅛	1 7/16	⅞	2¾	5/16	5½
× 64	17⅞	8¾	11/16	⅜	3/16	4⅛	15⅛	1⅜	13/16	2¾	¼	5½
W 18× 60	18¼	7½	11/16	7/16	3/16	3⅝	15⅞	1 3/16	11/16	2¾	¼	3½
× 55	18⅛	7½	⅝	⅜	3/16	3⅝	15⅞	1⅛	⅝	2¾	¼	3½
× 50	18	7½	9/16	⅜	3/16	3⅝	15⅞	1 1/16	⅝	2½	¼	3½
× 45	17⅞	7½	½	5/16	3/16	3⅝	15⅞	1	⅝	2½	¼	3½
W 18× 40	17⅞	6	½	5/16	3/16	2⅞	15¾	1 1/16	⅝	2½	¼	3½
× 35	17¾	6	7/16	5/16	⅛	2⅞	15¾	1	⅝	2½	3/16	3½
W 16× 96	16⅜	11½	⅞	9/16	¼	5½	13⅛	1⅝	⅞	2¾	5/16	5½
× 88	16⅛	11½	13/16	½	¼	5½	13⅛	1½	⅞	2¾	5/16	5½
W 16× 78	16⅜	8⅝	⅞	½	¼	4	13⅛	1⅝	⅞	2¾	5/16	5½
× 71	16⅛	8½	13/16	½	¼	4	13⅛	1½	⅞	2¾	5/16	5½
× 64	16	8½	11/16	7/16	¼	4	13⅛	1 7/16	⅞	2¾	5/16	5½
× 58	15⅞	8½	⅝	7/16	3/16	4	13⅛	1⅜	13/16	2¾	¼	5½
W 16× 50	16¼	7⅛	⅝	⅜	3/16	3⅜	13¾	1¼	¾	2¾	¼	3½
× 45	16⅛	7	9/16	⅜	3/16	3⅜	13¾	1 3/16	11/16	2½	¼	3½
× 40	16	7	½	5/16	⅛	3⅜	13¾	1⅛	11/16	2½	3/16	3½
× 36	15⅞	7	7/16	5/16	⅛	3⅜	13¾	1 1/16	11/16	2½	3/16	3½
W 16× 31	15⅞	5½	7/16	¼	⅛	2⅝	13¾	1 1/16	11/16	2½	3/16	2¾
× 26	15⅝	5½	⅜	¼	⅛	2⅝	13¾	15/16	⅝	2¼	3/16	2¾

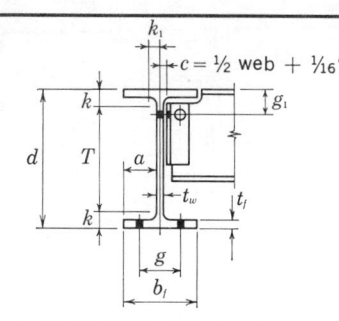

$c = \frac{1}{2}$ web $+ \frac{1}{16}''$

W SHAPES
Dimensions for detailing

Designation	Depth d	Flange Width b_f	Flange Thickness t_f	Web Thickness t_w	$\dfrac{t_w}{2}$	Distance a	T	k	k_1	g_1	c	Usual Gage g
	In.	In.	In.	In.	In.	In.	In.	In.	In.	In.	In.	In.
W 14×730	22½	17⅞	4¹⁵⁄₁₆	3¹⁄₁₆	1⁹⁄₁₆	7⅜	11¼	5⅝	2³⁄₁₆	7	1⅝	
×665	21⅝	17⅝	4½	2¹³⁄₁₆	1⁷⁄₁₆	7⅜	11¼	5³⁄₁₆	2¹⁄₁₆	6½	1½	
×605	21	17⅜	4³⁄₁₆	2⅝	1⁵⁄₁₆	7⅜	11¼	4⅞	1¹⁵⁄₁₆	6¼	1⅜	3-7½-3
×550	20¼	17¼	3¹³⁄₁₆	2⅜	1³⁄₁₆	7⅜	11¼	4½	1¹³⁄₁₆	5¾	1¼	
×500	19⅝	17	3½	2³⁄₁₆	1⅛	7⅜	11¼	4³⁄₁₆	1¾	5½	1³⁄₁₆	
×455	19	16⅞	3³⁄₁₆	2	1	7⅜	11¼	3⅞	1⅝	5¼	1¹⁄₁₆	
W 14×426	18¾	16¾	3¹⁄₁₆	1⅞	¹⁵⁄₁₆	7⅜	11¼	3¾	1⁹⁄₁₆	5	1	
×398	18¼	16⅝	2¹³⁄₁₆	1¾	⅞	7⅜	11¼	3½	1½	4¾	¹⁵⁄₁₆	
×370	18	16½	2¹¹⁄₁₆	1⅝	¹³⁄₁₆	7⅜	11¼	3⅜	1⁷⁄₁₆	4¾	⅞	3-5½-3
×342	17½	16⅜	2⁷⁄₁₆	1⁹⁄₁₆	¾	7⅜	11¼	3⅛	1⅜	4½	¹³⁄₁₆	
×314	17¼	16¼	2⁵⁄₁₆	1⁷⁄₁₆	¹¹⁄₁₆	7⅜	11¼	3	1⁵⁄₁₆	4¼	¾	
×287	16¾	16⅛	2¹⁄₁₆	1⁵⁄₁₆	⅝	7⅜	11¼	2¾	1⁵⁄₁₆	4	¹¹⁄₁₆	
×264	16½	16	1¹⁵⁄₁₆	1³⁄₁₆	⅝	7⅜	11¼	2⅝	1¼	4	¹¹⁄₁₆	
×246	16¼	16	1¹³⁄₁₆	1⅛	⁹⁄₁₆	7⅜	11¼	2½	1³⁄₁₆	3¾	⅝	
W 14×237	16⅛	15⅞	1¾	1¹⁄₁₆	⁹⁄₁₆	7⅜	11¼	2⁷⁄₁₆	1³⁄₁₆	3¾	⅝	
×228	16	15⅞	1¹¹⁄₁₆	1¹⁄₁₆	½	7⅜	11¼	2⅜	1⅛	3¾	⁹⁄₁₆	
×219	15⅞	15⅞	1⅝	1	½	7⅜	11¼	2⁵⁄₁₆	1⅛	3½	⁹⁄₁₆	
×211	15¾	15¾	1⁹⁄₁₆	1	½	7⅜	11¼	2¼	1⅛	3½	⁹⁄₁₆	
×202	15⅝	15¾	1½	¹⁵⁄₁₆	⁷⁄₁₆	7⅜	11¼	2³⁄₁₆	1⅛	3½	½	3-5½-3
×193	15½	15¾	1⁷⁄₁₆	⅞	⁷⁄₁₆	7⅜	11¼	2⅛	1¹⁄₁₆	3½	½	
×184	15⅜	15⅝	1⅜	¹³⁄₁₆	⁷⁄₁₆	7⅜	11¼	2¹⁄₁₆	1¹⁄₁₆	3½	½	
×176	15¼	15⅝	1⁵⁄₁₆	¹³⁄₁₆	⁷⁄₁₆	7⅜	11¼	2	1¹⁄₁₆	3¼	½	
×167	15⅛	15⅝	1¼	¾	⅜	7⅜	11¼	1¹⁵⁄₁₆	1	3¼	⁷⁄₁₆	
×158	15	15½	1³⁄₁₆	¾	⅜	7⅜	11¼	1⅞	1	3¼	⁷⁄₁₆	
×150	14⅞	15½	1⅛	¹¹⁄₁₆	⅜	7⅜	11¼	1¹³⁄₁₆	1	3¼	⁷⁄₁₆	
×142	14¾	15½	1¹⁄₁₆	¹¹⁄₁₆	⁵⁄₁₆	7⅜	11¼	1¾	1	3	⅜	
W 14×320	16¾	16¾	2¹⁄₁₆	1⅞	¹⁵⁄₁₆	7⅜	11¼	2¾	1⁹⁄₁₆	4	1	3-5½-3

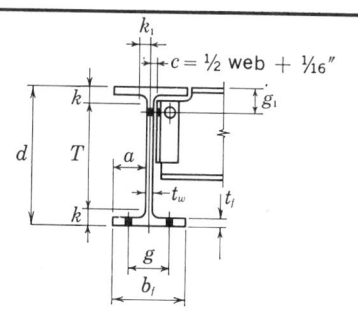

W SHAPES
Dimensions for detailing

Designation	Depth d	Flange Width b_f	Flange Thickness t_f	Web Thickness t_w	$\dfrac{t_w}{2}$	a	T	k	k_1	g_1	c	Usual Gage g
	In.	In.	In.	In.	In.	In.	In.	In.	In.	In.	In.	In.
W 14×136	14¾	14¾	1¹⁄₁₆	¹¹⁄₁₆	⁵⁄₁₆	7	11¼	1¾	¹⁵⁄₁₆	3	⅜	5½
×127	14⅝	14¾	1	⅝	⁵⁄₁₆	7	11¼	1¹¹⁄₁₆	¹⁵⁄₁₆	3	⅜	5½
×119	14½	14⅝	¹⁵⁄₁₆	⁹⁄₁₆	⁵⁄₁₆	7	11¼	1⅝	¹⁵⁄₁₆	3	⅜	5½
×111	14⅜	14⅝	⅞	⁹⁄₁₆	¼	7	11¼	1⁹⁄₁₆	⅞	2¾	⁵⁄₁₆	5½
×103	14¼	14⅝	¹³⁄₁₆	½	¼	7	11¼	1½	⅞	2¾	⁵⁄₁₆	5½
× 95	14⅛	14½	¾	⁷⁄₁₆	¼	7	11¼	1⁷⁄₁₆	⅞	2¾	⁵⁄₁₆	5½
× 87	14	14½	¹¹⁄₁₆	⁷⁄₁₆	³⁄₁₆	7	11¼	1⅜	¹³⁄₁₆	2¾	¼	5½
W 14× 84	14⅛	12	¾	⁷⁄₁₆	¼	5¾	11¼	1⁷⁄₁₆	⅞	2¾	⁵⁄₁₆	5½
× 78	14	12	¹¹⁄₁₆	⁷⁄₁₆	³⁄₁₆	5¾	11¼	1⅜	⅞	2¾	¼	5½
W 14× 74	14¼	10⅛	¹³⁄₁₆	⁷⁄₁₆	¼	4¾	11¼	1½	⅞	2¾	⁵⁄₁₆	5½
× 68	14	10	¹¹⁄₁₆	⁷⁄₁₆	³⁄₁₆	4¾	11¼	1⅜	¹³⁄₁₆	2¾	¼	5½
× 61	13⅞	10	⅝	⅜	³⁄₁₆	4¾	11¼	1⁵⁄₁₆	¹³⁄₁₆	2¾	¼	5½
W 14× 53	14	8	¹¹⁄₁₆	⅜	³⁄₁₆	3⅞	11¼	1⅜	¹³⁄₁₆	2¾	¼	5½
× 48	13¾	8	⁹⁄₁₆	⁵⁄₁₆	³⁄₁₆	3⅞	11¼	1¼	¹³⁄₁₆	2½	¼	5½
× 43	13⅝	8	½	⁵⁄₁₆	⅛	3⅞	11¼	1³⁄₁₆	¹³⁄₁₆	2½	³⁄₁₆	5½
W 14× 38	14⅛	6¾	½	⁵⁄₁₆	³⁄₁₆	3¼	11⅞	1⅛	¹¹⁄₁₆	2½	¼	3½
× 34	14	6¾	⁷⁄₁₆	⁵⁄₁₆	⅛	3¼	11⅞	1¹⁄₁₆	¹¹⁄₁₆	2½	³⁄₁₆	3½
× 30	13⅞	6¾	⅜	¼	⅛	3¼	11⅞	1	¹¹⁄₁₆	2½	³⁄₁₆	3½
W 14× 26	13⅞	5	⁷⁄₁₆	¼	⅛	2⅜	11⅞	1	¹¹⁄₁₆	2½	³⁄₁₆	2¾
× 22	13¾	5	⁵⁄₁₆	¼	⅛	2⅜	11⅞	¹⁵⁄₁₆	⅝	2¼	³⁄₁₆	2¾

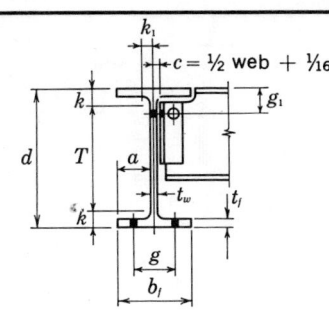

W SHAPES
Dimensions for detailing

Designation	Depth d	Flange Width b_f	Flange Thickness t_f	Web Thickness t_w	$\frac{t_w}{2}$	Distance a	T	k	k_1	g_1	c	Usual Gage g
	In.	In.	In.	In.	In.	In.	In.	In.	In.	In.	In.	In.
W 12×190	14⅜	12⅝	1¾	1¹⁄₁₆	½	5¾	9½	2⁷⁄₁₆	1³⁄₁₆	3¾	⁹⁄₁₆	5½
×161	13⅞	12½	1½	⅞	⁷⁄₁₆	5¾	9½	2³⁄₁₆	1¹⁄₁₆	3½	½	5½
×133	13⅜	12⅜	1¼	¾	⅜	5¾	9½	1¹⁵⁄₁₆	1	3¼	⁷⁄₁₆	5½
×120	13⅛	12⅜	1⅛	¹¹⁄₁₆	⅜	5¾	9½	1¹³⁄₁₆	1	3	⁷⁄₁₆	5½
×106	12⅞	12¼	1	⅝	⁵⁄₁₆	5¾	9½	1¹¹⁄₁₆	¹⁵⁄₁₆	3	⅜	5½
× 99	12¾	12¼	¹⁵⁄₁₆	⁹⁄₁₆	⁵⁄₁₆	5¾	9½	1⅝	¹⁵⁄₁₆	3	⅜	5½
× 92	12⅝	12⅛	⅞	⁹⁄₁₆	¼	5¾	9½	1⁹⁄₁₆	⅞	2¾	⁵⁄₁₆	5½
× 85	12½	12⅛	¹³⁄₁₆	½	¼	5¾	9½	1½	⅞	2¾	⁵⁄₁₆	5½
× 79	12⅜	12⅛	¾	½	¼	5¾	9½	1⁷⁄₁₆	⅞	2¾	⁵⁄₁₆	5½
× 72	12¼	12	¹¹⁄₁₆	⁷⁄₁₆	³⁄₁₆	5¾	9½	1⅜	⅞	2¾	¼	5½
× 65	12⅛	12	⅝	⅜	³⁄₁₆	5¾	9½	1⁵⁄₁₆	¹³⁄₁₆	2½	¼	5½
W 12× 58	12¼	10	⅝	⅜	³⁄₁₆	4⅞	9½	1⅜	¹³⁄₁₆	2¾	¼	5½
× 53	12	10	⁹⁄₁₆	⅜	³⁄₁₆	4⅞	9½	1¼	¹³⁄₁₆	2½	¼	5½
W 12× 50	12¼	8⅛	⅝	⅜	³⁄₁₆	3⅞	9½	1⅜	¹³⁄₁₆	2¾	¼	5½
× 45	12	8	⁹⁄₁₆	⁵⁄₁₆	³⁄₁₆	3⅞	9½	1¼	¹³⁄₁₆	2½	¼	5½
× 40	12	8	½	⁵⁄₁₆	⅛	3⅞	9½	1¼	¹³⁄₁₆	2½	³⁄₁₆	5½
W 12× 36	12¼	6⅝	⁹⁄₁₆	⁵⁄₁₆	⅛	3⅛	10⅛	1¹⁄₁₆	⅝	2½	³⁄₁₆	3½
× 31	12⅛	6½	⁷⁄₁₆	¼	⅛	3⅛	10⅛	1	⅝	2½	³⁄₁₆	3½
× 27	12	6½	⅜	¼	⅛	3⅛	10⅛	¹⁵⁄₁₆	⁹⁄₁₆	2½	³⁄₁₆	3½
W 12× 22	12¼	4	⁷⁄₁₆	¼	⅛	1⅞	10⅜	¹⁵⁄₁₆	⅝	2½	³⁄₁₆	2¼
× 19	12⅛	4	⅜	¼	⅛	1⅞	10⅜	⅞	⁹⁄₁₆	2¼	³⁄₁₆	2¼
× 16.5	12	4	¼	¼	⅛	1⅞	10⅜	¹³⁄₁₆	⁹⁄₁₆	2¼	³⁄₁₆	2¼
× 14	11⅞	4	¼	³⁄₁₆	⅛	1⅞	10⅜	¾	⁹⁄₁₆	2¼	³⁄₁₆	2¼

W SHAPES
Dimensions for detailing

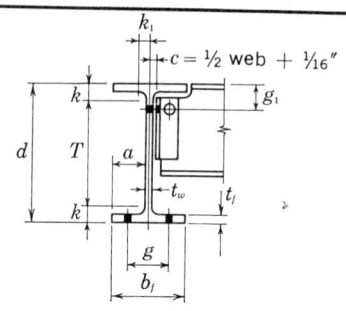

$c = \frac{1}{2}\ \text{web} + \frac{1}{16}''$

Designation	Depth d	Flange Width b_f	Flange Thickness t_f	Web Thickness t_w	$\frac{t_w}{2}$	a	T	k	k_1	g_1	c	Usual Gage g
	In.	In.	In.	In.	In.	In.	In.	In.	In.	In.	In.	In.
W 10×112	11⅜	10⅜	1¼	¾	⅜	4⅞	7¾	1 13/16	15/16	3	7/16	5½
×100	11⅛	10⅜	1⅛	11/16	5/16	4⅞	7¾	1 11/16	⅞	3	⅜	5½
× 89	10⅞	10¼	1	⅝	5/16	4⅞	7¾	1 9/16	13/16	2¾	⅜	5½
× 77	10⅝	10¼	⅞	9/16	¼	4⅞	7¾	1 7/16	13/16	2¾	5/16	5½
× 72	10½	10⅛	13/16	½	¼	4⅞	7¾	1⅜	13/16	2¾	5/16	5½
× 66	10⅜	10⅛	¾	7/16	¼	4⅞	7¾	1 5/16	¾	2½	5/16	5½
× 60	10¼	10⅛	11/16	7/16	3/16	4⅞	7¾	1¼	¾	2½	¼	5½
× 54	10⅛	10	⅝	⅜	3/16	4⅞	7¾	1 3/16	11/16	2½	¼	5½
× 49	10	10	9/16	5/16	3/16	4⅞	7¾	1⅛	11/16	2½	¼	5½
W 10× 45	10⅛	8	⅝	⅜	3/16	3⅞	7¾	1 3/16	11/16	2½	¼	5½
× 39	10	8	½	5/16	3/16	3⅞	7¾	1⅛	11/16	2½	¼	5½
× 33	9¾	8	7/16	5/16	⅛	3⅞	7¾	1	11/16	2¼	3/16	5½
W 10× 29	10¼	5¾	½	5/16	⅛	2¾	8⅛	1 1/16	⅝	2¼	3/16	2¾
× 25	10⅛	5¾	7/16	¼	⅛	2¾	8⅛	1	⅝	2¼	3/16	2¾
× 21	9⅞	5¾	5/16	¼	⅛	2¾	8⅛	⅞	9/16	2¼	3/16	2¾
W 10× 19	10¼	4	⅜	¼	⅛	1⅞	8⅜	15/16	⅝	2¼	3/16	2¼
× 17	10⅛	4	5/16	¼	⅛	1⅞	8⅜	⅞	9/16	2¼	3/16	2¼
× 15	10	4	¼	¼	⅛	1⅞	8⅜	13/16	9/16	2¼	3/16	2¼
× 11.5	9⅞	4	3/16	3/16	1/16	1⅞	8⅜	¾	9/16	2	⅛	2¼

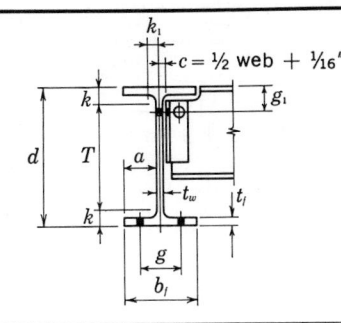

W SHAPES
Dimensions for detailing

Designation	Depth d	Flange Width b_f	Flange Thickness t_f	Web Thickness t_w	$\dfrac{t_w}{2}$	a	T	k	k_1	g_1	c	Usual Gage g
	In.	In.	In.	In.	In.	In.	In.	In.	In.	In.	In.	In.
W 8×67	9	8¼	15/16	9/16	5/16	3⅞	6⅛	1 7/16	¾	2¾	⅜	5½
×58	8¾	8¼	13/16	½	¼	3⅞	6⅛	1 5/16	11/16	2¾	5/16	5½
×48	8½	8⅛	11/16	⅜	3/16	3⅞	6⅛	1 3/16	⅝	2½	¼	5½
×40	8¼	8⅛	9/16	⅜	3/16	3⅞	6⅛	1 1/16	⅝	2½	¼	5½
×35	8⅛	8	½	5/16	3/16	3⅞	6⅛	1	⅝	2¼	¼	5½
×31	8	8	7/16	5/16	⅛	3⅞	6⅛	15/16	⅝	2¼	3/16	5½
W 8×28	8	6½	7/16	5/16	⅛	3⅛	6⅛	15/16	⅝	2¼	3/16	3½
×24	7⅞	6½	⅜	¼	⅛	3⅛	6⅛	⅞	9/16	2¼	3/16	3½
W 8×20	8⅛	5¼	⅜	¼	⅛	2½	6⅜	⅞	9/16	2¼	3/16	2¾
×17	8	5¼	5/16	¼	⅛	2½	6⅜	13/16	½	2¼	3/16	2¾
W 8×15	8⅛	4	5/16	¼	⅛	1⅞	6½	13/16	9/16	2¼	3/16	2¼
×13	8	4	¼	¼	⅛	1⅞	6½	¾	½	2¼	3/16	2¼
×10	7⅞	4	3/16	3/16	1/16	1⅞	6½	11/16	½	2	⅛	2¼
W 6×25	6⅜	6⅛	7/16	5/16	3/16	2⅞	4½	15/16	9/16	2¼	¼	3½
×20	6¼	6	⅜	¼	⅛	2⅞	4½	⅞	9/16	2¼	3/16	3½
×15.5	6	6	¼	¼	⅛	2⅞	4½	¾	½	2¼	3/16	3½
W 6×16	6¼	4	⅜	¼	⅛	1⅞	4½	⅞	9/16	2¼	3/16	2¼
×12	6	4	¼	¼	⅛	1⅞	4½	¾	½	2¼	3/16	2¼
× 8.5	5⅞	4	3/16	3/16	1/16	1⅞	4½	11/16	½	2	⅛	2¼
W 5×18.5	5⅛	5	7/16	¼	⅛	2⅜	3½	13/16	½	2¼	3/16	2¾
×16	5	5	⅜	¼	⅛	2⅜	3½	¾	7/16	2¼	3/16	2¾
W 4×13	4⅛	4	⅜	¼	⅛	1⅞	2½	13/16	9/16	2	3/16	2¼

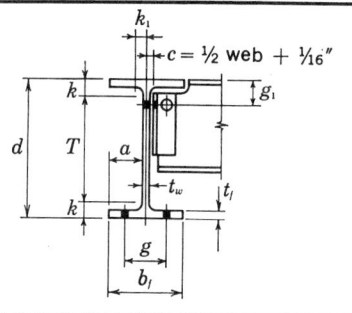

M SHAPES
Dimensions for detailing

$c = \frac{1}{2}$ web $+ \frac{1}{16}''$

Designation	Depth d	Flange Width b_f	Flange Thickness t_f	Web Thickness t_w	$\frac{t_w}{2}$	Distance a	T	k	k_1	g_1	c	Grip	Max. Flange Fastener	Usual Flange Gage g
	In.	In.	In.	In.	In.	In.	In.	In.	In.	In.	In.	In.	In.	In.
M 14×17.2	14	4	¼	³⁄₁₆	⅛	1⅞	12¾	⅝	⅜	2¼	³⁄₁₆	¼	¾	2¼
M 12×11.8	12	3⅛	¼	³⁄₁₆	¹⁄₁₆	1½	10⅞	⁹⁄₁₆	⅜	2¼	⅛	¼	—	—
M 10×29.1	9⅞	5⅞	⅜	⁷⁄₁₆	³⁄₁₆	2¾	8⅛	⅞	½	2½	¼	⁷⁄₁₆	⅞	2¾
×22.9	9⅞	5¾	⅜	¼	⅛	2¾	8⅛	⅞	⁷⁄₁₆	2½	³⁄₁₆	⅜	⅞	2¾
M 10× 9	10	2¾	³⁄₁₆	³⁄₁₆	¹⁄₁₆	1¼	9	½	⁵⁄₁₆	2	⅛	³⁄₁₆	—	—
M 8×34.3	8	8	⁷⁄₁₆	⅜	³⁄₁₆	3¾	5⅞	1¹⁄₁₆	⅝	2½	¼	⁷⁄₁₆	⅞	5½
×32.6	8	8	⁷⁄₁₆	⁵⁄₁₆	³⁄₁₆	3¾	5⅞	1¹⁄₁₆	⅝	2½	¼	⁷⁄₁₆	⅞	5½
M 8×22.5	8	5⅜	⅜	⅜	³⁄₁₆	2½	6¼	⅞	½	2¼	¼	⅜	⅞	2¾
×18.5	8	5¼	⅜	¼	⅛	2½	6¼	⅞	⁷⁄₁₆	2¼	³⁄₁₆	⅜	⅞	2¾
M 8× 6.5	8	2¼	³⁄₁₆	⅛	¹⁄₁₆	1⅛	7	½	¼	2	⅛	³⁄₁₆	—	—
M 7× 5.5	7	2⅛	³⁄₁₆	⅛	¹⁄₁₆	1	6⅛	⁷⁄₁₆	¼	2	⅛	³⁄₁₆	—	—
M 6×22.5	6	6	⅜	⅜	³⁄₁₆	2⅞	4⅜	¹³⁄₁₆	½	2¼	¼	⅜	⅞	3½
×20	6	6	⅜	¼	⅛	2⅞	4⅜	¹³⁄₁₆	⁷⁄₁₆	2¼	³⁄₁₆	⅜	⅞	3½
M 6× 4.4	6	1⅞	³⁄₁₆	⅛	¹⁄₁₆	⅞	5¼	⅜	¼	2	⅛	³⁄₁₆	—	—
M 5×18.9	5	5	⁷⁄₁₆	⁵⁄₁₆	³⁄₁₆	2⅜	3¼	⅞	½	2½	¼	⁷⁄₁₆	⅞	2¾
M 4×13.8	4	4	⅜	⁵⁄₁₆	³⁄₁₆	1⅞	2⅜	¹³⁄₁₆	½	2	¼	⅜	¾	2¼
×13	4	4	⅜	¼	⅛	1⅞	2⅜	¹³⁄₁₆	⁷⁄₁₆	2	³⁄₁₆	⅜	¾	2¼

Gage g permissible near beam ends; elsewhere Specification Sect. 1.16.5 may require reduction in fastener size.

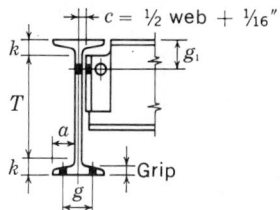

$c = \frac{1}{2}$ web $+ \frac{1}{16}''$

S SHAPES
Dimensions for detailing

Designation	Depth d	Flange Width b_f	Flange Thickness t_f	Web Thickness t_w	$\dfrac{t_w}{2}$	a	T	k	g_1	c	Grip	Max. Flange Fastener	Usual Flange Gage g
	In.	In.	In.	In.	In.	In.	In.	In.	In.	In.	In.	In.	In.
S 24×120	24	8	1⅛	¹³⁄₁₆	⅜	3⅝	20	2	3¼	⁷⁄₁₆	1⅛	1	4
×105.9	24	7⅞	1⅛	⅝	⁵⁄₁₆	3⅝	20	2	3¼	⅜	1⅛	1	4
S 24×100	24	7¼	⅞	¾	⅜	3¼	20½	1¾	3	⁷⁄₁₆	⅞	1	4
× 90	24	7⅛	⅞	⅝	⁵⁄₁₆	3¼	20½	1¾	3	⅜	⅞	1	4
× 79.9	24	7	⅞	½	¼	3¼	20½	1¾	3	⁵⁄₁₆	⅞	1	4
S 20× 95	20	7¼	¹⁵⁄₁₆	¹³⁄₁₆	⅜	3¼	16¼	1⅞	3	⁷⁄₁₆	¹⁵⁄₁₆	1	4
× 85	20	7	¹⁵⁄₁₆	⅝	⁵⁄₁₆	3¼	16¼	1⅞	3	⅜	⅞	1	4
S 20× 75	20	6⅜	¹³⁄₁₆	⅝	⁵⁄₁₆	2⅞	16¾	1⅝	3	⅜	¹³⁄₁₆	⅞	3½
× 65.4	20	6¼	¹³⁄₁₆	½	¼	2⅞	16¾	1⅝	3	⁵⁄₁₆	¾	⅞	3½
S 18× 70	18	6¼	¹¹⁄₁₆	¹¹⁄₁₆	⅜	2¾	15	1½	2¾	⁷⁄₁₆	¹¹⁄₁₆	⅞	3½
× 54.7	18	6	¹¹⁄₁₆	⁷⁄₁₆	¼	2¾	15	1½	2¾	⁵⁄₁₆	¹¹⁄₁₆	⅞	3½
S 15× 50	15	5⅝	⅝	⁹⁄₁₆	¼	2½	12¼	1⅜	2¾	⁵⁄₁₆	⁹⁄₁₆	¾	3½
× 42.9	15	5½	⅝	⁷⁄₁₆	³⁄₁₆	2½	12¼	1⅜	2¾	¼	⁹⁄₁₆	¾	3½
S 12× 50	12	5½	¹¹⁄₁₆	¹¹⁄₁₆	⁵⁄₁₆	2⅜	9⅛	1⁷⁄₁₆	2¾	⅜	¹¹⁄₁₆	¾	3
× 40.8	12	5¼	¹¹⁄₁₆	⁷⁄₁₆	¼	2⅜	9⅛	1⁷⁄₁₆	2¾	⁵⁄₁₆	⅝	¾	3
S 12× 35	12	5⅛	⁹⁄₁₆	⁷⁄₁₆	³⁄₁₆	2⅜	9⅝	1³⁄₁₆	2½	¼	½	¾	3
× 31.8	12	5	⁹⁄₁₆	⅜	³⁄₁₆	2⅜	9⅝	1³⁄₁₆	2½	¼	½	¾	3
S 10× 35	10	5	½	⅝	⁵⁄₁₆	2⅛	7¾	1⅛	2½	⅜	½	¾	2¾
× 25.4	10	4⅝	½	⁵⁄₁₆	⅛	2⅛	7¾	1⅛	2½	³⁄₁₆	½	¾	2¾
S 8× 23	8	4⅛	⁷⁄₁₆	⁷⁄₁₆	¼	1⅞	6	1	2½	⁵⁄₁₆	⁷⁄₁₆	¾	2¼
× 18.4	8	4	⁷⁄₁₆	¼	⅛	1⅞	6	1	2½	³⁄₁₆	⁷⁄₁₆	¾	2¼
S 7× 20	7	3⅞	⅜	⁷⁄₁₆	¼	1¾	5¼	⅞	2½	⁵⁄₁₆	⅜	⅝	2¼
× 15.3	7	3⅝	⅜	¼	⅛	1¾	5¼	⅞	2½	³⁄₁₆	⅜	⅝	2¼
S 6× 17.25	6	3⅝	⅜	⁷⁄₁₆	¼	1½	4⅜	¹³⁄₁₆	2¼	⁵⁄₁₆	⅜	⅝	2
× 12.5	6	3⅜	⅜	¼	⅛	1½	4⅜	¹³⁄₁₆	2¼	³⁄₁₆	⁵⁄₁₆	—	—
S 5× 14.75	5	3¼	⁵⁄₁₆	½	¼	1⅜	3½	¾	2¼	⁵⁄₁₆	⁵⁄₁₆	—	—
× 10	5	3	⁵⁄₁₆	³⁄₁₆	⅛	1⅜	3½	¾	2¼	³⁄₁₆	⁵⁄₁₆	—	—
S 4× 9.5	4	2¾	⁵⁄₁₆	⁵⁄₁₆	³⁄₁₆	1¼	2⅝	¹¹⁄₁₆	2	¼	⁵⁄₁₆	—	—
× 7.7	4	2⅝	⁵⁄₁₆	³⁄₁₆	⅛	1¼	2⅝	¹¹⁄₁₆	2	³⁄₁₆	⁵⁄₁₆	—	—
S 3× 7.5	3	2½	¼	⅜	³⁄₁₆	1⅛	1¾	⅝	—	¼	¼	—	—
× 5.7	3	2⅜	¼	³⁄₁₆	¹⁄₁₆	1⅛	1¾	⅝	—	⅛	¼	—	—

Gage g permissible near beam ends; elsewhere Specification Sect. 1.16.5 may require reduction in fastener size.

HP SHAPES
Dimensions for detailing

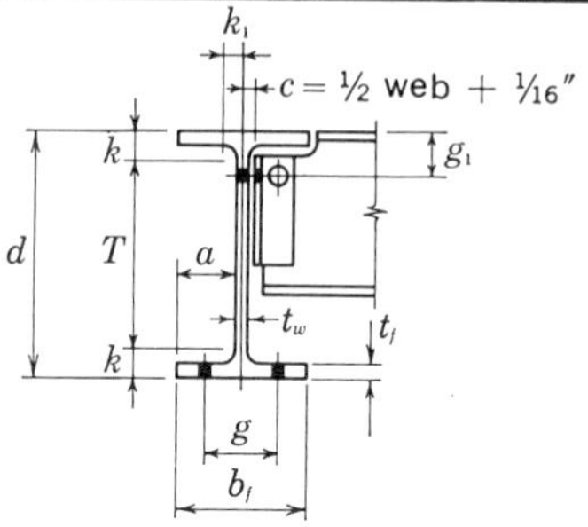

Designation	Depth d	Flange Width b_f	Flange Thickness t_f	Web Thickness t_w	$\frac{t_w}{2}$	Distance a	Distance T	Distance k	Distance k_1	Distance g_1	Distance c	Usual Gage g
	In.	In.	In.	In.	In.	In.	In.	In.	In.	In.	In.	In.
HP 14×117	14¼	14⅞	13/16	13/16	⅜	7	11¼	1½	1 1/16	2¾	7/16	5½
×102	14	14¾	11/16	11/16	⅜	7	11¼	1⅜	1	2¾	7/16	5½
× 89	13⅞	14¾	⅝	⅝	5/16	7	11¼	1 5/16	15/16	2½	⅜	5½
× 73	13⅝	14⅝	½	½	¼	7	11¼	1 3/16	⅞	2½	5/16	5½
HP 12× 74	12⅛	12¼	⅝	⅝	5/16	5¾	9½	1 5/16	15/16	2½	⅜	5½
× 53	11¾	12	7/16	7/16	3/16	5¾	9½	1⅛	⅞	2½	¼	5½
HP 10× 57	10	10¼	9/16	9/16	5/16	4⅞	7¾	1⅛	13/16	2½	⅜	5½
× 42	9¾	10⅛	7/16	7/16	3/16	4⅞	7¾	1	¾	2¼	¼	5½
HP 8× 36	8	8⅛	7/16	7/16	¼	3⅞	6⅛	15/16	⅝	2¼	5/16	5½

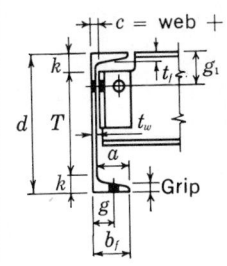

AMERICAN STANDARD CHANNELS
Dimensions for detailing

Designation	Depth of Section d In.	Flange Width b_f In.	Flange Avg. Thickness t_f In.	Web Thickness t_w In.	$\dfrac{t_w}{2}$ In.	Distance a In.	Distance T In.	Distance k In.	Distance g_1 In.	c In.	Grip In.	Max. Flange Fastener In.	Usual Flange Gage g In.
C 15×50	15	3¾	⅝	11/16	⅜	3	12⅛	1 7/16	2¾	¾	⅝	1	2¼
×40	15	3½	⅝	½	¼	3	12⅛	1 7/16	2¾	9/16	⅝	1	2
×33.9	15	3⅜	⅝	⅜	3/16	3	12⅛	1 7/16	2¾	7/16	⅝	1	2
C 12×30	12	3⅛	½	½	¼	2⅝	9¾	1⅛	2½	9/16	½	⅞	1¾
×25	12	3	½	⅜	3/16	2⅝	9¾	1⅛	2½	7/16	½	⅞	1¾
×20.7	12	3	½	5/16	⅛	2⅝	9¾	1⅛	2½	⅜	½	⅞	1¾
C 10×30	10	3	7/16	11/16	5/16	2⅜	8	1	2½	¾	7/16	¾	1¾
×25	10	2⅞	7/16	½	¼	2⅜	8	1	2½	9/16	7/16	¾	1¾
×20	10	2¾	7/16	⅜	3/16	2⅜	8	1	2½	7/16	7/16	¾	1½
×15.3	10	2⅝	7/16	¼	⅛	2⅜	8	1	2½	5/16	7/16	¾	1½
C 9×20	9	2⅝	7/16	7/16	¼	2¼	7⅛	15/16	2½	½	7/16	¾	1½
×15	9	2½	7/16	5/16	⅛	2¼	7⅛	15/16	2½	⅜	7/16	¾	1⅜
×13.4	9	2⅜	7/16	¼	⅛	2¼	7⅛	15/16	2½	5/16	7/16	¾	1⅜
C 8×18.75	8	2½	⅜	½	¼	2	6⅛	15/16	2½	9/16	⅜	¾	1½
×13.75	8	2⅜	⅜	5/16	⅛	2	6⅛	15/16	2½	⅜	⅜	¾	1⅜
×11.5	8	2¼	⅜	¼	⅛	2	6⅛	15/16	2½	5/16	⅜	¾	1⅜
C 7×14.75	7	2¼	⅜	7/16	3/16	1⅞	5¼	⅞	2½	½	⅜	⅝	1¼
×12.25	7	2¼	⅜	5/16	3/16	1⅞	5¼	⅞	2½	⅜	⅜	⅝	1¼
× 9.8	7	2⅛	⅜	3/16	⅛	1⅞	5¼	⅞	2½	¼	⅜	⅝	1¼
C 6×13	6	2⅛	5/16	7/16	3/16	1¾	4⅜	13/16	2¼	½	5/16	⅝	1⅜
×10.5	6	2	5/16	5/16	3/16	1¾	4⅜	13/16	2¼	⅜	⅜	⅝	1⅛
× 8.2	6	1⅞	5/16	3/16	⅛	1¾	4⅜	13/16	2¼	¼	5/16	⅝	1⅛
C 5× 9	5	1⅞	5/16	5/16	3/16	1½	3½	¾	2¼	⅜	5/16	⅝	1⅛
× 6.7	5	1¾	5/16	3/16	⅛	1½	3½	¾	2¼	¼	5/16	—	—
C 4× 7.25	4	1¾	5/16	5/16	3/16	1⅜	2⅝	11/16	2	⅜	5/16	⅝	1
× 5.4	4	1⅝	5/16	3/16	1/16	1⅜	2⅝	11/16	2	¼	¼	—	—
C 3× 6	3	1⅝	¼	⅜	3/16	1¼	1⅝	11/16	—	7/16	5/16	—	—
× 5	3	1½	¼	¼	⅛	1¼	1⅝	11/16	—	5/16	¼	—	—
× 4.1	3	1⅜	¼	3/16	1/16	1¼	1⅝	11/16	—	¼	¼	—	—

Gage g permissible near beam ends; elsewhere Specification Sect. 1.16.5 may require reduction in fastener size

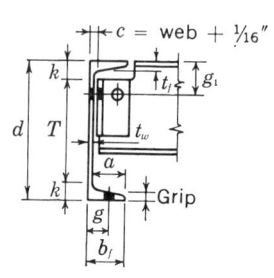

MISCELLANEOUS CHANNELS
Dimensions for detailing

c = web + $\frac{1}{16}''$

Designation	Depth of Section d	Flange Width b_f	Flange Avg. Thickness t_f	Web Thickness t_w	$\frac{t_w}{2}$	a	T	k	g_1	c	Grip	Max. Flange Fastener	Usual Flange Gage g
	In.	In.	In.	In.	In.	In.	In.	In.	In.	In.	In.	In.	In.
MC 18×58	18	4¼	⅝	11/16	⅜	3½	15¼	1⅜	2½	¾	⅝	1	2½
×51.9	18	4⅛	⅝	⅝	5/16	3½	15¼	1⅜	2½	11/16	⅝	1	2½
×45.8	18	4	⅝	½	¼	3½	15¼	1⅜	2½	9/16	⅝	1	2½
×42.7	18	4	⅝	7/16	¼	3½	15¼	1⅜	2½	½	⅝	1	2½
MC 13×50	13	4⅜	⅝	13/16	⅜	3⅝	10¼	1⅜	2¾	⅞	⅝	1	2½
×40	13	4⅛	⅝	9/16	¼	3⅝	10¼	1⅜	2¾	⅝	9/16	1	2½
×35	13	4⅛	⅝	7/16	¼	3⅝	10¼	1⅜	2¾	½	9/16	1	2½
×31.8	13	4	⅝	⅜	3/16	3⅝	10¼	1⅜	2¾	7/16	9/16	1	2½
MC 12×50	12	4⅛	11/16	13/16	7/16	3¼	9⅜	1 5/16	2½	⅞	11/16	1	2½
×45	12	4	11/16	11/16	⅜	3¼	9⅜	1 5/16	2½	¾	11/16	1	2½
×40	12	3⅞	11/16	9/16	5/16	3¼	9⅜	1 5/16	2½	⅝	11/16	1	2½
×35	12	3¾	11/16	7/16	¼	3¼	9⅜	1 5/16	2½	½	11/16	1	2½
MC 12×37	12	3⅝	⅝	⅝	5/16	3	9⅜	1 5/16	2½	11/16	⅝	⅞	2¼
×32.9	12	3½	⅝	½	¼	3	9⅜	1 5/16	2½	9/16	9/16	⅞	2¼
×30.9	12	3½	⅝	7/16	¼	3	9⅜	1 5/16	2½	½	9/16	⅞	2¼
MC 12×10.6	12	1½	5/16	3/16	⅛	1¼	10⅝	11/16	2¼	¼	¼	—	—
MC 10×41.1	10	4⅜	9/16	13/16	⅜	3½	7½	1¼	2½	⅞	9/16	⅞	2½
×33.6	10	4⅛	9/16	9/16	5/16	3½	7½	1¼	2½	⅝	9/16	⅞	2½
×28.5	10	4	9/16	7/16	3/16	3½	7½	1¼	2½	½	9/16	⅞	2½
MC 10×28.3	10	3½	9/16	½	¼	3	7½	1¼	2½	9/16	9/16	⅞	2
×25.3	10	3½	½	7/16	3/16	3⅛	7¾	1⅛	2½	½	½	⅞	2
×24.9	10	3⅜	9/16	⅜	3/16	3	7½	1¼	2½	7/16	9/16	⅞	2
×21.9	10	3½	½	5/16	3/16	3⅛	7¾	1⅛	2½	⅜	½	⅞	2
MC 10×8.4	10	1½	¼	3/16	1/16	1⅜	8⅝	11/16	2¼	¼	¼	—	—
MC 10×6.5	10	1⅛	3/16	⅛	1/16	1	9⅛	7/16	2¼	3/16	3/16	—	—

Gage g permissible near beam ends; elsewhere Specification Sect. 1.16.5 may require reduction in fastener size.

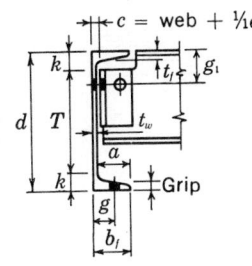

MISCELLANEOUS CHANNELS
Dimensions for detailing

Designation	Depth of Section d	Flange Width b_f	Flange Avg. Thickness t_f	Web Thickness t_w	$\frac{t_w}{2}$	a	T	k	g_1	c	Grip	Max. Flange Fastener	Usual Flange Gage g
	In.	In.	In.	In.	In.	In.	In.	In.	In.	In.	In.	In.	In.
MC 9×25.4	9	3½	9/16	7/16	¼	3	6⅝	1 3/16	2½	½	9/16	⅞	2
9×23.9	9	3½	9/16	⅜	3/16	3	6⅝	1 3/16	2½	7/16	9/16	⅞	2
MC 8×22.8	8	3½	½	7/16	3/16	3⅛	5⅝	1 3/16	2½	½	½	⅞	2
×21.4	8	3½	½	⅜	3/16	3⅛	5⅝	1 3/16	2½	7/16	½	⅞	2
MC 8×20	8	3	½	⅜	3/16	2⅝	5¾	1⅛	2½	7/16	½	⅞	2
×18.7	8	3	½	⅜	3/16	2⅝	5¾	1⅛	2½	7/16	½	⅞	2
MC 8× 8.5	8	1⅞	5/16	3/16	1/16	1¾	6½	¾	2¼	¼	5/16	⅝	1⅛
MC 7×22.7	7	3⅝	½	½	¼	3⅛	4¾	1⅛	2½	9/16	½	⅞	2
×19.1	7	3½	½	⅜	3/16	3⅛	4¾	1⅛	2½	7/16	½	⅞	2
MC 7×17.6	7	3	½	⅜	3/16	2⅝	4⅞	1 1/16	2½	7/16	½	¾	1¾
MC 6×18	6	3½	½	⅜	3/16	3⅛	3⅞	1 1/16	2½	7/16	½	⅞	2
×15.3	6	3½	⅜	5/16	3/16	3⅛	4¼	⅞	2¼	⅜	⅜	⅞	2
MC 6×16.3	6	3	½	⅜	3/16	2⅝	3⅞	1 1/16	2½	7/16	½	¾	1¾
×15.1	6	3	½	5/16	3/16	2⅝	3⅞	1 1/16	2½	⅜	½	¾	1¾
MC 6×12	6	2½	⅜	5/16	⅛	2⅛	4⅜	13/16	2¼	⅜	⅜	⅝	1½
MC 3× 9	3	2⅛	⅜	½	¼	1⅝	1¾	⅝	—	9/16	—	—	—
× 7.1	3	2	⅜	5/16	⅛	1⅝	1¾	⅝	—	⅜	—	—	—

Gage g permissible near beam ends; elsewhere Specification Sect. 1.16.5 may require reduction in fastener size.

Notes

PROPERTIES FOR DESIGNING
W Shapes
M Shapes
S Shapes
HP Shapes
American Standard Channels (C)
Miscellaneous Channels (MC)
Angles (L)

W SHAPES
Properties for designing

Designation	Area A	Depth d	Flange		Web Thickness t_w	Elastic Properties					
			Width b_f	Thickness t_f		Axis X-X			Axis Y-Y		
						I	S	r	I	S	r
	In.²	In.	In.	In.	In.	In.⁴	In.³	In.	In.⁴	In.³	In.
W 36×300	88.3	36.72	16.655	1.680	0.945	20300	1110	15.2	1300	156	3.83
×280	82.4	36.50	16.595	1.570	0.885	18900	1030	15.1	1200	144	3.81
×260	76.5	36.24	16.551	1.440	0.841	17300	952	15.0	1090	132	3.77
×245	72.1	36.06	16.512	1.350	0.802	16100	894	15.0	1010	123	3.75
×230	67.7	35.88	16.471	1.260	0.761	15000	837	14.9	940	114	3.73
W 36×194	57.2	36.48	12.117	1.260	0.770	12100	665	14.6	375	61.9	2.56
×182	53.6	36.32	12.072	1.180	0.725	11300	622	14.5	347	57.5	2.55
×170	50.0	36.16	12.027	1.100	0.680	10500	580	14.5	320	53.2	2.53
×160	47.1	36.00	12.000	1.020	0.653	9760	542	14.4	295	49.1	2.50
×150	44.2	35.84	11.972	0.940	0.625	9030	504	14.3	270	45.0	2.47
×135	39.8	35.55	11.945	0.794	0.598	7820	440	14.0	226	37.9	2.39
W 33×240	70.6	33.50	15.865	1.400	0.830	13600	813	13.9	933	118	3.64
×220	64.8	33.25	15.810	1.275	0.775	12300	742	13.8	841	106	3.60
×200	58.9	33.00	15.750	1.150	0.715	11100	671	13.7	750	95.2	3.57
W 33×152	44.8	33.50	11.565	1.055	0.635	8160	487	13.5	273	47.2	2.47
×141	41.6	33.31	11.535	0.960	0.605	7460	448	13.4	246	42.7	2.43
×130	38.3	33.10	11.510	0.855	0.580	6710	406	13.2	218	37.9	2.38
×118	34.8	32.86	11.484	0.738	0.554	5900	359	13.0	187	32.5	2.32
W 30×210	61.9	30.38	15.105	1.315	0.775	9890	651	12.6	757	100	3.50
×190	56.0	30.12	15.040	1.185	0.710	8850	587	12.6	673	89.5	3.47
×172	50.7	29.88	14.985	1.065	0.655	7910	530	12.5	598	79.8	3.43
W 30×132	38.9	30.30	10.551	1.000	0.615	5760	380	12.2	196	37.2	2.25
×124	36.5	30.16	10.521	0.930	0.585	5360	355	12.1	181	34.4	2.23
×116	34.2	30.00	10.500	0.850	0.564	4930	329	12.0	164	31.3	2.19
×108	31.8	29.82	10.484	0.760	0.548	4470	300	11.9	146	27.9	2.15
× 99	29.1	29.64	10.458	0.670	0.522	4000	270	11.7	128	24.5	2.10

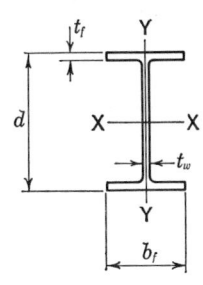

W SHAPES
Properties for designing

| Nominal Weight per Ft. | r_T | $\dfrac{d}{A_f}$ | Compact Section Criteria | | | | | Torsional Constant J | Warping Constant C_W | Plastic Modulus | |
| | | | $\dfrac{b_f}{2t_f}$ | F_y' | $\dfrac{d}{t_w}$ | F_y'' | F_y''' | | | Z_x | Z_y |
Lb.	In.			Ksi		Ksi	Ksi	In.⁴	In.⁶	In.³	In.³
300	4.46	1.31	4.96	—	38.9	—	43.7	64.2	398000	1260	241
280	4.43	1.40	5.29	—	41.2	—	38.8	52.6	365000	1170	223
260	4.40	1.52	5.75	—	43.1	—	35.6	41.6	330000	1080	204
245	4.38	1.62	6.12	—	45.0	—	32.7	34.7	306000	1010	190
230	4.36	1.73	6.54	63.8	47.1	—	29.7	28.6	282000	943	176
194	3.12	2.39	4.81	—	47.4	—	29.4	22.3	116000	768	97.8
182	3.10	2.55	5.12	—	50.1	—	26.3	18.4	107000	718	90.7
170	3.08	2.73	5.47	—	53.2	60.0	23.4	15.1	98300	668	83.7
160	3.06	2.94	5.88	—	55.1	55.8	21.7	12.4	90100	625	77.3
150	3.03	3.18	6.37	—	57.3	51.6	20.1	10.1	82100	581	70.9
135	2.97	3.75	7.52	48.2	59.4	48.0	18.7	7.03	68300	510	59.9
240	4.23	1.51	5.67	—	40.4	—	40.5	36.6	240000	919	182
220	4.20	1.65	6.20	—	42.9	—	35.9	28.2	215000	838	164
200	4.17	1.82	6.85	58.1	46.2	—	31.0	21.1	190000	756	147
152	2.98	2.75	5.48	—	52.8	61.0	23.7	12.4	71800	559	73.9
141	2.96	3.01	6.01	—	55.1	56.0	21.8	9.70	64400	514	66.9
130	2.92	3.36	6.73	60.1	57.1	52.1	20.3	7.37	56600	467	59.5
118	2.87	3.88	7.78	45.0	59.3	48.2	18.8	5.32	48200	415	51.3
210	4.05	1.53	5.74	—	39.2	—	43.0	28.5	160000	735	155
190	4.01	1.69	6.35	—	42.4	—	36.7	21.2	141000	661	138
172	3.98	1.87	7.04	55.1	45.6	—	31.7	15.7	124000	594	123
132	2.72	2.87	5.28	—	49.3	—	27.2	9.72	42100	437	58.5
124	2.70	3.08	5.66	—	51.6	63.9	24.8	7.99	38700	408	54.1
116	2.68	3.36	6.18	—	53.2	60.0	23.3	6.43	34900	378	49.3
108	2.64	3.74	6.90	57.3	54.4	57.3	22.3	5.02	30900	346	44.0
99	2.61	4.23	7.80	44.7	56.8	52.6	20.5	3.78	26900	313	38.7

I

W SHAPES
Properties for designing

Designation	Area A	Depth d	Flange		Web Thickness t_w	Elastic Properties					
			Width b_f	Thickness t_f		Axis X-X			Axis Y-Y		
						I	S	r	I	S	r
	In.²	In.	In.	In.	In.	In.⁴	In.³	In.	In.⁴	In.³	In.
W 27×177	52.2	27.31	14.090	1.190	0.725	6740	494	11.4	556	78.9	3.26
×160	47.1	27.08	14.023	1.075	0.658	6030	446	11.3	495	70.6	3.24
×145	42.7	26.88	13.965	0.975	0.600	5430	404	11.3	443	63.5	3.22
W 27×114	33.6	27.28	10.070	0.932	0.570	4090	300	11.0	159	31.6	2.18
×102	30.0	27.07	10.018	0.827	0.518	3610	267	11.0	139	27.7	2.15
× 94	27.7	26.91	9.990	0.747	0.490	3270	243	10.9	124	24.9	2.12
× 84	24.8	26.69	9.963	0.636	0.463	2830	212	10.7	105	21.1	2.06
W 24×160	47.1	24.72	14.091	1.135	0.656	5120	414	10.4	530	75.2	3.35
×145	42.7	24.49	14.043	1.020	0.608	4570	373	10.3	471	67.1	3.32
×130	38.3	24.25	14.000	0.900	0.565	4020	332	10.2	412	58.9	3.28
W 24×120	35.4	24.31	12.088	0.930	0.556	3650	300	10.2	274	45.4	2.78
×110	32.5	24.16	12.042	0.855	0.510	3330	276	10.1	249	41.4	2.77
×100	29.5	24.00	12.000	0.775	0.468	3000	250	10.1	223	37.2	2.75
W 24× 94	27.7	24.29	9.061	0.872	0.516	2690	221	9.86	108	23.9	1.98
× 84	24.7	24.09	9.015	0.772	0.470	2370	197	9.79	94.5	21.0	1.95
× 76	22.4	23.91	8.985	0.682	0.440	2100	176	9.69	82.6	18.4	1.92
× 68	20.0	23.71	8.961	0.582	0.416	1820	153	9.53	70.0	15.6	1.87
W 24× 61	18.0	23.72	7.023	0.591	0.419	1540	130	9.25	34.3	9.76	1.38
× 55	16.2	23.55	7.000	0.503	0.396	1340	114	9.10	28.9	8.25	1.34
W 21×142	41.8	21.46	13.132	1.095	0.659	3410	317	9.03	414	63.0	3.15
×127	37.4	21.24	13.061	0.985	0.588	3020	284	8.99	366	56.1	3.13
×112	33.0	21.00	13.000	0.865	0.527	2620	250	8.92	317	48.8	3.10
W 21× 96	28.3	21.14	9.038	0.935	0.575	2100	198	8.61	115	25.5	2.02
× 82	24.2	20.86	8.962	0.795	0.499	1760	169	8.53	95.6	21.3	1.99
W 21× 73	21.5	21.24	8.295	0.740	0.455	1600	151	8.64	70.6	17.0	1.81
× 68	20.0	21.13	8.270	0.685	0.430	1480	140	8.60	64.7	15.7	1.80
× 62	18.3	20.99	8.240	0.615	0.400	1330	127	8.54	57.5	13.9	1.77
× 55	16.2	20.80	8.215	0.522	0.375	1140	110	8.40	48.3	11.8	1.73
W 21× 49	14.4	20.82	6.520	0.532	0.368	971	93.3	8.21	24.7	7.57	1.31
× 44	13.0	20.66	6.500	0.451	0.348	843	81.6	8.07	20.7	6.38	1.27

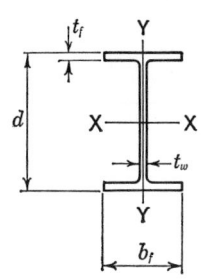

W SHAPES
Properties for designing

Nominal Weight per Ft.	r_T	$\dfrac{d}{A_f}$	$\dfrac{b_f}{2t_f}$	F_y'	$\dfrac{d}{t_w}$	F_y''	F_y'''	Torsional Constant J	Warping Constant C_W	Z_x	Z_y
Lb.	In.			Ksi		Ksi	Ksi	In.⁴	In.⁶	In.³	In.³
177	3.77	1.63	5.92	—	37.7	—	46.5	20.1	94800	557	122
160	3.75	1.80	6.52	64.1	41.2	—	39.0	14.9	83700	501	109
145	3.72	1.97	7.16	53.1	44.8	—	32.9	11.2	74300	453	97.6
114	2.62	2.91	5.40	—	47.9	—	28.8	7.36	27600	343	49.4
102	2.59	3.27	6.06	—	52.3	62.2	24.2	5.27	23900	305	43.3
94	2.56	3.61	6.69	60.9	54.9	56.3	21.9	4.06	21300	278	38.9
84	2.52	4.21	7.83	44.4	57.6	51.1	19.9	2.79	17800	244	33.0
160	3.82	1.55	6.21	—	37.7	—	46.5	16.5	73700	465	115
145	3.79	1.71	6.88	57.5	40.3	—	40.7	12.2	64900	417	103
130	3.76	1.92	7.78	45.0	42.9	—	35.9	8.67	56200	370	90.2
120	3.22	2.16	6.50	64.5	43.7	—	34.5	8.27	37500	338	69.9
110	3.20	2.35	7.04	54.9	47.4	—	29.4	6.45	33800	309	63.6
100	3.18	2.58	7.74	45.5	51.3	64.5	25.1	4.87	30100	280	57.2
94	2.37	3.07	5.20	—	47.1	—	29.8	5.23	14900	253	37.4
84	2.34	3.46	5.84	—	51.3	64.6	25.1	3.72	12800	224	32.7
76	2.32	3.90	6.59	62.8	54.3	57.5	22.4	2.70	11100	201	28.7
68	2.28	4.55	7.70	46.0	57.0	52.3	20.3	1.86	9350	176	24.4
61	1.74	5.71	5.94	—	56.6	53.0	20.6	1.66	4580	152	15.6
55	1.70	6.69	6.96	56.3	59.5	48.0	18.7	1.18	3840	134	13.3
142	3.58	1.49	6.00	—	32.6	—	62.3	13.8	42900	357	96.7
127	3.55	1.65	6.63	62.0	36.1	—	50.6	10.0	37600	318	85.8
112	3.52	1.87	7.51	48.3	39.8	—	41.6	6.87	32100	278	74.6
96	2.39	2.50	4.83	—	36.8	—	48.9	6.51	11800	227	39.9
82	2.35	2.93	5.64	—	41.8	—	37.8	4.09	9620	192	33.2
73	2.16	3.46	5.60	—	46.7	—	30.3	3.02	7410	172	26.6
68	2.15	3.73	6.04	—	49.1	—	27.4	2.45	6760	160	24.4
62	2.13	4.14	6.70	60.7	52.5	61.6	24.0	1.83	5960	144	21.7
55	2.10	4.85	7.87	44.0	55.5	55.2	21.5	1.24	4970	126	18.4
49	1.63	6.00	6.13	—	56.6	53.0	20.6	1.09	2540	108	12.0
44	1.59	7.05	7.21	52.5	59.4	48.2	18.7	0.768	2120	95.3	10.2

I W SHAPES
Properties for designing

Designation	Area A	Depth d	Flange Width b_f	Flange Thickness t_f	Web Thickness t_w	Axis X-X I	Axis X-X S	Axis X-X r	Axis Y-Y I	Axis Y-Y S	Axis Y-Y r
	In.²	In.	In.	In.	In.	In.⁴	In.³	In.	In.⁴	In.³	In.
W 18×114	33.5	18.48	11.833	0.991	0.595	2040	220	7.79	274	46.3	2.86
×105	30.9	18.32	11.792	0.911	0.554	1850	202	7.75	249	42.3	2.84
× 96	28.2	18.16	11.750	0.831	0.512	1680	185	7.70	225	38.3	2.82
W 18× 85	25.0	18.32	8.838	0.911	0.526	1440	157	7.57	105	23.8	2.05
× 77	22.7	18.16	8.787	0.831	0.475	1290	142	7.54	94.1	21.4	2.04
× 70	20.6	18.00	8.750	0.751	0.438	1160	129	7.50	84.0	19.2	2.02
× 64	18.9	17.87	8.715	0.686	0.403	1050	118	7.46	75.8	17.4	2.00
W 18× 60	17.7	18.25	7.558	0.695	0.416	986	108	7.47	50.1	13.3	1.68
× 55	16.2	18.12	7.532	0.630	0.390	891	98.4	7.42	45.0	11.9	1.67
× 50	14.7	18.00	7.500	0.570	0.358	802	89.1	7.38	40.2	10.7	1.65
× 45	13.2	17.86	7.477	0.499	0.335	706	79.0	7.30	34.8	9.32	1.62
W 18× 40	11.8	17.90	6.018	0.524	0.316	612	68.4	7.21	19.1	6.34	1.27
× 35	10.3	17.71	6.000	0.429	0.298	513	57.9	7.05	15.5	5.16	1.23
W 16× 96	28.2	16.32	11.533	0.875	0.535	1360	166	6.93	224	38.8	2.82
× 88	25.9	16.16	11.502	0.795	0.504	1220	151	6.87	202	35.1	2.79
W 16× 78	23.0	16.32	8.586	0.875	0.529	1050	128	6.75	92.5	21.6	2.01
× 71	20.9	16.16	8.543	0.795	0.486	941	116	6.71	82.8	19.4	1.99
× 64	18.8	16.00	8.500	0.715	0.443	836	104	6.66	73.3	17.3	1.97
× 58	17.1	15.86	8.464	0.645	0.407	748	94.4	6.62	65.3	15.4	1.96
W 16× 50	14.7	16.25	7.073	0.628	0.380	657	80.8	6.68	37.1	10.5	1.59
× 45	13.3	16.12	7.039	0.563	0.346	584	72.5	6.64	32.8	9.32	1.57
× 40	11.8	16.00	7.000	0.503	0.307	517	64.6	6.62	28.8	8.23	1.56
× 36	10.6	15.85	6.992	0.428	0.299	447	56.5	6.50	24.4	6.99	1.52
W 16× 31	9.13	15.84	5.525	0.442	0.275	374	47.2	6.40	12.5	4.51	1.17
× 26	7.67	15.65	5.500	0.345	0.250	300	38.3	6.25	9.59	3.49	1.12

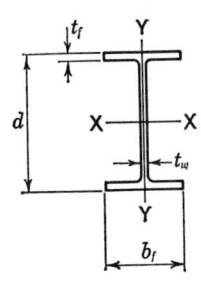

W SHAPES
Properties for designing

Nominal Weight per Ft.	r_T	$\dfrac{d}{A_f}$	Compact Section Criteria						Torsional Constant J	Warping Constant C_W	Plastic Modulus	
			$\dfrac{b_f}{2t_f}$	F_y'	$\dfrac{d}{t_w}$	F_y''	F_y'''				Z_x	Z_y
Lb.	In.			Ksi		Ksi	Ksi		In.⁴	In.⁶	In.³	In.³
114	3.23	1.58	5.97	—	31.1	—	—		9.13	21000	248	70.9
105	3.21	1.71	6.47	—	33.1	—	60.4		7.15	18900	227	64.7
96	3.19	1.86	7.07	54.5	35.5	—	52.5		5.48	16900	206	58.5
85	2.37	2.28	4.85	—	34.8	—	54.4		5.50	7960	178	36.8
77	2.36	2.49	5.29	—	38.2	—	45.2		4.16	7070	161	33.1
70	2.34	2.74	5.83	—	41.1	—	39.1		3.13	6250	145	29.6
64	2.32	2.99	6.35	—	44.3	—	33.6		2.41	5600	132	26.8
60	1.99	3.47	5.44	—	43.9	—	34.3		2.17	3860	123	20.6
55	1.98	3.82	5.98	—	46.5	—	30.6		1.66	3440	112	18.6
50	1.96	4.21	6.58	63.0	50.3	—	26.1		1.25	3050	101	16.6
45	1.94	4.79	7.49	48.5	53.3	59.7	23.2		0.889	2620	89.7	14.5
40	1.54	5.68	5.74	—	56.6	52.9	20.6		0.808	1440	78.4	9.94
35	1.51	6.88	6.99	55.7	59.4	48.1	18.7		0.511	1160	66.8	8.13
96	3.16	1.62	6.59	62.7	30.5	—	—		6.16	13400	186	59.3
88	3.14	1.77	7.23	52.1	32.1	—	64.2		4.72	11900	169	53.6
78	2.32	2.17	4.91	—	30.9	—	—		4.81	5520	146	33.4
71	2.30	2.38	5.37	—	33.3	—	59.7		3.65	4890	132	30.0
64	2.28	2.63	5.94	—	36.1	—	50.6		2.65	4280	118	26.6
58	2.26	2.91	6.56	63.3	39.0	—	43.5		1.98	3780	106	23.8
50	1.87	3.66	5.63	—	42.8	—	36.1		1.51	2260	91.8	16.3
45	1.85	4.07	6.25	—	46.6	—	30.4		1.11	1980	82.1	14.4
40	1.84	4.54	6.96	56.3	52.1	62.5	24.3		0.790	1730	72.8	12.7
36	1.81	5.30	8.17	40.8	53.0	60.4	23.5		0.545	1450	64.0	10.8
31	1.41	6.49	6.25	—	57.6	51.2	19.9		0.464	738	54.0	7.06
26	1.38	8.25	7.97	42.9	62.6	43.3	16.9		0.261	562	44.0	5.48

W SHAPES
Properties for designing

Designation	Area A	Depth d	Flange Width b_f	Flange Thickness t_f	Web Thickness t_w	Axis X-X I	Axis X-X S	Axis X-X r	Axis Y-Y I	Axis Y-Y S	Axis Y-Y r
	In.²	In.	In.	In.	In.	In.⁴	In.³	In.	In.⁴	In.³	In.
W 14×730	215	22.44	17.889	4.910	3.069	14400	1280	8.18	4720	527	4.69
×665	196	21.67	17.646	4.522	2.826	12500	1150	7.99	4170	472	4.62
×605	178	20.94	17.418	4.157	2.598	10900	1040	7.81	3680	423	4.55
×550	162	20.26	17.206	3.818	2.386	9450	933	7.64	3260	378	4.49
×500	147	19.63	17.008	3.501	2.188	8250	840	7.49	2880	339	4.43
×455	134	19.05	16.828	3.213	2.008	7220	758	7.35	2560	304	4.37
W 14×426	125	18.69	16.695	3.033	1.875	6610	707	7.26	2360	283	4.34
×398	117	18.31	16.590	2.843	1.770	6010	657	7.17	2170	262	4.31
×370	109	17.94	16.475	2.658	1.655	5450	608	7.08	1990	241	4.27
×342	101	17.56	16.365	2.468	1.545	4910	559	6.99	1810	221	4.24
×314	92.3	17.19	16.235	2.283	1.415	4400	512	6.90	1630	201	4.20
×287	84.4	16.81	16.130	2.093	1.310	3910	465	6.81	1470	182	4.17
×264	77.6	16.50	16.025	1.938	1.205	3530	427	6.74	1330	166	4.14
×246	72.3	16.25	15.945	1.813	1.125	3230	397	6.68	1230	154	4.12
W 14×237	69.7	16.12	15.910	1.748	1.090	3080	382	6.65	1170	148	4.11
×228	67.1	16.00	15.865	1.688	1.045	2940	368	6.62	1120	142	4.10
×219	64.4	15.87	15.825	1.623	1.005	2800	353	6.59	1070	136	4.08
×211	62.1	15.75	15.800	1.563	0.980	2670	339	6.56	1030	130	4.07
×202	59.4	15.63	15.750	1.503	0.930	2540	325	6.54	980	124	4.06
×193	56.7	15.50	15.710	1.438	0.890	2400	310	6.51	930	118	4.05
×184	54.1	15.38	15.660	1.378	0.840	2270	296	6.49	883	113	4.04
×176	51.7	15.25	15.640	1.313	0.820	2150	282	6.45	838	107	4.02
×167	49.1	15.12	15.600	1.248	0.780	2020	267	6.42	790	101	4.01
×158	46.5	15.00	15.550	1.188	0.730	1900	253	6.40	745	95.8	4.00
×150	44.1	14.88	15.515	1.128	0.695	1790	240	6.37	703	90.6	3.99
×142	41.8	14.75	15.500	1.063	0.680	1670	227	6.32	660	85.2	3.97
W 14×320	94.1	16.81	16.710	2.093	1.890	4140	493	6.63	1640	196	4.17

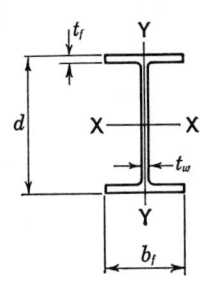

W SHAPES
Properties for designing

Nominal Weight per Ft.	r_T	$\dfrac{d}{A_f}$	Compact Section Criteria					Torsional Constant J	Warping Constant C_W	Plastic Modulus	
			$\dfrac{b_f}{2t_f}$	F_y'	$\dfrac{d}{t_w}$	F_y''	F_y'''			Z_x	Z_y
Lb.	In.			Ksi		Ksi	Ksi	In.⁴	In.⁶	In.³	In.³
730	5.27	0.255	1.82	—	7.31	—	—	1450	362000	1660	816
665	5.17	0.272	1.95	—	7.67	—	—	1120	306000	1480	730
605	5.08	0.289	2.10	—	8.06	—	—	869	259000	1320	652
550	5.00	0.308	2.25	—	8.49	—	—	670	220000	1180	584
500	4.92	0.330	2.43	—	8.97	—	—	514	187000	1050	522
455	4.85	0.352	2.62	—	9.49	—	—	396	161000	938	468
426	4.81	0.369	2.75	—	9.97	—	—	330	145000	869	434
398	4.76	0.388	2.92	—	10.3	—	—	272	130000	802	401
370	4.72	0.410	3.10	—	10.8	—	—	222	116000	737	370
342	4.68	0.435	3.32	—	11.4	—	—	178	103000	673	338
314	4.63	0.464	3.56	—	12.1	—	—	140	90600	611	307
287	4.58	0.498	3.85	—	12.8	—	—	108	79400	551	278
264	4.54	0.531	4.13	—	13.7	—	—	85.3	70600	502	254
246	4.51	0.562	4.40	—	14.4	—	—	69.7	63900	464	235
237	4.50	0.580	4.55	—	14.8	—	—	62.6	60700	445	225
228	4.48	0.597	4.70	—	15.3	—	—	56.2	57600	427	216
219	4.47	0.618	4.88	—	15.8	—	—	49.9	54500	408	207
211	4.46	0.638	5.05	—	16.1	—	—	44.8	51800	391	198
202	4.44	0.660	5.24	—	16.8	—	—	39.6	48900	373	189
193	4.42	0.686	5.46	—	17.4	—	—	34.7	46000	355	180
184	4.41	0.713	5.68	—	18.3	—	—	30.3	43300	338	171
176	4.39	0.743	5.96	—	18.6	—	—	26.5	40700	321	163
167	4.38	0.777	6.25	—	19.4	—	—	22.8	38000	303	154
158	4.36	0.812	6.54	63.6	20.5	—	—	19.5	35500	286	145
150	4.35	0.850	6.88	57.6	21.4	—	—	16.7	33200	270	137
142	4.33	0.895	7.29	51.3	21.7	—	—	14.2	30900	255	129
320	4.73	0.481	3.99	—	8.89	—	—	137	88500	592	304

W SHAPES
Properties for designing

Designation	Area A	Depth d	Flange Width b_f	Flange Thickness t_f	Web Thickness t_w	Axis X-X I	Axis X-X S	Axis X-X r	Axis Y-Y I	Axis Y-Y S	Axis Y-Y r
	In.²	In.	In.	In.	In.	In.⁴	In.³	In.	In.⁴	In.³	In.
W 14×136	40.0	14.75	14.740	1.063	0.660	1590	216	6.31	568	77.0	3.77
×127	37.3	14.62	14.690	0.998	0.610	1480	202	6.29	528	71.8	3.76
×119	35.0	14.50	14.650	0.938	0.570	1370	189	6.26	492	67.1	3.75
×111	32.7	14.37	14.620	0.873	0.540	1270	176	6.23	455	62.2	3.73
×103	30.3	14.25	14.575	0.813	0.495	1170	164	6.21	420	57.6	3.72
× 95	27.9	14.12	14.545	0.748	0.465	1060	151	6.17	384	52.8	3.71
× 87	25.6	14.00	14.500	0.688	0.420	967	138	6.15	350	48.2	3.70
W 14× 84	24.7	14.18	12.023	0.778	0.451	928	131	6.13	225	37.5	3.02
× 78	22.9	14.06	12.000	0.718	0.428	851	121	6.09	207	34.5	3.00
W 14× 74	21.8	14.19	10.072	0.783	0.450	797	112	6.05	133	26.5	2.48
× 68	20.0	14.06	10.040	0.718	0.418	724	103	6.02	121	24.1	2.46
× 61	17.9	13.91	10.000	0.643	0.378	641	92.2	5.98	107	21.5	2.45
W 14× 53	15.6	13.94	8.062	0.658	0.370	542	77.8	5.90	57.5	14.3	1.92
× 48	14.1	13.81	8.031	0.593	0.339	485	70.2	5.86	51.3	12.8	1.91
× 43	12.6	13.68	8.000	0.528	0.308	429	62.7	5.82	45.1	11.3	1.89
W 14× 38	11.2	14.12	6.776	0.513	0.313	386	54.7	5.88	26.6	7.86	1.54
× 34	10.0	14.00	6.750	0.453	0.287	340	48.6	5.83	23.3	6.89	1.52
× 30	8.83	13.86	6.733	0.383	0.270	290	41.9	5.74	19.5	5.80	1.49
W 14× 26	7.67	13.89	5.025	0.418	0.255	244	35.1	5.64	8.86	3.53	1.08
× 22	6.49	13.72	5.000	0.335	0.230	198	28.9	5.53	7.00	2.80	1.04

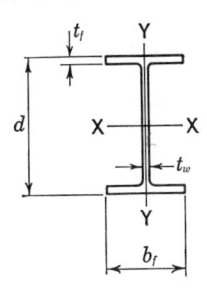

W SHAPES
Properties for designing

Nominal Weight per Ft.	r_T	$\dfrac{d}{A_f}$	Compact Section Criteria					Torsional Constant J	Warping Constant C_W	Plastic Modulus	
			$\dfrac{b_f}{2t_f}$	F_y'	$\dfrac{d}{t_w}$	F_y''	F_y'''			Z_x	Z_y
Lb.	In.			Ksi		Ksi	Ksi	In.⁴	In.⁶	In.³	In.³
136	4.12	0.941	6.93	56.7	22.3	—	—	13.5	26600	243	117
127	4.10	0.997	7.36	50.3	24.0	—	—	11.1	24500	226	109
119	4.08	1.06	7.81	44.7	25.4	—	—	9.20	22600	211	102
111	4.07	1.13	8.37	38.9	26.6	—	—	7.48	20700	196	94.3
103	4.05	1.20	8.96	33.9	28.8	—	—	6.02	18900	181	87.2
95	4.04	1.30	9.72	28.8	30.4	—	—	4.74	17200	166	79.9
87	4.02	1.40	10.5	24.5	33.3	—	59.4	3.68	15500	151	73.0
84	3.32	1.52	7.73	45.6	31.4	—	—	4.41	10100	145	57.0
78	3.31	1.63	8.36	39.0	32.9	—	61.2	3.52	9210	134	52.4
74	2.76	1.80	6.43	—	31.5	—	—	3.86	6000	126	40.5
68	2.74	1.95	6.99	55.7	33.6	—	58.4	3.01	5390	115	36.8
61	2.73	2.16	7.78	45.1	36.8	—	48.8	2.19	4720	102	32.7
53	2.18	2.63	6.13	—	37.7	—	46.5	1.93	2540	87.1	21.9
48	2.16	2.90	6.77	59.4	40.7	—	39.8	1.44	2240	78.4	19.6
43	2.14	3.24	7.58	47.5	44.4	—	33.5	1.05	1950	69.7	17.3
38	1.80	4.06	6.60	62.5	45.1	—	32.5	0.796	1230	61.6	12.1
34	1.78	4.58	7.45	49.1	48.8	—	27.8	0.567	1070	54.6	10.6
30	1.75	5.37	8.79	35.3	51.3	64.4	25.1	0.376	886	47.2	8.95
26	1.29	6.61	6.01	—	54.5	57.2	22.3	0.355	402	40.0	5.52
22	1.26	8.19	7.46	48.9	59.7	47.7	18.6	0.208	313	33.1	4.39

I

W SHAPES
Properties for designing

Designation	Area A	Depth d	Flange Width b_f	Flange Thickness t_f	Web Thickness t_w	Axis X-X I	Axis X-X S	Axis X-X r	Axis Y-Y I	Axis Y-Y S	Axis Y-Y r
	In.²	In.	In.	In.	In.	In.⁴	In.³	In.	In.⁴	In.³	In.
W 12×190	55.9	14.38	12.670	1.736	1.060	1890	263	5.82	590	93.1	3.25
×161	47.4	13.88	12.515	1.486	0.905	1540	222	5.70	486	77.7	3.20
×133	39.1	13.38	12.365	1.236	0.755	1220	183	5.59	390	63.1	3.16
×120	35.3	13.12	12.320	1.106	0.710	1070	163	5.51	345	56.0	3.13
×106	31.2	12.88	12.230	0.986	0.620	931	145	5.46	301	49.2	3.11
× 99	29.1	12.75	12.192	0.921	0.582	859	135	5.43	278	45.7	3.09
× 92	27.1	12.62	12.155	0.856	0.545	789	125	5.40	256	42.2	3.08
× 85	25.0	12.50	12.105	0.796	0.495	723	116	5.38	235	38.9	3.07
× 79	23.2	12.38	12.080	0.736	0.470	663	107	5.34	216	35.8	3.05
× 72	21.2	12.25	12.040	0.671	0.430	597	97.5	5.31	195	32.4	3.04
× 65	19.1	12.12	12.000	0.606	0.390	533	88.0	5.28	175	29.1	3.02
W 12× 58	17.1	12.19	10.014	0.641	0.359	476	78.1	5.28	107	21.4	2.51
× 53	15.6	12.06	10.000	0.576	0.345	426	70.7	5.23	96.1	19.2	2.48
W 12× 50	14.7	12.19	8.077	0.641	0.371	395	64.7	5.18	56.4	14.0	1.96
× 45	13.2	12.06	8.042	0.576	0.336	351	58.2	5.15	50.0	12.4	1.94
× 40	11.8	11.94	8.000	0.516	0.294	310	51.9	5.13	44.1	11.0	1.94
W 12× 36	10.6	12.24	6.565	0.540	0.305	281	46.0	5.15	25.5	7.77	1.55
× 31	9.13	12.09	6.525	0.465	0.265	239	39.5	5.12	21.6	6.61	1.54
× 27	7.95	11.96	6.497	0.400	0.237	204	34.2	5.07	18.3	5.63	1.52
W 12× 22	6.47	12.31	4.030	0.424	0.260	156	25.3	4.91	4.64	2.31	0.847
× 19	5.59	12.16	4.007	0.349	0.237	130	21.3	4.82	3.76	1.88	0.820
× 16.5	4.87	12.00	4.000	0.269	0.230	105	17.6	4.65	2.88	1.44	0.770
× 14	4.12	11.91	3.968	0.224	0.198	88.0	14.8	4.62	2.34	1.18	0.754

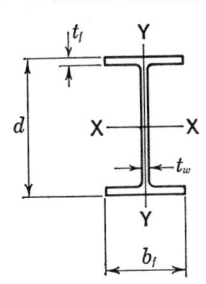

W SHAPES
Properties for designing

Nominal Weight per Ft.	r_T	$\dfrac{d}{A_f}$	Compact Section Criteria					Torsional Constant J	Warping Constant C_W	Plastic Modulus	
			$\dfrac{b_f}{2t_f}$	F_y'	$\dfrac{d}{t_w}$	F_y''	F_y'''			Z_x	Z_y
Lb.	In.			Ksi		Ksi	Ksi	In.⁴	In.⁶	In.³	In.³
190	3.59	0.654	3.65	—	13.6	—	—	48.9	23600	311	143
161	3.53	0.746	4.21	—	15.3	—	—	30.6	18700	259	119
133	3.47	0.875	5.00	—	17.7	—	—	17.6	14400	210	96.2
120	3.44	0.963	5.57	—	18.5	—	—	12.9	12500	186	85.5
106	3.41	1.07	6.20	—	20.8	—	—	9.10	10600	164	74.9
99	3.39	1.14	6.62	62.2	21.9	—	—	7.45	9740	152	69.5
92	3.38	1.21	7.10	54.1	23.2	—	—	6.01	8870	140	64.2
85	3.36	1.30	7.60	47.1	25.3	—	—	4.80	8060	129	59.1
79	3.34	1.39	8.21	40.5	26.3	—	—	3.85	7330	119	54.4
72	3.33	1.52	8.97	33.9	28.5	—	—	2.94	6550	108	49.2
65	3.31	1.67	9.90	27.8	31.1	—	—	2.19	5790	97.0	44.1
58	2.75	1.90	7.81	44.7	34.0	—	57.3	2.10	3580	86.5	32.6
53	2.74	2.09	8.68	36.2	35.0	—	54.1	1.59	3170	78.1	29.2
50	2.19	2.35	6.30	—	32.9	—	61.2	1.79	1880	72.5	21.4
45	2.18	2.60	6.98	55.9	35.9	—	51.3	1.32	1650	64.8	19.0
40	2.16	2.89	7.75	45.3	40.6	—	40.0	0.956	1440	57.5	16.8
36	1.77	3.45	6.08	—	40.1	—	41.0	0.830	873	51.6	11.9
31	1.75	3.98	7.02	55.4	45.6	—	31.7	0.536	728	44.1	10.1
27	1.74	4.60	8.12	41.3	50.5	—	25.9	0.351	611	38.0	8.62
22	1.03	7.20	4.75	—	47.3	—	29.5	0.292	164	29.3	3.65
19	1.01	8.70	5.74	—	51.3	64.5	25.1	0.181	131	24.7	2.98
16.5	0.975	11.2	7.43	49.3	52.2	62.4	24.3	0.112	99.2	20.6	2.32
14	0.957	13.4	8.86	34.7	60.2	46.9	18.3	0.069	80.0	17.3	1.89

W SHAPES
Properties for designing

Designation	Area A	Depth d	Flange		Web Thickness t_w	Elastic Properties					
			Width b_f	Thickness t_f		Axis X-X			Axis Y-Y		
						I	S	r	I	S	r
	In.²	In.	In.	In.	In.	In.⁴	In.³	In.	In.⁴	In.³	In.
W 10×112	32.9	11.38	10.415	1.248	0.755	719	126	4.67	235	45.2	2.67
×100	29.4	11.12	10.345	1.118	0.685	625	112	4.61	207	39.9	2.65
× 89	26.2	10.88	10.275	0.998	0.615	542	99.7	4.55	181	35.2	2.63
× 77	22.7	10.62	10.195	0.868	0.535	457	86.1	4.49	153	30.1	2.60
× 72	21.2	10.50	10.170	0.808	0.510	421	80.1	4.46	142	27.9	2.59
× 66	19.4	10.38	10.117	0.748	0.457	382	73.7	4.44	129	25.5	2.58
× 60	17.7	10.25	10.075	0.683	0.415	344	67.1	4.41	116	23.1	2.57
× 54	15.9	10.12	10.028	0.618	0.368	306	60.4	4.39	104	20.7	2.56
× 49	14.4	10.00	10.000	0.558	0.340	273	54.6	4.35	93.0	18.6	2.54
W 10× 45	13.2	10.12	8.022	0.618	0.350	249	49.1	4.33	53.2	13.3	2.00
× 39	11.5	9.94	7.990	0.528	0.318	210	42.2	4.27	44.9	11.2	1.98
× 33	9.71	9.75	7.964	0.433	0.292	171	35.0	4.20	36.5	9.16	1.94
W 10× 29	8.54	10.22	5.799	0.500	0.289	158	30.8	4.30	16.3	5.61	1.38
× 25	7.36	10.08	5.762	0.430	0.252	133	26.5	4.26	13.7	4.76	1.37
× 21	6.20	9.90	5.750	0.340	0.240	107	21.5	4.15	10.8	3.75	1.32
W 10× 19	5.61	10.25	4.020	0.394	0.250	96.3	18.8	4.14	4.28	2.13	0.874
× 17	4.99	10.12	4.010	0.329	0.240	81.9	16.2	4.05	3.55	1.77	0.844
× 15	4.41	10.00	4.000	0.269	0.230	68.9	13.8	3.95	2.88	1.44	0.809
× 11.5	3.39	9.87	3.950	0.204	0.180	52.0	10.5	3.92	2.10	1.06	0.787

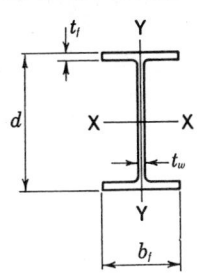

W SHAPES
Properties for designing

Nominal Weight per Ft.	r_T	$\dfrac{d}{A_f}$	Compact Section Criteria					Torsional Constant J	Warping Constant C_W	Plastic Modulus	
			$\dfrac{b_f}{2t_f}$	F_y'	$\dfrac{d}{t_w}$	F_y''	F_y'''			Z_x	Z_y
Lb.	In.			Ksi		Ksi	Ksi	In.⁴	In.⁶	In.³	In.³
112	2.94	0.876	4.17	—	15.1	—	—	15.0	6040	148	69.1
100	2.91	0.961	4.63	—	16.2	—	—	10.8	5170	130	61.0
89	2.88	1.06	5.15	—	17.7	—	—	7.74	4410	114	53.6
77	2.85	1.20	5.87	—	19.9	—	—	5.11	3650	97.8	45.8
72	2.84	1.28	6.29	—	20.6	—	—	4.17	3330	90.6	42.4
66	2.82	1.37	6.76	59.6	22.7	—	—	3.27	3000	82.8	38.8
60	2.80	1.49	7.38	50.1	24.7	—	—	2.49	2670	75.0	35.1
54	2.78	1.63	8.11	41.4	27.5	—	—	1.84	2350	67.1	31.4
49	2.77	1.79	8.96	33.9	29.4	—	—	1.38	2070	60.3	28.2
45	2.21	2.04	6.49	64.7	28.9	—	—	1.50	1200	54.9	20.2
39	2.19	2.36	7.57	47.6	31.3	—	—	0.971	995	46.9	17.1
33	2.16	2.83	9.20	32.2	33.4	—	59.2	0.580	792	38.8	14.0
29	1.57	3.52	5.80	—	35.4	—	52.8	0.579	384	34.7	8.62
25	1.56	4.07	6.70	60.7	40.0	—	41.3	0.373	320	29.6	7.30
21	1.53	5.06	8.46	38.1	41.3	—	38.8	0.210	246	24.1	5.77
19	1.05	6.47	5.10	—	41.0	—	39.3	0.232	104	21.6	3.35
17	1.03	7.67	6.09	—	42.2	—	37.1	0.155	85.1	18.6	2.80
15	1.00	9.29	7.43	49.3	43.5	—	34.9	0.104	68.2	16.0	2.29
11.5	0.975	12.2	9.68	29.1	54.8	56.5	22.0	0.049	49.1	12.2	1.68

I

W SHAPES
Properties for designing

Designation	Area A	Depth d	Flange Width b_f	Flange Thickness t_f	Web Thickness t_w	Axis X-X I	Axis X-X S	Axis X-X r	Axis Y-Y I	Axis Y-Y S	Axis Y-Y r
	In.²	In.	In.	In.	In.	In.⁴	In.³	In.	In.⁴	In.³	In.
W 8×67	19.7	9.00	8.287	0.933	0.575	272	60.4	3.71	88.6	21.4	2.12
×58	17.1	8.75	8.222	0.808	0.510	227	52.0	3.65	74.9	18.2	2.10
×48	14.1	8.50	8.117	0.683	0.405	184	43.2	3.61	60.9	15.0	2.08
×40	11.8	8.25	8.077	0.558	0.365	146	35.5	3.53	49.0	12.1	2.04
×35	10.3	8.12	8.027	0.493	0.315	126	31.1	3.50	42.5	10.6	2.03
×31	9.12	8.00	8.000	0.433	0.288	110	27.4	3.47	37.0	9.24	2.01
W 8×28	8.23	8.06	6.540	0.463	0.285	97.8	24.3	3.45	21.6	6.61	1.62
×24	7.06	7.93	6.500	0.398	0.245	82.5	20.8	3.42	18.2	5.61	1.61
W 8×20	5.89	8.14	5.268	0.378	0.248	69.4	17.0	3.43	9.22	3.50	1.25
×17	5.01	8.00	5.250	0.308	0.230	56.6	14.1	3.36	7.44	2.83	1.22
W 8×15	4.43	8.12	4.015	0.314	0.245	48.1	11.8	3.29	3.40	1.69	0.876
×13	3.83	8.00	4.000	0.254	0.230	39.6	9.90	3.21	2.72	1.36	0.842
×10	2.96	7.90	3.940	0.204	0.170	30.8	7.80	3.23	2.08	1.06	0.839
W 6×25	7.35	6.37	6.080	0.456	0.320	53.3	16.7	2.69	17.1	5.62	1.53
×20	5.88	6.20	6.018	0.367	0.258	41.5	13.4	2.66	13.3	4.43	1.51
×15.5	4.56	6.00	5.995	0.269	0.235	30.1	10.0	2.57	9.67	3.23	1.46
W 6×16	4.72	6.25	4.030	0.404	0.260	31.7	10.2	2.59	4.42	2.19	0.967
×12	3.54	6.00	4.000	0.279	0.230	21.7	7.25	2.48	2.98	1.49	0.918
× 8.5	2.51	5.83	3.940	0.194	0.170	14.8	5.08	2.43	1.98	1.01	0.889
W 5×18.5	5.43	5.12	5.025	0.420	0.265	25.4	9.94	2.16	8.89	3.54	1.28
×16	4.70	5.00	5.000	0.360	0.240	21.3	8.53	2.13	7.51	3.00	1.26
W 4×13	3.82	4.16	4.060	0.345	0.280	11.3	5.45	1.72	3.76	1.85	0.991

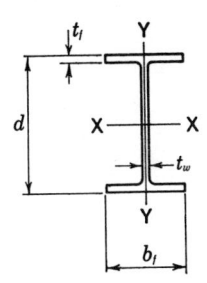

W SHAPES
Properties for designing

Nominal Weight per Ft.	r_T	$\dfrac{d}{A_f}$	Compact Section Criteria					Torsional Constant J	Warping Constant C_W	Plastic Modulus	
			$\dfrac{b_f}{2t_f}$	F_y'	$\dfrac{d}{t_w}$	F_y''	F_y'''			Z_x	Z_y
Lb.	In.			Ksi		Ksi	Ksi	In.⁴	In.⁶	In.³	In.³
67	2.33	1.16	4.44	—	15.7	—	—	5.05	1440	70.2	32.7
58	2.31	1.32	5.09	—	17.2	—	—	3.32	1180	59.7	27.8
48	2.27	1.53	5.94	—	21.0	—	—	1.96	931	49.0	22.8
40	2.24	1.83	7.24	52.0	22.6	—	—	1.12	725	39.8	18.5
35	2.22	2.05	8.14	41.1	25.8	—	—	0.768	618	34.7	16.1
31	2.21	2.31	9.24	31.9	27.8	—	—	0.534	529	30.4	14.0
28	1.80	2.66	7.06	54.6	28.3	—	—	0.533	312	27.1	10.1
24	1.78	3.07	8.17	40.9	32.4	—	63.0	0.343	259	23.1	8.54
20	1.42	4.09	6.97	56.1	32.8	—	61.3	0.245	139	19.1	5.37
17	1.40	4.95	8.52	37.5	34.8	—	54.6	0.147	110	15.9	4.36
15	1.04	6.44	6.39	—	33.1	—	60.1	0.136	51.8	13.6	2.66
13	1.02	7.87	7.87	43.9	34.8	—	54.6	0.087	40.8	11.4	2.15
10	1.00	9.83	9.66	29.2	46.5	—	30.6	0.042	30.9	8.86	1.65
25	1.69	2.30	6.67	61.3	19.9	—	—	0.463	150	18.9	8.58
20	1.66	2.81	8.20	40.5	24.0	—	—	0.243	113	15.0	6.75
15.5	1.63	3.72	11.1	21.9	25.5	—	—	0.111	79.4	11.1	4.92
16	1.10	3.84	4.99	—	24.0	—	—	0.222	37.7	11.6	3.38
12	1.07	5.38	7.17	53.0	26.1	—	—	0.090	24.4	8.23	2.31
8.5	1.04	7.63	10.2	26.4	34.3	—	56.2	0.033	15.7	5.71	1.55
18.5	1.40	2.43	5.98	—	19.3	—	—	0.295	49.1	11.3	5.39
16	1.39	2.78	6.94	56.5	20.8	—	—	0.192	40.4	9.61	4.58
13	1.11	2.97	5.88	—	14.9	—	—	0.154	13.7	6.27	2.88

M SHAPES
Properties for designing

Designation	Area A	Depth d	Flange Width b_f	Flange Thickness t_f	Web Thickness t_w	Axis X-X I	Axis X-X S	Axis X-X r	Axis Y-Y I	Axis Y-Y S	Axis Y-Y r
	In.²	In.	In.	In.	In.	In.⁴	In.³	In.	In.⁴	In.³	In.
M 14× 17.2	5.05	14.00	4.000	0.272	0.210	147	21.1	5.40	2.65	1.33	0.725
M 12× 11.8	3.47	12.00	3.065	0.225	0.177	71.9	12.0	4.55	0.980	0.639	0.532
M 10× 29.1	8.56	9.88	5.937	0.389	0.427	131	26.6	3.92	11.2	3.76	1.14
× 22.9	6.73	9.88	5.752	0.389	0.242	117	23.6	4.16	10.0	3.48	1.22
M 10× 9	2.65	10.00	2.690	0.206	0.157	38.8	7.76	3.83	0.609	0.453	0.480
M 8× 34.3	10.1	8.00	8.003	0.459	0.378	116	29.1	3.40	34.9	8.73	1.86
× 32.6	9.58	8.00	7.940	0.459	0.315	114	28.4	3.44	34.1	8.58	1.89
M 8× 22.5	6.60	8.00	5.395	0.353	0.375	68.2	17.1	3.22	7.48	2.77	1.06
× 18.5	5.44	8.00	5.250	0.353	0.230	62.0	15.5	3.38	6.82	2.60	1.12
M 8× 6.5	1.92	8.00	2.281	0.189	0.135	18.5	4.62	3.10	0.343	0.301	0.423
M 7× 5.5	1.62	7.00	2.080	0.180	0.128	12.0	3.44	2.73	0.249	0.239	0.392
M 6× 22.5	6.62	6.00	6.060	0.379	0.372	41.2	13.7	2.49	12.4	4.08	1.37
× 20	5.89	6.00	5.938	0.379	0.250	39.0	13.0	2.57	11.6	3.90	1.40
M 6× 4.4	1.29	6.00	1.844	0.171	0.114	7.20	2.40	2.36	0.165	0.179	0.358
M 5× 18.9	5.55	5.00	5.003	0.416	0.316	24.1	9.63	2.08	7.86	3.14	1.19
M 4× 13.8	4.06	4.00	4.000	0.371	0.313	10.8	5.42	1.63	3.58	1.79	0.939
× 13	3.81	4.00	3.940	0.371	0.254	10.5	5.24	1.66	3.36	1.71	0.939

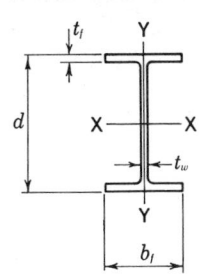

M SHAPES
Properties for designing

Nominal Weight per Ft.	r_T	$\dfrac{d}{A_f}$	Compact Section Criteria					Torsional Constant J	Warping Constant C_W	Plastic Modulus	
			$\dfrac{b_f}{2t_f}$	F_y'	$\dfrac{d}{t_w}$	F_y''	F_y'''			Z_x	Z_y
Lb.	In.			Ksi		Ksi	Ksi	In.⁴	In.⁶	In.³	In.³
17.2	0.925	12.8	7.34	50.6	66.7	38.2	14.9	0.110	125	24.8	2.21
11.8	0.690	17.4	6.81	58.7	67.8	36.9	14.4	0.053	34.0	14.3	1.09
29.1	1.40	4.28	7.63	46.8	23.1	—	—	0.587	251	30.9	6.51
22.9	1.40	4.42	7.39	49.8	40.8	—	39.6	0.343	226	26.4	5.80
9	0.616	18.0	6.53	63.9	63.7	41.8	16.3	0.033	14.6	9.19	0.765
34.3	2.08	2.18	8.72	35.9	21.2	—	—	0.747	497	32.6	13.9
32.6	2.08	2.20	8.65	36.4	25.4	—	—	0.673	484	31.6	13.6
22.5	1.28	4.20	7.64	46.7	21.3	—	—	0.374	109	19.7	4.79
18.5	1.28	4.32	7.44	49.3	34.8	—	54.6	0.243	99.8	17.4	4.35
6.5	0.535	18.6	6.03	—	59.3	48.3	18.8	0.019	5.23	5.42	0.502
5.5	0.493	18.7	5.78	—	54.7	56.8	22.1	0.015	2.89	4.03	0.398
22.5	1.55	2.61	7.98	42.7	16.1	—	—	0.385	97.7	15.6	6.63
20	1.54	2.66	7.82	44.5	24.0	—	—	0.295	91.5	14.5	6.25
4.4	0.444	19.0	5.39	—	52.6	61.3	23.8	0.010	1.40	2.80	0.296
18.9	1.32	2.40	6.01	—	15.8	—	—	0.344	41.3	11.0	5.02
13.8	1.05	2.69	5.38	—	12.8	—	—	0.216	11.8	6.31	2.88
13	1.04	2.73	5.30	—	15.7	—	—	0.190	11.1	6.06	2.74

I

S SHAPES
Properties for designing

Designation	Area A	Depth d	Flange Width b_f	Flange Thickness t_f	Web Thickness t_w	Axis X-X I	Axis X-X S	Axis X-X r	Axis Y-Y I	Axis Y-Y S	Axis Y-Y r
	In.²	In.	In.	In.	In.	In.⁴	In.³	In.	In.⁴	In.³	In.
S 24×120	35.3	24.00	8.048	1.102	0.798	3030	252	9.26	84.2	20.9	1.54
×105.9	31.1	24.00	7.875	1.102	0.625	2830	236	9.53	78.2	19.8	1.58
S 24×100	29.4	24.00	7.247	0.871	0.747	2390	199	9.01	47.8	13.2	1.27
× 90	26.5	24.00	7.124	0.871	0.624	2250	187	9.22	44.9	12.6	1.30
× 79.9	23.5	24.00	7.001	0.871	0.501	2110	175	9.47	42.3	12.1	1.34
S 20× 95	27.9	20.00	7.200	0.916	0.800	1610	161	7.60	49.7	13.8	1.33
× 85	25.0	20.00	7.053	0.916	0.653	1520	152	7.79	46.2	13.1	1.36
S 20× 75	22.1	20.00	6.391	0.789	0.641	1280	128	7.60	29.6	9.28	1.16
× 65.4	19.2	20.00	6.250	0.789	0.500	1180	118	7.84	27.4	8.77	1.19
S 18× 70	20.6	18.00	6.251	0.691	0.711	926	103	6.71	24.1	7.72	1.08
× 54.7	16.1	18.00	6.001	0.691	0.461	804	89.4	7.07	20.8	6.94	1.14
S 15× 50	14.7	15.00	5.640	0.622	0.550	486	64.8	5.75	15.7	5.57	1.03
× 42.9	12.6	15.00	5.501	0.622	0.411	447	59.6	5.95	14.4	5.23	1.07
S 12× 50	14.7	12.00	5.477	0.659	0.687	305	50.8	4.55	15.7	5.74	1.03
× 40.8	12.0	12.00	5.252	0.659	0.462	272	45.4	4.77	13.6	5.16	1.06
S 12× 35	10.3	12.00	5.078	0.544	0.428	229	38.2	4.72	9.87	3.89	0.980
× 31.8	9.35	12.00	5.000	0.544	0.350	218	36.4	4.83	9.36	3.74	1.00
S 10× 35	10.3	10.00	4.944	0.491	0.594	147	29.4	3.78	8.36	3.38	0.901
× 25.4	7.46	10.00	4.661	0.491	0.311	124	24.7	4.07	6.79	2.91	0.954
S 8× 23	6.77	8.00	4.171	0.425	0.441	64.9	16.2	3.10	4.31	2.07	0.798
× 18.4	5.41	8.00	4.001	0.425	0.271	57.6	14.4	3.26	3.73	1.86	0.831
S 7× 20	5.88	7.00	3.860	0.392	0.450	42.4	12.1	2.69	3.17	1.64	0.734
× 15.3	4.50	7.00	3.662	0.392	0.252	36.7	10.5	2.86	2.64	1.44	0.766
S 6× 17.25	5.07	6.00	3.565	0.359	0.465	26.3	8.77	2.28	2.31	1.30	0.675
× 12.5	3.67	6.00	3.332	0.359	0.232	22.1	7.37	2.45	1.82	1.09	0.705
S 5× 14.75	4.34	5.00	3.284	0.326	0.494	15.2	6.09	1.87	1.67	1.01	0.620
× 10	2.94	5.00	3.004	0.326	0.214	12.3	4.92	2.05	1.22	0.809	0.643
S 4× 9.5	2.79	4.00	2.796	0.293	0.326	6.79	3.39	1.56	0.903	0.646	0.569
× 7.7	2.26	4.00	2.663	0.293	0.193	6.08	3.04	1.64	0.764	0.574	0.581
S 3× 7.5	2.21	3.00	2.509	0.260	0.349	2.93	1.95	1.15	0.586	0.468	0.516
× 5.7	1.67	3.00	2.330	0.260	0.170	2.52	1.68	1.23	0.455	0.390	0.522

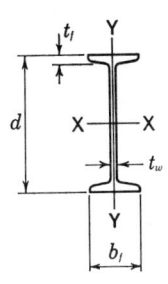

S SHAPES
Properties for designing

Nominal Weight per Ft.	r_T	$\dfrac{d}{A_f}$	Compact Section Criteria					Torsional Constant J	Warping Constant C_W	Plastic Modulus	
			$\dfrac{b_f}{2t_f}$	F_y'	$\dfrac{d}{t_w}$	F_y''	F_y'''			Z_x	Z_y
Lb.	In.			Ksi		Ksi	Ksi	In.⁴	In.⁶	In.³	In.³
120	1.93	2.71	3.65	—	30.1	—	—	13.0	11000	299	36.4
105.9	1.93	2.77	3.57	—	38.4	—	44.8	10.4	10200	274	33.5
100	1.65	3.80	4.16	—	32.1	—	64.0	7.63	6390	240	24.0
90	1.65	3.87	4.09	—	38.5	—	44.6	6.05	6010	222	22.3
79.9	1.66	3.94	4.02	—	47.9	—	28.8	4.90	5660	205	20.7
95	1.70	3.03	3.93	—	25.0	—	—	8.46	4520	194	24.7
85	1.69	3.09	3.85	—	30.6	—	—	6.63	4200	179	22.8
75	1.48	3.96	4.05	—	31.2	—	—	4.60	2730	153	16.6
65.4	1.48	4.05	3.96	—	40.0	—	41.3	3.50	2530	138	15.2
70	1.41	4.17	4.52	—	25.3	—	—	4.15	1810	125	14.4
54.7	1.41	4.34	4.34	—	39.0	—	43.3	2.37	1560	105	12.1
50	1.31	4.28	4.53	—	27.3	—	—	2.12	811	77.1	9.97
42.9	1.31	4.38	4.42	—	36.5	—	49.6	1.54	743	69.3	9.02
50	1.31	3.32	4.15	—	17.5	—	—	2.82	505	61.2	10.3
40.8	1.28	3.46	3.98	—	26.0	—	—	1.76	436	53.1	8.85
35	1.20	4.34	4.67	—	28.0	—	—	1.08	324	44.8	6.79
31.8	1.20	4.41	4.60	—	34.3	—	56.2	0.901	307	42.0	6.40
35	1.15	4.12	5.03	—	16.8	—	—	1.29	189	35.4	6.22
25.4	1.13	4.37	4.74	—	32.2	—	63.9	0.604	153	28.4	4.96
23	0.987	4.51	4.90	—	18.1	—	—	0.551	61.8	19.3	3.68
18.4	0.973	4.70	4.70	—	29.5	—	—	0.336	53.5	16.5	3.16
20	0.914	4.63	4.92	—	15.6	—	—	0.451	34.6	14.5	2.96
15.3	0.894	4.88	4.67	—	27.8	—	—	0.241	28.8	12.1	2.44
17.25	0.845	4.69	4.97	—	12.9	—	—	0.374	18.4	10.6	2.36
12.5	0.817	5.02	4.64	—	25.9	—	—	0.168	14.5	8.47	1.85
14.75	0.781	4.66	5.03	—	10.1	—	—	0.323	9.09	7.42	1.88
10	0.741	5.10	4.60	—	23.4	—	—	0.114	6.64	5.67	1.37
9.5	0.684	4.88	4.77	—	12.3	—	—	0.120	3.10	4.04	1.13
7.7	0.662	5.13	4.54	—	20.7	—	—	0.073	2.62	3.51	0.964
7.5	0.621	4.60	4.83	—	8.60	—	—	0.091	1.10	2.36	0.826
5.7	0.585	4.95	4.48	—	17.6	—	—	0.044	0.854	1.95	0.653

HP SHAPES
Properties for designing

Designation	Area A	Depth d	Flange Width b_f	Flange Thickness t_f	Web Thickness t_w	Axis X-X I	Axis X-X S	Axis X-X r	Axis Y-Y I	Axis Y-Y S	Axis Y-Y r
	In.²	In.	In.	In.	In.	In.⁴	In.³	In.	In.⁴	In.³	In.
HP 14×117	34.4	14.23	14.885	0.805	0.805	1230	173	5.97	443	59.5	3.59
×102	30.0	14.03	14.784	0.704	0.704	1050	150	5.93	380	51.3	3.56
× 89	26.2	13.86	14.696	0.616	0.616	910	131	5.89	326	44.4	3.53
× 73	21.5	13.64	14.586	0.506	0.506	734	108	5.85	262	35.9	3.49
HP 12× 74	21.8	12.12	12.217	0.607	0.607	566	93.4	5.10	185	30.2	2.91
× 53	15.6	11.78	12.046	0.436	0.436	394	66.9	5.03	127	21.1	2.86
HP 10× 57	16.8	10.01	10.224	0.564	0.564	295	58.8	4.19	101	19.7	2.45
× 42	12.4	9.72	10.078	0.418	0.418	211	43.4	4.13	71.4	14.2	2.40
HP 8× 36	10.6	8.03	8.158	0.446	0.446	120	29.9	3.36	40.4	9.91	1.95

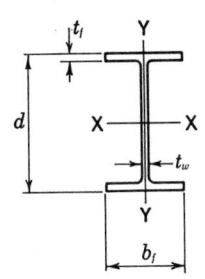

HP SHAPES
Properties for designing

Nominal Weight per Ft.	r_T	$\dfrac{d}{A_f}$	Compact Section Criteria					Torsional Constant J	Warping Constant C_W	Plastic Modulus	
			$\dfrac{b_f}{2t_f}$	F_y'	$\dfrac{d}{t_w}$	F_y''	F_y'''			Z_x	Z_y
Lb.	In.			Ksi		Ksi	Ksi	In.⁴	In.⁶	In.³	In.³
117	4.06	1.19	9.25	31.9	17.7	—	—	8.02	20000	195	91.4
102	4.02	1.35	10.5	24.7	19.9	—	—	5.38	16900	169	78.6
89	3.99	1.53	11.9	19.1	22.5	—	—	3.62	14300	146	67.9
73	3.94	1.85	14.4	13.1	27.0	—	—	2.03	11300	119	54.8
74	3.31	1.63	10.1	26.9	20.0	—	—	2.97	6120	105	46.4
53	3.23	2.24	13.8	14.3	27.0	—	—	1.13	4090	74.2	32.3
57	2.78	1.74	9.06	33.2	17.7	—	—	1.96	2240	66.5	30.3
42	2.72	2.31	12.1	18.8	23.3	—	—	0.811	1540	48.4	21.7
36	2.22	2.21	9.15	32.6	18.0	—	—	0.776	581	33.8	15.2

CHANNELS
AMERICAN STANDARD
Properties for designing

Designation	Area A	Depth d	Flange Width b_f	Flange Average thickness t_f	Web thickness t_w	$\dfrac{d}{A_f}$	Axis X-X I	Axis X-X S	Axis X-X r
	In.²	In.	In.	In.	In.		In.⁴	In.³	In.
C 15×50	14.7	15.00	3.716	0.650	0.716	6.21	404	53.8	5.24
×40	11.8	15.00	3.520	0.650	0.520	6.56	349	46.5	5.44
×33.9	9.96	15.00	3.400	0.650	0.400	6.79	315	42.0	5.62
C 12×30	8.82	12.00	3.170	0.501	0.510	7.55	162	27.0	4.29
×25	7.35	12.00	3.047	0.501	0.387	7.85	144	24.1	4.43
×20.7	6.09	12.00	2.942	0.501	0.282	8.13	129	21.5	4.61
C 10×30	8.82	10.00	3.033	0.436	0.673	7.55	103	20.7	3.42
×25	7.35	10.00	2.886	0.436	0.526	7.94	91.2	18.2	3.52
×20	5.88	10.00	2.739	0.436	0.379	8.36	78.9	15.8	3.66
×15.3	4.49	10.00	2.600	0.436	0.240	8.81	67.4	13.5	3.87
C 9×20	5.88	9.00	2.648	0.413	0.448	8.22	60.9	13.5	3.22
×15	4.41	9.00	2.485	0.413	0.285	8.76	51.0	11.3	3.40
×13.4	3.94	9.00	2.433	0.413	0.233	8.95	47.9	10.6	3.48
C 8×18.75	5.51	8.00	2.527	0.390	0.487	8.12	44.0	11.0	2.82
×13.75	4.04	8.00	2.343	0.390	0.303	8.75	36.1	9.03	2.99
×11.5	3.38	8.00	2.260	0.390	0.220	9.08	32.6	8.14	3.11
C 7×14.75	4.33	7.00	2.299	0.366	0.419	8.31	27.2	7.78	2.51
×12.25	3.60	7.00	2.194	0.366	0.314	8.71	24.2	6.93	2.60
× 9.8	2.87	7.00	2.090	0.366	0.210	9.14	21.3	6.08	2.72
C 6×13	3.83	6.00	2.157	0.343	0.437	8.10	17.4	5.80	2.13
×10.5	3.09	6.00	2.034	0.343	0.314	8.59	15.2	5.06	2.22
× 8.2	2.40	6.00	1.920	0.343	0.200	9.10	13.1	4.38	2.34
C 5× 9	2.64	5.00	1.885	0.320	0.325	8.29	8.90	3.56	1.83
× 6.7	1.97	5.00	1.750	0.320	0.190	8.93	7.49	3.00	1.95
C 4× 7.25	2.13	4.00	1.721	0.296	0.321	7.84	4.59	2.29	1.47
× 5.4	1.59	4.00	1.584	0.296	0.184	8.52	3.85	1.93	1.56
C 3× 6	1.76	3.00	1.596	0.273	0.356	6.87	2.07	1.38	1.08
× 5	1.47	3.00	1.498	0.273	0.258	7.32	1.85	1.24	1.12
× 4.1	1.21	3.00	1.410	0.273	0.170	7.78	1.66	1.10	1.17

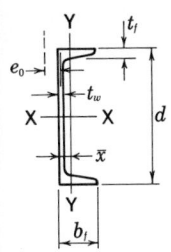

CHANNELS
AMERICAN STANDARD
Properties for designing

Nominal Weight per Ft.	Axis Y-Y			$\bar{x}$	Shear Center Location E_0	Torsional Constant J	Warping Constant C_w
	I	S	r				
	In.⁴	In.³	In.	In.	In.	In.⁴	In.⁶
50	11.0	3.78	0.867	0.799	0.941	2.66	492
40	9.23	3.36	0.886	0.778	1.03	1.46	410
33.9	8.13	3.11	0.904	0.787	1.10	1.01	358
30	5.14	2.06	0.763	0.674	0.873	0.865	151
25	4.47	1.88	0.780	0.674	0.940	0.541	131
20.7	3.88	1.73	0.799	0.698	1.01	0.371	112
30	3.94	1.65	0.669	0.649	0.705	1.22	79.5
25	3.36	1.48	0.676	0.617	0.757	0.690	68.4
20	2.81	1.32	0.691	0.606	0.826	0.370	57.0
15.3	2.28	1.16	0.713	0.634	0.916	0.211	45.5
20	2.42	1.17	0.642	0.583	0.739	0.429	39.5
15	1.93	1.01	0.661	0.586	0.824	0.209	31.0
13.4	1.76	0.962	0.668	0.601	0.859	0.169	28.2
18.75	1.98	1.01	0.599	0.565	0.674	0.436	25.1
13.75	1.53	0.853	0.615	0.553	0.756	0.187	19.3
11.5	1.32	0.781	0.625	0.571	0.807	0.131	16.5
14.75	1.38	0.779	0.564	0.532	0.651	0.268	13.1
12.25	1.17	0.702	0.571	0.525	0.695	0.161	11.2
9.8	0.968	0.625	0.581	0.541	0.752	0.100	9.16
13	1.05	0.642	0.525	0.514	0.599	0.241	7.21
10.5	0.865	0.564	0.529	0.500	0.643	0.131	5.94
8.2	0.692	0.492	0.537	0.512	0.699	0.075	4.73
9	0.632	0.449	0.489	0.478	0.590	0.109	2.93
6.7	0.478	0.378	0.493	0.484	0.647	0.055	2.22
7.25	0.432	0.343	0.450	0.459	0.546	0.082	1.24
5.4	0.319	0.283	0.449	0.458	0.594	0.040	0.923
6	0.305	0.268	0.416	0.455	0.500	0.073	0.463
5	0.247	0.233	0.410	0.438	0.521	0.043	0.380
4.1	0.197	0.202	0.404	0.437	0.546	0.027	0.307

[

CHANNELS
MISCELLANEOUS
Properties for designing

| Designation | Area A | Depth d | Flange | | Web thickness t_w | $\dfrac{d}{A_f}$ | Axis X-X | | |
			Width b_f	Average thickness t_f			I	S	r
	In.²	In.	In.	In.	In.		In.⁴	In.³	In.
MC 18×58	17.1	18.00	4.200	0.625	0.700	6.86	676	75.1	6.29
×51.9	15.3	18.00	4.100	0.625	0.600	7.02	627	69.7	6.41
×45.8	13.5	18.00	4.000	0.625	0.500	7.20	578	64.3	6.56
×42.7	12.6	18.00	3.950	0.625	0.450	7.29	554	61.6	6.64
MC 13×50	14.7	13.00	4.412	0.610	0.787	4.83	314	48.4	4.62
×40	11.8	13.00	4.185	0.610	0.560	5.09	273	42.0	4.82
×35	10.3	13.00	4.072	0.610	0.447	5.23	252	38.8	4.95
×31.8	9.35	13.00	4.000	0.610	0.375	5.33	239	36.8	5.06
MC 12×50	14.7	12.00	4.135	0.700	0.835	4.15	269	44.9	4.28
×45	13.2	12.00	4.012	0.700	0.712	4.27	252	42.0	4.36
×40	11.8	12.00	3.890	0.700	0.590	4.41	234	39.0	4.46
×35	10.3	12.00	3.767	0.700	0.467	4.55	216	36.1	4.59
MC 12×37	10.9	12.00	3.600	0.600	0.600	5.56	205	34.2	4.34
×32.9	9.67	12.00	3.500	0.600	0.500	5.71	191	31.8	4.44
×30.9	9.07	12.00	3.450	0.600	0.450	5.80	183	30.6	4.50
MC 12×10.6	3.10	12.00	1.500	0.309	0.190	25.9	55.4	9.23	4.22
MC 10×41.1	12.1	10.00	4.321	0.575	0.796	4.02	158	31.5	3.61
×33.6	9.87	10.00	4.100	0.575	0.575	4.24	139	27.8	3.75
×28.5	8.37	10.00	3.950	0.575	0.425	4.40	127	25.3	3.89
MC 10×28.3	8.32	10.00	3.502	0.575	0.477	4.97	118	23.6	3.77
×25.3	7.43	10.00	3.550	0.500	0.425	5.63	107	21.4	3.79
×24.9	7.32	10.00	3.402	0.575	0.377	5.11	110	22.0	3.87
×21.9	6.43	10.00	3.450	0.500	0.325	5.80	98.5	19.7	3.91
MC 10× 8.4	2.46	10.00	1.500	0.280	0.170	23.8	32.0	6.40	3.61
MC 10× 6.5	1.91	10.00	1.127	0.202	0.152	43.8	22.1	4.42	3.40

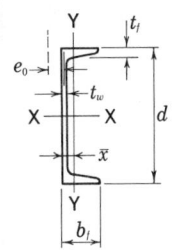

CHANNELS
MISCELLANEOUS
Properties for designing

Nominal Weight per Ft.	Axis Y-Y			$\bar{x}$	Shear Center Location E_0	Torsional Constant J	Warping Constant C_w
	I	S	r				
	In.⁴	In.³	In.	In.	In.	In.⁴	In.⁶
58	17.8	5.32	1.02	0.862	1.04	2.81	1070
51.9	16.4	5.07	1.04	0.858	1.10	2.03	986
45.8	15.1	4.82	1.06	0.866	1.16	1.45	898
42.7	14.4	4.69	1.07	0.877	1.19	1.23	852
50	16.5	4.79	1.06	0.974	1.21	2.97	558
40	13.7	4.26	1.08	0.964	1.31	1.55	462
35	12.3	3.99	1.10	0.980	1.38	1.13	413
31.8	11.4	3.81	1.11	1.00	1.43	0.938	380
50	17.4	5.65	1.09	1.05	1.16	3.23	411
45	15.8	5.33	1.09	1.04	1.20	2.34	374
40	14.3	5.00	1.10	1.04	1.25	1.70	336
35	12.7	4.67	1.11	1.05	1.30	1.25	298
37	9.81	3.59	0.950	0.866	1.05	1.43	247
32.9	8.91	3.39	0.960	0.867	1.09	1.04	224
30.9	8.46	3.28	0.966	0.873	1.12	0.895	212
10.6	0.382	0.310	0.351	0.269	0.379	0.060	11.7
41.1	15.8	4.88	1.14	1.09	1.26	2.26	269
33.6	13.2	4.38	1.16	1.08	1.35	1.20	224
28.5	11.4	4.02	1.17	1.12	1.43	0.792	193
28.3	8.21	3.20	0.993	0.933	1.17	0.842	139
25.3	7.61	2.89	1.01	0.918	1.19	0.576	132
24.9	7.32	2.99	1.00	0.954	1.22	0.633	124
21.9	6.74	2.70	1.02	0.954	1.25	0.417	116
8.4	0.328	0.270	0.365	0.284	0.417	0.041	7.01
6.5	0.112	0.118	0.242	0.180	0.243	0.018	2.46

CHANNELS
MISCELLANEOUS
Properties for designing

Designation	Area A	Depth d	Flange Width b_f	Flange Average thickness t_f	Web thickness t_w	$\dfrac{d}{A_f}$	Axis X-X I	S	r
	In.²	In.	In.	In.	In.		In.⁴	In.³	In.
MC 9×25.4	7.47	9.00	3.500	0.550	0.450	4.68	88.0	19.6	3.43
×23.9	7.02	9.00	3.450	0.550	0.400	4.74	85.0	18.9	3.48
MC 8×22.8	6.70	8.00	3.502	0.525	0.427	4.35	63.8	16.0	3.09
×21.4	6.28	8.00	3.450	0.525	0.375	4.42	61.6	15.4	3.13
MC 8×20	5.88	8.00	3.025	0.500	0.400	5.29	54.5	13.6	3.05
×18.7	5.50	8.00	2.978	0.500	0.353	5.37	52.5	13.1	3.09
MC 8×8.5	2.50	8.00	1.874	0.311	0.179	13.7	23.3	5.83	3.05
MC 7×22.7	6.67	7.00	3.603	0.500	0.503	3.89	47.5	13.6	2.67
×19.1	5.61	7.00	3.452	0.500	0.352	4.06	43.2	12.3	2.77
MC 7×17.6	5.17	7.00	3.000	0.475	0.375	4.91	37.6	10.8	2.70
MC 6×18	5.29	6.00	3.504	0.475	0.379	3.60	29.7	9.91	2.37
×15.3	4.50	6.00	3.500	0.385	0.340	4.45	25.4	8.47	2.38
MC 6×16.3	4.79	6.00	3.000	0.475	0.375	4.21	26.0	8.68	2.33
×15.1	4.44	6.00	2.941	0.475	0.316	4.29	25.0	8.32	2.37
MC 6×12	3.53	6.00	2.497	0.375	0.310	6.41	18.7	6.24	2.30
MC 3×9	2.65	3.00	2.122	0.351	0.497	4.02	3.15	2.10	1.09
×7.1	2.09	3.00	1.938	0.351	0.312	4.40	2.73	1.82	1.14

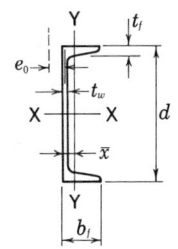

CHANNELS
MISCELLANEOUS
Properties for designing

Nominal Weight per Ft.	Axis Y-Y			$\bar{x}$	Shear Center Location E_0	Torsional Constant J	Warping Constant C_w
	I	S	r				
	In.⁴	In.³	In.	In.	In.	In.⁴	In.⁶
25.4	7.65	3.02	1.01	0.970	1.21	0.692	104
23.9	7.22	2.93	1.01	0.981	1.24	0.599	98.2
22.8	7.07	2.84	1.03	1.01	1.26	0.573	75.4
21.4	6.64	2.74	1.03	1.02	1.28	0.495	70.9
20	4.47	2.05	0.872	0.840	1.04	0.442	47.9
18.7	4.20	1.97	0.874	0.849	1.07	0.381	45.1
8.5	0.628	0.434	0.501	0.428	0.631	0.059	8.22
22.7	7.29	2.85	1.05	1.04	1.26	0.626	58.5
19.1	6.11	2.57	1.04	1.08	1.33	0.407	49.4
17.6	4.01	1.89	0.881	0.873	1.08	0.354	32.5
18	5.93	2.48	1.06	1.12	1.36	0.379	34.7
15.3	4.97	2.03	1.05	1.05	1.33	0.224	30.2
16.3	3.82	1.84	0.892	0.927	1.12	0.336	22.2
15.1	3.51	1.75	0.889	0.940	1.14	0.285	20.5
12	1.87	1.04	0.728	0.704	0.880	0.155	11.3
9	0.967	0.677	0.604	0.694	0.703	0.175	1.21
7.1	0.712	0.561	0.583	0.669	0.730	0.084	0.923

ANGLES
Equal legs
Properties for designing

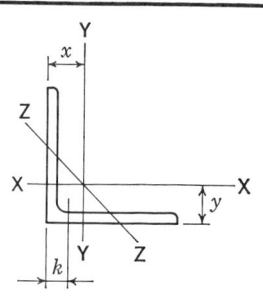

Size and Thickness	k	Weight per Foot	Area	AXIS X-X AND AXIS Y-Y				AXIS Z-Z
				I	S	r	x or y	r
In.	In.	Lb.	In.²	In.⁴	In.³	In.	In.	In.
L 8 × 8 × 1⅛	1¾	56.9	16.7	98.0	17.5	2.42	2.41	1.56
1	1⅝	51.0	15.0	89.0	15.8	2.44	2.37	1.56
⅞	1½	45.0	13.2	79.6	14.0	2.45	2.32	1.57
¾	1⅜	38.9	11.4	69.7	12.2	2.47	2.28	1.58
⅝	1¼	32.7	9.61	59.4	10.3	2.49	2.23	1.58
⁹⁄₁₆	1³⁄₁₆	29.6	8.68	54.1	9.34	2.50	2.21	1.59
½	1⅛	26.4	7.75	48.6	8.36	2.50	2.19	1.59
L 6 × 6 × 1	1½	37.4	11.0	35.5	8.57	1.80	1.86	1.17
⅞	1⅜	33.1	9.73	31.9	7.63	1.81	1.82	1.17
¾	1¼	28.7	8.44	28.2	6.66	1.83	1.78	1.17
⅝	1⅛	24.2	7.11	24.2	5.66	1.84	1.73	1.18
⁹⁄₁₆	1¹⁄₁₆	21.9	6.43	22.1	5.14	1.85	1.71	1.18
½	1	19.6	5.75	19.9	4.61	1.86	1.68	1.18
⁷⁄₁₆	¹⁵⁄₁₆	17.2	5.06	17.7	4.08	1.87	1.66	1.19
⅜	⅞	14.9	4.36	15.4	3.53	1.88	1.64	1.19
⁵⁄₁₆	¹³⁄₁₆	12.4	3.65	13.0	2.97	1.89	1.62	1.20
L 5 × 5 × ⅞	1⅜	27.2	7.98	17.8	5.17	1.49	1.57	.973
¾	1¼	23.6	6.94	15.7	4.53	1.51	1.52	.975
⅝	1⅛	20.0	5.86	13.6	3.86	1.52	1.48	.978
½	1	16.2	4.75	11.3	3.16	1.54	1.43	.983
⁷⁄₁₆	¹⁵⁄₁₆	14.3	4.18	10.0	2.79	1.55	1.41	.986
⅜	⅞	12.3	3.61	8.74	2.42	1.56	1.39	.990
⁵⁄₁₆	¹³⁄₁₆	10.3	3.03	7.42	2.04	1.57	1.37	.994
L 4 × 4 × ¾	1⅛	18.5	5.44	7.67	2.81	'1.19	1.27	.778
⅝	1	15.7	4.61	6.66	2.40	1.20	1.23	.779
½	⅞	12.8	3.75	5.56	1.97	1.22	1.18	.782
⁷⁄₁₆	¹³⁄₁₆	11.3	3.31	4.97	1.75	1.23	1.16	.785
⅜	¾	9.8	2.86	4.36	1.52	1.23	1.14	.788
⁵⁄₁₆	¹¹⁄₁₆	8.2	2.40	3.71	1.29	1.24	1.12	.791
¼	⅝	6.6	1.94	3.04	1.05	1.25	1.09	.795

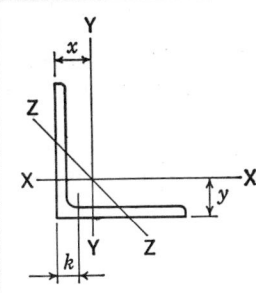

ANGLES
Equal legs

Properties for designing

Size and Thickness	k	Weight per Foot	Area	AXIS X-X AND AXIS Y-Y				AXIS Z-Z
				I	S	r	x or y	r
In.	In.	Lb.	In.²	In.⁴	In.³	In.	In.	In.
L 3½ × 3½ × ½	⅞	11.1	3.25	3.64	1.49	1.06	1.06	.683
⁷⁄₁₆	¹³⁄₁₆	9.8	2.87	3.26	1.32	1.07	1.04	.684
⅜	¾	8.5	2.48	2.87	1.15	1.07	1.01	.687
⁵⁄₁₆	¹¹⁄₁₆	7.2	2.09	2.45	.976	1.08	.990	.690
¼	⅝	5.8	1.69	2.01	.794	1.09	.968	.694
L 3 × 3 × ½	¹³⁄₁₆	9.4	2.75	2.22	1.07	.898	.932	.584
⁷⁄₁₆	¾	8.3	2.43	1.99	.954	.905	.910	.585
⅜	¹¹⁄₁₆	7.2	2.11	1.76	.833	.913	.888	.587
⁵⁄₁₆	⅝	6.1	1.78	1.51	.707	.922	.865	.589
¼	⁹⁄₁₆	4.9	1.44	1.24	.577	.930	.842	.592
³⁄₁₆	½	3.71	1.09	.962	.441	.939	.820	.596
L 2½ × 2½ × ½	¹³⁄₁₆	7.7	2.25	1.23	.724	.739	.806	.487
⅜	¹¹⁄₁₆	5.9	1.73	.984	.566	.753	.762	.487
⁵⁄₁₆	⅝	5.0	1.46	.849	.482	.761	.740	.489
¼	⁹⁄₁₆	4.1	1.19	.703	.394	.769	.717	.491
³⁄₁₆	½	3.07	.902	.547	.303	.778	.694	.495
L 2 × 2 × ⅜	¹¹⁄₁₆	4.7	1.36	.479	.351	.594	.636	.389
⁵⁄₁₆	⅝	3.92	1.15	.416	.300	.601	.614	.390
¼	⁹⁄₁₆	3.19	.938	.348	.247	.609	.592	.391
³⁄₁₆	½	2.44	.715	.272	.190	.617	.569	.394
⅛	⁷⁄₁₆	1.65	.484	.190	.131	.626	.546	.398
L 1¾ × 1¾ × ¼	½	2.77	.813	.227	.186	.529	.529	.341
³⁄₁₆	⁷⁄₁₆	2.12	.621	.179	.144	.537	.506	.343
⅛	⅜	1.44	.422	.126	.099	.546	.484	.347
L 1½ × 1½ × ¼	⁷⁄₁₆	2.34	.688	.139	.134	.449	.466	.292
³⁄₁₆	⅜	1.80	.527	.110	.104	.457	.444	.293
⁵⁄₃₂	⅜	1.52	.444	.094	.088	.461	.433	.295
⅛	⁵⁄₁₆	1.23	.359	.078	.072	.465	.421	.296
L 1¼ × 1¼ × ¼	⁷⁄₁₆	1.92	.563	.077	.091	.369	.403	.243
³⁄₁₆	⅜	1.48	.434	.061	.071	.377	.381	.244
⅛	⁵⁄₁₆	1.01	.297	.044	.049	.385	.359	.246
L 1 × 1 × ¼	⅜	1.49	.438	.037	.056	.290	.339	.196
³⁄₁₆	⁵⁄₁₆	1.16	.340	.030	.044	.297	.318	.195
⅛	¼	.80	.234	.022	.031	.304	.296	.196

ANGLES
Unequal legs
Properties for designing

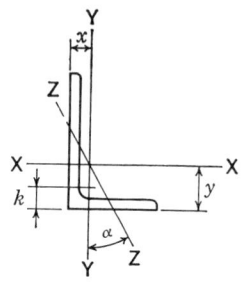

Size and Thickness	k	Weight per Foot	Area	AXIS X-X				AXIS Y-Y				AXIS Z-Z	
				I	S	r	y	I	S	r	x	r	Tan α
In.	In.	Lb.	In.²	In.⁴	In.³	In.	In.	In.⁴	In.³	In.	In.	In.	
L 9 × 4 × 1	1½	40.8	12.0	97.0	17.6	2.84	3.50	12.0	4.00	1.00	1.00	.834	.203
⅞	1⅜	36.1	10.6	86.8	15.7	2.86	3.45	10.8	3.56	1.01	.953	.836	.208
¾	1¼	31.3	9.19	76.1	13.6	2.88	3.41	9.63	3.11	1.02	.906	.841	.212
⅝	1⅛	26.3	7.73	64.9	11.5	2.90	3.36	8.32	2.65	1.04	.858	.847	.216
⁹⁄₁₆	1¹⁄₁₆	23.8	7.00	59.1	10.4	2.91	3.33	7.63	2.41	1.04	.834	.850	.218
½	1	21.3	6.25	53.2	9.34	2.92	3.31	6.92	2.17	1.05	.810	.854	.220
L 8 × 6 × 1	1½	44.2	13.0	80.8	15.1	2.49	2.65	38.8	8.92	1.73	1.65	1.28	.543
⅞	1⅜	39.1	11.5	72.3	13.4	2.51	2.61	34.9	7.94	1.74	1.61	1.28	.547
¾	1¼	33.8	9.94	63.4	11.7	2.53	2.56	30.7	6.92	1.76	1.56	1.29	.551
⅝	1⅛	28.5	8.36	54.1	9.87	2.54	2.52	26.3	5.88	1.77	1.52	1.29	.554
⁹⁄₁₆	1¹⁄₁₆	25.7	7.56	49.3	8.95	2.55	2.50	24.0	5.34	1.78	1.50	1.30	.556
½	1	23.0	6.75	44.3	8.02	2.56	2.47	21.7	4.79	1.79	1.47	1.30	.558
⁷⁄₁₆	¹⁵⁄₁₆	20.2	5.93	39.2	7.07	2.57	2.45	19.3	4.23	1.80	1.45	1.31	.560
L 8 × 4 × 1	1½	37.4	11.0	69.6	14.1	2.52	3.05	11.6	3.94	1.03	1.05	.846	.247
⅞	1⅜	33.1	9.73	62.5	12.5	2.53	3.00	10.5	3.51	1.04	.999	.848	.253
¾	1¼	28.7	8.44	54.9	10.9	2.55	2.95	9.36	3.07	1.05	.953	.852	.258
⅝	1⅛	24.2	7.11	46.9	9.21	2.57	2.91	8.10	2.62	1.07	.906	.857	.262
⁹⁄₁₆	1¹⁄₁₆	21.9	6.43	42.8	8.35	2.58	2.88	7.43	2.38	1.07	.882	.861	.265
½	1	19.6	5.75	38.5	7.49	2.59	2.86	6.74	2.15	1.08	.859	.865	.267
⁷⁄₁₆	¹⁵⁄₁₆	17.2	5.06	34.1	6.60	2.60	2.83	6.02	1.90	1.09	.835	.869	.269
L 7 × 4 × ⅞	1⅜	30.2	8.86	42.9	9.65	2.20	2.55	10.2	3.46	1.07	1.05	.856	.318
¾	1¼	26.2	7.69	37.8	8.42	2.22	2.51	9.05	3.03	1.09	1.01	.860	.324
⅝	1⅛	22.1	6.48	32.4	7.14	2.24	2.46	7.84	2.58	1.10	.963	.865	.329
⁹⁄₁₆	1¹⁄₁₆	20.0	5.87	29.6	6.48	2.24	2.44	7.19	2.35	1.11	.940	.868	.332
½	1	17.9	5.25	26.7	5.81	2.25	2.42	6.53	2.12	1.11	.917	.872	.335
⁷⁄₁₆	¹⁵⁄₁₆	15.8	4.62	23.7	5.13	2.26	2.39	5.83	1.88	1.12	.893	.876	.337
⅜	⅞	13.6	3.98	20.6	4.44	2.27	2.37	5.10	1.63	1.13	.870	.880	.340

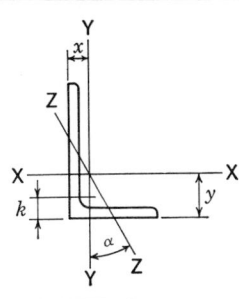

ANGLES
Unequal legs
Properties for designing

Size and Thickness	k	Weight per Foot	Area	AXIS X-X				AXIS Y-Y				AXIS Z-Z	
				I	S	r	y	I	S	r	x	r	Tan α
In.	In.	Lb.	In.²	In.⁴	In.³	In.	In.	In.⁴	In.³	In.	In.	In.	
L 6 × 4 × ⅞	1⅜	27.2	7.98	27.7	7.15	1.86	2.12	9.75	3.39	1.11	1.12	.857	.421
¾	1¼	23.6	6.94	24.5	6.25	1.88	2.08	8.68	2.97	1.12	1.08	.860	.428
⅝	1⅛	20.0	5.86	21.1	5.31	1.90	2.03	7.52	2.54	1.13	1.03	.864	.435
⁹⁄₁₆	1¹⁄₁₆	18.1	5.31	19.3	4.83	1.90	2.01	6.91	2.31	1.14	1.01	.866	.438
½	1	16.2	4.75	17.4	4.33	1.91	1.99	6.27	2.08	1.15	.987	.870	.440
⁷⁄₁₆	¹⁵⁄₁₆	14.3	4.18	15.5	3.83	1.92	1.96	5.60	1.85	1.16	.964	.873	.443
⅜	⅞	12.3	3.61	13.5	3.32	1.93	1.94	4.90	1.60	1.17	.941	.877	.446
⁵⁄₁₆	¹³⁄₁₆	10.3	3.03	11.4	2.79	1.94	1.92	4.18	1.35	1.17	.918	.882	.448
¼	¾	8.3	2.44	9.27	2.26	1.95	1.89	3.41	1.10	1.18	.894	.887	.451
L 6 × 3½ × ½	1	15.3	4.50	16.6	4.24	1.92	2.08	4.25	1.59	.972	.833	.759	.344
⅜	⅞	11.7	3.42	12.9	3.24	1.94	2.04	3.34	1.23	.988	.787	.767	.350
⁵⁄₁₆	¹³⁄₁₆	9.8	2.87	10.9	2.73	1.95	2.01	2.85	1.04	.996	.763	.772	.352
¼	¾	7.9	2.31	8.86	2.21	1.96	1.99	2.34	0.847	1.01	.740	.777	.355
L 5 × 3½ × ¾	1¼	19.8	5.81	13.9	4.28	1.55	1.75	5.55	2.22	.977	.996	.748	.464
⅝	1⅛	16.8	4.92	12.0	3.65	1.56	1.70	4.83	1.90	.991	.951	.751	.472
½	1	13.6	4.00	9.99	2.99	1.58	1.66	4.05	1.56	1.01	.906	.755	.479
⁷⁄₁₆	¹⁵⁄₁₆	12.0	3.53	8.90	2.64	1.59	1.63	3.63	1.39	1.01	.883	.758	.482
⅜	⅞	10.4	3.05	7.78	2.29	1.60	1.61	3.18	1.21	1.02	.861	.762	.486
⁵⁄₁₆	¹³⁄₁₆	8.7	2.56	6.60	1.94	1.61	1.59	2.72	1.02	1.03	.838	.766	.489
¼	¾	7.0	2.06	5.39	1.57	1.62	1.56	2.23	.830	1.04	.814	.770	.492
L 5 × 3 × ½	1	12.8	3.75	9.45	2.91	1.59	1.75	2.58	1.15	.829	.750	.648	.357
⁷⁄₁₆	¹⁵⁄₁₆	11.3	3.31	8.43	2.58	1.60	1.73	2.32	1.02	.837	.727	.651	.361
⅜	⅞	9.8	2.86	7.37	2.24	1.61	1.70	2.04	.888	.845	.704	.654	.364
⁵⁄₁₆	¹³⁄₁₆	8.2	2.40	6.26	1.89	1.61	1.68	1.75	.753	.853	.681	.658	.368
¼	¾	6.6	1.94	5.11	1.53	1.62	1.66	1.44	.614	.861	.657	.663	.371

ANGLES
Unequal legs
Properties for designing

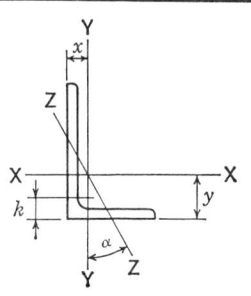

Size and Thickness	k	Weight per Foot	Area	AXIS X-X				AXIS Y-Y				AXIS Z-Z	
				I	S	r	y	I	S	r	x	r	Tan α
In.	In.	Lb.	In.²	In.⁴	In.³	In.	In.	In.⁴	In.³	In.	In.	In.	α
L 4 × 3½ × ⅝	1 1/16	14.7	4.30	6.37	2.35	1.22	1.29	4.52	1.84	1.03	1.04	.719	.745
½	15/16	11.9	3.50	5.32	1.94	1.23	1.25	3.79	1.52	1.04	1.00	.722	.750
7/16	⅞	10.6	3.09	4.76	1.72	1.24	1.23	3.40	1.35	1.05	.978	.724	.753
⅜	13/16	9.1	2.67	4.18	1.49	1.25	1.21	2.95	1.17	1.06	.955	.727	.755
5/16	¾	7.7	2.25	3.56	1.26	1.26	1.18	2.55	.994	1.07	.932	.730	.757
¼	11/16	6.2	1.81	2.91	1.03	1.27	1.16	2.09	.808	1.07	.909	.734	.759
L 4 × 3 × ⅝	1 1/16	13.6	3.98	6.03	2.30	1.23	1.37	2.87	1.35	.849	.871	.637	.534
½	15/16	11.1	3.25	5.05	1.89	1.25	1.33	2.42	1.12	.864	.827	.639	.543
7/16	⅞	9.8	2.87	4.52	1.68	1.25	1.30	2.18	.992	.871	.804	.641	.547
⅜	13/16	8.5	2.48	3.96	1.46	1.26	1.28	1.92	.866	.879	.782	.644	.551
5/16	¾	7.2	2.09	3.38	1.23	1.27	1.26	1.65	.734	.887	.759	.647	.554
¼	11/16	5.8	1.69	2.77	1.00	1.28	1.24	1.36	.599	.896	.736	.651	.558
L 3½ × 3 × ½	15/16	10.2	3.00	3.45	1.45	1.07	1.13	2.33	1.10	.881	.875	.621	.714
7/16	⅞	9.1	2.65	3.10	1.29	1.08	1.10	2.09	.975	.889	.853	.622	.718
⅜	13/16	7.9	2.30	2.72	1.13	1.09	1.08	1.85	.851	.897	.830	.625	.721
5/16	¾	6.6	1.93	2.33	.954	1.10	1.06	1.58	.722	.905	.808	.627	.724
¼	11/16	5.4	1.56	1.91	.776	1.11	1.04	1.30	.589	.914	.785	.631	.727
L 3½ × 2½ × ½	15/16	9.4	2.75	3.24	1.41	1.09	1.20	1.36	.760	.704	.705	.534	.486
7/16	⅞	8.3	2.43	2.91	1.26	1.09	1.18	1.23	.677	.711	.682	.535	.491
⅜	13/16	7.2	2.11	2.56	1.09	1.10	1.16	1.09	.592	.719	.660	.537	.496
5/16	¾	6.1	1.78	2.19	.927	1.11	1.14	.939	.504	.727	.637	.540	.501
¼	11/16	4.9	1.44	1.80	.755	1.12	1.11	.777	.412	.735	.614	.544	.506
L 3 × 2½ × ½	⅞	8.5	2.50	2.08	1.04	.913	1.00	1.30	.744	.722	.750	.520	.667
7/16	13/16	7.6	2.21	1.88	.928	.920	.978	1.18	.664	.729	.728	.521	.672
⅜	¾	6.6	1.92	1.66	.810	.928	.956	1.04	.581	.736	.706	.522	.676
5/16	11/16	5.6	1.62	1.42	.688	.937	.933	.898	.494	.744	.683	.525	.680
¼	⅝	4.5	1.31	1.17	.561	.945	.911	.743	.404	.753	.661	.528	.684
3/16	9/16	3.39	.996	.907	.430	.954	.888	.577	.310	.761	.638	.533	.688

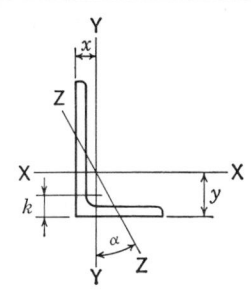

ANGLES
Unequal legs
Properties for designing

L

Size and Thickness	k	Weight per Foot	Area	AXIS X-X				AXIS Y-Y				AXIS Z-Z	
				I	S	r	y	I	S	r	x	r	Tan α
In.	In.	Lb.	In.²	In.⁴	In.³	In.	In.	In.⁴	In.³	In.	In.	In.	
L 3 × 2 × ½	13/16	7.7	2.25	1.92	1.00	.924	1.08	.672	.474	.546	.583	.428	.414
7/16	¾	6.8	2.00	1.73	.894	.932	1.06	.609	.424	.553	.561	.429	.421
⅜	11/16	5.9	1.73	1.53	.781	.940	1.04	.543	.371	.559	.539	.430	.428
5/16	⅝	5.0	1.46	1.32	.664	.948	1.02	.470	.317	.567	.516	.432	.435
¼	9/16	4.1	1.19	1.09	.542	.957	.993	.392	.260	.574	.493	.435	.440
3/16	½	3.07	.902	.842	.415	.966	.970	.307	.200	.583	.470	.439	.446
L 2½ × 2 × ⅜	11/16	5.3	1.55	.912	.547	.768	.831	.514	.363	.577	.581	.420	.614
5/16	⅝	4.5	1.31	.788	.466	.776	.809	.446	.310	.584	.559	.422	.620
¼	9/16	3.62	1.06	.654	.381	.784	.787	.372	.254	.592	.537	.424	.626
3/16	½	2.75	.809	.509	.293	.793	.764	.291	.196	.600	.514	.427	.631
L 2½ × 1½ × 5/16	⅝	3.92	1.15	.711	.444	.785	.898	.191	.174	.408	.398	.322	.349
¼	9/16	3.19	.938	.591	.364	.794	.875	.161	.143	.415	.375	.324	.357
3/16	½	2.44	.715	.461	.279	.803	.852	.127	.111	.422	.352	.327	.364
L 2 × 1½ × ¼	½	2.77	.813	.316	.236	.623	.663	.151	.139	.432	.413	.320	.543
3/16	7/16	2.12	.621	.248	.182	.632	.641	.120	.108	.440	.391	.322	.551
⅛	⅜	1.44	.422	.173	.125	.641	.618	.085	.075	.448	.368	.326	.558
L 2 × 1¼ × ¼	½	2.55	.750	.296	.229	.628	.708	.089	.097	.344	.333	.269	.378
3/16	7/16	1.96	.574	.232	.177	.636	.686	.071	.075	.351	.311	.271	.387
⅛	⅜	1.33	.391	.163	.122	.645	.663	.050	.052	.359	.287	.274	.396
L 1¾ × 1¼ × ¼	7/16	2.34	.688	.202	.176	.543	.602	.085	.095	.352	.352	.267	.486
3/16	⅜	1.80	.527	.160	.137	.551	.580	.068	.074	.359	.330	.269	.496
⅛	5/16	1.23	.359	.113	.094	.560	.557	.049	.051	.368	.307	.272	.506

Notes

DOUBLE ANGLES
Properties of Sections

Properties of double angles in contact and separated are listed in the following tables. Each left hand page in the table shows properties of double angles in contact and the radius of gyration about the Y-Y axis when the legs of the angles are separated; right hand facing pages show values of Q_s and C'_c for $F_y = 36$ ksi and $F_y = 50$ ksi for those angles exceeding the width-thickness ratios of AISC Specification Sect. 1.9.1. For these pairs of angles, the design stress is governed by the provisions of AISC Specification Appendix C, Sects. C2, C5, and C6. Where no values of Q_s and C'_c are shown, the double angles conform to the provisions of AISC Specification Sect. 1.9.1 and are considered fully effective.

USE OF TABLES

Use of the listed values of Q_s and C'_c affords the designer a means of rapid solution for values of allowable axial stress F_a.

For the design of double angles as axially loaded compression members when AISC Specification Appendix C governs, read the value of C'_c from the table for the double angles selected and the F_y value desired:

Compute $\dfrac{Kl/r}{C'_c}$

If $\dfrac{Kl/r}{C'_c} \geq 1.0$: Enter the table in AISC Specification Appendix A, pgs. **5** - 84 thru **5** - 92, for the desired F_y and Kl/r values. Read F_a directly.

If $\dfrac{Kl/r}{C'_c} < 1.0$: Enter Table 1-A, AISC Specification Appendix A, pg. **5** - 93 and read a value of C_a for the computed value $\dfrac{Kl/r}{C'_c}$.

$$F_a = Q_s C_a F_y$$

For the design of double angles subject to combined axial and flexural stress when AISC Specification Appendix C governs:

Use the smaller value obtained from:
$F_b = 0.6\ F_y Q_s$ or Specification Sect. 1.5.1.4.6.

DOUBLE ANGLES

Two equal angles

Properties of sections

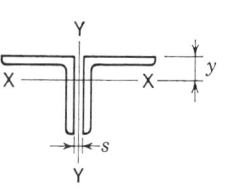

Designation	Wt. per Ft. 2 Angles Lb.	Area of 2 Angles In.²	AXIS X - X				Radii of Gyration About Axis Y - Y					
			I In.⁴	S In.³	r In.	y In.	Back to Back of Angles, Inches					
							0	¼	⅜	½	⅝	¾
L 8 × 8 × 1⅛	113.8	33.5	195.0	35.1	2.42	2.41	3.42	3.51	3.55	3.60	3.64	3.69
1	102.0	30.0	177.0	31.6	2.44	2.37	3.40	3.48	3.53	3.57	3.62	3.67
⅞	90.0	26.5	159.0	28.0	2.45	2.32	3.38	3.46	3.51	3.55	3.60	3.64
¾	77.8	22.9	139.0	24.4	2.47	2.28	3.36	3.44	3.49	3.53	3.58	3.62
⅝	65.4	19.2	118.0	20.6	2.49	2.23	3.34	3.43	3.47	3.51	3.56	3.60
⁹⁄₁₆	59.2	17.4	108.0	18.7	2.50	2.21	3.33	3.42	3.46	3.50	3.55	3.59
½	52.8	15.5	97.3	16.7	2.50	2.19	3.32	3.41	3.45	3.49	3.54	3.58
L 6 × 6 × 1	74.8	22.0	70.9	17.1	1.80	1.86	2.59	2.68	2.73	2.77	2.82	2.87
⅞	66.2	19.5	63.8	15.3	1.81	1.82	2.57	2.66	2.70	2.75	2.80	2.85
¾	57.4	16.9	56.3	13.3	1.83	1.78	2.55	2.64	2.68	2.73	2.77	2.82
⅝	48.4	14.2	48.3	11.3	1.84	1.73	2.53	2.62	2.66	2.71	2.75	2.80
⁹⁄₁₆	43.8	12.9	44.1	10.3	1.85	1.71	2.52	2.61	2.65	2.69	2.74	2.79
½	39.2	11.5	39.8	9.23	1.86	1.68	2.51	2.60	2.64	2.68	2.73	2.78
⁷⁄₁₆	34.4	10.1	35.4	8.15	1.87	1.66	2.50	2.59	2.63	2.67	2.72	2.76
⅜	29.8	8.72	30.8	7.06	1.88	1.64	2.49	2.58	2.62	2.66	2.71	2.75
⁵⁄₁₆	24.8	7.30	26.0	5.94	1.89	1.62	2.49	2.57	2.61	2.65	2.70	2.74
L 5 × 5 × ⅞	54.4	16.0	35.5	10.3	1.49	1.57	2.16	2.26	2.30	2.35	2.40	2.45
¾	47.2	13.9	31.5	9.06	1.51	1.52	2.14	2.23	2.28	2.33	2.37	2.42
⅝	40.0	11.7	27.2	7.71	1.52	1.48	2.12	2.21	2.26	2.30	2.35	2.40
½	32.4	9.50	22.5	6.31	1.54	1.43	2.10	2.19	2.24	2.28	2.33	2.38
⁷⁄₁₆	28.6	8.37	20.0	5.58	1.55	1.41	2.09	2.18	2.23	2.27	2.32	2.36
⅜	24.6	7.22	17.5	4.84	1.56	1.39	2.09	2.17	2.22	2.26	2.31	2.35
⁵⁄₁₆	20.6	6.05	14.8	4.08	1.57	1.37	2.08	2.16	2.21	2.25	2.30	2.34
L 4 × 4 × ¾	37.0	10.9	15.3	5.62	1.19	1.27	1.74	1.83	1.88	1.93	1.98	2.83
⅝	31.4	9.22	13.3	4.80	1.20	1.23	1.72	1.81	1.86	1.90	1.95	2.00
½	25.6	7.50	11.1	3.95	1.22	1.18	1.70	1.79	1.83	1.88	1.93	1.98
⁷⁄₁₆	22.6	6.62	9.95	3.50	1.23	1.16	1.69	1.78	1.82	1.87	1.92	1.97
⅜	19.6	5.72	8.72	3.05	1.23	1.14	1.68	1.77	1.81	1.86	1.91	1.95
⁵⁄₁₆	16.4	4.80	7.43	2.58	1.24	1.12	1.67	1.76	1.80	1.85	1.89	1.94
¼	13.2	3.88	6.08	2.09	1.25	1.09	1.66	1.75	1.79	1.84	1.88	1.93
L 3½ × 3½ × ½	22.2	6.50	7.27	2.98	1.06	1.06	1.50	1.59	1.63	1.68	1.73	1.78
⁷⁄₁₆	19.6	5.74	6.52	2.65	1.07	1.04	1.49	1.58	1.62	1.67	1.72	1.77
⅜	17.0	4.97	5.73	2.30	1.07	1.01	1.48	1.56	1.61	1.66	1.71	1.75
⁵⁄₁₆	14.4	4.18	4.90	1.95	1.08	.990	1.47	1.55	1.60	1.65	1.69	1.74
¼	11.6	3.38	4.02	1.59	1.09	.968	1.46	1.54	1.59	1.64	1.68	1.73

DOUBLE ANGLES
Two equal angles

$$C_c' = \sqrt{\frac{2\pi^2 E}{Q_s Q_a F_y}}$$

$$Q_a = 1.0$$

Properties of sections limited by width-thickness ratios
Per AISC Specification, Sect. 1.9.1

| Designation | Angles in Contact | | | | Angles Separated | | | |
| | $F_y = 36$ ksi | | $F_y = 50$ ksi | | $F_y = 36$ ksi | | $F_y = 50$ ksi | |
In.	Q_s	C_c'	Q_s	C_c'	Q_s	C_c'	Q_s	C_c'
L 8 ✕ 8 ✕ 1⅛	—	—	—	—	—	—	—	—
1	—	—	—	—	—	—	—	—
⅞	—	—	—	—	—	—	—	—
¾	—	—	—	—	--	—	—	—
⅝	—	—	—	—	0.997	126	0.935	111
⁹⁄₁₆	—	—	0.976	108	0.959	129	0.890	113
½	0.995	126	0.921	112	0.911	132	0.834	117
L 6 ✕ 6 ✕ 1	—	—	—	—	—	—	—	—
⅞	—	—	—	—	—	—	—	—
¾	—	—	—	—	—	—	—	—
⅝	—	—	—	—	—	—	—	—
⁹⁄₁₆	—	—	—	—	—	—	—	—
½	—	—	—	—	—	—	0.961	109
⁷⁄₁₆	—	—	0.991	107	0.972	128	0.907	112
⅜	0.995	126	0.921	112	0.911	132	0.834	117
⁵⁄₁₆	0.912	132	0.822	118	0.825	139	0.733	125
L 5 ✕ 5 ✕ ⅞	—	—	—	—	—	—	—	—
¾	—	—	—	—	—	—	—	—
⅝	—	—	—	—	—	—	—	—
½	—	—	—	—	—	—	—	—
⁷⁄₁₆	—	—	—	—	—	—	0.979	108
⅜	—	—	—	—	0.982	127	0.919	112
⁵⁄₁₆	0.995	126	0.921	112	0.911	132	0.834	117
L 4 ✕ 4 ✕ ¾	—	—	—	—	—	—	—	—
⅝	—	—	—	—	—	—	—	—
½	—	—	—	—	—	—	—	—
⁷⁄₁₆	—	—	—	—	—	—	—	—
⅜	—	—	—	—	—	—	—	—
⁵⁄₁₆	—	—	—	—	0.997	126	0.935	111
¼	0.995	126	0.921	112	0.911	132	0.834	117
L 3½ ✕ 3½ ✕ ½	—	—	—	—	—	—	—	—
⁷⁄₁₆	—	—	—	—	—	—	—	—
⅜	—	—	—	—	—	—	—	—
⁵⁄₁₆	—	—	—	—	—	—	0.986	108
¼	—	—	0.982	108	0.965	128	0.897	113

Where no value of C_c' or Q_s is shown, the angles comply with Specification Sect. 1.9.1.2 and may be considered fully effective.

AMERICAN INSTITUTE OF STEEL CONSTRUCTION

DOUBLE ANGLES

Two equal angles

Properties of sections

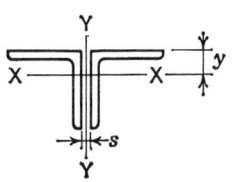

Designation	Wt. per Ft. 2 Angles	Area of 2 Angles	AXIS X - X				Radii of Gyration About Axis Y - Y Back to Back of Angles, Inches					
			I	S	r	y	0	¼	⅜	½	⅝	¾
	Lb.	In.²	In.⁴	In.³	In.	In.						
L 3 × 3 × ½	18.8	5.50	4.43	2.14	.898	.932	1.29	1.39	1.43	1.48	1.53	1.59
⁷⁄₁₆	16.6	4.87	3.99	1.91	.905	.910	1.28	1.37	1.42	1.47	1.52	1.57
⅜	14.4	4.22	3.52	1.67	.913	.888	1.27	1.36	1.41	1.46	1.51	1.56
⁵⁄₁₆	12.2	3.55	3.02	1.41	.922	.865	1.26	1.35	1.40	1.45	1.50	1.55
¼	9.8	2.88	2.49	1.15	.930	.842	1.26	1.34	1.39	1.43	1.48	1.53
³⁄₁₆	7.42	2.18	1.92	.882	.939	.820	1.25	1.33	1.38	1.42	1.47	1.52
L 2½ × 2½ × ½	15.4	4.50	2.45	1.45	.739	.806	1.09	1.19	1.24	1.29	1.34	1.39
⅜	11.8	3.47	1.97	1.13	.753	.762	1.07	1.16	1.21	1.26	1.31	1.36
⁵⁄₁₆	10.0	2.93	1.70	.964	.761	.740	1.06	1.15	1.20	1.25	1.30	1.35
¼	8.2	2.38	1.41	.789	.769	.717	1.05	1.14	1.19	1.24	1.29	1.34
³⁄₁₆	6.14	1.80	1.09	.685	.778	.694	1.04	1.13	1.18	1.22	1.27	1.32
L 2 × 2 × ⅜	9.4	2.72	.958	.702	.594	.636	.870	.965	1.01	1.07	1.12	1.17
⁵⁄₁₆	7.84	2.30	.832	.600	.601	.614	.859	.952	1.00	1.05	1.10	1.16
¼	6.38	1.88	.695	.494	.609	.592	.849	.940	.989	1.04	1.09	1.14
³⁄₁₆	4.88	1.43	.545	.381	.617	.569	.840	.929	.977	1.03	1.08	1.13
⅛	3.30	.960	.380	.261	.626	.546	.831	.918	.965	1.01	1.06	1.11
L 1¾ × 1¾ × ¼	5.54	1.63	.454	.372	.529	.529	.748	.841	.890	.941	.994	1.05
³⁄₁₆	4.24	1.24	.358	.288	.537	.506	.738	.829	.877	.928	.979	1.03
⅛	2.88	.844	.251	.198	.546	.484	.729	.818	.865	.914	.965	1.02
L 1½ × 1½ × ¼	4.38	1.38	.277	.268	.449	.466	.647	.742	.793	.845	.899	.953
³⁄₁₆	3.60	1.05	.220	.208	.457	.444	.637	.729	.779	.831	.883	.938
⁵⁄₃₂	3.04	.888	.189	.177	.461	.433	.632	.723	.773	.824	.876	.930
⅛	2.46	.719	.156	.144	.465	.421	.628	.717	.766	.817	.869	.922
L 1¼ × 1¼ × ¼	3.84	1.13	.153	.181	.369	.403	.546	.644	.696	.750	.805	.861
³⁄₁₆	2.96	.867	.123	.142	.377	.381	.536	.631	.682	.735	.789	.845
⅛	2.02	.594	.088	.099	.385	.359	.526	.618	.668	.720	.774	.820
L 1 × 1 × ¼	2.98	.875	.074	.112	.290	.339	.447	.548	.601	.657	.714	.771
³⁄₁₆	2.32	.680	.060	.088	.297	.318	.435	.533	.586	.641	.697	.754
⅛	1.60	.469	.043	.062	.304	.296	.425	.519	.571	.625	.680	.737

DOUBLE ANGLES
Two equal angles

$$C_c' = \sqrt{\frac{2\pi^2 E}{Q_s Q_a F_y}}$$

$Q_a = 1.0$

Properties of sections limited by width-thickness ratios

Per AISC Specification, Sect. 1.9.1

| Designation | Angles in Contact | | | | Angles Separated | | | |
| | $F_y = 36$ ksi | | $F_y = 50$ ksi | | $F_y = 36$ ksi | | $F_y = 50$ ksi | |
In.	Q_s	C_c'	Q_s	C_c'	Q_s	C_c'	Q_s	C_c'
L 3 × 3 × ½	—	—	—	—	—	—	—	—
7⁄16	—	—	—	—	—	—	—	—
3⁄8	—	—	—	—	—	—	—	—
5⁄16	—	—	—	—	—	—	—	—
¼	—	—	—	—	—	—	0.961	109
3⁄16	0.995	126	0.921	112	0.911	132	0.834	117
L 2½ × 2½ × ½	—	—	—	—	—	—	—	—
3⁄8	—	—	—	—	—	—	—	—
5⁄16	—	—	—	—	—	—	—	—
¼	—	—	—	—	—	—	—	—
3⁄16	—	—	—	—	0.982	127	0.919	112
L 2 × 2 × 3⁄8	—	—	—	—	—	—	—	—
5⁄16	—	—	—	—	—	—	—	—
¼	—	—	—	—	—	—	—	—
3⁄16	—	—	—	—	—	—	—	—
⅛	0.995	126	0.921	112	0.911	132	0.834	117
L 1¾ × 1¾ × ¼	—	—	—	—	—	—	—	—
3⁄16	—	—	—	—	—	—	—	—
⅛	—	—	0.982	108	0.965	128	0.897	113
L 1½ × 1½ × ¼	—	—	—	—	—	—	—	—
3⁄16	—	—	—	—	—	—	—	—
5⁄32	—	—	—	—	—	—	—	—
⅛	—	—	—	—	—	—	0.961	109
L 1¼ × 1¼ × ¼	—	—	—	—	—	—	—	—
3⁄16	—	—	—	—	—	—	—	—
⅛	—	—	—	—	—	—	—	—
L 1 × 1 × ¼	—	—	—	—	—	—	—	—
3⁄16	—	—	—	—	—	—	—	—
⅛	—	—	—	—	—	—	—	—

Where no value of C_c' or Q_s is shown, the angles comply with Specification Sect. 1.9.1.2 and may be considered fully effective.

AMERICAN INSTITUTE OF STEEL CONSTRUCTION

DOUBLE ANGLES
Two unequal angles
Properties of sections

Short legs back to back

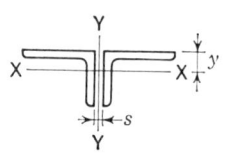

Designation	Wt. per Ft. 2 Angles	Area of 2 Angles	AXIS X - X				Radii of Gyration About Axis Y - Y Back to Back of Angles, Inches					
			I	S	r	y	0	¼	⅜	½	⅝	¾
	Lb.	In.²	In.⁴	In.³	In.	In.						
L 9 × 4 × 1	81.6	24.0	24.0	8.00	1.00	1.00	4.51	4.61	4.66	4.71	4.76	4.81
⅞	72.2	21.2	21.7	7.12	1.01	.953	4.48	4.58	4.63	4.68	4.73	4.78
¾	62.6	18.4	19.3	6.22	1.02	.906	4.46	4.56	4.60	4.65	4.70	4.75
⅝	52.6	15.5	16.6	5.30	1.04	.858	4.44	4.53	4.58	4.63	4.68	4.73
⁹⁄₁₆	47.6	14.0	15.3	4.82	1.04	.834	4.42	4.52	4.57	4.61	4.66	4.71
½	42.6	12.5	13.8	4.34	1.05	.810	4.41	4.51	4.55	4.60	4.65	4.70
L 8 × 6 × 1	88.4	26.0	77.6	17.8	1.73	1.65	3.64	3.73	3.78	3.83	3.87	3.92
⅞	78.2	23.0	69.7	15.9	1.74	1.61	3.62	3.71	3.76	3.80	3.85	3.90
¾	67.6	19.9	61.4	13.8	1.76	1.56	3.60	3.69	3.74	3.78	3.83	3.88
⅝	57.0	16.7	52.7	11.8	1.77	1.52	3.58	3.67	3.71	3.76	3.81	3.85
⁹⁄₁₆	51.4	15.1	48.1	10.7	1.78	1.50	3.57	3.66	3.70	3.75	3.79	3.84
½	46.0	13.5	43.4	9.58	1.79	1.47	3.56	3.65	3.69	3.74	3.78	3.83
⁷⁄₁₆	40.4	11.9	38.5	8.46	1.80	1.45	3.55	3.64	3.68	3.73	3.77	3.82
L 8 × 4 × 1	74.8	22.0	23.3	7.88	1.03	1.05	3.95	4.05	4.10	4.15	4.20	4.25
⅞	66.2	19.5	21.1	7.02	1.04	.999	3.93	4.02	4.07	4.12	4.17	4.22
¾	57.4	16.9	18.7	6.14	1.05	.953	3.90	4.00	4.05	4.09	4.14	4.19
⅝	48.4	14.2	16.2	5.24	1.07	.906	3.88	3.97	4.02	4.07	4.12	4.17
⁹⁄₁₆	43.8	12.9	14.9	4.27	1.07	.882	3.87	3.96	4.01	4.06	4.11	4.15
½	39.2	11.5	13.5	4.29	1.08	.859	3.86	3.95	4.00	4.04	4.09	4.14
⁷⁄₁₆	34.4	10.1	12.0	3.80	1.09	.835	3.84	3.94	3.98	4.03	4.08	4.13
L 7 × 4 × ⅞	60.4	17.7	20.4	6.91	1.07	1.05	3.37	3.47	3.52	3.57	3.61	3.66
¾	52.4	15.4	16.1	6.05	1.09	1.01	3.35	3.44	3.49	3.54	3.59	3.64
⅝	44.2	13.0	15.7	5.16	1.10	.963	3.33	3.42	3.47	3.52	3.56	3.61
⁹⁄₁₆	40.0	11.7	14.4	4.70	1.11	.940	3.31	3.41	3.46	3.50	3.55	3.60
½	35.8	10.5	13.1	4.23	1.11	.917	3.30	3.40	3.44	3.49	3.54	3.59
⁷⁄₁₆	31.6	9.24	11.7	3.75	1.12	.893	3.29	3.39	3.43	3.48	3.53	3.58
⅜	27.2	7.97	10.2	3.26	1.13	.870	3.28	3.37	3.42	3.47	3.52	3.56
L 6 × 4 × ⅞	54.4	16.0	19.5	6.78	1.11	1.12	2.82	2.92	2.97	3.02	3.07	3.12
¾	47.2	13.9	17.4	5.94	1.12	1.08	2.80	2.90	2.94	2.99	3.04	3.09
⅝	40.0	11.7	15.0	5.07	1.13	1.03	2.78	2.87	2.92	2.97	3.02	3.06
⁹⁄₁₆	36.2	10.6	13.8	4.62	1.14	1.01	2.77	2.86	2.91	2.96	3.00	3.05
½	32.4	9.50	12.5	4.16	1.15	.987	2.76	2.85	2.90	2.94	2.99	3.04
⁷⁄₁₆	28.6	8.37	11.2	3.69	1.16	.964	2.75	2.84	2.89	2.93	2.98	3.03
⅜	24.6	7.22	9.81	3.21	1.17	.941	2.74	2.83	2.87	2.92	2.97	3.02
⁵⁄₁₆	20.6	6.05	8.35	2.71	1.17	.918	2.73	2.82	2.86	2.91	2.96	3.00
¼	16.6	4.88	6.83	2.20	1.18	.894	2.72	2.81	2.85	2.90	2.95	2.99

DOUBLE ANGLES
Two unequal angles
Short legs back to back

$$C_c' = \sqrt{\frac{2\pi^2 E}{Q_s Q_a F_y}}$$

$$Q_a = 1.0$$

Properties of sections limited by width-thickness ratios
Per AISC Specification, Sect. 1.9.1.

| Designation | Angles in Contact | | | | Angles Separated | | | |
| | $F_y = 36$ ksi | | $F_y = 50$ ksi | | $F_y = 36$ ksi | | $F_y = 50$ ksi | |
In.	Q_s	C_c'	Q_s	C_c'	Q_s	C_c'	Q_s	C_c'
L 9 × 4 × 1	—	—	—	—	—	—	—	—
7/8	—	—	—	—	—	—	—	—
3/4	—	—	—	—	—	—	0.961	109
5/8	—	—	0.970	109	0.954	129	0.885	114
9/16	0.995	126	0.921	112	0.911	132	0.834	117
1/2	0.943	130	0.859	115	0.857	136	0.771	122
L 8 × 6 × 1	—	—	—	—	—	—	—	—
7/8	—	—	—	—	—	—	—	—
3/4	—	—	—	—	—	—	—	—
5/8	—	—	—	—	0.997	126	0.935	111
9/16	—	—	0.976	108	0.959	129	0.890	113
1/2	0.995	126	0.921	112	0.911	132	0.834	117
7/16	0.936	130	0.850	116	0.850	137	0.762	123
L 8 × 4 × 1	—	—	—	—	—	—	—	—
7/8	—	—	—	—	—	—	—	—
3/4	—	—	—	—	—	—	—	—
5/8	—	—	—	—	0.997	126	0.935	111
9/16	—	—	0.976	108	0.959	129	0.890	113
1/2	0.995	126	0.921	112	0.911	132	0.834	117
7/16	0.936	130	0.850	116	0.850	137	0.762	123
L 7 × 4 × 7/8	—	—	—	—	—	—	—	—
3/4	—	—	—	—	—	—	—	—
5/8	—	—	—	—	—	—	0.986	108
9/16	—	—	—	—	—	—	0.947	110
1/2	—	—	0.982	108	0.965	128	0.897	113
7/16	0.995	126	0.921	112	0.911	132	0.834	117
3/8	0.926	131	0.838	117	0.839	138	0.750	124
L 6 × 4 × 7/8	—	—	—	—	—	—	—	—
3/4	—	—	—	—	—	—	—	—
5/8	—	—	—	—	—	—	—	—
9/16	—	—	—	—	—	—	—	—
1/2	—	—	—	—	—	—	0.961	109
7/16	—	—	0.991	107	0.972	128	0.907	112
3/8	0.995	126	0.921	112	0.911	132	0.834	117
5/16	0.912	132	0.822	118	0.825	139	0.733	125
1/4	0.786	142	0.673	130	0.696	151	0.538	146

Where no value of C_c' or Q_s is shown, the angles comply with Specification Sect. 1.9.1.2 and may be considered fully effective.

DOUBLE ANGLES
Two unequal angles
Properties of sections

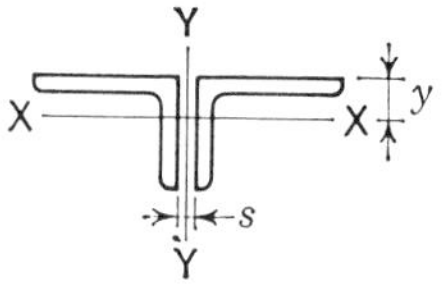

Short legs back to back

Designation	Wt. per Ft. 2 Angles	Area of 2 Angles	AXIS X - X				Radii of Gyration About Axis Y - Y, Back to Back of Angles, Inches					
			I	S	r	y	0	¼	⅜	½	⅝	¾
	Lb.	In.²	In.⁴	In.³	In.	In.						
L 6 × 3½ × ½	30.6	9.00	8.50	3.19	.972	.833	2.83	2.93	2.97	3.02	3.07	3.12
⅜	23.4	6.84	6.68	2.46	.988	.787	2.81	2.90	2.95	3.00	3.05	3.09
5⁄16	19.6	5.74	5.70	2.08	.996	.763	2.80	2.89	2.94	2.99	3.03	3.08
¼	15.8	4.63	4.67	1.69	1.01	.740	2.79	2.88	2.93	2.97	3.02	3.07
L 5 × 3½ × ¾	39.6	11.6	11.1	4.43	.977	.996	2.33	2.43	2.48	2.53	2.58	2.63
⅝	33.6	9.84	9.67	3.79	.991	.951	2.31	2.40	2.45	2.50	2.55	2.60
½	27.2	8.00	8.10	3.12	1.01	.906	2.29	2.38	2.43	2.48	2.52	2.57
7⁄16	24.0	7.05	7.25	2.77	1.01	.883	2.28	2.37	2.42	2.46	2.51	2.56
⅜	20.8	6.09	6.37	2.41	1.02	.861	2.27	2.36	2.41	2.45	2.50	2.55
5⁄16	17.4	5.12	5.44	2.04	1.03	.838	2.26	2.35	2.39	2.44	2.49	2.54
¼	14.0	4.13	4.46	1.66	1.04	.814	2.25	2.34	2.38	2.43	2.48	2.52
L 5 × 3 × ½	25.6	7.50	5.16	2.29	.829	.750	2.36	2.46	2.50	2.55	2.60	2.65
7⁄16	22.6	6.62	4.63	2.04	.837	.727	2.35	2.45	2.49	2.54	2.59	2.64
⅜	19.6	5.72	4.08	1.78	.845	.704	2.34	2.43	2.48	2.53	2.58	2.63
5⁄16	16.4	4.80	3.49	1.51	.853	.681	2.33	2.42	2.47	2.52	2.57	2.61
¼	13.2	3.88	2.88	1.23	.861	.657	2.32	2.41	2.46	2.50	2.55	2.60
L 4 × 3½ × ⅝	29.4	8.59	9.04	3.68	1.03	1.04	1.78	1.87	1.92	1.97	2.02	2.07
½	23.8	7.00	7.58	3.03	1.04	1.00	1.76	1.85	1.89	1.94	1.99	2.04
7⁄16	21.2	6.18	6.80	2.70	1.05	.978	1.75	1.84	1.88	1.93	1.98	2.03
⅜	18.2	5.34	5.97	2.35	1.06	.955	1.74	1.83	1.87	1.92	1.97	2.01
5⁄16	15.4	4.49	5.10	1.99	1.07	.932	1.73	1.81	1.86	1.91	1.95	2.00
¼	12.4	3.63	4.19	1.62	1.07	.909	1.72	1.80	1.85	1.90	1.94	1.99
L 4 × 3 × ⅝	27.2	7.97	5.75	2.70	.849	.871	1.84	1.94	1.99	2.04	2.09	2.14
½	22.2	6.50	4.85	2.23	.864	.827	1.82	1.91	1.96	2.01	2.06	2.11
7⁄16	19.6	5.74	4.36	1.98	.871	.804	1.81	1.90	1.95	2.00	2.05	2.10
⅜	17.0	4.97	3.84	1.73	.879	.782	1.80	1.89	1.94	1.99	2.03	2.08
5⁄16	14.4	4.18	3.29	1.47	.887	.759	1.79	1.88	1.93	1.97	2.02	2.07
¼	11.6	3.38	2.71	1.20	.896	.736	1.78	1.87	1.92	1.96	2.01	2.06
L 3½ × 3 × ½	20.4	6.00	4.66	2.19	.881	.875	1.55	1.65	1.70	1.74	1.79	1.84
7⁄16	18.2	5.30	4.19	1.95	.889	.853	1.54	1.64	1.68	1.73	1.78	1.83
⅜	15.8	4.59	3.69	1.70	.897	.830	1.53	1.62	1.67	1.72	1.77	1.82
5⁄16	13.2	3.87	3.17	1.44	.905	.808	1.52	1.61	1.66	1.71	1.76	1.80
¼	10.8	3.13	2.61	1.18	.914	.785	1.52	1.60	1.65	1.70	1.74	1.79

DOUBLE ANGLES
Two unequal angles
Short legs back to back

$$C_c' = \sqrt{\frac{2\pi^2 E}{Q_s Q_a F_y}}$$

$$Q_a = 1.0$$

Properties of sections limited by width-thickness ratios
Per AISC Specification, Sect. 1.9.1

| Designation | Angles in Contact | | | | Angles Separated | | | |
| | $F_y = 36$ ksi | | $F_y = 50$ ksi | | $F_y = 36$ ksi | | $F_y = 50$ ksi | |
In.	Q_s	C_c'	Q_s	C_c'	Q_s	C_c'	Q_s	C_c'
L 6 × 3½ × ½	—	—	—	—	—	—	0.961	109
⅜	0.995	126	0.921	112	0.911	132	0.834	117
⁵⁄₁₆	0.912	132	0.822	118	0.825	139	0.733	125
¼	0.786	142	0.673	130	0.696	151	0.538	146
L 5 × 3½ × ¾	—	—	—	—	—	—	—	—
⅝	—	—	—	—	—	—	—	—
½	—	—	—	—	—	—	—	—
⁷⁄₁₆	—	—	—	—	—	—	0.979	108
⅜	—	—	—	—	0.982	127	0.919	112
⁵⁄₁₆	0.995	126	0.921	112	0.911	132	0.834	117
¼	0.891	134	0.797	120	0.804	141	0.708	127
L 5 × 3 × ½	—	—	—	—	—	—	—	—
⁷⁄₁₆	—	—	—	—	—	—	0.979	108
⅜	—	—	—	—	0.982	127	0.919	112
⁵⁄₁₆	0.995	126	0.921	112	0.911	132	0.834	117
¼	0.891	134	0.797	120	0.804	141	0.708	127
L 4 × 3½ × ⅝	—	—	—	—	—	—	—	—
½	—	—	—	—	—	—	—	—
⁷⁄₁₆	—	—	—	—	—	—	—	—
⅜	—	—	—	—	—	—	—	—
⁵⁄₁₆	—	—	—	—	0.997	126	0.935	111
¼	0.995	126	0.921	112	0.911	132	0.834	117
L 4 × 3 × ⅝	—	—	—	—	—	—	—	—
½	—	—	—	—	—	—	—	—
⁷⁄₁₆	—	—	—	—	—	—	—	—
⅜	—	—	—	—	—	—	—	—
⁵⁄₁₆	—	—	—	—	0.997	126	0.935	111
¼	0.995	126	0.921	112	0.911	132	0.834	117
L 3½ × 3 × ½	—	—	—	—	—	—	—	—
⁷⁄₁₆	—	—	—	—	—	—	—	—
⅜	—	—	—	—	—	—	—	—
⁵⁄₁₆	—	—	—	—	—	—	0.986	108
¼	—	—	0.982	108	0.965	128	0.897	113

Where no value of C_c' or Q_s is shown, the angles comply with Specification Sect. 1.9.1.2 and may be considered fully effective.

AMERICAN INSTITUTE OF STEEL CONSTRUCTION

DOUBLE ANGLES
Two unequal angles
Properties of sections

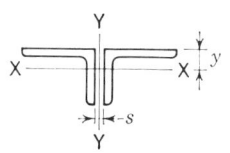

Short legs back to back

Designation	Wt. per Ft. 2 Angles	Area of 2 Angles	AXIS X - X				Radii of Gyration About Axis Y -Y Back to Back of Angles, Inches					
			I	S	r	y	0	¼	⅜	½	⅝	¾
	Lb.	In.²	In.⁴	In.³	In.	In.						
L 3½ × 2½ × ½	18.8	5.50	2.73	1.52	.704	.705	1.62	1.72	1.77	1.81	1.87	1.92
⁷⁄₁₆	16.6	4.87	2.46	1.35	.711	.682	1.61	1.70	1.75	1.80	1.85	1.90
⅜	14.4	4.22	2.18	1.18	.719	.660	1.60	1.69	1.74	1.79	1.84	1.89
⁵⁄₁₆	12.2	3.55	1.88	1.01	.727	.637	1.59	1.68	1.73	1.78	1.83	1.88
¼	9.8	2.88	1.55	.824	.735	.614	1.58	1.67	1.72	1.76	1.81	1.86
L 3 × 2½ × ½	17.0	5.00	2.60	1.49	.722	.750	1.35	1.45	1.50	1.55	1.60	1.65
⁷⁄₁₆	15.2	4.43	2.35	1.33	.729	.728	1.34	1.44	1.49	1.53	1.59	1.64
⅜	13.2	3.84	2.08	1.16	.736	.706	1.33	1.42	1.47	1.52	1.57	1.62
⁵⁄₁₆	11.2	3.24	1.80	.989	.744	.683	1.32	1.41	1.46	1.51	1.56	1.61
¼	9.0	2.63	1.49	.808	.753	.661	1.31	1.40	1.45	1.50	1.55	1.60
³⁄₁₆	6.77	1.99	1.15	.620	.761	.638	1.30	1.39	1.44	1.49	1.53	1.58
L 3 × 2 × ½	15.4	4.50	1.34	.949	.546	.583	1.42	1.52	1.57	1.62	1.67	1.73
⁷⁄₁₆	13.6	3.99	1.22	.847	.553	.561	1.41	1.51	1.56	1.61	1.66	1.71
⅜	11.8	3.47	1.09	.743	.559	.539	1.40	1.50	1.55	1.60	1.65	1.70
⁵⁄₁₆	10.0	2.93	.941	.634	.567	.516	1.39	1.48	1.53	1.58	1.63	1.68
¼	8.2	2.38	.784	.520	.574	.493	1.38	1.47	1.52	1.57	1.62	1.67
³⁄₁₆	6.1	1.80	.613	.401	.583	.470	1.37	1.46	1.51	1.56	1.61	1.66
L 2½ × 2 × ⅜	10.6	3.09	1.03	.725	.577	.581	1.13	1.23	1.28	1.33	1.38	1.43
⁵⁄₁₆	9.0	2.62	.893	.620	.584	.559	1.12	1.21	1.26	1.31	1.36	1.42
¼	7.2	2.13	.745	.509	.592	.537	1.11	1.20	1.25	1.30	1.35	1.40
³⁄₁₆	5.5	1.62	.583	.392	.600	.514	1.10	1.19	1.24	1.29	1.34	1.39
L 2½ × 1½ × ⁵⁄₁₆	7.84	2.30	.383	.347	.408	.398	1.19	1.29	1.34	1.39	1.44	1.50
¼	6.38	1.88	.322	.286	.415	.375	1.18	1.28	1.33	1.38	1.43	1.48
³⁄₁₆	4.88	1.43	.255	.222	.422	.352	1.17	1.26	1.31	1.36	1.41	1.47
L 2 × 1½ × ¼	5.54	1.63	.303	.279	.432	.413	.910	1.00	1.05	1.11	1.16	1.21
³⁄₁₆	4.24	1.24	.240	.216	.440	.391	.900	.993	1.04	1.09	1.14	1.20
⅛	2.88	.844	.169	.150	.448	.368	.890	.981	1.03	1.08	1.13	1.18
L 2 × 1¼ × ¼	5.10	1.50	.177	.193	.344	.333	.946	1.04	1.09	1.15	1.20	1.25
³⁄₁₆	3.92	1.15	.141	.150	.351	.311	.935	1.03	1.08	1.13	1.18	1.24
⅛	2.66	.781	.101	.105	.359	.287	.925	1.02	1.07	1.12	1.17	1.22
L 1¾ × 1¼ × ¼	4.68	1.38	.171	.190	.352	.352	.811	.907	.958	1.01	1.06	1.12
³⁄₁₆	3.60	1.05	.136	.148	.359	.330	.800	.895	.945	.996	1.05	1.10
⅛	2.46	.719	.097	.103	.368	.307	.790	.882	.931	.982	1.03	1.09

$C_c' = \sqrt{\dfrac{2\pi^2 E}{Q_s Q_a F_y}}$

$Q_a = 1.0$

DOUBLE ANGLES

Two unequal angles

Short legs back to back

Properties of sections limited by width-thickness ratios

Per AISC Specification, Sect. 1.9.1.

Designation	Angles in Contact				Angles Separated			
	$F_y = 36$ ksi		$F_y = 50$ ksi		$F_y = 36$ ksi		$F_y = 50$ ksi	
In.	Q_s	C_c'	Q_s	C_c'	Q_s	C_c'	Q_s	C_c'
L 3½ × 2½ × ½	—	—	—	—	—	—	—	—
7/16	—	—	—	—	—	—	—	—
3/8	—	—	—	—	—	—	—	—
5/16	—	—	—	—	—	—	0.986	108
1/4	—	—	0.982	108	0.965	128	0.897	113
L 3 × 2½ × ½	—	—	—	—	—	—	—	—
7/16	—	—	—	—	—	—	—	—
3/8	—	—	—	—	—	—	—	—
5/16	—	—	—	—	—	—	—	—
1/4	—	—	—	—	—	—	0.961	109
3/16	0.995	126	0.921	112	0.911	132	0.834	117
L 3 × 2 × ½	—	—	—	—	—	—	—	—
7/16	—	—	—	—	—	—	—	—
3/8	—	—	—	—	—	—	—	—
5/16	—	—	—	—	—	—	—	—
1/4	—	—	—	—	—	—	0.961	109
3/16	0.995	126	0.921	112	0.911	132	0.834	117
L 2½ × 2 × 3/8	—	—	—	—	—	—	—	—
5/16	—	—	—	—	—	—	—	—
1/4	—	—	—	—	—	—	—	—
3/16	—	—	—	—	0.982	127	0.919	112
L 2½ × 1½ × 5/16	—	—	—	—	—	—	—	—
1/4	—	—	—	—	—	—	—	—
3/16	—	—	—	—	0.982	127	0.919	112
L 2 × 1½ × ¼	—	—	—	—	—	—	—	—
3/16	—	—	—	—	—	—	—	—
1/8	0.995	126	0.921	112	0.911	132	0.834	117
L 2 × 1¼ × ¼	—	—	—	—	—	—	—	—
3/16	—	—	—	—	—	—	—	—
1/8	0.995	126	0.921	112	0.911	132	0.834	117
L 1¾ × 1¼ × ¼	—	—	—	—	—	—	—	—
3/16	—	—	—	—	—	—	—	—
1/8	—	—	0.982	108	0.965	128	0.897	113

Where no value of C_c' or Q_s is shown, the angles comply with Specification Sect. 1.9.1.2 and may be considered fully effective.

DOUBLE ANGLES
Two unequal angles
Properties of sections

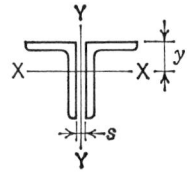

Long legs back to back

Designation	Wt. per Ft. 2 Angles	Area of 2 Angles	AXIS X - X				Radii of Gyration About Axis Y - Y					
			I	S	r	y	Back to Back of Angles, Inches					
	Lb.	In.²	In.⁴	In.³	In.	In.	0	¼	⅜	½	⅝	¾
L 9 × 4 × 1	81.6	24.0	194.0	35.3	2.84	3.50	1.41	1.51	1.55	1.60	1.65	1.70
⅞	72.2	21.2	173.0	31.3	2.86	3.45	1.39	1.48	1.52	1.57	1.62	1.67
¾	62.6	18.4	152.0	27.2	2.88	3.41	1.37	1.45	1.50	1.54	1.59	1.64
⅝	52.6	15.5	129.0	23.0	2.90	3.36	1.35	1.43	1.47	1.52	1.56	1.61
⁹⁄₁₆	47.6	14.0	118.0	20.9	2.91	3.33	1.34	1.42	1.46	1.51	1.55	1.60
½	42.6	12.5	106.0	18.7	2.92	3.31	1.33	1.41	1.45	1.49	1.54	1.58
L 8 × 6 × 1	88.4	26.0	161.0	30.2	2.49	2.65	2.39	2.48	2.52	2.57	2.62	2.66
⅞	78.2	23.0	144.0	26.8	2.51	2.61	2.37	2.46	2.50	2.55	2.59	2.64
¾	67.6	19.9	126.0	23.3	2.53	2.56	2.35	2.44	2.48	2.53	2.57	2.62
⅝	57.0	16.7	108.0	19.7	2.54	2.52	2.34	2.42	2.46	2.51	2.55	2.60
⁹⁄₁₆	51.4	15.1	98.5	17.9	2.55	2.50	2.33	2.41	2.45	2.50	2.54	2.58
½	46.0	13.5	88.6	16.0	2.56	2.47	2.32	2.40	2.44	2.49	2.53	2.57
⁷⁄₁₆	40.4	11.9	78.5	14.1	2.57	2.45	2.31	2.39	2.43	2.48	2.52	2.56
L 8 × 4 × 1	74.8	22.0	139.0	28.1	2.52	3.05	1.47	1.56	1.61	1.65	1.70	1.75
⅞	66.2	19.5	124.0	25.0	2.53	3.00	1.44	1.53	1.58	1.63	1.67	1.72
¾	57.4	16.9	109.0	21.8	2.55	2.95	1.42	1.51	1.55	1.60	1.65	1.69
⅝	48.4	14.2	93.8	18.4	2.57	2.91	1.40	1.48	1.53	1.57	1.62	1.67
⁹⁄₁₆	43.8	12.9	85.5	16.7	2.58	2.88	1.39	1.47	1.52	1.56	1.61	1.65
½	39.2	11.5	77.0	15.0	2.59	2.86	1.38	1.46	1.51	1.55	1.59	1.64
⁷⁄₁₆	34.4	10.1	68.2	13.2	2.60	2.83	1.37	1.45	1.50	1.54	1.58	1.63
L 7 × 4 × ⅞	60.4	17.7	85.8	19.3	2.20	2.55	1.50	1.59	1.64	1.69	1.74	1.79
¾	52.4	15.4	75.6	16.8	2.22	2.51	1.48	1.57	1.62	1.66	1.71	1.76
⅝	44.2	13.0	64.8	14.3	2.24	2.46	1.46	1.55	1.59	1.64	1.68	1.73
⁹⁄₁₆	40.0	11.7	59.1	13.0	2.24	2.44	1.45	1.54	1.58	1.63	1.67	1.72
½	35.8	10.5	53.3	11.6	2.25	2.42	1.44	1.53	1.57	1.61	1.66	1.71
⁷⁄₁₆	31.6	9.24	47.3	10.3	2.26	2.39	1.44	1.52	1.56	1.60	1.65	1.69
⅜	27.2	7.97	41.1	8.88	2.27	2.37	1.43	1.51	1.55	1.59	1.64	1.68
L 6 × 4 × ⅞	54.4	16.0	55.5	14.3	1.86	2.12	1.58	1.67	1.71	1.76	1.81	1.86
¾	47.2	13.9	49.0	12.5	1.88	2.08	1.55	1.64	1.69	1.74	1.78	1.83
⅝	40.0	11.7	42.1	10.6	1.90	2.03	1.53	1.62	1.67	1.71	1.76	1.81
⁹⁄₁₆	36.2	10.6	38.5	9.65	1.90	2.01	1.52	1.61	1.65	1.70	1.75	1.79
½	32.4	9.50	34.8	8.67	1.91	1.99	1.51	1.60	1.64	1.69	1.73	1.78
⁷⁄₁₆	28.6	8.37	30.9	7.66	1.92	1.96	1.51	1.59	1.63	1.68	1.72	1.77
⅜	24.6	7.22	26.9	6.64	1.93	1.94	1.50	1.58	1.62	1.67	1.71	1.76
⁵⁄₁₆	20.6	6.05	22.8	5.59	1.94	1.92	1.49	1.57	1.61	1.66	1.70	1.75
¼	16.6	4.88	18.5	4.52	1.95	1.89	1.48	1.56	1.60	1.65	1.69	1.74

DOUBLE ANGLES
Two unequal angles
Long legs back to back

$$C_c' = \sqrt{\frac{2\pi^2 E}{Q_s Q_a F_y}}$$

$$Q_a = 1.0$$

Properties of sections limited by width-thickness ratios
Per AISC Specification, Sect. 1.9.1

| Designation | Angles in Contact | | | | Angles Separated | | | |
| | $F_y = 36$ ksi | | $F_y = 50$ ksi | | $F_y = 36$ ksi | | $F_y = 50$ ksi | |
In.	Q_s	C_c'	Q_s	C_c'	Q_s	C_c'	Q_s	C_c'
L 9 × 4 × 1	—	—	—	—	—	—	—	—
7/8	—	—	—	—	—	—	—	—
3/4	—	—	—	—	—	—	0.961	109
5/8	—	—	—	—	0.954	129	0.885	114
9/16	—	—	—	—	0.911	132	0.834	117
1/2	—	—	—	—	0.857	136	0.771	122
L 8 × 6 × 1	—	—	—	—	—	—	—	—
7/8	—	—	—	—	—	—	—	—
3/4	—	—	—	—	—	—	—	—
5/8	—	—	—	—	0.997	126	0.935	111
9/16	—	—	—	—	0.959	129	0.890	113
1/2	—	—	—	—	0.911	132	0.834	117
7/16	—	—	0.991	107	0.850	137	0.762	123
L 8 × 4 × 1	—	—	—	—	—	—	—	—
7/8	—	—	—	—	—	—	—	—
3/4	—	—	—	—	—	—	—	—
5/8	—	—	—	—	0.997	126	0.935	111
9/16	—	—	—	—	0.959	129	0.890	113
1/2	—	—	—	—	0.911	132	0.834	117
7/16	—	—	—	—	0.850	137	0.762	123
L 7 × 4 × 7/8	—	—	—	—	—	—	—	—
3/4	—	—	—	—	—	—	—	—
5/8	—	—	—	—	—	—	0.986	108
9/16	—	—	—	—	—	—	0.947	110
1/2	—	—	—	—	0.965	128	0.897	113
7/16	—	—	—	—	0.911	132	0.834	117
3/8	—	—	—	—	0.839	138	0.750	124
L 6 × 4 × 7/8	—	—	—	—	—	—	—	—
3/4	—	—	—	—	—	—	—	—
5/8	—	—	—	—	—	—	—	—
9/16	—	—	—	—	—	—	—	—
1/2	—	—	—	—	—	—	0.961	109
7/16	—	—	—	—	0.972	128	0.907	112
3/8	—	—	—	—	0.911	132	0.834	117
5/16	—	—	—	—	0.825	139	0.733	125
1/4	0.995	126	0.921	112	0.696	151	0.538	146

Where no value of C_c' or Q_s is shown, the angles comply with Specification Sect. 1.9.1.2 and may be considered fully effective.

AMERICAN INSTITUTE OF STEEL CONSTRUCTION

DOUBLE ANGLES
Two unequal angles
Properties of sections
Long legs back to back

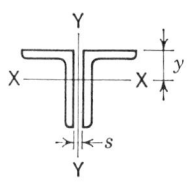

Designation		Wt. per Ft. 2 Angles	Area of 2 Angles	AXIS X - X				Radii of Gyration About Axis Y - Y Back to Back of Angles, Inches					
				I	S	r	y	0	¼	⅜	½	⅝	¾
		Lb.	In.²	In.⁴	In.³	In.	In.						
L 6	× 3½ × ½	30.6	9.00	33.2	8.47	1.92	2.08	1.28	1.36	1.41	1.46	1.50	1.55
	⅜	23.4	6.84	25.7	6.49	1.94	2.04	1.26	1.34	1.39	1.43	1.48	1.53
	⁵⁄₁₆	19.6	5.74	21.8	5.47	1.95	2.01	1.26	1.33	1.38	1.42	1.47	1.51
	¼	15.8	4.63	17.7	4.42	1.96	1.99	1.25	1.33	1.37	1.41	1.46	1.50
L 5	× 3½ × ¾	39.6	11.6	27.8	8.55	1.55	1.75	1.40	1.49	1.53	1.58	1.63	1.68
	⅝	33.6	9.84	24.1	7.29	1.56	1.70	1.37	1.46	1.51	1.56	1.61	1.66
	½	27.2	8.00	20.0	5.97	1.58	1.66	1.35	1.44	1.49	1.53	1.58	1.63
	⁷⁄₁₆	24.0	7.05	17.8	5.29	1.59	1.63	1.34	1.43	1.47	1.52	1.57	1.62
	⅜	20.8	6.09	15.6	4.59	1.60	1.61	1.34	1.42	1.46	1.51	1.56	1.60
	⁵⁄₁₆	17.4	5.12	13.2	3.87	1.61	1.59	1.33	1.41	1.45	1.50	1.54	1.59
	¼	14.0	4.13	10.8	3.14	1.62	1.56	1.32	1.40	1.44	1.49	1.53	1.58
L 5	× 3 × ½	25.6	7.50	18.9	5.82	1.59	1.75	1.12	1.21	1.25	1.30	1.35	1.40
	⁷⁄₁₆	22.6	6.62	16.9	5.15	1.60	1.73	1.11	1.19	1.24	1.29	1.33	1.38
	⅜	19.6	5.72	14.7	4.47	1.61	1.70	1.10	1.18	1.23	1.27	1.32	1.37
	⁵⁄₁₆	16.4	4.80	12.5	3.77	1.61	1.68	1.09	1.17	1.22	1.26	1.31	1.36
	¼	13.2	3.88	10.2	3.06	1.62	1.66	1.08	1.16	1.21	1.25	1.30	1.34
L 4	× 3½ × ⅝	29.4	8.59	12.7	4.71	1.22	1.29	1.46	1.56	1.60	1.65	1.70	1.75
	½	23.8	7.00	10.6	3.87	1.23	1.25	1.44	1.53	1.58	1.63	1.68	1.72
	⁷⁄₁₆	21.2	6.18	9.52	3.44	1.24	1.23	1.43	1.52	1.57	1.61	1.66	1.71
	⅜	18.2	5.34	8.35	2.99	1.25	1.21	1.42	1.51	1.56	1.60	1.65	1.70
	⁵⁄₁₆	15.4	4.49	7.12	2.53	1.26	1.18	1.42	1.50	1.55	1.59	1.64	1.69
	¼	12.4	3.63	5.83	2.05	1.27	1.16	1.41	1.49	1.54	1.58	1.63	1.67
L 4	× 3 × ⅝	27.2	7.97	12.1	4.59	1.23	1.37	1.22	1.31	1.36	1.41	1.46	1.51
	½	22.2	6.50	10.1	3.78	1.25	1.33	1.20	1.29	1.33	1.38	1.43	1.48
	⁷⁄₁₆	19.6	5.74	9.04	3.35	1.25	1.30	1.19	1.27	1.32	1.37	1.42	1.47
	⅜	17.0	4.97	7.93	2.92	1.26	1.28	1.18	1.26	1.31	1.36	1.40	1.45
	⁵⁄₁₆	14.4	4.18	6.76	2.47	1.27	1.26	1.17	1.25	1.30	1.34	1.39	1.44
	¼	11.6	3.38	5.54	2.00	1.28	1.24	1.16	1.24	1.29	1.33	1.38	1.43
L 3½ × 3	× ½	20.4	6.00	6.91	2.91	1.07	1.13	1.24	1.33	1.38	1.43	1.48	1.53
	⁷⁄₁₆	18.2	5.30	6.20	2.59	1.08	1.10	1.23	1.32	1.37	1.42	1.47	1.52
	⅜	15.8	4.59	5.45	2.25	1.09	1.08	1.22	1.31	1.36	1.40	1.45	1.50
	⁵⁄₁₆	13.2	3.87	4.66	1.91	1.10	1.06	1.21	1.30	1.35	1.39	1.44	1.49
	¼	10.8	3.13	3.83	1.55	1.11	1.04	1.20	1.29	1.33	1.38	1.43	1.48

$$C_c' = \sqrt{\frac{2\pi^2 E}{Q_s Q_a F_y}}$$

$$Q_a = 1.0$$

DOUBLE ANGLES
Two unequal angles
Long legs back to back

Properties of sections limited by width-thickness ratios
Per AISC Specification, Sect. 1.9.1

| Designation | Angles in Contact | | | | Angles Separated | | | |
| | F_y = 36 ksi | | F_y = 50 ksi | | F_y = 36 ksi | | F_y = 50 ksi | |
In.	Q_s	C_c'	Q_s	C_c'	Q_s	C_c'	Q_s	C_c'
L 6 × 3½ × ½	—	—	—	—	—	—	0.961	109
⅜	—	—	—	—	0.911	132	0.834	117
5⁄16	—	—	—	—	0.825	139	0.733	125
¼	—	—	0.982	108	0.696	151	0.538	146
L 5 × 3½ × ¾	—	—	—	—	—	—	—	—
⅝	—	—	—	—	—	—	—	—
½	—	—	—	—	—	—	—	—
7⁄16	—	—	—	—	—	—	0.979	108
⅜	—	—	—	—	0.982	127	0.919	112
5⁄16	—	—	—	—	0.911	132	0.834	117
¼	—	—	0.982	108	0.804	141	0.708	127
L 5 × 3 × ½	—	—	—	—	—	—	—	—
7⁄16	—	—	—	—	—	—	0.979	108
⅜	—	—	—	—	0.982	127	0.919	112
5⁄16	—	—	—	—	0.911	132	0.834	117
¼	—	—	—	—	0.804	141	0.708	127
L 4 × 3½ × ⅝	—	—	—	—	—	—	—	—
½	—	—	—	—	—	—	—	—
7⁄16	—	—	—	—	—	—	—	—
⅜	—	—	—	—	—	—	—	—
5⁄16	—	—	—	—	0.997	126	0.935	111
¼	—	—	0.982	108	0.911	132	0.834	117
L 4 × 3 × ⅝	—	—	—	—	—	—	—	—
½	—	—	—	—	—	—	—	—
7⁄16	—	—	—	—	—	—	—	—
⅜	—	—	—	—	—	—	—	—
5⁄16	—	—	—	—	0.997	126	0.935	111
¼	—	—	—	—	0.911	132	0.834	117
L 3½ × 3 × ½	—	—	—	—	—	—	—	—
7⁄16	—	—	—	—	—	—	—	—
⅜	—	—	—	—	—	—	—	—
5⁄16	—	—	—	—	—	—	0.986	108
¼	—	—	—	—	0.965	128	0.897	113

Where no value of C_c' or Q_s is shown, the angles comply with Specification Sect. 1.9.1.2 and may be considered fully effective.

DOUBLE ANGLES
Two unequal angles
Properties of sections
Long legs back to back

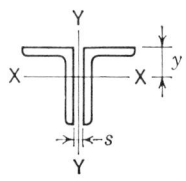

Designation	Wt. per Ft. 2 Angles Lb.	Area of 2 Angles In.²	AXIS X-X I In.⁴	S In.³	r In.	y In.	Radii of Gyration About Axis Y-Y, Back to Back of Angles, Inches 0	¼	⅜	½	⅝	¾
L 3½ × 2½ × ½	18.8	5.50	6.48	2.82	1.09	1.20	.996	1.09	1.14	1.19	1.24	1.29
7/16	16.6	4.87	5.82	2.51	1.09	1.18	.986	1.08	1.12	1.17	1.22	1.27
⅜	14.4	4.22	5.12	2.19	1.10	1.16	.976	1.06	1.11	1.16	1.21	1.26
5/16	12.2	3.55	4.38	1.85	1.11	1.14	.966	1.05	1.10	1.15	1.20	1.25
¼	9.8	2.88	3.60	1.51	1.12	1.11	.958	1.04	1.09	1.13	1.18	1.23
L 3 × 2½ × ½	17.0	5.00	4.17	2.08	.913	1.00	1.04	1.13	1.18	1.23	1.28	1.34
7/16	15.2	4.43	3.75	1.86	.920	.978	1.03	1.12	1.17	1.22	1.27	1.32
⅜	13.2	3.84	3.31	1.62	.928	.956	1.02	1.11	1.16	1.21	1.26	1.31
5/16	11.2	3.24	2.85	1.38	.937	.933	1.01	1.10	1.15	1.19	1.24	1.29
¼	9.0	2.63	2.35	1.12	.945	.911	1.00	1.09	1.13	1.18	1.23	1.28
3/16	6.77	1.99	1.81	.859	.954	.888	.993	1.08	1.12	1.17	1.22	1.27
L 3 × 2 × ½	15.4	4.50	3.84	2.01	.924	1.08	.799	.895	.945	.997	1.05	1.10
7/16	13.6	3.99	3.47	1.79	.932	1.06	.788	.881	.931	.982	1.03	1.09
⅜	11.8	3.47	3.06	1.56	.940	1.04	.777	.868	.917	.967	1.02	1.07
5/16	10.0	2.93	2.63	1.33	.948	1.02	.767	.856	.903	.953	1.00	1.06
¼	8.2	2.38	2.17	1.08	.957	.993	.757	.844	.891	.940	.990	1.04
3/16	6.1	1.80	1.68	.830	.966	.970	.749	.833	.879	.927	.976	1.03
L 2½ × 2 × ⅜	10.6	3.09	1.82	1.09	.768	.831	.819	.912	.961	1.01	1.06	1.12
5/16	9.0	2.62	1.58	.932	.776	.809	.809	.900	.948	.998	1.05	1.10
¼	7.2	2.13	1.31	.763	.784	.787	.799	.888	.935	.985	1.04	1.09
3/16	5.5	1.62	1.02	.586	.793	.764	.790	.877	.923	.972	1.02	1.07
L 2½ × 1½ × 5/16	7.84	2.30	1.42	.887	.785	.898	.570	.663	.713	.765	.819	.874
¼	6.38	1.88	1.18	.727	.794	.875	.559	.650	.699	.750	.803	.857
3/16	4.88	1.43	.921	.559	.803	.852	.550	.637	.685	.735	.787	.841
L 2 × 1½ × ¼	5.54	1.63	.631	.472	.623	.663	.598	.690	.740	.792	.845	.899
3/16	4.24	1.24	.496	.365	.632	.641	.588	.678	.726	.777	.829	.883
⅛	2.88	.844	.346	.250	.641	.618	.580	.666	.714	.763	.815	.868
L 2 × 1¼ × ¼	5.10	1.50	.591	.458	.628	.708	.479	.573	.624	.677	.732	.787
3/16	3.92	1.15	.465	.354	.636	.686	.469	.559	.609	.661	.715	.770
⅛	2.66	.781	.325	.243	.645	.663	.460	.547	.595	.646	.699	.753
L 1¾ × 1¼ × ¼	4.68	1.38	.405	.353	.543	.602	.498	.593	.644	.698	.752	.808
3/16	3.60	1.05	.320	.273	.551	.580	.488	.580	.630	.682	.736	.791
⅛	2.46	.719	.225	.189	.560	.557	.479	.567	.616	.667	.720	.775

DOUBLE ANGLES
Two unequal angles
Long legs back to back

Properties of sections limited by width-thickness ratios
Per AISC Specification, Sect. 1.9.1

$$C_c' = \sqrt{\frac{2\pi^2 E}{Q_s Q_a F_y}}$$

$$Q_a = 1.0$$

| Designation | Angles in Contact | | | | Angles Separated | | | |
| | $F_y = 36$ ksi | | $F_y = 50$ ksi | | $F_y = 36$ ksi | | $F_y = 50$ ksi | |
In.	Q_s	C_c'	Q_s	C_c'	Q_s	C_c'	Q_s	C_c'
L 3½ × 2½ × ½	—	—	—	—	—	—	—	—
⁷⁄₁₆	—	—	—	—	—	—	—	—
⅜	—	—	—	—	—	—	—	—
⁵⁄₁₆	—	—	—	—	—	—	0.986	108
¼	—	—	—	—	0.965	128	0.897	113
L 3 × 2½ × ½	—	—	—	—	—	—	—	—
⁷⁄₁₆	—	—	—	—	—	—	—	—
⅜	—	—	—	—	—	—	—	—
⁵⁄₁₆	—	—	—	—	—	—	—	—
¼	—	—	—	—	—	—	0.961	109
³⁄₁₆	—	—	—	—	0.911	132	0.834	117
L 3 × 2 × ½	—	—	—	—	—	—	—	—
⁷⁄₁₆	—	—	—	—	—	—	—	—
⅜	—	—	—	—	—	—	—	—
⁵⁄₁₆	—	—	—	—	—	—	—	—
¼	—	—	—	—	—	—	0.961	109
³⁄₁₆	—	—	—	—	0.911	132	0.834	117
L 2½ × 2 × ⅜	—	—	—	—	—	—	—	—
⁵⁄₁₆	—	—	—	—	—	—	—	—
¼	—	—	—	—	—	—	—	—
³⁄₁₆	—	—	—	—	0.982	127	0.919	112
L 2½ × 1½ × ⁵⁄₁₆	—	—	—	—	—	—	—	—
¼	—	—	—	—	—	—	—	—
³⁄₁₆	—	—	—	—	0.982	127	0.919	112
L 2 × 1½ × ¼	—	—	—	—	—	—	—	—
³⁄₁₆	—	—	—	—	—	—	—	—
⅛	—	—	—	—	0.911	132	0.834	117
L 2 × 1¼ × ¼	—	—	—	—	—	—	—	—
³⁄₁₆	—	—	—	—	—	—	—	—
⅛	—	—	—	—	0.911	132	0.834	117
L 1¾ × 1¼ × ¼	—	—	—	—	—	—	—	—
³⁄₁₆	—	—	—	—	—	—	—	—
⅛	—	—	—	—	0.965	128	0.897	113

Where no value of C_c' or Q_s is shown, the angles comply with Specification Sect. 1.9.1.2 and may be considered fully effective.

AMERICAN INSTITUTE OF STEEL CONSTRUCTION

Notes

STRUCTURAL TEES
Dimensions and Properties

Structural tees are obtained by splitting the webs of various beams, generally with the aid of rotary shears, and straightening to meet established tolerances listed in Standard Mill Practice in Part 1 of this Manual.

Although structural tees may be obtained by off-center splitting, or by splitting on two lines, as specified on order, the Dimensions and Properties for Designing are based on a depth of tee equal to ½ the published beam depth. Each left hand page in the table shows properties and dimensions for these full depth tees; right hand facing pages show values of Q_s and C_c' for various values of F_y, for those tees having stems which exceed the limiting width-thickness ratio of AISC Specification, Section 1.9.1. For these tees, the design stress is governed by the provisions of AISC Specification, Appendix C, Sections C2, C5 and C6. Where no value of Q_s and C_c' are shown, the tee conforms to AISC Specification, Section 1.9.1, and is considered as fully effective.

USE OF TABLES:

Use of the listed values of Q_s and C_c' affords the designer a means of rapid solution for values of allowable axial stress, F_a.

For the design of tees as axially loaded compression members when AISC Specification, Appendix C governs, read the value of C_c' from the table for the tee selected and the F_y value desired:

Compute $\dfrac{Kl/r}{C_c'}$

If $(Kl/r)/C_c' \geq 1.0$: Enter the table in AISC Specification, Appendix A, pages 5-84 through 5-92, for the desired F_y and Kl/r values. Read F_a direct.

If $(Kl/r)/C_c' < 1.0$: Enter Table 1-A, AISC Specification, Appendix A, page 5-93, and read a value of C_a for the computed value $(Kl/r)/C_c'$.

$$F_a = (Q_s)(C_a)(F_y)$$

For the design of tees subject to combined axial and flexural stress when AISC Specification, Appendix C, governs:

Use the smaller value obtained from:
$$F_b = 0.6(F_y)(Q_s) \text{ or Specification Section 1.5.1.4.6}$$

STRUCTURAL TEES
Cut from W shapes
Dimensions and properties for designing

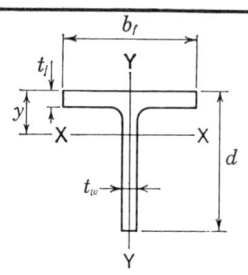

Designation	Area	Depth of Tee d	Flange		Stem Thickness t_w	$\dfrac{d}{t_w}$	AXIS X-X				AXIS Y-Y		
			Width b_f	Thickness t_f			I	S	r	y	I	S	r
	In.²	In.	In.	In.	In.		In.⁴	In.³	In.	In.	In.⁴	In.³	In.
WT 18 ✕ 150	44.1	18.36	16.655	1.680	0.945	19.4	1220	86.0	5.27	4.13	648	77.8	3.83
✕ 140	41.2	18.25	16.595	1.570	0.885	20.6	1130	80.0	5.25	4.06	599	72.2	3.81
✕ 130	38.2	18.12	16.551	1.440	0.841	21.5	1060	75.1	5.26	4.05	545	65.9	3.77
✕ 122.5	36.1	18.03	16.512	1.350	0.802	22.5	995	71.1	5.25	4.03	507	61.4	3.75
✕ 115	33.8	17.94	16.471	1.260	0.761	23.6	933	67.0	5.25	4.00	470	57.1	3.73
WT 18 ✕ 97	28.6	18.24	12.117	1.260	0.770	23.7	905	67.4	5.63	4.81	188	31.0	2.56
✕ 91	26.8	18.16	12.072	1.180	0.725	25.0	845	63.1	5.61	4.77	174	28.8	2.55
✕ 85	25.0	18.08	12.027	1.100	0.680	26.6	786	58.8	5.60	4.73	160	26.6	2.53
✕ 80	23.6	18.00	12.000	1.020	0.653	27.6	742	56.0	5.61	4.75	147	24.6	2.50
✕ 75	22.1	17.92	11.972	0.940	0.625	28.7	698	53.1	5.62	4.78	135	22.5	2.47
✕ 67.5	19.9	17.78	11.945	0.794	0.598	29.7	636	49.5	5.65	4.94	113	18.9	2.39
WT 16.5 ✕ 120	35.3	16.75	15.865	1.400	0.830	20.2	823	63.2	4.83	3.73	467	58.8	3.64
✕ 110	32.4	16.63	15.810	1.275	0.775	21.5	755	58.4	4.83	3.70	421	53.2	3.60
✕ 100	29.4	16.50	15.750	1.150	0.715	23.1	685	53.3	4.82	3.66	375	47.6	3.57
WT 16.5 ✕ 76	22.4	16.75	11.565	1.055	0.635	26.4	592	47.4	5.15	4.26	136	23.6	2.47
✕ 70.5	20.8	16.66	11.535	0.960	0.605	27.5	552	44.7	5.16	4.29	123	21.3	2.43
✕ 65	19.2	16.55	11.510	0.855	0.580	28.5	514	42.2	5.18	4.37	109	18.9	2.38
✕ 59	17.4	16.43	11.484	0.738	0.554	29.7	471	39.4	5.21	4.48	93.4	16.3	2.32
WT 15 ✕ 105	30.9	15.19	15.105	1.315	0.775	19.6	579	48.7	4.33	3.31	378	50.1	3.50
✕ 95	28.0	15.06	15.040	1.185	0.710	21.2	521	44.1	4.31	3.25	336	44.7	3.47
✕ 86	25.4	14.94	14.985	1.065	0.655	22.8	472	40.2	4.31	3.22	299	39.9	3.43
WT 15 ✕ 66	19.4	15.15	10.551	1.000	0.615	24.6	421	37.4	4.65	3.90	98.2	18.6	2.25
✕ 62	18.2	15.08	10.521	0.930	0.585	25.8	395	35.3	4.65	3.89	90.5	17.2	2.23
✕ 58	17.1	15.00	10.500	0.850	0.564	26.6	372	33.6	4.67	3.93	82.2	15.7	2.19
✕ 54	15.9	14.91	10.484	0.760	0.548	27.2	350	32.1	4.69	4.02	73.2	14.0	2.15
✕ 49.5	14.6	14.82	10.458	0.670	0.522	28.4	323	30.1	4.71	4.10	64.1	12.3	2.10
WT 13.5 ✕ 88.5	26.1	13.66	14.090	1.190	0.725	18.8	393	36.8	3.88	2.97	278	39.4	3.26
✕ 80	23.6	13.54	14.023	1.075	0.658	20.6	352	33.1	3.87	2.90	247	35.3	3.24
✕ 72.5	21.4	13.44	13.965	0.975	0.600	22.4	317	29.9	3.85	2.85	222	31.7	3.22

STRUCTURAL TEES
Cut from W shapes

Properties of sections limited by width-thickness ratios

Per AISC Specification, Sect. 1.9.1

$$C_c' = \sqrt{\frac{2\pi^2 E}{Q_s Q_a F_y}} \text{ where } Q_a = 1.0$$

Designation	$F_y = 36$ ksi		$F_y = 50$ ksi	
	Q_s	C_c'	Q_s	C_c'
WT 18 × 150	—	—	0.927	111
× 140	—	—	0.867	115
× 130	0.986	127	0.821	118
× 122.5	0.943	130	0.770	122
× 115	0.896	133	0.715	127
WT 18 × 97	0.891	134	0.710	127
× 91	0.836	138	0.640	134
× 85	0.767	144	0.565	142
× 80	0.724	148	0.525	148
× 75	0.677	153	0.486	154
× 67.5	0.630	159	0.453	159
WT 16.5 × 120	—	—	0.887	114
× 110	0.986	127	0.821	118
× 100	0.917	132	0.740	124
WT 16.5 × 76	0.775	143	0.574	141
× 70.5	0.728	148	0.529	147
× 65	0.685	152	0.492	152
× 59	0.630	159	0.453	159
WT 15 × 105	—	—	0.917	112
× 95	0.999	126	0.836	117
× 86	0.930	131	0.755	123
WT 15 × 66	0.853	137	0.664	131
× 62	0.801	141	0.601	138
× 58	0.767	144	0.565	142
× 54	0.741	146	0.541	146
× 49.5	0.690	152	0.496	152
WT 13.5 × 88.5	—	—	0.958	109
× 80	—	—	0.867	115
× 72.5	0.947	130	0.775	122

NOTE: Where no value of C_c' or Q_s is shown, the Tee complies with Specification Sect. 1.9.1.2 and may be considered fully effective.

STRUCTURAL TEES
Cut from W shapes
Dimensions and properties for designing

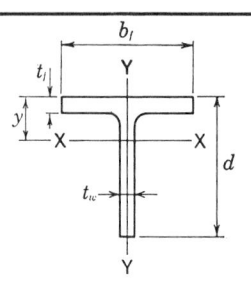

Designation	Area	Depth of Tee d	Flange Width b_f	Flange Thickness t_f	Stem Thickness t_w	$\dfrac{d}{t_w}$	AXIS X-X I	S	r	y	AXIS Y-Y I	S	r
	In.²	In.	In.	In.	In.		In.⁴	In.³	In.	In.	In.⁴	In.³	In.
WT 13.5 × 57	16.8	13.64	10.070	0.932	0.570	23.9	289	28.3	4.15	3.41	79.5	15.8	2.18
× 51	15.0	13.54	10.018	0.827	0.518	26.1	258	25.4	4.14	3.38	69.5	13.9	2.15
× 47	13.8	13.46	9.990	0.747	0.490	27.5	239	23.8	4.15	3.41	62.2	12.5	2.12
× 42	12.4	13.35	9.963	0.636	0.463	28.8	216	22.0	4.18	3.50	52.5	10.5	2.06
WT 12 × 80	23.6	12.36	14.091	1.135	0.656	18.8	272	27.6	3.40	2.50	265	37.6	3.35
× 72.5	21.4	12.25	14.043	1.020	0.608	20.1	247	25.2	3.40	2.47	236	33.6	3.32
× 65	19.2	12.13	14.000	0.900	0.565	21.5	223	23.1	3.41	2.46	206	29.4	3.28
WT 12 × 60	17.7	12.16	12.088	0.930	0.556	21.9	215	22.5	3.49	2.62	137	22.7	2.78
× 55	16.2	12.08	12.042	0.855	0.510	23.7	195	20.5	3.47	2.57	125	20.7	2.77
× 50	14.8	12.00	12.000	0.775	0.468	25.6	177	18.7	3.46	2.53	112	18.6	2.75
WT 12 × 47	13.8	12.15	9.061	0.872	0.516	23.5	186	20.3	3.67	3.00	54.2	12.0	1.98
× 42	12.4	12.05	9.015	0.772	0.470	25.6	166	18.3	3.66	2.97	47.2	10.5	1.95
× 38	11.2	11.96	8.985	0.682	0.440	27.2	151	16.9	3.68	2.99	41.3	9.20	1.92
× 34	10.0	11.86	8.961	0.582	0.416	28.5	137	15.6	3.70	3.07	35.0	7.81	1.87
WT 12 × 30.5	8.98	11.86	7.023	0.591	0.419	28.3	129	15.2	3.78	3.42	17.1	4.88	1.38
× 27.5	8.09	11.78	7.000	0.503	0.396	29.7	116	14.1	3.79	3.50	14.4	4.13	1.34
WT 10.5 × 71	20.9	10.73	13.132	1.095	0.659	16.3	177	20.8	2.92	2.18	207	31.5	3.15
× 63.5	18.7	10.62	13.061	0.985	0.588	18.1	156	18.3	2.89	2.11	183	28.0	3.13
× 56	16.5	10.50	13.000	0.865	0.527	19.9	137	16.2	2.88	2.06	159	24.4	3.10
WT 10.5 × 48	14.1	10.57	9.038	0.935	0.575	18.4	137	17.1	3.12	2.54	57.7	12.8	2.02
× 41	12.1	10.43	8.962	0.795	0.499	20.9	116	14.6	3.10	2.48	47.8	10.7	1.99
WT 10.5 × 36.5	10.7	10.62	8.295	0.740	0.455	23.3	110	13.8	3.21	2.60	35.3	8.51	1.81
× 34	10.0	10.57	8.270	0.685	0.430	24.6	103	12.9	3.20	2.59	32.4	7.83	1.80
× 31	9.13	10.50	8.240	0.615	0.400	26.2	93.8	11.9	3.21	2.58	28.7	6.97	1.77
× 27.5	8.10	10.40	8.215	0.522	0.375	27.7	84.4	10.9	3.23	2.64	24.2	5.88	1.73
WT 10.5 × 24.5	7.21	10.41	6.520	0.532	0.368	28.3	78.3	10.4	3.29	2.90	12.3	3.78	1.31
× 22	6.48	10.33	6.500	0.451	0.348	29.7	70.9	9.63	3.31	2.97	10.4	3.19	1.27

STRUCTURAL TEES
Cut from W shapes
Properties of sections limited by width-thickness ratios

Per AISC Specification, Sect. 1.9.1

| Designation | $C_c' = \sqrt{\dfrac{2\pi^2 E}{Q_s Q_a F_y}}$ where $Q_a = 1.0$ | | | |
| | $F_y = 36$ ksi | | $F_y = 50$ ksi | |
	Q_s	C_c'	Q_s	C_c'
WT 13.5 × 57	0.883	134	0.700	128
× 51	0.788	142	0.587	140
× 47	0.728	148	0.529	147
× 42	0.672	154	0.482	154
WT 12 × 80	—	—	0.958	109
× 72.5	—	—	0.892	113
× 65	0.986	127	0.821	118
WT 12 × 60	0.968	128	0.801	120
× 55	0.891	134	0.710	127
× 50	0.810	140	0.610	137
WT 12 × 47	0.900	133	0.720	126
× 42	0.810	140	0.610	137
× 38	0.741	146	0.541	146
× 34	0.685	152	0.492	152
WT 12 × 30.5	0.694	151	0.499	151
× 27.5	0.630	159	0.453	159
WT 10.5 × 71	—	—	—	—
× 63.5	—	—	0.993	107
× 56	—	—	0.902	113
WT 10.5 × 48	—	—	0.978	108
× 41	—	—	0.851	116
WT 10.5 × 36.5	0.908	132	0.730	125
× 34	0.853	137	0.664	131
× 31	0.784	142	0.583	140
× 27.5	0.720	149	0.521	148
WT 10.5 × 24.5	0.694	151	0.499	151
× 22	0.630	159	0.453	159

NOTE: Where no value of C_c' or Q_s is shown, the Tee complies with Specification Sect. 1.9.1.2 and may be considered fully effective.

AMERICAN INSTITUTE OF STEEL CONSTRUCTION

STRUCTURAL TEES
Cut from W shapes
Dimensions and properties for designing

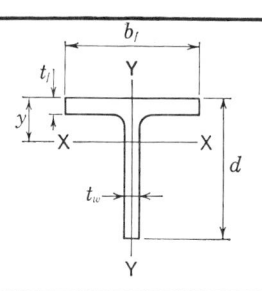

Designation	Area	Depth of Tee d	Flange Width b_f	Flange Thickness t_f	Stem Thickness t_w	$\dfrac{d}{t_w}$	AXIS X-X I	S	r	y	AXIS Y-Y I	S	r
	In.²	In.	In.	In.	In.		In.⁴	In.³	In.	In.	In.⁴	In.³	In.
WT 9 × 57	16.8	9.24	11.833	0.991	0.595	15.5	103	13.9	2.48	1.85	137	23.2	2.86
× 52.5	15.4	9.16	11.792	0.911	0.554	16.5	94.0	12.8	2.47	1.82	125	21.1	2.84
× 48	14.1	9.08	11.750	0.831	0.512	17.7	85.4	11.7	2.46	1.78	112	19.1	2.82
WT 9 × 42.5	12.5	9.16	8.838	0.911	0.526	17.4	84.4	11.9	2.60	2.05	52.5	11.9	2.05
× 38.5	11.4	9.08	8.787	0.831	0.475	19.1	75.3	10.6	2.58	1.99	47.1	10.7	2.04
× 35	10.3	9.00	8.750	0.751	0.438	20.5	68.2	9.68	2.57	1.96	42.0	9.60	2.02
× 32	9.43	8.94	8.715	0.686	0.403	22.2	61.9	8.83	2.56	1.92	37.9	8.70	2.00
WT 9 × 30	8.83	9.13	7.558	0.695	0.416	21.9	64.9	9.32	2.71	2.16	25.1	6.63	1.68
× 27.5	8.10	9.06	7.532	0.630	0.390	23.2	59.6	8.64	2.71	2.16	22.5	5.97	1.67
× 25	7.36	9.00	7.500	0.570	0.358	25.1	54.0	7.86	2.71	2.13	20.1	5.35	1.65
× 22.5	6.62	8.93	7.477	0.499	0.335	26.7	49.0	7.24	2.72	2.16	17.4	4.66	1.62
WT 9 × 20	5.88	8.95	6.018	0.524	0.316	28.3	44.9	6.75	2.76	2.29	9.54	3.17	1.27
× 17.5	5.15	8.86	6.000	0.429	0.298	29.7	40.1	6.18	2.79	2.38	7.74	2.58	1.23
WT 8 × 48	14.1	8.16	11.533	0.875	0.535	15.3	64.7	9.82	2.14	1.57	112	19.4	2.82
× 44	12.9	8.08	11.502	0.795	0.504	16.0	59.5	9.11	2.14	1.55	101	17.5	2.79
WT 8 × 39	11.5	8.16	8.586	0.875	0.529	15.4	60.0	9.45	2.28	1.81	46.3	10.8	2.01
× 35.5	10.5	8.08	8.543	0.795	0.486	16.6	54.1	8.57	2.27	1.77	41.4	9.69	1.99
× 32	9.41	8.08	8.500	0.715	0.443	18.1	48.3	7.72	2.27	1.73	36.7	8.63	1.97
× 29	8.53	7.93	8.464	0.645	0.407	19.5	43.6	7.01	2.26	1.71	32.6	7.71	1.96
WT 8 × 25	7.36	8.13	7.073	0.628	0.380	21.4	42.2	6.77	2.40	1.89	18.6	5.25	1.59
× 22.5	6.63	8.06	7.039	0.563	0.346	23.3	37.8	6.10	2.39	1.86	16.4	4.66	1.57
× 20	5.89	8.00	7.000	0.503	0.307	26.1	33.2	5.38	2.37	1.82	14.4	4.11	1.56
× 18	5.30	7.93	6.992	0.428	0.299	26.5	30.8	5.11	2.41	1.89	12.2	3.49	1.52
WT 8 × 15.5	4.57	7.92	5.53	0.442	0.275	28.8	27.3	4.62	2.44	2.01	6.23	2.25	1.17
× 13	3.84	7.82	5.50	0.345	0.250	31.3	23.3	4.07	2.47	2.08	4.80	1.74	1.12

STRUCTURAL TEES
Cut from W shapes

Properties of sections limited by width-thickness ratios

Per AISC Specification, Sect. 1.9.1

| Designation | $C_c' = \sqrt{\dfrac{2\pi^2 E}{Q_s Q_a F_y}}$ where $Q_a = 1.0$ | | | |
| | $F_y = 36$ ksi | | $F_y = 50$ ksi | |
	Q_s	C_c'	Q_s	C_c'
WT 9 × 57	—	—	—	—
× 52.5	—	—	—	—
× 48	—	—	—	—
WT 9 × 42.5	—	—	—	—
× 38.5	—	—	0.942	110
× 35	—	—	0.872	115
× 32	0.956	129	0.786	121
WT 9 × 30	0.968	128	0.801	120
× 27.5	0.913	132	0.735	125
× 25	0.831	138	0.635	134
× 22.5	0.763	144	0.561	143
WT 9 × 20	0.694	151	0.499	151
× 17.5	0.630	159	0.453	159
WT 8 × 48	—	—	—	—
× 44	—	—	—	—
WT 8 × 39	—	—	—	—
× 35.5	—	—	—	—
× 32	—	—	0.993	107
× 29	—	—	0.922	111
WT 8 × 25	0.990	127	0.826	118
× 22.5	0.908	132	0.730	125
× 20	0.788	142	0.587	140
× 18	0.771	144	0.570	142
WT 8 × 15.5	0.672	154	0.482	154
× 13	0.567	167	0.408	167

NOTE: Where no value of C_c' or Q_s is shown, the Tee complies with Specification Sect. 1.9.1.2 and may be considered fully effective.

STRUCTURAL TEES
Cut from W shapes
Dimensions and
properties for designing

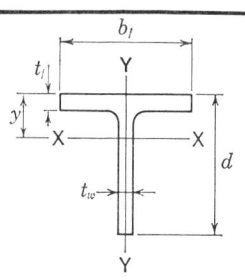

Designation	Area	Depth of Tee d	Flange		Stem Thickness t_w	$\dfrac{d}{t_w}$	AXIS X-X				AXIS Y-Y		
			Width b_f	Thickness t_f			I	S	r	y	I	S	r
	In.²	In.	In.	In.	In.		In.⁴	In.³	In.	In.	In.⁴	In.³	In.
WT 7 × 365	107.0	11.22	17.889	4.910	3.069	3.66	740	95.6	2.63	3.47	2360	264	4.69
× 332.5	97.8	10.84	17.646	4.522	2.826	3.83	623	82.2	2.52	3.25	2080	236	4.62
× 302.5	89.0	10.47	17.418	4.157	2.598	4.03	525	70.8	2.43	3.05	1840	211	4.55
× 275	80.9	10.13	17.206	3.818	2.386	4.25	444	61.1	2.34	2.86	1630	189	4.49
× 250	73.5	9.82	17.008	3.501	2.188	4.49	377	52.8	2.26	2.68	1440	169	4.43
× 227.5	66.9	9.53	16.828	3.213	2.008	4.74	322	45.9	2.19	2.51	1280	152	4.37
WT 7 × 213	62.6	9.35	16.695	3.033	1.875	4.98	288	41.4	2.14	2.40	1180	141	4.34
× 199	58.5	9.16	16.590	2.843	1.770	5.17	258	37.7	2.10	2.30	1080	131	4.31
× 185	54.4	8.97	16.475	2.658	1.655	5.42	230	34.0	2.06	2.19	993	121	4.27
× 171	50.3	8.78	16.365	2.468	1.545	5.68	204	30.5	2.02	2.09	903	110	4.24
× 157	46.2	8.60	16.235	2.283	1.415	6.07	179	27.0	1.97	1.98	816	100	4.20
× 143.5	42.2	8.41	16.130	2.093	1.310	6.42	157	24.1	1.93	1.87	733	90.9	4.17
× 132	38.8	8.25	16.025	1.938	1.205	6.85	139	21.5	1.89	1.78	666	83.1	4.14
× 123	36.2	8.13	15.945	1.813	1.125	7.22	126	19.6	1.86	1.71	613	76.9	4.12
WT 7 × 118.5	34.8	8.06	15.910	1.748	1.090	7.39	120	18.7	1.85	1.67	587	73.8	4.11
× 114	33.5	8.00	15.865	1.688	1.045	7.66	113	17.7	1.84	1.64	562	70.9	4.10
× 109.5	32.2	7.94	15.825	1.623	1.005	7.90	107	16.9	1.82	1.60	537	67.8	4.08
× 105.5	31.0	7.88	15.800	1.563	0.980	8.04	102	16.2	1.82	1.57	514	65.1	4.07
× 101	29.7	7.82	15.750	1.503	0.930	8.40	95.8	15.2	1.80	1.53	490	62.2	4.06
× 96.5	28.4	7.75	15.710	1.438	0.890	8.71	90.1	14.4	1.78	1.49	465	59.2	4.05
× 92	27.0	7.69	15.660	1.378	0.840	9.15	83.9	13.4	1.76	1.45	441	56.4	4.04
× 88	25.9	7.63	15.640	1.313	0.820	9.30	80.2	12.9	1.76	1.42	419	53.6	4.02
× 83.5	24.5	7.56	15.600	1.248	0.780	9.69	75.0	12.2	1.75	1.39	395	50.7	4.01
× 79	23.2	7.50	15.550	1.188	0.730	10.3	69.3	11.3	1.73	1.34	372	47.9	4.00
× 75	22.0	7.44	15.515	1.128	0.695	10.7	65.0	10.6	1.72	1.31	351	45.3	3.99
× 71	20.9	7.38	15.500	1.063	0.680	10.8	62.1	10.2	1.72	1.29	330	42.6	3.97
WT 7 × 160	47.1	8.41	16.710	2.093	1.890	4.45	209	33.3	2.11	2.12	818	97.8	4.17

STRUCTURAL TEES
Cut from W shapes
Properties of sections limited by width-thickness ratios
Per AISC Specification, Sect. 1.9.1

$$C_c' = \sqrt{\frac{2\pi^2 E}{Q_s Q_a F_y}} \text{ where } Q_a = 1.0$$

Designation	$F_y = 36$ ksi		$F_y = 50$ ksi	
	Q_s	C_c'	Q_s	C_c'
WT 7 × 365	—	—	—	—
× 332.5	—	—	—	—
× 302.5	—	—	—	—
× 275	—	—	—	—
× 250	—	—	—	—
× 227.5	—	—	—	—
WT 7 × 213	—	—	—	—
× 199	—	—	—	—
× 185	—	—	—	—
× 171	—	—	—	—
× 157	—	—	—	—
× 143.5	—	—	—	—
× 132	—	—	—	—
× 123	—	—	—	—
WT 7 × 118.5	—	—	—	—
× 114	—	—	—	—
× 109.5	—	—	—	—
× 105.5	—	—	—	—
× 101	—	—	—	—
× 96.5	—	—	—	—
× 92	—	—	—	—
× 88	—	—	—	—
× 83.5	—	—	—	—
× 79	—	—	—	—
× 75	—	—	—	—
× 71	—	—	—	—
WT 7 × 160	—	—	—	—

NOTE: Where no value of C_c' or Q_s is shown, the Tee complies with Specification Sect. 1.9.1.2 and may be considered fully effective.

AMERICAN INSTITUTE OF STEEL CONSTRUCTION

STRUCTURAL TEES
Cut from W shapes
Dimensions and properties for designing

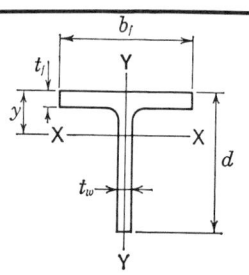

Designation	Area	Depth of Tee d	Flange		Stem Thickness t_w	$\dfrac{d}{t_w}$	AXIS X-X				AXIS Y-Y		
			Width b_f	Thickness t_f			I	S	r	y	I	S	r
	In.²	In.	In.	In.	In.		In.⁴	In.³	In.	In.	In.⁴	In.³	In.
WT 7 × 68	20.0	7.38	14.740	1.063	0.660	11.2	60.1	9.89	1.73	1.31	284	38.5	3.77
× 63.5	18.7	7.31	14.690	0.998	0.610	12.0	54.7	9.05	1.71	1.26	264	35.9	3.76
× 59.5	17.5	7.25	14.650	0.938	0.570	12.7	50.4	8.36	1.70	1.22	246	33.6	3.75
× 55.5	16.3	7.19	14.620	0.873	0.540	13.3	46.9	7.82	1.69	1.19	227	31.1	3.73
× 51.5	15.1	7.13	14.575	0.813	0.495	14.4	42.4	7.10	1.67	1.15	210	28.8	3.72
× 47.5	14.0	7.06	14.545	0.748	0.465	15.2	39.1	6.58	1.67	1.12	192	26.4	3.71
× 43.5	12.8	7.00	14.500	0.688	0.420	16.7	34.9	5.88	1.65	1.08	175	24.1	3.70
WT 7 × 42	12.4	7.09	12.023	0.778	0.451	15.7	37.4	6.36	1.74	1.21	113	18.8	3.02
× 39	11.5	7.03	12.000	0.718	0.428	16.4	34.8	5.96	1.74	1.19	103	17.2	3.00
WT 7 × 37	10.9	7.10	10.072	0.783	0.450	15.8	36.1	6.26	1.82	1.32	66.7	13.3	2.48
× 34	10.0	7.03	10.040	0.718	0.418	16.8	33.0	5.75	1.82	1.29	60.6	12.1	2.46
× 30.5	8.97	6.96	10.000	0.643	0.378	18.4	29.2	5.13	1.80	1.25	53.6	10.7	2.45
WT 7 × 26.5	7.79	6.97	8.062	0.658	0.370	18.8	27.7	4.96	1.88	1.38	28.8	7.14	1.92
× 24	7.06	6.91	8.031	0.593	0.339	20.4	24.9	4.49	1.88	1.35	25.6	6.38	1.91
× 21.5	6.32	6.84	8.000	0.528	0.308	22.2	22.2	4.02	1.87	1.33	22.6	5.64	1.89
WT 7 × 19	5.59	7.06	6.776	0.513	0.313	22.6	23.5	4.27	2.05	1.55	13.3	3.93	1.54
× 17	5.01	7.00	6.750	0.453	0.287	24.4	21.1	3.87	2.05	1.54	11.6	3.44	1.52
× 15	4.42	6.93	6.733	0.383	0.270	25.7	19.0	3.56	2.08	1.58	9.76	2.90	1.49
WT 7 × 13	3.83	6.95	5.025	0.418	0.255	27.2	17.2	3.30	2.12	1.72	4.43	1.76	1.08
× 11	3.24	6.86	5.000	0.335	0.230	29.8	14.8	2.90	2.13	1.76	3.50	1.40	1.04
WT 6 × 95	27.9	7.19	12.670	1.736	1.060	6.78	79.0	14.2	1.68	1.62	295	46.5	3.25
× 80.5	23.7	6.94	12.515	1.486	0.905	7.67	62.6	11.5	1.63	1.47	243	38.9	3.20
× 66.5	19.6	6.69	12.365	1.236	0.755	8.86	48.4	9.04	1.57	1.33	195	31.5	3.16
× 60	17.7	6.56	12.320	1.106	0.710	9.24	43.4	8.22	1.57	1.28	173	28.0	3.13
× 53	15.6	6.44	12.230	0.986	0.620	10.4	36.7	7.01	1.53	1.20	150	24.6	3.11
× 49.5	14.6	6.38	12.192	0.921	0.582	11.0	33.8	6.48	1.52	1.16	139	22.8	3.09
× 46	13.5	6.31	12.155	0.856	0.545	11.6	31.0	5.99	1.51	1.13	128	21.1	3.08
× 42.5	12.5	6.25	12.105	0.796	0.495	12.6	27.8	5.38	1.49	1.08	118	19.5	3.07
× 39.5	11.6	6.19	12.080	0.736	0.470	13.2	25.8	5.03	1.49	1.06	108	17.9	3.05
× 36	10.6	6.13	12.040	0.671	0.430	14.2	23.2	4.54	1.48	1.02	97.6	16.2	3.04
× 32.5	9.55	6.06	12.000	0.606	0.390	15.5	20.6	4.06	1.47	0.985	87.3	14.6	3.02

AMERICAN INSTITUTE OF STEEL CONSTRUCTION

STRUCTURAL TEES
Cut from W shapes

Properties of sections limited by width-thickness ratios

Per AISC Specification, Sect. 1.9.1

| Designation | $C_c' = \sqrt{\dfrac{2\pi^2 E}{Q_s Q_a F_y}}$ where $Q_a = 1.0$ | | | |
| | $F_y = 36$ ksi | | $F_y = 50$ ksi | |
	Q_s	C_c'	Q_s	C_c'
WT 7 × 68	—	—	—	—
× 63.5	—	—	—	—
× 59.5	—	—	—	—
× 55.5	—	—	—	—
× 51.5	—	—	—	—
× 47.5	—	—	—	—
× 43.5	—	—	—	—
WT 7 × 42	—	—	—	—
× 39	—	—	—	—
WT 7 × 37	—	—	—	—
× 34	—	—	—	—
× 30.5	—	—	0.978	108
WT 7 × 26.5	—	—	0.958	109
× 24	—	—	0.877	114
× 21.5	0.956	129	0.786	121
WT 7 × 19	0.938	130	0.765	122
× 17	0.861	136	0.674	130
× 15	0.805	141	0.606	137
WT 7 × 13	0.741	146	0.541	146
× 11	0.626	159	0.450	159
WT 6 × 95	—	—	—	—
× 80.5	—	—	—	—
× 66.5	—	—	—	—
× 60	—	—	—	—
× 53	—	—	—	—
× 49.5	—	—	—	—
× 46	—	—	—	—
× 42.5	—	—	—	—
× 39.5	—	—	—	—
× 36	—	—	—	—
× 32.5	—	—	—	—

NOTE: Where no value of C_c' or Q_s is shown, the Tee complies with Specification Sect. 1.9.1.2 and may be considered fully effective.

AMERICAN INSTITUTE OF STEEL CONSTRUCTION

STRUCTURAL TEES
Cut from W shapes
Dimensions and properties for designing

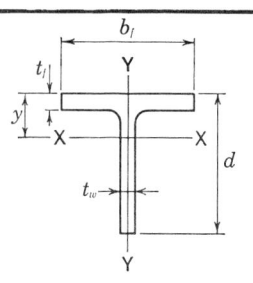

Designation	Area	Depth of Tee d	Flange		Stem Thickness t_w	$\dfrac{d}{t_w}$	AXIS X-X				AXIS Y-Y		
			Width b_f	Thickness t_f			I	S	r	y	I	S	r
	In.²	In.	In.	In.	In.		In.⁴	In.³	In.	In.	In.⁴	In.³	In.
WT 6 × 29	8.53	6.10	10.014	0.641	0.359	17.0	19.0	3.75	1.49	1.03	53.7	10.7	2.51
× 26.5	7.80	6.03	10.000	0.576	0.345	17.5	17.7	3.54	1.51	1.02	48.0	9.61	2.48
WT 6 × 25	7.36	6.10	8.077	0.641	0.371	16.4	18.7	3.80	1.60	1.17	28.2	6.98	1.96
× 22.5	6.62	6.03	8.042	0.576	0.336	17.9	16.6	3.40	1.59	1.13	25.0	6.22	1.94
× 20	5.89	5.97	8.000	0.516	0.294	20.3	14.4	2.94	1.56	1.08	22.0	5.51	1.94
WT 6 × 18	5.30	6.12	6.565	0.540	0.305	20.1	15.3	3.14	1.70	1.26	12.7	3.88	1.55
× 15.5	4.57	6.05	6.525	0.465	0.265	22.8	13.0	2.69	1.69	1.22	10.8	3.30	1.54
× 13.5	3.97	5.98	6.497	0.400	0.237	25.2	11.3	2.37	1.69	1.20	9.15	2.82	1.52
WT 6 × 11	3.24	6.16	4.030	0.424	0.260	23.7	11.7	2.59	1.90	1.63	2.32	1.15	0.847
× 9.5	2.80	6.08	4.007	0.349	0.237	25.7	10.2	2.30	1.91	1.65	1.88	0.938	0.820
× 8.25	2.43	6.00	4.000	0.269	0.230	26.1	9.03	2.13	1.93	1.76	1.44	0.721	0.770
× 7	2.06	5.96	3.968	0.224	0.198	30.1	7.61	1.81	1.92	1.75	1.17	0.590	0.754
WT 5 × 56	16.5	5.69	10.415	1.248	0.755	7.54	28.8	6.42	1.32	1.21	118	22.6	2.67
× 50	14.7	5.56	10.345	1.118	0.685	8.12	24.8	5.62	1.30	1.14	103	20.0	2.65
× 44.5	13.1	5.44	10.275	0.998	0.615	8.85	21.3	4.88	1.28	1.07	90.3	17.6	2.63
× 38.5	11.3	5.31	10.195	0.868	0.535	9.93	17.7	4.10	1.25	0.996	76.7	15.1	2.60
× 36	10.6	5.25	10.170	0.808	0.510	10.3	16.4	3.83	1.24	0.971	70.9	13.9	2.59
× 33	9.70	5.19	10.117	0.748	0.457	11.4	14.5	3.39	1.22	0.922	64.6	12.8	2.58
× 30	8.83	5.13	10.075	0.683	0.415	12.3	12.8	3.03	1.21	0.882	58.2	11.6	2.57
× 27	7.94	5.06	10.028	0.618	0.368	13.8	11.2	2.64	1.19	0.836	52.0	10.4	2.56
× 24.5	7.20	5.00	10.000	0.558	0.340	14.7	10.1	2.40	1.18	0.809	46.5	9.30	2.54
WT 5 × 22.5	6.62	5.06	8.022	0.618	0.350	14.5	10.3	2.48	1.25	0.910	26.6	6.63	2.00
× 19.5	5.74	4.97	7.990	0.528	0.318	15.6	8.96	2.19	1.25	0.883	22.5	5.62	1.98
× 16.5	4.85	4.88	7.964	0.433	0.292	16.7	7.80	1.95	1.27	0.875	18.2	4.58	1.94
WT 5 × 14.5	4.27	5.11	5.799	0.500	0.289	17.7	8.39	2.07	1.40	1.05	8.14	2.81	1.38
× 12.5	3.68	5.04	5.762	0.430	0.252	20.0	7.13	1.77	1.39	1.01	6.86	2.38	1.37
× 10.5	3.10	4.95	5.750	0.340	0.240	20.6	6.32	1.62	1.43	1.06	5.39	1.88	1.32

STRUCTURAL TEES
Cut from W shapes

Properties of sections limited by width-thickness ratios

Per AISC Specification, Sect. 1.9.1

| Designation | $C_c' = \sqrt{\dfrac{2\pi^2 E}{Q_s Q_a F_y}}$ where $Q_a = 1.0$ | | | |
| | $F_y = 36$ ksi | | $F_y = 50$ ksi | |
	Q_s	C_c'	Q_s	C_c'
WT 6 × 29	—	—	—	—
× 26.5	—	—	—	—
WT 6 × 25	—	—	—	—
× 22.5	—	—	—	—
× 20	—	—	0.882	114
WT 6 × 18	—	—	0.892	113
× 15.5	0.930	131	0.755	123
× 13.5	0.827	139	0.630	135
WT 6 × 11	0.891	134	0.710	127
× 9.5	0.805	141	0.606	137
× 8.25	0.788	142	0.587	140
× 7	0.613	161	0.441	161
WT 5 × 56	—	—	—	—
× 50	—	—	—	—
× 44.5	—	—	—	—
× 38.5	—	—	—	—
× 36	—	—	—	—
× 33	—	—	—	—
× 30	—	—	—	—
× 27	—	—	—	—
× 24.5	—	—	—	—
WT 5 × 22.5	—	—	—	—
× 19.5	—	—	—	—
× 16.5	—	—	—	—
WT 5 × 14.5	—	—	—	—
× 12.5	—	—	0.897	113
× 10.5	—	—	0.867	115

NOTE: Where no value of C_c' or Q_s is shown, the Tee complies with Specification Sect. 1.9.1.2 and may be considered fully effective.

STRUCTURAL TEES
Cut from W shapes
Dimensions and properties for designing

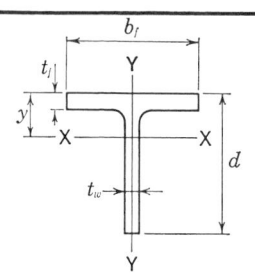

Designation	Area	Depth of Tee d	Flange Width b_f	Flange Thick-ness t_f	Stem Thick-ness t_w	$\dfrac{d}{t_w}$	AXIS X-X I	S	r	y	AXIS Y-Y I	S	r
	In.²	In.	In.	In.	In.		In.⁴	In.³	In.	In.	In.⁴	In.³	In.
WT 5 ✕ 9.5	2.81	5.13	4.020	0.394	0.250	20.5	6.70	1.74	1.55	1.28	2.14	1.06	0.874
✕ 8.5	2.49	5.06	4.010	0.329	0.240	21.1	6.07	1.62	1.56	1.32	1.77	0.885	0.844
✕ 7.5	2.20	5.00	4.000	0.269	0.230	21.7	5.46	1.51	1.57	1.37	1.44	0.720	0.809
✕ 5.75	1.70	4.94	3.950	0.204	0.180	27.4	4.16	1.16	1.57	1.34	1.05	0.532	0.787
WT 4 ✕ 33.5	9.85	4.50	8.287	0.933	0.575	7.83	10.9	3.07	1.05	0.939	44.3	10.7	2.12
✕ 29	8.53	4.38	8.222	0.808	0.510	8.58	9.12	2.61	1.03	0.874	37.5	9.12	2.10
✕ 24	7.06	4.25	8.117	0.683	0.405	10.5	6.92	2.00	0.990	0.781	30.5	7.51	2.08
✕ 20	5.88	4.13	8.077	0.558	0.365	11.3	5.80	1.71	0.993	0.740	24.5	6.07	2.04
✕ 17.5	5.15	4.06	8.027	0.493	0.315	12.9	4.88	1.45	0.973	0.694	21.3	5.30	2.03
✕ 15.5	4.56	4.00	8.000	0.433	0.288	13.9	4.31	1.30	0.973	0.672	18.5	4.62	2.01
WT 4 ✕ 14	4.11	4.03	6.540	0.463	0.285	14.1	4.22	1.28	1.01	0.735	10.8	3.30	1.62
✕ 12	3.53	3.97	6.500	0.398	0.245	16.2	3.53	1.08	1.00	0.695	9.12	2.80	1.61
WT 4 ✕ 10	2.95	4.07	5.268	0.378	0.248	16.4	3.67	1.13	1.12	0.825	4.61	1.75	1.25
✕ 8.5	2.50	4.00	5.250	0.308	0.230	17.4	3.21	1.02	1.13	0.835	3.72	1.42	1.22
WT 4 ✕ 7.5	2.22	4.06	4.015	0.314	0.245	16.6	3.29	1.07	1.22	1.00	1.70	0.847	0.876
✕ 6.5	1.92	4.00	4.000	0.254	0.230	17.4	2.90	0.976	1.23	1.03	1.36	0.680	0.842
✕ 5	1.48	3.95	3.940	0.204	0.170	23.2	2.15	0.719	1.21	0.957	1.04	0.529	0.839
WT 3 ✕ 12.5	3.67	3.19	6.080	0.456	0.320	9.95	2.27	0.883	0.787	0.609	8.55	2.81	1.53
✕ 10	2.94	3.10	6.018	0.367	0.258	12.0	1.75	0.688	0.771	0.557	6.67	2.22	1.51
✕ 7.75	2.28	3.00	5.995	0.269	0.235	12.8	1.44	0.591	0.795	0.559	4.83	1.61	1.46
WT 3 ✕ 8	2.36	3.13	4.030	0.404	0.260	12.0	1.66	0.679	0.839	0.673	2.21	1.10	0.967
✕ 6	1.77	3.00	4.000	0.279	0.230	13.0	1.30	0.558	0.857	0.673	1.49	0.746	0.918
✕ 4.25	1.25	2.92	3.940	0.194	0.170	17.1	0.904	0.397	0.849	0.638	0.990	0.503	0.889
WT 2.5 ✕ 9.25	2.72	2.56	5.025	0.420	0.265	9.66	0.980	0.471	0.601	0.481	4.45	1.77	1.28
✕ 8	2.35	2.50	5.000	0.360	0.240	10.4	0.840	0.411	0.598	0.457	3.75	1.50	1.26
WT 2 ✕ 6.5	1.91	2.08	4.060	0.345	0.280	7.43	0.526	0.321	0.524	0.440	1.88	0.926	0.991

STRUCTURAL TEES
Cut from W shapes

Properties of sections limited by width-thickness ratios

Per AISC Specification, Sect. 1.9.1

$$C_c' = \sqrt{\frac{2\pi^2 E}{Q_s Q_a F_y}} \text{ where } Q_a = 1.0$$

Designation	$F_y = 36$ ksi		$F_y = 50$ ksi	
	Q_s	C_c'	Q_s	C_c'
WT 5 × 9.5	—	—	0.872	115
× 8.5	—	—	0.841	117
× 7.5	0.977	128	0.811	119
× 5.75	0.733	147	0.533	147
WT 4 × 33.5	—	—	—	—
× 29	—	—	—	—
× 24	—	—	—	—
× 20	—	—	—	—
× 17.5	—	—	—	—
× 15.5	—	—	—	—
WT 4 × 14	—	—	—	—
× 12	—	—	—	—
WT 4 × 10	—	—	—	—
× 8.5	—	—	—	—
WT 4 × 7.5	—	—	—	—
× 6.5	—	—	—	—
× 5	0.913	132	0.735	125
WT 3 × 12.5	—	—	—	—
× 10	—	—	—	—
× 7.75	—	—	—	—
WT 3 × 8	—	—	—	—
× 6	—	—	—	—
× 4.25	—	—	—	—
WT 2.5 × 9.25	—	—	—	—
× 8	—	—	—	—
WT 2 × 6.5	—	—	—	—

NOTE: Where no value of C_c' or Q_s is shown, the Tee complies with Specification Sect. 1.9.1.2 and may be considered fully effective.

AMERICAN INSTITUTE OF STEEL CONSTRUCTION

STRUCTURAL TEES
Cut from M shapes
Dimensions and
properties for designing

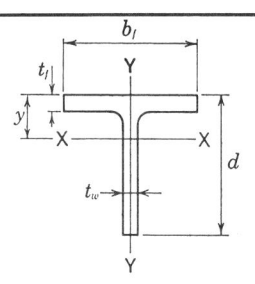

Designation	Area	Depth of Tee d	Flange		Stem Thickness t_w	$\dfrac{d}{t_w}$	AXIS X-X				AXIS Y-Y		
			Width b_f	Thickness t_f			I	S	r	y	I	S	r
	In.²	In.	In.	In.	In.		In.⁴	In.³	In.	In.	In.⁴	In.³	In.
MT 7 × 8.6	2.53	7.00	4.000	0.272	0.210	33.3	12.9	2.64	2.26	2.10	1.33	0.663	0.725
MT 6 × 5.9	1.73	6.00	3.065	0.225	0.177	33.9	6.60	1.60	1.95	1.89	0.490	0.320	0.532
MT 5 × 14.55	4.28	4.94	5.937	0.389	0.427	11.6	9.79	2.71	1.51	1.32	5.58	1.88	1.14
× 11.45	3.36	4.94	5.752	0.389	0.242	20.4	6.41	1.63	1.38	1.01	5.01	1.74	1.22
MT 5 × 4.5	1.32	5.00	2.690	0.206	0.157	31.8	3.46	0.997	1.62	1.53	0.305	0.227	0.480
MT 4 × 18.85	5.54	4.06	8.002	0.521	0.377	10.8	5.65	1.71	1.01	0.755	20.2	5.05	1.91
× 17.15	5.04	4.00	8.003	0.459	0.378	10.6	5.38	1.66	1.03	0.766	17.5	4.37	1.86
× 16.3	4.79	4.00	7.940	0.459	0.315	12.7	4.64	1.41	0.984	0.701	17.0	4.29	1.89
MT 4 × 11.25	3.30	4.00	5.395	0.353	0.375	10.7	4.70	1.57	1.19	1.01	3.74	1.39	1.06
× 9.25	2.72	4.00	5.250	0.353	0.230	17.4	3.24	1.01	1.09	0.804	3.41	1.30	1.12
MT 4 × 3.25	0.958	4.00	2.281	0.189	0.135	29.6	1.57	0.556	1.28	1.17	0.172	0.150	0.423
MT 3.5 × 2.75	0.809	3.50	2.080	0.180	0.128	27.3	1.01	0.404	1.12	1.01	0.124	0.120	0.392
MT 3 × 16.875	4.96	3.13	6.114	0.605	0.488	6.40	3.02	1.24	0.779	0.695	10.7	3.49	1.47
× 11.25	3.31	3.00	6.060	0.379	0.372	8.06	2.12	0.898	0.801	0.638	6.19	2.04	1.37
× 10	2.94	3.00	5.938	0.379	0.250	12.0	1.54	0.624	0.724	0.531	5.80	1.95	1.40
MT 3 × 2.2	0.646	3.00	1.844	0.171	0.114	26.3	0.577	0.267	0.945	0.836	0.083	0.090	0.358
MT 2.5 × 9.45	2.78	2.50	5.003	0.416	0.316	7.91	1.05	0.527	0.615	0.511	3.93	1.57	1.19
MT 2 × 8.15	2.40	2.10	3.938	0.472	0.312	6.73	0.587	0.359	0.495	0.465	2.22	1.13	0.962
× 6.9	2.03	2.00	4.000	0.371	0.313	6.39	0.509	0.327	0.501	0.444	1.79	0.894	0.939
× 6.5	1.90	2.00	3.940	0.371	0.254	7.87	0.431	0.271	0.475	0.410	1.68	0.853	0.939

STRUCTURAL TEES
Cut from M shapes

Properties of sections limited by width-thickness ratios

Per AISC Specification, Sect. 1.9.1

$$C_c' = \sqrt{\frac{2\pi^2 E}{Q_s Q_a F_y}} \text{ where } Q_a = 1.0$$

Designation	$F_y = 36$ ksi		$F_y = 50$ ksi	
	Q_s	C_c'	Q_s	C_c'
MT 7 × 8.6	0.501	178	0.361	178
MT 6 × 5.9	0.483	181	0.348	181
MT 5 × 14.55	—	—	—	—
× 11.45	—	—	0.877	114
MT 5 × 4.5	0.549	170	0.396	170
MT 4 × 18.85	—	—	—	—
× 17.15	—	—	—	—
× 16.3	—	—	—	—
MT 4 × 11.25	—	—	—	—
× 9.25	—	—	—	—
MT 4 × 3.25	0.634	158	0.457	158
MT 3.5 × 2.75	0.737	147	0.537	146
MT 3 × 16.875	—	—	—	—
× 11.25	—	—	—	—
× 10	—	—	—	—
MT 3 × 2.2	0.780	143	0.578	141
MT 2.5 × 9.45	—	—	—	—
MT 2 × 8.15	—	—	—	—
× 6.9	—	—	—	—
× 6.5	—	—	—	--

NOTE: Where no value of C_c' or Q_s is shown, the Tee complies with Specification Sect. 1.9.1.2 and may be considered fully effective.

STRUCTURAL TEES
Cut from S shapes
Dimensions and properties for designing

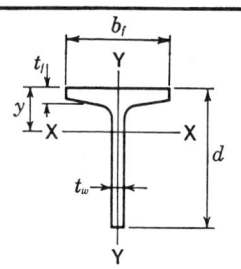

Designation	Area	Depth of Tee d	Flange Width b_f	Flange Thick-ness t_f	Stem Thick-ness t_w	$\dfrac{d}{t_w}$	AXIS X-X I	S	r	y	AXIS Y-Y I	S	r
	In.²	In.	In.	In.	In.		In.⁴	In.³	In.	In.	In.⁴	In.³	In.
ST 12 × 60	17.6	12.00	8.048	1.102	0.798	15.0	245	28.9	3.72	3.52	42.1	10.5	1.54
× 52.95	15.6	12.00	7.875	1.102	0.625	19.2	205	23.3	3.63	3.19	39.1	9.92	1.58
ST 12 × 50	14.7	12.00	7.247	0.871	0.747	16.1	215	26.4	3.83	3.84	23.9	6.59	1.27
× 45	13.2	12.00	7.124	0.871	0.624	19.2	190	22.6	3.79	3.60	22.5	6.31	1.30
× 39.95	11.8	12.00	7.001	0.871	0.501	24.0	163	18.7	3.72	3.30	21.1	6.04	1.34
ST 10 × 47.5	14.0	10.00	7.200	0.916	0.800	12.5	137	19.7	3.13	3.07	24.8	6.90	1.33
× 42.5	12.5	10.00	7.053	0.916	0.653	15.3	118	16.6	3.08	2.85	23.1	6.55	1.36
ST 10 × 37.5	11.0	10.00	6.391	0.789	0.641	15.6	110	15.9	3.16	3.08	14.8	4.64	1.16
× 32.7	9.62	10.00	6.250	0.789	0.500	20.0	92.3	12.8	3.10	2.80	13.7	4.38	1.19
ST 9 × 35	10.3	9.00	6.251	0.691	0.711	12.7	84.7	14.0	2.87	2.94	12.1	3.86	1.08
× 27.35	8.04	9.00	6.001	0.691	0.461	19.5	62.4	9.61	2.79	2.50	10.4	3.47	1.14
ST 7.5 × 25	7.35	7.50	5.640	0.622	0.550	13.6	40.6	7.73	2.35	2.25	7.85	2.78	1.03
× 21.45	6.31	7.50	5.501	0.622	0.411	18.2	33.0	6.00	2.29	2.01	7.19	2.61	1.07
ST 6 × 25	7.35	6.00	5.477	0.659	0.687	8.73	25.2	6.05	1.85	1.84	7.85	2.87	1.03
× 20.4	6.00	6.00	5.252	0.659	0.462	13.0	18.9	4.28	1.78	1.58	6.78	2.58	1.06
ST 6 × 17.5	5.14	6.00	5.078	0.544	0.428	14.0	17.2	3.95	1.83	1.65	4.93	1.94	0.980
× 15.9	4.68	6.00	5.000	0.544	0.350	17.1	14.9	3.31	1.78	1.51	4.68	1.87	1.00
ST 5 × 17.5	5.15	5.00	4.944	0.491	0.594	8.42	12.5	3.63	1.56	1.56	4.18	1.69	0.901
× 12.7	3.73	5.00	4.661	0.491	0.311	16.1	7.83	2.06	1.45	1.20	3.39	1.46	0.954
ST 4 × 11.5	3.38	4.00	4.171	0.425	0.441	9.07	5.03	1.77	1.22	1.15	2.15	1.03	0.798
× 9.2	2.70	4.00	4.001	0.425	0.271	14.8	3.51	1.15	1.14	0.941	1.86	0.932	0.831
ST 3.5 × 10	2.94	3.50	3.860	0.392	0.450	7.78	3.36	1.36	1.07	1.04	1.59	0.821	0.734
× 7.65	2.25	3.50	3.662	0.392	0.252	13.9	2.19	0.816	0.987	0.817	1.32	0.720	0.766
ST 3 × 8.625	2.53	3.00	3.565	0.359	0.465	6.45	2.13	1.02	0.917	0.914	1.15	0.648	0.675
× 6.25	1.83	3.00	3.332	0.359	0.232	12.9	1.27	0.552	0.833	0.691	0.911	0.547	0.705
ST 2.5 × 7.375	2.17	2.50	3.284	0.326	0.494	5.06	1.27	0.740	0.764	0.789	0.833	0.507	0.620
' × 5	1.47	2.50	3.004	0.326	0.214	11.7	0.681	0.353	0.681	0.569	0.608	0.405	0.643
ST 2 × 4.75	1.40	2.00	2.796	0.293	0.326	6.13	0.470	0.325	0.580	0.553	0.451	0.323	0.569
× 3.85	1.13	2.00	2.663	0.293	0.193	10.4	0.316	0.203	0.528	0.448	0.382	0.287	0.581
ST 1.5 × 3.75	1.10	1.50	2.509	0.260	0.349	4.30	0.204	0.191	0.430	0.432	0.293	0.234	0.516
× 2.85	0.835	1.50	2.330	0.260	0.170	8.82	0.118	0.101	0.376	0.329	0.227	0.195	0.522

STRUCTURAL TEES
Cut from S shapes
Properties of sections limited by width-thickness ratios

Per AISC Specification, Sect. 1.9.1

Designation	$C_c' = \sqrt{\dfrac{2\pi^2 E}{Q_s Q_a F_y}}$ where $Q_a = 1.0$			
	$F_y = 36$ ksi		$F_y = 50$ ksi	
	Q_s	C_c'	Q_s	C_c'
ST 12 × 60	—	—	—	—
× 52.95	—	—	0.937	111
ST 12 × 50	—	—	—	—
× 45	—	—	0.937	111
× 39.95	0.878	135	0.695	128
ST 10 × 47.5	—	—	—	—
× 42.5	—	—	—	—
ST 10 × 37.5	—	—	—	—
× 32.7	—	—	0.897	113
ST 9 × 35	—	—	—	—
× 27.35	—	—	0.922	111
ST 7.5 × 25	—	—	—	—
× 21.45	—	—	0.988	108
ST 6 × 25	—	—	—	—
× 20.4	—	—	—	—
ST 6 × 17.5	—	—	—	—
× 15.9	—	—	—	—
ST 5 × 17.5	—	—	—	—
× 12.7	—	—	—	—
ST 4 × 11.5	—	—	—	—
× 9.2	—	—	—	—
ST 3.5 × 10	—	—	—	—
× 7.65	—	—	—	—
ST 3 × 8.625	—	—	—	—
× 6.25	—	—	—	—
ST 2.5 × 7.375	—	—	—	—
× 5	—	—	—	—
ST 2 × 4.75	—	—	—	—
× 3.85	—	—	—	—
ST 1.5 × 3.75	—	—	—	—
× 2.85	—	—	—	—

NOTE: Where no value of C_c' or Q_s is shown, the Tee complies with Specification Sect. 1.9.1.2 and may be considered fully effective.

Notes

STEEL PIPE AND STRUCTURAL TUBING
Dimensions and properties

GENERAL

When designing and specifying steel pipe or tubing for structural use, refer to comments in the notes for Columns, Steel Pipe and Structural Tubing, page 3 - 37.

STEEL PIPE

The tables of dimensions and properties of steel pipe (unfilled) list a selected range of diameters of Standard, Extra Strong, and Double-Extra Strong pipe ranging from $\frac{1}{2}$ in. diameter up to 12 in. diameter as available in ASTM A501, F_y = 36 ksi, and ASTM A53, Types E or S, Grade B, F_y = 35 ksi.

STRUCTURAL TUBING

The tables of dimensions and properties of square and rectangular structural tubing (unfilled) do not cover the complete range of sizes manufactured. The sizes listed have been selected as those that will most frequently be used as structural members. For dimensions and properties of other sizes refer to manufacturers' catalogs.

Structural tubing is available in ASTM A501, F_y = 36 ksi; ASTM A500, Grade B, F_y = 46 ksi; and ASTM A618, F_y = 50 ksi.

PIPE
Dimensions and properties

Nominal Diameter In.	Outside Diameter In.	Inside Diameter In.	Wall Thickness In.	Weight per Foot Lbs. Plain Ends	A In.^{2}	I In.^{4}	S In.^{3}	r In.
	Dimension				Properties			

Standard Weight

Nominal Diameter In.	Outside Diameter In.	Inside Diameter In.	Wall Thickness In.	Weight per Foot Lbs. Plain Ends	A In.^{2}	I In.^{4}	S In.^{3}	r In.
½	.840	.622	.109	.85	.250	.017	.041	.261
¾	1.050	.824	.113	1.13	.333	.037	.071	.334
1	1.315	1.049	.133	1.68	.494	.087	.133	.421
1¼	1.660	1.380	.140	2.27	.669	.195	.235	.540
1½	1.900	1.610	.145	2.72	.799	.310	.326	.623
2	2.375	2.067	.154	3.65	1.07	.666	.561	.787
2½	2.875	2.469	.203	5.79	1.70	1.53	1.06	.947
3	3.500	3.068	.216	7.58	2.23	3.02	1.72	1.16
3½	4.000	3.548	.226	9.11	2.68	4.79	2.39	1.34
4	4.500	4.026	.237	10.79	3.17	7.23	3.21	1.51
5	5.563	5.047	.258	14.62	4.30	15.2	5.45	1.88
6	6.625	6.065	.280	18.97	5.58	28.1	8.50	2.25
8	8.625	7.981	.322	28.55	8.40	72.5	16.8	2.94
10	10.750	10.020	.365	40.48	11.9	161	29.9	3.67
12	12.750	12.000	.375	49.56	14.6	279	43.8	4.38

Extra Strong

Nominal Diameter In.	Outside Diameter In.	Inside Diameter In.	Wall Thickness In.	Weight per Foot Lbs. Plain Ends	A In.^{2}	I In.^{4}	S In.^{3}	r In.
½	.840	.546	.147	1.09	.320	.020	.048	.250
¾	1.050	.742	.154	1.47	.433	.045	.085	.321
1	1.315	.957	.179	2.17	.639	.106	.161	.407
1¼	1.660	1.278	.191	3.00	.881	.242	.291	.524
1½	1.900	1.500	.200	3.63	1.07	.391	.412	.605
2	2.375	1.939	.218	5.02	1.48	.868	.731	.766
2½	2.875	2.323	.276	7.66	2.25	1.92	1.34	.924
3	3.500	2.900	.300	10.25	3.02	3.89	2.23	1.14
3½	4.000	3.364	.318	12.50	3.68	6.28	3.14	1.31
4	4.500	3.826	.337	14.98	4.41	9.61	4.27	1.48
5	5.563	4.813	.375	20.78	6.11	20.7	7.43	1.84
6	6.625	5.761	.432	28.57	8.40	40.5	12.2	2.19
8	8.625	7.625	.500	43.39	12.8	106	24.5	2.88
10	10.750	9.750	.500	54.74	16.1	212	39.4	3.63
12	12.750	11.750	.500	65.42	19.2	362	56.7	4.33

Double-Extra Strong

Nominal Diameter In.	Outside Diameter In.	Inside Diameter In.	Wall Thickness In.	Weight per Foot Lbs. Plain Ends	A In.^{2}	I In.^{4}	S In.^{3}	r In.
2	2.375	1.503	.436	9.03	2.66	1.31	1.10	.703
2½	2.875	1.771	.552	13.69	4.03	2.87	2.00	.844
3	3.500	2.300	.600	18.58	5.47	5.99	3.42	1.05
4	4.500	3.152	.674	27.54	8.10	15.3	6.79	1.37
5	5.563	4.063	.750	38.55	11.3	33.6	12.1	1.72
6	6.625	4.897	.864	53.16	15.6	66.3	20.0	2.06
8	8.625	6.875	.875	72.42	21.3	162	37.6	2.76

The listed sections are available in conformance with ASTM Specification A53 Grade B or A501. Other sections are made to these specifications. Consult with pipe manufacturers or distributors for availability.

AMERICAN INSTITUTE OF STEEL CONSTRUCTION

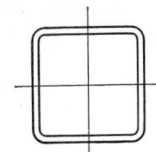

STRUCTURAL TUBING
Square
Dimensions and properties

	DIMENSIONS			PROPERTIES			
Nominal* Size	Wall Thickness		Weight per Foot	Area	I	S	r
In.	In.		Lb.	In.²	In.⁴	In.³	In.
10 × 10	.6250	⅝	73.98	21.8	304.	60.7	3.74
	.5000	½	60.95	17.9	260.	52.0	3.81
	.3750	⅜	47.03	13.8	208.	41.7	3.88
	.3125	⁵⁄₁₆	‡39.74	11.7	179.	35.8	3.92
	.2500	¼	†32.23	9.48	148.	29.6	3.95
	.1875	³⁄₁₆	†24.50	7.21	114.	22.9	3.98
8 × 8	.6250	⅝	56.98	16.8	142.	35.5	2.91
	.5000	½	47.35	13.9	124.	31.1	2.99
	.3750	⅜	36.83	10.8	102.	25.4	3.06
	.3125	⁵⁄₁₆	31.24	9.19	88.1	22.0	3.10
	.2500	¼	‡25.44	7.48	73.4	18.4	3.13
	.1875	³⁄₁₆	†19.41	5.71	57.2	14.3	3.17
7 × 7	.5000	½	40.55	11.9	79.2	22.6	2.58
	.3750	⅜	31.73	9.33	65.6	18.8	2.65
	.3125	⁵⁄₁₆	26.99	7.94	57.4	16.4	2.69
	.2500	¼	22.04	6.48	48.1	13.7	2.72
	.1875	³⁄₁₆	†16.85	4.96	37.7	10.8	2.76
6 × 6	.5000	½	34.48	10.1	48.6	16.2	2.19
	.3750	⅜	27.04	7.95	40.5	13.5	2.26
	.3125	⁵⁄₁₆	23.02	6.77	35.5	11.8	2.29
	.2500	¼	18.82	5.54	29.9	9.95	2.32
	.1875	³⁄₁₆	‡14.41	4.24	23.5	7.83	2.35
5 × 5	.5000	½	27.68	8.14	25.7	10.3	1.78
	.3750	⅜	21.94	6.45	22.0	8.80	1.85
	.3125	⁵⁄₁₆	18.77	5.52	19.5	7.81	1.88
	.2500	¼	15.42	4.54	16.6	6.64	1.91
	.1875	³⁄₁₆	11.86	3.49	13.2	5.28	1.95
4 × 4	.5000	½	20.88	6.14	11.4	5.70	1.36
	.3750	⅜	16.84	4.95	10.2	5.10	1.44
	.3125	⁵⁄₁₆	14.52	4.27	9.23	4.61	1.47
	.2500	¼	12.02	3.54	8.00	4.00	1.50
	.1875	³⁄₁₆	9.31	2.74	6.47	3.24	1.54
3½ × 3½	.2500	¼	10.50	3.09	5.29	3.02	1.31
	.1875	³⁄₁₆	8.14	2.39	4.29	2.45	1.34
3 × 3	.2500	¼	8.80	2.59	3.16	2.10	1.10
	.1875	³⁄₁₆	6.86	2.02	2.60	1.73	1.13
2 × 2	.2500	¼	5.40	1.59	.766	.766	.694
	.1875	³⁄₁₆	4.31	1.27	.668	.668	.726

* Outside dimensions across flat sides.
† Non-compact section for $F_y = 36$ ksi and $F_y = 46$ ksi, bending only.
‡ Non-compact section for $F_y = 46$ ksi, bending only.
Sections subjected to axial compression or compression due to bending should be checked for compliance with Specification Sect. 1.9.2.2.

STRUCTURAL TUBING
Rectangular
Dimensions and properties

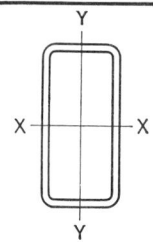

	DIMENSIONS				PROPERTIES					
Nominal* Size	Wall Thickness		Weight per Foot	Area	X - X AXIS			Y - Y AXIS		
					I_x	S_x	r_x	I_y	S_y	r_y
In.	In.		Lb.	In.²	In.⁴	In.³	In.	In.⁴	In.³	In.
12 × 8	.5000	½	60.95	17.9	337.	56.2	4.34	181.	45.2	3.18
	.3750	⅜	47.03	13.8	270.	45.0	4.42	145.	36.3	3.24
	.3125	�5⁄16	39.74	11.7	232.	38.7	4.46	125.	31.3	3.27
	.2500	¼	‡32.23	9.48	192.	32.0	4.50	103.	25.9	3.30
	.1875	³⁄16	†24.50	7.21	148.	24.7	4.54	80.1	20.0	3.33
12 × 6	.5000	½	54.15	15.9	271.	45.2	4.13	92.0	30.7	2.40
	.3750	⅜	41.93	12.3	220.	36.6	4.22	75.0	25.0	2.47
	.3125	�5⁄16	35.49	10.4	190.	31.6	4.26	65.1	21.7	2.50
	.2500	¼	28.83	8.48	157.	26.2	4.31	54.2	18.1	2.53
	.1875	³⁄16	‡21.96	6.46	122.	20.4	4.35	42.2	14.1	2.56
12 × 4	.5000	½	47.35	13.9	205.	34.2	3.84	35.2	17.6	1.59
	.3750	⅜	36.83	10.8	169.	28.1	3.95	29.5	14.7	1.65
	.3125	�5⁄16	31.24	9.19	147.	24.5	4.00	25.9	13.0	1.68
	.2500	¼	25.44	7.48	123.	20.5	4.05	21.9	10.9	1.71
	.1875	³⁄16	‡19.41	5.71	96.0	16.0	4.10	17.3	8.63	1.74
12 × 2	.3750	⅜	31.73	9.33	118.	19.7	3.56	5.62	5.62	.776
	.3125	�5⁄16	26.99	7.94	104.	17.4	3.62	5.14	5.14	.805
	.2500	¼	22.04	6.48	88.3	14.7	3.69	4.51	4.51	.834
	.1875	³⁄16	‡16.85	4.96	69.8	11.6	3.75	3.70	3.70	.863
10 × 8	.5000	½	54.15	15.9	215.	43.0	3.67	153.	38.1	3.10
	.3750	⅜	41.93	12.3	174.	34.7	3.75	123.	30.8	3.16
	.3125	�5⁄16	35.49	10.4	150.	30.0	3.79	107.	26.7	3.20
	.2500	¼	‡28.83	8.48	124.	24.8	3.83	88.4	22.1	3.23
	.1875	³⁄16	†21.96	6.46	96.3	19.3	3.86	68.7	17.2	3.26
10 × 6	.5000	½	47.35	13.9	170.	34.0	3.49	76.9	25.6	2.35
	.3750	⅜	36.83	10.8	139.	27.8	3.58	63.1	21.0	2.41
	.3125	�5⁄16	31.24	9.19	120.	24.1	3.62	55.0	18.3	2.45
	.2500	¼	25.44	7.48	100.	20.1	3.66	45.9	15.3	2.48
	.1875	³⁄16	‡19.41	5.71	78.3	15.7	3.70	35.9	12.0	2.51

* Outside dimensions across flat sides.

† Non-compact section for $F_y = 36$ ksi and $F_y = 46$ ksi, when bending occurs about X - X axis.

‡ Non-compact section for $F_y = 46$ ksi, when bending occurs about X - X axis.

Shapes subjected to combined axial load and bending may not be compact under Specification Sect. 1.5.1.4.1. Check all shapes for compliance with this section.

Shapes subjected to axial compression or compression due to bending should be checked for compliance with Specification Sect. 1.9.2.2.

Shapes subjected to bending about the Y - Y axis may not be compact under Specification Sect. 1.5.1.4.1.

AMERICAN INSTITUTE OF STEEL CONSTRUCTION

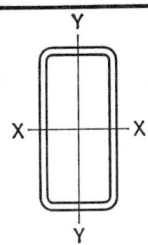

STRUCTURAL TUBING
Rectangular
Dimensions and properties

	DIMENSIONS				PROPERTIES					
					X - X AXIS			Y - Y AXIS		
Nominal* Size	Wall Thickness		Weight per Foot	Area	I_x	S_x	r_x	I_y	S_y	r_y
In.	In.		Lb.	In.²	In.⁴	In.³	In.	In.⁴	In.³	In.
10 × 4	.5000	½	40.55	11.9	125.	24.9	3.23	29.0	14.5	1.56
	.3750	⅜	31.73	9.33	104.	20.8	3.34	24.5	12.3	1.62
	.3125	⁵⁄₁₆	26.99	7.94	91.2	18.2	3.39	21.7	10.8	1.65
	.2500	¼	22.04	6.48	76.6	15.3	3.44	18.3	9.17	1.68
	.1875	³⁄₁₆	16.85	4.96	60.2	12.0	3.48	14.5	7.26	1.71
10 × 2	.3750	⅜	27.04	7.95	72.4	14.5	3.02	4.74	4.74	.772
	.3125	⁵⁄₁₆	23.02	6.77	64.0	12.8	3.07	4.33	4.33	.800
	.2500	¼	18.82	5.54	54.2	10.8	3.13	3.80	3.80	.828
	.1875	³⁄₁₆	14.41	4.24	42.9	8.58	3.18	3.11	3.11	.857
8 × 6	.5000	½	40.55	11.9	96.2	24.1	2.84	61.7	20.6	2.27
	.3750	⅜	31.73	9.33	79.7	19.9	2.92	51.2	17.1	2.34
	.3125	⁵⁄₁₆	26.99	7.94	69.7	17.4	2.96	44.8	14.9	2.38
	.2500	¼	22.04	6.48	58.4	14.6	3.00	37.6	12.5	2.41
	.1875	³⁄₁₆	‡16.85	4.96	45.8	11.4	3.04	29.6	9.85	2.44
8 × 4	.5000	½	34.48	10.1	71.6	17.9	2.66	23.7	11.9	1.53
	.3750	⅜	27.04	7.95	59.9	15.0	2.74	20.1	10.0	1.59
	.3125	⁵⁄₁₆	23.02	6.77	52.6	13.1	2.79	17.7	8.87	1.62
	.2500	¼	18.82	5.54	44.2	11.1	2.83	15.0	7.52	1.65
	.1875	³⁄₁₆	14.41	4.24	34.8	8.71	2.87	11.9	5.96	1.68
8 × 3	.5000	½	31.08	9.14	57.6	14.4	2.51	11.6	7.74	1.13
	.3750	⅜	24.49	7.20	49.0	12.3	2.61	10.1	6.74	1.18
	.3125	⁵⁄₁₆	20.90	6.15	43.3	10.8	2.65	9.05	6.04	1.21
	.2500	¼	17.12	5.04	36.7	9.18	2.70	7.77	5.18	1.24
	.1875	³⁄₁₆	13.13	3.86	29.1	7.28	2.74	6.24	4.16	1.27
8 × 2	.3750	⅜	21.94	6.45	38.1	9.52	2.43	3.73	3.73	.760
	.3125	⁵⁄₁₆	18.77	5.52	34.1	8.52	2.48	3.43	3.43	.788
	.2500	¼	15.42	4.54	29.2	7.31	2.54	3.03	3.03	.817
	.1875	³⁄₁₆	11.86	3.49	23.4	5.85	2.59	2.49	2.49	.845
7 × 5	.5000	½	34.48	10.1	60.8	17.4	2.45	35.9	14.3	1.88
	.3750	⅜	27.04	7.95	50.7	14.5	2.52	30.0	12.0	1.94
	.3125	⁵⁄₁₆	23.02	6.77	44.4	12.7	2.56	26.4	10.6	1.97
	.2500	¼	18.82	5.54	37.4	10.7	2.60	22.3	8.90	2.00
	.1875	³⁄₁₆	14.41	4.24	29.4	8.40	2.63	17.6	7.02	2.04

* Outside dimensions across flat sides.

‡ Non-compact section for $F_y = 46$ ksi, when bending occurs about X - X axis.

Shapes subjected to combined axial load and bending may not be compact under Specification Sect. 1.5.1.4.1. Check all shapes for compliance with this section.

Shapes subjected to axial compression or compression due to bending should be checked for compliance with Specification Sect. 1.9.2.2.

Shapes subjected to bending about the Y - Y axis may not be compact under Specification Sect. 1.5.1.4.1.

AMERICAN INSTITUTE OF STEEL CONSTRUCTION

STRUCTURAL TUBING
Rectangular
Dimensions and properties

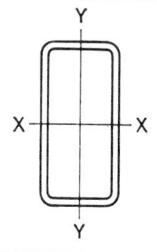

Nominal* Size	Wall Thickness		Weight per Foot	Area	X - X AXIS			Y - Y AXIS		
					I_x	S_x	r_x	I_y	S_y	r_y
In.	In.		Lb.	In.²	In.⁴	In.³	In.	In.⁴	In.³	In.
6 × 4	.5000	½	27.68	8.14	33.4	11.1	2.02	17.6	8.79	1.47
	.3750	⅜	21.94	6.45	28.6	9.54	2.11	15.2	7.58	1.53
	.3125	⁵⁄₁₆	18.77	5.52	25.4	8.46	2.14	13.5	6.74	1.56
	.2500	¼	15.42	4.54	21.6	7.19	2.18	11.5	5.76	1.59
	.1875	³⁄₁₆	11.86	3.49	17.2	5.72	2.22	9.20	4.60	1.62
6 × 3	.5000	½	24.28	7.14	25.8	8.60	1.90	8.44	5.63	1.09
	.3750	⅜	19.39	5.70	22.7	7.56	1.99	7.51	5.01	1.15
	.3125	⁵⁄₁₆	16.65	4.90	20.3	6.77	2.04	6.79	4.52	1.18
	.2500	¼	13.72	4.04	17.4	5.82	2.08	5.88	3.92	1.21
	.1875	³⁄₁₆	10.58	3.11	14.0	4.66	2.12	4.76	3.17	1.24
6 × 2	.3750	⅜	16.84	4.95	16.7	5.57	1.84	2.72	2.72	.741
	.3125	⁵⁄₁₆	14.52	4.27	15.3	5.08	1.89	2.53	2.53	.770
	.2500	¼	12.02	3.54	13.3	4.44	1.94	2.25	2.25	.799
	.1875	³⁄₁₆	9.31	2.74	10.8	3.61	1.99	1.87	1.87	.827
5 × 3	.5000	½	20.88	6.14	15.5	6.21	1.59	6.86	4.57	1.06
	.3750	⅜	16.84	4.95	14.0	5.58	1.68	6.21	4.14	1.12
	.3125	⁵⁄₁₆	14.52	4.27	12.6	5.06	1.72	5.65	3.77	1.15
	.2500	¼	12.02	3.54	11.0	4.38	1.76	4.93	3.29	1.18
	.1875	³⁄₁₆	9.31	2.74	8.87	3.55	1.80	4.02	2.68	1.21
5 × 2	.2500	¼	10.50	3.09	8.48	3.39	1.66	1.92	1.92	.789
	.1875	³⁄₁₆	8.14	2.39	6.89	2.75	1.70	1.60	1.60	.816
4 × 3	.2500	¼	10.50	3.09	6.45	3.23	1.45	4.10	2.74	1.15
	.1875	³⁄₁₆	8.14	2.39	5.23	2.62	1.48	3.34	2.23	1.18
4 × 2	.2500	¼	8.80	2.59	4.69	2.35	1.35	1.54	1.54	.770
	.1875	³⁄₁₆	6.86	2.02	3.87	1.93	1.38	1.29	1.29	.798
3 × 2	.2500	¼	7.10	2.09	2.21	1.47	1.03	1.15	1.15	.742
	.1875	³⁄₁₆	5.59	1.64	1.86	1.24	1.06	.977	.977	.771

* Outside dimensions across flat sides.

Shapes subjected to combined axial load and bending may not be compact under Specification Sect. 1.5.1.4.1. Check all shapes for compliance with this section.

Shapes subjected to axial compression or compression due to bending should be checked for compliance with Specification Sect. 1.9.2.2.

Shapes subjected to bending about the Y - Y axis may not be compact under Specification Sect. 1.5.1.4.1.

AMERICAN INSTITUTE OF STEEL CONSTRUCTION

Notes

BARS AND PLATES
Product availability

Plates and bars are readily available in eight of the structural steel specifications listed in Section 1.4.1 of the AISC Specification. These are ASTM A36, A242, A440, A441, A529, A572, A588, and A514. Table 1, page 1 - 6 shows the availability of each steel in terms of plate thickness. The Manual user is referred to the discussion on Selection of the Appropriate Structural Steel, page 1 - 3, for guidance in selection of both plate and structural shapes. For additional information designers should consult the steel producers.

The Summary of ASTM Specifications in Part 5 of this Manual lists the scope and principal tensile properties of each of these eight structural steels. For complete information, refer to the appropriate specification.

CLASSIFICATION

Bars and plates are generally classified as follows:

Bars: 6 in. or less in width, .203 in. and over in thickness.

        6 in. to 8 in. in width, .230 in. and over in thickness.

Plates: Over 8 in. in width, .230 in. and over in thickness.

        Over 48 in. in width, .180 in. and over in thickness.

For complete classification, see bottom of page 6 - 3.

BARS

Bars are available from many mills in varying widths and in all necessary thicknesses and lengths. Specifying widths in $\frac{1}{4}$ in. and thicknesses in $\frac{1}{8}$ in. increments is the preferred practice.

PLATES

Defined according to rolling procedure:

Sheared plates are rolled between horizontal rolls and trimmed (sheared or gas cut) on all edges.

Universal (UM) plates are rolled between horizontal and vertical rolls and trimmed (sheared or gas cut) on ends only.

Sizes

Plate mills are located in various districts, but the sizes of plates produced differ greatly and the catalogs of individual mills should be consulted for detail data. The extreme width of UM plates currently rolled is 60 in. and for sheared plates it is 200 in., but their availability together with limiting thicknesses and lengths should be checked with the mills before specifying. The preferred increments for width and thickness are:

Widths: Vary by even inches, though smaller increments are obtainable.

Thickness: $\frac{1}{32}$ in. increments up to $\frac{1}{2}$ in.

            $\frac{1}{16}$ in. increments over $\frac{1}{2}$ to 2 in.

            $\frac{1}{8}$ in. increments over 2 in. to 6 in.

            $\frac{1}{4}$ in. increments over 6 in.

Ordering

Plate thickness may be specified in inches or by weight per square foot, but no decimal edge thickness can be assured by latter method. Separate tolerance tables apply to each method.

"Sketch" plates (i.e., plates whose dimensions and cuts are detailed), exclusive of those with re-entrant cuts, can be supplied by most mills by shearing or gas cutting, depending on thickness.

"Full circles" are also available, either by shearing up to 1 in. thickness, or by gas cutting for heavier gages.

Invoicing

Standard practice is to invoice plates to the fabricator at theoretical weight at point of shipment. Permissible variations in weight are limited in accordance with the tables of allowances in the standard specification ASTM Designation A6.

All sketch plates, including circles, are invoiced at theoretical weight and, except as noted, are subject to the same weight variations as apply to rectangular plates. Odd shapes in most instances require gas cutting, for which gas cutting extras are applicable.

All plates ordered gas cut for whatever reason, or beyond published shearing limits, take extras for gas cutting in addition to all other extras. Rolled steel bearing plates are often gas cut to prevent distortion due to shearing but would also take the regular extra for the thickness involved.

Extras for thickness, width, length, cutting, quality and quantity, etc., which are added to the base price of plates, are subject to revision, and should be obtained by inquiry of the producer. The foregoing general statements are made as a guide toward economy in design.

FLOOR PLATES

Skid resistant raised pattern plates are available from several mills, each offering their own style of surface projections and in a variety of widths, thicknesses and lengths. The maximum combination of width and length is 96 in. and 50 feet, with a corresponding thickness of $\frac{7}{8}$ in. A maximum thickness of 2 in. is available, but matching widths and lengths should be checked with the producer. Floor plates are generally not specified to chemical composition limits or mechanical property requirements; a commercial grade of carbon steel is furnished. However, when strength or corrosion resistance is a consideration, raised pattern floor plates are procurable in any of the regular steel specifications. As in the case of plain plates, the individual manufacturers should be consulted for precise information. The nominal or ordered thickness is that of the flat plate, exclusive of the height of raised pattern. The usual weights are as follows:

Nominal Thickness, Inches	$\frac{1}{8}$	$\frac{3}{16}$	$\frac{1}{4}$	$\frac{5}{16}$	$\frac{3}{8}$	$\frac{7}{16}$	$\frac{1}{2}$	$\frac{9}{16}$	$\frac{5}{8}$	$\frac{3}{4}$	$\frac{7}{8}$	1
Theoretical Weight, Lb. per Sq. Ft.	6.15	8.70	11.25	13.80	16.35	18.90	21.45	24.00	26.55	31.65	36.75	41.85

SQUARE AND ROUND BARS
Weight and area

Size Inches	Weight Lb. per Foot ■	●	Area Square Inches ▨	◎	Size Inches	Weight Lb. per Foot ■	●	Area Square Inches ▨	◎
0					3	30.60	24.03	9.000	7.069
1/16	.013	.010	.0039	.0031	1/16	31.89	25.05	9.379	7.366
1/8	.053	.042	.0156	.0123	1/8	33.20	26.08	9.766	7.670
3/16	.120	.094	.0352	.0276	3/16	34.54	27.13	10.160	7.980
1/4	.213	.167	.0625	.0491	1/4	35.91	28.21	10.563	8.296
5/16	.332	.261	.0977	.0767	5/16	37.31	29.30	10.973	8.618
3/8	.478	.376	.1406	.1105	3/8	38.73	30.42	11.391	8.946
7/16	.651	.511	.1914	.1503	7/16	40.18	31.55	11.816	9.281
1/2	.850	.668	.2500	.1963	1/2	41.65	32.71	12.250	9.621
9/16	1.076	.845	.3164	.2485	9/16	43.15	33.89	12.691	9.968
5/8	1.328	1.043	.3906	.3068	5/8	44.68	35.09	13.141	10.321
11/16	1.607	1.262	.4727	.3712	11/16	46.23	36.31	13.598	10.680
3/4	1.913	1.502	.5625	.4418	3/4	47.81	37.55	14.063	11.045
13/16	2.245	1.763	.6602	.5185	13/16	49.42	38.81	14.535	11.416
7/8	2.603	2.044	.7656	.6013	7/8	51.05	40.10	15.016	11.793
15/16	2.988	2.347	.8789	.6903	15/16	52.71	41.40	15.504	12.177
1	3.400	2.670	1.0000	.7854	4	54.40	42.73	16.000	12.566
1/16	3.838	3.015	1.1289	.8866	1/16	56.11	44.07	16.504	12.962
1/8	4.303	3.380	1.2656	.9940	1/8	57.85	45.44	17.016	13.364
3/16	4.795	3.766	1.4102	1.1075	3/16	59.62	46.83	17.535	13.772
1/4	5.313	4.172	1.5625	1.2272	1/4	61.41	48.23	18.063	14.186
5/16	5.857	4.600	1.7227	1.3530	5/16	63.23	49.66	18.598	14.607
3/8	6.428	5.049	1.8906	1.4849	3/8	65.08	51.11	19.141	15.033
7/16	7.026	5.518	2.0664	1.6230	7/16	66.95	52.58	19.691	15.466
1/2	7.650	6.008	2.2500	1.7671	1/2	68.85	54.07	20.250	15.904
9/16	8.301	6.519	2.4414	1.9175	9/16	70.78	55.59	20.816	16.349
5/8	8.978	7.051	2.6406	2.0739	5/8	72.73	57.12	21.391	16.800
11/16	9.682	7.604	2.8477	2.2365	11/16	74.71	58.67	21.973	17.257
3/4	10.413	8.178	3.0625	2.4053	3/4	76.71	60.25	22.563	17.721
13/16	11.170	8.773	3.2852	2.5802	13/16	78.74	61.85	23.160	18.190
7/8	11.953	9.388	3.5156	2.7612	7/8	80.80	63.46	23.766	18.665
15/16	12.763	10.024	3.7539	2.9483	15/16	82.89	65.10	24.379	19.147
2	13.600	10.681	4.0000	3.1416	5	85.00	66.76	25.000	19.635
1/16	14.463	11.359	4.2539	3.3410	1/16	87.14	68.44	25.629	20.129
1/8	15.353	12.058	4.5156	3.5466	1/8	89.30	70.14	26.266	20.629
3/16	16.270	12.778	4.7852	3.7583	3/16	91.49	71.86	26.910	21.135
1/4	17.213	13.519	5.0625	3.9761	1/4	93.71	73.60	27.563	21.648
5/16	18.182	14.280	5.3477	4.2000	5/16	95.96	75.36	28.223	22.166
3/8	19.178	15.062	5.6406	4.4301	3/8	98.23	77.15	28.891	22.691
7/16	20.201	15.866	5.9414	4.6664	7/16	100.53	78.95	29.566	23.221
1/2	21.250	16.690	6.2500	4.9087	1/2	102.85	80.78	30.250	23.758
9/16	22.326	17.534	6.5664	5.1572	9/16	105.20	82.62	30.941	24.301
5/8	23.428	18.400	6.8906	5.4119	5/8	107.58	84.49	31.641	24.850
11/16	24.557	19.287	7.2227	5.6727	11/16	109.98	86.38	32.348	25.406
3/4	25.713	20.195	7.5625	5.9396	3/4	112.41	88.29	33.063	25.967
13/16	26.895	21.123	7.9102	6.2126	13/16	114.87	90.22	33.785	26.535
7/8	28.103	22.072	8.2656	6.4918	7/8	117.35	92.17	34.516	27.109
15/16	29.338	23.042	8.6289	6.7771	15/16	119.86	94.14	35.254	27.688
3	30.600	24.033	9.0000	7.0686	6	122.40	96.13	36.000	28.274

SQUARE AND ROUND BARS
Weight and area

Size Inches	Weight Lb. per Foot ■	Weight Lb. per Foot ●	Area Square Inches ▨	Area Square Inches ◎	Size Inches	Weight Lb. per Foot ■	Weight Lb. per Foot ●	Area Square Inches ▨	Area Square Inches ◎
6	122.40	96.13	36.000	28.274	9	275.40	216.30	81.000	63.617
1/16	124.96	98.15	36.754	28.866	1/16	279.24	219.31	82.129	64.504
1/8	127.55	100.18	37.516	29.465	1/8	283.10	222.35	83.266	65.397
3/16	130.17	102.23	38.285	30.069	3/16	286.99	225.41	84.410	66.296
1/4	132.81	104.31	39.063	30.680	1/4	290.91	228.48	85.563	67.201
5/16	135.48	106.41	39.848	31.296	5/16	294.86	231.58	86.723	68.112
3/8	138.18	108.53	40.641	31.919	3/8	298.83	234.70	87.891	69.029
7/16	140.90	110.66	41.441	32.548	7/16	302.83	237.84	89.066	69.953
1/2	143.65	112.82	42.250	33.183	1/2	306.85	241.00	90.250	70.882
9/16	146.43	115.00	43.066	33.824	9/16	310.90	244.18	91.441	71.818
5/8	149.23	117.20	43.891	34.472	5/8	314.98	247.38	92.641	72.760
11/16	152.06	119.43	44.723	35.125	11/16	319.08	250.61	93.848	73.708
3/4	154.91	121.67	45.563	35.785	3/4	323.21	253.85	95.063	74.662
13/16	157.79	123.93	46.410	36.450	13/16	327.37	257.12	96.285	75.622
7/8	160.70	126.22	47.266	37.122	7/8	331.55	260.40	97.516	76.589
15/16	163.64	128.52	48.129	37.800	15/16	335.76	263.71	98.754	77.561
7	166.60	130.85	49.000	38.485	10	340.00	267.04	100.000	78.540
1/16	169.59	133.19	49.879	39.175	1/16	344.26	270.38	101.254	79.525
1/8	172.60	135.56	50.766	39.871	1/8	348.55	273.75	102.516	80.516
3/16	175.64	137.95	51.660	40.574	3/16	352.87	277.14	103.785	81.513
1/4	178.71	140.36	52.563	41.282	1/4	357.21	280.55	105.063	82.516
5/16	181.81	142.79	53.473	41.997	5/16	361.58	283.99	106.348	83.525
3/8	184.93	145.24	54.391	42.718	3/8	365.98	287.44	107.641	84.541
7/16	188.07	147.71	55.316	43.445	7/16	370.40	290.91	108.941	85.563
1/2	191.25	150.21	56.250	44.179	1/2	374.85	294.41	110.250	86.590
9/16	194.45	152.72	57.191	44.918	9/16	379.33	297.92	111.566	87.624
5/8	197.68	155.26	58.141	45.664	5/8	383.83	301.46	112.891	88.664
11/16	200.93	157.81	59.098	46.415	11/16	388.36	305.02	114.223	89.710
3/4	204.21	160.39	60.063	47.173	3/4	392.91	308.59	115.563	90.763
13/16	207.52	162.99	61.035	47.937	13/16	397.49	312.19	116.910	91.821
7/8	210.85	165.60	62.016	48.707	7/8	402.10	315.81	118.266	92.886
15/16	214.21	168.24	63.004	49.483	15/16	406.74	319.45	119.629	93.957
8	217.60	170.90	64.000	50.265	11	411.40	323.11	121.000	95.033
1/16	221.01	173.58	65.004	51.054	1/16	416.09	326.80	122.379	96.116
1/8	224.45	176.29	66.016	51.849	1/8	420.80	330.50	123.766	97.205
3/16	227.92	179.01	67.035	52.649	3/16	425.54	334.22	125.160	98.301
1/4	231.41	181.75	68.063	53.456	1/4	430.31	337.97	126.563	99.402
5/16	234.93	184.52	69.098	54.269	5/16	435.11	341.73	127.973	100.510
3/8	238.48	187.30	70.141	55.088	3/8	439.93	345.52	129.391	101.623
7/16	242.05	190.11	71.191	55.914	7/16	444.78	349.33	130.816	102.743
1/2	245.65	192.93	72.250	56.745	1/2	449.65	353.16	132.250	103.869
9/16	249.28	195.78	73.316	57.583	9/16	454.55	357.00	133.691	105.001
5/8	252.93	198.65	74.391	58.426	5/8	459.48	360.87	135.141	106.139
11/16	256.61	201.54	75.473	59.276	11/16	464.43	364.76	136.598	107.284
3/4	260.31	204.45	76.563	60.132	3/4	469.41	368.68	138.063	108.434
13/16	264.04	207.38	77.660	60.994	13/16	474.42	372.61	139.535	109.591
7/8	267.80	210.33	78.766	61.863	7/8	479.45	376.56	141.016	110.754
15/16	271.59	213.31	79.879	62.737	15/16	484.51	380.54	142.504	111.923
9	275.40	216.30	81.000	63.617	12	489.60	384.53	144.000	113.098

AMERICAN INSTITUTE OF STEEL CONSTRUCTION

WEIGHT OF RECTANGULAR SECTIONS
Pounds per linear foot

Width In.	Thickness, Inches													
	3/16	1/4	5/16	3/8	7/16	1/2	9/16	5/8	11/16	3/4	13/16	7/8	15/16	1
1/4	.16	.21	.27	.32	.37	.43	.48	.53	.58	.64	.69	.74	.80	.85
1/2	.32	.43	.53	.64	.74	.85	.96	1.06	1.17	1.28	1.38	1.49	1.59	1.70
3/4	.48	.64	.80	.96	1.12	1.28	1.43	1.59	1.75	1.91	2.07	2.23	2.39	2.55
1	.64	.85	1.06	1.28	1.49	1.70	1.91	2.13	2.34	2.55	2.76	2.98	3.19	3.40
1 1/4	.80	1.06	1.33	1.59	1.86	2.13	2.39	2.66	2.92	3.19	3.45	3.72	3.98	4.25
1 1/2	.96	1.28	1.59	1.91	2.23	2.55	2.87	3.19	3.51	3.83	4.14	4.46	4.78	5.10
1 3/4	1.12	1.49	1.86	2.23	2.60	2.98	3.35	3.72	4.09	4.46	4.83	5.21	5.58	5.95
2	1.28	1.70	2.13	2.55	2.98	3.40	3.83	4.25	4.68	5.10	5.53	5.95	6.38	6.80
2 1/4	1.43	1.91	2.39	2.87	3.35	3.83	4.30	4.78	5.26	5.74	6.22	6.69	7.17	7.65
2 1/2	1.59	2.13	2.66	3.19	3.72	4.25	4.78	5.31	5.84	6.38	6.91	7.44	7.97	8.50
2 3/4	1.75	2.34	2.92	3.51	4.09	4.68	5.26	5.84	6.43	7.01	7.60	8.18	8.77	9.35
3	1.91	2.55	3.19	3.83	4.46	5.10	5.74	6.38	7.01	7.65	8.29	8.93	9.56	10.2
3 1/4	2.07	2.76	3.45	4.14	4.83	5.53	6.22	6.91	7.60	8.29	8.98	9.67	10.4	11.1
3 1/2	2.23	2.98	3.72	4.46	5.21	5.95	6.69	7.44	8.18	8.93	9.67	10.4	11.2	11.9
3 3/4	2.39	3.19	3.98	4.78	5.58	6.38	7.17	7.97	8.77	9.56	10.4	11.2	12.0	12.8
4	2.55	3.40	4.25	5.10	5.95	6.80	7.65	8.50	9.35	10.2	11.1	11.9	12.8	13.6
4 1/4	2.71	3.61	4.52	5.42	6.32	7.23	8.13	9.03	9.93	10.8	11.7	12.6	13.6	14.5
4 1/2	2.87	3.83	4.78	5.74	6.69	7.65	8.61	9.56	10.5	11.5	12.4	13.4	14.3	15.3
4 3/4	3.03	4.04	5.05	6.06	7.07	8.08	9.08	10.1	11.1	12.1	13.1	14.1	15.1	16.2
5	3.19	4.25	5.31	6.38	7.44	8.50	9.56	10.6	11.7	12.8	13.8	14.9	15.9	17.0
5 1/4	3.35	4.46	5.58	6.69	7.81	8.93	10.0	11.2	12.3	13.4	14.5	15.6	16.7	17.9
5 1/2	3.51	4.68	5.84	7.01	8.18	9.35	10.5	11.7	12.9	14.0	15.2	16.4	17.5	18.7
5 3/4	3.67	4.89	6.11	7.33	8.55	9.78	11.0	12.2	13.4	14.7	15.9	17.1	18.3	19.6
6	3.83	5.10	6.38	7.65	8.93	10.2	11.5	12.8	14.0	15.3	16.6	17.9	19.1	20.4
6 1/4	3.98	5.31	6.64	7.97	9.30	10.6	12.0	13.3	14.6	15.9	17.3	18.6	19.9	21.3
6 1/2	4.14	5.53	6.91	8.29	9.67	11.1	12.4	13.8	15.2	16.6	18.0	19.3	20.7	22.1
6 3/4	4.30	5.74	7.17	8.61	10.0	11.5	12.9	14.3	15.8	17.2	18.7	20.1	21.5	23.0
7	4.46	5.95	7.44	8.93	10.4	11.9	13.4	14.9	16.4	17.9	19.3	20.8	22.3	23.8
7 1/4	4.62	6.16	7.70	9.24	10.8	12.3	13.9	15.4	17.0	18.5	20.0	21.6	23.1	24.7
7 1/2	4.78	6.38	7.97	9.56	11.2	12.8	14.3	15.9	17.5	19.1	20.7	22.3	23.9	25.5
7 3/4	4.94	6.59	8.23	9.88	11.5	13.2	14.8	16.5	18.1	19.8	21.4	23.1	24.7	26.4
8	5.10	6.80	8.50	10.2	11.9	13.6	15.3	17.0	18.7	20.4	22.1	23.8	25.5	27.2
8 1/4	5.26	7.01	8.77	10.5	12.3	14.0	15.8	17.5	19.3	21.0	22.8	24.5	26.3	28.1
8 1/2	5.42	7.23	9.03	10.8	12.6	14.5	16.3	18.1	19.9	21.7	23.5	25.3	27.1	28.9
8 3/4	5.58	7.44	9.30	11.2	13.0	14.9	16.7	18.6	20.5	22.3	24.2	26.0	27.9	29.8
9	5.74	7.65	9.56	11.5	13.4	15.3	17.2	19.1	21.0	23.0	24.9	26.8	28.7	30.6
9 1/4	5.90	7.86	9.83	11.8	13.8	15.7	17.7	19.7	21.6	23.6	25.6	27.5	29.5	31.5
9 1/2	6.06	8.08	10.1	12.1	14.1	16.2	18.2	20.2	22.2	24.2	26.2	28.3	30.3	32.3
9 3/4	6.22	8.29	10.4	12.4	14.5	16.6	18.7	20.7	22.8	24.9	26.9	29.0	31.1	33.2
10	6.38	8.50	10.6	12.8	14.9	17.0	19.1	21.3	23.4	25.5	27.6	29.8	31.9	34.0

WEIGHT OF RECTANGULAR SECTIONS
Pounds per linear foot

Width In.	Thickness, Inches													
	$3/16$	$1/4$	$5/16$	$3/8$	$7/16$	$1/2$	$9/16$	$5/8$	$11/16$	$3/4$	$13/16$	$7/8$	$15/16$	1
$10\frac{1}{4}$	6.53	8.71	10.9	13.1	15.3	17.4	19.6	21.8	24.0	26.1	28.3	30.5	32.7	34.9
$10\frac{1}{2}$	6.69	8.93	11.2	13.4	15.6	17.9	20.1	22.3	24.5	26.8	29.0	31.2	33.5	35.7
$10\frac{3}{4}$	6.85	9.14	11.4	13.7	16.0	18.3	20.6	22.8	25.1	27.4	29.7	32.0	34.3	36.6
11	7.01	9.35	11.7	14.0	16.4	18.7	21.0	23.4	25.7	28.1	30.4	32.7	35.1	37.4
$11\frac{1}{4}$	7.17	9.55	12.0	14.3	16.7	19.1	21.5	23.9	26.3	28.7	31.1	33.5	35.9	38.3
$11\frac{1}{2}$	7.33	9.78	12.2	14.7	17.1	19.6	22.0	24.4	26.9	29.3	31.8	34.2	36.7	39.1
$11\frac{3}{4}$	7.49	9.99	12.5	15.0	17.5	20.0	22.5	25.0	27.5	30.0	32.5	35.0	37.5	40.0
12	7.65	10.2	12.8	15.3	17.9	20.4	23.0	25.5	28.1	30.6	33.2	35.7	38.3	40.8
$12\frac{1}{2}$	7.97	10.6	13.3	15.9	18.6	21.3	23.9	26.6	29.2	31.9	34.5	37.2	39.8	42.5
13	8.29	11.1	13.8	16.6	19.3	22.1	24.9	27.6	30.4	33.2	35.9	38.7	41.4	44.2
$13\frac{1}{2}$	8.61	11.5	14.3	17.2	20.1	23.0	25.8	28.7	31.6	34.4	37.3	40.2	43.0	45.9
14	8.93	11.9	14.9	17.9	20.8	23.8	26.8	29.8	32.7	35.7	38.7	41.7	44.6	47.6
$14\frac{1}{2}$	9.24	12.3	15.4	18.5	21.6	24.7	27.7	30.8	33.9	37.0	40.1	43.1	46.2	49.3
15	9.56	12.8	15.9	19.1	22.3	25.5	28.7	31.9	35.1	38.3	41.4	44.6	47.8	51.0
$15\frac{1}{2}$	9.88	13.2	16.5	19.8	23.1	26.4	29.6	32.9	36.2	39.5	42.8	46.1	49.4	52.7
16	10.2	13.6	17.0	20.4	23.8	27.2	30.6	34.0	37.4	40.8	44.2	47.6	51.0	54.4
$16\frac{1}{2}$	10.5	14.0	17.5	21.0	24.5	28.1	31.6	35.1	38.6	42.1	45.6	49.1	52.6	56.1
17	10.8	14.5	18.1	21.7	25.3	28.9	32.5	36.1	39.7	43.4	47.0	50.6	54.2	57.8
$17\frac{1}{2}$	11.2	14.9	18.6	22.3	26.0	29.8	33.5	37.2	40.9	44.6	48.3	52.1	55.8	59.5
18	11.5	15.3	19.1	23.0	26.8	30.6	34.4	38.3	42.1	45.9	49.7	53.6	57.4	61.2
$18\frac{1}{2}$	11.8	15.7	19.7	23.6	27.5	31.5	35.4	39.3	43.2	47.2	51.1	55.0	59.0	62.9
19	12.1	16.2	20.2	24.2	28.3	32.3	36.3	40.4	44.4	48.5	52.5	56.5	60.6	64.6
$19\frac{1}{2}$	12.4	16.6	20.7	24.9	29.0	33.2	37.3	41.4	45.6	49.7	53.9	58.0	62.2	66.3
20	12.8	17.0	21.3	25.5	29.8	34.0	38.3	42.5	46.8	51.0	55.3	59.5	63.8	68.0
$20\frac{1}{2}$	13.1	17.4	21.8	26.1	30.5	34.9	39.2	43.6	47.9	52.3	56.6	61.0	65.3	69.7
21	13.4	17.9	22.3	26.8	31.2	35.7	40.2	44.6	49.1	53.6	58.0	62.5	66.9	71.4
$21\frac{1}{2}$	13.7	18.3	22.8	27.4	32.0	36.6	41.1	45.7	50.3	54.8	59.4	64.0	68.5	73.1
22	14.0	18.7	23.4	28.1	32.7	37.4	42.1	46.8	51.4	56.1	60.8	65.5	70.1	74.8
$22\frac{1}{2}$	14.3	19.1	23.9	28.7	33.5	38.3	43.0	47.8	52.6	57.4	62.2	66.9	71.7	76.5
23	14.7	19.6	24.4	29.3	34.2	39.1	44.0	48.9	53.8	58.7	63.5	68.4	73.3	78.2
$23\frac{1}{2}$	15.0	20.0	25.0	30.0	35.0	40.0	44.9	49.9	54.9	59.9	64.9	69.9	74.9	79.9
24	15.3	20.4	25.5	30.6	35.7	40.8	45.9	51.0	56.1	61.2	66.3	71.4	76.5	81.6
25	15.9	21.3	26.6	31.9	37.2	42.5	47.8	53.1	58.4	63.8	69.1	74.4	79.9	85.0
26	16.6	22.1	27.6	33.2	38.7	44.2	49.7	55.3	60.8	66.3	71.8	77.4	82.9	88.4
27	17.2	23.0	28.7	34.4	40.2	45.9	51.6	57.4	63.1	68.9	74.6	80.3	86.1	91.8
28	17.9	23.8	29.8	35.7	41.7	47.6	53.6	59.5	65.5	71.4	77.4	83.3	89.3	95.2
29	18.5	24.7	30.8	37.0	43.1	49.3	55.5	61.6	67.8	74.0	80.1	86.3	92.4	98.6
30	19.1	25.5	31.9	38.3	44.6	51.0	57.4	63.8	70.1	76.5	82.9	89.3	95.6	102
31	19.8	26.4	32.9	39.5	46.1	52.7	59.3	65.9	72.5	79.1	85.6	92.2	98.8	105
32	20.4	27.2	34.0	40.8	47.6	54.4	61.2	68.0	74.8	81.6	88.4	95.2	102	109

AMERICAN INSTITUTE OF STEEL CONSTRUCTION

WEIGHT OF RECTANGULAR SECTIONS
Pounds per linear foot

Width In.	Thickness, Inches													
	$3/16$	$1/4$	$5/16$	$3/8$	$7/16$	$1/2$	$9/16$	$5/8$	$11/16$	$3/4$	$13/16$	$7/8$	$15/16$	1
33	21.0	28.1	35.1	42.1	49.1	56.1	63.1	70.1	77.1	84.2	91.2	98.2	105	112
34	21.7	28.9	36.1	43.4	50.6	57.8	65.0	72.3	79.5	86.7	93.9	101	108	116
35	22.3	29.8	37.2	44.6	52.1	59.5	66.9	74.4	81.8	89.3	96.1	104	112	119
36	23.0	30.6	38.3	45.9	53.6	61.2	68.9	76.5	84.2	91.8	99.5	107	115	122
37	23.6	31.5	39.3	47.2	55.0	62.9	70.8	78.6	86.5	94.4	102	110	118	126
38	24.2	32.3	40.4	48.5	56.5	64.6	72.7	80.8	88.8	96.9	105	113	121	129
39	24.9	33.2	41.4	49.7	58.0	66.3	74.6	82.9	91.2	99.5	108	116	124	133
40	25.5	34.0	42.5	51.0	59.5	68.0	76.5	85.0	93.5	102	111	119	128	136
41	26.1	34.9	43.6	52.3	61.0	69.7	78.4	87.1	95.8	105	113	122	131	139
42	26.8	35.7	44.6	53.6	62.5	71.4	80.3	89.3	98.2	107	116	125	134	143
43	27.4	36.6	45.7	54.8	64.0	73.1	82.2	91.4	101	110	119	128	137	146
44	28.1	37.4	46.8	56.1	65.5	74.8	84.2	93.5	103	112	122	131	140	150
45	28.7	38.3	47.8	57.4	66.9	76.5	86.1	95.6	105	115	124	134	143	153
46	29.3	39.1	48.9	58.7	68.4	78.2	88.0	97.8	108	117	127	137	147	156
47	30.0	40.0	49.9	59.9	69.9	79.9	89.9	99.9	110	120	130	140	150	160
48	30.6	40.8	51.0	61.2	71.4	81.6	91.8	102	112	122	133	143	153	163
49	31.2	41.7	52.1	62.5	72.9	83.3	93.7	104	115	125	135	146	156	167
50	31.9	42.5	53.1	63.8	74.4	85.0	95.6	106	117	128	138	149	159	170
51	32.5	43.4	54.2	65.0	75.9	86.7	97.5	108	119	130	141	152	163	173
52	33.2	44.2	55.3	66.3	77.4	88.4	99.5	111	122	133	144	155	166	177
53	33.8	45.1	56.3	67.6	78.8	90.1	101	113	124	135	146	158	169	180
54	34.4	45.9	57.4	68.9	80.3	91.8	103	115	126	138	149	161	172	184
55	35.1	46.8	58.4	70.1	81.8	93.5	105	117	129	140	152	164	175	187
56	35.7	47.6	59.5	71.4	83.3	95.2	107	119	131	143	155	167	179	190
57	36.3	48.5	60.6	72.7	84.8	96.9	109	121	133	145	158	170	182	194
58	37.0	49.3	61.6	74.0	86.3	98.6	111	123	136	148	160	173	185	197
59	37.6	50.2	62.7	75.2	87.8	100	113	125	138	151	163	176	188	201
60	38.3	51.0	63.8	76.5	89.3	102	115	128	140	153	166	179	191	204
61	38.9	51.9	64.8	77.8	90.7	104	117	130	143	156	169	182	194	207
62	39.5	52.7	65.9	79.1	92.2	105	119	132	145	158	171	185	198	211
63	40.2	53.6	66.9	80.3	93.7	107	121	134	147	161	174	187	201	214
64	40.8	54.4	68.0	81.6	95.2	109	122	136	150	163	177	190	204	218
65	41.4	55.3	69.1	82.9	96.7	111	124	138	152	166	180	193	207	221
66	42.1	56.1	70.1	84.2	98.2	112	126	140	154	168	182	196	210	224
67	42.7	57.0	71.2	85.4	99.7	114	128	142	157	171	185	199	214	228
68	43.4	57.8	72.3	86.7	101	116	130	145	159	173	188	202	217	231
69	44.0	58.7	73.3	88.0	103	117	132	147	161	176	191	205	220	235
70	44.6	59.5	74.4	89.3	104	119	134	149	164	179	193	208	223	238
71	45.3	60.4	75.4	90.5	106	121	136	151	166	181	196	211	226	241
72	45.9	61.2	76.5	91.8	107	122	138	153	168	184	199	214	230	245

WEIGHT OF RECTANGULAR SECTIONS
Pounds per linear foot

Width In.	Thickness, Inches													
	$3/16$	$1/4$	$5/16$	$3/8$	$7/16$	$1/2$	$9/16$	$5/8$	$11/16$	$3/4$	$13/16$	$7/8$	$15/16$	1
73	46.5	62.1	77.6	93.1	109	124	140	155	171	186	202	217	233	248
74	47.2	62.9	78.6	94.4	110	126	142	157	173	189	204	220	236	252
75	47.8	63.8	79.7	95.6	112	128	143	159	175	191	207	223	239	255
76	48.5	64.6	80.8	96.9	113	129	145	162	178	194	210	226	242	258
77	49.1	65.5	81.8	98.2	115	131	147	164	180	196	213	229	245	262
78	49.7	66.3	82.9	99.5	116	133	149	166	182	199	216	232	249	265
79	50.4	67.2	83.9	101	118	134	151	168	185	202	218	235	252	269
80	51.0	68.0	85.0	102	119	136	153	170	187	204	221	238	255	272
81	51.6	68.9	86.1	103	121	138	155	172	189	207	224	241	258	275
82	52.3	69.7	87.1	105	122	139	157	174	192	209	227	244	261	279
83	52.9	70.6	88.2	106	124	141	159	176	194	212	229	247	265	282
84	53.6	71.4	89.3	107	125	143	161	179	196	214	232	250	268	286
85	54.2	72.3	90.3	108	126	145	163	181	199	217	235	253	271	289
86	54.8	73.1	91.4	110	128	146	165	183	201	219	238	256	274	292
87	55.5	74.0	92.4	111	129	148	166	185	203	222	240	259	277	296
88	56.1	74.8	93.5	112	131	150	168	187	206	224	243	262	281	299
89	56.7	75.7	94.6	114	132	151	170	189	208	227	246	265	284	303
90	57.4	76.5	95.6	115	134	153	172	191	210	230	249	268	287	306
91	...	77.4	96.7	116	135	155	174	193	213	232	251	271	290	309
92	...	78.2	97.8	117	137	156	176	196	215	235	254	274	293	313
93	...	79.1	98.8	119	138	158	178	198	217	237	257	277	296	316
94	...	79.9	99.9	120	140	160	180	200	220	240	260	280	300	320
95	...	80.8	101	121	141	162	182	202	222	242	262	283	303	328
96	...	81.6	102	122	143	163	184	204	224	245	265	286	306	326
98	...	83.3	104	125	146	167	187	208	229	250	271	292	312	333
100	...	85.0	106	128	149	170	191	213	234	255	276	298	319	340
102	...	85.7	108	130	152	173	195	217	238	260	282	304	325	347
104	...	88.4	111	133	155	177	199	221	243	265	287	309	332	354
106	...	90.1	113	135	158	180	203	225	248	270	293	315	338	360
108	...	91.8	115	138	161	184	207	230	253	275	298	321	344	367
110	...	93.5	117	140	164	187	210	234	257	281	304	327	351	374
112	...	95.2	119	143	167	190	214	238	262	286	309	333	357	381
114	...	96.9	121	145	170	194	218	242	267	291	315	339	363	388
116	...	98.6	123	148	173	197	222	247	271	296	321	345	370	394
118	...	100	125	151	176	201	226	251	276	301	326	351	376	401
120	...	102	128	153	179	204	230	255	281	306	332	357	383	408
122	...	104	130	156	182	207	233	259	285	311	337	363	389	415
124	...	105	132	158	185	211	237	264	290	316	343	369	395	422
126	...	107	134	161	187	214	241	268	295	321	348	375	402	428
128	...	109	136	163	190	218	245	272	299	326	354	381	408	435

WEIGHT OF RECTANGULAR SECTIONS
Pounds per linear foot

Width In.	Thickness, Inches												
	¼	⁵⁄₁₆	⅜	⁷⁄₁₆	½	⁹⁄₁₆	⅝	¹¹⁄₁₆	¾	¹³⁄₁₆	⅞	¹⁵⁄₁₆	1
130	111	138	166	193	221	249	276	304	332	359	387	414	442
132	112	140	168	196	224	252	281	309	337	365	393	421	449
134	114	142	171	199	228	256	285	313	342	370	399	427	456
136	116	145	173	202	231	260	289	318	347	376	405	434	462
138	117	147	176	205	235	264	293	323	352	381	411	440	469
140	119	149	179	208	238	268	298	327	357	387	417	446	476
142	121	151	181	211	241	272	302	332	362	392	422	453	483
144	122	153	184	214	245	275	306	337	367	398	428	459	490
146	124	155	186	217	248	279	310	341	372	403	434	465	496
148	126	157	189	220	252	283	315	346	377	409	440	472	503
150	128	159	191	223	255	287	319	351	383	414	446	478	510
152	129	162	194	226	258	291	323	355	388	420	452	485	517
154	131	164	196	229	262	295	327	360	393	425	458	491	524
156	133	166	199	232	265	298	332	365	398	431	464	497	530
158	134	168	201	235	269	302	336	369	403	436	470	504	537
160	136	170	204	238	272	306	340	374	408	442	476	510	544
162	138	172	207	241	275	310	344	379	413	448	482	516	551
164	139	174	209	244	279	314	349	383	418	453	488	523	558
166	141	176	212	247	282	317	353	388	423	459	494	529	564
168	143	179	214	250	286	321	357	393	428	464	500	536	571
170	145	181	217	253	289	325	361	397	434	470	506	542	578

AREA OF RECTANGULAR SECTIONS
Square inches

Width In.	Thickness, Inches													
	3/16	1/4	5/16	3/8	7/16	1/2	9/16	5/8	11/16	3/4	13/16	7/8	15/16	1
1/4	.047	.063	.078	.094	.109	.125	.141	.156	.172	.188	.203	.219	.234	.250
1/2	.094	.125	.156	.188	.219	.250	.281	.313	.344	.375	.406	.438	.469	.500
3/4	.141	.188	.234	.281	.328	.375	.422	.469	.516	.563	.609	.656	.703	.750
1	.188	.250	.313	.375	.438	.500	.563	.625	.688	.750	.813	.875	.938	1.00
1¼	.234	.313	.391	.469	.547	.625	.703	.781	.859	.938	1.02	1.09	1.17	1.25
1½	.281	.375	.469	.563	.656	.750	.844	.938	1.03	1.13	1.22	1.31	1.41	1.50
1¾	.328	.438	.547	.656	.766	.875	.984	1.09	1.20	1.31	1.42	1.53	1.64	1.75
2	.375	.500	.625	.750	.875	1.00	1.13	1.25	1.38	1.50	1.63	1.75	1.88	2.00
2¼	.422	.563	.703	.844	.984	1.13	1.27	1.41	1.55	1.69	1.83	1.97	2.11	2.25
2½	.469	.625	.781	.938	1.09	1.25	1.41	1.56	1.72	1.88	2.03	2.19	2.34	2.50
2¾	.516	.688	.859	1.03	1.20	1.38	1.55	1.72	1.89	2.06	2.23	2.41	2.58	2.75
3	.563	.750	.938	1.13	1.31	1.50	1.69	1.88	2.06	2.25	2.44	2.63	2.81	3.00
3¼	.609	.813	1.02	1.22	1.42	1.63	1.83	2.03	2.23	2.44	2.64	2.84	3.05	3.25
3½	.656	.875	1.09	1.31	1.53	1.75	1.97	2.19	2.41	2.63	2.84	3.06	3.28	3.50
3¾	.703	.938	1.17	1.41	1.64	1.88	2.11	2.34	2.58	2.81	3.05	3.28	3.52	3.75
4	.750	1.00	1.25	1.50	1.75	2.00	2.25	2.50	2.75	3.00	3.25	3.50	3.75	4.00
4¼	.797	1.06	1.33	1.59	1.86	2.13	2.39	2.66	2.92	3.19	3.45	3.72	3.98	4.25
4½	.844	1.13	1.41	1.69	1.97	2.25	2.53	2.81	3.09	3.38	3.66	3.94	4.22	4.50
4¾	.891	1.19	1.48	1.78	2.09	2.38	2.67	2.97	3.27	3.56	3.86	4.16	4.45	4.75
5	.938	1.25	1.56	1.88	2.19	2.50	2.81	3.13	3.44	3.75	4.06	4.38	4.69	5.00
5¼	.984	1.31	1.64	1.97	2.30	2.63	2.95	3.28	3.61	3.94	4.27	4.59	4.92	5.25
5½	1.03	1.38	1.72	2.06	2.41	2.75	3.09	3.44	3.78	4.13	4.47	4.81	5.16	5.50
5¾	1.08	1.44	1.80	2.16	2.52	2.88	3.23	3.59	3.95	4.31	4.67	5.03	5.39	5.75
6	1.13	1.50	1.88	2.25	2.63	3.00	3.38	3.75	4.13	4.50	4.88	5.25	5.63	6.00
6¼	1.17	1.56	1.95	2.34	2.73	3.13	3.52	3.91	4.30	4.69	5.08	5.47	5.86	6.25
6½	1.22	1.63	2.03	2.44	2.84	3.25	3.66	4.06	4.47	4.88	5.28	5.69	6.09	6.50
6¾	1.27	1.69	2.10	2.53	2.95	3.38	3.80	4.22	4.64	5.06	5.48	5.91	6.33	6.75
7	1.31	1.75	2.19	2.63	3.06	3.50	3.94	4.38	4.81	5.25	5.69	6.13	6.56	7.00
7¼	1.36	1.81	2.27	2.72	3.17	3.63	4.08	4.53	4.98	5.44	5.89	6.34	6.80	7.25
7½	1.41	1.88	2.34	2.81	3.28	3.75	4.22	4.69	5.16	5.63	6.09	6.56	7.03	7.50
7¾	1.45	1.94	2.42	2.91	3.39	3.88	4.36	4.84	5.33	5.81	6.30	6.78	7.27	7.75
8	1.50	2.00	2.50	3.00	3.50	4.00	4.50	5.00	5.50	6.00	6.50	7.00	7.50	8.00
8¼	1.55	2.06	2.58	3.09	3.61	4.13	4.64	5.16	5.67	6.19	6.70	7.22	7.73	8.25
8½	1.59	2.13	2.66	3.19	3.72	4.25	4.78	5.31	5.84	6.38	6.91	7.44	7.97	8.50
8¾	1.64	2.19	2.73	3.28	3.83	4.38	4.92	5.47	6.02	6.56	7.11	7.66	8.20	8.75
9	1.69	2.25	2.81	3.38	3.94	4.50	5.06	5.63	6.19	6.75	7.31	7.88	8.44	9.00
9¼	1.73	2.31	2.89	3.47	4.05	4.63	5.20	5.78	6.36	6.94	7.52	8.09	8.67	9.25
9½	1.78	2.38	2.97	3.56	4.16	4.75	5.34	5.94	6.53	7.13	7.72	8.31	8.91	9.50
9¾	1.83	2.44	3.05	3.66	4.27	4.88	5.48	6.09	6.70	7.31	7.92	8.53	9.14	9.75
10	1.88	2.50	3.13	3.75	4.38	5.00	5.63	6.25	6.88	7.50	8.13	8.75	9.38	10.00

AMERICAN INSTITUTE OF STEEL CONSTRUCTION

AREA OF RECTANGULAR SECTIONS
Square inches

Width In.	Thickness, Inches															
	$3/16$	$1/4$	$5/16$	$3/8$	$7/16$	$1/2$	$9/16$	$5/8$	$11/16$	$3/4$	$13/16$	$7/8$	$15/16$	1
$10\frac{1}{4}$	1.92	2.56	3.20	3.84	4.48	5.13	5.77	6.41	7.05	7.69	8.33	8.97	9.61	10.25
$10\frac{1}{2}$	1.97	2.63	3.28	3.94	4.59	5.25	5.91	6.56	7.22	7.88	8.53	9.19	9.84	10.50
$10\frac{3}{4}$	2.02	2.69	3.36	4.03	4.70	5.38	6.05	6.72	7.39	8.06	8.73	9.41	10.08	10.75
11	2.06	2.75	3.44	4.13	4.81	5.50	6.19	6.88	7.56	8.25	8.94	9.63	10.31	11.00
$11\frac{1}{4}$	2.11	2.81	3.52	4.22	4.92	5.63	6.33	7.03	7.73	8.44	9.14	9.84	10.55	11.25
$11\frac{1}{2}$	2.16	2.88	3.59	4.31	5.03	5.75	6.47	7.19	7.91	8.63	9.34	10.06	10.78	11.50
$11\frac{3}{4}$	2.20	2.94	3.67	4.41	5.14	5.88	6.61	7.34	8.08	8.81	9.55	10.28	11.02	11.75
12	2.25	3.00	3.75	4.50	5.25	6.00	6.75	7.50	8.25	9.00	9.75	10.50	11.25	12.00
$12\frac{1}{2}$	2.34	3.13	3.91	4.69	5.47	6.25	7.03	7.81	8.59	9.38	10.16	10.94	11.72	12.50
13	2.44	3.25	4.06	4.88	5.69	6.50	7.31	8.13	8.94	9.75	10.56	11.38	12.19	13.00
$13\frac{1}{2}$	2.53	3.38	4.22	5.06	5.91	6.75	7.59	8.44	9.28	10.13	10.97	11.81	12.66	13.50
14	2.63	3.50	4.38	5.25	6.13	7.00	7.88	8.75	9.63	10.50	11.38	12.25	13.13	14.00
$14\frac{1}{2}$	2.72	3.63	4.53	5.44	6.34	7.25	8.16	9.06	9.97	10.88	11.78	12.69	13.59	14.50
15	2.81	3.75	4.69	5.63	6.56	7.50	8.44	9.38	10.31	11.25	12.19	13.13	14.06	15.00
$15\frac{1}{2}$	2.91	3.88	4.84	5.81	6.78	7.75	8.72	9.69	10.66	11.63	12.59	13.56	14.53	15.50
16	3.00	4.00	5.00	6.00	7.00	8.00	9.00	10.00	11.00	12.00	13.00	14.00	15.00	16.00
$16\frac{1}{2}$	3.09	4.13	5.16	6.19	7.22	8.25	9.28	10.31	11.34	12.38	13.41	14.44	15.47	16.50
17	3.19	4.25	5.31	6.38	7.44	8.50	9.56	10.63	11.69	12.75	13.81	14.88	15.94	17.00
$17\frac{1}{2}$	3.28	4.38	5.47	6.56	7.66	8.75	9.84	10.94	12.03	13.13	14.22	15.31	16.41	17.50
18	3.38	4.50	5.63	6.75	7.88	9.00	10.13	11.25	12.38	13.50	14.63	15.75	16.88	18.00
$18\frac{1}{2}$	3.47	4.63	5.78	6.94	8.09	9.25	10.41	11.56	12.72	13.88	15.03	161.9	17.34	18.50
19	3.56	4.75	5.94	7.13	8.31	9.50	10.69	11.88	13.06	14.25	15.44	16.63	17.81	19.00
$19\frac{1}{2}$	3.66	4.88	6.09	7.31	8.53	9.75	10.97	12.19	13.41	14.63	15.84	17.06	18.28	19.50
20	3.75	5.00	6.25	7.50	8.75	10.00	11.25	12.50	13.75	15.00	16.25	17.50	18.75	20.00
$20\frac{1}{2}$	3.84	5.13	6.41	7.69	8.97	10.25	11.53	12.81	14.09	15.38	16.66	17.94	19.22	20.50
21	3.94	5.25	6.56	7.88	9.19	10.50	11.81	13.13	14.44	15.75	17.06	18.38	19.69	21.00
$21\frac{1}{2}$	4.03	5.38	6.72	8.06	9.41	10.75	12.09	13.44	14.78	16.13	17.47	18.81	20.16	21.50
22	4.13	5.50	6.88	8.25	9.63	11.00	12.38	13.75	15.13	16.50	17.88	19.25	20.63	22.00
$22\frac{1}{2}$	4.22	5.63	7.03	8.44	9.84	11.25	12.66	14.06	15.47	16.88	18.28	19.69	21.09	22.50
23	4.31	5.75	7.19	8.63	10.06	11.50	12.94	14.38	15.81	17.25	18.69	20.13	21.56	23.00
$23\frac{1}{2}$	4.41	5.88	7.34	8.81	10.28	11.75	13.22	14.69	16.16	17.63	19.09	20.56	22.03	23.50
24	4.50	6.00	7.50	9.00	10.50	12.00	13.50	15.00	16.50	18.00	19.50	21.00	22.50	24.00
25	4.69	6.25	7.81	9.38	10.94	12.50	14.06	15.63	17.19	18.75	20.31	21.88	23.44	25.00
26	4.88	6.50	8.13	9.75	11.38	13.00	14.63	16.25	17.88	19.50	21.13	22.75	24.38	26.00
27	5.06	6.75	8.44	10.13	11.81	13.50	15.19	16.88	18.56	20.25	21.94	23.63	25.31	27.00
28	5.25	7.00	8.75	10.50	12.25	14.00	15.75	17.50	19.25	21.00	22.75	24.50	26.25	28.00
29	5.44	7.25	9.06	10.88	12.69	14.50	16.31	18.13	19.94	21.75	23.56	25.38	27.19	29.00
30	5.63	7.50	9.38	11.25	13.13	15.00	16.88	18.75	20.63	22.50	24.38	26.25	28.13	30.00
31	5.81	7.75	9.69	11.63	13.56	15.50	17.44	19.38	21.31	23.25	25.19	27.13	29.06	31.00
32	6.00	8.00	10.00	12.00	14.00	16.00	18.00	20.00	22.00	24.00	26.00	28.00	30.00	32.00

AREA OF RECTANGULAR SECTIONS
Square inches

Width In.	Thickness, Inches													
	$3/16$	$1/4$	$5/16$	$3/8$	$7/16$	$1/2$	$9/16$	$5/8$	$11/16$	$3/4$	$13/16$	$7/8$	$15/16$	1
33	6.19	8.25	10.31	12.38	14.44	16.50	18.56	20.63	22.69	24.75	26.81	28.88	30.94	33.00
34	6.38	8.50	10.63	12.75	14.88	17.00	19.13	21.25	23.38	25.50	27.63	29.75	31.88	34.00
35	6.56	8.75	10.94	13.13	15.31	17.50	19.69	21.88	24.06	26.25	28.44	30.63	32.81	35.00
36	6.75	9.00	11.25	13.50	15.75	18.00	20.25	22.50	24.75	27.00	29.25	31.50	33.75	36.00
37	6.94	9.25	11.56	13.88	16.19	18.50	20.81	23.13	25.44	27.75	30.06	32.38	34.69	37.00
38	7.13	9.50	11.88	14.25	16.63	19.00	21.38	23.75	26.13	28.50	30.88	33.25	35.63	38.00
39	7.31	9.75	12.19	14.63	17.06	19.50	21.94	24.38	26.81	29.25	31.69	34.13	36.56	39.00
40	7.50	10.00	12.50	15.00	17.50	20.00	22.50	25.00	27.50	30.00	32.50	35.00	37.50	40.00
41	7.69	10.25	12.81	15.38	17.94	20.50	23.06	25.63	28.19	30.75	33.31	35.88	38.44	41.00
42	7.88	10.50	13.13	15.75	18.38	21.00	23.63	26.25	28.88	31.50	34.13	36.75	39.38	42.00
43	8.06	10.75	13.44	16.13	18.81	21.50	24.19	26.88	29.56	32.25	34.94	37.63	40.31	43.00
44	8.25	11.00	13.75	16.50	19.25	22.00	24.75	27.50	30.25	33.00	35.75	38.50	41.25	44.00
45	8.44	11.25	14.06	16.88	19.69	22.50	25.31	28.13	30.94	33.75	36.56	39.38	42.19	45.00
46	8.63	11.50	14.38	17.25	20.13	23.00	25.88	28.75	31.63	34.50	37.38	40.25	43.13	46.00
47	8.81	11.75	14.69	17.63	20.56	23.50	26.44	29.38	32.31	35.25	38.19	41.13	44.06	47.00
48	9.00	12.00	15.00	18.00	21.00	24.00	27.00	30.00	33.00	36.00	39.00	42.00	45.00	48.00
49	9.19	12.25	15.31	18.38	21.44	24.50	27.56	30.63	33.69	36.75	39.81	42.88	45.94	49.00
50	9.38	12.50	15.63	18.75	21.88	25.00	28.13	31.25	34.38	37.50	40.63	43.75	46.88	50.00
51	9.56	12.75	15.94	19.13	22.31	25.50	28.69	31.88	35.06	38.25	41.44	44.63	47.81	51.00
52	9.75	13.00	16.25	19.50	22.75	26.00	29.25	32.50	35.75	39.00	42.25	45.50	48.75	52.00
53	9.94	13.25	16.56	19.88	23.19	26.50	29.81	33.13	36.44	39.75	43.06	46.38	49.69	53.00
54	10.13	13.50	16.88	20.25	23.63	27.00	30.38	33.75	37.13	40.50	43.88	47.25	50.63	54.00
55	10.31	13.75	17.19	20.63	24.06	27.50	30.94	34.38	37.81	41.25	44.69	48.13	51.56	55.00
56	10.50	14.00	17.50	21.00	24.50	28.00	31.50	35.00	38.50	42.00	45.50	49.00	52.50	56.00
57	10.69	14.25	17.81	21.38	24.94	28.50	32.06	35.63	39.19	42.75	46.31	49.88	53.44	57.00
58	10.88	14.50	18.13	21.75	25.38	29.00	32.63	36.25	39.88	43.50	47.13	50.75	54.38	58.00
59	11.06	14.75	18.44	22.13	25.81	29.50	33.19	36.88	40.56	44.25	47.94	51.63	55.31	59.00
60	11.25	15.00	18.75	22.50	26.25	30.00	33.75	37.50	41.25	45.00	48.75	52.50	56.25	60.00
61	11.44	15.25	19.06	22.88	26.69	30.50	34.31	38.13	41.94	45.75	49.56	53.38	57.19	61.00
62	11.63	15.50	19.38	23.25	27.13	31.00	34.88	38.75	42.63	46.50	50.38	54.25	58.13	62.00
63	11.81	15.75	19.69	23.63	27.56	31.50	35.44	39.38	43.31	47.25	51.19	55.13	59.06	63.00
64	12.00	16.00	20.00	24.00	28.00	32.00	36.00	40.00	44.00	48.00	52.00	56.00	60.00	64.00
65	12.19	16.25	20.31	24.38	28.44	32.50	36.56	40.63	44.69	48.75	52.81	56.88	60.94	65.00
66	12.38	16.50	20.63	24.75	28.88	33.00	37.13	41.25	45.38	49.50	53.63	57.75	61.88	66.00
67	12.56	16.75	20.94	25.13	29.31	33.50	37.69	41.88	46.06	50.25	54.44	58.63	62.81	67.00
68	12.75	17.00	21.25	25.50	29.75	34.00	38.25	42.50	46.75	51.00	55.25	59.50	63.75	68.00
69	12.94	17.25	21.56	25.88	30.19	34.50	38.81	43.13	47.44	51.75	56.06	60.38	64.69	69.00
70	13.13	17.50	21.88	26.25	30.63	35.00	39.38	43.75	48.13	52.50	56.88	61.25	65.63	70.00
71	13.31	17.75	22.19	26.63	31.06	35.50	39.94	44.38	48.81	53.25	57.69	62.13	66.56	71.00
72	13.50	18.00	22.50	27.00	31.50	36.00	40.50	45.00	49.50	54.00	58.50	63.00	67.50	72.00

AREA OF RECTANGULAR SECTIONS
Square inches

Width In.	Thickness, Inches													
	$3/16$	$1/4$	$5/16$	$3/8$	$7/16$	$1/2$	$9/16$	$5/8$	$11/16$	$3/4$	$13/16$	$7/8$	$15/16$	1
73	13.69	18.25	22.81	27.38	31.94	36.50	41.06	45.63	50.19	54.75	59.31	63.88	68.44	73.00
74	13.88	18.50	23.13	27.75	32.38	37.00	41.63	46.25	50.88	55.50	60.13	64.75	69.38	74.00
75	14.06	18.75	23.44	28.13	32.81	37.50	42.19	46.88	51.56	56.25	60.94	65.63	70.31	75.00
76	14.25	19.00	23.75	28.50	33.25	38.00	42.75	47.50	52.25	57.00	61.75	66.50	71.25	76.00
77	14.44	19.25	24.06	28.88	33.69	38.50	43.31	48.13	52.94	57.75	62.56	67.38	72.19	77.00
78	14.63	19.50	24.38	29.25	34.13	39.00	43.88	48.75	53.63	58.50	63.38	68.25	73.13	78.00
79	14.81	19.75	24.69	29.63	34.56	39.50	44.44	49.38	54.31	59.25	64.19	69.13	74.06	79.00
80	15.00	20.00	25.00	30.00	35.00	40.00	45.00	50.00	55.00	60.00	65.00	70.00	75.00	80.00
81	15.19	20.25	25.31	30.38	35.44	40.50	45.56	50.63	55.69	60.75	65.81	70.88	75.94	81.00
82	15.38	20.50	25.63	30.75	35.88	41.00	46.13	51.25	56.38	61.50	66.63	71.75	76.88	82.00
83	15.56	20.75	25.94	31.13	36.31	41.50	46.69	51.88	57.06	62.25	67.44	72.63	77.81	83.00
84	15.75	21.00	26.25	31.50	36.75	42.00	47.25	52.50	57.75	63.00	68.25	73.50	78.75	84.00
85	15.94	21.25	26.56	31.88	37.19	42.50	47.81	53.13	58.44	63.75	69.06	74.38	79.69	85.00
86	16.13	21.50	26.88	32.25	37.63	43.00	48.38	53.75	59.13	64.50	69.88	75.25	80.63	86.00
87	16.31	21.75	27.19	32.63	38.06	43.50	48.94	54.38	59.81	65.25	70.69	76.13	81.56	87.00
88	16.50	22.00	27.50	33.00	38.50	44.00	49.50	55.00	60.50	66.00	71.50	77.00	82.50	88.00
89	16.69	22.25	27.81	33.38	38.94	44.50	50.06	55.63	61.19	66.75	72.31	77.88	83.44	89.00
90	16.88	22.50	28.13	33.75	39.38	45.00	50.63	56.25	61.88	67.50	73.13	78.75	84.38	90.00
91	...	22.75	28.44	34.13	39.81	45.50	51.19	56.88	62.56	68.25	73.94	79.63	85.31	91.00
92	...	23.00	28.75	34.50	40.25	46.00	51.75	57.50	63.25	69.00	74.75	80.50	86.25	92.00
93	...	23.25	29.06	34.88	40.69	46.50	52.31	58.13	63.94	69.75	75.56	81.38	87.19	93.00
94	...	23.50	29.38	35.25	41.13	47.00	52.88	58.75	64.63	70.50	76.38	82.25	88.13	94.00
95	...	23.75	29.69	35.63	41.56	47.50	53.44	59.38	65.31	71.25	77.19	83.13	89.06	95.00
96	...	24.00	30.00	36.00	42.00	48.00	54.00	60.00	66.00	72.00	78.00	84.00	90.00	96.00
98	...	24.50	30.63	36.75	42.88	49.00	55.13	61.25	67.38	73.50	79.63	85.75	91.88	98.00
100	...	25.00	31.25	37.50	43.75	50.00	56.25	62.50	68.75	75.00	81.25	87.50	93.75	100.00
102	...	25.50	31.88	38.25	44.63	51.00	57.38	63.75	70.13	76.50	82.88	89.25	95.63	102.00
104	...	26.00	32.50	39.00	45.50	52.00	58.50	65.00	71.50	78.00	84.50	91.00	97.50	104.00
106	...	26.50	33.13	39.75	46.38	53.00	59.63	66.25	72.88	79.50	86.13	92.75	99.38	106.00
108	...	27.00	33.75	40.50	47.25	54.00	60.75	67.50	74.25	81.00	87.75	94.50	101.25	108.00
110	...	27.50	34.38	41.25	48.13	55.00	61.88	68.75	75.63	82.50	89.38	96.25	103.13	110.00
112	...	28.00	35.00	42.00	49.00	56.00	63.00	70.00	77.00	84.00	91.00	98.00	105.00	112.00
114	...	28.50	35.63	42.75	49.88	57.00	64.13	71.25	78.38	85.50	92.63	99.75	106.88	114.00
116	...	29.00	36.25	43.50	50.75	58.00	65.25	72.50	79.75	87.00	94.25	101.50	108.75	116.00
118	...	29.50	36.88	44.25	51.63	59.00	66.38	73.75	81.13	88.50	95.88	103.25	110.63	118.00
120	...	30.00	37.50	45.00	52.50	60.00	67.50	75.00	82.50	90.00	97.50	105.00	112.50	120.00
122	...	30.50	38.13	45.75	53.38	61.00	68.63	76.25	83.88	91.50	99.13	106.75	114.38	122.00
124	...	31.00	38.75	46.50	54.25	62.00	69.75	77.50	85.25	93.00	100.75	108.50	116.25	124.00
126	...	31.50	39.38	47.25	55.13	63.00	70.88	78.75	86.63	94.50	102.38	110.25	118.13	126.00
128	...	32.00	40.00	48.00	56.00	64.00	72.00	80.00	88.00	96.00	104.00	112.00	120.00	128.00

AREA OF RECTANGULAR SECTIONS
Square inches

Width In.	Thickness, Inches												
	¼	⁵⁄₁₆	⅜	⁷⁄₁₆	½	⁹⁄₁₆	⅝	¹¹⁄₁₆	¾	¹³⁄₁₆	⅞	¹⁵⁄₁₆	1
130	32.50	40.63	48.75	56.88	65.00	73.13	81.25	89.38	97.50	105.63	113.75	121.88	130.00
132	33.00	41.25	49.50	57.75	66.00	74.25	82.50	90.75	99.00	107.25	115.50	123.75	132.00
134	33.50	41.88	50.25	58.63	67.00	75.38	83.75	92.13	100.50	108.88	117.25	125.63	134.00
136	34.00	42.50	51.00	59.50	68.00	76.50	85.00	93.50	102.00	110.50	119.00	127.50	136.00
138	34.50	43.13	51.75	60.38	69.00	77.63	86.25	94.88	103.50	112.13	120.75	129.38	138.00
140	35.00	43.75	52.50	61.25	70.00	78.75	87.50	96.25	105.00	113.75	122.50	131.25	140.00
142	35.50	44.38	53.25	62.13	71.00	79.88	88.75	97.63	106.50	115.38	124.25	133.13	142.00
144	36.00	45.00	54.00	63.00	72.00	81.00	90.00	99.00	108.00	117.00	126.00	135.00	144.00
146	36.50	45.63	54.75	63.88	73.00	82.13	91.25	100.38	109.50	118.63	127.75	136.88	146.00
148	37.00	46.25	55.50	64.75	74.00	83.25	92.50	101.75	111.00	120.25	129.50	138.75	148.00
150	37.50	46.88	56.25	65.63	75.00	84.38	93.75	103.13	112.50	121.88	131.25	140.63	150.00
152	38.00	47.50	57.00	66.50	76.00	85.50	95.00	104.50	114.00	123.50	133.00	142.50	152.00
154	38.50	48.13	57.75	67.38	77.00	86.63	96.25	105.88	115.50	125.13	134.75	144.38	154.00
156	39.00	48.75	58.50	68.25	78.00	87.75	97.50	107.25	117.00	126.75	136.50	146.25	156.00
158	39.50	49.38	59.25	69.13	79.00	88.88	98.75	108.63	118.50	128.38	138.25	148.13	158.00
160	40.00	50.00	60.00	70.00	80.00	90.00	100.00	110.00	120.00	130.00	140.00	150.00	160.00
162	40.50	50.63	60.75	70.88	81.00	91.13	101.25	111.38	121.50	131.63	141.75	151.88	162.00
164	41.00	51.25	61.50	71.75	82.00	92.25	102.50	112.75	123.00	133.25	143.50	153.75	164.00
166	41.50	51.88	62.25	72.63	83.00	93.38	103.75	114.13	124.50	134.88	145.25	155.63	166.00
168	42.00	52.50	63.00	73.50	84.00	94.50	105.00	115.50	126.00	136.50	147.00	157.50	168.00
170	42.50	53.13	63.75	74.38	85.00	95.63	106.25	116.88	127.50	138.13	148.75	159.38	170.00

Notes

STANDARD MILL PRACTICE
General information

Rolling structural shapes and plates involves such factors as roll wear, subsequent roll dressing, temperature variations, etc., which cause the finished product to vary from published profiles. Such variations are limited by the provisions of the American Society for Testing and Materials Designation A6. Contained in this section is a summary of these provisions, not a reproduction of the complete specification. In its entirety, A6 covers a group of common requirements, which, unless otherwise specified in the purchase order or in an individual specification, shall apply to rolled steel plates, shapes, sheet piling and bars.

In accordance with the Scope clause of A6, *carbon steel* refers to ASTM Designations A36 and A529; *high-strength steel* and *high-strength low-alloy steel* refers to Designations A242, A440, A441, A572 and A588; *alloy steel* refers to Designation A514.

For further information on mill practices, including tolerances for rolled tees, zees and bulb angles in structural and bar sizes, pipe, tubing, sheets and strip and for other grades of steel, see ASTM A6, A53, A375, A500, A501 and A570,* and the AISI Steel Products Manuals and Producers' Catalogs.

The data on spreading rolls to increase areas and weights and mill cambering of beams is not a part of A6.

Additional material on mill practice is included in the descriptive material preceding the "properties tables" for shapes and plates.

Letter symbols representing dimensions on sketches shown herein are in accordance with ASTM A6, AISI and mill catalogs and **not necessarily as defined by the general nomenclature of this manual.**

* Also see Section 1.4.1 of Supplement Nos. 1 and 2 to the 1969 AISC Specification for additional permitted steels.

AMERICAN INSTITUTE OF STEEL CONSTRUCTION

STANDARD MILL PRACTICE
Methods of increasing areas and weights by spreading rolls

W SHAPES

To vary the area and weight within a given nominal size, the flange width, the flange thickness, and the web thickness are changed as shown in Figure 1.

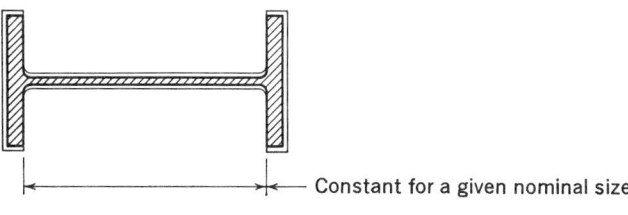

— Constant for a given nominal size

Fig. 1

S SHAPES AND AMERICAN STANDARD CHANNELS

To vary the area and weight within a given nominal size, the web thickness and the flange width are changed by an equal amount as shown in Figures 2 and 3.

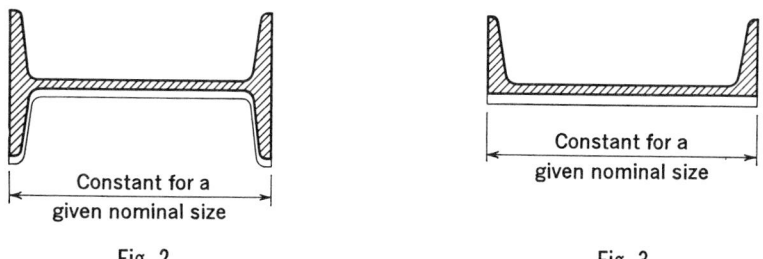

Constant for a given nominal size

Constant for a given nominal size

Fig. 2

Fig. 3

ANGLES

To vary area and weight for a given leg length, the thickness of each leg is changed. Note that leg length is changed slightly by this method (see Figure 4).

Fig. 4

AMERICAN INSTITUTE OF STEEL CONSTRUCTION

STANDARD MILL PRACTICE
Cambering of rolled beams

All beams are straightened after rolling to meet sweep and camber tolerances listed hereinafter for W shapes and S shapes. The following data refers to the subsequent cold cambering of beams to produce a predetermined design.

The maximum lengths that can be cambered depend on the length to which a given section can be rolled, with a maximum of 100 feet. The following table outlines the maximum and minimum camber of W shapes and S shapes.

MAXIMUM AND MINIMUM CAMBER

Sections Nominal Depth in.	Specified Length of Beam, ft.				
	Over 30 to 42, incl.	Over 42 to 52, incl.	Over 52 to 65, incl.	Over 65 to 85, incl.	Over 85 to 100, incl.
	Range of Max. and Min. Camber Acceptable, in.				
W shapes, 24 and over	1 to 2, incl.	1 to 3, incl.	2 to 4, incl.	3 to 5, incl.	3 to 6, incl.
W shapes, 14 to 21, incl. and S shapes, 12 in. and over	¾ to 2½, incl.	1 to 3, incl.	2 to 4, incl.	2½ to 5, incl.	Inquire

Consult the producer for specific camber and/or lengths outside the above listed available lengths and sections.

Retention of mill camber in beams of less depth than tabulated cannot be guaranteed.

A single minimum value for camber, within the ranges shown above for the length ordered, should be specified.

Camber is measured at the mill and will not necessarily be present in the same amount in the section of beam as received due to release of stress induced during the cambering operation. In general, 75% of the specified camber is likely to remain.

Camber will approximate a simple regular curve nearly the full length of the beam, or between any two points specified.

Camber is ordinarily specified by the ordinate at the mid-length of the portion of the beam to be curved. Ordinates at other points should not be specified.

Although mill cambering to achieve reverse or other compound curves is not considered practical, fabricating shop facilities for cambering by heat can accomplish such results as well as form regular curves in excess of the limits tabulated above. Refer to Effect of Heat on Steel, Part 6 of this Manual, for further information.

CAMBER ORDINATE TOLERANCES

Lengths	Plus Tolerance	Minus Tolerance
50 ft. and Less	½ inch	0
Over 50 ft.	½ inch plus ⅛ inch for each 10 ft. or fraction thereof in excess of 50 ft.	0

AMERICAN INSTITUTE OF STEEL CONSTRUCTION

STANDARD MILL PRACTICE
Positions for measuring camber and sweep

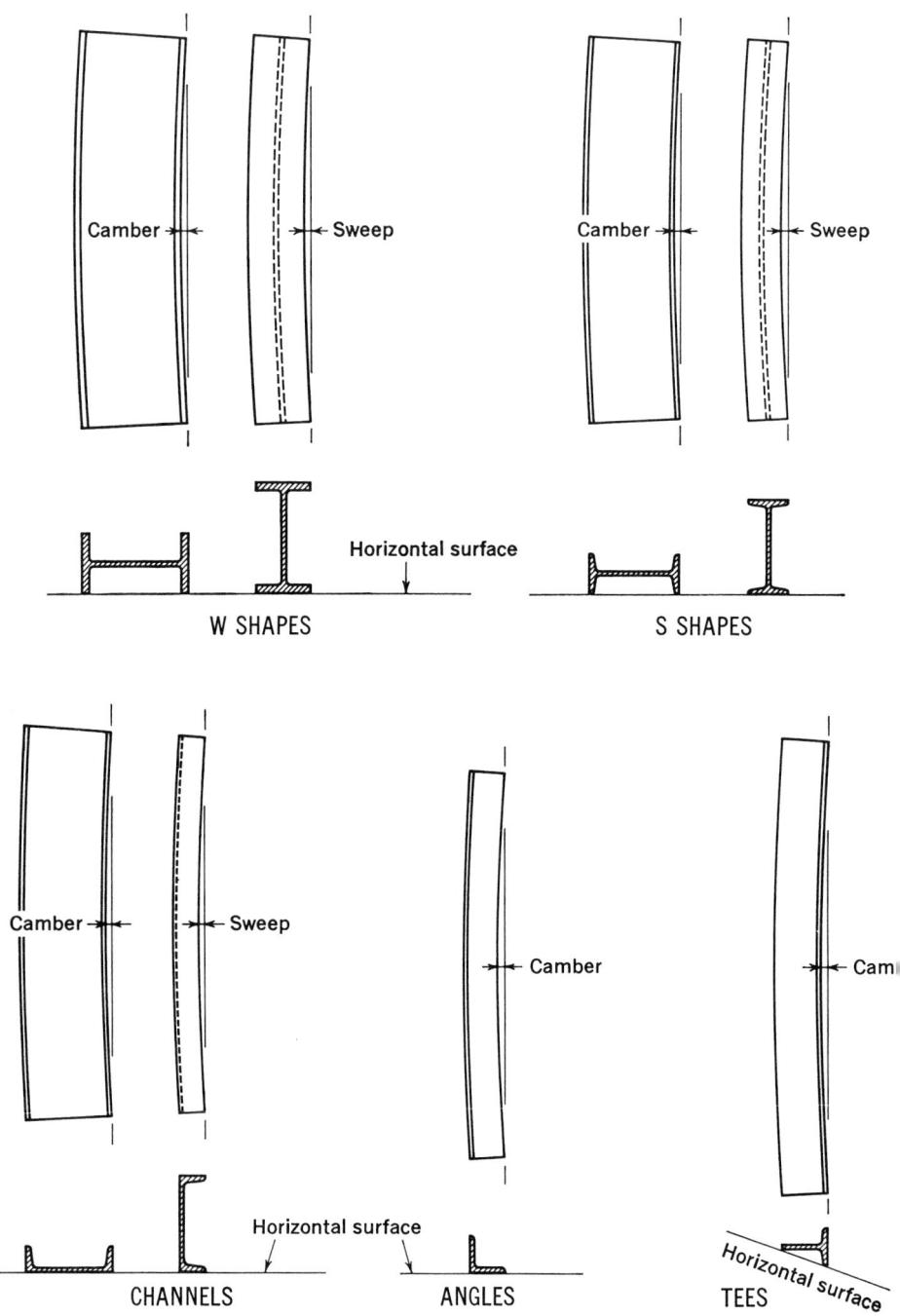

Camber → ←   → ← Sweep   Camber → ←   → ← Sweep

Horizontal surface

W SHAPES   **S SHAPES**

Camber → ←   → ← Sweep   → ← Camber   → ← Cam

Horizontal surface   Horizontal surface

CHANNELS   **ANGLES**   **TEES**

AMERICAN INSTITUTE OF STEEL CONSTRUCTION

STANDARD MILL PRACTICE
W shapes

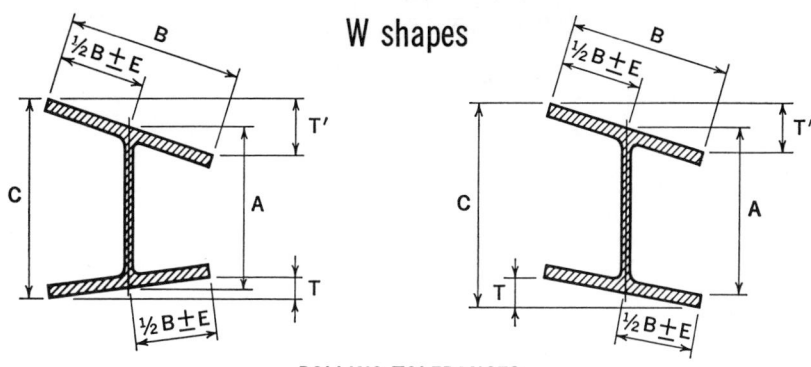

ROLLING TOLERANCES

Section Nominal Size, in.	A, Depth, in.		B, Flg. Width, in.		T + T', Flanges, Out of Square, max, in.	aE, Web off Center, max, in.	C, Max. Depth at any Cross-Section over Theoretical Depth, in.
	Over Theoretical	Under Theoretical	Over Theoretical	Under Theoretical			
To 12, incl.	⅛	⅛	¼	3⁄16	¼	3⁄16	¼
Over 12	⅛	⅛	¼	3⁄16	5⁄16	3⁄16	¼

a Variation of 5⁄16-in. max. for sections over 426 lb./ft.

CUTTING TOLERANCES

W Shapes	Variations from Specified Length for Lengths Given, in.			
	30 ft. and Under		Over 30 ft.	
	Over	Under	Over	Under
Beams 24 in. and under in nominal depth	⅜	⅜	⅜ plus 1⁄16 for each additional 5 ft. or fraction thereof	⅜
Beams over 24 in. nom. depth; all columns	½	½	½ plus 1⁄16 for each additional 5 ft. or fraction thereof	½

OTHER TOLERANCES

Area and Weight Variation: ±2.5% theoretical or specified amount.

Ends Out-of-Square: 1/64 in. per in. of depth, or of flange width if it is greater than the depth.

Camber and Sweep:

Sizes	Length	Permissible Variation, in.	
		Camber	Sweep
All sizes unless otherwise noted	All	$⅛ \text{ in.} \times \dfrac{\text{(total length, ft.)}^c}{10}$	
Sizes with flange width less than 6 in.	All	$⅛ \text{ in.} \times \dfrac{\text{(total length, ft.)}}{10}$	$⅛ \text{ in.} \times \dfrac{\text{(total length, ft.)}}{5}$
b Certain sections with a flange width approx. equal to depth & specified on order as columns	45 ft. and under	$⅛ \text{ in.} \times \dfrac{\text{(total length, ft.)}}{10}$ with ⅜ in. max.	
	Over 45 ft.	$⅜ \text{ in.} + \left[⅛ \text{ in.} \times \dfrac{\text{(total length, ft. } -45)}{10} \right]$	

b Applies only to: W 8 × 31 and heavier, W 12 × 65 and heavier, W 10 × 49 and heavier, W 14 × 78 and heavier. If other sections are specified on the order as columns, the tolerance will be subject to negotiation with the manufacturer.

c For sections with flange width less than 6 in., tolerance for sweep $= ⅛ \text{ in.} \times \dfrac{\text{(total length, ft.)}}{5}$.

AMERICAN INSTITUTE OF STEEL CONSTRUCTION

STANDARD MILL PRACTICE
S shapes and channels
ROLLING TOLERANCES

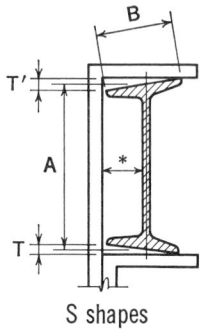

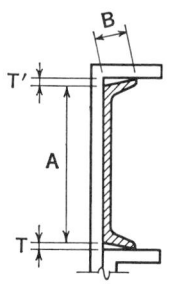

S shapes

Channels

* Back of square and centerline of web to be parallel when measuring "out-of-square."

T + T' applies when flanges of channels are toed in or out.

Section	Nominal Size, in.	^{a}A, Depth, in.		B, Flange Width, in.		T + T', Out of Square per Inch of B, in.
		Over Theoretical	Under Theoretical	Over Theoretical	Under Theoretical	
S shapes	3 to 7, incl.	3/32	1/16	1/8	1/8	1/32
	Over 7 to 14, incl.	1/8	3/32	5/32	5/32	1/32
	Over 14 to 24, incl.	3/16	1/8	3/16	3/16	1/32
Channels	3 to 7, incl.	3/32	1/16	1/8	1/8	1/32
	Over 7 to 14, incl.	1/8	3/32	1/8	5/32	1/32
	Over 14	3/16	1/8	1/8	3/16	1/32

^{a} A is measured at center line of web for beams; and at back of web for channels.

CUTTING TOLERANCES

Section	Variations from Specified Length for Lengths Given, in.									
	To 30 ft., incl.		Over 30 to 40 ft., incl.		Over 40 to 50 ft., incl.		Over 50 to 65 ft., incl.		Over 65 ft.	
	Over	Under	Over	Under	Over	Under	Over	Under	Over	Under
S shapes and American Standard channels	1/2	1/4	3/4	1/4	1	1/4	1 1/8	1/4	1 1/4	1/4

OTHER TOLERANCES

Area and Weight Variation: ±2.5% theoretical or specified amount.

Ends Out-of-Square: S shapes and channels 1/64 in. per in. of depth.

Camber: 1/8 in. $\times \dfrac{\text{total length, ft.}}{5}$

Sweep: Due to extreme flexibility of S shapes and channels straightness tolerances are subject to negotiations between the manufacturer and the purchaser.

AMERICAN INSTITUTE OF STEEL CONSTRUCTION

STANDARD MILL PRACTICE
Tees split from W, M, and S shapes
Angles split from American Standard channels

DEPTH TOLERANCES

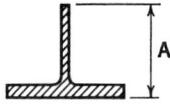 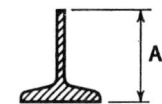 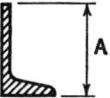

Dimension A may be approximately 1/2 beam or channel depth, or any dimension resulting from off-center splitting, or splitting on two lines as specified on the order.

Depth of Beam from which Tees or Angles are Split	Variations in Depth A Over and Under	
	Tees	Angles
To 6 in, excl.	⅛	⅛
6 to 16, excl.	³⁄₁₆	³⁄₁₆
16 to 20, excl.	¼	¼
20 to 24, excl.	⁵⁄₁₆	...
24 and over	⅜	...

The above tolerances for depths of tees or angles include the allowable tolerances in depth for the beams and channels before splitting.

OTHER TOLERANCES

Other rolling tolerances, as well as cutting tolerances, Area and Weight variation, and ends out-of-square will correspond to those of the beam or channel before splitting, except

$$\text{camber} = 1/8 \text{ in.} \times \frac{\text{total length, ft.}}{5}$$

Sweep tolerances for tees cut from all shapes $= 1/8$ in. $\times \dfrac{\text{total length, ft.}}{5}$

STANDARD MILL PRACTICE
Angles, structural size

ROLLING TOLERANCES

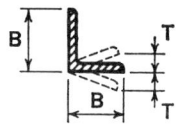

Section	*Nominal Size, in.	B Length of Leg, in.		T, Out of Square per Inch of B, in.
		Over Theoretical	Under Theoretical	
Angles	3 to 4, incl.	⅛	³⁄₃₂	*b* 3/128
	Over 4 to 6, incl.	⅛	⅛	*b* 3/128
	Over 6	³⁄₁₆	⅛	*b* 3/128

a For unequal leg angles, longer leg determines classification.
b 3/128 in. per in. = 1½ deg.

CUTTING TOLERANCES

Section	Variations from Specified Length for Lengths Given, in.									
	To 30 ft., incl.		Over 30 to 40 ft., incl.		Over 40 to 50 ft., incl.		Over 50 to 65 ft. incl.		Over 65 ft.	
Angles	Over	Under	Over	Under	Over	Under	Over	Under	Over	Under
	½	¼	¾	¼	1	¼	1⅛	¼	1¼	¼

OTHER TOLERANCES

Area and Weight Variation: ±2.5% theoretical or specified amount.

Ends Out-of-Square: 3/128 in. per in. of leg length, or 1½ degrees. Tolerances based on the longer leg of an unequal angle.

Camber: ⅛ in. $\times \dfrac{\text{total length, ft.,}}{5}$, applied to either leg.

Sweep: Not applicable; see camber tolerance.

STANDARD MILL PRACTICE
*Angles, bar size

ROLLING TOLERANCES

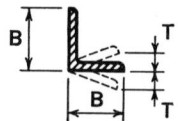

^aSpecified Length of Leg, in.	Variations from Thickness for Thicknesses Given, Over and Under, in.			B Length of Leg, Over and Under, in.	T, Out of Square per Inch of B, in.
	³⁄₁₆ and Under	Over ³⁄₁₆ to ³⁄₈, incl.	Over ³⁄₈		
1 and under	0.008	0.010	...	¹⁄₃₂	^b³⁄₁₂₈
Over 1 to 2 incl.	0.010	0.010	0.012	³⁄₆₄	^b³⁄₁₂₈
Over 2 to 3, excl.	0.012	0.015	0.015	¹⁄₁₆	^b³⁄₁₂₈

^a The longer leg of an unequal angle determines the size for permissible variations.
^b3/128- in. per in. = 1 ½ degrees.

CUTTING TOLERANCES
(Hot cut)

Section	Variations Over Specified Length for Lengths Given No Variation Under				
	5 to 10 ft., excl.	10 to 20 ft., excl.	20 to 30 ft., excl.	30 to 40 ft., excl.	40 to 60 ft., incl.
All Sizes of Bar-Size Angles	⅝	1	1½	2	2½

OTHER TOLERANCES

Camber: ¼ inch in any 5 feet, or ¼ in. $\times \dfrac{\text{total length, ft.}}{5}$

Sweep: Not applicable; see camber tolerance.

Straightness: Because of warpage, straightness tolerances do not apply to bars if any subsequent heating operation has been performed.

Ends Out-of-Square: 3/128 in. per in. of leg length or 1½ degrees. Tolerance based on longer leg of an unequal angle.

---

* A member is "bar size" when its greatest cross-sectional dimension is less than 3 in.

STANDARD MILL PRACTICE
Steel pipe and tubing
DIMENSIONS AND WEIGHT TOLERANCES

ROUND TUBING AND PIPE

ASTM A53

Weight—The weight of the pipe as specified shall not vary by more than the following amounts:
Extra-strong and lighter wall thickness:

±5 per cent

Heavier than extra-strong wall thickness:

±10 per cent

Note that the weight tolerance of ±5 per cent or ±10 per cent, as the case may be, is determined from the weights of the customary lifts of pipe as produced for shipment by the mill, divided by the number of feet of pipe in the lift. On pipe sizes over 4 in. where individual lengths may be weighed, the weight tolerance is applicable to the individual length.

Diameter—For pipe 2 in. and over in nominal diameter, the outside diameter shall not vary more than ±1 per cent from the standard specified.

Thickness—The minimum wall thickness at any point shall be not more than 12.5 per cent under the nominal wall thickness specified.

ASTM A501

Outside Dimensions—For round hot formed structural tubing 2 in. and over in nominal size, the outside diameter shall not vary more than ±1 per cent from the standard specified.

Weight—The weight of the structural tubing shall not be less than the specified value by more than 3.5 per cent.

Length—Structural tubing is commonly produced in random mill lengths, in multiple lengths, and in definite cut lengths. When cut lengths are specified for structural tubing, the length tolerances shall be in accordance with the following table:

	22 feet and Under		Over 22 to 44 feet, incl.	
	Over	Under	Over	Under
Length tolerance for specified cut lengths, in.	½	¼	¾	¼

Straightness—The permissible variation for straightness of structural tubing shall be ⅛ in. times the number of feet of total length divided by 5.

SQUARE AND RECTANGULAR TUBING

ASTM A501 and ASTM A500

Outside Dimensions—The specified dimensions, measured across the flats at positions at least 2 in. from either end of square or rectangular tubing and including an allowance for convexity or concavity, shall not exceed the plus and minus tolerance shown in the following table:

Largest Outside Dimension, Across Flats, in.	Tolerance[a] plus and minus, in.
2½ and under	0.020
Over 2½ to 3½, incl.	0.025
Over 3½ to 5½, incl.	0.030
Over 5½	1 per cent

[a] The respective outside dimension tolerances include the allowances for convexity and concavity.

Length—Structural tubing is commonly produced in random lengths, in multiple lengths, and in definite cut lengths. When cut lengths are specified for structural tubing, the length tolerances shall be in accordance with the following table:

	22 Feet and Under		Over 22 to 44 feet, incl.	
	Over	Under	Over	Under
Length tolerance for specified cut lengths, in.	½	¼	¾	¼

Weight (A501 only)—The weight of the structural tubing, as specified in Tables 4 and 5, shall not be less than the specified value by more than 3.5 per cent.

Straightness—The permissible variation for straightness of structural tubing shall be ⅛ in. times the number of feet of total length divided by 5.

Squareness of Sides—For square or rectangular structural tubing, adjacent sides may deviate from 90 deg. by a tolerance of plus or minus 2 deg. max.

Radius of Corners—For square or rectangular structural tubing, the radius of any outside corner of the section shall not exceed three times the specified wall thickness.

Twist—The tolerances for twist or variation with respect to axial alignment of the section, for square and rectangular structural tubing, shall be as shown in the following Table:

Specified Dimension of Longest Side, in.	Maximum Twist in 3 ft, in.
1½ and under	0.050
Over 1½ to 2½, incl.	0.062
Over 2½ to 4 incl.	0.075
Over 4 to 6, incl.	0.087
Over 6 to 8, incl.	0.100
Over 8	0.112

Twist is measured by holding down one end of a square or rectangular tube on a flat surface plate with the bottom side of the tube parallel to the surface plate and noting the height that either corner, at the opposite end of the bottom side of the tube, extends above the surface plate.

Wall Thickness (A500 only)—The tolerance for wall thickness exclusive of the weld area shall be plus and minus 10 per cent of the nominal wall thickness specified. The wall thickness is to be measured at the center of the flat.

AMERICAN INSTITUTE OF STEEL CONSTRUCTION

STANDARD MILL PRACTICE

Rectangular sheared plates and Universal mill plates

WIDTH AND LENGTH TOLERANCE FOR SHEARED PLATES
(1½ in. and under in thickness)

LENGTH TOLERANCE ONLY FOR UNIVERSAL MILL PLATES
(2½ in. and under in thickness)

Specified Dimensions, in.		Variations over Specified Width and Length for Thicknesses, in., and Equivalent Weights, lb. per sq. ft., Given							
		To ⅜, excl.		⅜ to ⅝, excl.		⅝ to 1, excl.		1 to 2, incl.[a]	
Length	Width	To 15.3, excl.		15.3 to 25.5, excl.		25.5 to 40.8, excl.		40.8 to 81.6, incl.	
		Width	Length	Width	Length	Width	Length	Width	Length
To 120, excl.	To 60, excl.	⅜	½	7/16	⅝	½	¾	⅝	1
	60 to 84, excl.	7/16	⅝	½	11/16	⅝	⅞	¾	1
	84 to 108, excl.	½	¾	⅝	⅞	¾	1	1	1⅛
	108 and over	⅝	⅞	¾	1	⅞	1⅛	1⅛	1¼
120 to 240, excl.	To 60, excl.	⅜	¾	½	⅞	⅝	1	¾	1⅛
	60 to 84, excl.	½	¾	⅝	⅞	¾	1	⅞	1¼
	84 to 108, excl.	9/16	⅞	11/16	15/16	13/16	1⅛	1	1⅜
	108 and over	⅝	1	¾	1⅛	⅞	1¼	1⅛	1⅜
240 to 360, excl.	To 60, excl.	⅜	1	½	1⅛	⅝	1¼	¾	1½
	60 to 84, excl.	½	1	⅝	1⅛	¾	1¼	⅞	1½
	84 to 108, excl.	9/16	1	11/16	1⅛	⅞	1⅜	1	1½
	108 and over	11/16	1⅛	⅞	1¼	1	1⅜	1¼	1¾
360 to 480, excl.	To 60, excl.	7/16	1⅛	½	1¼	⅝	1⅜	¾	1⅝
	60 to 84, excl.	½	1¼	⅝	1⅜	¾	1½	⅞	1⅝
	84 to 108, excl.	9/16	1¼	¾	1⅜	⅞	1½	1	1⅞
	108 and over	¾	1⅜	⅞	1½	1	1⅝	1¼	1⅞
480 to 600, excl.	To 60, excl.	7/16	1¼	½	1½	⅝	1⅝	¾	1⅞
	60 to 84, excl.	½	1⅜	⅝	1½	¾	1⅝	⅞	1⅞
	84 to 108, excl.	⅝	1⅜	¾	1½	⅞	1⅝	1	1⅞
	108 and over	¾	1½	⅞	1⅝	1	1¾	1¼	1⅞
600 to 720, excl.	To 60, excl.	½	1¾	⅝	1⅞	¾	1⅞	⅞	2¼
	60 to 84, excl.	⅝	1¾	¾	1⅞	⅞	1⅞	1	2¼
	84 to 108, excl.	⅝	1¾	¾	1⅞	⅞	1⅞	1⅛	2¼
	108 and over	⅞	1¾	1	2	1⅛	2¼	1¼	2½
720 and over	To 60, excl.	9/16	2	¾	2⅛	⅞	2¼	1	2¾
	60 to 84, excl.	¾	2	⅞	2⅛	1	2¼	1⅛	2¾
	84 to 108, excl.	¾	2	⅞	2⅛	1	2¼	1¼	2¾
	108 and over	1	2	1⅛	2⅜	1¼	2½	1⅜	3

[a] Permissible variations in length apply also to Universal Mill plates up to 12 in. in width for thicknesses over 2 to 2½ in., incl. except for alloy steels up to 1¾ in. thick.

Notes: Permissible variations under specified width and length, ¼ in.

(Table applies to all steels listed ASTM A6 unless noted.)

STANDARD MILL PRACTICE
Rectangular sheared plates and Universal mill plates

WIDTH TOLERANCE FOR UNIVERSAL MILL PLATES
(15 in. and under in thickness)

Specified Width, in.	Variations Over Specified Width for Thickness, in., and Equivalent Weights, lb. per sq. ft., Given					
	To ⅜, excl.	⅜ to ⅝, excl.	⅝ to 1, excl.	1 to 2, incl.	Over 2 to 10, incl.	Over 10 to 15, incl.
	To 15.3, excl.	15.3 to 25.5, excl.	25.5 to 40.8, excl.	40.8 to 81.6, incl.	81.6 to 408.0, incl.	408.0 to 612.0, incl.
Over 8 to 20, excl.	⅛	⅛	³⁄₁₆	¼	⅜	½
20 to 36, excl.	³⁄₁₆	¼	⁵⁄₁₆	⅜	⁷⁄₁₆	⁹⁄₁₆
36 and over	⁵⁄₁₆	⅜	⁷⁄₁₆	½	⁹⁄₁₆	⅝

Notes: Permissible variation under specified width, ⅛ in.
Table applies to all steels listed in ASTM A6.

CAMBER TOLERANCE FOR CARBON STEEL
SHEARED AND GAS CUT RECTANGULAR PLATES

Maximum permissible camber, in. (all thicknesses) = ⅛ in. $\times$ (total length, ft./5)

CAMBER TOLERANCE FOR CARBON STEEL UNIVERSAL MILL PLATES

Dimension, in.		Camber for Thicknesses and Widths Given
Thickness	Width	
To 2, incl.	All	⅛ in. $\times$ (total length, ft./5)
Over 2 to 15, incl.	To 30, incl.	³⁄₁₆ in. $\times$ (total length, ft./5)
Over 2 to 15, incl.	Over 30 to 60, incl.	¼ in. $\times$ (total length, ft./5)

CAMBER TOLERANCE FOR HIGH-STRENGTH AND HIGH-STRENGTH LOW-ALLOY
STEEL SHEARED AND GAS CUT RECTANGULAR PLATES, UNIVERSAL MILL
PLATES, SPECIAL CUT PLATES

Dimension, in.		Camber for Thicknesses and Widths Given
Thickness	Width	
To 2, incl.	All	⅛ in. $\times$ (total length, ft./5)
Over 2 to 15, incl.	To 30, incl.	³⁄₁₆ in. $\times$ (total length, ft./5)
Over 2 to 15, incl.	Over 30 to 60, incl.	¼ in. $\times$ (total length, ft./5)

AMERICAN INSTITUTE OF STEEL CONSTRUCTION

Notes

CRANE RAILS

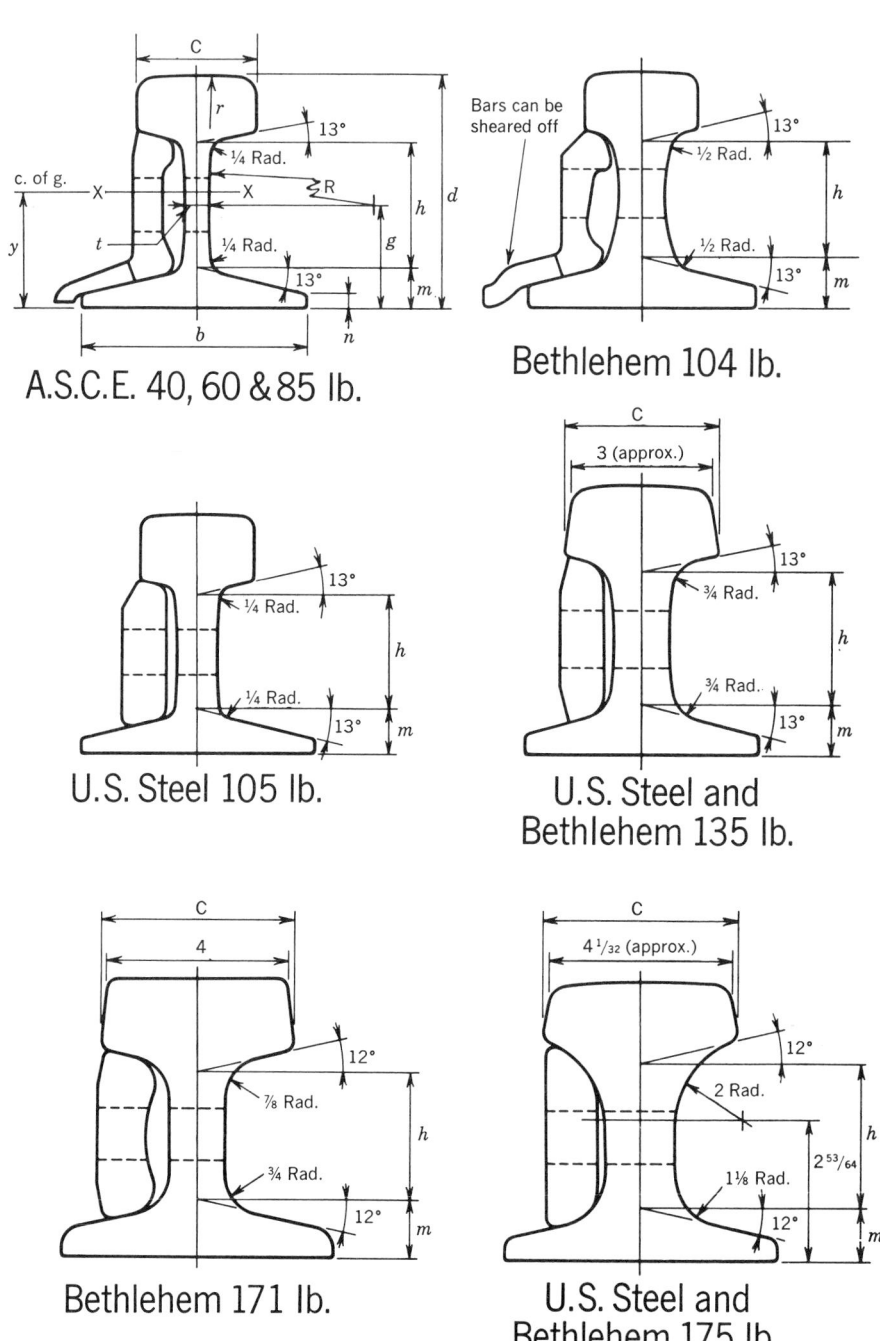

A.S.C.E. 40, 60 & 85 lb.

Bethlehem 104 lb.

U.S. Steel 105 lb.

U.S. Steel and Bethlehem 135 lb.

Bethlehem 171 lb.

U.S. Steel and Bethlehem 175 lb.

Nomenclature of sketch for A.S.C.E. rails also applies to the other sections.

CRANE RAILS

GENERAL NOTES

The A.S.C.E. rails and the 104 to 175 pound crane rails listed below are recommended for crane runway use. For complete details and for profiles and properties of rails not listed, consult manufacturers' catalogs.

Rails should be arranged so that joints on opposite sides of the crane runway will be staggered with respect to each other and with respect to the wheelbase of the crane. Rail joints should not occur at crane girder splices. Light 40 pound rails are available in 30 foot lengths, 60 pound rails in 30, 33 or 39 foot lengths, standard rails in 33 or 39 foot lengths and crane rails up to 60 feet. Consult manufacturer for availability of other lengths. Odd lengths, which must be included to complete a run or obtain the necessary stagger, should not be less than 10 feet long. For crane rail service, 40 pound rails and crane rails are furnished to manufacturers' specifications and tolerances. 60 and 85 pound rails may be furnished to manufacturers' specifications and tolerances, or to ASTM A1. Rails will be furnished with standard drilling (see page 1 - 139) in both standard and odd lengths unless stipulated otherwise on order. For controlled cooling, heat treatment and rail end preparation, see manufacturers' catalogs. Purchase orders for crane rails should be noted "For crane service."

DIMENSIONS AND PROPERTIES

Type	Classification	Nominal Wt. per Yd.	d	Gage g	Base			Head		Web			Properties—Axis X - X				
					b	m	n	c	r	t	h	R	Area	I	S Hd.	S Bse.	y
		Lb.	In.	In.	In.	In.	In.	In.	In.	In.	In.	In.	In.^{2}	In.^{4}	In.^{3}	In.^{3}	In.
A.S.C.E.	Light	40	3½	1 71/128	3½	⅝	7/32	1⅞	12	25/64	1 55/64	12	3.94	6.54	3.59	3.89	1.68
A.S.C.E.	Light	60	4¼	1 115/128	4¼	49/64	9/32	2⅜	12	31/64	2 17/64	12	5.93	14.6	6.64	7.12	2.05
A.S.C.E.	Std.	85	5 3/16	2 17/64	5 3/16	57/64	19/64	2 9/16	12	9/16	2¾	12	8.33	30.1	11.1	12.2	2.47
Bethlehem	Crane	104	5	2 7/16	5	1 1/16	½	2½	12	1	2 7/16	3½	10.3	29.8	10.7	13.5	2.21
U.S.S.	Crane	105	5 3/16	2 13/64	5 3/16	1	13/32	2 9/16	12	15/16	2 13/32	12	10.3	34.4	12.4	14.3	2.41
U.S.S. & Beth.	Crane	135	5¾	2 15/32	5 3/16	1 1/16	15/32	3 7/16	14	1¼	2 13/16	12	13.3	50.6	17.2	18.0	2.81
Bethlehem	Crane	171	6	2⅝	6	1¼	⅝	4.3	Flat	1¼	2¾	Vert.	16.8	73.4	24.5	24.4	3.01
U.S.S. & Beth.	Crane	175	6	2 21/32	6	1 9/64	½	4¼	18	1½	3 7/64	Vert.	17.1	70.2	23.5	23.3	3.02

For maximum wheel loadings see manufacturers' catalogs.

CRANE RAILS
Splices

WELDED SPLICES

When welded splices are specified, consult the manufacturer for recommended rail end preparation, welding procedure and method of ordering. Although joint continuity, made possible by this method of splicing, is desirable, it should be cautioned that the careful control required in all stages of the welding operation may be difficult to meet during crane runway construction.

In any event, rails should not be spliced by welding straps in the webs, nor should they be attached to structural supports by welding. Rails with holes for joint bar bolts should not be used in making welded splices.

BOLTED SPLICES

It is often more desirable to use properly installed and maintained bolted splice bars in making up rail joints for crane service.

Standard rail drilling and joint bar punching, as furnished by manufacturers of light and standard rails for track work, includes round holes in rail ends and slotted holes in joint bars to receive standard oval neck track bolts. Holes in rails are oversize and punching in joint bars is spaced to allow $\frac{1}{16}$ to $\frac{1}{8}$ inch clearance between rail ends. (See manufacturers' catalogs for spacing and dimensions of holes and slots.) Although this construction is satisfactory for track and light crane service, its use in general crane service may lead to joint failure.

For best service in bolted splices, it is recommended that tight joints be stipulated for all rails for crane service. This will require rail ends to be finished by milling or grinding, and the special rail drilling and joint bar punching tabulated below. Special rail drilling is accepted by some mills, or rails may be ordered blank for shop drilling. End finishing of standard rails can be done at the mill; light rails must be end finished in the fabricating shop or ground at the site prior to erection. In the crane rail range, from 104 to 175 pounds per yard, rails and joint bars are manufactured to obtain a tight fit and no further special end finishing, drilling or punching is required. Because of cumulative tolerance variations in holes, bolt diameters and rail ends, a slight gap may sometimes occur in the so-called tight joints. Conversely, it may sometimes be necessary to ream holes through joint bar and rail to permit entry of bolts.

Joint bars for crane service are provided in various sections to match the rails. Joint bars for light and standard rails may be purchased blank for special shop punching to obtain tight joints. See manufacturers' catalogs for dimensions, material specifications and the identification necessary to match the crane rail section.

Joint bar bolts, as distinguished from oval neck track bolts, have straight shanks to the head and are manufactured to ASTM A449 specifications. Nuts are manufactured to ASTM A563 Gr B specifications. ASTM A325 bolts and nuts may be used. Bolt assembly includes an alloy steel spring washer, furnished to A.R.E.A. specification.

After installation, bolts should be retightened within 30 days and every three months thereafter.

CRANE RAILS
Splices
For tight joints

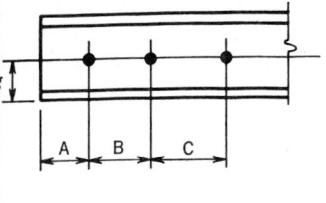

Rail End

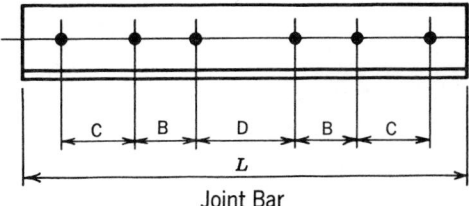

Joint Bar

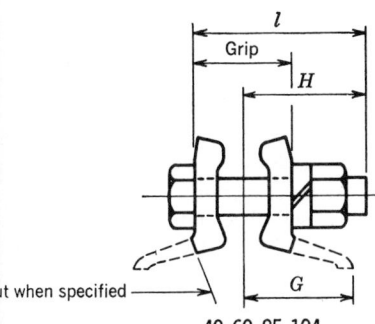

...t when specified

40·60·85·104

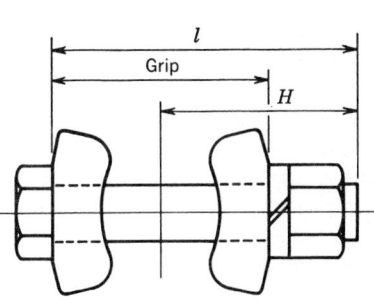

105·135·171·175

	Rail					Joint Bar						Bolt				Washer		Wt. 2 Bars Bolts, Nuts Washers	
Wt. per yard	Drilling					Punching				L	G					In-side Diam.	Thick-ness & Width		
	g	Hole Diam.	A	B	C	Hole Diam.	D	B	C			Diam.	Grip	l	H			With Flg.	Less Flg.
Lb.	In.	In.	In.	In.	In.	In.	In.	In.	In.	In.	In.	In.	In.	In.	In.	In.	In.	Lb.	Lb.
40	$1\frac{71}{128}$	* $\frac{13}{16}$	$2\frac{1}{2}$	5	...	* $\frac{13}{16}$	*$4\frac{15}{16}$	5	...	20	$2\frac{3}{16}$	$\frac{3}{4}$	$1\frac{15}{16}$	$3\frac{1}{2}$	$2\frac{1}{2}$	$\frac{13}{16}$	$\frac{7}{16}\times\frac{3}{8}$	20.0	16.5
60	$1\frac{115}{128}$	* $\frac{13}{16}$	$2\frac{1}{2}$	5	...	* $\frac{13}{16}$	*$4\frac{15}{16}$	5	...	24	$2\frac{11}{16}$	$\frac{3}{4}$	$2\frac{19}{32}$	4	$2\frac{11}{16}$	$\frac{13}{16}$	$\frac{7}{16}\times\frac{3}{8}$	36.5	29.6
85	$2\frac{17}{64}$	* $\frac{15}{16}$	$2\frac{1}{2}$	5	...	* $\frac{15}{16}$	*$4\frac{15}{16}$	5	...	24	$3\frac{11}{32}$	$\frac{7}{8}$	$3\frac{5}{32}$	$4\frac{3}{4}$	$3\frac{3}{16}$	$\frac{15}{16}$	$\frac{7}{16}\times\frac{3}{8}$	56.6	45.3
104	$2\frac{7}{16}$	$1\frac{1}{16}$	4	5	6	$1\frac{1}{16}$	$7\frac{5}{16}$	5	6	34	$3\frac{1}{2}$	1	$3\frac{1}{2}$	$5\frac{1}{4}$	$3\frac{1}{2}$	$1\frac{1}{16}$	$\frac{7}{16}\times\frac{1}{2}$	73.5	55.4
105	$2\frac{13}{64}$	$\frac{15}{16}$	4	5	6	$\frac{15}{16}$	$7\frac{5}{16}$	5	6	34	...	$\frac{7}{8}$	$3\frac{3}{8}$	5	$3\frac{5}{16}$	$\frac{15}{16}$	$\frac{7}{16}\times\frac{3}{8}$	...	61.0
135	$2\frac{15}{32}$	$1\frac{3}{16}$	4	5	6	$1\frac{3}{16}$	$7\frac{5}{16}$	5	6	34	...	$1\frac{1}{8}$	$3\frac{5}{8}$	$5\frac{1}{2}$	$3\frac{11}{16}$	$1\frac{3}{16}$	$\frac{7}{16}\times\frac{1}{2}$	...	75.3
171	$2\frac{5}{8}$	$1\frac{3}{16}$	4	5	6	$1\frac{3}{16}$	$7\frac{5}{16}$	5	6	34	...	$1\frac{1}{8}$	$4\frac{7}{16}$	$6\frac{1}{4}$	$4\frac{1}{16}$	$1\frac{3}{16}$	$\frac{7}{16}\times\frac{1}{2}$	...	90.8
175	$2\frac{21}{32}$	$1\frac{3}{16}$	4	5	6	$1\frac{3}{16}$	$7\frac{15}{16}$	5	6	34	...	$1\frac{1}{8}$	$4\frac{1}{8}$	6	$3\frac{15}{16}$	$1\frac{3}{16}$	$\frac{7}{16}\times\frac{1}{2}$	...	87.7

* Special rail drilling and joint bar punching.

CRANE RAILS
Fastenings

HOOK BOLTS

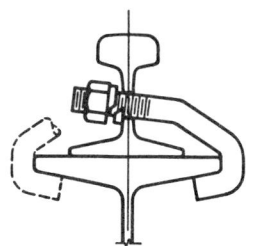

Hook bolts are used primarily with light rails when attached to beams with flanges too narrow for clamps. Rail adjustment up to $\pm \frac{1}{2}$ inch is inherent in the threaded shank. Hook bolts are paired alternately, 3 to 4 inches apart, spaced at about 24 inch centers. The special rail drilling required is accepted by some manufacturers, or may be done at the fabricator's shop.

RAIL CLAMPS

Although a variety of satisfactory rail clamps are available from track accessory manufacturers, two, frequently recommended for crane runway use, are the fixed and floating types illustrated below. These are available in forgings or pressed steel, either for single bolts or for double bolts as shown. The fixed type features adjustment through eccentric punching of fillers and positive attachment of rail to support. The floating type permits longitudinal and controlled transverse movement through clamp clearances and filler adjustment, useful in allowing for thermal expansion and contraction of rails, and possible misalignment of supports. Both types should be spaced 3 feet or less apart.

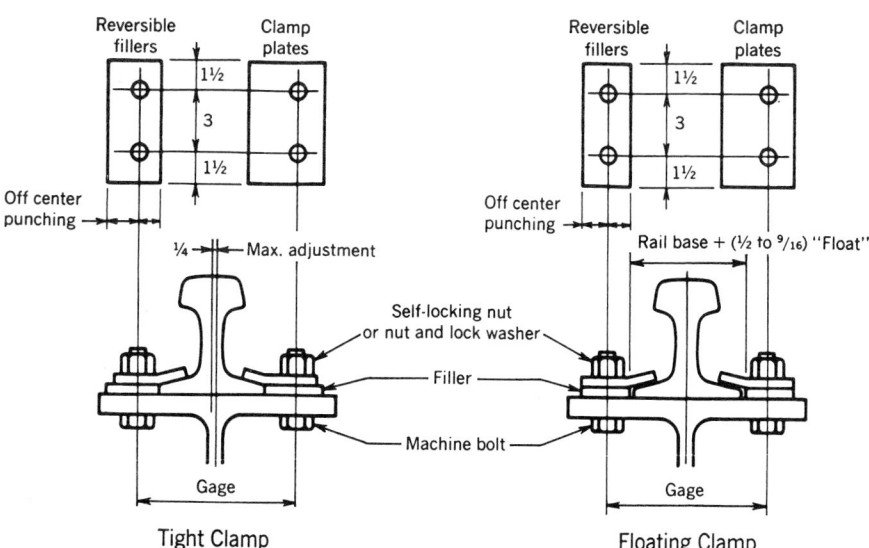

Tight Clamp   Floating Clamp

Dimensions shown above are suggested. See manufacturers' catalogs for recommended gages, bolt sizes and detail dimensions not shown.

Notes

PART 2
Beam and Girder Design

ALLOWABLE STRESS DESIGN SELECTION TABLE S_x
For shapes used as beams

This table is provided to facilitate the selection of flexural members designed on the basis of allowable bending stress in accordance with Section 1.5.1.4 of the AISC Specification. It includes W, M, and S shapes, and American Standard and Miscellaneous channels (C, MC). A beam can be selected by entering the table with either the required section modulus, or with the design bending moment, and comparing these with the tabulated values of S_x and M_R, respectively.

The table is applicable to adequately braced beams for which maximum limiting values of allowable stress are permitted by the Specification. For beams not meeting these bracing requirements, the charts of allowable moments, pages 2-87 through 2-105, are recommended.

For most loading conditions, it is convenient to use the selection table. However, for adequately braced simply supported beams with a uniform load over the full length, or equivalent symmetrical loading, tables of Allowable Loads on Beams, pages 2-28 through 2-81, can also be used.

In this table the shapes are listed in groups by descending order of section modulus, S_x, and include corresponding values of F'_y and F''_y.

Included also for steels of F_y = 36 ksi and F_y = 50 ksi are values for the maximum resisting moment M_R and the limiting values of unbraced lengths L_c and L_u. The lightest shape is listed at the top of each group, and is shown in boldface type; however, due to the difference in allowable stress for compact and non-compact shapes, the respective M_R values may not be in corresponding order.

The values of M_R are valid for beams with unbraced lengths less than or equal to L_c. When the value of L_c does not appear, the M_R values are valid for unbraced lengths up to L_u.

The symbols used in this table and their Specification references are:

S_x = elastic section modulus, X-X axis

F'_y = theoretical yield stress at which the shape becomes non-compact as defined by flange criteria (Section 1.5.1.4.1b)

F''_y = theoretical yield stress at which the shape becomes non-compact as defined by web criteria (Section 1.5.1.4.1d)*

L_c = maximum unbraced length, in feet, of the compression flange at which the allowable bending stress may be taken at 0.66 F_y or from AISC Formula (1.5-5) when applicable. (See Appendix A of AISC Specification, Section 1.5.1.4.1e)

L_u = maximum unbraced length, in feet, of the compression flange for which the allowable bending stress may be taken at 0.60 F_y when $C_b = 1$

M_R = beam resisting moment = $F_b S_x/12$,
where F_b = 0.66 F_y if shape is compact;

F_b = $F_y [0.733 - 0.0014 (b_f/2t_f) \sqrt{F_y}]$ if shape is non-compact due to F'_y;

F_b = 0.60 F_y if shape is not included in Section 1.5.1.4.1 or is non-compact due to F''_y.

---

* Also see Sect. 1.5.1.4.1 of Supplement No. 1 to the 1969 AISC Specification.

AMERICAN INSTITUTE OF STEEL CONSTRUCTION

USE OF THE TABLE

Determine the required elastic section modulus, S_x, from the maximum design moment using the appropriate F_b for the desired yield strength steel. Enter the column headed S_x and find a value equal to or next larger than the section modulus required. Alternately, enter the M_R column and find a value of M_R equal to or greater than the design moment. The beam opposite this value in the shape column, and all beams above it, have sufficient bending capacity. The first beam that appears in boldface type adjacent to or above the required S_x or M_R is the lightest that will serve for F_y = 36 ksi steel. For beams of F_y = 50 ksi steel, the tables must be scanned in the vicinity of the required values to determine whether a lighter weight section is suitable (due to variation of allowable stress for compact and non-compact shapes). If the beam must not exceed a certain depth, proceed up the column headed "Shape" until a beam within the required depth is reached; then check to see that no lighter beam of the same depth appears higher in the column.

After a shape has been selected, the following checks should be made: The lateral bracing of the compression flange should be spaced no greater than L_c when an allowable stress of 0.66 F_y or an allowable stress determined from Formula (1.5-5) was used in calculating the required S_x, or when the M_R value is used as a basis for design. If an allowable stress of 0.60 F_y was used, or when the value of L_c does not appear, the spacing of lateral bracing of the compression flange should not exceed the L_u value. For beams with unbraced lengths greater than these limits, it is recommended that the charts of Allowable Moments in Beams with Unbraced Lengths Greater than L_u be used. A check should be made for web shear capacity of the selected beam by referring to beam load tables or by use of the formula $V = F_v dt$. Also, if a deflection limitation exists, the adequacy of the selected beam should be checked.

Where torsional or other special loading conditions occur, proper provisions must be made in the design. Consult textbooks for such conditions.

EXAMPLE 1

Given:

Select a beam of F_y = 36 ksi steel subjected to a bending moment of 125 kip-ft., having its compression flange braced at 6.0 ft. intervals.	Specification or Manual Reference

Solution (S_x method):

Assume F_b = 0.66 F_y = 24 ksi

$$S \text{ (req'd)} = \frac{M}{F_b} = \frac{125 \times 12}{24} = 62.5 \text{ in.}^3$$

Enter the Beam Selection Table and find that the nearest tabulated value of S_x is 62.7 in.³, which corresponds to a W14 ×43. However, this beam is not in bold face type. Proceed up the shape column and locate the first beam in boldface, W16 ×40.	pg. **2**-10
A check of the F_y' and F_y'' columns shows the respective values of 56.3 ksi and 62.5 ksi are greater than 36 ksi. Therefore, the shape is compact and the assumed allowable stress of F_b = 0.66 F_y is correct.	**1.5.1.4.1b** **1.5.1.4.1d**

From the table, $L_c = 7.4 > 6.0$ ft.   Therefore the bracing is adequate.

1.5.1.4.1e

Use: W16 ×40

Alternate Solution (M_R method):

Enter the column of M_R values and note the tabulated value nearest the design moment equals 125 kip-ft., which corresponds to a W14 ×43. Scanning the M_R values for shapes listed higher in the column, a W16 ×40 is found to be the lightest suitable shape.

pg. **2 - 10**

Observe that $L_c = 7.4 > 6.0$ ft.

Use: W16 ×40

EXAMPLE 2

Given:

Determine the moment capacity of a W16 ×40 of $F_y = 36$ ksi steel with the compression flange braced at intervals of 9.0 ft.

Solution:

Enter the Beam Selection Table and note that:

pg. **2 - 10**

$L_u = 10.2$ ft. and $L_c = 7.4$ ft.

$L_u > 9.0$ ft. $> L_c \therefore F_b = 0.60 F_y = 22$ ksi

1.5.1.4.6a

$S_x = 64.6$ in.³

$$M = \frac{22 \times 64.6}{12} = \textbf{118.4 kip-ft.}$$

EXAMPLE 3

Given:

Select a beam of $F_y = 50$ ksi steel subjected to a bending moment of 110 kip-ft. having its compression flange braced at 6.0 ft. intervals.

Solution (S_x method):

Assume $F_b = 0.66 F_y = 33$ ksi

$$S \text{ (req'd)} = \frac{M}{F_b} = \frac{110 \times 12}{33} = 40.0 \text{ in.}^3$$

Enter the Beam Selection Table and note that the nearest tabulated value of S_x is 41.9 in.³ for a W14 ×30, which is in bold face type and therefore the lightest weight section.

pg. **2 - 10**

$L_c = 6.0 \geq 6.0$ ft.; therefore, the bracing is adequate.

1.5.1.4.1e

A check of the F_y' and F_y'' columns shows the respective values to be 35.3 ksi and 64.4 ksi.   Since F_y' is less than 50 ksi, the shape is non-compact due to flange criteria.   Therefore the allowable stress is less than $0.66 F_y$ and must be de-

1.5.1.4.1b
1.5.1.4.1d

1.5.1.4.2

termined from Formula (1.5-5). (Alternately, this value may be selected from the Beam Load Tables; see the value in parentheses at bottom of load column.)

pg. 2 - 74

From Properties Tables for W shapes, Part 1, $b_f/2t_f$ for a W14×30 equals 8.79. From Section 1.5.1.4.2 in Specification Appendix A, the allowable stress is determined to be F_b = 32.3 ksi.

Formula
(1.5-5)
Appendix A
pg. 5 - 69

$$f_b = \frac{110 \times 12}{41.9} = 31.5 < 32.3$$

Use: W14×30

Solution (M_R method):

Enter the column of M_R values for F_y = 50 ksi and note that the value of M_R = 113 kip-ft. for a W14×30 is greater than the applied bending moment of 110 kip-ft.

pg. 2 - 10

Use: W14×30

ALLOWABLE STRESS DESIGN SELECTION TABLE S_x
For shapes used as beams

$F_y = 50$ ksi			S_x	Shape	$F_{y'}$	F_y''	$F_y = 36$ ksi		
L_c	L_u	M_R					L_c	L_u	M_R
Ft.	Ft.	Kip-ft.	In.³		Ksi	Ksi	Ft.	Ft.	Kip-ft.
14.9	25.4	3053	1110	W 36 × 300	—	—	17.6	35.3	2220
14.9	23.8	2833	1030	W 36 × 280	—	—	17.5	33.1	2060
14.8	21.9	2618	952	W 36 × 260	—	—	17.5	30.5	1904
14.8	20.6	2459	894	W 36 × 245	—	—	17.4	28.6	1788
14.8	19.3	2302	837	W 36 × 230	63.8	—	17.4	26.8	1674
14.2	22.1	2236	813	W 33 × 240	—	—	16.7	30.7	1626
14.2	20.2	2041	742	W 33 × 220	—	—	16.7	28.1	1484
14.1	18.3	1845	671	W 33 × 200	58.1	—	16.6	25.4	1342
10.9	13.9	1829	665	W 36 × 194	—	—	12.8	19.4	1330
13.5	21.8	1790	651	W 30 × 210	—	—	15.9	30.3	1302
10.8	13.1	1711	622	W 36 × 182	—	—	12.7	18.2	1244
13.5	19.7	1614	587	W 30 × 190	—	—	15.9	27.4	1174
10.8	12.2	1595	580	W 36 × 170	—	60.0	12.7	17.0	1160
10.7	11.5	1491	542	W 36 × 160	—	55.8	12.7	15.7	1084
13.4	17.8	1458	530	W 30 × 172	55.1	—	15.8	24.8	1060
10.5	11.4	1386	504	W 36 × 150	—	51.6	12.6	14.6	1008
12.6	20.4	1359	494	W 27 × 177	—	—	14.9	28.4	988
10.4	12.1	1339	487	W 33 × 152	—	61.0	12.2	16.8	974
10.3	11.1	1232	448	W 33 × 141	—	56.0	12.2	15.4	896
12.6	18.5	1227	446	W 27 × 160	64.1	—	14.8	25.7	892
—	11.2	1100	440	W 36 × 135	48.2	48.0	12.3	13.2	880
12.6	21.5	1139	414	W 24 × 160	—	—	14.9	29.9	828
9.9	11.0	1117	406	W 33 × 130	60.1	52.1	12.1	13.8	812
12.5	16.9	1111	404	W 27 × 145	53.1	—	14.7	23.5	808
9.5	11.6	1045	380	W 30 × 132	—	—	11.1	16.1	760
12.6	19.5	1026	373	W 24 × 145	57.5	—	14.8	27.1	746
—	10.8	898	359	W 33 × 118	45.0	48.2	11.9	12.7	718
9.4	10.8	976	355	W 30 × 124	—	63.9	11.1	15.0	710
12.5	17.4	907	332	W 24 × 130	45.0	—	14.8	24.1	664
9.4	10.1	905	329	W 30 × 116	—	60.0	11.1	13.8	658
11.8	22.4	872	317	W 21 × 142	—	—	13.9	31.1	634
$F_y = 50$ ksi							$F_y = 36$ ksi		

S_x ALLOWABLE STRESS DESIGN SELECTION TABLE
For shapes used as beams

$F_y = 50$ ksi			S_x	Shape	F_y'	F_y''	$F_y = 36$ ksi		
L_c	L_u	M_R					L_c	L_u	M_R
Ft.	Ft.	Kip-ft.	In.³		Ksi	Ksi	Ft.	Ft.	Kip-ft.
8.9	9.9	825	300	W 30 × 108	57.3	57.3	11.1	12.4	600
9.0	11.5	825	300	W 27 × 114	—	—	10.6	15.9	600
10.8	15.4	825	300	W 24 × 120	64.5	—	12.8	21.4	600
11.7	20.2	781	284	W 21 × 127	62.0	—	13.8	28.1	568
10.8	14.2	759	276	W 24 × 110	54.9	—	12.7	19.7	552
7.9	9.8	738	270	W 30 × 99	44.7	52.6	10.9	11.6	540
9.0	10.2	734	267	W 27 × 102	—	62.2	10.6	14.2	534
7.2	12.3	693	252	S 24 × 120	—	—	8.5	17.1	504
10.7	12.9	684	250	W 24 × 100	45.5	64.5	12.7	17.9	500
11.6	17.8	686	250	W 21 × 112	48.3	—	13.7	24.8	500
8.9	9.6	668	243	W 27 × 94	60.9	56.3	10.5	12.8	486
7.1	12.0	649	236	S 24 × 105.9	—	—	8.3	16.7	472
8.1	10.9	608	221	W 24 × 94	—	—	9.6	15.1	442
10.6	21.1	605	220	W 18 × 114	—	—	12.5	29.3	440
7.9	9.5	579	212	W 27 × 84	44.4	51.1	10.5	11.2	424
10.6	19.5	556	202	W 18 × 105	—	—	12.4	27.1	404
6.5	8.8	547	199	S 24 × 100	—	—	7.6	12.2	398
8.1	13.3	545	198	W 21 × 96	—	—	9.5	18.5	396
8.1	9.6	542	197	W 24 × 84	—	64.6	9.5	13.4	394
13.1	31.4	516	189	W 14 × 119	44.7	—	15.5	43.7	378
6.4	8.6	514	187	S 24 × 90	—	—	7.5	12.0	374
10.5	17.9	509	185	W 18 × 96	54.5	—	12.4	24.9	370
8.0	8.7	484	176	W 24 × 76	62.8	57.5	9.5	11.9	352
13.1	29.5	477	176	W 14 × 111	38.9	—	15.4	41.0	352
6.3	8.5	481	175	S 24 × 79.9	—	—	7.4	11.8	350
8.0	11.4	465	169	W 21 × 82	—	—	9.5	15.8	338
10.3	20.6	457	166	W 16 × 96	62.7	—	12.2	28.6	332
13.1	27.8	440	164	W 14 × 103	33.9	—	15.4	38.6	324
6.4	11.0	443	161	S 20 × 95	—	—	7.6	15.3	322
7.9	14.6	432	157	W 18 × 85	—	—	9.3	20.3	314
7.3	8.6	419	153	W 24 × 68	46.0	52.3	9.5	10.2	306
6.3	10.8	418	152	S 20 × 85	—	—	7.4	15.0	304
7.4	9.6	415	151	W 21 × 73	—	—	8.8	13.4	302
10.3	18.8	415	151	W 16 × 88	52.1	—	12.1	26.2	302
13.0	25.6	401	151	W 14 × 95	28.8	—	15.4	35.6	295
7.9	13.4	391	142	W 18 × 77	—	—	9.3	18.6	284
7.4	8.9	385	140	W 21 × 68	—	—	8.7	12.4	280
13.0	23.8	362	138	W 14 × 87	24.5	—	15.3	33.1	267
10.8	21.9	358	131	W 14 × 84	45.6	—	12.7	30.5	262
	$F_y = 50$ ksi							$F_y = 36$ ksi	

ALLOWABLE STRESS DESIGN SELECTION TABLE S_x
For shapes used as beams

$F_y = 50$ ksi			S_x	Shape	F_y'	F_y''	$F_y = 36$ ksi		
L_c	L_u	M_R					L_c	L_u	M_R
Ft.	Ft.	Kip-ft.	In.³		Ksi	Ksi	Ft.	Ft.	Kip-ft.
5.8	6.5	358	130	W 24 × 61	—	53.0	7.4	8.1	260
7.8	12.2	355	129	W 18 × 70	—	—	9.2	16.9	258
5.7	8.4	352	128	S 20 × 75	—	—	6.7	11.7	256
7.7	15.4	352	128	W 16 × 78	—	—	9.1	21.3	256
7.4	8.1	349	127	W 21 × 62	60.7	61.6	8.7	11.2	254
10.7	20.4	328	121	W 14 × 78	39.0	—	12.7	28.4	242
5.6	8.2	325	118	S 20 × 65.4	—	—	6.6	11.4	236
7.8	11.1	325	118	W 18 × 64	—	—	9.2	15.5	236
7.7	14.0	319	116	W 16 × 71	—	—	9.0	19.5	232
10.8	25.6	318	116	W 12 × 85	47.1	—	12.8	35.6	232
—	6.4	285	114	W 24 × 55	56.3	48.0	6.9	7.5	228
9.0	18.5	308	112	W 14 × 74	—	—	10.6	25.7	224
6.9	7.9	300	110	W 21 × 55	44.0	55.2	8.7	9.5	220
6.8	9.6	297	108	W 18 × 60	—	—	8.0	13.3	216
10.8	24.0	291	107	W 12 × 79	40.5	—	12.8	33.3	214
7.6	12.7	286	104	W 16 × 64	—	—	9.0	17.6	208
5.6	8.0	283	103	S 18 × 70	—	—	6.6	11.1	206
9.0	17.1	283	103	W 14 × 68	55.7	—	10.6	23.7	206
6.7	8.7	271	98.4	W 18 × 55	—	—	8.0	12.1	197
10.8	21.9	262	97.5	W 12 × 72	33.9	—	12.7	30.5	192
7.6	11.5	260	94.4	W 16 × 58	63.3	—	8.9	15.9	189
5.6	6.1	257	93.3	W 21 × 49	—	53.0	6.9	7.7	187
9.0	15.4	252	92.2	W 14 × 61	45.1	—	10.6	21.4	184
5.4	7.7	246	89.4	S 18 × 54.7	—	—	6.3	10.7	179
6.7	7.9	245	89.1	W 18 × 50	63.0	—	7.9	11.0	178
10.7	20.0	233	88.0	W 12 × 65	27.8	—	12.7	27.7	172
—	6.0	204	81.6	W 21 × 44	52.5	48.2	6.6	7.1	163
6.3	9.1	222	80.8	W 16 × 50	—	—	7.5	12.6	162
6.7	7.3	217	79.0	W 18 × 45	48.5	59.7	7.9	9.7	158
9.0	17.5	213	78.1	W 12 × 58	44.7	—	10.6	24.4	156
7.2	12.7	214	77.8	W 14 × 53	—	—	8.5	17.6	156
—	4.9	188	75.1	MC 18 × 58	—	—	—	6.7	138
9.1	24.3	203	73.7	W 10 × 66	59.6	—	10.7	33.8	147
6.3	8.2	199	72.5	W 16 × 45	—	—	7.4	11.4	145
9.0	15.9	191	70.7	W 12 × 53	36.2	—	10.6	22.2	141
7.2	11.5	193	70.2	W 14 × 48	59.4	—	8.5	16.0	140
—	4.7	174	69.7	MC 18 × 51.9	—	—	—	6.6	128
$F_y = 50$ ksi							$F_y = 36$ ksi		

S_x ALLOWABLE STRESS DESIGN SELECTION TABLE
For shapes used as beams

$F_y = 50$ ksi			S_x	Shape	F_y'	F_y''	$F_y = 36$ ksi		
L_c	L_u	M_R					L_c	L_u	M_R
Ft.	Ft.	Kip-ft.	In.³		Ksi	Ksi	Ft.	Ft.	Kip-ft.
5.4	5.9	188	68.4	**W 18 × 40**	—	52.9	6.4	8.2	137
9.0	22.4	185	67.1	W 10 × 60	50.1	—	10.6	31.1	134
5.1	7.8	178	64.8	S 15 × 50	—	—	6.0	10.8	130
7.2	14.2	178	64.7	W 12 × 50	—	—	8.5	19.7	129
6.3	7.3	178	64.6	**W 16 × 40**	56.3	62.5	7.4	10.2	129
—	4.6	161	64.3	MC 18 × 45.8	—	—	—	6.4	118
7.2	10.3	172	62.7	W 14 × 43	47.5	—	8.4	14.3	125
—	4.6	154	61.6	MC 18 × 42.7	—	—	—	6.4	113
9.0	20.4	164	60.4	W 10 × 54	41.4	—	10.6	28.4	121
4.9	7.6	164	59.6	S 15 × 42.9	—	—	5.8	10.6	119
7.2	12.8	160	58.2	W 12 × 45	55.9	—	8.5	17.8	116
—	5.7	145	57.9	**W 18 × 35**	55.7	48.1	6.3	6.7	116
6.3	6.8	154	56.5	W 16 × 36	40.8	60.4	7.4	8.7	113
6.1	8.2	150	54.7	W 14 × 38	62.5	—	7.2	11.4	109
9.0	18.6	147	54.6	W 10 × 49	33.9	—	10.6	25.9	108
—	5.4	135	53.8	C 15 × 50	—	—	—	7.5	99
7.2	11.5	142	51.9	W 12 × 40	45.3	—	8.4	16.0	104
4.9	10.0	140	50.8	S 12 × 50	—	—	5.8	13.9	102
7.2	16.3	135	49.1	W 10 × 45	64.7	—	8.5	22.7	98
6.0	7.3	133	48.6	**W 14 × 34**	49.1	—	7.1	10.1	97
4.9	5.3	130	47.2	**W 16 × 31**	—	51.2	5.8	7.1	94
—	5.1	116	46.5	C 15 × 40	—	—	—	7.1	85
5.9	9.7	127	46.0	W 12 × 36	—	—	6.9	13.4	92
4.7	9.6	125	45.4	S 12 × 40.8	—	—	5.5	13.4	91
7.2	14.1	116	42.2	W 10 × 39	47.6	—	8.4	19.6	84
—	4.9	105	42.0	C 15 × 33.9	—	—	—	6.8	77
6.0	6.6	113	41.9	**W 14 × 30**	35.3	64.4	7.1	8.6	83
5.8	8.4	109	39.5	W 12 × 31	55.4	—	6.9	11.6	79
—	5.2	96	38.3	**W 16 × 26**	42.9	43.3	5.6	6.1	77
4.5	7.7	105	38.2	S 12 × 35	—	—	5.4	10.7	76
4.5	7.6	100	36.4	S 12 × 31.8	—	—	5.3	10.5	73
4.5	5.0	97	35.1	**W 14 × 26**	—	57.2	5.3	7.0	70
7.1	11.8	94	35.0	W 10 × 33	32.2	—	8.4	16.4	69
5.8	7.2	93	34.2	W 12 × 27	41.3	—	6.9	10.1	68
7.2	16.3	85	31.1	W 8 × 35	41.1	—	8.5	22.6	62
5.2	9.5	85	30.8	W 10 × 29	—	—	6.1	13.2	62
4.4	8.1	81	29.4	S 10 × 35	—	—	5.2	11.2	59
$F_y = 50$ ksi							$F_y = 36$ ksi		

ALLOWABLE STRESS DESIGN SELECTION TABLE S_x
For shapes used as beams

$F_y = 50$ ksi			S_x	Shape	F_y'	F_y''	$F_y = 36$ ksi		
L_c	L_u	M_R					L_c	L_u	M_R
Ft.	Ft.	Kip-ft.	In.³		Ksi	Ksi	Ft.	Ft.	Kip-ft.
—	4.7	72	28.9	**W 14 × 22**	48.9	47.7	5.3	5.7	58
7.2	14.4	73	27.4	W 8 × 31	31.9	—	8.4	20.0	54
—	4.4	68	27.0	C 12 × 30	—	—	—	6.1	50
5.3	7.8	73	26.6	M 10 × 29.1	46.8	—	6.3	10.8	53
5.2	8.2	73	26.5	W 10 × 25	60.7	—	6.1	11.4	53
3.6	4.6	70	25.3	**W 12 × 22**	—	—	4.3	6.4	51
4.2	7.6	68	24.7	S 10 × 25.4	—	—	4.9	10.6	49
5.9	12.5	67	24.3	W 8 × 28	54.6	—	6.9	17.4	49
—	4.2	60	24.1	C 12 × 25	—	—	—	5.9	44
5.2	7.5	65	23.6	M 10 × 22.9	49.8	—	6.1	10.5	47
—	4.1	54	21.5	**C 12 × 20.7**	—	—	—	5.7	39
5.2	6.6	58	21.5	W 10 × 21	38.1	—	6.1	9.1	43
3.6	3.8	59	21.3	**W 12 × 19**	—	64.5	4.2	5.3	43
—	3.5	53	21.1	**M 14 × 17.2**	50.6	38.2	3.6	4.1	42
5.8	10.9	57	20.8	W 8 × 24	40.9	—	6.9	15.1	42
—	4.4	52	20.7	C 10 × 30	—	—	—	6.1	38
3.6	5.2	52	18.8	**W 10 × 19**	—	—	4.2	7.2	38
—	4.2	46	18.2	C 10 × 25	—	—	—	5.8	33
3.0	3.7	48	17.6	**W 12 × 16.5**	49.3	62.4	4.1	4.3	35
4.7	8.1	47	17.0	W 8 × 20	56.1	—	5.6	11.3	34
5.4	14.5	46	16.7	W 6 × 25	61.3	—	6.4	20.1	33
3.6	4.3	45	16.2	W 10 × 17	—	—	4.2	6.0	32
3.7	7.4	45	16.2	S 8 × 23	—	—	4.4	10.3	32
—	4.0	40	15.8	C 10 × 20	—	—	—	5.5	29
—	3.6	37	14.8	**W 12 × 14**	34.7	46.9	3.5	4.2	29
3.6	7.1	40	14.4	S 8 × 18.4	—	—	4.2	9.9	29
4.7	6.7	38	14.1	W 8 × 17	37.5	—	5.5	9.4	28
3.6	3.8	38	13.8	W 10 × 15	49.3	—	4.2	5.0	28
—	3.8	34	13.5	C 10 × 15.3	—	—	—	5.3	25
—	4.1	34	13.5	C 9 × 20	—	—	—	5.6	25
5.4	11.9	36	13.4	W 6 × 20	40.5	—	6.4	16.5	27
3.5	7.2	33	12.1	S 7 × 20	—	—	4.1	10.0	24
—	2.6	30	12.0	**M 12 × 11.8**	58.7	36.9	2.7	3.1	24
3.6	5.2	32	11.8	W 8 × 15	—	—	4.2	7.2	24
—	3.8	28	11.3	C 9 × 15	—	—	—	5.3	21
—	4.1	28	11.0	C 8 × 18.75	—	—	—	5.7	20
—	3.7	27	10.6	C 9 × 13.4	—	—	—	5.2	19
$F_y = 50$ ksi							$F_y = 36$ ksi		

S_x ALLOWABLE STRESS DESIGN SELECTION TABLE
For shapes used as beams

$F_y = 50$ ksi			S_x	Shape	F_y'	F_y''	$F_y = 36$ ksi		
L_c	L_u	M_R'					L_c	L_u	M_R
Ft.	Ft.	Kip-ft.	In.³		Ksi	Ksi	Ft.	Ft.	Kip-ft.
2.7	3.7	28	10.5	W 10 × 11.5	29.1	56.5	3.8	4.3	21
3.3	6.8	29	10.5	S 7 × 15.3	—	—	3.9	9.5	21
3.6	8.7	28	10.2	W 6 × 16	—	—	4.3	12.1	20
5.4	9.0	26	10.0	W 6 × 15.5	21.9	—	6.3	12.4	19
3.6	4.2	27	9.90	W 8 × 13	43.9	—	4.2	5.9	20
—	1.3	23	9.23	MC 12 × 10.6	—	—	—	1.8	17
—	3.8	23	9.03	C 8 × 13.75	—	—	—	5.3	17
3.2	7.1	24	8.77	S 6 × 17.25	—	—	3.8	9.9	18
—	3.7	20	8.14	C 8 × 11.5	—	—	—	5.1	15
—	2.3	19	7.76	M 10 × 9	63.9	41.8	2.6	2.7	16
3.4	3.8	21	7.80	W 8 × 10	29.2	—	4.2	4.7	15
—	4.0	19	7.78	C 7 × 14.75	—	—	—	5.6	14
3.0	6.6	20	7.37	S 6 × 12.5	—	—	3.5	9.2	15
3.6	6.2	20	7.25	W 6 × 12	53.0	—	4.2	8.6	15
—	3.8	17	6.93	C 7 × 12.25	—	—	—	5.3	13
—	1.4	16	6.40	MC 10 × 8.4	—	—	—	1.9	12
—	3.6	15	6.08	C 7 × 9.8	—	—	—	5.1	11
2.9	7.2	17	6.09	S 5 × 14.75	—	—	3.5	9.9	12
—	4.1	15	5.80	C 6 × 13	—	—	—	5.7	11
3.5	4.4	13	5.08	W 6 × 8.5	26.4	—	4.2	6.1	10
—	3.9	13	5.06	C 6 × 10.5	—	—	—	5.4	9
2.7	6.5	14	4.92	S 5 × 10	—	—	3.2	9.1	10
—	2.0	12	4.62	M 8 × 6.5	—	48.3	2.4	2.5	9
—	0.8	11	4.42	MC 10 × 6.5	—	—	—	1.1	8
—	3.7	11	4.38	C 6 × 8.2	—	—	—	5.1	8
—	4.0	9	3.56	C 5 × 9	—	—	—	5.6	7
1.8	1.9	9	3.44	M 7 × 5.5	—	56.8	2.2	2.5	7
2.5	6.8	9	3.39	S 4 × 9.5	—	—	3.0	9.5	7
—	3.7	8	3.00	C 5 × 6.7	—	—	—	5.2	6
2.4	6.5	8	3.04	S 4 × 7.7	—	—	2.8	9.0	6
1.7	1.8	7	2.40	M 6 × 4.4	—	61.3	1.9	2.4	5
—	4.3	6	2.29	C 4 × 7.25	—	—	—	5.9	4
2.2	7.2	5	1.95	S 3 × 7.5	—	—	2.6	10.1	4
—	3.9	5	1.93	C 4 × 5.4	—	—	—	5.4	4
2.1	6.7	5	1.68	S 3 × 5.7	—	—	2.5	9.4	3
—	4.9	3	1.38	C 3 × 6	—	—	—	6.7	3
—	4.6	3	1.24	C 3 × 5	—	—	—	6.3	2
—	4.3	3	1.10	C 3 × 4.1	—	—	—	6.0	2
$F_y = 50$ ksi							$F_y = 36$ ksi		

AMERICAN INSTITUTE OF STEEL CONSTRUCTION

Notes

Z_x PLASTIC DESIGN SELECTION TABLE

For shapes used as beams or columns

When plastic design is used in proportioning continuous beams and structural frames, bending capacity based on ultimate strength is determined by the plastic section modulus of a shape. Fundamentals of plastic design are discussed in various publications, including *Plastic Design of Braced Multistory Frames,* published by the American Iron and Steel Institute in cooperation with AISC, and the earlier AISC manual, *Plastic Design in Steel.*

The AISC Specification permits plastic design with steels of yield strengths up to 65 ksi. Section 2.2 of the Specification lists the ASTM steels that may be used.

In this table, the plastic section modulus Z_x has been tabulated for hot-rolled shapes which satisfy the requirements of Part 2 of the AISC Specification. Included are W, M, and S shapes of $F_y = 36$ ksi and $F_y = 50$ ksi steel. When no axial load is present, all shapes included in the table can be classified as "plastic design sections" except for those shapes of $F_y = 50$ ksi steel where the values of M_p and P_y do not appear. When axial load is present, shapes marked with an asterisk (*) must be checked for compliance with Formulas (2.7-1a) and (2.7-1b). Additionally, the tabulated values are valid only for members laterally braced in accordance with Specification Section 2.9.

The use of the Plastic Design Selection Table in determining the lightest shape for the design requirements is similar to the procedure previously outlined for the Allowable Stress Design Selection Table. The boldface type identifies the shapes that are the lightest in weight in each particular group.

The symbols used in the table are defined below:

Z_x = plastic section modulus, X-X axis

A = area of the shape

d/t_w = depth-thickness ratio of the web. Used to check compliance with Formulas (2.7-1a) and (2.7-1b)

r_x = radius of gyration with respect to the X-X axis, in inches. Used in determining the slenderness ratio of columns about the X-X axis.

r_y = radius of gyration with respect to the Y-Y axis, in inches. Used in determining the slenderness ratio of columns about the Y-Y axis. Also used to determine P_{cr} and M_m, and to determine the lateral bracing requirements in accordance with Section 2.9 of the Specification.

M_p = plastic moment, in kip-ft, $= (F_y \times Z_x)/12$

P_y = plastic axial load, in kips, $= (F_y \times A)$

PLASTIC DESIGN SELECTION TABLE Z_x
For shapes used as beams or columns

Z_x	Shape	A	$\dfrac{d}{t_w}$	r_x	r_y	$F_y = 36$ ksi		$F_y = 50$ ksi	
						M_p	P_y	M_p	P_y
In.³		In.²		In.	In.	Kip-ft.	Kips	Kip-ft.	Kips
1660	W 14 × 730	215	7.31	8.18	4.69	4980	7740	ᵃ6360	ᵃ9890
1480	W 14 × 665	196	7.67	7.99	4.62	4440	7060	ᵃ5670	ᵃ9020
1320	W 14 × 605	178	8.06	7.81	4.55	3960	6410	ᵃ5060	ᵃ8190
1260	W 36 × 300	88.3	38.9	15.2	3.83	3780	3180	5250	*4420
1180	W 14 × 550	162	8.49	7.64	4.49	3540	5830	4920	8100
1170	W 36 × 280	82.4	41.2	15.1	3.81	3510	2970	4880	*4120
1080	W 36 × 260	76.5	43.1	15.0	3.77	3240	*2750	4500	*3830
1050	W 14 × 500	147	8.97	7.49	4.43	3150	5290	4380	7350
1010	W 36 × 245	72.1	45.0	15.0	3.75	3030	*2600	4210	*3610
943	W 36 × 230	67.7	47.1	14.9	3.73	2830	*2440	3930	*3390
938	W 14 × 455	134	9.49	7.35	4.37	2810	4820	3910	6700
919	W 33 × 240	70.6	40.4	13.9	3.64	2760	2540	3830	*3530
869	W 14 × 426	125	9.97	7.26	4.34	2610	4500	3620	6250
838	W 33 × 220	64.8	42.9	13.8	3.60	2510	*2330	3490	*3240
802	W 14 × 398	117	10.3	7.17	4.31	2410	4210	3340	5850
768	W 36 × 194	57.2	47.4	14.6	2.56	2300	*2060	3200	*2860
756	W 33 × 200	58.9	46.2	13.7	3.57	2270	*2120	3150	*2950
737	W 14 × 370	109	10.8	7.08	4.27	2210	3920	3070	5450
735	W 30 × 210	61.9	39.2	12.6	3.50	2210	2230	3060	*3100
718	W 36 × 182	53.6	50.1	14.5	2.55	2150	*1930	2990	*2680
673	W 14 × 342	101	11.4	6.99	4.24	2020	3640	2800	5050
668	W 36 × 170	50.0	53.2	14.5	2.53	2000	*1800	2780	*2500
661	W 30 × 190	56.0	42.4	12.6	3.47	1980	2020	2750	*2800
625	W 36 × 160	47.1	55.1	14.4	2.50	1880	*1700	2600	*2360
611	W 14 × 314	92.3	12.1	6.90	4.20	1830	3320	2550	4620
594	W 30 × 172	50.7	45.6	12.5	3.43	1780	*1830	2480	*2540
592	W 14 × 320	94.1	8.89	6.63	4.17	1780	3390	2470	4710
581	W 36 × 150	44.2	57.3	14.3	2.47	1740	*1590	2420	*2210
559	W 33 × 152	44.8	52.8	13.5	2.47	1680	*1610	2330	*2240
557	W 27 × 177	52.2	37.7	11.4	3.26	1670	1880	2320	*2610
551	W 14 × 287	84.4	12.8	6.81	4.17	1650	3040	2300	4220
514	W 33 × 141	41.6	55.1	13.4	2.43	1540	*1500	2140	*2080

* Check shape for compliance with Formulas (2.7-1a) or (2.7-1b), Section 2.7, AISC Specification, as applicable, when subjected to combined axial force and bending moment at ultimate loading.

ᵃ Values of M_p and P_y for these shapes computed on the basis of $F_y = 46$ ksi.

AMERICAN INSTITUTE OF STEEL CONSTRUCTION

Z_x PLASTIC DESIGN SELECTION TABLE
For shapes used as beams or columns

Z_x	Shape	A	$\dfrac{d}{t_w}$	r_x	r_y	$F_y = 36$ ksi		$F_y = 50$ ksi	
						M_p	P_y	M_p	P_y
In.³		In.²		In.	In.	Kip-ft.	Kips	Kip-ft.	Kips
510	**W 36 × 135**	39.8	59.4	14.0	2.39	1530	*1430	—	—
502	W 14 × 264	77.6	13.7	6.74	4.14	1510	2790	2090	3880
501	W 27 × 160	47.1	41.2	11.3	3.24	1500	1700	2090	*2360
467	**W 33 × 130**	38.3	57.1	13.2	2.38	1400	*1380	1950	*1920
465	W 24 × 160	47.1	37.7	10.4	3.35	1400	1700	1940	*2360
464	W 14 × 246	72.3	14.4	6.68	4.12	1390	2600	1930	3620
453	W 27 × 145	42.7	44.8	11.3	3.22	1360	*1540	—	—
445	W 14 × 237	69.7	14.8	6.65	4.11	1340	2510	1850	3490
437	W 30 × 132	38.9	49.3	12.2	2.25	1310	*1400	1820	*1950
427	W 14 × 228	67.1	15.3	6.62	4.10	1280	2420	1780	3360
417	W 24 × 145	42.7	40.3	10.3	3.32	1250	1540	1740	*2140
415	**W 33 × 118**	34.8	59.3	13.0	2.32	1250	*1250	—	—
408	W 30 × 124	36.5	51.6	12.1	2.23	1220	*1310	1700	*1830
408	W 14 × 219	64.4	15.8	6.59	4.08	1220	2320	1700	3220
391	W 14 × 211	62.1	16.1	6.56	4.07	1170	2240	1630	3110
378	**W 30 × 116**	34.2	53.2	12.0	2.19	1130	*1230	1580	*1710
373	W 14 × 202	59.4	16.8	6.54	4.06	1120	2140	1550	2970
370	W 24 × 130	38.3	42.9	10.2	3.28	1110	*1380	—	—
357	W 21 × 142	41.8	32.6	9.03	3.15	1070	1500	1490	2090
355	W 14 × 193	56.7	17.4	6.51	4.05	1070	2040	1480	2840
346	**W 30 × 108**	31.8	54.4	11.9	2.15	1040	*1140	1440	*1590
343	W 27 × 114	33.6	47.9	11.0	2.18	1030	*1210	1430	*1680
338	W 24 × 120	35.4	43.7	10.2	2.78	1010	*1270	1410	*1770
338	W 14 × 184	54.1	18.3	6.49	4.04	1010	1950	1410	2710
321	W 14 × 176	51.7	18.6	6.45	4.02	963	1860	1340	2590
318	W 21 × 127	37.4	36.1	8.99	3.13	954	1350	1330	1870
313	**W 30 × 99**	29.1	56.8	11.7	2.10	939	*1050	—	—
311	W 12 × 190	55.9	13.6	5.82	3.25	933	2010	1300	2800
309	W 24 × 110	32.5	47.4	10.1	2.77	927	1170	1290	*1630
305	W 27 × 102	30.0	52.3	11.0	2.15	915	*1080	1270	*1500
303	W 14 × 167	49.1	19.4	6.42	4.01	909	1770	1260	2460
299	S 24 × 120	35.3	30.1	9.26	1.54	897	1270	1250	1770
286	W 14 × 158	46.5	20.5	6.40	4.00	858	1670	1190	2330
280	W 24 × 100	29.5	51.3	10.1	2.75	840	*1060	—	—
278	**W 27 × 94**	27.7	54.9	10.9	2.12	834	* 997	1160	*1390
278	W 21 × 112	33.0	39.8	8.92	3.10	834	1190	—	—
274	S 24 × 105.9	31.1	38.4	9.53	1.58	822	1120	1140	*1560
270	W 14 × 150	44.1	21.4	6.37	3.99	810	1590	1130	2210
259	W 12 × 161	47.4	15.3	5.70	3.20	777	1710	1080	2370
255	W 14 × 142	41.8	21.7	6.32	3.97	765	1500	—	—

* Check shape for compliance with Formulas (2.7-1a) or (2.7-1b), Section 2.7, AISC Specification, as applicable, when subjected to combined axial force and bending moment at ultimate loading.

PLASTIC DESIGN SELECTION TABLE Z_x

For shapes used as beams or columns

Z_x	Shape	A	$\dfrac{d}{t_w}$	r_x	r_y	$F_y = 36$ ksi		$F_y = 50$ ksi	
						M_p	P_y	M_p	P_y
In.³		In.²		In.	In.	Kip-ft.	Kips	Kip-ft.	Kips
253	**W 24 × 94**	27.7	47.1	9.86	1.98	759	* 997	1050	*1390
248	W 18 × 114	33.5	31.1	7.79	2.86	744	1210	1030	1680
244	**W 27 × 84**	24.8	57.6	10.7	2.06	732	* 893	—	—
243	W 14 × 136	40.0	22.3	6.31	3.77	729	1440	1010	2000
240	S 24 × 100	29.4	32.1	9.01	1.27	720	1060	1000	1470
227	W 21 × 96	28.3	36.8	8.61	2.02	681	1020	946	*1420
227	W 18 × 105	30.9	33.1	7.75	2.84	681	1110	946	1550
226	W 14 × 127	37.3	24.0	6.29	3.76	678	1340	—	—
224	**W 24 × 84**	24.7	51.3	9.79	1.95	672	* 889	933	*1240
222	S 24 × 90	26.5	38.5	9.22	1.30	666	954	925	*1330
211	W 14 × 119	35.0	25.4	6.26	3.75	633	1260	—	—
210	W 12 × 133	39.1	17.7	5.59	3.16	630	1410	875	1960
206	W 18 × 96	28.2	35.5	7.70	2.82	618	1020	—	—
205	**S 24 × 79.9**	23.5	47.9	9.47	1.34	615	* 846	854	*1180
201	**W 24 × 76**	22.4	54.3	9.69	1.92	603	* 806	838	*1120
196	W 14 × 111	32.7	26.6	6.23	3.73	588	1180	—	—
194	S 20 × 95	27.9	25.0	7.60	1.33	582	1000	808	1400
192	W 21 × 82	24.2	41.8	8.53	1.99	576	871	800	*1210
186	W 16 × 96	28.2	30.5	6.93	2.82	558	1020	775	1410
186	W 12 × 120	35.3	18.5	5.51	3.13	558	1270	775	1770
179	S 20 × 85	25.0	30.6	7.79	1.36	537	900	746	1250
178	W 18 × 85	25.0	34.8	7.57	2.05	534	900	742	1250
176	**W 24 × 68**	20.0	57.0	9.53	1.87	528	* 720	—	—
172	W 21 × 73	21.5	46.7	8.64	1.81	516	* 774	717	*1080
169	W 16 × 88	25.9	32.1	6.87	2.79	507	932	—	—
164	W 12 × 106	31.2	20.8	5.46	3.11	492	1120	683	1560
161	W 18 × 77	22.7	38.2	7.54	2.04	483	817	671	*1140
160	**W 21 × 68**	20.0	49.1	8.60	1.80	480	* 720	667	*1000
153	S 20 × 75	22.1	31.2	7.60	1.16	459	796	638	1110
152	**W 24 × 61**	18.0	56.6	9.25	1.38	456	* 648	633	* 900
152	W 12 × 99	29.1	21.9	5.43	3.09	456	1050	633	1460
148	W 10 × 112	32.9	15.1	4.67	2.67	444	1180	617	1650
146	W 16 × 78	23.0	30.9	6.75	2.01	438	828	608	1150
145	W 18 × 70	20.6	41.1	7.50	2.02	435	742	604	*1030
145	W 14 × 84	24.7	31.4	6.13	3.02	435	889	—	—
144	W 21 × 62	18.3	52.5	8.54	1.77	432	* 659	600	* 915
140	W 12 × 92	27.1	23.2	5.40	3.08	420	976	—	—
138	S 20 × 65.4	19.2	40.0	7.84	1.19	414	691	575	* 960

* Check shape for compliance with Formulas (2.7-1a) or (2.7-1b), Section 2.7, AISC Specification,
as applicable, when subjected to combined axial force and bending moment at ultimate
loading.

AMERICAN INSTITUTE OF STEEL CONSTRUCTION

Z_x PLASTIC DESIGN SELECTION TABLE

For shapes used as beams or columns

Z_x	Shape	A	$\dfrac{d}{t_w}$	r_x	r_y	$F_y = 36$ ksi		$F_y = 50$ ksi	
						M_p	P_y	M_p	P_y
In.³		In.²		In.	In.	Kip-ft.	Kips	Kip-ft.	Kips
134	**W 24 × 55**	16.2	59.5	9.10	1.34	402	* 583	—	—
134	W 14 × 78	22.9	32.9	6.09	3.00	402	824	—	—
132	W 18 × 64	18.9	44.3	7.46	2.00	396	* 680	550	* 945
132	W 16 × 71	20.9	33.3	6.71	1.99	396	752	550	1050
130	W 10 × 100	29.4	16.2	4.61	2.65	390	1060	542	1470
129	W 12 × 85	25.0	25.3	5.38	3.07	387	900	—	—
126	**W 21 × 55**	16.2	55.5	8.40	1.73	378	* 583	—	—
126	W 14 × 74	21.8	31.5	6.05	2.48	378	785	525	1090
125	S 18 × 70	20.6	25.3	6.71	1.08	375	742	521	1030
123	W 18 × 60	17.7	43.9	7.47	1.68	369	* 637	513	* 885
119	W 12 × 79	23.2	26.3	5.34	3.05	357	835	—	—
118	W 16 × 64	18.8	36.1	6.66	1.97	354	677	492	940
115	W 14 × 68	20.0	33.6	6.02	2.46	345	720	479	1000
114	W 10 × 89	26.2	17.7	4.55	2.63	342	943	475	1310
112	**W 18 × 55**	16.2	46.5	7.42	1.67	336	* 583	467	* 810
108	**W 21 × 49**	14.4	56.6	8.21	1.31	324	* 518	450	* 720
106	W 16 × 58	17.1	39.0	6.62	1.96	318	616	442	* 855
105	S 18 × 54.7	16.1	39.0	7.07	1.14	315	580	438	* 805
102	W 14 × 61	17.9	36.8	5.98	2.45	306	644	—	—
101	W 18 × 50	14.7	50.3	7.38	1.65	303	* 529	421	* 735
97.8	W 10 × 77	22.7	19.9	4.49	2.60	293	817	408	1140
95.3	**W 21 × 44**	13.0	59.4	8.07	1.27	286	* 468	—	—
91.8	W 16 × 50	14.7	42.8	6.68	1.59	275	529	383	* 735
90.6	W 10 × 72	21.2	20.6	4.46	2.59	272	763	378	1060
89.7	W 18 × 45	13.2	53.3	7.30	1.62	269	* 475	—	—
87.1	W 14 × 53	15.6	37.7	5.90	1.92	261	562	363	* 780
86.5	W 12 × 58	17.1	34.0	5.28	2.51	260	616	—	—
82.8	W 10 × 66	19.4	22.7	4.44	2.58	248	698	345	970
82.1	W 16 × 45	13.3	46.6	6.64	1.57	246	* 479	342	* 665
78.4	**W 18 × 40**	11.8	56.6	7.21	1.27	235	* 425	327	* 590
78.4	W 14 × 48	14.1	40.7	5.86	1.91	235	508	327	* 705
77.1	S 15 × 50	14.7	27.3	5.75	1.03	231	529	321	735
75.0	W 10 × 60	17.7	24.7	4.41	2.57	225	637	—	—
72.8	**W 16 × 40**	11.8	52.1	6.62	1.56	218	* 425	303	* 590
72.5	W 12 × 50	14.7	32.9	5.18	1.96	218	529	302	735
70.2	W 8 × 67	19.7	15.7	3.71	2.12	211	709	293	985
69.7	W 14 × 43	12.6	44.4	5.82	1.89	209	* 454	—	—
69.3	S 15 × 42.9	12.6	36.5	5.95	1.07	208	454	289	* 630
67.1	W 10 × 54	15.9	27.5	4.39	2.56	201	572	—	—

* Check shape for compliance with Formulas (2.7-1a) or (2.7-1b), Section 2.7, AISC Specification, as applicable, when subjected to combined axial force and bending moment at ultimate loading.

PLASTIC DESIGN SELECTION TABLE Z_x

For shapes used as beams or columns

Z_x	Shape	A	$\dfrac{d}{t_w}$	r_x	r_y	$F_y = 36$ ksi		$F_y = 50$ ksi	
						M_p	P_y	M_p	P_y
In.³		In.²		In.	In.	Kip-ft.	Kips	Kip-ft.	Kips
66.8	**W 18 × 35**	10.3	59.4	7.05	1.23	200	*371	—	—
64.8	W 12 × 45	13.2	35.9	5.15	1.94	194	475	270	660
64.0	W 16 × 36	10.6	53.0	6.50	1.52	192	*382	—	—
61.6	W 14 × 38	11.2	45.1	5.88	1.54	185	*403	257	*560
61.2	S 12 × 50	14.7	17.5	4.55	1.03	184	529	255	735
59.7	W 8 × 58	17.1	17.2	3.65	2.10	179	616	249	855
57.5	W 12 × 40	11.8	40.6	5.13	1.94	173	425	—	—
54.9	W 10 × 45	13.2	28.9	4.33	2.00	165	475	229	660
54.6	**W 14 × 34**	10.0	48.8	5.83	1.52	164	*360	—	—
54.0	**W 16 × 31**	9.13	57.6	6.40	1.17	162	*329	225	*457
53.1	S 12 × 40.8	12.0	26.0	4.77	1.06	159	432	221	600
51.6	W 12 × 36	10.6	40.1	5.15	1.55	155	382	215	*530
49.0	W 8 × 48	14.1	21.0	3.61	2.08	147	508	204	705
46.9	W 10 × 39	11.5	31.3	4.27	1.98	141	414	—	—
44.8	S 12 × 35	10.3	28.0	4.72	0.98	134	371	187	515
44.1	**W 12 × 31**	9.13	45.6	5.12	1.54	132	*329	184	*457
44.0	**W 16 × 26**	7.67	62.6	6.25	1.12	132	*276	—	—
42.0	S 12 × 31.8	9.35	34.3	4.83	1.00	126	337	175	468
40.0	**W 14 × 26**	7.67	54.5	5.64	1.08	120	*276	167	*384
39.8	W 8 × 40	11.8	22.6	3.53	2.04	119	425	—	—
38.0	W 12 × 27	7.95	50.5	5.07	1.52	114	*286	—	—
35.4	S 10 × 35	10.3	16.8	3.78	0.901	106	371	148	515
34.7	W 10 × 29	8.54	35.4	4.30	1.38	104	307	145	427
34.7	W 8 × 35	10.3	25.8	3.50	2.03	104	371	—	—
33.1	**W 14 × 22**	6.49	59.7	5.53	1.04	99.3	*234	—	—
30.9	M 10 × 29.1	8.56	23.1	3.92	1.14	92.7	308	—	—
29.6	W 10 × 25	7.36	40.0	4.26	1.37	88.8	265	123	*368
29.3	**W 12 × 22**	6.47	47.3	4.91	0.847	87.9	*233	122	*324
28.4	S 10 × 25.4	7.46	32.2	4.07	0.954	85.2	269	118	373
27.1	W 8 × 28	8.23	28.3	3.45	1.62	81.3	296	—	—
26.4	M 10 × 22.9	6.73	40.8	4.16	1.22	79.2	242	—	—
24.8	**M 14 × 17.2**	5.05	66.7	5.40	0.725	74.4	*182	—	—
24.7	W 12 × 19	5.59	51.3	4.82	0.820	74.1	*201	103	*280
24.1	W 10 × 21	6.20	41.3	4.15	1.32	72.3	223	—	—
23.1	W 8 × 24	7.06	32.4	3.42	1.61	69.3	254	—	—
21.6	W 10 × 19	5.61	41.0	4.14	0.874	64.8	202	90.0	*281

* Check shape for compliance with Formulas (2.7-1a) or (2.7-1b), Section 2.7, AISC Specification, as applicable, when subjected to combined axial force and bending moment at ultimate loading.

Z_x PLASTIC DESIGN SELECTION TABLE

For shapes used as beams or columns

Z_x	Shape	A	$\dfrac{d}{t_w}$	r_x	r_y	$F_y = 36$ ksi		$F_y = 50$ ksi	
						M_p	P_y	M_p	P_y
In.³		In.²		In.	In.	Kip-ft.	Kips	Kip-ft.	Kips
20.6	W 12 × 16.5	4.87	52.2	4.65	0.770	61.8	*175	—	—
19.7	M 8 × 22.5	6.60	21.3	3.22	1.06	59.1	238	—	—
19.3	S 8 × 23	6.77	18.1	3.10	0.798	57.9	244	80.4	339
19.1	W 8 × 20	5.89	32.8	3.43	1.25	57.3	212	79.6	295
18.9	W 6 × 25	7.35	19.9	2.69	1.53	56.7	265	78.8	368
18.6	W 10 × 17	4.99	42.2	4.05	0.844	55.8	180	77.5	*250
17.4	M 8 × 18.5	5.44	34.8	3.38	1.12	52.2	196	—	—
16.5	S 8 × 18.4	5.41	29.5	3.26	0.831	49.5	195	68.8	271
16.0	W 10 × 15	4.41	43.5	3.95	0.809	48.0	*159	—	—
15.9	W 8 × 17	5.01	34.8	3.36	1.22	47.7	180	—	—
15.6	M 6 × 22.5	6.62	16.1	2.49	1.37	46.8	238	—	—
15.0	W 6 × 20	5.88	24.0	2.66	1.51	45.0	212	—	—
14.5	S 7 × 20	5.88	15.6	2.69	0.734	43.5	212	60.4	294
14.5	M 6 × 20	5.89	24.0	2.57	1.40	43.5	212	—	—
14.3	M 12 × 11.8	3.47	67.8	4.55	0.532	42.9	*125	—	—
13.6	W 8 × 15	4.43	33.1	3.29	0.876	40.8	159	56.7	222
12.1	S 7 × 15.3	4.50	27.8	2.86	0.766	36.3	162	50.4	225
11.6	W 6 × 16	4.72	24.0	2.59	0.967	34.8	170	48.3	236
11.4	W 8 × 13	3.83	34.8	3.21	0.842	34.2	138	—	—
11.3	W 5 × 18.5	5.43	19.3	2.16	1.28	33.9	195	47.1	272
11.0	M 5 × 18.9	5.55	15.8	2.08	1.19	33.0	200	45.8	278
10.6	S 6 × 17.25	5.07	12.9	2.28	0.675	31.8	183	44.2	254
9.61	W 5 × 16	4.70	20.8	2.13	1.26	28.8	169	40.0	235
9.19	M 10 × 9	2.65	63.7	3.83	0.480	27.6	* 95.4	—	—
8.47	S 6 × 12.5	3.67	25.9	2.45	0.705	25.4	132	35.3	184
8.23	W 6 × 12	3.54	26.1	2.48	0.918	24.7	127	—	—
7.42	S 5 × 14.75	4.34	10.1	1.87	0.620	22.3	156	30.9	217
6.31	M 4 × 13.8	4.06	12.8	1.63	0.939	18.9	146	26.3	203
6.27	W 4 × 13	3.82	14.9	1.72	0.991	18.8	138	26.1	191
6.06	M 4 × 13	3.81	15.7	1.66	0.939	18.2	137	25.3	191
5.67	S 5 × 10	2.94	23.4	2.05	0.643	17.0	106	23.6	147
5.42	M 8 × 6.5	1.92	59.3	3.10	0.423	16.3	* 69.1	—	—
4.04	S 4 × 9.5	2.79	12.3	1.56	0.569	12.1	100	16.8	140
4.03	M 7 × 5.5	1.62	54.7	2.73	0.392	12.1	* 58.3	16.8	* 81.0
3.51	S 4 × 7.7	2.26	20.7	1.64	0.581	10.5	81.4	14.6	113
2.80	M 6 × 4.4	1.29	52.6	2.36	0.358	8.40	* 46.4	11.7	* 64.5
2.36	S 3 × 7.5	2.21	8.6	1.15	0.516	7.08	79.6	9.83	111
1.95	S 3 × 5.7	1.67	17.6	1.23	0.522	5.85	60.1	8.13	83.5

*Check shape for compliance with Formulas (2.7-1a) or (2.7-1b), Section 2.7, AISC Specification, as applicable, when subjected to combined axial force and bending moment at ultimate loading.

ALLOWABLE LOADS ON BEAMS
GENERAL NOTES

The tables of allowable loads for W, M, and S shapes, channels (C, MC), and angles (L), used as simple beams, give the total allowable uniformly distributed loads in kips for laterally supported steel beams. The tables are based on the allowable stresses specified in Section 1.5.1.4 of the AISC Specification. Separate tables are presented for $F_y = 36$ ksi and $F_y = 50$ ksi. The tabulated loads include the weight of the beam, which should be deducted to arrive at the net load the beam will support.

The tables are also applicable to laterally supported simple beams for concentrated loading conditions. A method to determine the beam load capacity for several cases is shown in the discussion on "Use of Tables."

It is assumed in all cases that the loads are applied normal to the X-X axis, shown in the tables of properties of shapes in Part 1 of this Manual, and that the beam deflects vertically in the plane of bending. If the conditions of loading involve forces outside of this plane, allowable loads must be determined from the general theory of flexure in accordance with the character of the load and its mode of application.

LATERAL SUPPORT OF BEAMS

The allowable bending stress and resultant allowable load capacity of a beam is dependent upon lateral support of its compression flange in addition to its section properties. In these tables, the notation L_c is used to denote the maximum unbraced length of compression flange, in feet, for which the allowable loads for compact symmetrical shapes are calculated with an allowable stress of 0.66 F_y and for which certain non-compact shapes are calculated with a value of allowable stress between 0.60 F_y and 0.66 F_y, as permitted by Section 1.5.1.4.2. The value of L_c is equal to the smaller value determined from the expressions

$$76b_f/(12\sqrt{F_y}) \quad \text{or} \quad 20{,}000/[12\ (d/A_f)\ F_y]$$

in accordance with Section 1.5.1.4.1, requirement (e).

The notation L_u is the maximum unbraced length of the compression flange, in feet, beyond which the allowable bending stress is less than 0.60 F_y, in accordance with the provisions of Section 1.5.1.4.6a, when $C_b = 1.0$. For most shapes the value of L_u, in feet, for steel of $F_y = 36$ ksi, is $556/[12(d/A_f)]$ and for $F_y = 50$ ksi is $400/[12(d/A_f)]$, as derived from Formula (1.5-7). For a few shapes, L_u is derived from Formula (1.5-6a) where this is more liberal.

These tables are not applicable for beams with unbraced lengths greater than L_u. For such cases, use of the charts of "Allowable Moments in Beams with Unbraced Length Greater than L_u" is recommended.

FLEXURAL STRESS AND TABULATED LOADS

For the symmetrical rolled shapes designated W, M and S, the allowable bending stress and resultant allowable loads are based on the assumption that the compression flanges of the beams are laterally supported at intervals not greater than L_c. When the value of L_c does not appear, L_u is the maximum unbraced length for which the loads are valid.

For compact shapes, the tabulated load is based on an allowable stress of 24 ksi for $F_y = 36$ ksi steel and 33 ksi for $F_y = 50$ ksi steel (see Section 1.5.1.4.1 of the Specification). For non-compact shapes, the tabulated load is based on an allowable stress of $0.60\,F_y$ or a value between $0.60\ F_y$ and $0.66\,F_y$, depending upon the web depth-thickness or flange width-thickness ratios. (See Sections 1.5.1.4.2 and 1.5.1.4.6a.) For non-compact shapes, the magnitude of allowable stress used to compute the tabulated loads is noted in parentheses (in ksi) at the bottom of the allowable load column.

When the unbraced length of a symmetrical member is greater than L_c but less than L_u, the tabulated load must be reduced by the ratio of $0.60\,F_y$ over the allowable stress used to compute its capacity.

In the case of American Standard channels (C) used as beams, the tabulated loads are based on an allowable stress of 22 ksi for $F_y = 36$ ksi, in accordance with Section 1.5.1.4.6a, and the assumption that the compression flanges are laterally supported at intervals not greater than L_u.

Tabulated loads for angles are based on an allowable stress of $0.60\,F_y$, which presumes adequate lateral support of the angle leg subjected to compression. Since the compression stress due to bending varies linearly across a partial width of angle leg, the width and thickness terms defined in Section 1.9 of the Specification are as shown:

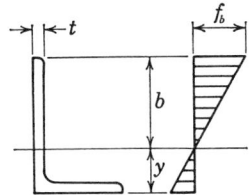

For the angle sizes tabulated, the width-thickness ratios calculated on this basis do not exceed the provisions of Section 1.9.

The tables are not applicable for angles laterally unsupported or subjected to torsion; for such members a special investigation is necessary.

SHEARING STRESSES

For relatively short spans, the allowable loads for beams and channels may be limited by the shearing stress in the web, instead of by the maximum bending stress in the flanges. This limit is indicated in the tables by solid horizontal lines. Loads shown above these lines will produce the maximum allowable shear in the beam web.

CRIPPLING VALUES OF BEAM WEBS

AISC Specification Section 1.10.10 requires that beams with unstiffened webs be designed so that the compression stress in the web at the toe of the fillet, resulting from reactions or concentrated loads, must not exceed $0.75\,F_y$. (For limiting stress values see Specification Appendix A, Section 1.10.10.1.)

When the following values are exceeded, the webs of the beams should be reinforced, or the length of bearing increased. In all cases proper lateral support must be provided for the top flanges of beams at the reaction point, to prevent a decrease in the beam web crippling strength.

Maximum end reaction $= 0.75\ F_y t\ (N + k)$
Maximum interior load $= 0.75\ F_y t\ (N + 2k)$

where

t = thickness of web, in inches
k = distance from outer face of flange to web toe of fillet, in inches
N = length of bearing or length of concentrated load, in inches (not less than k for end reactions)

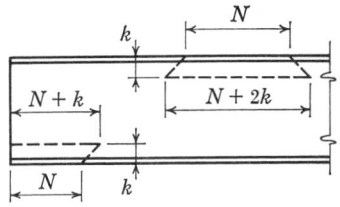

VERTICAL DEFLECTION

For rolled shapes designated W, S, and C, the column at the right of each group of nominal depths gives the deflection for beams of various spans when supporting the full tabulated allowable loads. These deflections are based on the nominal depth of the beams. The following equation may be used for calculating the maximum deflection of any symmetrical, uniformly loaded beam or girder:

$$\Delta = \frac{5Wl^3}{384EI}$$

where

Δ = deflection, in inches
W = total uniform load, including weight of beam, in kips
l = span, in inches

For $E = 29,000$ ksi and specific values of F_b, this equation reduces to the expressions shown in the table below. In this table, L = span, in feet, and d = depth of beam, in inches.

	F_b, ksi	Deflection, in.
$F_y = 50$ ksi	33	$0.03414L^2/d$
	30	$0.03103L^2/d$
$F_y = 36$ ksi	24	$0.02483L^2/d$
	22	$0.02276L^2/d$

The deflections tabulated for W and S shapes are calculated on the basis of 24 ksi for $F_y = 36$ ksi, and 33 ksi for $F_y = 50$ ksi, regardless of whether the sections are compact or non-compact. Therefore, the tabulated deflections must be reduced to correspond to the lower allowable stresses used to calculate the tabulated loads for non-compact shapes, or compact shapes with unsupported length between L_c and L_u. The table that follows lists the reduction factors.

REDUCTION FACTORS FOR TABULATED DEFLECTION

	Unbraced length, L_b	Compact	Non-compact
$F_y = 36$ ksi	$L_c \geq L_b$	$1.0 \times \Delta$	$\dfrac{(*)}{24} \times \Delta$
	$L_u \geq L_b > L_c$	$\dfrac{22}{24} \times \Delta$	
$F_y = 50$ ksi	$L_c \geq L_b$	$1.0 \times \Delta$	$\dfrac{(*)}{33} \times \Delta$
	$L_u \geq L_b > L_c$	$\dfrac{30}{33} \times \Delta$	

* Value listed in parentheses at bottom of allowable load column in tables

The deflections tabulated for channels are calculated on the basis of 22 ksi.

The live load deflection of floor beams supporting plastered ceilings should be limited to not more than $\frac{1}{360}$ of the span length. This limit is not reached for the span lengths tabulated when the ratio of live load to dead load is approximately 1.0.

Deflections are not tabulated for the M shapes or angles included in the tables. When required, they may be calculated from the general expression for deflection given above.

ALLOWABLE LOADS ON BEAMS

USE OF TABLES

FOR F_y = 36 KSI STEEL

The loads tabulated for steel of F_y = 36 ksi are based on allowable bending stresses of 24 ksi for compact shapes, and a reduced stress for non-compact shapes, shown in parentheses at the bottom of the load column. The beams must be adequately braced and have an axis of symmetry in the plane of loading. Loads may be read directly from the table when the distance between points of lateral support of the compression flange, L_b, does not exceed L_c for compact and non-compact symmetrical shapes, or L_u for channels.

When $L_u \geq L_b > L_c$, the tabulated loads must be reduced as follows:

1. For compact shape, multiply load by 22/24.
2. For non-compact shape, multiply load by 22 ÷ stress shown in parentheses at bottom of load column.

When $L_b > L_u$, the allowable bending stress is less than 22 ksi and the tables are not applicable. Use of the charts of "Allowable Moments in Beams with Unbraced Lengths Greater than L_u" is recommended.

FOR F_y = 50 KSI STEEL

The loads tabulated for steel of F_y = 50 ksi are based on allowable bending stresses of 33 ksi for compact shapes, and a reduced stress for non-compact shapes, shown in parentheses at the bottom of the load column. The beams must be adequately braced and have an axis of symmetry in the plane of loading. Loads may be read directly from the table when the distance between points of lateral support, L_b, does not exceed L_c for compact and non-compact W and M shapes.

When $L_u \geq L_b > L_c$, the tabulated loads must be reduced as follows:

1. For compact shape, multiply load by 30/33
2. For non-compact shape, multiply load by 30 ÷ stress shown in parentheses at bottom of load column

When $L_b > L_u$, the allowable bending stress is less than 30 ksi and the tables are not applicable. Use of the charts of "Allowable Moments in Beams with Unbraced Lengths Greater than L_u" is recommended.

CONCENTRATED LOAD CONDITIONS

The load tables are also applicable to laterally supported simple beams with equal concentrated loads spaced as shown in the following table of equivalent uniform loads. Except for short spans where shear controls the design, the beam load tables may be entered with an equivalent uniform load, equivalent in effect to the sum of the concentrated loads on the beam. Loads which will produce the maximum allowable shear in the beam web are shown in the load tables above the heavy horizontal lines. Deflections listed in the load tables must be multiplied by the proper deflection coefficient to determine the concentrated load deflection.

AMERICAN INSTITUTE OF STEEL CONSTRUCTION

TABLE OF EQUIVALENT UNIFORM LOADS

Type of Loading: Equal Loads, Equal Spaces	Equivalent Uniform Load	Deflection Coefficient
P $L/2$ $L/2$	2.00 P	0.80
P P $L/3$ $L/3$ $L/3$	2.67 P	1.02
P P P $L/4$ $L/4$ $L/4$ $L/4$	4.00 P	0.95
P P P P $L/5$ $L/5$ $L/5$ $L/5$ $L/5$	4.80 P	1.01

EXAMPLE

Given:

Using F_y = 36 ksi steel, select an 18-in. deep beam to span 30 ft. and support three equal concentrated loads of 20 kips located at the quarter points of the span.

Solution:

Refer to the table of equivalent uniform loads and note that:

    Equivalent uniform load = 4.0 P

    Deflection coefficient = 0.95

1. Equivalent uniform load = 4.0 × 20 = 80 kips
2. Enter beam load tables for W18 and 30 ft. span length. Select W18 ×85 with allowable load = 84 kips
3. Check deflection:

    From load table, uniform load deflection = 1.24 in.

$$\text{Concentrated load deflection} = 0.95 \times 1.24 \times \frac{80}{84} = 1.12 \text{ in.}$$

If the beam depth is not restricted, a shape with less weight can usually be selected by scanning the load tables for deeper sections. For example; W21 ×73, allowable load = 81 kips; W24 ×68, allowable load = 82 kips.

ALLOWABLE LOADS ON BEAMS

REFERENCE NOTES ON TABLES

1. L_c = Maximum unbraced length of compression flange, in feet. Allowable loads for a compact symmetrical shape are calculated with an allowable bending stress of $F_b = 0.66 F_y$; allowable loads for a non-compact symmetrical shape, as determined by $b_f/2t_f$, are calculated with an allowable bending stress of $F_b = F_y [0.733 - 0.0014 (b_f/2t_f)\sqrt{F_y}]$, Formula (1.5-5).

2. L_u = Maximum unbraced length of compression flange, in feet, beyond which the allowable bending stress would be less than $0.6 F_y$ when $C_b = 1$ due to moment gradient. Listed table values for most shapes are derived from the expression $L_u = 20,000/[12(d/A_f)F_y]$. For some shapes the expression $L_u = \sqrt{(102 \times 10^3 r_T{}^2)/(144 F_y)}$ will give a more liberal value and in such cases this latter value is shown.

3. L_b = Unbraced length of compression flange, feet.

4. S = Section modulus, inches³.

5. Formulas for reaction values:
   Values of V, R, R_i, and N_e used for connection design and design checks are included at the bottom of the tables for each shape. These symbols and corresponding formulas are defined in the table below:

Definition of symbols	$F_y = 36$ ksi	$F_y = 50$ ksi
V = Maximum web shear, kips	$14.5 dt$	$20 dt$
R = Maximum end reaction for 3½-in. bearing, kips	$27 t (3.5 + k)$	$37.5 t (3.5 + k)$
R_i = Increase in R for each additional inch of bearing, kips	$27 t$	$37.5 t$
N_e = Length of bearing to develop V, inches	$(V/R_i) - k$	$(V/R_i) - k$

6. Load above the heavy line in the load column is limited by maximum allowable web shear.

7. Value in parentheses at bottom of load column indicates the allowable stress, in ksi, used to tabulate the loads for non-compact shapes.

| $F_y = 36$ ksi | | | BEAMS | | | W 36 |

BEAMS
W shapes
Allowable uniform loads in kips
for beams laterally supported
For beams laterally unsupported, see page 2 - 84

Designation				W36			
Weight per Foot		300	280	260	245	230	Deflection Inches
Flange Width		16⅝	16⅝	16½	16½	16½	
L_c		17.6	17.5	17.5	17.4	17.4	
L_u		35.3	33.1	30.5	28.6	26.8	
	16					792	0.18
	17	1006	937	884	839	788	0.20
	18	987	916	846	795	744	0.22
	19	935	867	802	753	705	0.25
	20	888	824	762	715	670	0.28
	21	846	785	725	681	638	0.30
	22	807	749	692	650	609	0.33
	23	772	717	662	622	582	0.36
	24	740	687	635	596	558	0.40
	25	710	659	609	572	536	0.43
	26	683	634	586	550	515	0.47
	27	658	610	564	530	496	0.50
	28	634	589	544	511	478	0.54
	29	612	568	525	493	462	0.58
	30	592	549	508	477	446	0.62
	31	573	532	491	461	432	0.66
	32	555	515	476	447	419	0.71
	34	522	485	448	421	394	0.80
	36	493	458	423	397	372	0.89
	38	467	434	401	376	352	1.00
	40	444	412	381	358	335	1.10
	42	423	392	363	341	319	1.22
	44	404	375	346	325	304	1.34
	46	386	358	331	311	291	1.46
	48	370	343	317	298	279	1.59
	50	355	330	305	286	268	1.72
	52	342	317	293	275	258	1.86
	54	329	305	282	265	248	2.01
	56	317	294	272	255	239	2.16
	58	306	284	263	247	231	2.32
	60	296	275	254	238	223	2.48
	62	286	266	246	231	216	2.65
	64	278	258	238	224	209	2.82
	66	269	250	231	217	203	3.00
	68	261	242	224	210	197	3.19
	70	254	235	218	204	191	3.38
	72	247	229	212	199	186	3.58

(Side label: Span in Feet; $F_y = 36$ ksi)

Properties and Reaction Values

	300	280	260	245	230	
S in.³	1110	1030	952	894	837	For explanation of deflection see page 2 - 23
V kips	503	468	442	419	396	
R kips	161	148	138	129	121	
R_i kips	25.5	23.9	22.7	21.7	20.5	
N_e in.	16.9	16.9	16.9	16.9	16.9	

Load above heavy line is limited by maximum allowable web shear.

W 36		BEAMS					$F_y = 36$ ksi

BEAMS
W shapes

Allowable uniform loads in kips
for beams laterally supported

For beams laterally unsupported, see page 2 - 84

Designation					W36			
Weight per Foot		194	182	170	160	150	135	Deflection Inches
Flange Width		12⅛	12⅛	12	12	12	12	
L_c		12.8	12.7	12.7	12.7	12.6	12.3	
L_u		19.4	18.2	17.0	15.7	14.6	13.2	
	11						617	0.08
	12				682	650	587	0.10
	13	815	764	713	667	620	542	0.12
	14	760	711	663	619	576	503	0.14
	15	709	663	619	578	538	469	0.16
	16	665	622	580	542	504	440	0.18
	17	626	585	546	510	474	414	0.20
	18	591	553	516	482	448	391	0.22
	19	560	524	488	456	424	371	0.25
	20	532	498	464	434	403	352	0.28
	21	507	474	442	413	384	335	0.30
	22	484	452	422	394	367	320	0.33
	24	443	415	387	361	336	293	0.40
	26	409	383	357	334	310	271	0.47
	28	380	355	331	310	288	251	0.54
	30	355	332	309	289	269	235	0.62
	32	333	311	290	271	252	220	0.71
	34	313	293	273	255	237	207	0.80
	36	296	276	258	241	224	196	0.89
	38	280	262	244	228	212	185	1.00
	40	266	249	232	217	202	176	1.10
	42	253	237	221	206	192	168	1.22
	44	242	226	211	197	183	160	1.34
	46	231	216	202	189	175	153	1.46
	48	222	207	193	181	168	147	1.59
	50	213	199	186	173	161	141	1.72
	52	205	191	178	167	155	135	1.86
	54	197	184	172	161	149	130	2.01
	56	190	178	166	155	144	126	2.16
	58	183	172	160	150	139	121	2.32
	60	177	166	155	145	134	117	2.48
	62	172	161	150	140	130	114	2.65
	64	166	156	¹45	136	126	110	2.82
	66	161	151	₁41	131	122	107	3.00
	68	156	146	136	128	119	104	3.19
	70	152	142	133	124	115	101	3.38
	72	148	138	129	120	112	98	3.58

(Span in Feet — left margin; $F_y = 36$ ksi — far left margin)

Properties and Reaction Values

	194	182	170	160	150	135	
S in.³	665	622	580	542	504	440	For explanation of deflection see page 2 - 23
V kips	407	382	357	341	325	308	
R kips	118	110	101	96	91	84	
R_i kips	20.8	19.6	18.4	17.6	16.9	16.1	
N_e in.	17.4	17.4	17.4	17.4	17.4	17.4	

Load above heavy line is limited by maximum allowable web shear.

AMERICAN INSTITUTE OF STEEL CONSTRUCTION

F_y = 36 ksi

BEAMS
W shapes

W 33

Allowable uniform loads in kips
for beams laterally supported

For beams laterally unsupported, see page 2 - 84

Designation	W33			W33				Deflection Inches
Weight per Foot	240	220	200	152	141	130	118	
Flange Width	15⅞	15¾	15¾	11⅝	11½	11½	11½	
L_c	16.7	16.7	16.6	12.2	12.2	12.1	11.9	
L_u	30.7	28.1	25.4	16.8	15.4	13.8	12.7	
F_y = 36 ksi — Span in Feet								
10							528	0.08
11						557	522	0.09
12				617	584	541	479	0.11
13				599	551	500	442	0.13
14				557	512	464	410	0.15
15		747	684	519	478	433	383	0.17
16	806	742	671	487	448	406	359	0.19
17	765	698	632	458	422	382	338	0.22
18	723	660	596	433	398	361	319	0.24
19	685	625	565	410	377	342	302	0.27
20	650	594	537	390	358	325	287	0.30
21	619	565	511	371	341	309	274	0.33
22	591	540	488	354	326	295	261	0.36
23	566	516	467	339	312	282	250	0.40
24	542	495	447	325	299	271	239	0.43
25	520	475	429	312	287	260	230	0.47
26	500	457	413	300	276	250	221	0.51
28	465	424	383	278	256	232	205	0.59
30	434	396	358	260	239	217	191	0.68
32	407	371	336	244	224	203	180	0.77
34	383	349	316	229	211	191	169	0.87
36	361	330	298	216	199	180	160	0.98
38	342	312	283	205	189	171	151	1.09
40	325	297	268	195	179	162	144	1.20
42	310	283	256	186	171	155	137	1.33
44	296	270	244	177	163	148	131	1.46
46	283	258	233	169	156	141	125	1.59
48	271	247	224	162	149	135	120	1.73
50	260	237	215	156	143	130	115	1.88
52	250	228	206	150	138	125	110	2.03
54	241	220	199	144	133	120	106	2.19
56	232	212	192	139	128	116	103	2.36
58	224	205	185	134	124	112	99	2.53
60	217	198	179	130	119	108	96	2.71
62	210	191	173	126	116	105	93	2.89
64	203	186	168	122	112	102	90	3.08
66	197	180	163	118	109	98	87	3.28
Properties and Reaction Values								
S in.^{3}	813	742	671	487	448	406	359	For explanation of deflection see page 2 - 23
V kips	403	374	342	308	292	278	264	
R kips	133	122	110	92	86	81	76	
R_i kips	22.4	20.9	19.3	17.1	16.3	15.7	15.0	
N_e in.	15.6	15.5	15.5	16.1	16.1	16.1	16.1	

Load above heavy line is limited by maximum allowable web shear.

W 30

I

BEAMS
W shapes

Allowable uniform loads in kips
for beams laterally supported
For beams laterally unsupported, see page **2-84**

$F_y = 36$ ksi

$F_y = 36$ ksi

Designation		W30				W30			
Weight per Foot	210	190	172	132	124	116	108	99	Deflection Inches
Flange Width	15⅛	15	15	10½	10½	10½	10½	10½	
L_c	15.9	15.9	15.8	11.1	11.1	11.1	11.1	10.9	
L_u	30.3	27.4	24.8	16.1	15.0	13.8	12.4	11.6	

Span in Feet — $F_y = 36$ ksi

Span	210	190	172	132	124	116	108	99	Deflection
9								449	0.07
10						491	474	432	0.08
11				540	512	479	436	393	0.10
12				507	473	439	400	360	0.12
13				468	437	405	369	332	0.14
14			568	434	406	376	343	309	0.16
15	683	620	565	405	379	351	320	288	0.19
16	651	587	530	380	355	329	300	270	0.21
17	613	552	499	358	334	310	282	254	0.24
18	579	522	471	338	316	292	267	240	0.27
19	548	494	446	320	299	277	253	227	0.30
20	521	470	424	304	284	263	240	216	0.33
21	496	447	404	290	270	251	229	206	0.36
22	473	427	385	276	258	239	218	196	0.40
23	453	408	369	264	247	229	209	188	0.44
24	434	391	353	253	237	219	200	180	0.48
25	417	376	339	243	227	211	192	173	0.52
26	401	361	326	234	218	202	185	166	0.56
27	386	348	314	225	210	195	178	160	0.60
28	372	335	303	217	203	188	171	154	0.65
29	359	324	292	210	196	182	166	149	0.70
30	347	313	283	203	189	175	160	144	0.74
32	326	294	265	190	178	165	150	135	0.85
34	306	276	249	179	167	155	141	127	0.96
36	289	261	236	169	158	146	133	120	1.07
38	274	247	223	160	149	139	126	114	1.20
40	260	235	212	152	142	132	120	108	1.32
42	248	224	202	145	135	125	114	103	1.46
44	237	213	193	138	129	120	109	98	1.60
46	226	204	184	132	123	114	104	94	1.75
48	217	196	177	127	118	110	100	90	1.91
50	208	188	170	122	114	105	96	86	2.07
52	200	181	163	117	109	101	92	83	2.24
54	193	174	157	113	105	97	89	80	2.41
56	186	168	151	109	101	94	86	77	2.60
58	180	162	146	105	98	91	83	74	2.78
60	174	157	141	101	95	88	80	72	2.98

Properties and Reaction Values

	210	190	172	132	124	116	108	99	
S in.³	651	587	530	380	355	329	300	270	For explanation of deflection see page **2-23**
V kips	341	310	284	270	256	245	237	224	
R kips	122	109	98	87	82	78	75	70	
R_i kips	20.9	19.2	17.7	16.6	15.8	15.2	14.8	14.1	
N_e in.	14.0	14.0	14.0	14.5	14.5	14.5	14.5	14.5	

Load above heavy line is limited by maximum allowable web shear.

AMERICAN INSTITUTE OF STEEL CONSTRUCTION

| $F_y = 36$ ksi | | | **BEAMS**
W shapes
Allowable uniform loads in kips
for beams laterally supported
For beams laterally unsupported, see page 2 - 84 | | | | **W 27**
I |

Designation		W27			W27				
Weight per Foot		177	160	145	114	102	94	84	Deflection Inches
Flange Width		14⅛	14	14	10⅛	10	10	10	
L_c		14.9	14.8	14.7	10.6	10.6	10.5	10.5	
L_u		28.4	25.7	23.5	15.9	14.2	12.8	11.2	
	9							358	0.07
	10				451	407	382	339	0.09
	11				436	388	353	308	0.11
	12				400	356	324	283	0.13
	13	574	517	468	369	329	299	261	0.16
	14	565	510	462	343	305	278	242	0.18
	15	527	476	431	320	285	259	226	0.21
	16	494	446	404	300	267	243	212	0.24
	17	465	420	380	282	251	229	200	0.27
	18	439	396	359	267	237	216	188	0.30
	19	416	376	340	253	225	205	179	0.33
	20	395	357	323	240	214	194	170	0.37
	21	376	340	308	229	203	185	162	0.41
	22	359	324	294	218	194	177	154	0.45
	23	344	310	281	209	186	169	147	0.49
	24	329	297	269	200	178	162	141	0.53
	25	316	285	259	192	171	156	136	0.57
	26	304	274	249	185	164	150	130	0.62
	27	293	264	239	178	158	144	126	0.67
	28	282	255	231	171	153	139	121	0.72
	29	273	246	223	166	147	134	117	0.77
	30	263	238	215	160	142	130	113	0.83
	31	255	230	209	155	138	125	109	0.88
	32	247	223	202	150	134	122	106	0.94
	33	240	216	196	145	129	118	103	1.00
	34	232	210	190	141	126	114	100	1.06
	35	226	204	185	137	122	111	97	1.13
	36	220	198	180	133	119	108	94	1.19
	38	208	188	170	126	112	102	89	1.33
	40	198	178	162	120	107	97	85	1.47
	42	188	170	154	114	102	93	81	1.62
	44	180	162	147	109	97	88	77	1.78
	46	172	155	141	104	93	85	74	1.95
	48	165	149	135	100	89	81	71	2.12
	50	158	143	129	96	85	78	68	2.30
	52	152	137	124	92	82	75	65	2.49
	54	146	132	120	89	79	72	63	2.68

Span in Feet — $F_y = 36$ ksi

Properties and Reaction Values									
S in.³		494	446	404	300	267	243	212	For explanation of deflection see page 2 - 23
V kips		287	258	234	225	203	191	179	
R kips		110	99	88	80	72	66	62	
R_i kips		19.6	17.8	16.2	15.4	14.0	13.2	12.5	
N_e in.		12.5	12.5	12.5	13.0	12.9	13.0	12.9	

Load above heavy line is limited by maximum allowable web shear.

W 24

I

BEAMS
W shapes

Allowable uniform loads in kips
for beams laterally supported

For beams laterally unsupported, see page **2** - 84

$F_y = 36$ ksi

Designation		W24			W24			
Weight per Foot		160	145	130	120	110	100	Deflection Inches
Flange Width		14⅛	14	14	12⅛	12	12	
L_c		14.9	14.8	14.8	12.8	12.7	12.7	
L_u		29.9	27.1	24.1	21.4	19.7	17.9	
	12				392	357	326	0.15
	13		432	397	369	340	308	0.17
	14	470	426	379	343	315	286	0.20
	15	442	398	354	320	294	267	0.23
	16	414	373	332	300	276	250	0.26
	17	390	351	312	282	260	235	0.30
	18	368	332	295	267	245	222	0.34
	19	349	314	280	253	232	211	0.37
	20	331	298	266	240	221	200	0.41
	21	315	284	253	229	210	190	0.46
	22	301	271	241	218	201	182	0.50
	23	288	259	231	209	192	174	0.55
	24	276	249	221	200	184	167	0.60
	25	265	239	212	192	177	160	0.65
	26	255	230	204	185	170	154	0.70
	27	245	221	197	178	164	148	0.75
	28	237	213	190	171	158	143	0.81
	29	228	206	183	166	152	138	0.87
	30	221	199	177	160	147	133	0.93
	31	214	193	171	155	142	129	0.99
	32	207	187	166	150	138	125	1.06
	33	201	181	161	145	134	121	1.13
	34	195	176	156	141	130	118	1.20
	35	189	171	152	137	126	114	1.27
	36	184	166	148	133	123	111	1.34
	37	179	161	144	130	119	108	1.42
	38	174	157	140	126	116	105	1.49
	39	170	153	136	123	113	103	1.57
	40	166	149	133	120	110	100	1.66
	41	162	146	130	117	108	98	1.74
	42	158	142	126	114	105	95	1.82
	43	154	139	124	112	103	93	1.91
	44	151	136	121	109	100	91	2.00
	45	147	133	118	107	98	89	2.09
	46	144	130	115	104	96	87	2.19
	48	138	124	111	100	92	83	2.38
	50	132	119	106	96	88	80	2.59

Span in Feet (left side label) — $F_y = 36$ ksi (left margin)

Properties and Reaction Values

S in.³		414	373	332	300	276	250	For explanation of deflection see page **2** - 23
V kips		235	216	199	196	179	163	
R kips		96	87	79	78	71	64	
R_i kips		17.7	16.4	15.3	15.0	13.8	12.6	
N_e in.		11.3	11.3	11.3	11.4	11.3	11.3	

Load above heavy line is limited by maximum allowable web shear.

AMERICAN INSTITUTE OF STEEL CONSTRUCTION

$F_y = 36$ ksi	BEAMS	W 24

BEAMS
W shapes

Allowable uniform loads in kips
for beams laterally supported
For beams laterally unsupported, see page **2 - 84**

Designation		W24				W24		Deflection Inches
Weight per Foot		94	84	76	68	61	55	
Flange Width		9	9	9	9	7	7	
L_c		9.6	9.5	9.5	9.5	7.4	6.9	
L_u		15.1	13.4	11.9	10.2	8.1	7.5	
	6						270	0.04
	7					288	261	0.05
	8				286	260	228	0.07
	9	363	328	305	272	231	203	0.08
	10	354	315	282	245	208	182	0.10
	11	321	287	256	223	189	166	0.13
	12	295	263	235	204	173	152	0.15
	13	272	242	217	188	160	140	0.17
	14	253	225	201	175	149	130	0.20
	15	236	210	188	163	139	122	0.23
	16	221	197	176	153	130	114	0.26
	17	208	185	166	144	122	107	0.30
	18	196	175	156	136	116	101	0.34
	19	186	166	148	129	109	96	0.37
	20	177	158	141	122	104	91	0.41
	21	168	150	134	117	99	87	0.46
	22	161	143	128	111	95	83	0.50
	23	154	137	122	106	90	79	0.55
	24	147	131	117	102	87	76	0.60
	25	141	126	113	98	83	73	0.65
	26	136	121	108	94	80	70	0.70
	27	131	117	104	91	77	68	0.75
	28	126	113	101	87	74	65	0.81
	29	122	109	97	84	72	63	0.87
	30	118	105	94	82	69	61	0.93
	31	114	102	91	79	67	59	0.99
	32	111	99	88	77	65	57	1.06
	33	107	96	85	74	63	55	1.13
	34	104	93	83	72	61	54	1.20
	36	98	88	78	68	58	51	1.34
	38	93	83	74	64	55	48	1.49
	40	88	79	70	61	52	46	1.66
	42	84	75	67	58	50	43	1.82
	44	80	72	64	56	47	41	2.00
	46	77	69	61	53	45	40	2.19
	48	74	66	59	51	43	38	2.38
	50	71	63	56	49	42	36	2.59

Span in Feet — $F_y = 36$ ksi

Properties and Reaction Values

							For explanation of deflection see page **2 - 23**
S in.^{3}	221	197	176	153	130	114	
V kips	182	164	153	143	144	135	
R kips	71	64	59	55	55	51	
R_i kips	13.9	12.7	11.9	11.2	11.3	10.7	
N_e in.	11.4	11.4	11.4	11.4	11.4	11.4	

Load above heavy line is limited by maximum allowable web shear.

AMERICAN INSTITUTE OF STEEL CONSTRUCTION

W 21

BEAMS
W shapes

Allowable uniform loads in kips
for beams laterally supported
For beams laterally unsupported, see page 2 - 84

$F_y = 36$ ksi

Designation	W21			W21		Deflection Inches
Weight per Foot	142	127	112	96	82	
Flange Width	13⅛	13	13	9	9	
L_c	13.9	13.8	13.7	9.5	9.5	
L_u	31.1	28.1	24.8	18.5	15.8	
Span in Feet						
8				353	302	0.08
9				352	300	0.10
10				317	270	0.12
11				288	246	0.14
12	410	362	321	264	225	0.17
13	390	350	308	244	208	0.20
14	362	325	286	226	193	0.23
15	338	303	267	211	180	0.27
16	317	284	250	198	169	0.30
17	298	267	235	186	159	0.34
18	282	252	222	176	150	0.38
19	267	239	211	167	142	0.43
20	254	227	200	158	135	0.47
21	242	216	190	151	129	0.52
22	231	207	182	144	123	0.57
23	221	198	174	138	118	0.63
24	211	189	167	132	113	0.68
25	203	182	160	127	108	0.74
26	195	175	154	122	104	0.80
27	188	168	148	117	100	0.86
28	181	162	143	113	97	0.93
29	175	157	138	109	93	0.99
30	169	151	133	106	90	1.06
31	164	147	129	102	87	1.14
32	159	142	125	99	85	1.21
33	154	138	121	96	82	1.29
34	149	134	118	93	80	1.37
35	145	130	114	91	77	1.45
36	141	126	111	88	75	1.53
37	137	123	108	86	73	1.62
38	133	120	105	83	71	1.71
39	130	117	103	81	69	1.80
40	127	114	100	79	68	1.89
41	124	111	98	77	66	1.99
42	121	108	95	75	64	2.09
43	118	106	93	74	63	2.19
44	115	103	91	72	61	2.29

Properties and Reaction Values

						For explanation of deflection see page 2 - 23
S in.³	317	284	250	198	169	
V kips	205	181	160	176	151	
R kips	96	83	73	81	68	
R_i kips	17.8	15.9	14.2	15.5	13.5	
N_e in.	9.6	9.7	9.7	9.7	9.6	

Load above heavy line is limited by maximum allowable web shear.

$F_y = 36$ ksi

AMERICAN INSTITUTE OF STEEL CONSTRUCTION

| $F_y = 36$ ksi | | **BEAMS**
W shapes
Allowable uniform loads in kips
for beams laterally supported
For beams laterally unsupported, see page 2 - 84 | | | | | **W 21** |

Designation		W21				W21		
Weight per Foot		73	68	62	55	49	44	Deflection Inches
Flange Width		8¼	8¼	8¼	8¼	6½	6½	
L_c		8.8	8.7	8.7	8.7	6.9	6.6	
L_u		13.4	12.4	11.2	9.5	7.7	7.1	
	6					222	209	0.04
	7				226	213	187	0.06
	8	280	263	243	220	187	163	0.08
	9	268	249	226	196	166	145	0.10
	10	242	224	203	176	149	131	0.12
	11	220	204	185	160	136	119	0.14
	12	201	187	169	147	124	109	0.17
	13	186	172	156	135	115	100	0.20
	14	173	160	145	126	107	93	0.23
	15	161	149	135	117	100	87	0.27
	16	151	140	127	110	93	82	0.30
	17	142	132	120	104	88	77	0.34
	18	134	124	113	98	83	73	0.38
	19	127	118	107	93	79	69	0.43
	20	121	112	102	88	75	65	0.47
	22	110	102	92	80	68	59	0.57
	24	101	93	85	73	62	54	0.68
	26	93	86	78	68	57	50	0.80
	28	86	80	73	63	53	47	0.93
	30	81	75	68	59	50	44	1.06
	32	76	70	64	55	47	41	1.21
	34	71	66	60	52	44	38	1.37
	36	67	62	56	49	41	36	1.53
	38	64	59	53	46	39	34	1.71
	40	60	56	51	44	37	33	1.89
	42	58	53	48	42	36	31	2.09
	44	55	51	46	40	34	30	2.29

Span in Feet — $F_y = 36$ ksi

Properties and Reaction Values								
S in.^{3}		151	140	127	110	93.3	81.6	For explanation of deflection see page 2 - 23
V kips		140	132	122	113	111	104	
R kips		60	56	51	47	47	43	
R_i kips		12.3	11.6	10.8	10.1	9.9	9.4	
N_e in.		10.0	10.0	10.0	10.0	10.0	10.0	

Load above heavy line is limited by maximum allowable web shear.

W 18

BEAMS
W shapes
Allowable uniform loads in kips
for beams laterally supported
For beams laterally unsupported, see page 2 - 84

$$F_y = 36 \text{ ksi}$$

Designation		W18			W18				
Weight per Foot		114	105	96	85	77	70	64	Deflection Inches
Flange Width		11⅞	11¾	11¾	8⅞	8¾	8¾	8¾	
L_c		12.5	12.4	12.4	9.3	9.3	9.2	9.2	
L_u		29.3	27.1	24.9	20.3	18.6	16.9	15.5	
	9				279	250	229	209	0.11
	10			270	251	227	206	189	0.14
	11	319	294	269	228	207	188	172	0.17
	12	293	269	247	209	189	172	157	0.20
	13	271	249	228	193	175	159	145	0.23
	14	251	231	211	179	162	147	135	0.27
	15	235	215	197	167	151	138	126	0.31
	16	220	202	185	157	142	129	118	0.35
	17	207	190	174	148	134	121	111	0.40
	18	196	180	164	140	126	115	105	0.45
	19	185	170	156	132	120	109	99	0.50
	20	176	162	148	126	114	103	94	0.55
	21	168	154	141	120	108	98	90	0.61
	22	160	147	135	114	103	94	86	0.67
	23	153	141	129	109	99	90	82	0.73
	24	147	135	123	105	95	86	79	0.79
	25	141	129	118	100	91	83	76	0.86
	26	135	124	114	97	87	79	73	0.93
	27	130	120	110	93	84	76	70	1.01
	28	126	115	106	90	81	74	67	1.08
	29	121	111	102	87	78	71	65	1.16
	30	117	108	99	84	76	69	63	1.24
	31	114	104	95	81	73	67	61	1.33
	32	110	101	93	78	71	65	59	1.41
	33	107	98	90	76	69	63	57	1.50
	34	104	95	87	74	67	61	56	1.59
	35	101	92	85	72	65	59	54	1.69
	36	98	90	82	70	63	57	52	1.79
	37	95	87	80	68	61	56	51	1.89
	38	93	85	78	66	60	54	50	1.99

(Left margin: $F_y = 36$ ksi — Span in Feet)

Properties and Reaction Values

S in.³		220	202	185	157	142	129	118	For explanation of deflection see page 2 - 23
V kips		159	147	135	140	125	114	104	
R kips		83	77	69	73	64	58	53	
R_i kips		16.1	15.0	13.8	14.2	12.8	11.8	10.9	
N_e in.		8.2	8.2	8.3	8.2	8.3	8.2	8.2	

Load above heavy line is limited by maximum allowable web shear.

AMERICAN INSTITUTE OF STEEL CONSTRUCTION

$F_y = 36$ ksi

BEAMS
W shapes

W 18

Allowable uniform loads in kips
for beams laterally supported

For beams laterally unsupported, see page **2** - 84

Designation	W18				W18		Deflection Inches
Weight per Foot	60	55	50	45	40	35	
Flange Width	7½	7½	7½	7½	6	6	
L_c	8.0	8.0	7.9	7.9	6.4	6.3	
L_u	13.3	12.1	11.0	9.7	8.2	6.7	
$F_y = 36$ ksi — Span in Feet							
6					164	153	0.05
7	220	205	187	174	156	132	0.07
8	216	197	178	158	137	116	0.09
9	192	175	158	140	122	103	0.11
10	173	157	143	126	109	93	0.14
11	157	143	130	115	99	84	0.17
12	144	131	119	105	91	77	0.20
13	133	121	110	97	84	71	0.23
14	123	112	102	90	78	66	0.27
15	115	105	95	84	73	62	0.31
16	108	98	89	79	68	58	0.35
17	102	93	84	74	64	54	0.40
18	96	87	79	70	61	51	0.45
19	91	83	75	67	58	49	0.50
20	86	79	71	63	55	46	0.55
21	82	75	68	60	52	44	0.61
22	79	72	65	57	50	42	0.67
23	75	68	62	55	48	40	0.73
24	72	66	59	53	46	39	0.79
25	69	63	57	51	44	37	0.86
26	66	61	55	49	42	36	0.93
27	64	58	53	47	41	34	1.01
28	62	56	51	45	39	33	1.08
29	60	54	49	44	38	32	1.16
30	58	52	48	42	36	31	1.24
31	56	51	46	41	35	30	1.33
32	54	49	45	40	34	29	1.41
33	52	48	43	38	33	28	1.50
34	51	46	42	37	32	27	1.59
35	49	45	41	36	31	26	1.69
36	48	44	40	35	30	26	1.79
37	47	43	39	34	30	25	1.89
38	45	41	38	33	29	24	1.99

Properties and Reaction Values

	60	55	50	45	40	35	
S in.³	108	98.4	89.1	79.0	68.4	57.9	For explanation of deflection see page **2** - 23
V kips	110	102	93	87	82	77	
R kips	53	49	44	41	39	36	
R_i kips	11.2	10.5	9.7	9.0	8.5	8.0	
N_e in.	8.6	8.6	8.6	8.6	8.6	8.5	

Load above heavy line is limited by maximum allowable web shear.

W 16

BEAMS
W shapes
Allowable uniform loads in kips
for beams laterally supported
For beams laterally unsupported, see page **2-84**

$F_y = 36$ ksi

$F_y = 36$ ksi

Designation		W16		W16				
Weight per Foot		96	88	78	71	64	58	Deflection Inches
Flange Width		11½	11½	8⅝	8½	8½	8½	
L_c		12.2	12.1	9.1	9.0	9.0	8.9	
L_u		28.6	26.2	21.3	19.5	17.6	15.9	
Span in Feet	8			250	228	206	187	0.10
	9			228	206	185	168	0.13
	10	253	236	205	186	166	151	0.16
	11	241	220	186	169	151	137	0.19
	12	221	201	171	155	139	126	0.22
	13	204	186	158	143	128	116	0.26
	14	190	173	146	133	119	108	0.30
	15	177	161	137	124	111	101	0.35
	16	166	151	128	116	104	94	0.40
	17	156	142	120	109	98	89	0.45
	18	148	134	114	103	92	84	0.50
	19	140	127	108	98	88	79	0.56
	20	133	121	102	93	83	76	0.62
	21	126	115	98	88	79	72	0.68
	22	121	110	93	84	76	69	0.75
	23	115	105	89	81	72	66	0.82
	24	111	101	85	77	69	63	0.89
	25	106	97	82	74	67	60	0.97
	26	102	93	79	71	64	58	1.05
	27	98	89	76	69	62	56	1.13
	28	95	86	73	66	59	54	1.22
	29	92	83	71	64	57	52	1.31
	30	89	81	68	62	55	50	1.40
	31	86	78	66	60	54	49	1.49
	32	83	76	64	58	52	47	1.59
	33	80	73	62	56	50	46	1.69
	34	78	71	60	55	49	44	1.79

Properties and Reaction Values

	96	88	78	71	64	58	
S in.³	166	151	128	116	104	94.4	For explanation of deflection see page **2-23**
V kips	127	118	125	114	103	94	
R kips	74	68	73	66	59	54	
R_i kips	14.4	13.6	14.3	13.1	12.0	11.0	
N_e in.	7.1	7.2	7.1	7.2	7.2	7.1	

Load above heavy line is limited by maximum allowable web shear.

| $F_y = 36$ ksi | BEADS W shapes | | | | | W 16 |

BEAMS
W shapes
Allowable uniform loads in kips
for beams laterally supported
For beams laterally unsupported, see page 2 - 84

W 16

Designation		W16				W16		Deflection Inches
Weight per Foot		50	45	40	36	31	26	
Flange Width		7⅛	7	7	7	5½	5½	
L_c		7.5	7.4	7.4	7.4	5.8	5.6	
L_u		12.6	11.4	10.2	8.7	7.1	6.1	
Span in Feet	5						113	0.04
	6				137	126	102	0.06
	7	179	162	142	129	108	88	0.08
	8	162	145	129	113	94	77	0.10
	9	144	129	115	100	84	68	0.13
	10	129	116	103	90	76	61	0.16
	11	118	105	94	82	69	56	0.19
	12	108	97	86	75	63	51	0.22
	13	99	89	80	70	58	47	0.26
	14	92	83	74	65	54	44	0.30
	15	86	77	69	60	50	41	0.35
	16	81	73	65	57	47	38	0.40
	17	76	68	61	53	44	36	0.45
	18	72	64	57	50	42	34	0.50
	19	68	61	54	48	40	32	0.56
	20	65	58	52	45	38	31	0.62
	21	62	55	49	43	36	29	0.68
	22	59	53	47	41	34	28	0.75
	23	56	50	45	39	33	27	0.82
	24	54	48	43	38	31	26	0.89
	25	52	46	41	36	30	25	0.97
	26	50	45	40	35	29	24	1.05
	27	48	43	38	33	28	23	1.13
	28	46	41	37	32	27	22	1.22
	29	45	40	36	31	26	21	1.31
	30	43	39	34	30	25	20	1.40
	31	42	37	33	29	24	20	1.49
	32	40	36	32	28	24	19	1.59
	33	39	35	31	27	23	19	1.69
	34	38	34	30	27	22	18	1.79

Properties and Reaction Values

	50	45	40	36	31	26	
S in.³	80.8	72.5	64.6	56.5	47.2	38.3	For explanation of deflection see page 2 - 23
V kips	90	81	71	69	63	57	
R kips	49	44	38	37	34	30	
R_i kips	10.3	9.3	8.3	8.1	7.4	6.8	
N_e in.	7.5	7.5	7.5	7.4	7.4	7.5	

Load above heavy line is limited by maximum allowable web shear.

W 14

I

BEAMS
W shapes

$F_y = 36$ ksi

Allowable uniform loads in kips
for beams laterally supported
For beams laterally unsupported, see page 2-84

Designation	W14					W14		W14			Deflection Inches
Weight per Foot	119	111	*103	*95	*87	84	78	74	68	61	
Flange Width	14⅝	14⅝	14⅝	14½	14½	12	12	10⅛	10	10	
L_c	15.5	15.4	15.4	15.4	15.3	12.7	12.7	10.6	10.6	10.6	
L_u	43.7	41.0	38.6	35.6	33.1	30.5	28.4	25.7	23.7	21.4	
Span in Feet											
9								185	170	152	0.14
10								179	165	148	0.18
11						185	175	163	150	134	0.21
12	240	225	205	190	171	175	161	149	137	123	0.26
13	233	217	199	182	164	161	149	138	127	113	0.30
14	216	201	185	169	153	150	138	128	118	105	0.35
15	202	188	173	157	142	140	129	119	110	98	0.40
16	189	176	162	148	133	131	121	112	103	92	0.45
17	178	166	152	139	126	123	114	105	97	87	0.51
18	168	156	144	131	119	116	108	100	92	82	0.57
19	159	148	136	124	112	110	102	94	87	78	0.64
20	151	141	129	118	107	105	97	90	82	74	0.71
21	144	134	123	112	102	100	92	85	78	70	0.78
22	137	128	118	107	97	95	88	81	75	67	0.86
23	131	122	113	103	93	91	84	78	72	64	0.94
24	126	117	108	98	89	87	81	75	69	61	1.02
25	121	113	104	94	85	84	77	72	66	59	1.11
26	116	108	100	91	82	81	74	69	63	57	1.20
27	112	104	96	87	79	78	72	66	61	55	1.29
28	108	101	92	84	76	75	69	64	59	53	1.39
29	104	97	89	81	74	72	67	62	57	51	1.49
30	101	94	86	79	71	70	65	60	55	49	1.60
31	98	91	84	76	69						
32	95	88	81	74	67						
33	92	85	78	72	65						
34	89	83	76	69							
35	86	80	74	67							
36	84	78	72								
37	82	76	70								
38	80	74	68								
			(23.7)	(23.4)	(23.2)						

Properties and Reaction Values

											For explanation of deflection see page 2-23
S in.³	189	176	164	151	138	131	121	112	103	92.2	
V kips	120	113	102	95	85	93	87	93	85	76	
R kips	79	74	67	62	55	60	56	61	55	49	
R_i kips	15.4	14.6	13.4	12.6	11.3	12.2	11.6	12.2	11.3	10.2	
N_e in.	6.2	6.2	6.2	6.1	6.1	6.2	6.2	6.1	6.2	6.2	

Load above heavy line is limited by maximum allowable web shear.

* Tabulated loads for this shape are computed with the allowable stress (ksi) shown in parentheses at the bottom of the allowable load column.

AMERICAN INSTITUTE OF STEEL CONSTRUCTION

$F_y = 36$ ksi		BEAMS W shapes					W 14		

**Allowable uniform loads in kips
for beams laterally supported**

For beams laterally unsupported, see page **2**-84

Designation		W14			W14			W14		
Weight per Foot		53	48	43	38	34	*30	26	22	Deflection Inches
Flange Width		8	8	8	6¾	6¾	6¾	5	5	
L_c		8.5	8.5	8.4	7.2	7.1	7.1	5.3	5.3	
L_u		17.6	16.0	14.3	11.4	10.1	8.6	7.0	5.7	
	5							103	92	0.04
	6				128	117	109	94	77	0.06
	7				125	111	95	80	66	0.09
	8	150	136	122	109	97	83	70	58	0.11
	9	138	125	111	97	86	74	62	51	0.14
	10	124	112	100	88	78	66	56	46	0.18
	11	113	102	91	80	71	60	51	42	0.21
	12	104	94	84	73	65	55	47	39	0.26
	13	96	86	77	67	60	51	43	36	0.30
	14	89	80	72	63	56	47	40	33	0.35
	15	83	75	67	58	52	44	37	31	0.40
	16	78	70	63	55	49	41	35	29	0.45
	17	73	66	59	51	46	39	33	27	0.51
	18	69	62	56	49	43	37	31	26	0.57
	19	66	59	53	46	41	35	30	24	0.64
	20	62	56	50	44	39	33	28	23	0.71
	21	59	53	48	42	37	32	27	22	0.78
	22	57	51	46	40	35	30	26	21	0.86
	23	54	49	44	38	34	29	24	20	0.94
	24	52	47	42	36	32	28	23	19	1.02
	25	50	45	40	35	31	27	22	18	1.11
	26	48	43	39	34	30	25	22	18	1.20
	27	46	42	37	32	29	25	21	17	1.29
	28	44	40	36	31	28	24	20	17	1.39
	29	43	39	35	30	27	23	19	16	1.49
	30	41	37	33	29	26	22	19	15	1.60
							(23.7)			

Span in Feet (left vertical label); $F_y = 36$ ksi (left vertical label)

Properties and Reaction Values										
S in.³		77.8	70.2	62.7	54.7	48.6	41.9	35.1	28.9	For explanation of deflection see page **2** - 23
V kips		75	68	61	64	58	54	51	46	
R kips		49	43	39	39	35	33	31	28	
R_i kips		10.0	9.2	8.3	8.5	7.7	7.3	6.9	6.2	
N_e in.		6.1	6.2	6.2	6.5	6.5	6.4	6.5	6.4	

Load above heavy line is limited by maximum allowable web shear.

*Tabulated loads for this shape are computed with the allowable stress (ksi) shown in
parentheses at the bottom of the allowable load column.

AMERICAN INSTITUTE OF STEEL CONSTRUCTION

W 12

BEAMS
W shapes

Allowable uniform loads in kips
for beams laterally supported

For beams laterally unsupported, see page **2-84**

$F_y = 36$ ksi

Designation		W12				W12		W12			
Weight per Foot		85	79	*72	*65	58	53	50	45	40	Deflection Inches
Flange Width		12⅛	12⅛	12	12	10	10	8⅛	8	8	
L_c		12.8	12.8	12.7	12.7	10.6	10.6	8.5	8.5	8.4	
L_u		35.6	33.3	30.5	27.7	24.4	22.2	19.7	17.8	16.0	
Span in Feet	7							131	118		0.10
	8							129	116	102	0.13
	9					127	121	115	103	92	0.17
	10	179	169	153	137	125	113	104	93	83	0.21
	11	169	156	140	125	114	103	94	85	75	0.25
	12	155	143	128	114	104	94	86	78	69	0.30
	13	143	132	118	106	96	87	80	72	64	0.35
	14	133	122	110	98	89	81	74	67	59	0.41
	15	124	114	103	91	83	75	69	62	55	0.47
	16	116	107	96	86	78	71	65	58	52	0.53
	17	109	101	91	81	74	67	61	55	49	0.60
	18	103	95	85	76	69	63	58	52	46	0.67
	19	98	90	81	72	66	60	54	49	44	0.75
	20	93	86	77	69	62	57	52	47	42	0.83
	21	88	82	73	65	60	54	49	44	40	0.91
	22	84	78	70	62	57	51	47	42	38	1.00
	23	81	74	67	60	54	49	45	40	36	1.09
	24	77	71	64	57	52	47	43	39	35	1.19
	25	74	68	62	55	50	45	41	37	33	1.29
	26	71	66	59	53						
	27	69	63	57	51						
	28	66	61	55							
	29	64	59	53							
	30	62	57	51							
	31	60	55								
	32	58	54								
	33	56	52								
	34	55									
	35	53									
				(23.7)	(23.4)						

Properties and Reaction Values											For
S	in.³	116	107	97.5	88.0	78.1	70.7	64.7	58.2	51.9	explana-
V	kips	90	84	76	69	63	60	66	59	51	tion of
R	kips	67	63	57	51	47	44	49	43	38	deflection
R_i	kips	13.4	12.7	11.6	10.5	9.7	9.3	10.0	9.1	7.9	see page
N_e	in.	5.2	5.2	5.2	5.2	5.2	5.2	5.2	5.2	5.2	**2-23**

Load above heavy line is limited by maximum allowable web shear.

*Tabulated loads for this shape are computed with the allowable stress (ksi) shown in parentheses at the bottom of the allowable load column.

AMERICAN INSTITUTE OF STEEL CONSTRUCTION

$F_y = 36$ ksi		BEAMS						W 12

BEAMS
W shapes
Allowable uniform loads in kips
for beams laterally supported
For beams laterally unsupported, see page 2-84

Designation		W12			W12				
Weight per Foot		36	31	27	22	19	16.5	*14	Deflection Inches
Flange Width		6⅝	6½	6½	4	4	4	4	
L_c		6.9	6.9	6.9	4.3	4.2	4.1	3.5	
L_u		13.4	11.6	10.1	6.4	5.3	4.3	4.2	
	3						80.0	68.4	0.02
	4				92.8	83.6	70.4	58.5	0.03
	5				81.0	68.2	56.3	46.8	0.05
	6	108.3	92.9	82.2	67.5	56.8	46.9	39.0	0.07
	7	105.1	90.3	78.2	57.8	48.7	40.2	33.4	0.10
	8	92.0	79.0	68.4	50.6	42.6	35.2	29.2	0.13
	9	81.8	70.2	60.8	45.0	37.9	31.3	26.0	0.17
	10	73.6	63.2	54.7	40.5	34.1	28.2	23.4	0.21
	11	66.9	57.5	49.7	36.8	31.0	25.6	21.3	0.25
	12	61.3	52.7	45.6	33.7	28.4	23.5	19.5	0.30
	13	56.6	48.6	42.1	31.1	26.2	21.7	18.0	0.35
	14	52.6	45.1	39.1	28.9	24.3	20.1	16.7	0.41
	15	49.1	42.1	36.5	27.0	22.7	18.8	15.6	0.47
	16	46.0	39.5	34.2	25.3	21.3	17.6	14.6	0.53
	17	43.3	37.2	32.2	23.8	20.0	16.6	13.8	0.60
	18	40.9	35.1	30.4	22.5	18.9	15.6	13.0	0.67
	19	38.7	33.3	28.8	21.3	17.9	14.8	12.3	0.75
	20	36.8	31.6	27.4	20.2	17.0	14.1	11.7	0.83
	21	35.0	30.1	26.1	19.3	16.2	13.4	11.1	0.91
	22	33.5	28.7	24.9	18.4	15.5	12.8	10.6	1.00
	23	32.0	27.5	23.8	17.6	14.8	12.2	10.2	1.09
	24	30.7	26.3	22.8	16.9	14.2	11.7	9.7	1.19
	25	29.4	25.3	21.9	16.2	13.6	11.3	9.4	1.29
								(23.7)	

Span in Feet

$F_y = 36$ ksi

Properties and Reaction Values

	S in.³	46.0	39.5	34.2	25.3	21.3	17.6	14.8	For explanation of deflection see page 2-23
	V kips	54.1	46.5	41.1	46.4	41.8	40.0	34.2	
	R kips	37.6	32.2	28.4	31.2	28.0	26.8	22.7	
	R_i kips	8.2	7.2	6.4	7.0	6.4	6.2	5.3	
	N_e in.	5.5	5.5	5.5	5.7	5.7	5.6	5.6	

Load above heavy line is limited by maximum allowable web shear.

* Tabulated loads for this shape are computed with the allowable stress (ksi) shown in parentheses at the bottom of the allowable load column.

AMERICAN INSTITUTE OF STEEL CONSTRUCTION

W 10

BEAMS
W shapes

Allowable uniform loads in kips
for beams laterally supported
For beams laterally unsupported, see page 2 - 84

$F_y = 36$ ksi

Designation		W10				W10			
Weight per Foot	66	60	54	*49	45	39	*33	Deflection Inches
Flange Width	10⅛	10⅛	10	10	8	8	8	
L_c	10.7	10.6	10.6	10.6	8.5	8.4	8.4	
L_u	33.8	31.1	28.4	25.9	22.7	19.6	16.4	

Span in Feet									Deflection Inches
6							83	0.09
7					103	92	79	0.12
8	138	123	108	99	98	84	69	0.16
9	131	119	107	96	87	75	61	0.20
10	118	107	97	86	79	68	55	0.25
11	107	98	88	78	71	61	50	0.30
12	98	89	81	72	65	56	46	0.36
13	91	83	74	66	60	52	42	0.42
14	84	77	69	62	56	48	39	0.49
15	79	72	64	57	52	45	37	0.56
16	74	67	60	54	49	42	34	0.64
17	69	63	57	51	46	40	32	0.72
18	66	60	54	48	44	38	31	0.80
19	62	57	51	45	41	36	29	0.90
20	59	54	48	43	39	34	28	0.99
21	56	51	46	41	37	32	26	1.09
22	54	49	44	39	36	31	25	1.20
23	51	47	42	37				
24	49	45	40	36				
25	47	43	39	34				
26	45	41	37					
27	44	40	36					
28	42	38	35					
29	41	37						
30	39	36						
				(23.7)			(23.6)	

Properties and Reaction Values

	66	60	54	*49	45	39	*33	
S in.³	73.7	67.1	60.4	54.6	49.1	42.2	35.0	For explanation of deflection see page 2 - 23
V kips	69	62	54	49	51	46	41	
R kips	59	53	47	42	44	40	35	
R_i kips	12.3	11.2	9.9	9.2	9.5	8.6	7.9	
N_e in.	4.3	4.3	4.2	4.2	4.2	4.2	4.2	

Load above heavy line is limited by maximum allowable web shear.

*Tabulated loads for this shape are computed with the allowable stress (ksi) shown in parentheses at the bottom of the allowable load column.

AMERICAN INSTITUTE OF STEEL CONSTRUCTION

$F_y = 36$ ksi		BEADS W shapes							W 10

BEAMS
W shapes
Allowable uniform loads in kips
for beams laterally supported
For beams laterally unsupported, see page **2** - 84

Designation			W10			W10				
Weight per Foot		29	25	21	19	17	15	*11.5	Deflection
Flange Width		5¾	5¾	5¾	4	4	4	4	Inches
L_c		6.1	6.1	6.1	4.2	4.2	4.2	3.8	
L_u		13.2	11.4	9.1	7.2	6.0	5.0	4.3	

Span in Feet		W10 29	W10 25	W10 21	W10 19	W10 17	W10 15	W10 *11.5	Deflection Inches
	3					70.4	66.7	51.5	0.02
	4			68.9	74.3	64.8	55.2	41.1	0.04
	5	85.7	73.7	68.8	60.2	51.8	44.2	32.8	0.06
	6	82.1	70.7	57.3	50.1	43.2	36.8	27.4	0.09
	7	70.4	60.6	49.1	43.0	37.0	31.5	23.5	0.12
	8	61.6	53.0	43.0	37.6	32.4	27.6	20.5	0.16
	9	54.8	47.1	38.2	33.4	28.8	24.5	18.2	0.20
	10	49.3	42.4	34.4	30.1	25.9	22.1	16.4	0.25
	11	44.8	38.5	31.3	27.3	23.6	20.1	14.9	0.30
	12	41.1	35.3	28.7	25.1	21.6	18.4	13.7	0.36
	13	37.9	32.6	26.5	23.1	19.9	17.0	12.6	0.42
	14	35.2	30.3	24.6	21.5	18.5	15.8	11.7	0.49
	15	32.9	28.3	22.9	20.1	17.3	14.7	10.9	0.56
	16	30.8	26.5	21.5	18.8	16.2	13.8	10.3	0.64
	17	29.0	24.9	20.2	17.7	15.2	13.0	9.7	0.72
	18	27.4	23.6	19.1	16.7	14.4	12.3	9.1	0.80
	19	25.9	22.3	18.1	15.8	13.6	11.6	8.6	0.90
	20	24.6	21.2	17.2	15.0	13.0	11.0	8.2	0.99
	21	23.5	20.2	16.4	14.3	12.3	10.5	7.8	1.09
	22	22.4	19.3	15.6	13.7	11.8	10.0	7.5	1.20
								(23.5)	

Properties and Reaction Values

		29	25	21	19	17	15	*11.5	
S	in.³	30.8	26.5	21.5	18.8	16.2	13.8	10.5	For explanation of deflection see page **2** - 23
V	kips	42.8	36.8	34.5	37.2	35.2	33.4	25.8	
R	kips	35.6	30.6	28.4	30.0	28.4	26.8	20.7	
R_i	kips	7.8	6.8	6.5	6.8	6.5	6.2	4.9	
N_e	in.	4.4	4.4	4.4	4.6	4.6	4.6	4.6	

Load above heavy line is limited by maximum allowable web shear.

*Tabulated loads for this shape are computed with the allowable stress (ksi) shown in parentheses at the bottom of the allowable load column.

W 8

BEAMS
W shapes

Allowable uniform loads in kips
for beams laterally supported
For beams laterally unsupported, see page 2 - 84

$F_y = 36\,ksi$

$F_y = 36\,ksi$ (Span in Feet)

Designation	W8		W8		W8		W8			Deflection Inches
Weight per Foot	35	*31	28	24	20	17	15	13	*10	
Flange Width	8	8	6½	6½	5¼	5¼	4	4	4	
L_c	8.5	8.4	6.9	6.9	5.6	5.5	4.2	4.2	4.2	
L_u	22.6	20.0	17.4	15.1	11.3	9.4	7.2	5.9	4.7	
2								53.4		0.01
3							57.7	52.8	38.9	0.03
4					58.5	53.4	47.2	39.6	30.5	0.05
5			66.6	56.3	54.4	45.1	37.8	31.7	24.4	0.08
6	74.2	66.8	64.8	55.5	45.3	37.6	31.5	26.4	20.3	0.11
7	71.1	61.6	55.5	47.5	38.9	32.2	27.0	22.6	17.4	0.15
8	62.2	53.9	48.6	41.6	34.0	28.2	23.6	19.8	15.3	0.20
9	55.3	47.9	43.2	37.0	30.2	25.1	21.0	17.6	13.6	0.25
10	49.8	43.1	38.9	33.3	27.2	22.6	18.9	15.8	12.2	0.31
11	45.2	39.2	35.3	30.3	24.7	20.5	17.2	14.4	11.1	0.38
12	41.5	35.9	32.4	27.7	22.7	18.8	15.7	13.2	10.2	0.45
13	38.3	33.2	29.9	25.6	20.9	17.4	14.5	12.2	9.4	0.52
14	35.5	30.8	27.8	23.8	19.4	16.1	13.5	11.3	8.7	0.61
15	33.2	28.7	25.9	22.2	18.1	15.0	12.6	10.6	8.1	0.70
16	31.1	26.9	24.3	20.8	17.0	14.1	11.8	9.9	7.6	0.79
17	29.3	25.4	22.9	19.6	16.0	13.3	11.1	9.3	7.2	0.90
18	27.6	23.9								
19	26.2	22.7								
20	24.9	21.5								
21	23.7	20.5								
22	22.6	19.6								
			(23.6)						(23.5)	

Properties and Reaction Values

	35	*31	28	24	20	17	15	13	*10	
S in.³	31.1	27.4	24.3	20.8	17.0	14.1	11.8	9.9	7.8	For explanation of deflection see page 2-23
V kips	37.1	33.4	33.3	28.2	29.3	26.7	28.8	26.7	19.5	
R kips	**38.3**	**34.5**	**34.1**	**28.9**	29.3	**26.8**	28.5	26.4	19.2	
R_i kips	8.5	7.8	7.7	6.6	6.7	6.2	6.6	6.2	4.6	
N_e in.	3.4	3.4	3.4	3.4	3.5	3.5	3.5	3.5	3.6	

Load above heavy line is limited by maximum allowable web shear.

Values of R in **bold face** exceed maximum web shear V.

*Tabulated loads for this shape are computed with the allowable stress (ksi) shown in parentheses at the bottom of the allowable load column.

$F_y = 36$ ksi

BEAMS
W shapes

Allowable uniform loads in kips
for beams laterally supported
For beams laterally unsupported, see page 2 - 84

W 6

Designation		W6			W6			Deflection Inches
Weight per Foot		25	20	*15.5	16	12	*8.5	
Flange Width		6⅛	6	6	4	4	4	
L_c		6.4	6.4	6.3	4.3	4.2	4.2	
L_u		20.1	16.5	12.4	12.1	8.6	6.1	
	2					40.0	28.7	0.02
	3			40.9	47.1	38.7	26.3	0.04
	4	59.1	46.4	38.4	40.8	29.0	19.7	0.07
	5	53.4	42.9	30.7	32.6	23.2	15.8	0.10
	6	44.5	35.7	25.6	27.2	19.3	13.2	0.15
	7	38.2	30.6	21.9	23.3	16.6	11.3	0.20
	8	33.4	26.8	19.2	20.4	14.5	9.9	0.26
	9	29.7	23.8	17.1	18.1	12.9	8.8	0.34
	10	26.7	21.4	15.4	16.3	11.6	7.9	0.41
	11	24.3	19.5	14.0	14.8	10.5	7.2	0.50
	12	22.3	17.9	12.8	13.6	9.7	6.6	0.60
	13	20.6	16.5	11.8	12.6	8.9	6.1	0.70
	14	19.1	15.3	11.0				
	15	17.8	14.3	10.2				
				(23.0)			(23.3)	

Span in Feet (left vertical label)
$F_y = 36$ ksi (left vertical label)

Properties and Reaction Values

	25	20	*15.5	16	12	*8.5	
S in.³	16.7	13.4	10.0	10.2	7.3	5.1	For explanation of deflection see page 2 - 23
V kips	29.6	23.2	20.4	23.6	20.0	14.4	
R kips	**38.3**	**30.5**	**27.0**	**30.7**	**26.4**	**19.2**	
R_i kips	8.6	7.0	6.3	7.0	6.2	4.6	
N_e in.	2.5	2.5	2.5	2.5	2.5	2.4	

Load above heavy line is limited by maximum allowable web shear.
Values of R in **bold face** exceed maximum web shear V.
*Tabulated loads for this shape are computed with the allowable stress (ksi) shown in parentheses at the bottom of the allowable load column.

M 14-12-10-8-7-6

BEAMS
M shapes

$$F_y = 36 \text{ ksi}$$

Allowable uniform loads in kips for beams laterally supported

For beams laterally unsupported, see page **2-84**

Designation		M14	M12	M10		M10	M8	M7	M6
Weight per Foot		17.2	11.8	29.1	22.9	9	6.5	5.5	4.4
Flange Width		4	3⅛	5⅞	5¾	2¾	2¼	2⅛	1⅞
L_c		3.6	2.7	6.3	6.1	2.6	2.4	2.2	1.9
L_u		4.1	3.1	10.8	10.5	2.7	2.5	2.5	2.4
Span in Feet	1								19.8
	2					45.5	31.3	26.0	19.2
	3	85.3	61.6	122.3		41.4	24.6	18.3	12.8
	4	84.4	48.0	106.4		31.0	18.5	13.8	9.6
	5	67.5	38.4	85.1	69.3	24.8	14.8	11.0	7.7
	6	56.3	32.0	70.9	62.9	20.7	12.3	9.2	6.4
	7	48.2	27.4	60.8	53.9	17.7	10.6	7.9	5.5
	8	42.2	24.0	53.2	47.2	15.5	9.2	6.9	4.8
	9	37.5	21.3	47.3	42.0	13.8	8.2	6.1	4.3
	10	33.8	19.2	42.6	37.8	12.4	7.4	5.5	3.8
	11	30.7	17.5	38.7	34.3	11.3	6.7	5.0	3.5
	12	28.1	16.0	35.5	31.5	10.3	6.2	4.6	3.2
	13	26.0	14.8	32.7	29.0	9.6	5.7	4.2	3.0
	14	24.1	13.7	30.4	27.0	8.9	5.3	3.9	
	15	22.5	12.8	28.4	25.2	8.3	4.9	3.7	
	16	21.1	12.0	26.6	23.6	7.8	4.6		
	17	19.9	11.3	25.0	22.2	7.3	4.3		
	18	18.8	10.7	23.6	21.0	6.9			
	19	17.8	10.1	22.4	19.9	6.5			
	20	16.9	9.6	21.3	18.9	6.2			
	21	16.1	9.1	20.3	18.0	5.9			
	22	15.3	8.7						
	23	14.7	8.3						
	24	14.1	8.0						
	25	13.5	7.7						
	26	13.0							
	27	12.5							
	28	12.1							
	29	11.6							
	30	11.3							

$F_y = 36$ ksi

Properties and Reaction Values

	M14	M12	M10		M10	M8	M7	M6
S in.³	21.1	12.0	26.6	23.6	7.8	4.6	3.4	2.4
V kips	42.6	30.8	61.2	34.7	22.8	15.7	13.0	9.9
R kips	23.4	19.4	50.4	28.6	17.0	14.6	**13.6**	**11.9**
R_i kips	5.7	4.8	11.5	6.5	4.2	3.6	3.5	3.1
N_e in.	6.9	5.9	4.4	4.4	4.9	3.8	3.3	2.8

Load above heavy line is limited by maximum allowable web shear.
Values of R in **bold face** exceed maximum web shear V.

AMERICAN INSTITUTE OF STEEL CONSTRUCTION

| $F_y = 36$ ksi | | BEAMS | | | | | | S 24-20 | | |

S shapes

Allowable uniform loads in kips for beams laterally supported

Designation	S24		S24			Deflection Inches	S20		S20		Deflection Inches
Weight per Foot	120	105.9	100	90	79.9		95	85	75	65.4	
Flange Width	8	7⅞	7¼	7⅛	7		7¼	7	6⅜	6¼	
L_c	8.5	8.3	7.6	7.5	7.4		7.6	7.4	6.7	6.6	
L_u	17.1	16.7	12.2	12.0	11.8		15.3	15.0	11.7	11.4	
5							464		372		0.03
6			520	434		0.04	429	379	341	290	0.04
7	555		455	427		0.05	368	347	293	270	0.06
8	504	435	398	374	349	0.07	322	304	256	236	0.08
9	448	420	354	332	311	0.08	286	270	228	210	0.10
10	403	378	318	299	280	0.10	258	243	205	189	0.12
11	367	343	289	272	255	0.13	234	221	186	172	0.15
12	336	315	265	249	233	0.15	215	203	171	157	0.18
13	310	290	245	230	215	0.17	198	187	158	145	0.21
14	288	270	227	214	200	0.20	184	174	146	135	0.24
15	269	252	212	199	187	0.23	172	162	137	126	0.28
16	252	236	199	187	175	0.26	161	152	128	118	0.32
17	237	222	187	176	165	0.30	152	143	120	111	0.36
18	224	210	177	166	156	0.34	143	135	114	105	0.40
19	212	199	168	157	147	0.37	136	128	108	99	0.45
20	202	189	159	150	140	0.41	129	122	102	94	0.50
21	192	180	152	142	133	0.46	123	116	98	90	0.55
22	183	172	145	136	127	0.50	117	111	93	86	0.60
23	175	164	138	130	122	0.55	112	106	89	82	0.66
24	168	157	133	125	117	0.60	107	101	85	79	0.72
25	161	151	127	120	112	0.65	103	97	82	76	0.78
26	155	145	122	115	108	0.70	99	94	79	73	0.84
27	149	140	118	111	104	0.75	95	90	76	70	0.90
28	144	135	114	107	100	0.81	92	87	73	67	0.97
29	139	130	110	103	97	0.87	89	84	71	65	1.04
30	134	126	106	100	93	0.93	86	81	68	63	1.12
32	126	118	100	94	88	1.06	81	76	64	59	1.27
34	119	111	94	88	82	1.20	76	72	60	56	1.44
36	112	105	88	83	78	1.34	72	68	57	52	1.61
38	106	99	84	79	74	1.49	68	64	54	50	1.79
40	101	94	80	75	70	1.66	64	61	51	47	1.99
42	96	90	76	71	67	1.82	61	58	49	45	2.19
44	92	86	72	68	64	2.00					
46	88	82	69	65	61	2.19					
48	84	79	66	62	58	2.38					
50	81	76	64	60	56	2.59					

Span in Feet (left axis), $F_y = 36$ ksi

Properties and Reaction Values

S in.³	252	236	199	187	175	For explanation of deflection see page 2-23	161	152	128	118
V kips	278	218	260	217	174		232	189	186	145
R kips	119	93	106	88	71		116	95	89	69
R_i kips	21.5	16.9	20.2	16.8	13.5		21.6	17.6	17.3	13.5
N_e in.	10.9	10.9	11.1	11.1	11.1		8.9	8.9	9.1	9.1

(right-hand deflection column: For explanation of deflection see page 2-23)

Load above heavy line is limited by maximum allowable web shear.

S 18-15-12 — BEAMS

S shapes

$F_y = 36$ ksi

Allowable uniform loads in kips
for beams laterally supported

$F_y = 36$ ksi — Span in Feet

Designation	S18	S18	Deflection Inches	S15	S15	Deflection Inches	S12	S12	S12	S12	Deflection Inches
Weight per Foot	70	54.7		50	42.9		50	40.8	35	31.8	
Flange Width	6¼	6		5⅝	5½		5½	5¼	5⅛	5	
L_c	6.6	6.3		6.0	5.8		5.8	5.5	5.4	5.3	
L_u	11.1	10.7		10.8	10.6		13.9	13.4	10.7	10.5	
3							239				0.02
4	371		0.02	239		0.03	203	161	149	122	0.03
5	330	241	0.03	207	179	0.04	163	145	122	116	0.05
6	275	238	0.05	173	159	0.06	135	121	102	97	0.07
7	235	204	0.07	148	136	0.08	116	104	87	83	0.10
8	206	179	0.09	130	119	0.11	102	91	76	73	0.13
9	183	159	0.11	115	106	0.13	90	81	68	65	0.17
10	165	143	0.14	104	95	0.17	81	73	61	58	0.21
11	150	130	0.17	94	87	0.20	74	66	56	53	0.25
12	137	119	0.20	86	79	0.24	68	61	51	49	0.30
13	127	110	0.23	80	73	0.28	63	56	47	45	0.35
14	118	102	0.27	74	68	0.32	58	52	44	42	0.41
15	110	95	0.31	69	64	0.37	54	48	41	39	0.47
16	103	89	0.35	65	60	0.42	51	45	38	36	0.53
17	97	84	0.40	61	56	0.48	48	43	36	34	0.60
18	92	79	0.45	58	53	0.54	45	40	34	32	0.67
19	87	75	0.50	55	50	0.60	43	38	32	31	0.75
20	82	72	0.55	52	48	0.66	41	36	31	29	0.83
21	78	68	0.61	49	45	0.73	39	35	29	28	0.91
22	75	65	0.67	47	43	0.80	37	33	28	26	1.00
23	72	62	0.73	45	41	0.88	35	32	27	25	1.09
24	69	60	0.79	43	40	0.95	34	30	25	24	1.19
25	66	57	0.86	41	38	1.03	33	29	24	23	1.29
26	63	55	0.93	40	37	1.12					
27	61	53	1.01	38	35	1.21					
28	59	51	1.08	37	34	1.30					
29	57	49	1.16	36	33	1.39					
30	55	48	1.24	35	32	1.49					
31	53	46	1.33	33	31	1.59					
32	52	45	1.41	32	30	1.69					
33	50	43	1.50								
34	48	42	1.59								
35	47	41	1.69								
36	46	40	1.79								
37	45	39	1.89								
38	43	38	1.99								

Properties and Reaction Values

S in.³	103	89.4	For explanation of deflection see page 2 - 23	64.8	59.6	For explanation of deflection see page 2 - 23	50.8	45.4	38.2	36.4	For explanation of deflection see page 2 - 23
V kips	186	120		120	89		120	80	74	61	
R kips	96	62		72	54		92	62	54	44	
R_i kips	19.2	12.4		14.9	11.1		18.5	12.5	11.6	9.5	
N_e in.	8.2	8.2		6.7	6.7		5.0	5.0	5.3	5.3	

Load above heavy line is limited by maximum allowable web shear.

$F_y = 36$ ksi				BEAMS					S 10-8-7

BEAMS
S shapes

Allowable uniform loads in kips
for beams laterally supported

Designation		S10			S8			S7		
Weight per Foot		35	25.4	Deflection Inches	23	18.4	Deflection Inches	20	15.3	Deflection Inches
Flange Width		5	4⅝		4⅛	4		3⅞	3⅝	
L_c		5.2	4.9		4.4	4.2		4.1	3.9	
L_u		11.2	10.6		10.3	9.9		10.0	9.5	
	2	172.3		0.01	102.3		0.01	91.4		0.01
	3	156.8		0.02	86.4	62.9	0.03	64.5	51.2	0.03
	4	117.6	90.2	0.04	64.8	57.6	0.05	48.4	42.0	0.06
	5	94.1	79.0	0.06	51.8	46.1	0.08	38.7	33.6	0.09
	6	78.4	65.9	0.09	43.2	38.4	0.11	32.3	28.0	0.13
	7	67.2	56.5	0.12	37.0	32.9	0.15	27.7	24.0	0.17
	8	58.8	49.4	0.16	32.4	28.8	0.20	24.2	21.0	0.23
	9	52.3	43.9	0.20	28.8	25.6	0.25	21.5	18.7	0.29
	10	47.0	39.5	0.25	25.9	23.0	0.31	19.4	16.8	0.35
	11	42.8	35.9	0.30	23.6	20.9	0.38	17.6	15.3	0.43
	12	39.2	32.9	0.36	21.6	19.2	0.45	16.1	14.0	0.51
	13	36.2	30.4	0.42	19.9	17.7	0.52	14.9	12.9	0.60
	14	33.6	28.2	0.49	18.5	16.5	0.61	13.8	12.0	0.70
	15	31.4	26.3	0.56	17.3	15.4	0.70	12.9	11.2	0.80
	16	29.4	24.7	0.64	16.2	14.4	0.79			
	17	27.7	23.2	0.72	15.2	13.6	0.90			
	18	26.1	22.0	0.80						
	19	24.8	20.8	0.90						
	20	23.5	19.8	0.99						
	21	22.4	18.8	1.09						

$F_y = 36$ ksi — Span in Feet

Properties and Reaction Values

S in.³		29.4	24.7	For explana-tion of deflection see page **2 - 23**	16.2	14.4	For explana-tion of deflection see page **2 - 23**	12.1	10.5	For explana-tion of deflection see page **2 - 23**
V kips		86	45		51	31		46	26	
R kips		74	39		**54**	**33**		**53**	**30**	
R_i kips		16.0	8.4		11.9	7.3		12.2	6.8	
N_e in.		4.2	4.2		3.3	3.3		2.9	2.9	

Load above heavy line is limited by maximum allowable web shear.
Values of R in **bold face** exceed maximum web shear V.

AMERICAN INSTITUTE OF STEEL CONSTRUCTION

S 6-5-4-3

BEAMS
S shapes

$$F_y = 36 \text{ ksi}$$

Allowable uniform loads in kips
for beams laterally supported

Designation		S6			S5			S4			S3		
Weight per Foot		17.25	12.5	Deflec-	14.75	10	Deflec-	9.5	7.7	Deflec-	7.5	5.7	Deflec-
Flange Width		3⅝	3⅝	tion	3¼	3	tion	2¾	2⅝	tion	2½	2⅜	tion
L_c		3.8	3.5	Inches	3.5	3.2	Inches	3.0	2.8	Inches	2.6	2.5	Inches
L_u		9.9	9.2		9.9	9.1		9.5	9.0		10.1	9.4	
	1	80.9		0.00	71.6		0.00	37.8		0.01	30.4	14.8	0.01
	2	70.2	40.4	0.02	48.7	31.0	0.02	27.1	22.4	0.02	15.6	13.4	0.03
	3	46.8	39.3	0.04	32.5	26.2	0.04	18.1	16.2	0.06	10.4	9.0	0.07
	4	35.1	29.5	0.07	24.4	19.7	0.08	13.6	12.2	0.10	7.8	6.7	0.13
	5	28.1	23.6	0.10	19.5	15.7	0.12	10.8	9.7	0.16	6.2	5.4	0.21
	6	23.4	19.7	0.15	16.2	13.1	0.18	9.0	8.1	0.22	5.2	4.5	0.30
	7	20.0	16.8	0.20	13.9	11.2	0.24	7.7	6.9	0.30	4.5	3.8	0.41
	8	17.5	14.7	0.26	12.2	9.8	0.32	6.8	6.1	0.40			
	9	15.6	13.1	0.34	10.8	8.7	0.40	6.0	5.4	0.50			
	10	14.0	11.8	0.41	9.7	7.9	0.50						
	11	12.8	10.7	0.50	8.9	7.2	0.60						
	12	11.7	9.8	0.60									
	13	10.8	9.1	0.70									

$F_y = 36$ ksi

Span in Feet

Properties and Reaction Values

			For			For			For			For
S in.³	8.8	7.4	explana-	6.1	4.9	explana-	3.4	3.0	explana-	2.0	1.7	explana-
V kips	40.5	20.2	tion of	35.8	15.5	tion of	18.9	11.2	tion of	15.2	7.4	tion of
R kips	54.1	27.0	deflec-	56.7	24.6	deflec-	36.9	21.8	deflec-	38.9	18.9	deflec-
R_i kips	12.6	6.3	tion see	13.3	5.8	tion see	8.8	5.2	tion see	9.4	4.6	tion see
N_e in.	2.4	2.4	page 2-23	1.9	1.9	page 2-23	1.5	1.5	page 2-23	1.0	1.0	page 2-23

Load above heavy line is limited by maximum allowable web shear.
Values of R in **bold face** exceed maximum web shear V.

AMERICAN INSTITUTE OF STEEL CONSTRUCTION

$F_y = 36$ ksi			BEAMS				18-15
			Channels				

Allowable uniform loads in kips
for channels laterally supported

Designation		MC18					C15			
Weight per Foot		58	51.9	45.8	42.7	Deflection	50	40	33.9	Deflection
Flange Width		4¼	4⅛	4	4	Inches	3¾	3½	3⅜	Inches
L_u		6.7	6.6	6.4	6.4		7.5	7.1	6.8	
	2						311.5			0.01
	3	365.4	313.2	261.0	234.9	0.01	263.0	226.2	174.0	0.01
	4	275.4	255.6	235.8	225.9	0.02	197.3	170.5	154.0	0.02
	5	220.3	204.5	188.6	180.7	0.03	157.8	136.4	123.2	0.04
	6	183.6	170.4	157.2	150.6	0.05	131.5	113.7	102.7	0.05
	7	157.4	146.0	134.7	129.1	0.06	112.7	97.4	88.0	0.07
	8	137.7	127.8	117.9	112.9	0.08	98.6	85.3	77.0	0.10
	9	122.4	113.6	104.8	100.4	0.10	87.7	75.8	68.4	0.12
	10	110.1	102.2	94.3	90.3	0.13	78.9	68.2	61.6	0.15
	11	100.1	92.9	85.7	82.1	0.15	71.7	62.0	56.0	0.18
	12	91.8	85.2	78.6	75.3	0.18	65.8	56.8	51.3	0.22
	13	84.7	78.6	72.5	69.5	0.21	60.7	52.5	47.4	0.26
	14	78.7	73.0	67.4	64.5	0.25	56.4	48.7	44.0	0.30
	15	73.4	68.2	62.9	60.2	0.28	52.6	45.5	41.1	0.34
	16	68.8	63.9	58.9	56.5	0.32	49.3	42.6	38.5	0.39
	17	64.8	60.1	55.5	53.1	0.37	46.4	40.1	36.2	0.44
	18	61.2	56.8	52.4	50.2	0.41	43.8	37.9	34.2	0.49
	19	58.0	53.8	49.6	47.6	0.46	41.5	35.9	32.4	0.55
	20	55.1	51.1	47.2	45.2	0.51	39.5	34.1	30.8	0.61
	21	52.5	48.7	44.9	43.0	0.56	37.6	32.5	29.3	0.67
	22	50.1	46.5	42.9	41.1	0.61	35.9	31.0	28.0	0.73
	23	47.9	44.4	41.0	39.3	0.67	34.3	29.7	26.8	0.80
	24	45.9	42.6	39.3	37.6	0.73	32.9	28.4	25.7	0.87
	25	44.1	40.9	37.7	36.1	0.79	31.6	27.3	24.6	0.95
	26	42.4	39.3	36.3	34.7	0.85	30.3	26.2	23.7	1.03
	27	40.8	37.9	34.9	33.5	0.92	29.2	25.3	22.8	1.11
	28	39.3	36.5	33.7	32.3	0.99	28.2	24.4	22.0	1.19
	29	38.0	35.3	32.5	31.2	1.06	27.2	23.5	21.2	1.28
	30	36.7	34.1	31.4	30.1	1.14	26.3	22.7	20.5	1.37
	31	35.5	33.0	30.4	29.1	1.22	25.5	22.0	19.9	1.46
	32	34.4	31.9	29.5	28.2	1.29	24.7	21.3	19.3	1.55
	33	33.4	31.0	28.6	27.4	1.38	23.9	20.7	18.7	1.65
	34	32.4	30.1	27.7	26.6	1.46	23.2	20.1	18.1	1.75
	35	31.5	29.2	26.9	25.8	1.55	22.5	19.5	17.6	1.86
	36	30.6	28.4	26.2	25.1	1.64	21.9	18.9	17.1	1.97
	37	29.8	27.6	25.5	24.4	1.73	21.3	18.4	16.6	2.08
	38	29.0	26.9	24.8	23.8	1.83	20.8	17.9	16.2	2.19
	39	28.2	26.2	24.2	23.2	1.92				
	40	27.5	25.6	23.6	22.6	2.02				
	42	26.2	24.3	22.5	21.5	2.23				
	44	25.0	23.2	21.4	20.5	2.45				

(left margin, vertical: $F_y = 36$ ksi ; Span in Feet)

Properties and Reaction Values

S	in.³	75.1	69.7	64.3	61.6	For	53.8	46.5	42.0	For
V	kips	182.7	156.6	130.5	117.5	explanation	155.7	113.1	87.0	explanation
R	kips	92.1	79.0	65.8	59.2	of deflection	95.5	69.3	53.3	of deflection
R_i	kips	18.9	16.2	13.5	12.2	see page	19.3	14.0	10.8	see page
N_e	in.	8.3	8.3	8.3	8.3	2-23	6.6	6.6	6.6	2-23

Load above heavy line is limited by maximum allowable web shear.

12-10   BEAMS $F_y = 36$ ksi

Channels

Allowable uniform loads in kips for channels laterally supported

$F_y = 36$ ksi

Span in Feet

Designation	C12			MC12	Deflection Inches	C10				MC10		Deflection Inches
Weight per Foot	30	25	20.7	10.6		30	25	20	15.3	8.4	6.5	
Flange Width	3⅛	3	3	1½		3	2⅞	2¾	2⅝	1½	1⅛	
L_u	6.1	5.9	5.7	1.8		6.1	5.8	5.5	5.3	1.9	1.1	
1						195.2	152.5			49.3	44.1	0.00
2	177.5	134.7		66.1	0.01	151.8	133.5	109.9	69.6	46.9	32.4	0.01
3	132.0	117.8	98.1	45.1	0.02	101.2	89.0	77.2	66.0	31.3	21.6	0.02
4	99.0	88.4	78.8	33.8	0.03	75.9	66.7	57.9	49.5	23.5	16.2	0.04
5	79.2	70.7	63.1	27.1	0.05	60.7	53.4	46.3	39.6	18.8	13.0	0.06
6	66.0	58.9	52.6	22.6	0.07	50.6	44.5	38.6	33.0	15.6	10.8	0.08
7	56.6	50.5	45.0	19.3	0.09	43.4	38.1	33.1	28.3	13.4	9.3	0.11
8	49.5	44.2	39.4	16.9	0.12	38.0	33.4	29.0	24.8	11.7	8.1	0.15
9	44.0	39.3	35.0	15.0	0.15	33.7	29.7	25.7	22.0	10.4	7.2	0.18
10	39.6	35.3	31.5	13.5	0.19	30.4	26.7	23.2	19.8	9.4	6.5	0.23
11	36.0	32.1	28.7	12.3	0.23	27.6	24.3	21.1	18.0	8.5		0.28
12	33.0	29.5	26.3	11.3	0.27	25.3	22.2	19.3	16.5	7.8		0.33
13	30.5	27.2	24.3	10.4	0.32	23.4	20.5	17.8	15.2	7.2		0.38
14	28.3	25.2	22.5	9.7	0.37	21.7	19.1	16.6	14.1			0.45
15	26.4	23.6	21.0	9.0	0.43	20.2	17.8	15.4	13.2			0.51
16	24.8	22.1	19.7	8.5	0.49	19.0	16.7	14.5	12.4			0.58
17	23.3	20.8	18.5	8.0	0.55	17.9	15.7	13.6	11.6			0.66
18	22.0	19.6	17.5		0.61	16.9	14.8	12.9	11.0			0.74
19	20.8	18.6	16.6		0.68	16.0	14.0	12.2	10.4			0.82
20	19.8	17.7	15.8		0.76	15.2	13.3	11.6	9.9			0.91
21	18.9	16.8	15.0		0.84	14.5	12.7	11.0	9.4			1.00
22	18.0	16.1	14.3		0.92	13.8	12.1	10.5	9.0			1.10
23	17.2	15.4	13.7		1.00	13.2	11.6	10.1	8.6			1.20
24	16.5	14.7	13.1		1.09	12.7	11.1	9.7	8.3			1.31
25	15.8	14.1	12.6		1.19	12.1	10.7	9.3	7.9			1.42
26	15.2	13.6	12.1		1.28							
27	14.7	13.1	11.7		1.38							
28	14.1	12.6	11.3		1.49							
29	13.7	12.2	10.9		1.60							
30	13.2	11.8	10.5		1.71							

Properties and Reaction Values

	C12			MC12		C10				MC10		
S in.³	27.0	24.1	21.5	9.2	For explanation of deflection see page **2 - 23**	20.7	18.2	15.8	13.5	6.4	4.4	For explanation of deflection see page **2 - 23**
V kips	88.7	67.3	49.1	33.1		97.6	76.3	55.0	34.8	24.7	22.0	
R kips	63.7	48.3	35.2	21.5		81.8	63.9	46.0	29.2	19.2	16.2	
R_i kips	13.8	10.4	7.6	5.1		18.2	14.2	10.2	6.5	4.6	4.1	
N_e in.	5.3	5.3	5.3	5.8		4.4	4.4	4.4	4.4	4.7	4.9	

Load above heavy line is limited by maximum allowable web shear.

AMERICAN INSTITUTE OF STEEL CONSTRUCTION

$F_y = 36$ ksi

BEAMS
Channels

9-8-7

Allowable uniform loads in kips
for channels laterally supported

Designation	C9			Deflection Inches	C8			Deflection Inches	C7			Deflection Inches
Weight per Foot	20	15	13.4		18.75	13.75	11.5		14.75	12.25	9.8	
Flange Width	2⅝	2½	2⅜		2½	2⅜	2¼		2¼	2¼	2⅛	
L_u	5.6	5.3	5.2		5.7	5.3	5.1		5.6	5.3	5.1	
$F_y = 36$ ksi — Span in Feet												
1	116.9			0.00	113.0	70.3		0.00	85.1	63.7		0.00
2	99.0	74.4	60.8	0.01	80.7	66.2	51.0	0.01	57.1	50.8	42.6	0.01
3	66.0	55.2	51.8	0.02	53.8	44.1	39.8	0.03	38.0	33.9	29.7	0.03
4	49.5	41.4	38.9	0.04	40.3	33.1	29.8	0.05	28.5	25.4	22.3	0.05
5	39.6	33.1	31.1	0.06	32.3	26.5	23.9	0.07	22.8	20.3	17.8	0.08
6	33.0	27.6	25.9	0.09	26.9	22.1	19.9	0.10	19.0	16.9	14.9	0.12
7	28.3	23.7	22.2	0.12	23.0	18.9	17.1	0.14	16.3	14.5	12.7	0.16
8	24.8	20.7	19.4	0.16	20.2	16.6	14.9	0.18	14.3	12.7	11.1	0.21
9	22.0	18.4	17.3	0.20	17.9	14.7	13.3	0.23	12.7	11.3	9.9	0.26
10	19.8	16.6	15.5	0.25	16.1	13.2	11.9	0.28	11.4	10.2	8.9	0.33
11	18.0	15.1	14.1	0.31	14.7	12.0	10.9	0.34	10.4	9.2	8.1	0.39
12	16.5	13.8	13.0	0.36	13.4	11.0	9.9	0.41	9.5	8.5	7.4	0.47
13	15.2	12.7	12.0	0.43	12.4	10.2	9.2	0.48	8.8	7.8	6.9	0.55
14	14.1	11.8	11.1	0.50	11.5	9.5	8.5	0.56	8.2	7.3	6.4	0.64
15	13.2	11.0	10.4	0.57	10.8	8.8	8.0	0.64	7.6	6.8	5.9	0.73
16	12.4	10.4	9.7	0.65	10.1	8.3	7.5	0.73	7.1	6.4	5.6	0.83
17	11.6	9.7	9.1	0.73	9.5	7.8	7.0	0.82	6.7	6.0	5.2	0.94
18	11.0	9.2	8.6	0.82	9.0	7.4	6.6	0.92	6.3	5.6	5.0	1.05
19	10.4	8.7	8.2	0.91	8.5	7.0	6.3	1.03				
20	9.9	8.3	7.8	1.01	8.1	6.6	6.0	1.14				
21	9.4	7.9	7.4	1.12								
22	9.0	7.5	7.1	1.22								
23	8.6	7.2	6.8	1.34								

Properties and Reaction Values

	C9 20	C9 15	C9 13.4		C8 18.75	C8 13.75	C8 11.5		C7 14.75	C7 12.25	C7 9.8	
S in.^{3}	13.5	11.3	10.6	For explanation of deflection see page **2 - 23**	11.0	9.0	8.1	For explanation of deflection see page **2 - 23**	7.8	6.9	6.1	For explanation of deflection see page **2 - 23**
V kips	58.5	37.2	30.4		56.5	35.1	25.5		42.5	31.9	21.3	
R kips	53.7	34.1	27.9		**58.3**	**36.3**	**26.4**		**49.5**	**37.1**	**24.8**	
R_i kips	12.1	7.7	6.3		13.1	8.2	5.9		11.3	8.5	5.7	
N_e in.	3.9	3.9	3.9		3.4	3.4	3.4		2.9	2.9	2.9	

Load above heavy line is limited by maximum allowable web shear.
Values of R in **bold face** exceed maximum web shear V.

6-5-4-3 · BEAMS · Channels · $F_y = 36$ ksi

[

Allowable uniform loads in kips
for channels laterally supported

Designation	C6			Deflection Inches	C5		Deflection Inches	C4		Deflection Inches	C3			Deflection Inches
Weight per Foot	13	10.5	8.2		9	6.7		7.25	5.4		6	5	4.1	
Flange Width	2⅛	2	1⅞		1⅞	1¾		1¾	1⅝		1⅝	1½	1⅜	
L_u	5.7	5.4	5.1		5.6	5.2		5.9	5.4		6.7	6.3	6.0	
1	76.0	54.6	34.8	0.00	47.1	27.6	0.00	33.6	21.3	0.01	20.2	18.2	14.8	0.01
2	42.5	37.1	32.1	0.02	26.1	22.0	0.02	16.8	14.2	0.02	10.1	9.1	8.1	0.03
3	28.4	24.7	21.4	0.03	17.4	14.7	0.04	11.2	9.4	0.05	6.7	6.1	5.4	0.07
4	21.3	18.6	16.1	0.06	13.1	11.0	0.07	8.4	7.1	0.09	5.1	4.5	4.0	0.12
5	17.0	14.8	12.8	0.09	10.4	8.8	0.11	6.7	5.7	0.14	4.0	3.6	3.2	0.19
6	14.2	12.4	10.7	0.14	8.7	7.3	0.16	5.6	4.7	0.20	3.4	3.0	2.7	0.27
7	12.2	10.6	9.2	0.19	7.5	6.3	0.22	4.8	4.0	0.28	2.9	2.6	2.3	0.37
8	10.6	9.3	8.0	0.24	6.5	5.5	0.29	4.2	3.5	0.36	2.5	2.3	2.0	0.49
9	9.5	8.2	7.1	0.31	5.8	4.9	0.37	3.7	3.1	0.46				
10	8.5	7.4	6.4	0.38	5.2	4.4	0.46	3.4	2.8	0.57				
11	7.7	6.7	5.8	0.46	4.7	4.0	0.55							
12	7.1	6.2	5.4	0.55	4.4	3.7	0.66							
13	6.5	5.7	4.9	0.64	4.0	3.4	0.77							
14	6.1	5.3	4.6	0.74										
15	5.7	4.9	4.3	0.85										

$F_y = 36$ ksi · Span in Feet

Properties and Reaction Values

	C6				C5			C4			C3			
S in.³	5.8	5.1	4.4	For explanation of deflection see page **2** - 23	3.6	3.0	For explanation of deflection see page **2** - 23	2.3	1.9	For explanation of deflection see page **2** - 23	1.4	1.2	1.1	For explanation of deflection see page **2** - 23
V kips	38.0	27.3	17.4		23.6	13.8		18.6	10.7		15.5	11.2	7.4	
R kips	**50.9**	**36.6**	**23.3**		**37.3**	**21.8**		**36.3**	**20.8**		**40.3**	**29.2**	**19.2**	
R_i kips	11.8	8.5	5.4		8.8	5.1		8.7	5.0		9.6	7.0	4.6	
N_e in.	2.4	2.4	2.4		1.9	1.9		1.5	1.5		0.9	0.9	0.9	

Load above heavy line is limited by maximum allowable web shear.
Values of R in **bold face** exceed maximum web shear V.

AMERICAN INSTITUTE OF STEEL CONSTRUCTION

$F_y = 36$ ksi

BEAMS
Angles

Allowable uniform loads in kips
for angles laterally supported

Neutral axis parallel to horizontal leg

For angles laterally unsupported, allowable loads must be reduced.
For angles subject to torsion, make special investigation.

Horizontal leg	Angle		Wt. per Ft.	Span in Feet										
				4	5	6	7	8	9	10	12	14	16	18
8	L 8×8 ×	1	51.0	57.9	46.3	38.6	33.1	29.0	25.7	23.2	19.3	16.6	14.5	12.9
		7/8	45.0	51.3	41.1	34.2	29.3	25.7	22.8	20.5	17.1	14.7	12.8	11.4
		3/4	38.9	44.7	35.8	29.8	25.6	22.4	19.9	17.9	14.9	12.8	11.2	9.9
		5/8	32.7	37.8	30.2	25.2	21.6	18.9	16.8	15.1	12.6	10.8	9.4	8.4
		1/2	26.4	30.8	24.6	20.5	17.6	15.4	13.7	12.3	10.3	8.8	7.7	6.8
	L 8×6 ×	9/16	25.7	19.4	15.5	13.0	11.1	9.7	8.6	7.8	6.5	5.6		
		7/16	20.2	15.4	12.3	10.3	8.8	7.7	6.8	6.2	5.1	4.4		
	L 8×4 ×	7/16	17.2	7.0	5.6	4.6	4.0	3.5	3.1	2.8				
7	L 7×4 ×	3/4	26.2	11.0	8.8	7.3	6.3	5.5	4.9					
		5/8	22.1	9.5	7.6	6.4	5.4	4.8	4.2					
		1/2	17.9	7.7	6.2	5.1	4.4	3.8	3.4					
		7/16	15.8	7.0	5.6	4.6	4.0	3.5	3.1					
6	L 8×6 ×	3/4	33.8	42.9	34.3	28.6	24.5	21.4	19.1	17.2	14.3	12.3	10.7	
		5/8	28.5	36.3	29.0	24.2	20.7	18.1	16.1	14.5	12.1	10.4	9.1	
		1/2	23.0	29.3	23.5	19.6	16.8	14.7	13.0	11.7	9.8	8.4	7.3	
		7/16	20.2	26.0	20.8	17.4	14.9	13.0	11.6	10.4	8.7	7.4	6.5	
	L 6×6 ×	7/16	17.2	15.0	12.0	10.0	8.6	7.5	6.7	6.0	5.0	4.3		
		3/8	14.9	12.8	10.3	8.6	7.3	6.4	5.7	5.1	4.3	3.7		
	L 6×4 ×	7/16	14.3	7.0	5.6	4.6	4.0	3.5	3.1					
5	L 5×5 ×	5/8	20.0	14.3	11.4	9.5	8.2	7.1	6.4	5.7				
		1/2	16.2	11.7	9.4	7.8	6.7	5.9	5.2	4.7				
		3/8	12.3	8.8	7.0	5.9	5.0	4.4	3.9	3.5				
	L 5×3½×	3/8	10.4	4.4	3.5	2.9	2.5	2.2						
		5/16	8.7	3.7	2.9	2.4	2.1	1.8						
4	L 9×4 ×	1	40.8	64.5	51.6	43.0	36.9	32.3	28.7	25.8	21.5	18.4	16.1	
		7/8	36.1	57.6	46.1	38.4	32.9	28.8	25.6	23.0	19.2	16.4	14.4	
		3/4	31.3	49.9	39.9	33.2	28.5	24.9	22.2	19.9	16.6	14.2	12.5	
		5/8	26.3	42.2	33.7	28.1	24.1	21.1	18.7	16.9	14.1	12.0	10.5	
		9/16	23.8	38.1	30.5	25.4	21.8	19.1	16.9	15.3	12.7	10.9	9.5	
		1/2	21.3	34.1	27.3	22.7	19.5	17.0	15.2	13.6	11.4	9.7	8.5	
4	L 8×4 ×	5/8	24.2	33.7	27.0	22.5	19.3	16.9	15.0	13.5	11.2	9.6	8.4	
		1/2	19.6	27.5	22.0	18.3	15.7	13.7	12.2	11.0	9.2	7.9	6.9	
		7/16	17.2	24.2	19.4	16.1	13.8	12.1	10.8	9.7	8.1	6.9	6.0	

AMERICAN INSTITUTE OF STEEL CONSTRUCTION

BEAMS
Angles

$$F_y = 36 \text{ ksi}$$

L

Allowable uniform loads in kips
for angles laterally supported
Neutral axis parallel to horizontal leg

**For angles laterally unsupported, allowable loads must be reduced.
For angles subject to torsion, make special investigation.**

Horizontal leg	Angle	Wt. per Ft.	Span in Feet										
			2	3	4	5	6	7	8	9	10	12	14
4	L 7 ×4 ×7⁄16	15.8	..	..	18.7	15.0	12.5	10.7	9.3	8.3	7.5	6.2	5.3
	3⁄8	13.6	..	..	16.1	12.9	10.8	9.2	8.1	7.2	6.5	5.4	4.6
	L 6 ×4 ×3⁄8	12.3	..	..	12.1	9.7	8.1	6.9	6.0	5.4	4.8	4.0	
	L 4 ×4 ×3⁄8	9.8	..	..	5.5	4.4	3.7	3.1	2.7	2.4			
	5⁄16	8.2	..	..	4.8	3.8	3.2	2.7	2.4	2.1			
	L 4 ×3½×5⁄16	7.7	..	..	3.7	2.9	2.4	2.1	1.8				
	L 4 ×3 ×5⁄16	7.2	..	..	2.7	2.1	1.8	1.5					
	1⁄4	5.8	..	..	2.2	1.8	1.5	1.3					
3½	L 5 ×3½×½	13.6	22.0	14.7	11.0	8.8	7.3	6.3	5.5	4.9	4.4		
	3⁄8	10.4	16.9	11.2	8.4	6.7	5.6	4.8	4.2	3.7	3.4		
	5⁄16	8.7	13.9	9.3	7.0	5.6	4.6	4.0	3.5	3.1	2.8		
	L 4 ×3½×5⁄16	7.7	9.5	6.4	4.8	3.8	3.2	2.7	2.4	2.1			
	L 3½×3½×5⁄16	7.2	7.2	4.8	3.6	2.9	2.4	2.1	1.8				
	1⁄4	5.8	5.8	3.9	2.9	2.3	1.9	1.7	1.4				
	L 3½×3 ×1⁄4	5.4	4.3	2.9	2.2	1.7	1.4	1.2					
3	L 4 ×3 ×½	11.1	13.9	9.3	7.0	5.6	4.6	4.0	3.5				
	3⁄8	8.5	11.0	7.3	5.5	4.4	3.7	3.1	2.7				
	5⁄16	7.2	8.8	5.9	4.4	3.5	2.9	2.5	2.2				
	1⁄4	5.8	7.3	4.9	3.7	2.9	2.4	2.1	1.8				
	L 3½×3 ×1⁄4	5.4	5.7	3.8	2.9	2.3	1.9	1.6					
	L 3 ×3 ×1⁄4	4.9	4.3	2.8	2.1	1.7	1.4						
	L 3 ×2½×1⁄4	4.5	2.9	2.0	1.5	1.2							
2½	L 3 ×2½×3⁄8	6.6	5.9	4.0	3.0	2.4	2.0						
	5⁄16	5.6	5.1	3.4	2.5	2.0	1.7						
	1⁄4	4.5	4.1	2.7	2.1	1.6	1.4						
	L 2½×2½×1⁄4	4.1	2.9	1.9	1.4	1.1							
	L 2½×2 ×1⁄4	3.62	1.8	1.2	0.9								

| $F_y = 50$ ksi | | | **BEAMS**
W shapes
Allowable uniform loads in kips
for beams laterally supported
For beams laterally unsupported, see page 2 - 84 | | | | **W 36** |

Designation		W36					
Weight per Foot		300	280	260	245	230	Deflection Inches
Flange Width		16⅝	16⅝	16½	16½	16½	
L_c		14.9	14.9	14.8	14.8	14.8	
L_u		25.4	23.8	21.9	20.6	19.3	
	16					1092	0.24
	17	1388	1292	1219	1157	1083	0.27
	18	1357	1259	1164	1093	1023	0.31
	19	1285	1193	1102	1035	969	0.34
	20	1221	1133	1047	983	921	0.38
	21	1163	1079	997	937	877	0.42
	22	1110	1030	952	894	837	0.46
	23	1062	985	911	855	801	0.50
	24	1018	944	873	820	767	0.55
	25	977	906	838	787	737	0.59
	26	939	872	806	756	708	0.64
	27	904	839	776	728	682	0.69
	28	872	809	748	702	658	0.74
	29	842	781	722	678	635	0.80
	30	814	755	698	656	614	0.85
	31	788	731	676	634	594	0.91
	32	763	708	655	615	575	0.97
	34	718	666	616	578	542	1.10
	36	678	629	582	546	512	1.23
	38	643	596	551	518	485	1.37
	40	611	567	524	492	460	1.52
	42	581	540	499	468	438	1.67
	44	555	515	476	447	419	1.84
	46	531	493	455	428	400	2.01
	48	509	472	436	410	384	2.18
	50	488	453	419	393	368	2.37
	52	470	436	403	378	354	2.56
	54	452	420	388	364	341	2.77
	56	436	405	374	351	329	2.97
	58	421	391	361	339	317	3.19
	60	407	378	349	328	307	3.41
	62	394	365	338	317	297	3.65
	64	382	354	327	307	288	3.88
	66	370	343	317	298	279	4.13
	68	359	333	308	289	271	4.38
	70	349	324	299	281	263	4.65
	72	339	315	291	273	256	

Span in Feet — $F_y = 50$ ksi

Properties and Reaction Values

S in.³	1110	1030	952	894	837	For explanation of deflection see page 2 - 23
V kips	694	646	610	578	546	
R kips	224	205	191	179	168	
R_i kips	35.4	33.2	31.5	30.1	28.5	
N_e in.	16.8	16.8	16.8	16.8	16.8	

Load above heavy line is limited by maximum allowable web shear.

W 36

BEAMS
W shapes

Allowable uniform loads in kips
for beams laterally supported

For beams laterally unsupported, see page 2 - 84

$F_y = 50$ ksi

Designation		W36						
Weight per Foot		194	182	170	160	150	*135	Deflection Inches
Flange Width		12⅛	12⅛	12	12	12	12	
L_c		10.9	10.8	10.8	10.7	10.5	—	
L_u		13.9	13.1	12.2	11.5	11.4	11.2	
	10						850	0.09
	11						800	0.11
	12			984	940	896	733	0.14
	13	1124	1053	982	917	853	677	0.16
	14	1045	977	911	852	792	629	0.19
	15	975	912	851	795	739	587	0.21
	16	914	855	798	745	693	550	0.24
	17	861	805	751	701	652	518	0.27
	18	813	760	709	662	616	489	0.31
	19	770	720	672	628	584	463	0.34
	20	732	684	638	596	554	440	0.38
	21	697	652	608	568	528	419	0.42
	22	665	622	580	542	504	400	0.46
	24	610	570	532	497	462	367	0.55
	26	563	526	491	459	426	338	0.64
	28	523	489	456	426	396	314	0.74
	30	488	456	425	397	370	293	0.85
	32	457	428	399	373	347	275	0.97
	34	430	402	375	351	326	259	1.10
	36	406	380	354	331	308	244	1.23
	38	385	360	336	314	292	232	1.37
	40	366	342	319	298	277	220	1.52
	42	348	326	304	284	264	210	1.67
	44	333	311	290	271	252	200	1.84
	46	318	297	277	259	241	191	2.01
	48	305	285	266	248	231	183	2.18
	50	293	274	255	238	222	176	2.37
	52	281	263	245	229	213	169	2.56
	54	271	253	236	221	205	163	2.77
	56	261	244	228	213	198	157	2.97
	58	252	236	220	206	191	152	3.19
	60	244	228	213	199	185	147	3.41
	62	236	221	206	192	179	142	3.65
	64	229	214	199	186	173	138	3.88
	66	222	207	193	181	168	133	4.13
	68	215	201	188	175	163	129	4.38
	70	209	195	182	170	158	126	4.65
	72	203	190	177	166	154	122	
							(30.0)	

Span in Feet

Properties and Reaction Values

S in.³	665	622	580	542	504	440	For explanation of deflection see page 2 - 23
V kips	562	527	492	470	448	425	
R kips	164	153	140	133	126	116	
R_i kips	28.9	27.2	25.5	24.5	23.4	22.4	
N_e in.	17.3	17.2	17.3	17.3	17.2	17.3	

Load above heavy line is limited by maximum allowable web shear.

* Tabulated loads for this shape are computed with the allowable stress (ksi) shown in parentheses at the bottom of the allowable load column.

AMERICAN INSTITUTE OF STEEL CONSTRUCTION

$F_y = 50$ ksi	BEAMS W shapes	W 33

Allowable uniform loads in kips
for beams laterally supported

For beams laterally unsupported, see page **2 - 84**

Designation		W33			W33				Deflection Inches
Weight per Foot		240	220	200	152	141	130	*118	
Flange Width		15⅞	15¾	15¾	11⅝	11½	11½	11½	
L_c		14.2	14.2	14.1	10.4	10.3	9.9	—	
L_u		22.1	20.2	18.3	12.1	11.1	11.0	10.8	
	9							728	0.08
	10							718	0.10
	11						768	653	0.13
	12				851	806	744	598	0.15
	13				824	758	687	552	0.17
	14				765	704	638	513	0.20
	15		1031	944	714	657	595	479	0.23
	16	1112	1020	923	670	616	558	449	0.26
	17	1052	960	868	630	580	525	422	0.30
	18	994	907	820	595	548	496	399	0.34
	19	941	859	777	564	519	470	378	0.37
	20	894	816	738	536	493	447	359	0.41
	21	852	777	703	510	469	425	342	0.46
	22	813	742	671	487	448	406	326	0.50
	23	778	710	642	466	429	388	312	0.55
	24	745	680	615	446	411	372	299	0.60
	25	715	653	590	429	394	357	287	0.65
	26	688	628	568	412	379	344	276	0.70
	28	639	583	527	383	352	319	256	0.81
	30	596	544	492	357	329	298	239	0.93
	32	559	510	461	335	308	279	224	1.06
	34	526	480	434	315	290	263	211	1.20
	36	497	453	410	298	274	248	199	1.34
	38	471	430	388	282	259	235	189	1.49
	40	447	408	369	268	246	223	180	1.66
	42	426	389	351	255	235	213	171	1.82
	44	407	371	336	244	224	203	163	2.00
	46	389	355	321	233	214	194	156	2.19
	48	373	340	308	223	205	186	150	2.38
	50	358	326	295	214	197	179	144	2.59
	52	344	314	284	206	190	172	138	2.80
	54	331	302	273	198	183	165	133	3.02
	56	319	292	264	191	176	160	128	3.24
	58	308	281	255	185	170	154	124	3.48
	60	298	272	246	179	164	149	120	3.72
	62	288	263	238	173	159	144	116	3.98
	64	279	255	231	167	154	140	112	4.24
	66	271	247	224	162	149	135	109	
								(30.0)	

Properties and Reaction Values

S in.³		813	742	671	487	448	406	359	For
V kips		556	515	472	425	403	384	364	explanation
R kips		185	169	152	128	119	113	105	of deflection
R_i kips		31.1	29.1	26.8	23.8	22.7	21.8	20.8	see page 2 - 23
N_e in.		15.4	15.4	15.4	16.0	16.0	16.0	16.0	

Load above heavy line is limited by maximum allowable web shear.

* Tabulated loads for this shape are computed with the allowable stress (ksi) shown in parentheses at the bottom of the allowable load column.

W 30

$$F_y = 50 \text{ ksi}$$

BEAMS
W shapes

Allowable uniform loads in kips
for beams laterally supported
For beams laterally unsupported, see page 2 - 84

Designation	W30			W30					
Weight per Foot	210	190	172	132	124	116	108	*99	Deflection Inches
Flange Width	15⅛	15	15	10½	10½	10½	10½	10½	
L_c	13.5	13.5	13.4	9.5	9.4	9.4	8.9	7.9	
L_u	21.8	19.7	17.8	11.6	10.8	10.1	9.9	9.8	

Span in Feet										Deflection
9								619	0.09
10						677	654	590	0.11
11				745	706	658	600	537	0.14
12				697	651	603	550	492	0.16
13				643	601	557	508	454	0.19
14			783	597	558	517	471	422	0.22
15	942	855	777	557	521	483	440	393	0.26
16	895	807	729	523	488	452	413	369	0.29
17	842	760	686	492	459	426	388	347	0.33
18	796	717	648	464	434	402	367	328	0.37
19	754	680	614	440	411	381	347	311	0.41
20	716	646	583	418	391	362	330	295	0.46
21	682	615	555	398	372	345	314	281	0.50
22	651	587	530	380	355	329	300	268	0.55
23	623	561	507	363	340	315	287	257	0.60
24	597	538	486	348	325	302	275	246	0.66
25	573	517	466	334	312	290	264	236	0.71
26	551	497	448	322	300	278	254	227	0.77
27	530	478	432	310	289	268	244	219	0.83
28	512	461	416	299	279	259	236	211	0.89
29	494	445	402	288	269	250	228	204	0.96
30	477	430	389	279	260	241	220	197	1.02
32	448	404	364	261	244	226	206	184	1.17
34	421	380	343	246	230	213	194	174	1.32
36	398	359	324	232	217	201	183	164	1.47
38	377	340	307	220	206	190	174	155	1.64
40	358	323	292	209	195	181	165	148	1.82
42	341	307	278	199	186	172	157	141	2.01
44	326	294	265	190	178	165	150	134	2.20
46	311	281	253	182	170	157	143	128	2.41
48	298	269	243	174	163	151	138	123	2.62
50	286	258	233	167	156	145	132	118	2.84
52	275	248	224	161	150	139	127	114	3.08
54	265	239	216	155	145	134	122	109	3.32
56	256	231	208	149	139	129	118	105	3.57
58	247	223	201	144	135	125	114	102	3.83
60	239	215	194	139	130	121	110	98	
								(32.8)	

$F_y = 50 \text{ ksi}$

Properties and Reaction Values

S in.³	651	587	530	380	355	329	300	270	For explanation of deflection see page 2 - 23
V kips	471	428	391	373	353	338	327	309	
R kips	169	151	137	121	114	108	104	97	
R_i kips	29.1	26.6	24.6	23.1	21.9	21.2	20.6	19.6	
N_e in.	13.9	13.9	13.9	14.4	14.4	14.4	14.3	14.4	

Load above heavy line is limited by maximum allowable web shear.
* Tabulated loads for this shape are computed with the allowable stress (ksi) shown in parentheses at the bottom of the allowable load column.

AMERICAN INSTITUTE OF STEEL CONSTRUCTION

$F_y = 50$ ksi

BEAMS
W shapes

Allowable uniform loads in kips
for beams laterally supported

For beams laterally unsupported, see page **2 - 84**

W 27

Designation		W27			W27				Deflection Inches
Weight per Foot		177	160	145	114	102	94	*84	
Flange Width		14⅛	14	14	10⅛	10	10	10	
L_c		12.6	12.6	12.5	9.0	9.0	8.9	7.9	
L_u		20.4	18.5	16.9	11.5	10.2	9.6	9.5	
Span in Feet 9								494	0.10
10					622	561	527	463	0.13
11					600	534	486	421	0.15
12					550	490	446	386	0.18
13		792	713	645	508	452	411	356	0.21
14		776	701	635	471	420	382	331	0.25
15		725	654	593	440	392	356	309	0.28
16		679	613	556	413	367	334	290	0.32
17		639	577	523	388	346	314	272	0.37
18		604	545	494	367	326	297	257	0.41
19		572	516	468	347	309	281	244	0.46
20		543	491	444	330	294	267	232	0.51
21		518	467	423	314	280	255	221	0.56
22		494	446	404	300	267	243	211	0.61
23		473	427	386	287	255	232	201	0.67
24		453	409	370	275	245	223	193	0.73
25		435	392	356	264	235	214	185	0.79
26		418	377	342	254	226	206	178	0.85
27		403	363	329	244	218	198	172	0.92
28		388	350	317	236	210	191	165	0.99
29		375	338	306	228	203	184	160	1.06
30		362	327	296	220	196	178	154	1.14
31		351	317	287	213	189	172	149	1.22
32		340	307	278	206	184	167	145	1.29
33		329	297	269	200	178	162	140	1.38
34		320	289	261	194	173	157	136	1.46
35		311	280	254	189	168	153	132	1.55
36		302	273	247	183	163	149	129	1.64
38		286	258	234	174	155	141	122	1.83
40		272	245	222	165	147	134	116	2.02
42		259	234	212	157	140	127	110	2.23
44		247	223	202	150	134	122	105	2.45
46		236	213	193	143	128	116	101	2.68
48		226	204	185	138	122	111	97	2.91
50		217	196	178	132	117	107	93	3.16
52		209	189	171	127	113	103	89	3.42
54		201	182	165	122	109	99	86	
								(32.8)	

Properties and Reaction Values

		177	160	145	114	102	94	*84	
S in.³		494	446	404	300	267	243	212	For explanation of deflection see page 2 - 23
V kips		396	356	323	311	280	264	247	
R kips		153	137	122	111	100	92	86	
R_i kips		27.2	24.7	22.5	21.4	19.4	18.4	17.4	
N_e in.		12.4	12.4	12.4	12.9	12.8	12.9	12.8	

Load above heavy line is limited by maximum allowable web shear.

*Tabulated loads for this shape are computed with the allowable stress (ksi) shown in parentheses at the bottom of the allowable load column.

AMERICAN INSTITUTE OF STEEL CONSTRUCTION

W 24

BEAMS
W shapes

Allowable uniform loads in kips
for beams laterally supported

For beams laterally unsupported, see page 2 - 84

$$F_y = 50 \text{ ksi}$$

$F_y = 50$ ksi

Designation		W24			W24			
Weight per Foot		160	145	*130	120	110	*100	Deflection Inches
Flange Width		14⅛	14	14	12⅛	12	12	
L_c		12.6	12.6	12.5	10.8	10.8	10.7	
L_u		21.5	19.5	17.4	15.4	14.2	12.9	
Span in Feet	12				541	493	449	0.20
	13		596	548	508	467	421	0.24
	14	649	586	519	471	434	391	0.28
	15	607	547	484	440	405	365	0.32
	16	569	513	454	413	380	342	0.36
	17	536	483	427	388	357	322	0.41
	18	506	456	403	367	337	304	0.46
	19	479	432	382	347	320	288	0.51
	20	455	410	363	330	304	273	0.57
	21	434	391	346	314	289	260	0.63
	22	414	373	330	300	276	249	0.69
	23	396	357	316	287	264	238	0.75
	24	380	342	302	275	253	228	0.82
	25	364	328	290	264	243	219	0.89
	26	350	316	279	254	234	210	0.96
	27	337	304	269	244	225	203	1.04
	28	325	293	259	236	217	195	1.12
	29	314	283	250	228	209	189	1.20
	30	304	274	242	220	202	182	1.28
	31	294	265	234	213	196	176	1.37
	32	285	256	227	206	190	171	1.46
	33	276	249	220	200	184	166	1.55
	34	268	241	214	194	179	161	1.64
	35	260	234	207	189	173	156	1.74
	36	253	228	202	183	169	152	1.84
	37	246	222	196	178	164	148	1.95
	38	240	216	191	174	160	144	2.05
	39	234	210	186	169	156	140	2.16
	40	228	205	181	165	152	137	2.28
	41	222	200	177	161	148	133	2.39
	42	217	195	173	157	145	130	2.51
	43	212	191	169	153	141	127	2.63
	44	207	187	165	150	138	124	2.75
	45	202	182	161	147	135	122	2.88
	46	198	178	158	143	132	119	3.01
	48	190	171	151	138	127	114	
	50	182	164	145	132	121	109	
				(32.8)			(32.8)	

Properties and Reaction Values

	414	373	332	300	276	250	
S in.³	414	373	332	300	276	250	For explanation of deflection see page 2 - 23
V kips	324	298	274	270	246	225	
R kips	134	121	110	108	98	89	
R_i kips	24.6	22.8	21.2	20.9	19.1	17.6	
N_e in.	11.2	11.2	11.2	11.3	11.3	11.2	

Load above heavy line is limited by maximum allowable web shear.

* Tabulated loads for this shape are computed with the allowable stress (ksi) shown in parentheses at the bottom of the allowable load column.

AMERICAN INSTITUTE OF STEEL CONSTRUCTION

| $F_y = 50$ ksi | BEAMS W shapes | W 24 |

BEAMS
W shapes
Allowable uniform loads in kips
for beams laterally supported
For beams laterally unsupported, see page **2 - 84**

Designation		W24				W24		
Weight per Foot		94	84	76	*68	61	*55	Deflection Inches
Flange Width		9	9	9	9	7	7	
L_c		8.1	8.1	8.0	7.3	5.8	—	
L_u		10.9	9.6	8.7	8.6	6.5	6.4	
	6						373	0.05
	7					398	326	0.07
	8				395	358	285	0.09
	9	501	453	421	372	318	253	0.12
	10	486	433	387	335	286	228	0.14
	11	442	394	352	305	260	207	0.17
	12	405	361	323	279	238	190	0.20
	13	374	333	298	258	220	175	0.24
	14	347	310	277	239	204	163	0.28
	15	324	289	258	223	191	152	0.32
	16	304	271	242	209	179	143	0.36
	17	286	255	228	197	168	134	0.41
	18	270	241	215	186	159	127	0.46
	19	256	228	204	176	151	120	0.51
	20	243	217	194	167	143	114	0.57
	21	232	206	184	160	136	109	0.63
	22	221	197	176	152	130	104	0.69
	23	211	188	168	146	124	99	0.75
	24	203	181	161	140	119	95	0.82
	25	194	173	155	134	114	91	0.89
	26	187	167	149	129	110	88	0.96
	27	180	161	143	124	106	84	1.04
	28	174	155	138	120	102	81	1.12
	29	168	149	134	116	99	79	1.20
	30	162	144	129	112	95	76	1.28
	31	157	140	125	108	92	74	1.37
	32	152	135	121	105	89	71	1.46
	33	147	131	117	102	87	69	1.55
	34	143	127	114	99	84	67	1.64
	36	135	120	108	93	79	63	1.84
	38	128	114	102	88	75	60	2.05
	40	122	108	97	84	72	57	2.28
	42	116	103	92	80	68	54	2.51
	44	111	99	88	76	65	52	2.75
	46	106	94	84	73	62	50	3.01
	48	101	90	81	70	60	48	
	50	97	87	77	67	57	46	
					(32.8)		(30.0)	

Properties and Reaction Values

	94	84	76	68	61	55	
S in.³	221	197	176	153	130	114	For explanation of deflection see page **2 - 23**
V kips	251	226	210	197	199	187	
R kips	99	89	81	76	77	71	
R_i kips	19.4	17.6	16.5	15.6	15.7	14.9	
N_e in.	11.3	11.3	11.3	11.3	11.3	11.3	

Load above heavy line is limited by maximum allowable web shear.

* Tabulated loads for this shape are computed with the allowable stress (ksi) shown in parentheses at the bottom of the allowable load column.

W 21

BEAMS
W shapes

Allowable uniform loads in kips
for beams laterally supported
For beams laterally unsupported, see page 2 - 84

$F_y = 50$ ksi

$F_y = 50$ ksi

Designation		W21			W21		Deflection Inches
Weight per Foot		142	127	*112	96	82	
Flange Width		13⅛	13	13	9	9	
L_c		11.8	11.7	11.6	8.1	8.0	
L_u		22.4	20.2	17.8	13.3	11.4	
Span in Feet	8				486	416	0.10
	9				484	413	0.13
	10				436	372	0.16
	11				396	338	0.20
	12	566	500	443	363	310	0.23
	13	536	481	422	335	286	0.27
	14	498	446	392	311	266	0.32
	15	465	417	366	290	248	0.37
	16	436	391	343	272	232	0.42
	17	410	368	323	256	219	0.47
	18	387	347	305	242	207	0.53
	19	367	329	289	229	196	0.59
	20	349	312	274	218	186	0.65
	21	332	298	261	207	177	0.72
	22	317	284	249	198	169	0.79
	23	303	272	239	189	162	0.86
	24	291	260	229	182	155	0.94
	25	279	250	220	174	149	1.02
	26	268	240	211	168	143	1.10
	27	258	231	203	161	138	1.19
	28	249	223	196	156	133	1.27
	29	240	215	189	150	128	1.37
	30	232	208	183	145	124	1.46
	31	225	202	177	141	120	1.56
	32	218	195	172	136	116	1.66
	33	211	189	166	132	113	1.77
	34	205	184	161	128	109	1.88
	35	199	179	157	124	106	1.99
	36	194	174	152	121	103	2.11
	37	188	169	148	118	100	2.23
	38	184	164	144	115	98	2.35
	39	179	160	141	112	95	2.47
	40	174	156	137	109	93	2.60
	41	170	152	134	106	91	
	42	166	149	131	104	89	
	43	162	145	128	101	86	
	44	159	142	125	99	85	
				(32.9)			

Properties and Reaction Values

S in.³		317	284	250	198	169	For explanation of deflection see page 2 - 23
V kips		283	250	221	243	208	
R kips		133	116	101	112	95	
R_i kips		24.7	22.1	19.8	21.6	18.7	
N_e in.		9.6	9.6	9.6	9.6	9.6	

Load above heavy line is limited by maximum allowable web shear.

* Tabulated loads for this shape are computed with the allowable stress (ksi) shown in parentheses at the bottom of the allowable load column.

AMERICAN INSTITUTE OF STEEL CONSTRUCTION

$F_y = 50$ ksi — BEAMS — W 21

BEAMS
W shapes
Allowable uniform loads in kips
for beams laterally supported
For beams laterally unsupported, see page 2 - 84

Designation		W21				W21		
Weight per Foot		73	68	62	*55	49	*44	Deflection Inches
Flange Width		8¼	8¼	8¼	8¼	6½	6½	
L_c		7.4	7.4	7.4	6.9	5.6	—	
L_u		9.6	8.9	8.1	7.9	6.1	6.0	
Span in Feet	5						288	0.04
	6					306	272	0.06
	7				312	293	233	0.08
	8	387	363	336	300	257	204	0.10
	9	369	342	310	267	228	181	0.13
	10	332	308	279	240	205	163	0.16
	11	302	280	254	218	187	148	0.20
	12	277	257	233	200	171	136	0.23
	13	256	237	215	185	158	126	0.27
	14	237	220	200	172	147	117	0.32
	15	221	205	186	160	137	109	0.37
	16	208	193	175	150	128	102	0.42
	17	195	181	164	141	121	96	0.47
	18	185	171	155	133	114	91	0.53
	19	175	162	147	126	108	86	0.59
	20	166	154	140	120	103	82	0.65
	22	151	140	127	109	93	74	0.79
	24	138	128	116	100	86	68	0.94
	26	128	118	107	92	79	63	1.10
	28	119	110	100	86	73	58	1.27
	30	111	103	93	80	68	54	1.46
	32	104	96	87	75	64	51	1.66
	34	98	91	82	71	60	48	1.88
	36	92	86	78	67	57	45	2.11
	38	87	81	74	63	54	43	2.35
	40	83	77	70	60	51	41	2.60
	42	79	73	67	57	49	39	
	44	76	70	64	55	47	37	
					(32.8)		(30.0)	

Properties and Reaction Values

S in.³		151	140	127	110	93	81	For explanation of deflection see page 2 - 23
V kips		193	182	168	156	153	144	
R kips		83	78	71	65	65	60	
R_i kips		17.1	16.1	15.0	14.1	13.8	13.1	
N_e in.		10.0	10.0	9.9	10.0	9.9	10.0	

Load above heavy line is limited by maximum allowable web shear.

* Tabulated loads for this shape are computed with the allowable stress (ksi) shown in parentheses at the bottom of the allowable load column.

AMERICAN INSTITUTE OF STEEL CONSTRUCTION

W 18

BEAMS
W shapes

Allowable uniform loads in kips
for beams laterally supported
For beams laterally unsupported, see page 2 - 84

$$F_y = 50 \text{ ksi}$$

$$F_y = 50 \text{ ksi}$$

Designation		W18			W18			Deflection Inches
Weight per Foot	114	105	96	85	77	70	64	
Flange Width	11⅞	11¾	11¾	8⅞	8¾	8¾	8¾	
L_c	10.6	10.6	10.5	7.9	7.9	7.8	7.8	
L_u	21.1	19.5	17.9	14.6	13.4	12.2	11.1	

Span in Feet	114	105	96	85	77	70	64	Deflection Inches
8				385				0.12
9				384	345	315	288	0.15
10		406	372	345	312	284	260	0.19
11	440	404	370	314	284	258	236	0.23
12	403	370	339	288	260	237	216	0.27
13	372	342	313	266	240	218	200	0.32
14	346	317	291	247	223	203	185	0.37
15	323	296	271	230	208	189	173	0.43
16	303	278	254	216	195	177	162	0.49
17	285	261	239	203	184	167	153	0.55
18	269	247	226	192	174	158	144	0.61
19	255	234	214	182	164	149	137	0.68
20	242	222	204	173	156	142	130	0.76
21	230	212	194	164	149	135	124	0.84
22	220	202	185	157	142	129	118	0.92
23	210	193	177	150	136	123	113	1.00
24	202	185	170	144	130	118	108	1.09
25	194	178	163	138	125	114	104	1.19
26	186	171	157	133	120	109	100	1.28
27	179	165	151	128	116	105	96	1.38
28	173	159	145	123	112	101	93	1.49
29	167	153	140	119	108	98	90	1.60
30	161	148	136	115	104	95	87	1.71
31	156	143	131	111	101	92	84	1.82
32	151	139	127	108	98	89	81	1.94
33	147	135	123	105	95	86	79	2.07
34	142	131	120	102	92	83	76	2.19
35	138	127	116	99	89	81	74	2.32
36	134	123	113	96	87	79	72	
37	131	120	110	93	84	77	70	
38	127	117	107	91	82	75	68	

Properties and Reaction Values

	114	105	96	85	77	70	64	
S in.³	220	202	185	157	142	129	118	For explanation of deflection see page 2 - 23
V kips	220	203	186	193	173	158	144	
R kips	116	106	96	101	89	81	74	
R_i kips	22.3	20.8	19.2	19.7	17.8	16.4	15.1	
N_e in.	8.2	8.1	8.2	8.1	8.2	8.2	8.2	

Load above heavy line is limited by maximum allowable web shear.

| $F_y = 50$ ksi | | BEAMS | | | | | | W 18 |

BEAMS
W shapes
Allowable uniform loads in kips
for beams laterally supported
For beams laterally unsupported, see page 2 - 84

Designation		W18				W18		
Weight per Foot		60	55	50	*45	40	*35	Deflection Inches
Flange Width		7½	7½	7½	7½	6	6	
L_c		6.8	6.7	6.7	6.7	5.4	—	
L_u		9.6	8.7	7.9	7.3	5.9	5.7	
	5						211	0.05
	6					226	193	0.07
	7	304	283	258	239	215	165	0.09
	8	297	271	245	217	188	145	0.12
	9	264	241	218	193	167	129	0.15
	10	238	216	196	173	150	116	0.19
	11	216	197	178	158	137	105	0.23
	12	198	180	163	145	125	97	0.27
	13	183	167	151	133	116	89	0.32
	14	170	155	140	124	107	83	0.37
	15	158	144	131	116	100	77	0.43
	16	149	135	123	108	94	72	0.49
	17	140	127	115	102	89	68	0.55
	18	132	120	109	96	84	64	0.61
	19	125	114	103	91	79	61	0.68
	20	119	108	98	87	75	58	0.76
	21	113	103	93	83	72	55	0.84
	22	108	98	89	79	68	53	0.92
	23	103	94	85	75	65	50	1.00
	24	99	90	82	72	63	48	1.09
	25	95	87	78	69	60	46	1.19
	26	91	83	75	67	58	45	1.28
	27	88	80	73	64	56	43	1.38
	28	85	77	70	62	54	41	1.49
	29	82	75	68	60	52	40	1.60
	30	79	72	65	58	50	39	1.71
	31	77	70	63	56	49	37	1.82
	32	74	68	61	54	47	36	1.94
	33	72	66	59	53	46	35	2.07
	34	70	64	58	51	44	34	2.19
	35	68	62	56	50	43	33	2.32
	36	66	60	54	48	42	32	
	37	64	59	53	47	41	31	
	38	63	57	52	46	40	30	
					(32.9)		(30.0)	

Span in Feet

$F_y = 50$ ksi

Properties and Reaction Values

S in.³	108	98.4	89.1	79.0	68.4	57.9	For explanation of deflection see page 2 - 23
V kips	152	141	129	120	113	106	
R kips	73	68	61	57	54	50	
R_i kips	15.6	14.6	13.4	12.6	11.9	11.2	
N_e in.	8.5	8.5	8.5	8.5	8.5	8.4	

Load above heavy line is limited by maximum allowable web shear.

*Tabulated loads for this shape are computed with the allowable stress (ksi) shown in parentheses at the bottom of the allowable load column.

W 16

BEAMS
W shapes

Allowable uniform loads in kips
for beams laterally supported
For beams laterally unsupported, see page 2 - 84

$F_y = 50$ ksi

$F_y = 50$ ksi

Designation			W16		W16				
Weight per Foot		96	88	78	71	64	58		Deflection Inches
Flange Width		11½	11½	8⅝	8½	8½	8½		
L_c		10.3	10.3	7.7	7.7	7.6	7.6		
L_u		20.6	18.8	15.4	14.0	12.7	11.5		
Span in Feet	8			345	314	284	258		0.14
	9			313	284	254	231		0.17
	10	349	326	282	255	229	208		0.21
	11	332	302	256	232	208	189		0.26
	12	304	277	235	213	191	173		0.31
	13	281	256	217	196	176	160		0.36
	14	261	237	201	182	163	148		0.42
	15	243	221	188	170	153	138		0.48
	16	228	208	176	160	143	130		0.55
	17	215	195	166	150	135	122		0.62
	18	203	185	156	142	127	115		0.69
	19	192	175	148	134	120	109		0.77
	20	183	166	141	128	114	104		0.85
	21	174	158	134	122	109	99		0.94
	22	166	151	128	116	104	94		1.03
	23	159	144	122	111	99	90		1.13
	24	152	138	117	106	95	87		1.23
	25	146	133	113	102	92	83		1.33
	26	140	128	108	98	88	80		1.44
	27	135	123	104	95	85	77		1.56
	28	130	119	101	91	82	74		1.67
	29	126	115	97	88	79	72		1.79
	30	122	111	94	85	76	69		1.92
	31	118	107	91	82	74	67		2.05
	32	114	104	88	80	72	65		
	33	111	101	85	77	69	63		
	34	107	98	83	75	67	61		

Properties and Reaction Values

S in.³	166	151	128	116	104	94.4		For explanation of deflection see page 2 - 23
V kips	175	163	173	157	142	129		
R kips	103	95	102	91	82	74		
R_i kips	20.1	18.9	19.8	18.2	16.6	15.3		
N_e in.	7.1	7.1	7.1	7.1	7.1	7.1		

Load above heavy line is limited by maximum allowable web shear.

AMERICAN INSTITUTE OF STEEL CONSTRUCTION

| $F_y = 50$ ksi | | | | **BEAMS**
W shapes
Allowable uniform loads in kips
for beams laterally supported
For beams laterally unsupported, see page **2 - 84** | | | | **W 16** |

Designation		W16				W16		
Weight per Foot		50	45	40	*36	31	*26	Deflection
Flange Width		7⅛	7	7	7	5½	5½	Inches
L_c		6.3	6.3	6.3	6.3	4.9	—	
L_u		9.1	8.2	7.3	6.8	5.3	5.2	

	Span in Feet	50	45	40	*36	31	*26	Deflection Inches
	4						157	0.03
	5					174	153	0.05
	6				190	173	128	0.08
	7	247	223	196	175	148	109	0.10
	8	222	199	178	154	130	96	0.14
	9	198	177	158	136	115	85	0.17
	10	178	160	142	123	104	77	0.21
	11	162	145	129	112	94	70	0.26
	12	148	133	118	102	87	64	0.31
	13	137	123	109	94	80	59	0.36
	14	127	114	102	88	74	55	0.42
	15	119	106	95	82	69	51	0.48
	16	111	100	89	77	65	48	0.55
	17	105	94	84	72	61	45	0.62
	18	99	89	79	68	58	43	0.69
	19	94	84	75	65	55	40	0.77
	20	89	80	71	61	52	38	0.85
	21	85	76	68	58	49	36	0.94
	22	81	73	65	56	47	35	1.03
	23	77	69	62	53	45	33	1.13
	24	74	66	59	51	43	32	1.23
	25	71	64	57	49	42	31	1.33
	26	68	61	55	47	40	29	1.44
	27	66	59	53	45	38	28	1.56
	28	63	57	51	44	37	27	1.67
	29	61	55	49	42	36	26	1.79
	30	59	53	47	41	35	26	1.92
	31	57	51	46	40	33	25	2.05
	32	56	50	44	38	32	24	
	33	54	48	43	37	31	23	
	34	52	47	42	36	31	23	
					(32.6)		(30.0)	

Properties and Reaction Values								
S in.³		80.8	72.5	64.6	56.5	47.2	38.3	For explanation of deflection see page **2 - 23**
V kips		124	112	98	95	87	78	
R kips		68	61	53	51	47	42	
R_i kips		14.3	13.0	11.5	11.2	10.3	9.4	
N_e in.		7.4	7.4	7.4	7.4	7.4	7.4	

Load above heavy line is limited by maximum allowable web shear.

* Tabulated loads for this shape are computed with the allowable stress (ksi) shown in parentheses at the bottom of the allowable load column.

AMERICAN INSTITUTE OF STEEL CONSTRUCTION

W 14

I

BEAMS
W shapes

$F_y = 50$ ksi

Allowable uniform loads in kips
for beams laterally supported
For beams laterally unsupported, see page **2 - 84**

Designation	W14					W14		W14			
Weight per Foot	*119	*111	*103	*95	*87	*84	*78	74	68	*61	Deflection Inches
Flange Width	14⅝	14⅝	14⅝	14½	14½	12	12	10⅛	10	10	
L_c	13.1	13.1	13.1	13.0	13.0	10.8	10.7	9.0	9.0	9.0	
L_u	31.4	29.5	27.8	25.6	23.8	21.9	20.4	18.5	17.1	15.4	
9								255	235	210	0.20
10							241	246	227	202	0.24
11						256	238	224	206	183	0.30
12	331	310	282	263	235	239	219	205	189	168	0.35
13	318	293	271	247	223	221	202	190	174	155	0.41
14	295	272	252	229	207	205	187	176	162	144	0.48
15	275	254	235	214	193	191	175	164	151	134	0.55
16	258	238	220	200	181	179	164	154	142	126	0.62
17	243	224	207	189	170	169	154	145	133	119	0.70
18	229	212	196	178	161	159	146	137	126	112	0.79
19	217	201	185	169	152	151	138	130	119	106	0.88
20	207	191	176	160	145	143	131	123	113	101	0.98
21	197	182	168	153	138	137	125	117	108	96	1.08
22	188	173	160	146	132	130	119	112	103	92	1.18
23	180	166	153	139	126	125	114	107	99	88	1.29
24	172	159	147	134	121	119	109	103	94	84	1.40
25	165	153	141	128	116	115	105	99	91	81	1.52
26	159	147	135	123	111	110	101	95	87	78	1.65
27	153	141	130	119	107	106	97	91	84	75	1.78
28	148	136	126	114	103	102	94	88	81	72	
29	142	132	121	111	100	99	90	85	78	70	
30	138	127	117	107	96	96	87	82	76	67	
31	133	123	114	103	93						
32	129	119	110	100	90						
33	125	116	107	97	88						
34	121	112	104	94							
35	118	109	101	92							
36	115	106	98								
37	112	103	95								
38	109	100	93								
	(32.8)	(32.5)	(32.2)	(31.8)	(31.5)	(32.8)	(32.5)			(32.8)	

Properties and Reaction Values

S in.³	189	176	164	151	138	131	121	112	103	92.2	For explanation of deflection see page **2 - 23**
V kips	165	155	141	131	118	128	120	128	118	105	
R kips	110	103	93	86	77	84	78	84	76	68	
R_i kips	21.4	20.3	18.6	17.4	15.8	16.9	16.1	16.9	15.7	14.2	
N_e in.	6.1	6.1	6.1	6.1	6.1	6.1	6.1	6.1	6.1	6.1	

Load above heavy line is limited by maximum allowable web shear.
* Tabulated loads for this shape are computed with the allowable stress (ksi) shown in parentheses at the bottom of the allowable load column.

$F_y = 50$ ksi

Span in Feet

AMERICAN INSTITUTE OF STEEL CONSTRUCTION

| $F_y = 50$ ksi | | BEAMS
W shapes | | | | | | W 14 |

BEAMS
W shapes
Allowable uniform loads in kips
for beams laterally supported
For beams laterally unsupported, see page 2 - 84

Designation		W14			W14			W14		
Weight per Foot		53	48	*43	38	*34	*30	26	*22	Deflection Inches
Flange Width		8	8	8	6¾	6¾	6¾	5	5	
L_c		7.2	7.2	7.2	6.1	6.0	6.0	4.5	—	
L_u		12.7	11.5	10.3	8.2	7.3	6.6	5.0	4.7	
Span in Feet	4								126	0.04
	5							142	116	0.06
	6				177	161	150	129	96	0.09
	7				172	153	129	110	83	0.12
	8	206	187	169	150	133	113	97	72	0.16
	9	190	172	153	134	119	100	86	64	0.20
	10	171	154	138	120	107	90	77	58	0.24
	11	156	140	125	109	97	82	70	53	0.30
	12	143	129	115	100	89	75	64	48	0.35
	13	132	119	106	93	82	69	59	44	0.41
	14	122	110	98	86	76	64	55	41	0.48
	15	114	103	92	80	71	60	51	39	0.55
	16	107	97	86	75	67	56	48	36	0.62
	17	101	91	81	71	63	53	45	34	0.70
	18	95	86	76	67	59	50	43	32	0.79
	19	90	81	72	63	56	47	41	30	0.88
	20	86	77	69	60	53	45	39	29	0.98
	21	82	74	65	57	51	43	37	28	1.08
	22	78	70	63	55	49	41	35	26	1.18
	23	74	67	60	52	46	39	34	25	1.29
	24	71	64	57	50	44	38	32	24	1.40
	25	68	62	55	48	43	36	31	23	1.52
	26	66	59	53	46	41	35	30	22	1.65
	27	63	57	51	45	40	33	29	21	1.78
	28	61	55	49	43	38	32	28	21	
	29	59	53	47	41	37	31	27	20	
	30	57	51	46	40	36	30	26	19	
				(32.9)		(33.0)	(32.3)		(30.0)	

Properties and Reaction Values

S in.³		77.8	70.2	62.7	54.7	48.6	41.9	35.1	28.9	
V kips		103	94	84	88	80	75	71	63	For explanation
R kips		68	60	54	54	49	46	43	38	of deflection
R_i kips		13.9	12.7	11.6	11.7	10.8	10.1	9.6	8.6	see page 2 - 23
N_e in.		6.1	6.1	6.1	6.4	6.4	6.4	6.4	6.4	

Load above heavy line is limited by maximum allowable web shear.

* Tabulated loads for this shape are computed with the allowable stress (ksi) shown in parentheses at the bottom of the allowable load column.

AMERICAN INSTITUTE OF STEEL CONSTRUCTION

W 12

BEAMS
W shapes

$F_y = 50$ ksi

Allowable uniform loads in kips
for beams laterally supported
For beams laterally unsupported, see page 2 - 84

Designation		W12				W12			W12		
Weight per Foot		*85	*79	*72	*65	*58	*53	50	45	*40	Deflection Inches
Flange Width		12⅛	12⅛	12	12	10	10	8⅛	8	8	
L_c		10.8	10.8	10.8	10.7	9.0	9.0	7.2	7.2	7.2	
L_u		25.6	24.0	21.9	20.0	17.5	15.9	14.2	12.8	11.5	
	7							181	162		0.14
	8							178	160	140	0.18
	9		233	211	189	175	166	158	142	126	0.23
	10	248	232	209	186	171	152	142	128	114	0.28
	11	231	211	190	169	155	139	129	116	103	0.34
	12	212	194	174	155	142	127	119	107	95	0.41
	13	196	179	161	143	131	117	109	98	87	0.48
	14	182	166	150	133	122	109	102	91	81	0.56
	15	170	155	140	124	114	102	95	85	76	0.64
	16	159	145	131	116	107	95	89	80	71	0.73
	17	150	137	123	110	100	90	84	75	67	0.82
	18	141	129	116	103	95	85	79	71	63	0.92
	19	134	122	110	98	90	80	75	67	60	1.03
	20	127	116	105	93	85	76	71	64	57	1.14
	21	121	111	100	89	81	73	68	61	54	1.25
	22	116	106	95	85	78	69	65	58	52	1.38
	23	111	101	91	81	74	66	62	56	49	1.50
	24	106	97	87	78	71	64	59	53	47	
	25	102	93	84	75	68	61	57	51	45	
	26	98	89	81	72						
	27	94	86	78	69						
	28	91	83	75							
	29	88	80	72							
	30	85	77	70							
	31	82	75								
	32	79	73								
	33	77	70								
	34	75									
	35	73									
		(32.9)	(32.6)	(32.2)	(31.7)	(32.8)	(32.4)			(32.8)	

Properties and Reaction Values

S in.³		116	107	97	88	78.1	70.7	64.7	58.2	51.9	For
V kips		124	116	105	95	88	83	90	81	70	explana-
R kips		93	87	79	70	66	61	68	60	52	tion of
R_i kips		18.6	17.6	16.1	14.6	13.5	12.9	13.9	12.6	11.0	deflection
N_e in.		5.2	5.2	5.2	5.2	5.1	5.2	5.1	5.2	5.1	see page 2 - 23

Load above heavy line is limited by maximum allowable web shear.

*Tabulated loads for this shape are computed with the allowable stress (ksi) shown in parentheses at the bottom of the allowable load column.

AMERICAN INSTITUTE OF STEEL CONSTRUCTION

| $F_y = 50$ ksi | | BEAMS | | | | | | W 12 |

BEAMS
W shapes
Allowable uniform loads in kips
for beams laterally supported
For beams laterally unsupported, see page 2 - 84

Designation		W12			W12				
Weight per Foot		36	31	*27	22	19	*16.5	*14	Deflection Inches
Flange Width		6⅝	6½	6½	4	4	4	4	
L_c		5.9	5.8	5.8	3.6	3.6	3.0	—	
L_u		9.7	8.4	7.2	4.6	3.8	3.7	3.6	
	3						110.4	94.3	0.03
	4				128.0	115.3	96.7	74.0	0.05
	5				111.3	93.7	77.4	59.2	0.07
	6	149.3	128.2	113.4	92.8	78.1	64.5	49.3	0.10
	7	144.6	124.1	106.3	79.5	66.9	55.3	42.3	0.14
	8	126.5	108.6	93.0	69.6	58.6	48.4	37.0	0.18
	9	112.4	96.6	82.7	61.8	52.1	43.0	32.9	0.23
	10	101.2	86.9	74.4	55.7	46.9	38.7	29.6	0.28
	11	92.0	79.0	67.6	50.6	42.6	35.2	26.9	0.34
	12	84.3	72.4	62.0	46.4	39.0	32.2	24.7	0.41
	13	77.8	66.8	57.2	42.8	36.0	29.8	22.8	0.48
	14	72.3	62.1	53.1	39.8	33.5	27.6	21.1	0.56
	15	67.5	57.9	49.6	37.1	31.2	25.8	19.7	0.64
	16	63.3	54.3	46.5	34.8	29.3	24.2	18.5	0.73
	17	59.5	51.1	43.8	32.7	27.6	22.8	17.4	0.82
	18	56.2	48.3	41.3	30.9	26.0	21.5	16.4	0.92
	19	53.3	45.7	39.2	29.3	24.7	20.4	15.6	1.03
	20	50.6	43.5	37.2	27.8	23.4	19.3	14.8	1.14
	21	48.2	41.4	35.4	26.5	22.3	18.4	14.1	1.25
	22	46.0	39.5	33.8	25.3	21.3	17.6	13.5	1.38
	23	44.0	37.8	32.3	24.2	20.4	16.8	12.9	1.50
	24	42.2	36.2	31.0	23.2	19.5	16.1	12.3	
	25	40.5	34.8	29.8	22.3	18.7	15.5	11.8	
				(32.6)			(33.0)	(30.0)	

$F_y = 50$ ksi — Span in Feet

Properties and Reaction Values

	36	31	*27	22	19	*16.5	*14	
S in.³	46.0	39.5	34.2	25.3	21.3	17.6	14.8	For explanation of deflection see page 2 - 23
V kips	74.7	64.1	56.7	64.0	57.6	55.2	47.2	
R kips	52.2	44.7	39.4	43.3	38.9	37.2	31.6	
R_i kips	11.4	9.9	8.9	9.8	8.9	8.6	7.4	
N_e in.	5.5	5.4	5.4	5.6	5.6	5.6	5.6	

Load above heavy line is limited by maximum allowable web shear.

* Tabulated loads for this shape are computed with the allowable stress (ksi) shown in parentheses at the bottom of the allowable load column.

AMERICAN INSTITUTE OF STEEL CONSTRUCTION

W 10

BEAMS
W shapes

$F_y = 50$ ksi

Allowable uniform loads in kips
for beams laterally supported
For beams laterally unsupported, see page **2 - 84**

Designation		W10				W10			
Wt. per Foot		66	60	*54	*49	45	*39	*33	Deflection Inches
Flange Width		10⅛	10⅛	10	10	8	8	8	
L_c		9.1	9.0	9.0	9.0	7.2	7.2	7.1	
L_u		24.3	22.4	20.4	18.6	16.3	14.1	11.8	
	6							114	0.12
	7					142	126	107	0.17
	8	190	170	149	136	135	116	94	0.22
	9	180	164	146	130	120	103	83	0.28
	10	162	148	131	117	108	93	75	0.34
	11	147	134	119	107	98	84	68	0.41
	12	135	123	110	98	90	77	62	0.49
	13	125	114	101	90	83	71	58	0.58
	14	116	105	94	84	77	66	53	0.67
	15	108	98	88	78	72	62	50	0.77
	16	101	92	82	73	68	58	47	0.87
	17	95	87	77	69	64	54	44	0.99
	18	90	82	73	65	60	51	42	1.11
	19	85	78	69	62	57	49	39	1.23
	20	81	74	66	59	54	46	37	
	21	77	70	63	56	51	44	36	
	22	74	67	60	53	49	42	34	
	23	70	64	57	51				
	24	68	62	55	49				
	25	65	59	53	47				
	26	62	57	51					
	27	60	55	49					
	28	58	53	47					
	29	56	51						
	30	54	49						
				(32.6)	(32.2)		(32.9)	(32.1)	

Span in Feet

$F_y = 50$ ksi

Properties and Reaction Values

	66	60	*54	*49	45	*39	*33	
S in.³	73.7	67.1	60.4	54.6	49.1	42.2	35.0	For explanation of deflection see page **2 - 23**
V kips	95	85	74	68	71	63	57	
R kips	82	74	65	59	62	55	49	
R_i kips	17.1	15.6	13.8	12.8	13.1	11.9	11.0	
N_e in.	4.2	4.2	4.2	4.2	4.2	4.2	4.2	

Load above heavy line is limited by maximum allowable web shear.

* Tabulated loads for this shape are computed with the allowable stress (ksi) shown in parentheses at the bottom of the allowable load column.

AMERICAN INSTITUTE OF STEEL CONSTRUCTION

| $F_y = 50$ ksi | | | BEAMS | | | | | | W 10 |

BEAMS
W shapes
Allowable uniform loads in kips
for beams laterally supported
For beams laterally unsupported, see page 2 - 84

Designation		W10				W10			
Weight per Foot		29	25	*21	19	17	*15	*11.5	Deflection Inches
Flange Width		5¾	5¾	5¾	4	4	4	4	
L_c		5.2	5.2	5.2	3.6	3.6	3.6	2.7	
L_u		9.5	8.2	6.6	5.2	4.3	3.8	3.7	
Span in Feet	3					97.2	92.0	71.1	0.03
	4			95.0	102.5	89.1	75.8	55.8	0.05
	5	118.1	101.6	93.1	82.7	71.3	60.7	44.6	0.09
	6	112.9	97.2	77.5	68.9	59.4	50.6	37.2	0.12
	7	96.8	83.3	66.5	59.1	50.9	43.3	31.9	0.17
	8	84.7	72.9	58.2	51.7	44.5	37.9	27.9	0.22
	9	75.3	64.8	51.7	46.0	39.6	33.7	24.8	0.28
	10	67.8	58.3	46.5	41.4	35.6	30.3	22.3	0.34
	11	61.6	53.0	42.3	37.6	32.4	27.6	20.3	0.41
	12	56.5	48.6	38.8	34.5	29.7	25.3	18.6	0.49
	13	52.1	44.8	35.8	31.8	27.4	23.3	17.2	0.58
	14	48.4	41.6	33.2	29.5	25.5	21.7	15.9	0.67
	15	45.2	38.9	31.0	27.6	23.8	20.2	14.9	0.77
	16	42.4	36.4	29.1	25.9	22.3	19.0	13.9	0.87
	17	39.9	34.3	27.4	24.3	21.0	17.8	13.1	0.99
	18	37.6	32.4	25.8	23.0	19.8	16.9	12.4	1.11
	19	35.7	30.7	24.5	21.8	18.8	16.0	11.7	1.23
	20	33.9	29.2	23.3	20.7	17.8	15.2	11.2	
	21	32.3	27.8	22.2	19.7	17.0	14.4	10.6	
	22	30.8	26.5	21.1	18.8	16.2	13.8	10.1	
				(32.5)			(33.0)	(31.9)	

Properties and Reaction Values

	29	25	*21	19	17	*15	*11.5	
S in.³	30.8	26.5	21.5	18.8	16.2	13.8	10.5	For explanation of deflection see page 2 - 23
V kips	59.1	50.8	47.5	51.3	48.6	46.0	35.5	
R kips	49.4	42.5	39.4	41.6	39.4	37.2	28.7	
R_i kips	10.8	9.5	9.0	9.4	9.0	8.6	6.8	
N_e in.	4.4	4.4	4.4	4.5	4.5	4.5	4.5	

Load above heavy line is limited by maximum allowable web shear.
*Tabulated loads for this shape are computed with the allowable stress (ksi) shown in parentheses at the bottom of the allowable load column.

AMERICAN INSTITUTE OF STEEL CONSTRUCTION

W 8

BEAMS
W shapes

$F_y = 50$ ksi

Allowable uniform loads in kips
for beams laterally supported

For beams laterally unsupported, see page **2-84**

Designation	W8		W8		W8		W8			
Weight per Foot	*35	*31	28	*24	20	*17	15	*13	*10	Deflection Inches
Flange Width	8	8	6½	6½	5¼	5¼	4	4	4	
L_c	7.2	7.2	5.9	5.8	4.7	4.7	3.6	3.6	3.4	
L_u	16.3	14.4	12.5	10.9	8.1	6.7	5.2	4.2	3.8	
Span in Feet										
2								73.6		0.02
3							79.6	72.1	53.7	0.04
4					80.7	73.6	64.9	54.0	41.4	0.07
5			91.9	77.7	74.8	61.0	51.9	43.2	33.1	0.11
6	102.3	92.2	89.1	75.4	62.3	50.8	43.3	36.0	27.6	0.15
7	96.6	83.7	76.4	64.6	53.4	43.6	37.1	30.9	23.7	0.21
8	84.5	73.2	66.8	56.5	46.8	38.1	32.5	27.0	20.7	0.27
9	75.1	65.1	59.4	50.2	41.6	33.9	28.8	24.0	18.4	0.35
10	67.6	58.6	53.5	45.2	37.4	30.5	26.0	21.6	16.6	0.43
11	61.5	53.3	48.6	41.1	34.0	27.7	23.6	19.7	15.1	0.52
12	56.4	48.8	44.5	37.7	31.2	25.4	21.6	18.0	13.8	0.61
13	52.0	45.1	41.1	34.8	28.8	23.5	20.0	16.6	12.7	0.72
14	48.3	41.9	38.2	32.3	26.7	21.8	18.5	15.4	11.8	0.84
15	45.1	39.1	35.6	30.1	24.9	20.3	17.3	14.4	11.0	0.96
16	42.3	36.6	33.4	28.3	23.4	19.1	16.2	13.5	10.4	
17	39.8	34.5	31.4	26.6	22.0	17.9	15.3	12.7	9.7	
18	37.6	32.6								
19	35.6	30.8								
20	33.8	29.3								
21	32.2	27.9								
22	30.7	26.6								
	(32.6)	(32.1)		(32.6)		(32.4)		(32.8)	(31.9)	

Properties and Reaction Values

S in.³	31.1	27.4	24.3	20.8	17.0	14.1	11.8	9.9	7.8	For explanation of deflection see page **2-23**
V kips	51.2	46.1	45.9	38.9	40.4	36.8	39.8	36.8	26.9	
R kips	**53.2**	**47.9**	**47.4**	**40.2**	**40.7**	**37.2**	39.6	36.7	26.7	
R_i kips	11.8	10.8	10.7	9.2	9.3	8.6	9.2	8.6	6.4	
N_e in.	3.3	3.3	3.4	3.4	3.5	3.5	3.5	3.5	3.5	

Load above heavy line is limited by maximum allowable web shear.

Values of R in **bold face** exceed maximum web shear V.

*Tabulated loads for this shape are computed with the allowable stress (ksi) shown in parentheses at the bottom of the allowable load column.

AMERICAN INSTITUTE OF STEEL CONSTRUCTION

$F_y = 50$ ksi

BEAMS
W shapes

Allowable uniform loads in kips
for beams laterally supported
For beams laterally unsupported, see page 2 - 84

W 6

Designation		W6			W6			Deflection Inches
Weight per Foot		25	*20	*15.5	16	12	*8.5	
Flange Width		6⅛	6	6	4	4	4	
L_c		5.4	5.4	5.4	3.6	3.6	3.5	
L_u		14.5	11.9	9.0	8.7	6.2	4.4	
	2					55.2	39.6	0.02
	3			56.4	65.0	53.2	35.7	0.05
	4	81.5	64.0	51.9	56.1	39.9	26.8	0.09
	5	73.5	58.2	41.5	44.9	31.9	21.4	0.14
	6	61.2	48.5	34.6	37.4	26.6	17.8	0.20
	7	52.5	41.6	29.7	32.1	22.8	15.3	0.28
	8	45.9	36.4	26.0	28.1	19.9	13.4	0.36
	9	40.8	32.3	23.1	24.9	17.7	11.9	0.46
	10	36.7	29.1	20.8	22.4	16.0	10.7	0.57
	11	33.4	26.5	18.9	20.4	14.5	9.7	0.69
	12	30.6	24.3	17.3	18.7	13.3	8.9	
	13	28.3	22.4	16.0	17.3	12.3	8.2	
	14	26.2	20.8	14.8				
	15	24.5	19.4	13.8				
		(32.6)	(31.2)			(31.6)		

$F_y = 50$ ksi — Span in Feet

Properties and Reaction Values

S in.³	16.7	13.4	10.0	10.2	7.3	5.1	For explanation of deflection see page 2 - 23
V kips	40.8	32.0	28.2	32.5	27.6	19.8	
R kips	**53.2**	**42.3**	**37.5**	**42.7**	**36.7**	**26.7**	
R_i kips	12.0	9.7	8.8	9.8	8.6	6.4	
N_e in.	2.5	2.4	2.5	2.5	2.5	2.4	

Load above heavy line is limited by maximum allowable web shear.

Values of R in **bold face** exceed maximum web shear V.

*Tabulated loads for this shape are computed with the allowable stress (ksi) shown in parentheses at the bottom of the allowable load column.

AMERICAN INSTITUTE OF STEEL CONSTRUCTION

M 14-12-10-8-7-6	BEAMS M shapes	$F_y = 50$ ksi

**Allowable uniform loads in kips
for beams laterally supported**

For beams laterally unsupported, see page 2 - 84

Designation	M14	M12	M10		M10	M8	M7	M6
Weight per Foot	*17.2	*11.8	*29.1	*22.9	*9	*6.5	5.5	4.4
Flange Width	4	3⅛	5⅞	5¾	2¾	2¼	2⅛	1⅞
L_c	—	—	5.3	5.2	—	—	1.8	1.7
L_u	3.5	2.6	7.8	7.5	2.3	2.0	1.9	1.8
1								27.4
2		85.0			62.8	43.2	35.8	26.4
3	117.6	80.0	168.8		51.7	30.8	25.2	17.6
4	105.5	60.0	145.7		38.8	23.1	18.9	13.2
5	84.4	48.0	116.6	95.6	31.0	18.5	15.1	10.6
6	70.3	40.0	97.2	86.5	25.9	15.4	12.6	8.8
7	60.3	34.3	83.3	74.2	22.2	13.2	10.8	7.5
8	52.7	30.0	72.9	64.9	19.4	11.6	9.5	6.6
9	46.9	26.7	64.8	57.7	17.2	10.3	8.4	5.9
10	42.2	24.0	58.3	51.9	15.5	9.2	7.6	5.3
11	38.4	21.8	53.0	47.2	14.1	8.4	6.9	4.8
12	35.2	20.0	48.6	43.3	12.9	7.7	6.3	4.4
13	32.5	18.5	44.8	39.9	11.9	7.1	5.8	4.1
14	30.1	17.1	41.6	37.1	11.1	6.6	5.4	
15	28.1	16.0	38.9	34.6	10.3	6.2	5.0	
16	26.4	15.0	36.4	32.4	9.7	5.8		
17	24.8	14.1	34.3	30.5	9.1	5.4		
18	23.4	13.3	32.4	28.8	8.6			
19	22.2	12.6	30.7	27.3	8.2			
20	21.1	12.0	29.1	26.0	7.8			
21	20.1	11.4	27.8	24.7	7.4			
22	19.2	10.9						
23	18.3	10.4						
24	17.6	10.0						
25	16.9	9.6						
26	16.2							
27	15.6							
28	15.1							
29	14.6							
30	14.1							
	(30.0)	(30.0)	(32.9)	(33.0)	(30.0)	(30.0)		

Properties and Reaction Values								
S in.³	21.1	12.0	26.6	23.6	7.8	4.6	3.4	2.4
V kips	58.8	42.5	84.4	47.8	31.4	21.6	17.9	13.7
R kips	32.5	27.0	70.1	39.7	23.6	20.3	**18.9**	**16.6**
R_i kips	7.9	6.6	16.0	9.1	5.9	5.1	4.8	4.3
N_e in.	6.8	5.8	4.4	4.4	4.8	3.8	3.3	2.8

Load above heavy line is limited by maximum allowable web shear.

Values of R in **bold face** exceed maximum web shear V.

* Tabulated loads for this shape are computed with the allowable stress (ksi) shown in parentheses at the bottom of the allowable load column.

AMERICAN INSTITUTE OF STEEL CONSTRUCTION

(Span in Feet)

$F_y = 50$ ksi

BEAMS
Design of bearing plates

When a beam is supported by a masonry wall or pilaster, it is essential that the beam reaction be distributed over an area sufficient to keep the average pressure on the masonry within allowable limits. In the absence of code provisions, an allowable F_p, depending on the type of construction, may be selected from AISC Specification Section 1.5.5.

The following method of design is recommended:

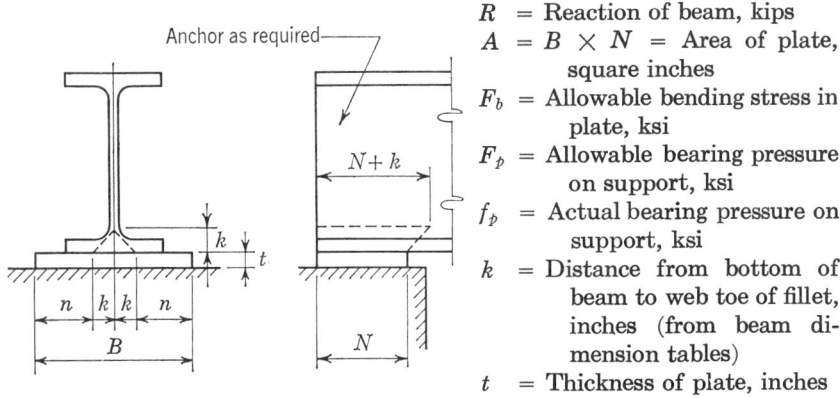

R = Reaction of beam, kips
$A = B \times N$ = Area of plate, square inches
F_b = Allowable bending stress in plate, ksi
F_p = Allowable bearing pressure on support, ksi
f_p = Actual bearing pressure on support, ksi
k = Distance from bottom of beam to web toe of fillet, inches (from beam dimension tables)
t = Thickness of plate, inches

The beam reaction, R, is assumed to be uniformly distributed to the plate over the area $N \times 2k$. The bearing plate is assumed to distribute this load uniformly over the masonry support.

1. Establish F_b, ksi and F_p, ksi.
2. Determine the required area, $A = R/F_p$, square inches.
3. Establish N and solve for $B = A/N$. The length of bearing, N, is usually governed by the available wall thickness or some other structural consideration. B and N should preferably be in full inches, and B rounded off so that $B \times N \geq A$.
4. Determine the actual bearing pressure, $f_p = R/(B \times N)$.
5. Determine $n = (B/2) - k$ and, using the actual f_p, solve for t in the formula:

$$t = \sqrt{\frac{3 f_p n^2}{F_b}}$$

6. Check web crippling on length $N + k$.

$$\frac{R}{(N + k) \times \text{web thickness}} \leq .75 \, F_y$$

EXAMPLE

A W18 ×50 beam, F_y = 36 ksi, for which web thickness = 0.358 inch and k = $1\frac{1}{16}$ inches, has a reaction of 49 kips and is to be supported by a masonry wall with an allowable F_p = 0.25 ksi. The length of bearing, N, is limited to 10 inches. Using F_b = 27.0 ksi (AISC Specification, Sect. 1.5.1.4.3), design a bearing plate for the beam.

A (req'd.) = 49/.250
    = 196 sq. in.

B = 196/10 = 19.6 in.;
    use 20 in.

A = 10 × 20
    = 200 ≥ 196

f_p = 49/(10 × 20)
    = .245 ksi

n = 20/2 − 1.06
    = 8.94 in.

$$t = \sqrt{\frac{3 \times .245 \times 8.94^2}{27.0}}$$

    = 1.48 inches; use $1\frac{1}{2}$ in.

Check for web crippling:
.75 F_y = 27.0 ksi (allowable)

$$\frac{49}{(10 + 1.06) \times .358} = 12.38 \text{ ksi}$$

12.38 ≤ 27.0 **o.k.**

Use: Bearing plate $1\frac{1}{2}$ × 10 × 1'-8

Steel bearing plates are usually shipped separately and grouted in place prior to erection of the beam. Beams are generally not attached to the bearing plates, but should be properly anchored to the wall. Recommended anchorage details are shown in Part 4, Suggested Details.

In the event light loads or high allowable bearing pressures reduce the bearing area required sufficiently to permit support of the beam without bearing plates, it is recommended that the beam flange be investigated for bending by the formula,

$$F_b \text{ (allowable)} = \frac{3 F_p n^2}{t^2}$$

in which

t = thickness of flange, inches
n = (flange width/2) − k, inches
F_b = 0.75 F_y, ksi, allowable bending stress in flange when acting as a bearing plate

ALLOWABLE MOMENTS IN BEAMS
With unbraced length greater than L_u

GENERAL NOTES

Spacing of lateral bracing at distances greater than L_u creates a problem in which the designer is confronted with a given laterally unbraced length (usually less than the total span) along the compression flange, and a calculated required bending moment. The beam cannot be selected from its section modulus alone, since depth and flange proportions have an influence on its bending strength.

The following charts show the total allowable bending moment for W and M shapes of $F_y = 36$ ksi and $F_y = 50$ ksi steels, used as beams, with respect to the maximum unbraced length for which this moment is permissible. The charts are limited to a maximum unbraced length of 24 feet for the smaller beams, since greater lengths are infrequently encountered in design practice.

The total allowable bending moment, in kip-feet, is plotted with respect to unbraced length with no consideration of the moment due to weight of the beam. Total allowable moments are shown for unbraced lengths in feet of spans up to L_c, of spans between L_c and L_u, and of spans beyond L_u.

The unbraced length is the maximum laterally unbraced length of the compression flange corresponding to the total allowable moment. It may be either the total span or any part of the total span between braced points. The curves shown in these charts were computed for beams subjected to loading conditions which produce bending moments within the unbraced length greater than that at both ends of this length. In these cases, C_b is taken as unity in accordance with Section 1.5.1.4.6a. When the unbraced length is greater than L_u and the bending moment within the unbraced length is smaller than that at either end of this length, C_b is larger than unity and the section may provide a more liberal moment capacity. In these cases the allowable moment can be determined using the provisions of Section 1.5.1.4.6a of the Specification.

The unbraced length L_c, in feet, with the limit indicated by a solid symbol (●), is the maximum unbraced length of the compression flange for which the allowable bending stress F_b may be taken at $0.66\,F_y$ for compact sections by Specification Section 1.5.1.4.1, and for which certain non-compact shapes are permitted an allowable stress higher than $0.60\,F_y$ by Section 1.5.1.4.2. For these non-compact shapes, which meet the requirements of compact sections except that $b_f/2t_f$ exceeds $52.2/\sqrt{F_y}$, but is less than $95.0/\sqrt{F_y}$, the allowable bending stress is obtained from Formula (1.5-5). L_c is equal to the smaller value obtained from the expressions $76.0\,b_f/\sqrt{F_y}$ and $20,000/[(d/A_f)\,F_y]$.

The unbraced length L_u, in feet, with the limit indicated by an open symbol (○), is the maximum unbraced length of the compression flange beyond which the allowable bending stress F_b is less than $0.60\,F_y$. L_u is equal to the greater value obtained from Formulas (1.5-6a) and (1.5-7) when F_b is $0.60\,F_y$ and C_b equals unity. For lengths greater than L_c, but not greater than L_u, F_b may be taken at 22 ksi for $F_y = 36$ ksi steel and 30 ksi for $F_y = 50$ ksi steel. In no case is L_c taken greater than L_u.

For shapes which do not qualify as compact sections, and for non-compact sections which do not meet the requirements of Section 1.5.1.4.2, the allowable bending stress F_b is 22 ksi for F_y = 36 ksi steel and is 30 ksi for F_y = 50 ksi steel, for all laterally unbraced lengths up to L_u.

In all cases where the unbraced length of the compression flange exceeds L_u, F_b must be calculated according to the provisions of Section 1.5.1.4.6a, and may neither exceed the larger value given by the following formulas, nor 0.60 F_y:

When $l/r_T \leqslant \sqrt{\dfrac{102 \times 10^3 \times C_b}{F_y}}$: $\quad F_b = 0.60F_y$

When $\sqrt{\dfrac{102 \times 10^3 C_b}{F_y}} \leqslant \dfrac{l}{r_T} \leqslant \sqrt{\dfrac{510 \times 10^3 C_b}{F_y}}$:

$$F_b = \left[\frac{2}{3} - \frac{F_y (l/r_T)^2}{1{,}530 \times 10^3 C_b} \right] F_y \qquad (1.5\text{-}6a)$$

When $l/r_T \geqslant \sqrt{\dfrac{510 \times 10^3 C_b}{F_y}}$: $\quad F_b = \dfrac{170 \times 10^3 C_b}{(l/r_T)^2} \qquad (1.5\text{-}6b)$

Or, when the compression flange is solid and approximately rectangular in cross-section and its area is not less than that of the tension flange

$$F_b = \frac{12 \times 10^3 C_b}{ld/A_f} \qquad (1.5\text{-}7)$$

Formulas (1.5-6a) and (1.5-6b) are simplified for each grade of steel as shown in Specification Appendix A. Formula (1.5-7) is independent of yield stress and applies equally to all grades of steel.

In computing the points for the curves, C_b in the above formulas was taken as unity; the radius of gyration r_T about an axis in the plane of the web is taken from the tables of Properties for Designing, Part 1 of this Manual.

Over a limited range of length, a given beam is the lightest available for various combinations of unbraced length and total moment. The charts are designed to assist in selection of the lightest available beam for the given combination.

The solid portion of each curve indicates the most economical section by weight. The dashed portion of each curve indicates ranges in which a lighter weight beam will satisfy the loading conditions. For beams of equal weight, where both would satisfy the loading conditions, the deeper beam is indicated as a dashed curve to assist in making a selection for reduced deflection or a limited depth condition. The dashed lines have been terminated at the point beyond which any further extension would not be practical from a normal design standpoint. In no case is the dashed line or the solid line extended beyond the point where the allowable bending stress is less than 11 ksi for F_y = 36 ksi steel, or 15 ksi for F_y = 50 ksi steel.

The following example illustrates use of the charts for selection of a proper size beam with an unbraced length greater than L_u:

AMERICAN INSTITUTE OF STEEL CONSTRUCTION

EXAMPLE

Given: Using F_y = 36 ksi steel, determine the size of a "simple" framed girder with a span of 35 ft., which supports two equal concentrated loads located 10 ft. from its left and right reaction points. The compression flange is laterally supported at the concentrated load points only. The loads produce a maximum calculated moment of 220 kip-ft. in the center 15-ft. section between the loads.

Solution:

For this loading condition, C_b = 1.0.

Center section of 15 ft. is longest unbraced length.

With total span equal to 35 ft. and M = 220 kip-ft., assume approximate weight of beam at 70 lbs/ft. (equal to 0.07 kips/ft.)

$$\text{Total } M = 220 + \frac{0.07 \times (35)^2}{8} = 231 \text{ kip-ft.}$$

Entering chart, with unbraced length equal to 15 ft. on the bottom scale (abscissa), proceed upward to meet the horizontal line corresponding to a moment equal to 231 kip-ft. on the left hand scale (ordinate). Any beam listed above and to the right of the point so located satisfies the allowable bending stress requirement. In this case, the lightest section satisfying this criterion is a W24 × 68, for which the total allowable moment with an unbraced length of 15 ft. is 238 kip-ft.

Use: **W24 ×68**

Note: If depth is limited, a W18×70 could be selected, provided deflection conditions are not critical.

ALLOWABLE MOMENTS IN BEAMS

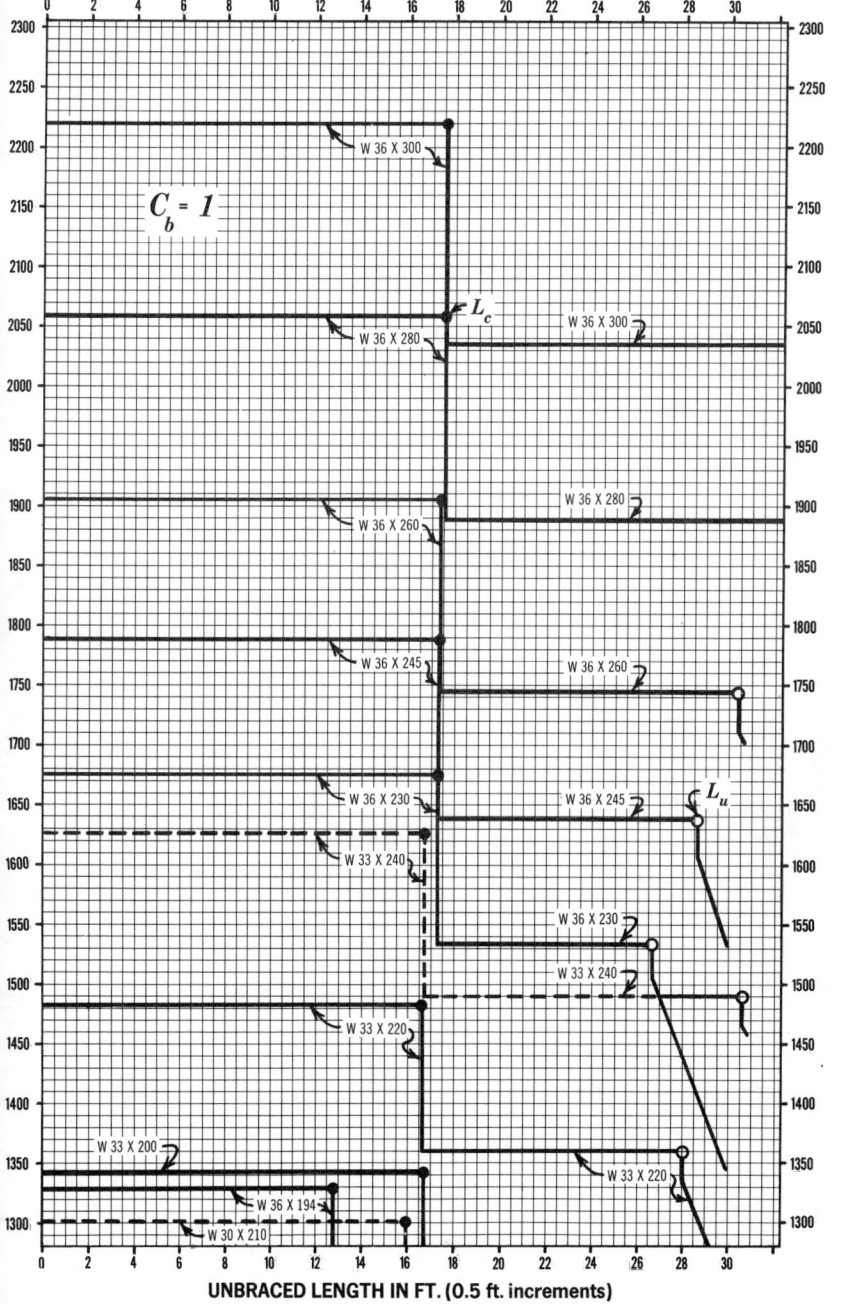

$F_Y = 36\ ksi$

$C_b = 1$

L_c

L_u

W 36 X 300
W 36 X 280
W 36 X 260
W 36 X 245
W 36 X 230
W 33 X 240
W 33 X 220
W 33 X 200
W 36 X 194
W 30 X 210

UNBRACED LENGTH IN FT. (0.5 ft. increments)

AMERICAN INSTITUTE OF STEEL CONSTRUCTION

ALLOWABLE MOMENTS IN BEAMS

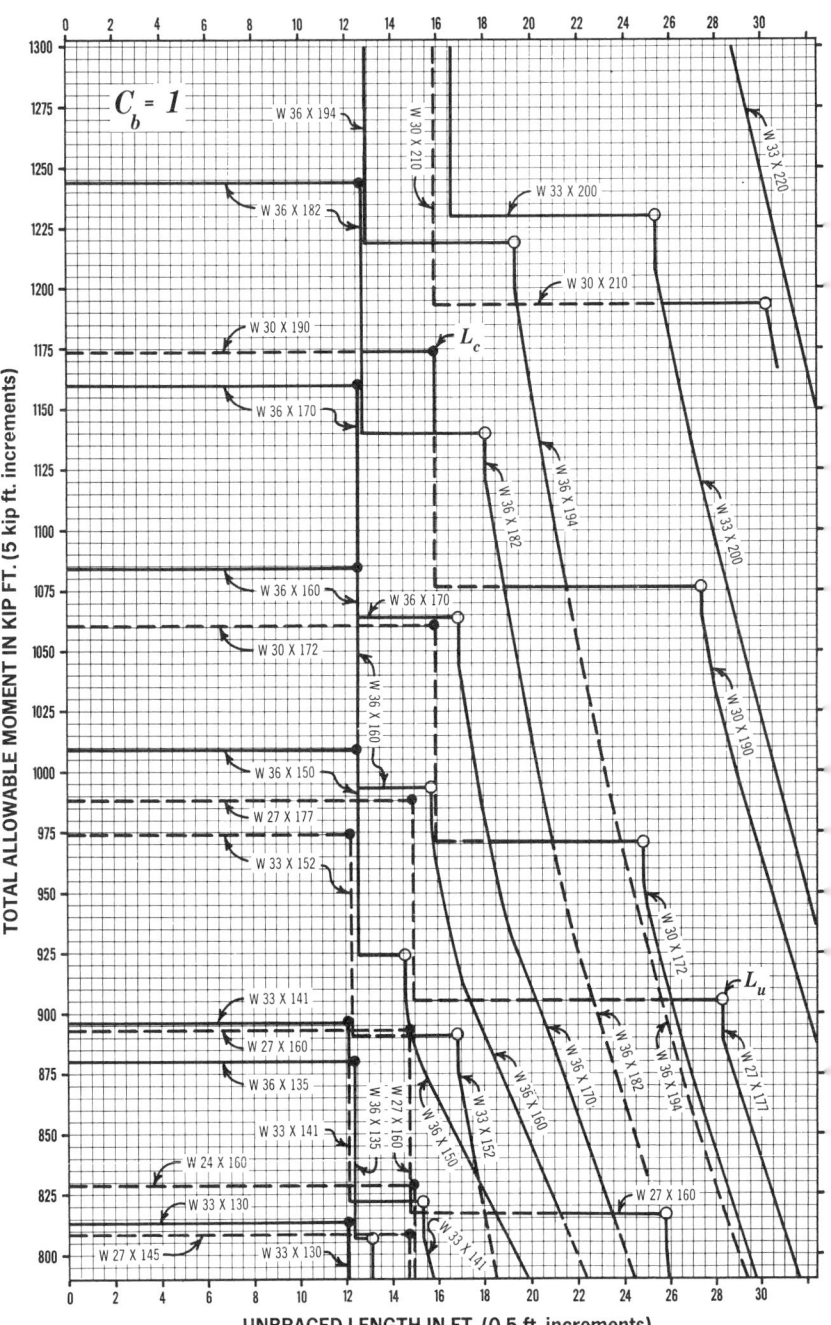

$F_Y = 36$ ksi

TOTAL ALLOWABLE MOMENT IN KIP FT. (5 kip ft. increments)

UNBRACED LENGTH IN FT. (0.5 ft. increments)

AMERICAN INSTITUTE OF STEEL CONSTRUCTION

ALLOWABLE MOMENTS IN BEAMS

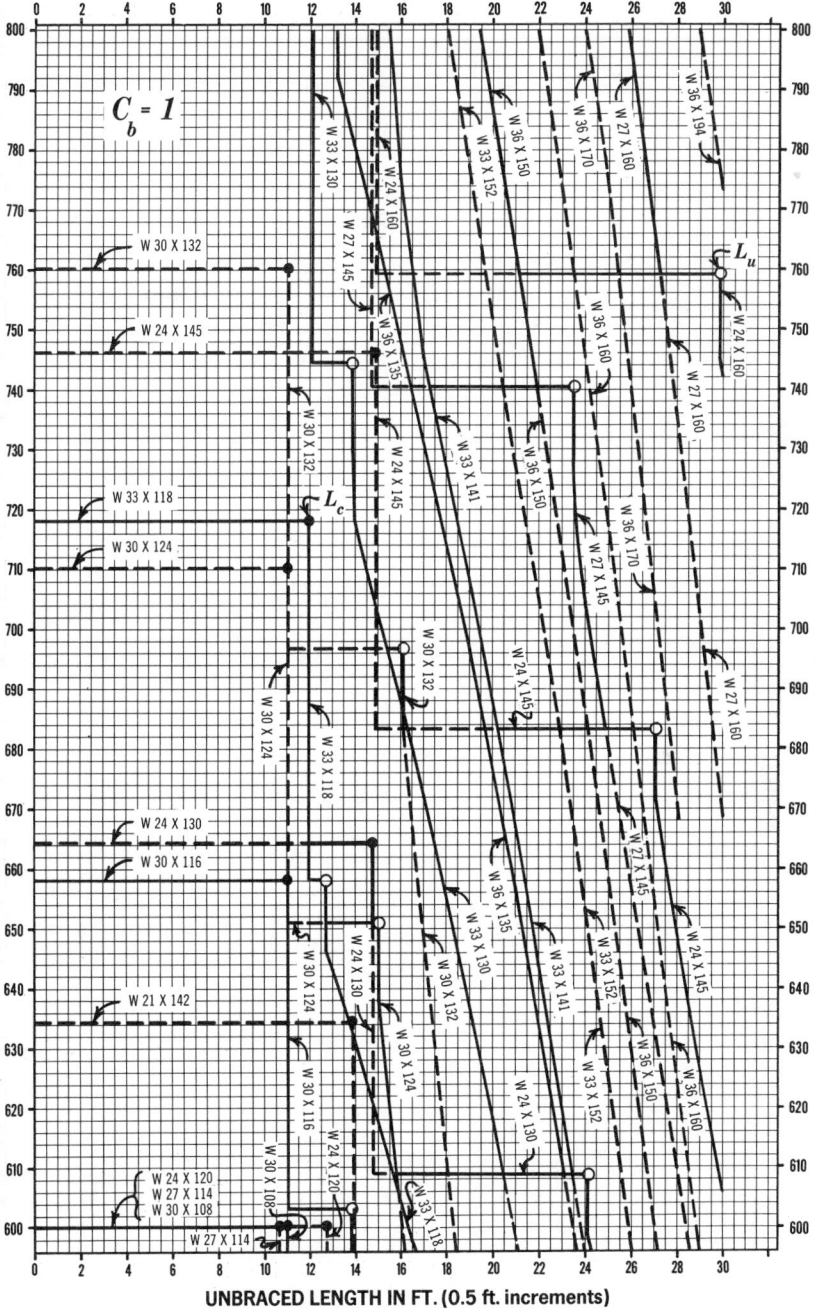

UNBRACED LENGTH IN FT. (0.5 ft. increments)

AMERICAN INSTITUTE OF STEEL CONSTRUCTION

ALLOWABLE MOMENTS IN BEAMS

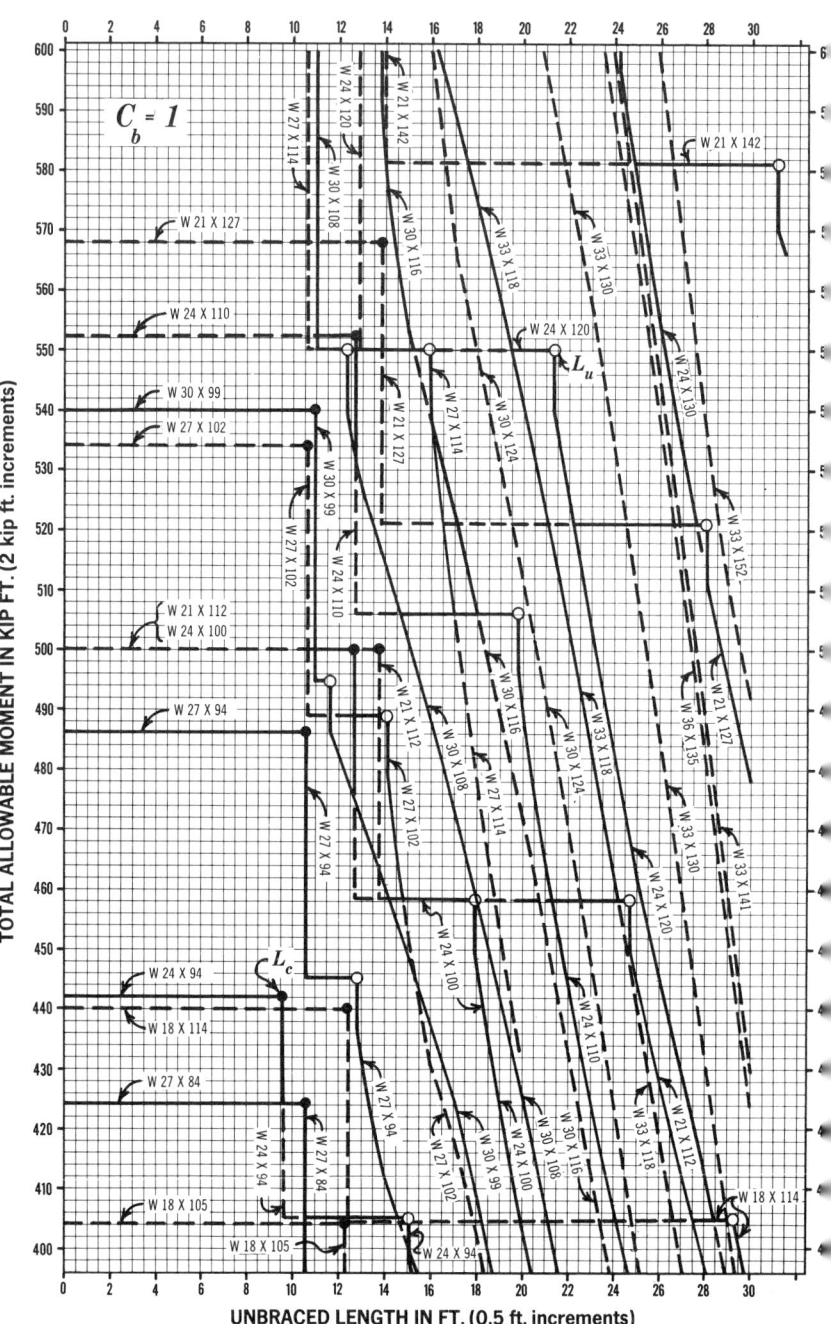

$F_Y = 36$ ksi

$C_b = 1$

TOTAL ALLOWABLE MOMENT IN KIP FT. (2 kip ft. increments)

UNBRACED LENGTH IN FT. (0.5 ft. increments)

AMERICAN INSTITUTE OF STEEL CONSTRUCTION

ALLOWABLE MOMENTS IN BEAMS

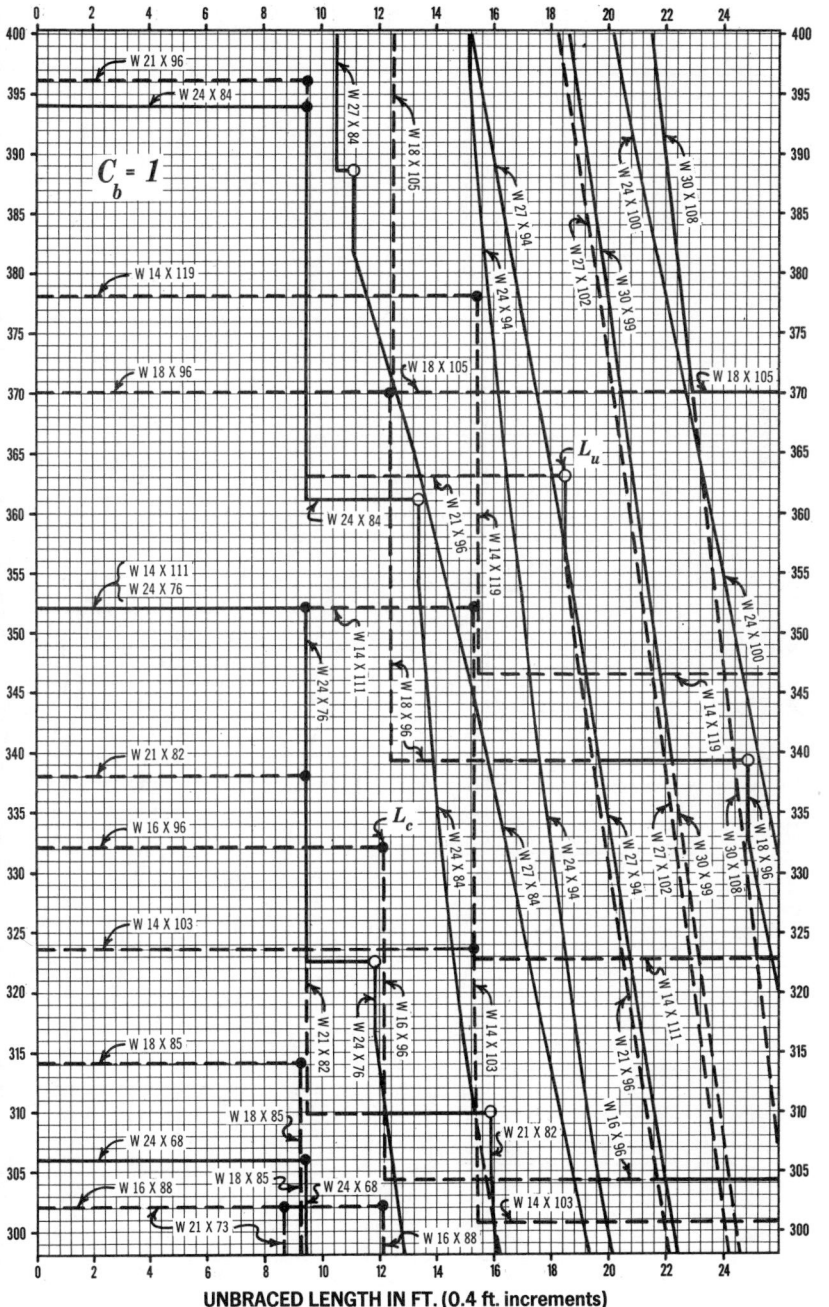

UNBRACED LENGTH IN FT. (0.4 ft. increments)

AMERICAN INSTITUTE OF STEEL CONSTRUCTION

$F_Y = 36\ ksi$

ALLOWABLE MOMENTS IN BEAMS

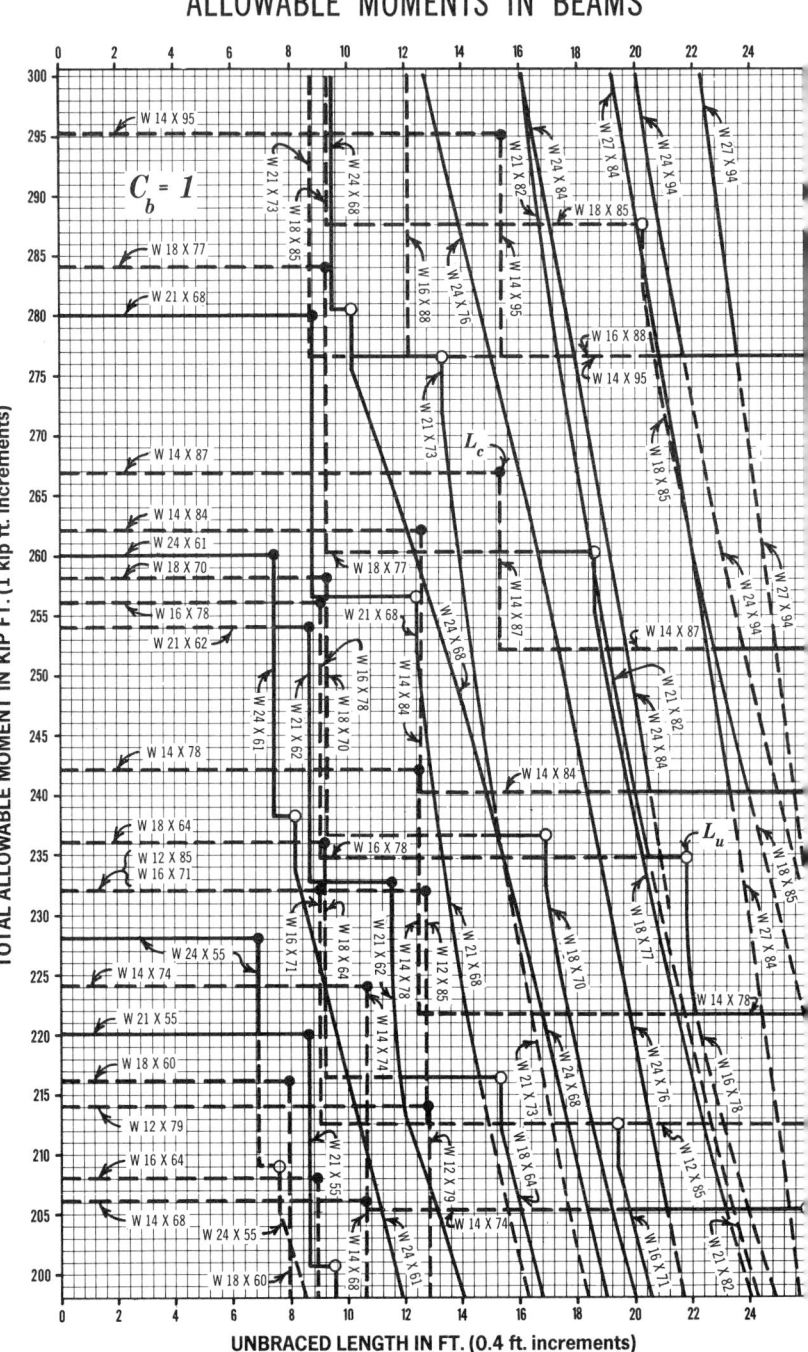

$F_Y = 36\ ksi$

$C_b = 1$

TOTAL ALLOWABLE MOMENT IN KIP FT. (1 kip ft. increments)

UNBRACED LENGTH IN FT. (0.4 ft. increments)

AMERICAN INSTITUTE OF STEEL CONSTRUCTION

ALLOWABLE MOMENTS IN BEAMS

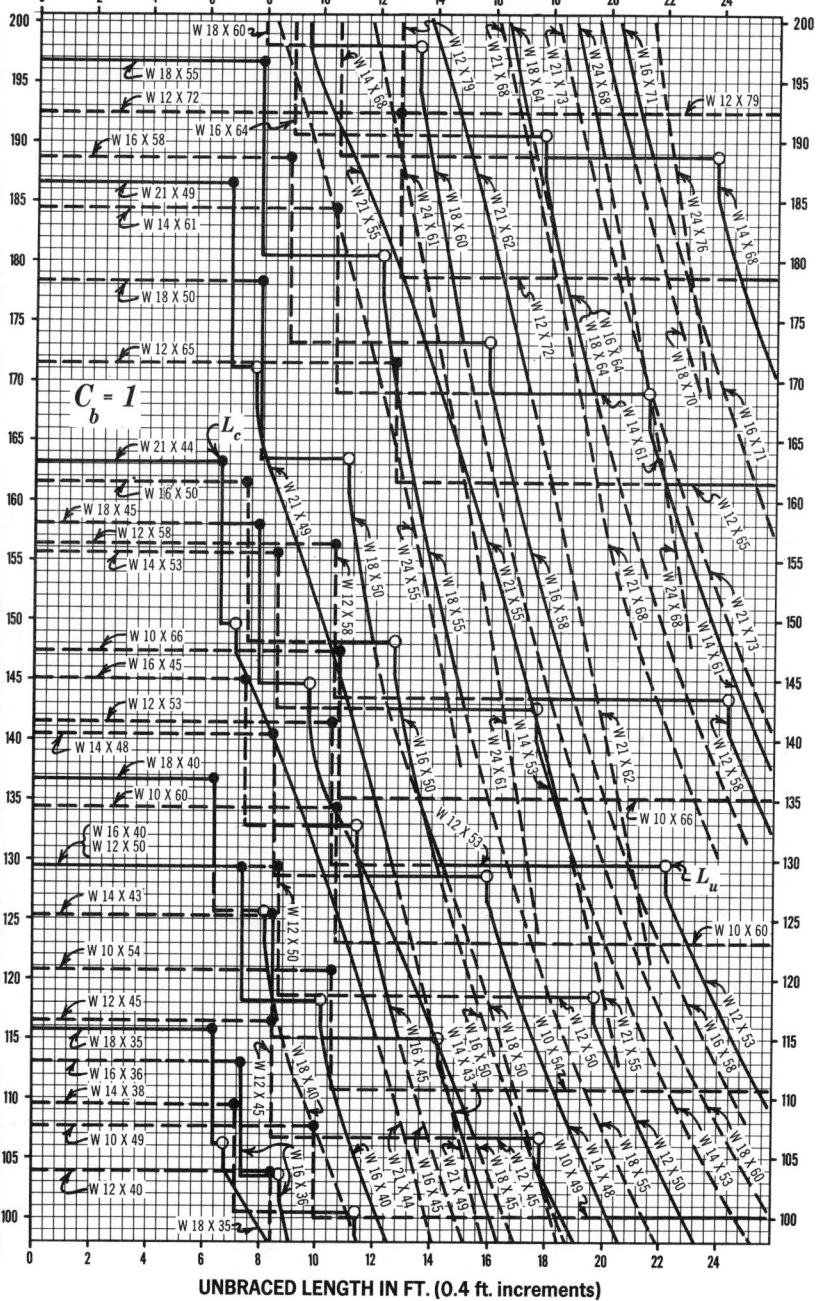

UNBRACED LENGTH IN FT. (0.4 ft. increments)

$F_Y = 36$ ksi

AMERICAN INSTITUTE OF STEEL CONSTRUCTION

ALLOWABLE MOMENTS IN BEAMS

$F_Y = 36\ ksi$

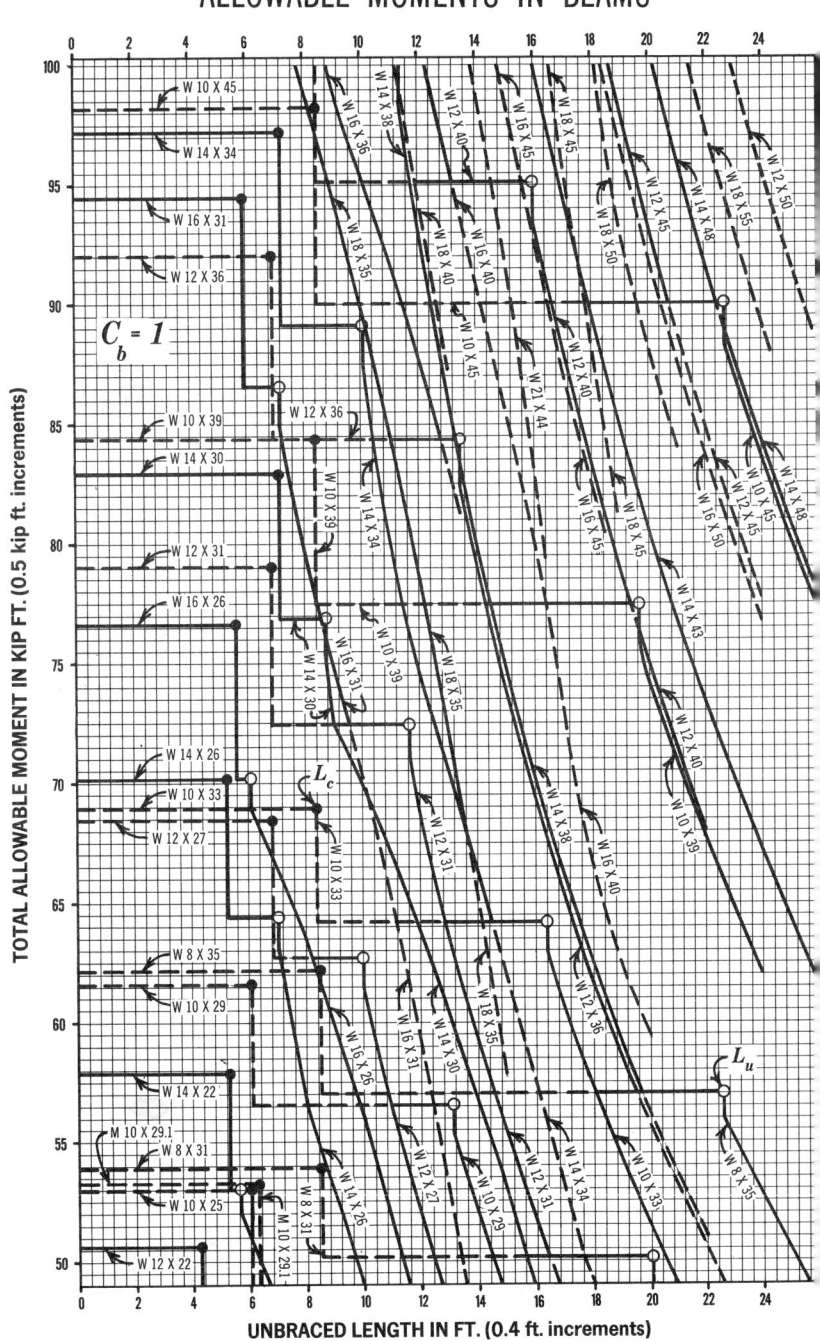

TOTAL ALLOWABLE MOMENT IN KIP FT. (0.5 kip ft. increments)

UNBRACED LENGTH IN FT. (0.4 ft. increments)

$C_b = 1$

AMERICAN INSTITUTE OF STEEL CONSTRUCTION

ALLOWABLE MOMENTS IN BEAMS

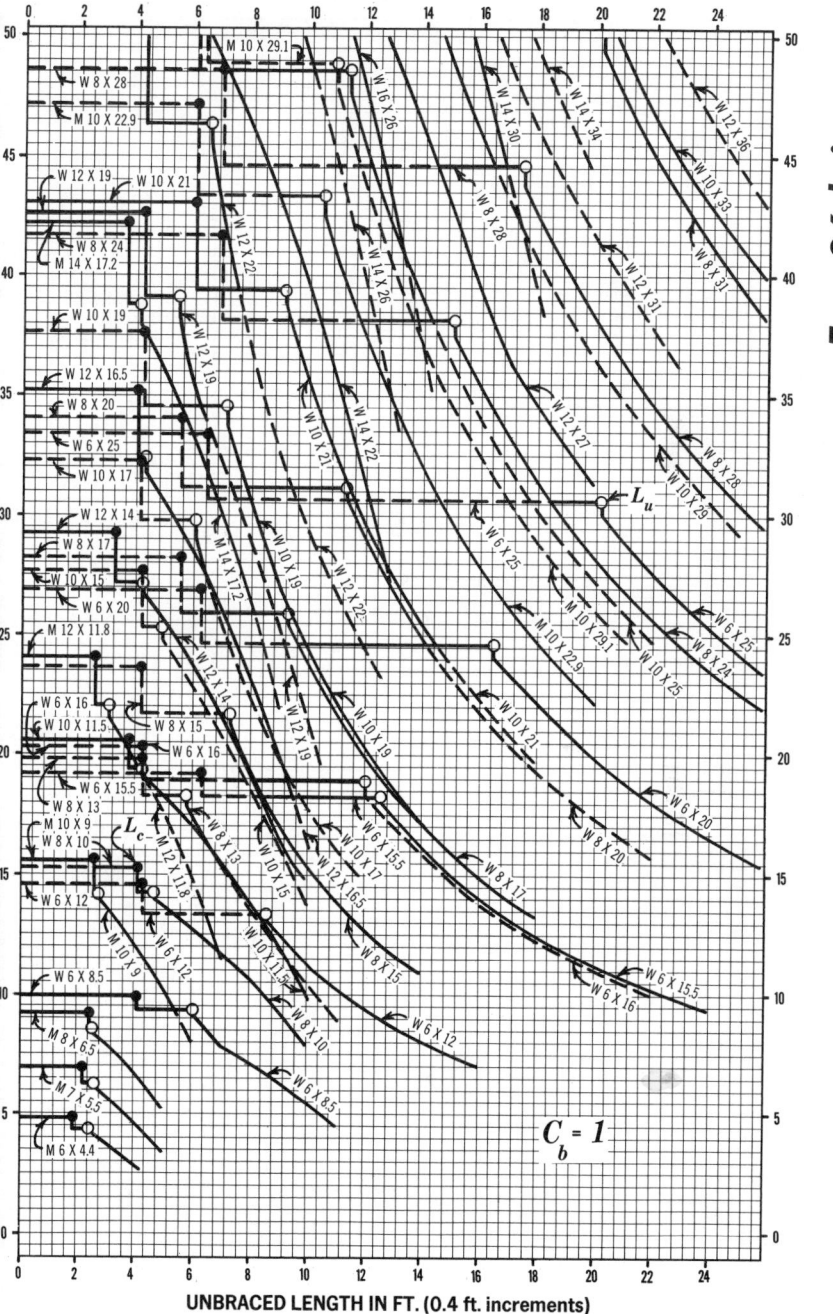

UNBRACED LENGTH IN FT. (0.4 ft. increments)

$F_Y = 36\ ksi$

$C_b = 1$

ALLOWABLE MOMENTS IN BEAMS

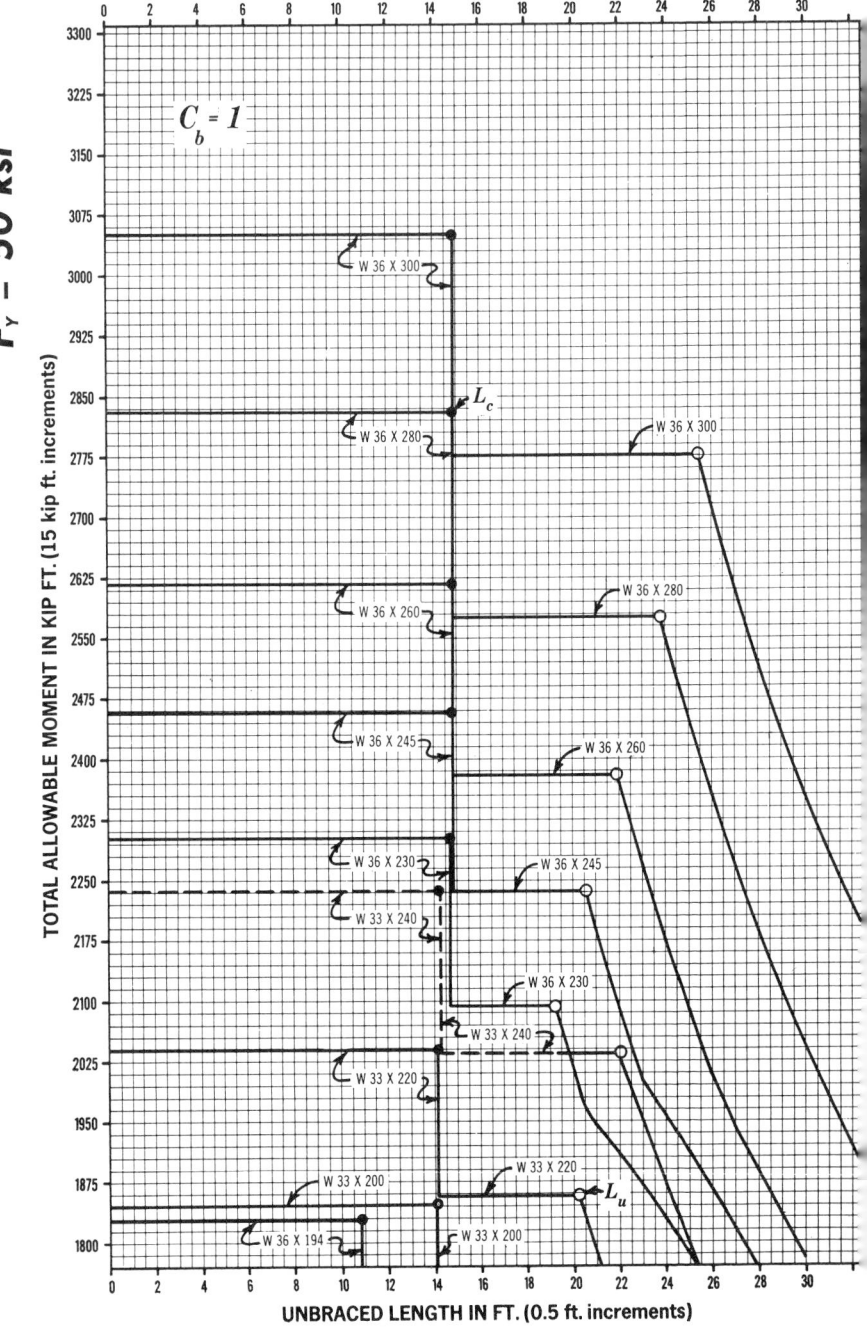

$F_Y = 50\ ksi$

$C_b = 1$

TOTAL ALLOWABLE MOMENT IN KIP FT. (15 kip ft. increments)

W 36 X 300

L_c

W 36 X 280

W 36 X 300

W 36 X 260

W 36 X 280

W 36 X 245

W 36 X 260

W 36 X 230

W 36 X 245

W 33 X 240

W 36 X 230

W 33 X 240

W 33 X 220

W 33 X 200

W 33 X 220

L_u

W 36 X 194

W 33 X 200

UNBRACED LENGTH IN FT. (0.5 ft. increments)

AMERICAN INSTITUTE OF STEEL CONSTRUCTION

ALLOWABLE MOMENTS IN BEAMS

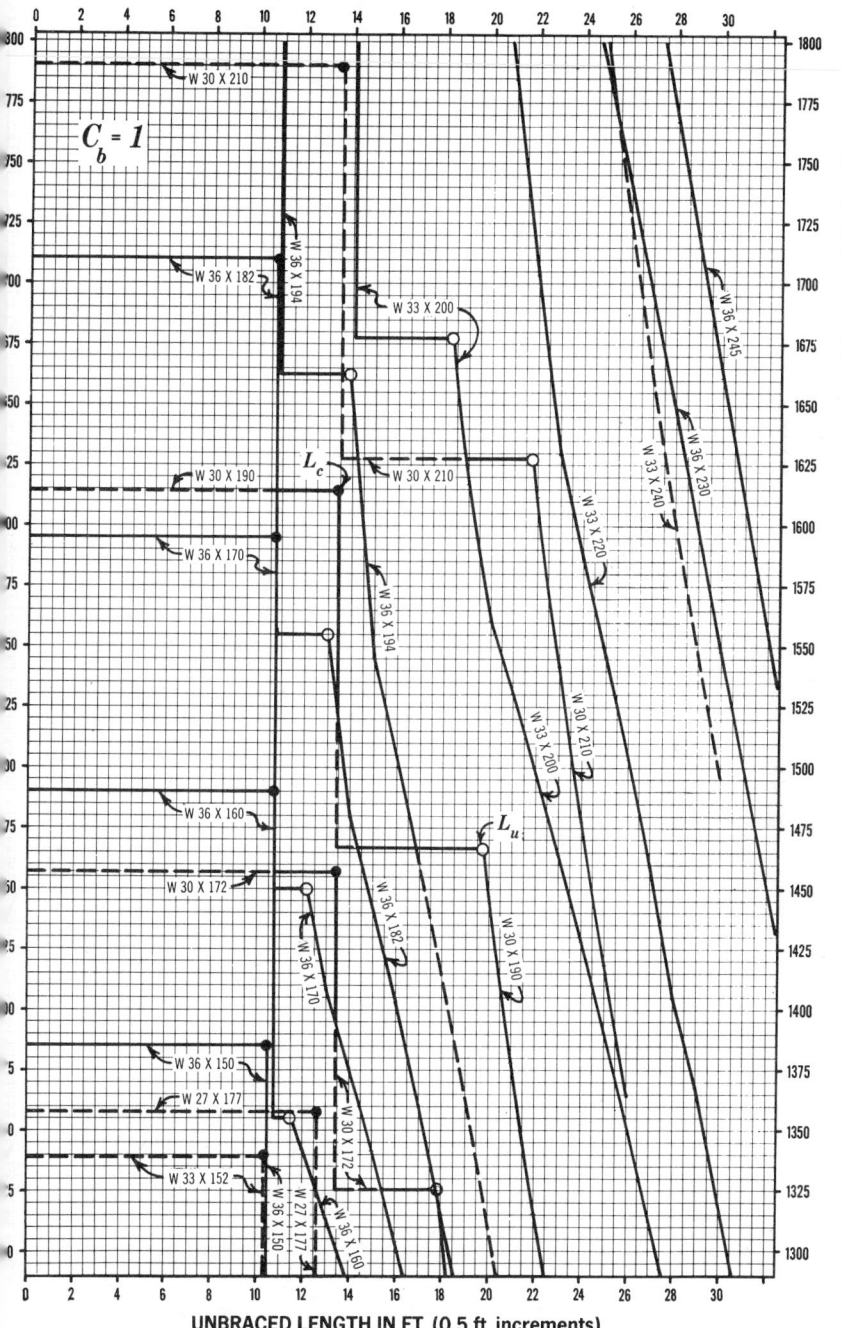

$C_b = 1$

$F_Y = 50$ ksi

UNBRACED LENGTH IN FT. (0.5 ft. increments)

AMERICAN INSTITUTE OF STEEL CONSTRUCTION

ALLOWABLE MOMENTS IN BEAMS

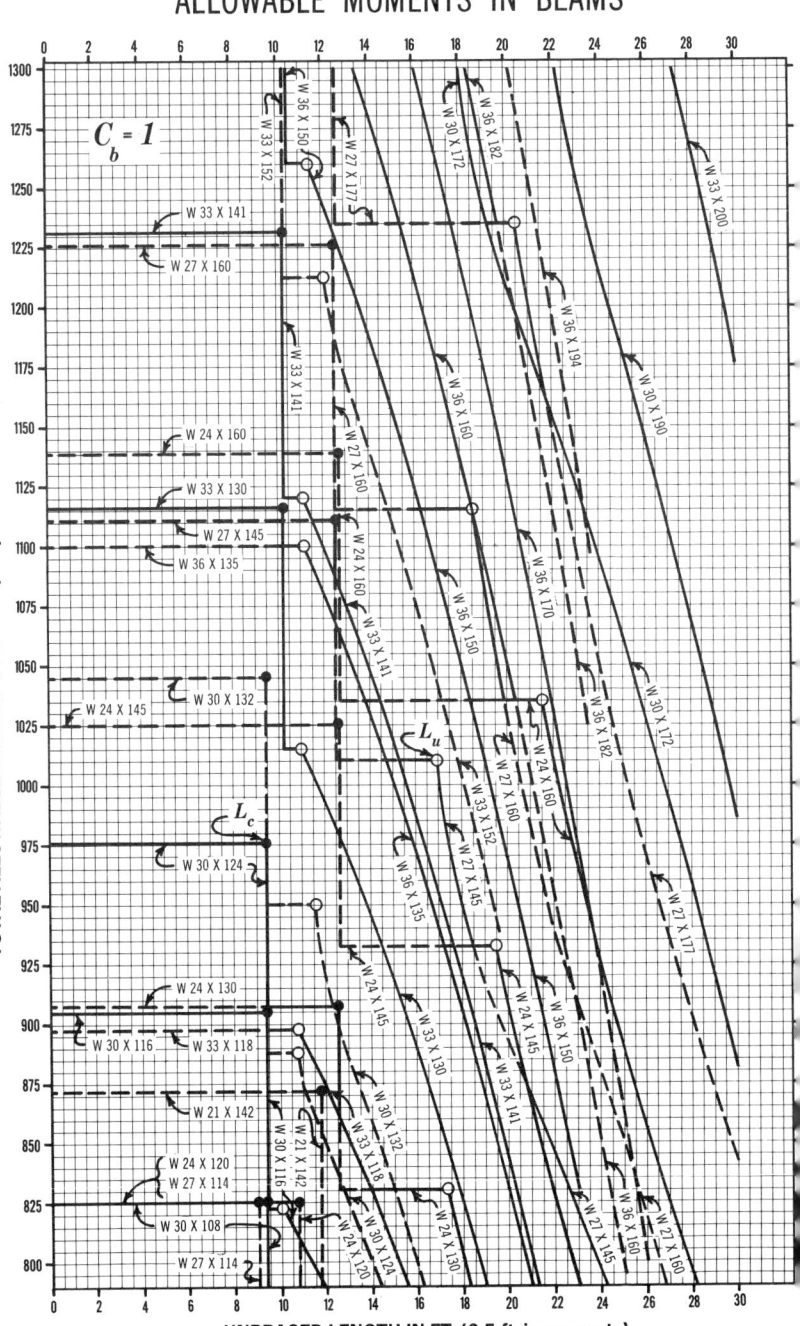

$F_Y = 50$ ksi

$C_b = 1$

TOTAL ALLOWABLE MOMENT IN KIP FT. (5 kip ft. increments)

UNBRACED LENGTH IN FT. (0.5 ft. increments)

AMERICAN INSTITUTE OF STEEL CONSTRUCTION

ALLOWABLE MOMENTS IN BEAMS

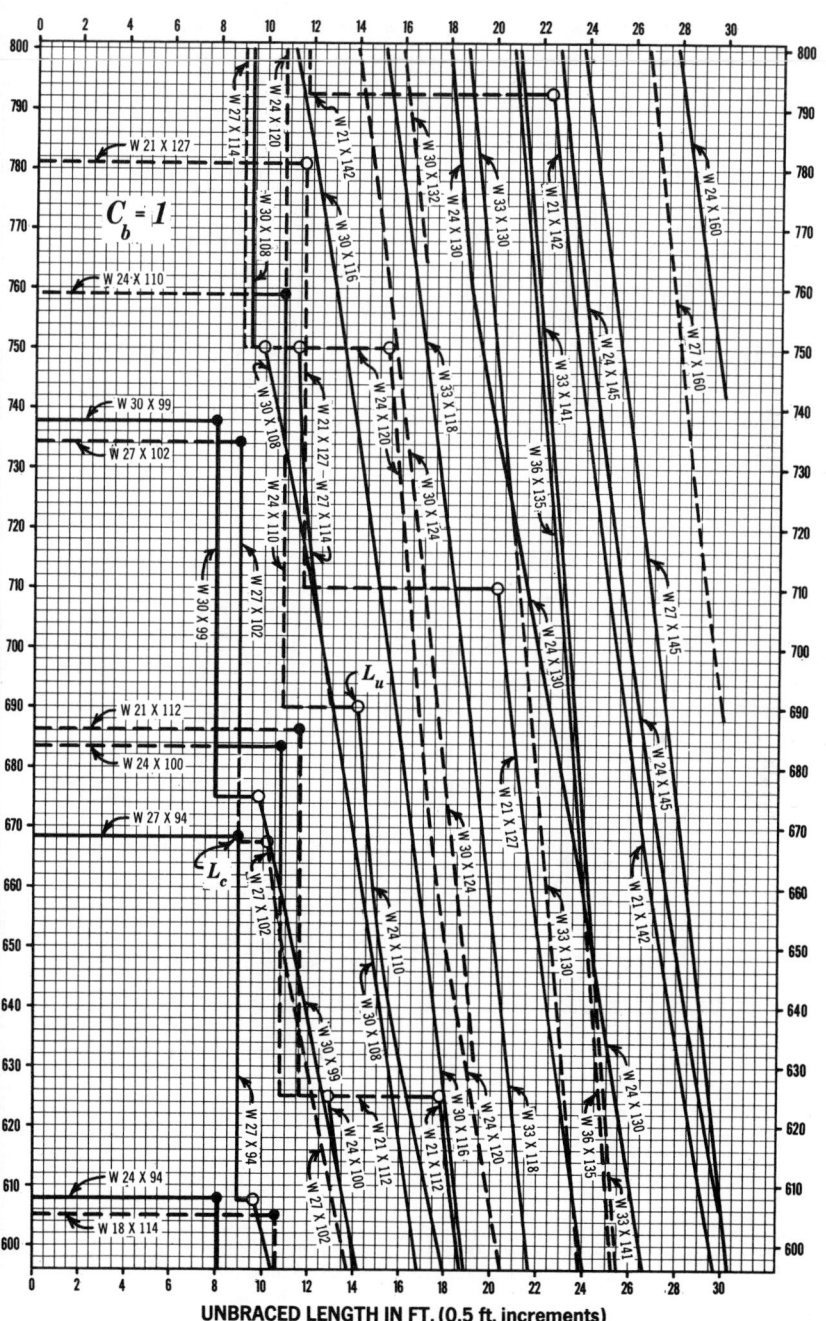

$F_Y = 50\ ksi$

$C_b = 1$

UNBRACED LENGTH IN FT. (0.5 ft. increments)

AMERICAN INSTITUTE OF STEEL CONSTRUCTION

ALLOWABLE MOMENTS IN BEAMS

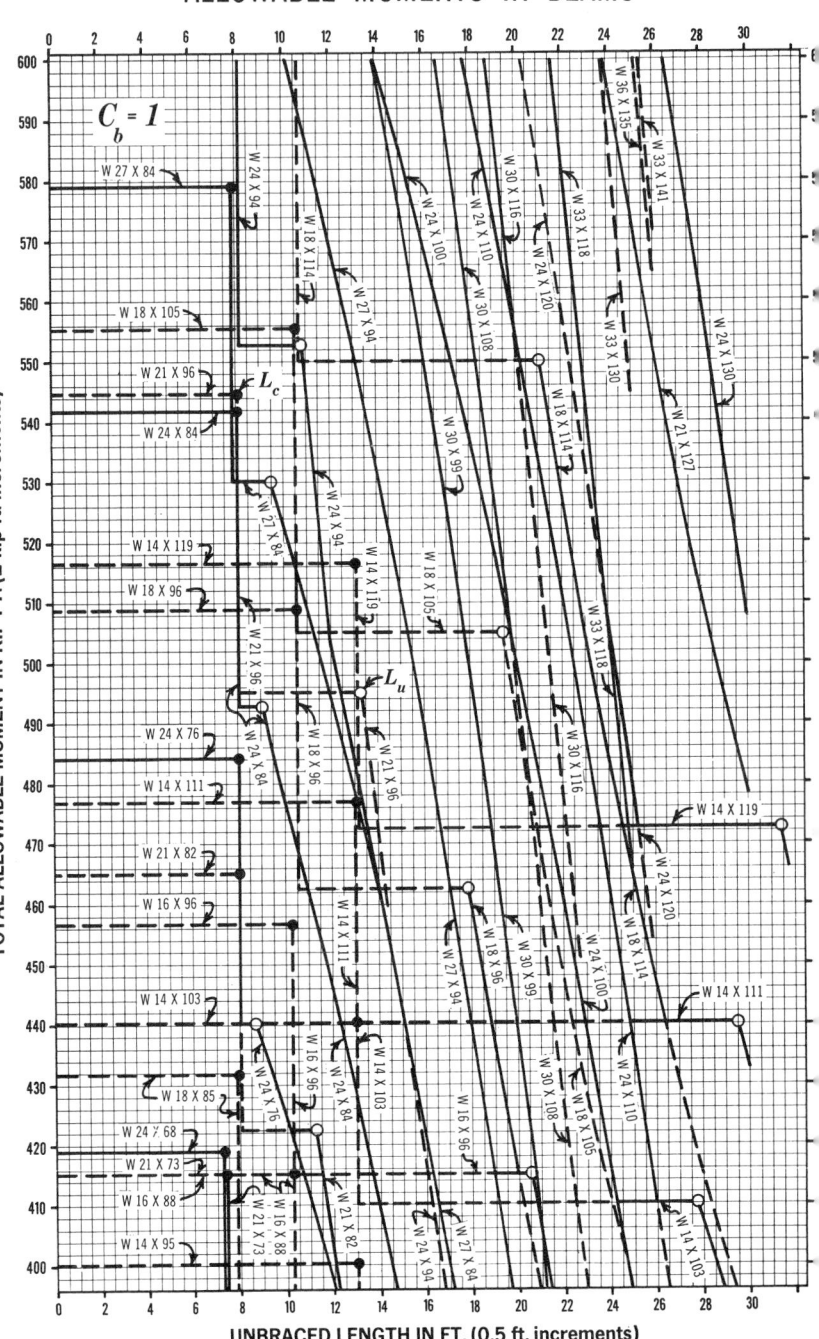

$F_Y = 50$ ksi

$C_b = 1$

TOTAL ALLOWABLE MOMENT IN KIP FT. (2 kip ft. increments)

UNBRACED LENGTH IN FT. (0.5 ft. increments)

AMERICAN INSTITUTE OF STEEL CONSTRUCTION

ALLOWABLE MOMENTS IN BEAMS

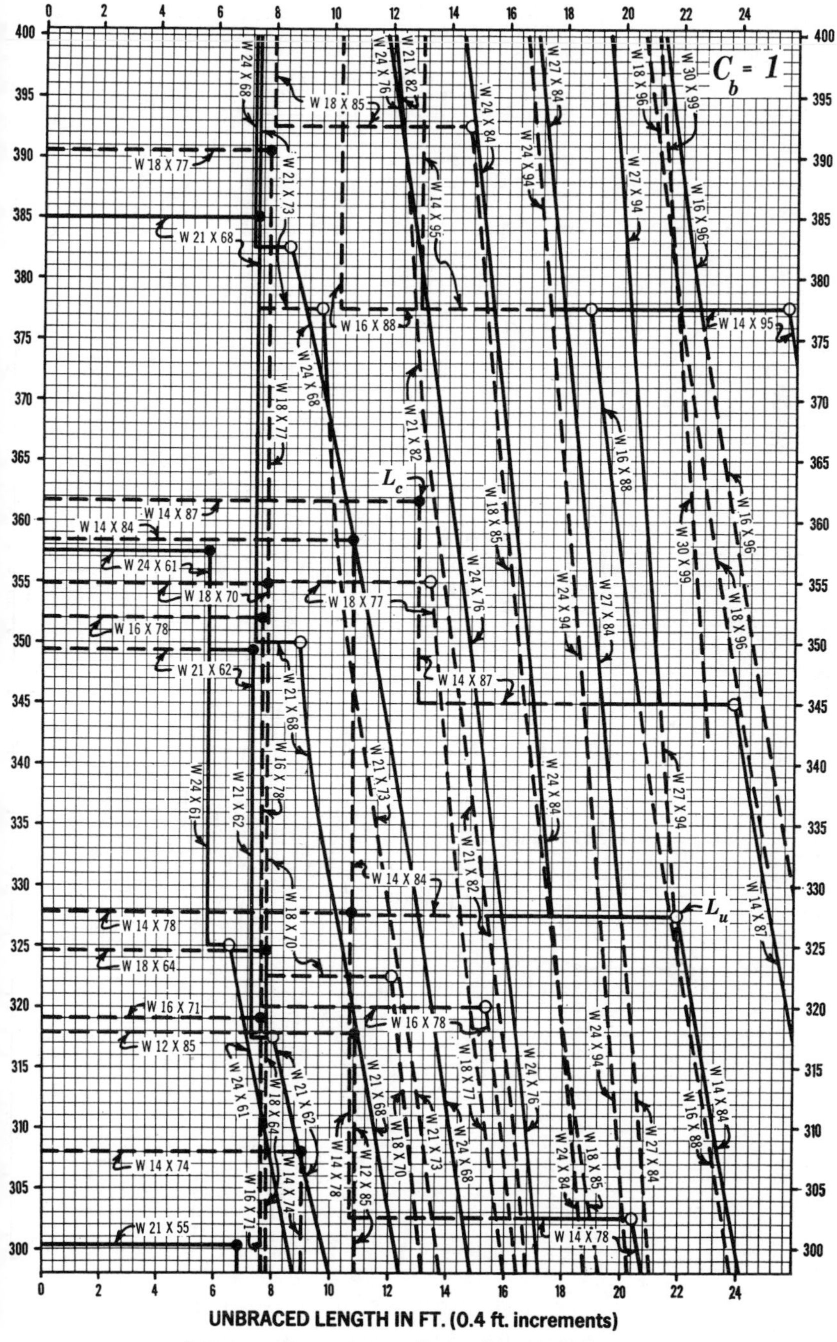

$C_b = 1$

$F_Y = 50\ ksi$

UNBRACED LENGTH IN FT. (0.4 ft. increments)

AMERICAN INSTITUTE OF STEEL CONSTRUCTION

ALLOWABLE MOMENTS IN BEAMS

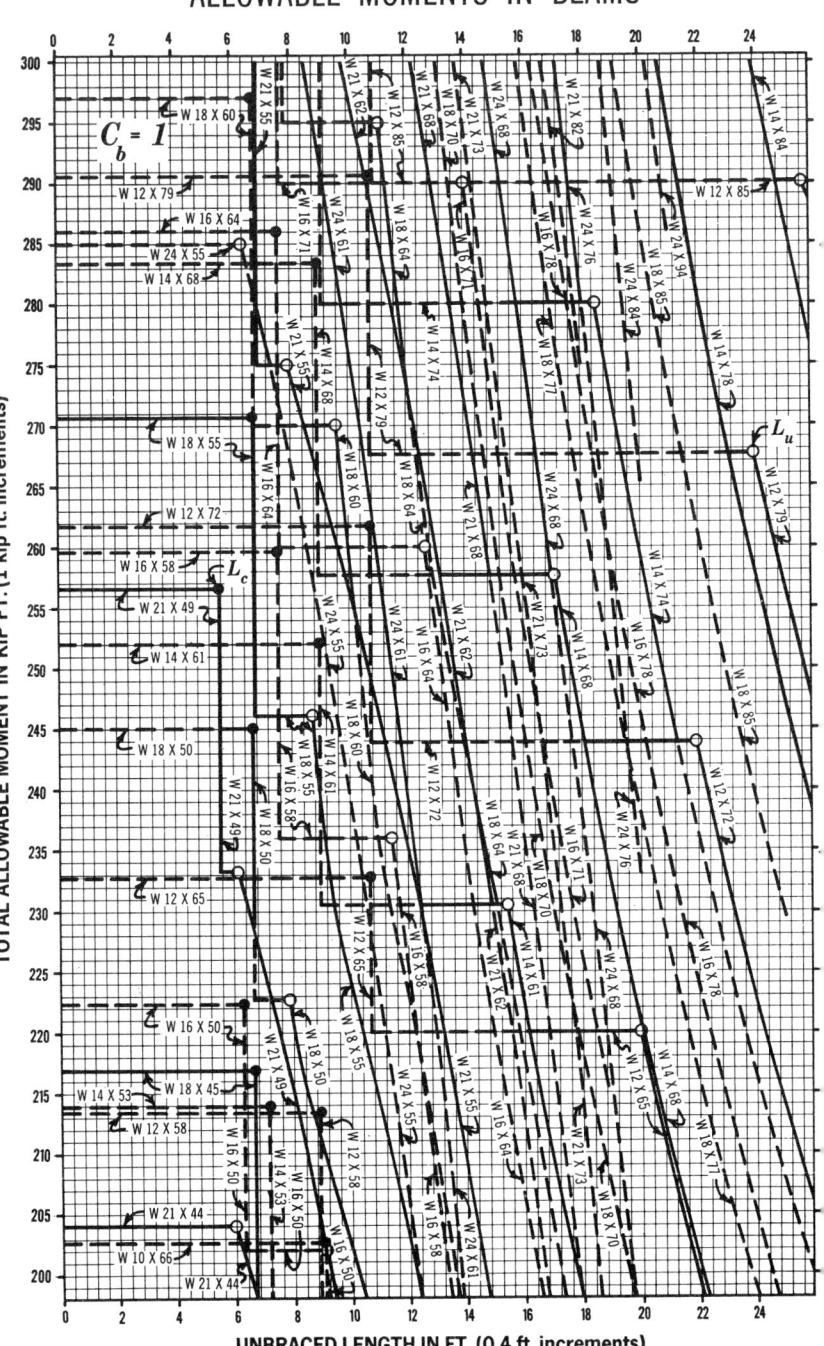

$F_Y = 50$ ksi

TOTAL ALLOWABLE MOMENT IN KIP FT. (1 kip ft. increments)

UNBRACED LENGTH IN FT. (0.4 ft. increments)

AMERICAN INSTITUTE OF STEEL CONSTRUCTION

ALLOWABLE MOMENTS IN BEAMS

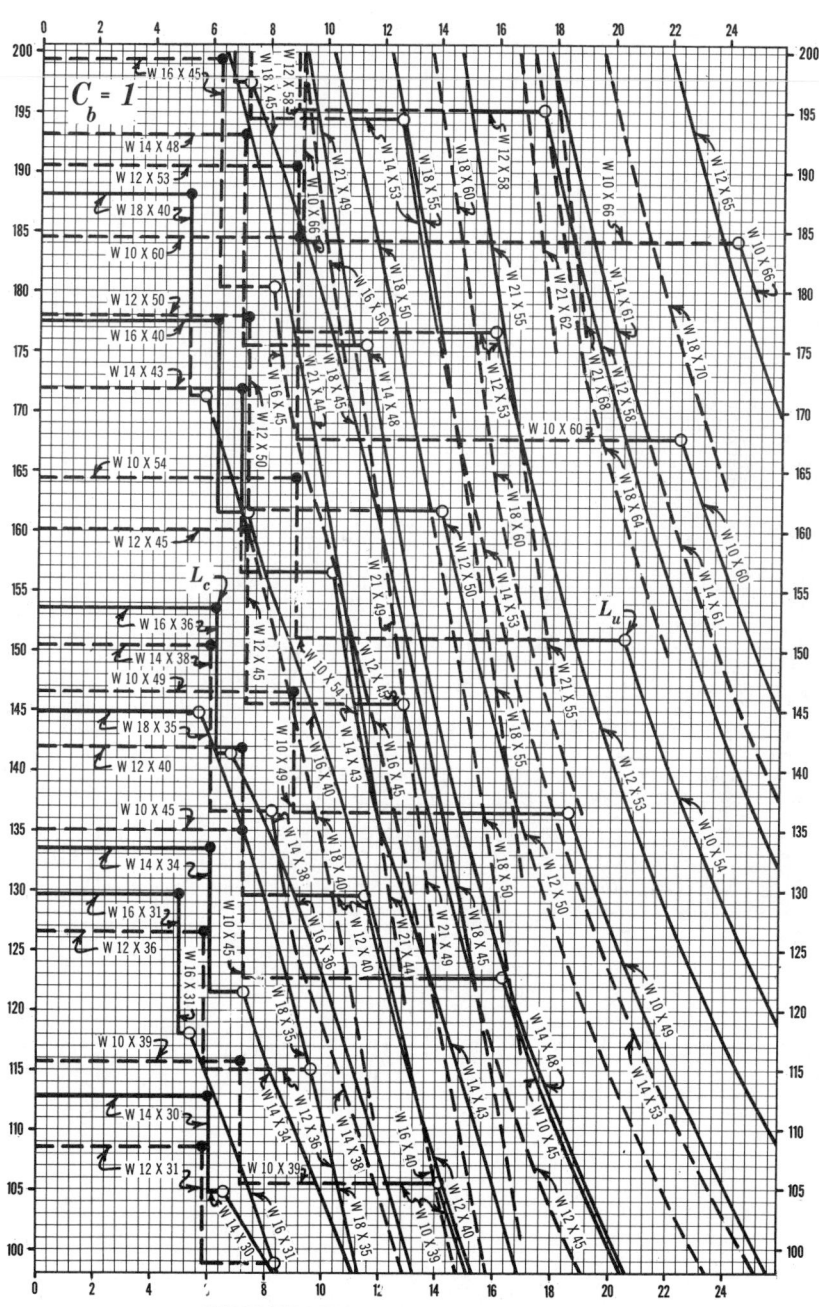

TOTAL ALLOWABLE MOMENT IN KIP FT. (1 kip ft. increments)

UNBRACED LENGTH IN FT. (0.4 ft. increments)

$C_b = 1$

$F_Y = 50\ ksi$

AMERICAN INSTITUTE OF STEEL CONSTRUCTION

ALLOWABLE MOMENTS IN BEAMS

$F_Y = 50$ ksi

AMERICAN INSTITUTE OF STEEL CONSTRUCTION

ALLOWABLE MOMENTS IN BEAMS

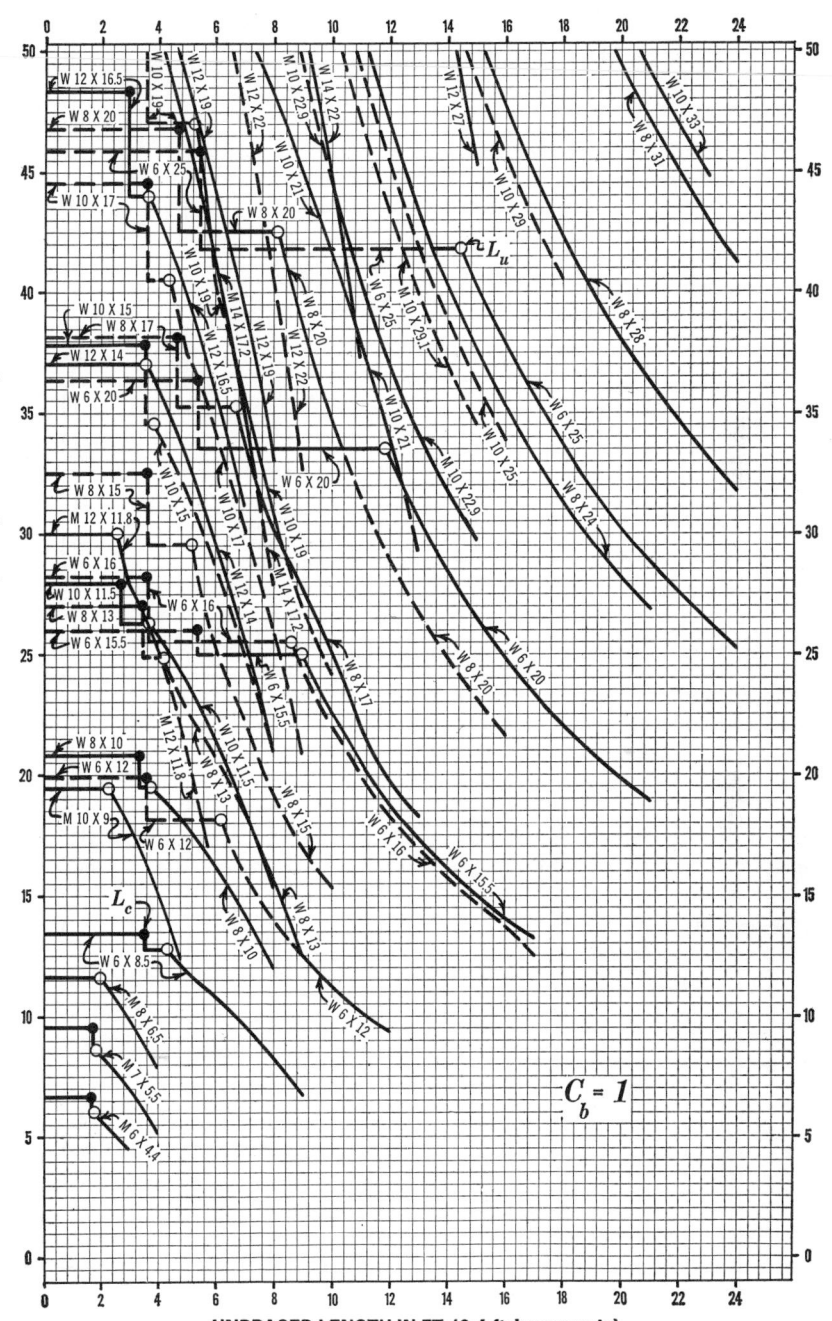

$F_Y = 50$ ksi

TOTAL ALLOWABLE MOMENT IN KIP FT. (0.5 kip ft. increments)

UNBRACED LENGTH IN FT. (0.4 ft. increments)

$C_b = 1$

AMERICAN INSTITUTE OF STEEL CONSTRUCTION

PLATE GIRDERS

Design
Use of AISC Specification and Manual Tables

The *Specification for the Design, Fabrication and Erection of Structural Steel for Buildings*, adopted by the American Institute of Steel Construction in February 1969,* continues virtually unchanged the rules for conventional plate girder design previously adopted in April 1963. New provisions in the Specification relate to hybrid girders whose flanges are fabricated from a stronger grade of steel than that in their web.

Tables pertaining solely to riveted fabrication that appeared in previous editions of the Manual have been omitted to conform with general fabrication practice, although riveted construction is permitted by the Specification. New to the Manual are the table of coefficients C_h for determining the maximum allowable bending stress in hybrid girders and the table of allowable shear stress in webs (tension field action neglected), aids for use in the design of hybrid girders. Also new is a section modulus nomograph to assist in rapidly selecting a trial section of either conventional or hybrid construction.

TABLE OF DIMENSIONS AND PROPERTIES OF WELDED PLATE GIRDERS

This table serves as a guide for selecting welded plate girders of economical proportions. It provides dimensions and properties for a wide range of sections with nominal depths from 41 to 86 in.

To facilitate selection of a girder whose depth is intermediate to those listed in the table, only one width of flange plate is given. Several thicknesses are listed for each flange plate width to afford a fairly uniform variation in bending strength for a given web plate depth. No preference is intended for the flange plate dimensions tabulated, as compared to other flange plates having the same area. Substitution of wider but thinner flange plates, without change in flange area, will result in a slight reduction in section modulus.

The thinnest flange plate listed in each case has a width-thickness ratio that complies with the provisions of Section 1.9 of the AISC Specification for $F_y = 36$ ksi steel. If thinner flange plates are used, or if steels of higher yield stresses are used, the properties of girder sections should be checked for compliance with Section 1.9.

In long girders it may prove economical to reduce the size of flange plates at one or more points near the girder ends, where the bending moment is substantially less. In analyzing overall economy, weight savings must be balanced against higher fabrication costs incurred in splicing the flanges. Economy, through reduction of flange plate sizes, will most likely occur with long girders where flanges must be spliced in any case.

Only one thickness of web plate is given for each depth of girder. When the ratio of maximum shear to maximum moment is relatively large, overall economy may dictate selection of a thicker web plate. The resulting in-

* Also see Sect. 1.10 of Supplement Nos. 1 and 2 to the 1969 AISC Specification.

crease in section modulus can be obtained by multiplying the value S', given in the table, by the number of sixteenths of an inch increase in web thickness, and adding the value so obtained to the section modulus value S for the girder profile shown in the table.

Overall economy may often be obtained by using a web plate of such thickness that intermediate stiffeners are not required. However, this is not always the case. The girder sections listed in the table will provide a "balanced" design with respect to bending moment and web shear without excessive use of intermediate stiffeners. When stiffeners are required, their proper spacing can be determined with the help of the appropriate Table 3 in Appendix A of the AISC Specification. For hybrid girders, the table on page 2-133, Allowable Shear Stress in Webs (Tension Field Action Neglected), may be used instead of Table 3.

The maximum end reaction permissible without intermediate stiffeners for the tabulated web plate thicknesses for F_y = 36 ksi steel is listed in the table column headed R. If a thicker web plate is used, the value R will be increased in proportion to the increase in web plate area. Use of a thicker web plate will also result in an increase in the allowable shear stress through reduction of web depth-thickness ratio h/t. In Table 3 (Specification Appendix A) and in the similar table for hybrid girders (page 2-133), allowable values for shear stress in the case where intermediate stiffeners are not required are given in the right hand column headed "Over 3".

DESIGN EXAMPLES

Design of a plate girder by the moment of inertia method recommended in the AISC Specification should start with the preliminary design or selection of a trial section. The initial choice may require one or more adjustments before a final cross section is obtained that satisfies all the provisions of the Specification with maximum economy. In the following design examples all applicable provisions of the Specification and page numbers of appropriate information that appear elsewhere in the Manual are listed on the right of each page.

Example 1 illustrates a recommended procedure for designing a welded plate girder of constant depth. The selection of a suitable trial cross section is obtained by the "flange area method" and then checked by the "moment of inertia" method.

Example 2 illustrates a recommended procedure for designing a welded hybrid girder of constant depth. In selecting a trial section use is made of a section modulus nomograph, page 2-124. (The nomograph is also applicable to conventional girders.) The somewhat tedious determination of stiffener requirements is simplified by use of a diagram showing the relationship of web shear to stiffener spacing throughout the girder.

Example 3 illustrates use of the table of dimensions and properties of welded plate girders, pages 2-122 and 2-123, to obtain an efficient trial profile. The 52 in. depth specified for this example demonstrates how the tabular data may be used for girder depths intermediate to those listed. The final girder cross section is checked using the "the moment of inertia" method. Another design requirement in this example is the omission of intermediate web stiffeners.

Example 4 is similar to Example 3 except that it illustrates the selection of a girder section whose web requires intermediate stiffeners.

EXAMPLE 1

Design a welded plate girder to support a uniform load of 3 kips per ft. and two concentrated loads of 70 kips located 17 ft. from each end. The compression flange of the girder will be laterally supported only at points of concentrated load.

Given: *Maximum bending moment:* 2054 kip-ft.
Maximum vertical shear: 142 kips
Span: 48 ft.
Maximum depth: 72 in.
Steel: $F_y = 36$ ksi

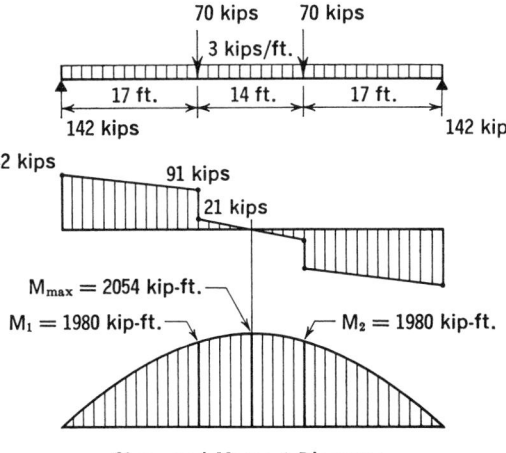

Shear and Moment Diagrams

Specification
or Manual
Reference

Solution:

A. *Preliminary web design*

1. Assume web depth, $h = 70$ in.

For no reduction in flange stress, $\dfrac{h}{t} \leq \dfrac{760}{\sqrt{22}} = 162$ **1.10.6**

Corresponding thickness of web $= \dfrac{70}{162} = 0.43$ in.

2. Minimum thickness of web $= \dfrac{70}{322} = 0.22$ in.   **1.10.2**
and
Appendix
pg. **5 - 74**

Try web plate: $\frac{5}{16} \times 70$; $A_w = 21.9$ sq. in.; $\dfrac{h}{t} = \dfrac{70}{0.313} = 224$

B. *Preliminary flange design*

1. Required flange area:

Assume flanges $\frac{3}{4}$-in. thick and allowable bending stress   Appendix
$F_b = 22$ ksi   pg. **5 - 70**

$$A_f \cong \frac{2054 \times 12}{70.75 \times 22} - \frac{1}{3} \times \frac{21.9}{2} \cong 12.18 \text{ sq. in.}$$

Try: $\frac{3}{4} \times 18$ plate; $A_f = 13.5$ sq. in. > 12.18 sq. in. **o.k.**

AMERICAN INSTITUTE OF STEEL CONSTRUCTION

2. Check local buckling:

$$\frac{9}{0.75} = 12 < 15.8 \text{ o.k.}$$

C. *Trial girder section*

1 web $\frac{5}{16} \times 70$; 2 flange plates $\frac{3}{4} \times 18$

1. Check by "moment of inertia" method:

Section	A in.^{2}	y in.	Ay^2 in.^{4}	I_0 in.^{4}	I_{gr} in.^{4}
1 web $\frac{5}{16} \times 70$	21.9			8932	8932
1 flange $\frac{3}{4} \times 18$	13.5 ⎫	35.375	^{a}33791		1
1 flange $\frac{3}{4} \times 18$	13.5 ⎭				33792
Effective moment of inertia,					42724

^{a} Enter table, pg. 2 - 126 with $2y = 70.75$. By interpolation, obtain value of 2503. Multiply this value by the area of one flange 13.5 sq. in. Equal to 2503 × 13.5 = 33791 in.^{4}

Section modulus furnished $= \dfrac{42724}{35.75} = 1195$ in.^{3}

Section modulus required $= \dfrac{2054 \times 12}{22} = 1120$ in.^{3} **o.k.**

2. Check lateral buckling:

Maximum bending stress at midspan $= f_b = \dfrac{2054 \times 12}{1195} = 20.6$ ksi

Moment of inertia of flange plus $\frac{1}{6}$ web about Y - Y axis $=$

$$I_{0y} = \frac{3}{4} \times \frac{18^3}{12} = 365 \text{ in.}^4$$

$A_f + \frac{1}{6} A_w = 13.5 + \frac{1}{6}(21.9) = 17.15$ sq. in.
$r_T = \sqrt{365/17.15} = 4.61$ in.

a. From moment diagram, check bending stress in 14 ft. panel:
$M_{max} > M_1$ and M_2 ∴ $C_b = 1$

$$\frac{l}{r_T} = \frac{14 \times 12}{4.61} = 36.4 < 53\sqrt{C_b} = 53$$

∴ Allowable stress in 14 ft. panel: $F_b = 0.60 F_y = 22$ ksi

Allowable flange stress in 14 ft. panel:

$$F'_b = 22.0 \left[1.0 - 0.0005 \frac{21.9}{13.5} \left(\frac{70}{0.313} - \frac{760}{\sqrt{22}} \right) \right] = 20.9 \text{ ksi}$$

20.9 ksi > 20.6 ksi **o.k.**

b. From moment diagram check bending stress in 17 ft. long panel:

$$C_b = 1.75 + 1.05 \frac{M_1}{M_2} + 0.3 \left(\frac{M_1}{M_2} \right)^2$$

where $M_1 = 0$; then $\dfrac{M_1}{M_2} = 0$ ∴ $C_b = 1.75$

Calculated bending stress in 17 ft. panel:

$$f_b = \frac{1980 \times 12}{1195} = 19.88 \text{ ksi}$$

$$\frac{l}{r_T} = \frac{17 \times 12}{4.61} = 44.3 < 53\sqrt{C_b}$$

∴ Allowable stress in 17 ft. panel:
$F_b = 0.60F_y = 22 \text{ ksi}$

Allowable flange stress in 17 ft. panel:

$$F'_b = 22.0 \left[1.0 - 0.0005 \frac{21.9}{13.5} \left(\frac{70}{0.313} - \frac{760}{\sqrt{22}} \right) \right] = 20.9 \text{ ksi}$$

20.9 ksi > 19.88 ksi **o.k.**

Use: Web: **1 plate** $\frac{5}{16} \times$ **70**
       Flanges: **2 plates** $\frac{3}{4} \times$ **18**

D. *Stiffener requirements*

1. End panel spacing:

Calculated shear stress: $f_v = \frac{142}{21.9} = 6.48 \text{ ksi}$

Allowable clear distance between end panel stiffeners: (tension field action)

$$a \leqslant \frac{348 \times \frac{5}{16}}{\sqrt{6.48}} = 42.7 \text{ in.}$$

∴ Space stiffeners 42 in. from each end of girder.

2. *Provide bearing stiffeners under concentrated loads

∴ Clear distance between end stiffeners and concentrated loads =
$(17 \times 12) - 42 = 162 \text{ in.}$

3. Check intermediate stiffener requirements:

$\frac{h}{t} = 224 < 260$ **o.k.**

Check allowable shear stress in 162 in. panel:

$$\frac{a}{h} = \frac{162}{70} = 2.31 > 1.0$$

$$k = 5.34 + \frac{4.00}{(2.31)^2} = 6.09$$

$$C_v = \frac{45000 \times 6.09}{36 \times (224)^2} = 0.152 < 0.8$$

$$F_v = \frac{36}{2.89} \times 0.152 = 1.89 \text{ ksi} < 0.4 \times 36 = 14.4 \text{ ksi}$$

* Stiffeners are required at unframed girder ends. However, at concentrated loads, their need is governed by Section 1.10.10.1 of the Specification. For purposes of this example bearing stiffeners are assumed required under concentrated loads.

AMERICAN INSTITUTE OF STEEL CONSTRUCTION

Vertical shear 42 in. from end of girder:

$V = 142 - (3 \times 3.5) = 131.5$ kips (max. in 162 in. panel)

Calculated shear stress:

$f_v = \dfrac{131.5}{21.9} = 6.00$ ksi > 1.89 ksi   (does not satisfy)

$\therefore$ Space intermediate stiffener at $\dfrac{162}{2} = 81$ in. o.c.

Maximum spacing between intermediate stiffeners: **1.10.5.3**

$\dfrac{a}{h} = \left(\dfrac{260 \times 0.313}{70}\right)^2 = 1.35$

$a = 1.35 \times 70 = 94.5$ in. > 81 in. **o.k.**

From Table 3 - 36:

For $\dfrac{a}{h} = \dfrac{81}{70} = 1.16$ and $\dfrac{h}{t} = 224$,   Appendix
Table
3 - 36

allowable shear stress: $F_v = 8.20$ ksi > 6.00 ksi **o.k.**

4. Check interaction at concentrated loads: **1.10.7**

Required shear stress: $f_v = \dfrac{91.0}{21.9} = 4.16$ ksi

Allowable bending tensile stress:

$F_b = \left[0.825 - \left(0.375 \times \dfrac{4.16}{8.20}\right)\right] \times 36 = 22.9$ ksi > 22.0 ksi   Formula
(1.10-7)

$\therefore$ 22 ksi permitted

Use: End spacing: 42 in.

 Intermediate spacing: 81 in. o.c.

5. Check 14 ft. midspan panel: $\dfrac{h}{t} = 224 < 260$ **o.k.**   **1.10.5.3**

Max. vertical shear from shear diagram: $V = 21$ kips

Calculated shear stress: $f_v = \dfrac{21}{21.9} = 0.96$ ksi

Clear distance between stiffeners: $a = 14 \times 12 = 168$ in.;

$\dfrac{a}{h} = \dfrac{168}{70} = 2.40 > 1.0$

$k = 5.34 + \dfrac{4.00}{(2.40)^2} = 6.03$ **1.10.5.2**

$C_v = \dfrac{45,000 \times 6.03}{36 \times (224)^2} = 0.150 < 0.80$

Allowable shear stress:

$F_v = \dfrac{36}{2.89} \times 0.150 = 1.87 > 0.96$ ksi and < 14.4 ksi **o.k.**   Formula
(1.10-1)

6. Check web crippling (assume construction prevents compression flange rotation):

1.10.10

Uniform load = 3 kips per ft.

Calculated compressive stress = $\dfrac{3}{12 \times 0.313}$ = 0.8 ksi

1.10.10.2
Formula
(1.10-10)

Allowable compressive stress =

$$\left[5.5 + \frac{4}{(2.40)^2} \right] \times \frac{10000}{(224)^2} = 1.23 \text{ ksi} > 0.8 \text{ ksi } \textbf{o.k.}$$

No stiffener required at midspan.
Summary: Space stiffeners as shown:

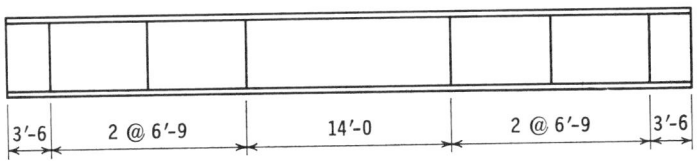

E. *Stiffener size*
  1. For intermediate stiffeners:
     a. *From Table 3 - 36:

Appendix
pg. 5 - 95

Area required: A_{st} = 0.111 × 21.9 = 2.43 sq. in.

$\left.\begin{array}{l} F_v = 8.20 \text{ ksi} \\ f_v \leqslant 6.00 \text{ ksi} \end{array}\right\}$ see step D3

Actual area required = $\dfrac{6.00}{8.20}$ × 2.43 = 1.78 sq. in.

Try 2 bars 4 × ¼ = 2.0 sq. in. > 1.78 sq. in. **o.k.**

b. Check width-thickness ratio:

1.9.1.2
and
Appendix
pg. 5 - 72

$\dfrac{4}{0.25}$ = 16 ≅ 15.8 (say **o.k.**)

c. Check moment of inertia:

$$I_{req} = \left(\frac{70}{50} \right)^4 = 3.84 \text{ in.}^4$$

1.10.5.4

$$I_{furn} = \frac{1}{12} (0.25) (8.31)^3 = 11.96 \text{ in.}^4 > 3.84 \text{ in.}^4 \textbf{ o.k.}$$

d. Length required = 70 − (4 × 5⁄16) = 68¾ in.

1.10.5.4

Use for intermediate stiffeners: 2 bars 4 × ¼ × 5′-8¾ bearing on compression flange of girder.

---

* Since values of a/h and h/t are close to 1.0 and 220, respectively (see Table 3-36) percent of web area = 11.1 is used. The percent of web area may also be computed with Formula (1.10-3).

2. For bearing stiffeners: Under concentrated loads and at end of girder, design for end reaction. | **1.10.5.1**

Try 2 - 8 $\times$ ½ in. bars.

1.9.1.2

a. Check width-thickness ratio: | and
Appendix
pg. **5 - 72**

$$\frac{8}{0.5} = 16 \cong 15.8 \text{ (say } \textbf{o.k.})$$

b. Check compressive stress (end bearing): | **1.10.5.1**

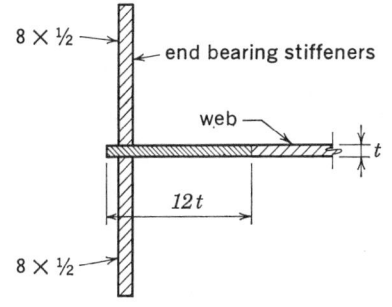

Effective Area

$$I = \frac{1}{2} \times \frac{(16.31)^3}{12} = 181 \text{ in.}^4$$

$$A_{eff} = [2 \times 8 \times \tfrac{1}{2}] + [12 \times (\tfrac{5}{16})^2] = 9.17 \text{ sq. in.}$$

$$r = \sqrt{\frac{181}{9.17}} = 4.44 \text{ in.}$$

$$l = \tfrac{3}{4} \times 70 = 52.5 \text{ in.}$$

$$\frac{l}{r} = \frac{52.5}{4.44} = 11.8$$

From Table 1 - 36, for $\dfrac{Kl}{r} = 11.8(K$ assumed 1.0): | Appendix
pg. **5 - 84**

Allowable stress: $F_a = 21.06$ ksi

$$f_a = \frac{142}{9.17} = 15.49 \text{ ksi} < 21.06 \text{ ksi } \textbf{o.k.}$$

Use for bearing stiffeners: 2 bars 8 $\times$ ½ $\times$ 5'-9¾ with close bearing on compression flange receiving reaction and concentrated loads.

*****Use same size stiffeners for bearing under concentrated loads.**

---

* In this example bearing stiffeners were designed for end bearing; however, $25t$ may be used in determining effective area of web for bearing stiffeners under concentrated loads at interior panels (Sect. 1.10.5.1).

EXAMPLE 2

Design a hybrid girder to support a uniform load of 2 kips per ft. and three concentrated loads of 200 kips located at the quarter points. The girder depth must be limited to 5 ft. The compression flange will be laterally supported throughout its length.

Given: *Maximum bending moment:* 9,600 kip-ft.
Maximum vertical shear: 380 kips
Span: 80 ft.
Maximum depth: 60 in.
Steel: Flanges: $F_y = 50$ ksi
Web: $F_y = 36$ ksi

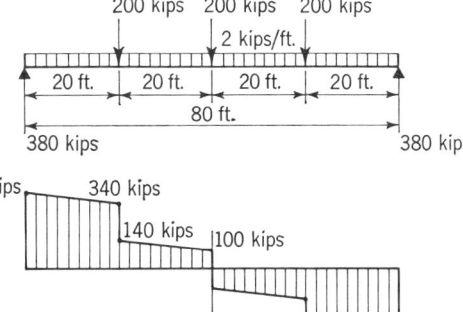

Shear and Moment Diagrams

	Specification or Manual Reference
Solution:	
A. *Preliminary web design*	
1. Assume web depth, $h = 54$ in.	
For no reduction in flange stress, $\dfrac{h}{t} \leqslant \dfrac{760}{\sqrt{30}} = 139$	**1.10.6**
2. Minimum t required for maximum allowable shear stress of 14.5 ksi:	
$t = \dfrac{380}{14.5 \times 54} = 0.486$ in.	**1.5.1.2**

Minimum thickness of web $= \dfrac{54}{243} = 0.22$ in.

Try web plate $\frac{9}{16} \times 54$; $A_w = 30.38$ sq. in.

$f_v = \dfrac{380}{30.38} = 12.5$ ksi < 14.5 ksi **o.k.**; $\dfrac{h}{t} = \dfrac{54}{0.563} = 96$

B. *Preliminary flange design*

1. Required flange area:

$t = \frac{9}{16}$ in., $h = 54$ in.; assume $F'_b = 30$ ksi

Section modulus required $= \dfrac{9600 \times 12}{30} = 3840$ in.³

$\dfrac{S}{h} = \dfrac{3840}{54} = 71.3$; assume $b = 24$ in.

From the section modulus nomograph:
Try $t_f = 3$ in.

2. Check local buckling:

$\dfrac{12}{3} = 4 < 13.4$ **o.k.**

C. *Trial girder section*

1 web: $\frac{9}{16} \times 54$
2 flange plates: 3×24

1. Check by "moment of inertia" method:

Section	A in.²	y in.	Ay^2 in.⁴	I_0 in.⁴	I_{gr} in.⁴
1 web $\frac{9}{16} \times 54$	30.38			7380	7380
1 flange 3×24	72 ⎱	28.5	ᵃ117000		
1 flange 3×24	72 ⎰			108	117108
Effective moment of inertia					124488

ᵃ Enter table, pg. **2** - 126 with $2y = 57.0$. Read table to obtain value of 1625. Multiply this value by the area of one flange 72.0 sq. in. Equal to $1625 \times 72.0 = 117000$ in.⁴

Section modulus furnished $= \dfrac{124488}{30} = 4150$ in.³

2. Check allowable flange stresses:

a. Compression flange is supported laterally for full length.

$F_b = 30$ ksi; $\dfrac{h}{t} \leq \dfrac{760}{\sqrt{30}} = 139 > 96$

∴ No reduction in either flange stress by Formula (1.10-5) is required.

b. Check allowable flange stress (applies to either flange)
by Formula (1.10-6):

$$\frac{A_w}{A_f} = \frac{30.38}{72} = 0.422, \; \alpha = \frac{F_y \text{ (web)}}{F_y \text{ (flange)}} = \frac{36}{50} = 0.72$$

From Table of Coefficients for Formula (1.10-6), $C_h =$ 0.99.

pg. 2 - 132

$F'_b = 0.99 F_b = 0.99 \; (30) = 29.7$ ksi

Use allowable flange stress of $F_b = 29.7$ ksi

Section modulus required $= \dfrac{9600 \times 12}{29.7} = 3880$ in.^{3}

4150 in.$^3 >$ 3880 in.^{3} **o.k.**

Use: Web: 1 plate $\frac{9}{16} \times 54$ ($F_y = 36$ ksi)
Flanges: 2 plates 3×24 ($F_y = 50$ ksi)

D. *Stiffener requirements*

1.10.5

1. The Specification does not permit tension field action in hybrid girder design. Therefore, determine need for intermediate stiffeners by use of Formula (1.10-1) or by Table of Allowable Shear Stress in Webs (Tension Field Action Neglected).

1.10.5.2
and
pg. 5 - 144
pg. 2 - 133

Checking the requirement for intermediate stiffeners between end bearing stiffener and bearing stiffener under concentrated load 20 ft. from end:

$$\frac{a}{h} > 3.0, \; F_y \text{ (web)} = 36 \text{ ksi}, \; \frac{h}{t} = 96 < 260$$

1.10.5.3

Allowable shear stress: $F_v = 9.0$ ksi

pg. 2 - 133

Vertical shear at end of girder from shear diagram:
$V = 380$ kips

Calculated shear stress: $f_v = \dfrac{380}{30.38} = 12.5$ ksi

12.5 ksi $>$ 9.0 ksi $\therefore$ intermediate stiffeners required

2. Intermediate stiffeners
   a. Determine spacing by graphical method:
      Plot the curve for F_v versus panel length a. On the same chart, plot calculated f_v versus x, the distance from the left reaction. Use a single ordinate scale for F_v and f_v, but separate abscissa scales for x and a.
      Values for F_v may be obtained from Formula (1.10-1) or the table on pg. 2-133. Values for $f_v = V/A_w$.
      For this example, x is extended to include the first concentrated load at 240 inches. The minimum and maximum values of a for construction of the a abscissa scale may be determined by inspection of table, pg. 2-133.

AMERICAN INSTITUTE OF STEEL CONSTRUCTION

To determine the first stiffener location, enter the graph at $x = 0$; from $f_v = 12.5$ ksi, project horizontally to intersect the F_v curve, then drop vertically to the a-abscissa to read $a_1 = 54$ in. For the second stiffener, enter at $x = 54$ in. (Σ of a-distances thus far), project vertically to the f_v curve, project horizontally to the F_v curve; drop vertically to read $a_2 = 58$ in. For the third spacing, enter at $x = 112$ in. ($a_1 + a_2$), project vertically to the f_v curve, project horizontally to the F_v curve; drop vertically to the a-abscissa to read $a_3 = 62$ in. Continue this process for the remainder of the panel. These spacings represent maximums; closer spacing can be used to adjust for a desired overall spacing pattern. Additionally, requirements for bearing stiffeners at points of concentrated loads must be checked (see step E-3).

1.10.5.1

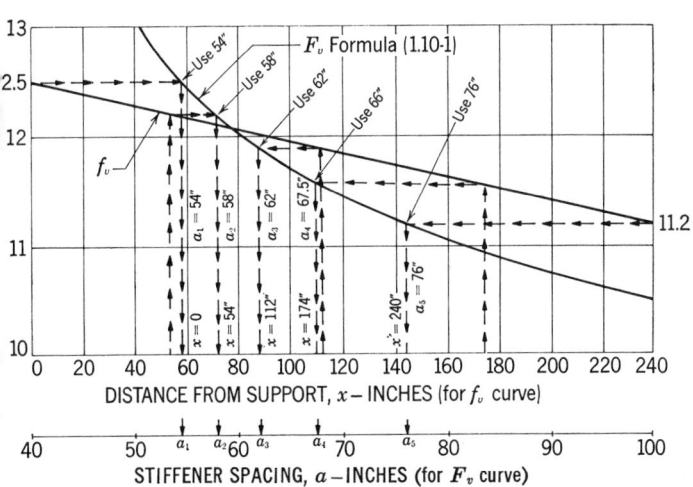

Figure 1

From Fig. 1 use the following intermediate stiffener spacing:

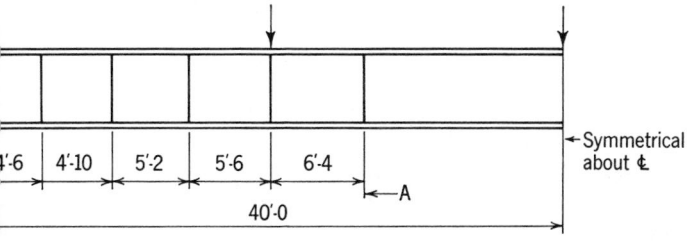

Figure 2

From shear diagram, f_v at point **A** = 4.6 ksi

$$\frac{a}{h} > 3.0, \quad \frac{h}{t} = 96 < 260, \quad F_v = 9.0 \text{ ksi} > 4.6 \text{ ksi } \textbf{o.k.}$$

Intermediate stiffeners are not required beyond point **A** (**Fig. 2**).

3. Check web crippling for the uniform load: **1.10.10**
   Assume construction prevents compression flange rotation. Check in area where intermediate stiffeners are not required.

   Uniform load = 2 kips per ft.

   Calculated compressive stress on web = $\dfrac{2}{12 \times 0.5625}$ = 0.30 ksi   **1.10.10.**

   $a = 2(40 - \Sigma a) = 13$ ft.-8 in.

   $\dfrac{a}{h} = \dfrac{164}{54} = 3.04$, use 3.0

   Allowable compressive stress =   Formul
   $$\left[5.5 + \frac{4}{(3.0)^2} \right] \times \frac{10000}{(96)^2} = 6.5 \text{ ksi} > 0.30 \textbf{ o.k.}$$ (1.10-1(

E. *Stiffener size*
   1. Intermediate stiffeners:
      a. Check width-thickness ratio:
         Assume $4 \times \frac{5}{16}$ bars, $F_y = 36$ ksi

         $$\frac{4}{0.313} = 12.8 < 15.8 \textbf{ o.k.}$$ **1.9.1.**
         and
         Append
         pg. 5 -
      b. Check moment of inertia: **1.10.5.**
         $$I_{req} \geq \left(\frac{54}{50} \right)^4 = 1.36 \text{ in.}^4$$

         $$I_{furn} = \frac{1}{12} (0.313)(8.5625)^3 = 16.37 \text{ in.}^4 > 1.36 \text{ in.}^4 \textbf{ o.k.}$$

      c. Length required = $54 - (4 \times 0.5625) = 51.75$ in.   **1.10.5.**
         (Use 52 in.)

      Use for intermediate stiffeners: 2 bars 4 $\times$ $\frac{5}{16}$ $\times$ 4'-4" bearing on compression flange of girder.

   2. Bearing stiffeners at ends of girder: **1.10.5.**
      For design of end bearing stiffener, see step E-2, Example 1.
      Use: 2 plates $\frac{3}{4} \times 11 \times$ 4'-5$\frac{3}{4}$ with close bearing on flange receiving reaction.

   3. Bearing stiffener at concentrated loads: **1.10.5.**
      a. Check web crippling by Formula (1.10-8):   **1.10.1**
         $R = 200$ kips
         Assume $N = 10$ in., $k = 3$ in.

Allowable compressive stress = $0.75F_y$
$$= 0.75 \times 36 = 27 \text{ ksi}$$

Computed compressive stress $= \dfrac{200}{\frac{9}{16}[10 + (2 \times 3)]}$

$$\cong 22 \text{ ksi} < 27 \text{ ksi } \textbf{o.k.}$$

b. Check web crippling by Formula (1.10-10):

Since the flange is restrained against rotation:
Allowable compressive stress = 6.5   (Step D3)
To compute the compressive stress, the concentrated load
must be divided by the lesser of the girder depth $\times t$
or the length of panel in which the load is placed.   For
this case, girder depth controls.

Computed compressive stress $= \dfrac{200}{60 \times 0.5625}$
$$= 5.93 \text{ ksi} < 6.5 \textbf{ o.k.}$$

∴ **Bearing stiffeners at points of concentrated loads
are not required.**

EXAMPLE 3

Given: Using $F_y = 36$ ksi, design the section of a 52 in. deep
welded plate girder with no intermediate stiffeners to support a
uniform load of 2.4 kips per linear foot on an 85 ft. span. The
girder will be framed between columns and its compression
flange will be laterally supported for its entire length.

Solution:

$F_b = 22$ ksi

Required section modulus $= \dfrac{2.4 \times 85 \times 85 \times 12}{8 \times 22}$
$$= 1182 \text{ in.}^3$$

Maximum vertical shear = $2.4 \times 85/2 = 102$ kips

Enter Table of Welded Plate Girders, Dimensions and   pg. 2 - 123
Properties:

For girder having $\frac{3}{8} \times 48$ web with $1\frac{1}{4} \times 16$ flange plates,
$S = 1100$ in.$^3 < 1182$ in.^{3}

For girder having $\frac{3}{8} \times 52$ web with $1\frac{1}{4} \times 18$ flange plates,
$S = 1330$ in.$^3 > 1182$ in.^{3}

A. *Determine web required:*   Appendix
Table
3-36
Try: Web = $\frac{3}{8} \times 50$; $A_w = 18.75$ sq. in.

Check web:
For $h/t = 50/0.375 = 133$; from Table 3-36 under column
headed "Over 3", allowable shear stress without intermediate stiffeners, by interpolation = 4.7 ksi

Allowable vertical shear $= 18.75 \times 4.7$
$= 88$ kips < 102 kips
Try: Web $= \frac{7}{16} \times 50$; $A_w = 21.8$ sq. in.
For $h/t = 50/0.4375 = 114$; re-enter Table 3-36; allowable shear stress without intermediate stiffeners, by interpolation $= 6.5$ ksi

Allowable vertical shear $= 21.8 \times 6.5$
$= 141.7$ kips > 102 kips **o.k.**

B. *Determine flange required:*
Try flange thickness $= 1\frac{1}{8}$ in.; $d = 52.25$ in.
Required moment of inertia $=$
$1182 \times 52.25/2 = 30880$ in.^{4} | pg. **2** - 1‖
Less moment of inertia of $\frac{7}{16} \times 50$ web $\quad = \quad \underline{4557 \text{ in.}^4}$
Required moment of inertia 2 flanges $\quad = 26323$ in.^{4}
Distance between flange centroids $= 2y = 51.125$ in.;
then $2y^2 = 1307$ sq. in. | pg. **2** - 1‖
*Req'd area of one flange $= 26323/1307 = 20.14$ sq. in.
$1\frac{1}{8} \times 18 = 20.25$ sq. in. > 20.14 sq. in. **o.k.**

Use: Web $\frac{7}{16} \times 50$
2 flange plates $= 1\frac{1}{8} \times 18$

EXAMPLE 4

Given: Design conditions are the same as given in Example 3 except intermediate stiffeners are to be used.

Solution:

A. *Determine web stiffeners required:*
Try: Web $= \frac{5}{16} \times 50$; $A_w = 15.63$ sq. in.
  1. Check stiffener spacing at ends of girder:
     Calculated shear stress at ends of girder:
     $f_v = 102/15.63 = 6.53$ ksi
     Allowable clear distance between end panel stiffeners $=$ | 1.10.5.‖
     $$a = \frac{348 \times 0.313}{\sqrt{6.53}} = 42.6 \text{ in., say 42 in.} = 3.5 \text{ ft.}$$
  2. Check intermediate stiffener requirements:
     Calculated shear stress 3.5 ft. from end of girder:
     $$f_v = \frac{102 - (3.5 \times 2.4)}{15.63} = 5.99 \text{ ksi}$$
     Allowable clear distance between intermediate stiffeners: | 1.10.5.‖
     $$a/h = \left(\frac{260 \times 0.313}{50}\right)^2 = 2.64, \text{ say } 2.5$$
     $$a = 50 \times 2.5 = 125 \text{ in.}$$

* In long girders, it may prove economical to reduce the size of flange plates ne‖ the girder ends where the moment gradient is small. See discussion of Welded Plate Gird‖ table.

From Table 3-36 for $a/h = 2.5$,
$h/t = 50/0.313 = 160$

$F_v = 6.5$ ksi > 5.99 ksi **o.k.**

Area of stiffener required $= \dfrac{5.99}{6.5} (.063 \times 15.63)$

$= 0.91$ sq. in.

Try: 2 bars $6 \times \frac{3}{8}$;

$A_{st} = 4.5$ sq. in. > 0.91 sq. in. **o.k.**

Width-thickness ratio $= \dfrac{6}{0.375} = 16 \cong 15.8$ **o.k.**

Distance between end stiffeners $= (85 - 7) \times 12$
$= 936$ in.

No. of panels required between intermediate

stiffeners $= \dfrac{936}{125} = 7.5$, say 8

Space intermediate stiffeners at $\dfrac{936}{8} = 117$ in. $= 9.75$ ft.

**Use: Web $\frac{5}{16} \times 50$ with 9 pairs of $6 \times \frac{3}{8}$
stiffeners. Space as follows:**
2 at 3.5 ft. from each end = 7.0 ft.
7 at 9.75 ft. (8 panels)   = 78.0 ft.
                        85.0 ft.

B. *Determine flange required:*

Try flange thickness $= \frac{7}{8}$ in.; $d = 51.75$ in.

Required moment of inertia
$= 1182 \times 51.75/2 = 30584$ in.⁴

Moment of inertia of $\frac{5}{16} \times 50$ web
$= 10417 \times \frac{5}{16} = \underline{3255}$ in.⁴

Required moment of inertia of 2 flanges $= 27329$ in.⁴

Distance between flange centroids $= 2y = 50.875$ in.;
then $2y^2 = 1294$ sq. in.

*Req'd area of one flange $= 27329/1294 = 21.1$ sq. in.
$25 \times \frac{7}{8} = 21.9 > 21.1$ sq. in. **o.k.**
$25/(2 \times 0.875) = 14.3 < 15.8$ **o.k.**

Use: 2 flange plates $\frac{7}{8} \times 25$

Appendix
Table
3-36

1.10.5.4

1.9.1.2
and
pg. 5 - 72

pg. 2 - 130

pg. 2 - 126

1.9.1.2

---

* In long girders, it may prove economical to reduce the size of flange plates near
.e girder ends where the moment gradient is small.   See discussion of Welded Plate Girder
ble.

86-61

WELDED PLATE GIRDERS
Dimensions and properties

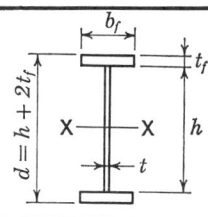

Nominal Size / h/t Ratio	Wt. per Foot	Area	Depth d	Flange Width b_f	Flange Thick t_f	Web Depth h	Web Thick t	Axis X-X I	Axis X-X S	Axis X-X $^aS'$	$^b r_T$	$^c R$	$\dfrac{d}{A_f}$
In.	Lb.	In.²	In.	In.	In.	In.	In.	In.⁴	In.³	In.³	In.	Kips	In.⁻
86 × 28	750	220	90.00	28	3	84	5/8	349000	7750	68.6	7.69	241.6	1.0
h/t = 134	654	192	89.00	28	2½	84	5/8	293000	6580	69.4	7.62	241.6	1.2
	559	164	88.00	28	2	84	5/8	238000	5410	70.2	7.52	241.6	1.5
	512	150	87.50	28	1¾	84	5/8	211000	4820	70.6	7.45	241.6	1.7
	464	136	87.00	28	1½	84	5/8	184000	4240	71.0	7.35	241.6	2.0
	416	122	86.50	28	1¼	84	5/8	158000	3650	71.4	7.23	241.6	2.4
	369	108	86.00	28	1	84	5/8	132000	3070	71.8	7.06	241.6	3.0
80 × 26	696	205	84.00	26	3	78	5/8	281000	6680	58.8	7.14	260.2	1.0
h/t = 125	608	179	83.00	26	2½	78	5/8	235000	5670	59.6	7.08	260.2	1.2
	519	153	82.00	26	2	78	5/8	191000	4660	60.3	6.98	260.2	1.5
	475	140	81.50	26	1¾	78	5/8	169000	4160	60.7	6.91	260.2	1.7
	431	127	81.00	26	1½	78	5/8	148000	3650	61.0	6.83	260.2	2.0
	387	114	80.50	26	1¼	78	5/8	127000	3150	61.4	6.71	260.2	2.4
	343	101	80.00	26	1	78	5/8	106000	2690	61.8	6.55	260.2	3.0
	320	94.2	79.75	26	7/8	78	5/8	95500	2390	62.0	6.44	260.2	3.5
74 × 24	627	184	78.00	24	3	72	9/16	220000	5640	49.8	6.62	205.5	1.0
h/t = 128	546	160	77.00	24	2½	72	9/16	184000	4780	50.5	6.57	205.5	1.2
	464	136	76.00	24	2	72	9/16	149000	3920	51.2	6.49	205.5	1.5
	423	124	75.50	24	1¾	72	9/16	132000	3490	51.5	6.43	205.5	1.8
	382	112	75.00	24	1½	72	9/16	115000	3060	51.8	6.36	205.5	2.0
	342	100	74.50	24	1¼	72	9/16	98000	2630	52.2	6.26	205.5	2.4
	301	88.5	74.00	24	1	72	9/16	81400	2200	52.5	6.12	205.5	3.0
	280	82.5	73.75	24	7/8	72	9/16	73300	1990	52.7	6.03	205.5	3.5
68 × 22	561	165	72.00	22	3	66	½	169000	4700	41.6	6.10	157.5	1.0
h/t = 132	486	143	71.00	22	2½	66	½	141000	3970	42.2	6.06	157.5	1.2
	411	121	70.00	22	2	66	½	114000	3250	42.8	5.99	157.5	1.5
	374	110	69.50	22	1¾	66	½	100000	2890	43.1	5.94	157.5	1.8
	337	99.0	69.00	22	1½	66	½	87200	2530	43.4	5.88	157.5	2.0
	299	88.0	68.50	22	1¼	66	½	74200	2170	43.7	5.80	157.5	2.4
	262	77.0	68.00	22	1	66	½	61400	1800	44.0	5.68	157.5	3.0
	243	71.5	67.75	22	7/8	66	½	55000	1620	44.2	5.60	157.5	3.5
	224	66.0	67.50	22	¾	66	½	48700	1440	44.4	5.50	157.5	4.0
61 × 20	429	126	65.00	20	2½	60	7/16	106000	3250	34.6	5.54	116.0	1.3
h/t = 137	361	106	64.00	20	2	60	7/16	84800	2650	35.2	5.48	116.0	1.6
	327	96.2	63.50	20	1¾	60	7/16	74600	2350	35.4	5.44	116.0	1.8
	293	86.2	63.00	20	1½	60	7/16	64600	2090	35.7	5.39	116.0	2.1
	259	76.2	62.50	20	1¼	60	7/16	54800	1750	36.0	5.33	116.0	2.5
	225	66.2	62.00	20	1	60	7/16	45100	1450	36.3	5.23	116.0	3.1
	208	61.2	61.75	20	7/8	60	7/16	40300	1310	36.4	5.16	116.0	3.5
	191	56.2	61.50	20	¾	60	7/16	35600	1160	36.6	5.08	116.0	4.1

^{a} S' = Additional section modulus corresponding to $\frac{1}{16}''$ increase in web thickness.

^{b} r_T = Radius of gyration of the "T" section comprising the compression flange plus $\frac{1}{3}$ of the compression web area, about an axis in the plane of the web.

^{c} R = Maximum end reaction permissible without intermediate stiffeners for tabulated web plate.

The width-thickness ratios for girders in this table comply with AISC Specification Section 1.9 for F_y = 36 ksi steel. For steels of higher yield strengths, check flanges for compliance with this section.

See Section 1.10.5 for design of stiffeners.

Welds not included in tabulated weight per foot.

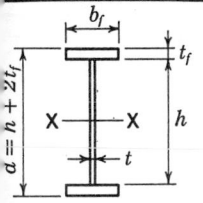

57-41

WELDED PLATE GIRDERS
Dimensions and properties

Nominal Size / t Ratio	Wt. per Foot	Area	Depth d	Flange Width b_f	Flange Thick t_f	Web Depth h	Web Thick t	Axis X-X I	S	$^aS'$	$^b r_T$	$^c R$	$\dfrac{d}{A_f}$
In.	Lb.	In.²	In.	In.	In.	In.	In.	In.⁴	In.³	In.³	In.	Kips	In.⁻¹
×18 t=128	389	115	61.00	18	2½	56	7/16	83500	2740	30.0	4.98	124.3	1.36
	328	96.5	60.00	18	2	56	7/16	67000	2230	30.5	4.92	124.3	1.67
	298	87.5	59.50	18	1¾	56	7/16	58900	1980	30.7	4.89	124.3	1.89
	267	78.5	59.00	18	1½	56	7/16	51000	1730	31.0	4.84	124.3	2.19
	236	69.5	58.50	18	1¼	56	7/16	43300	1480	31.3	4.78	124.3	2.60
	206	60.5	58.00	18	1	56	7/16	35600	1230	31.5	4.69	124.3	3.22
	190	56.0	57.75	18	7/8	56	7/16	31900	1100	31.7	4.63	124.3	3.67
	175	51.5	57.50	18	3/4	56	7/16	28100	979	31.8	4.55	124.3	4.26
	160	47.0	57.25	18	5/8	56	7/16	24400	854	32.0	4.45	124.3	5.09
×18 t=138	342	100	56.50	18	2¼	52	3/8	64000	2270	25.9	5.00	84.3	1.40
	311	91.5	56.00	18	2	52	3/8	56900	2030	26.2	4.98	84.3	1.56
	280	82.5	55.50	18	1¾	52	3/8	49900	1800	26.4	4.95	84.3	1.76
	250	73.5	55.00	18	1½	52	3/8	43000	1566	26.6	4.91	84.3	2.04
	219	64.5	54.50	18	1¼	52	3/8	36300	1330	26.9	4.86	84.3	2.42
	189	55.5	54.00	18	1	52	3/8	29700	1100	27.1	4.78	84.3	3.00
	173	51.0	53.75	18	7/8	52	3/8	26400	983	27.2	4.73	84.3	3.41
	158	46.5	53.50	18	3/4	52	3/8	23200	866	27.4	4.67	84.3	3.96
	143	42.0	53.25	18	5/8	52	3/8	20000	750	27.5	4.58	84.3	4.73
×16 t=128	306	90.0	52.50	16	2¼	48	3/8	48900	1860	21.9	4.44	91.3	1.46
	279	82.0	52.00	16	2	48	3/8	43500	1670	22.2	4.42	91.3	1.63
	252	74.0	51.50	16	1¾	48	3/8	38100	1480	22.4	4.39	91.3	1.84
	224	66.0	51.00	16	1½	48	3/8	32900	1290	22.6	4.35	91.3	2.13
	197	58.0	50.50	16	1¼	48	3/8	27700	1100	22.8	4.31	91.3	2.53
	170	50.0	50.00	16	1	48	3/8	22700	907	23.0	4.24	91.3	3.13
	156	46.0	49.75	16	7/8	48	3/8	20200	811	23.2	4.19	91.3	3.55
	143	42.0	49.50	16	3/4	48	3/8	17700	716	23.3	4.13	91.3	4.13
	129	38.0	49.25	16	5/8	48	3/8	15300	620	23.4	4.05	91.3	4.93
×16 t=141	237	69.8	47.50	16	1¾	44	5/16	31500	1330	18.7	4.44	57.7	1.70
	210	61.8	47.00	16	1½	44	5/16	27100	1150	18.9	4.41	57.7	1.96
	183	53.8	46.50	16	1¼	44	5/16	22700	976	19.1	4.38	57.7	2.33
	156	45.8	46.00	16	1	44	5/16	18400	801	19.3	4.32	57.7	2.88
	142	41.8	45.75	16	7/8	44	5/16	16300	713	19.4	4.28	57.7	3.27
	128	37.8	45.50	16	3/4	44	5/16	14200	626	19.5	4.23	57.7	3.79
	115	33.8	45.25	16	5/8	44	5/16	12200	538	19.6	4.17	57.7	4.53
×14 t=128	209	61.5	43.50	14	1¾	40	5/16	23000	1060	15.3	3.88	63.4	1.78
	185	54.5	43.00	14	1½	40	5/16	19800	919	15.5	3.85	63.4	2.05
	162	47.5	42.50	14	1¼	40	5/16	16600	779	15.7	3.82	63.4	2.43
	138	40.5	42.00	14	1	40	5/16	13400	640	15.9	3.77	63.4	3.00
	126	37.0	41.75	14	7/8	40	5/16	11900	570	16.0	3.74	63.4	3.41
	114	33.5	41.50	14	3/4	40	5/16	10400	500	16.1	3.69	63.4	3.95
	102	30.0	41.25	14	5/8	40	5/16	8890	431	16.2	3.63	63.4	4.71
	90.1	26.5	41.00	14	½	40	5/16	7410	361	16.3	3.55	63.4	5.86

^{a} S' = Additional section modulus corresponding to $\frac{1}{16}''$ increase in web thickness.

^{b} r_T = Radius of gyration of the "T" section comprising the compression flange plus ⅓ of the compression web area, about an axis in the plane of the web.

^{c} R = Maximum end reaction permissible without intermediate stiffeners for tabulated web plate.

The width-thickness ratios for girders in this table comply with AISC Specification Section 1.9 for F_y = 36 ksi steel. For steels of higher yield strengths, check flanges for compliance with this section.

See Section 1.10.5 for design of stiffeners.

Welds not included in tabulated weight per foot.

AMERICAN INSTITUTE OF STEEL CONSTRUCTION

PLATE GIRDERS
Section Modulus Nomograph
(for symmetrical cross-section girders)

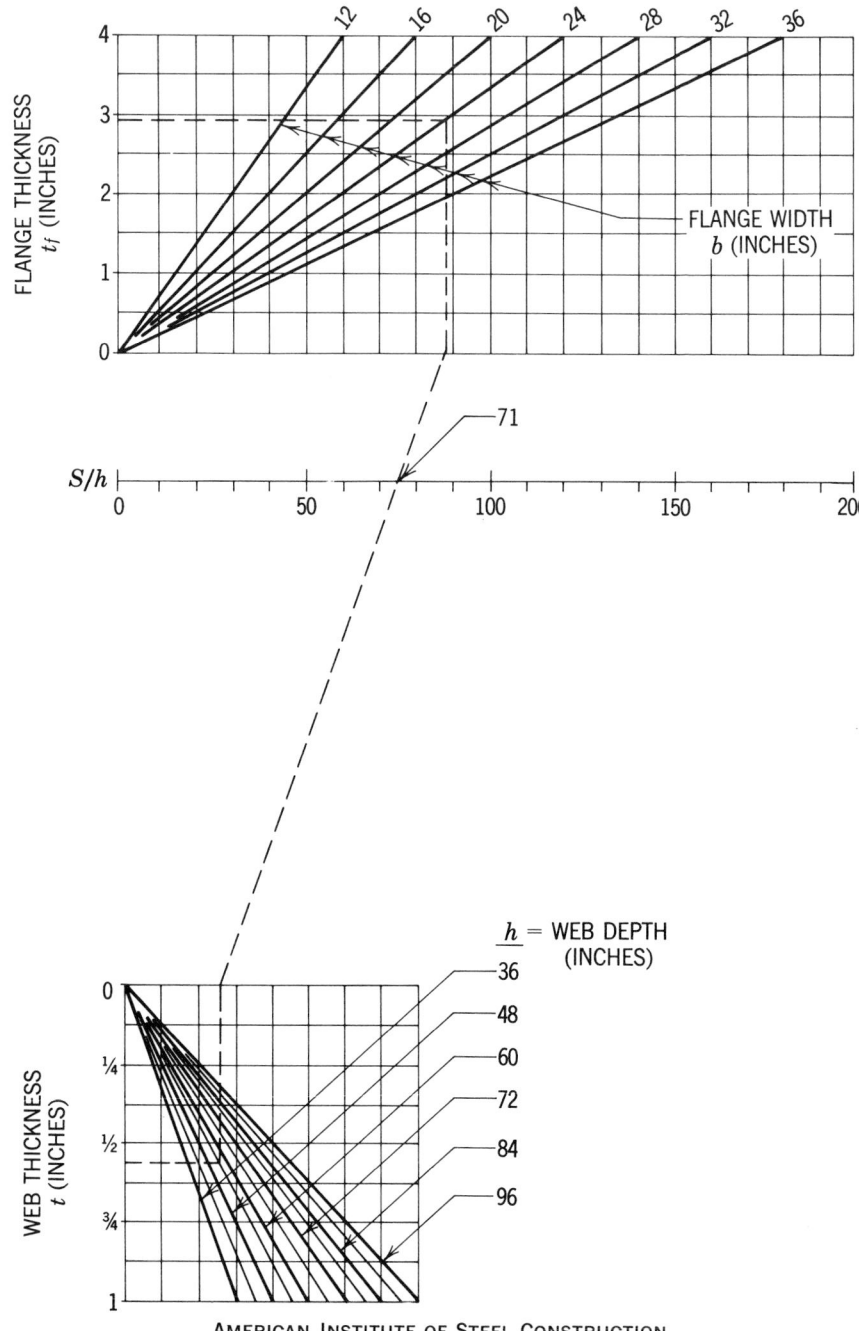

AMERICAN INSTITUTE OF STEEL CONSTRUCTION

PLATE GIRDERS

Values of $2y^2$ for computing Moment of Inertia of areas about axis X-X

$(\Sigma Ay^2 = \text{Area of one flange} \times 2y^2)$

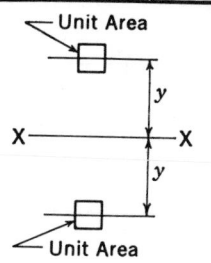

$2y$	.0	.1	.2	.3	.4	.5	.6	.7	.8	.9
10	50	51	52	53	54	55	56	57	58	59
11	61	62	63	64	65	66	67	68	70	71
12	72	73	74	76	77	78	79	81	82	83
13	85	86	87	88	90	91	92	94	95	97
14	98	99	101	102	104	105	107	108	110	111
15	113	114	116	117	119	120	122	123	125	126
16	128	130	131	133	134	136	138	139	141	143
17	145	146	148	150	151	153	155	157	158	160
18	162	164	166	167	169	171	173	175	177	179
19	181	182	184	186	188	190	192	194	196	198
20	200	202	204	206	208	210	212	214	216	218
21	221	223	225	227	229	231	233	235	238	240
22	242	244	246	249	251	253	255	258	260	262
23	265	267	269	271	274	276	278	281	283	286
24	288	290	293	295	298	300	303	305	308	310
25	313	315	318	320	323	325	328	330	333	335
26	338	341	343	346	348	351	354	356	359	362
27	365	367	370	373	375	378	381	384	386	389
28	392	395	398	400	403	406	409	412	415	418
29	421	423	426	429	432	435	438	441	444	447
30	450	453	456	459	462	465	468	471	474	477
31	481	484	487	490	493	496	499	502	506	509
32	512	515	518	522	525	528	531	535	538	541
33	545	548	551	554	558	561	564	568	571	575
34	578	581	585	588	592	595	599	602	606	609
35	613	616	620	623	627	630	634	637	641	644
36	648	652	655	659	662	666	670	673	677	681
37	685	688	692	696	699	703	707	711	714	718
38	722	726	730	733	737	741	745	749	753	757
39	761	764	768	772	776	780	784	788	792	796
40	800	804	808	812	816	820	824	828	832	836
41	841	845	849	853	857	861	865	869	874	878
42	882	886	890	895	899	903	907	912	916	920
43	925	929	933	937	942	946	950	955	959	964
44	968	972	977	981	986	990	995	999	1004	1008
45	1013	1017	1022	1026	1031	1035	1040	1044	1049	1053
46	1058	1063	1067	1072	1076	1081	1086	1090	1095	1100
47	1105	1109	1114	1119	1123	1128	1133	1138	1142	1147
48	1152	1157	1162	1166	1171	1176	1181	1186	1191	1196
49	1201	1205	1210	1215	1220	1225	1230	1235	1240	1245

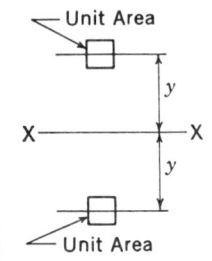

Unit Area

Unit Area

PLATE GIRDERS

Values of $2y^2$ for computing Moment of Inertia of areas about axis X-X

$(\Sigma Ay^2 = \text{Area of one flange} \times 2y^2)$

2y	.0	.1	.2	.3	.4	.5	.6	.7	.8	.9
50	1250	1255	1260	1265	1270	1275	1280	1285	1290	1295
51	1301	1306	1311	1316	1321	1326	1331	1336	1342	1347
52	1352	1357	1362	1368	1373	1378	1383	1389	1394	1399
53	1405	1410	1415	1420	1426	1431	1436	1442	1447	1453
54	1458	1463	1469	1474	1480	1485	1491	1496	1502	1507
55	1513	1518	1524	1529	1535	1540	1546	1551	1557	1562
56	1568	1574	1579	1585	1590	1596	1602	1607	1613	1619
57	1625	1630	1636	1642	1647	1653	1659	1665	1670	1676
58	1682	1688	1694	1699	1705	1711	1717	1723	1729	1735
59	1741	1746	1752	1758	1764	1770	1776	1782	1788	1794
60	1800	1806	1812	1818	1824	1830	1836	1842	1848	1854
61	1861	1867	1873	1879	1885	1891	1897	1903	1910	1916
62	1922	1928	1934	1941	1947	1953	1959	1966	1972	1978
63	1985	1991	1997	2003	2010	2016	2022	2029	2035	2042
64	2048	2054	2061	2067	2074	2080	2087	2093	2100	2106
65	2113	2119	2126	2132	2139	2145	2152	2158	2165	2171
66	2178	2185	2191	2198	2204	2211	2218	2224	2231	2238
67	2245	2251	2258	2265	2271	2278	2285	2292	2298	2305
68	2312	2319	2326	2332	2339	2346	2353	2360	2367	2374
69	2381	2387	2394	2401	2408	2415	2422	2429	2436	2443
70	2450	2457	2464	2471	2478	2485	2492	2499	2506	2513
71	2521	2528	2535	2542	2549	2556	2563	2570	2578	2585
72	2592	2599	2606	2614	2621	2628	2635	2643	2650	2657
73	2665	2672	2679	2686	2694	2701	2708	2716	2723	2731
74	2738	2745	2753	2760	2768	2775	2783	2790	2798	2805
75	2813	2820	2828	2835	2843	2850	2858	2865	2873	2880
76	2888	2896	2903	2911	2918	2926	2934	2941	2949	2957
77	2965	2972	2980	2988	2995	3003	3011	3019	3026	3034
78	3042	3050	3058	3065	3073	3081	3089	3097	3105	3113
79	3121	3128	3136	3144	3152	3160	3168	3176	3184	3192
80	3200	3208	3216	3224	3232	3240	3248	3256	3264	3272
81	3281	3289	3297	3305	3313	3321	3329	3337	3346	3354
82	3362	3370	3378	3387	3395	3403	3411	3420	3428	3436
83	3445	3453	3461	3469	3478	3486	3494	3503	3511	3520
84	3528	3536	3545	3553	3562	3570	3579	3587	3596	3604
85	3613	3621	3630	3638	3647	3655	3664	3672	3681	3689
86	3698	3707	3715	3724	3732	3741	3750	3758	3767	3776
87	3785	3793	3802	3811	3819	3828	3837	3846	3854	3863
88	3872	3881	3890	3898	3907	3916	3925	3934	3943	3952
89	3961	3969	3978	3987	3996	4005	4014	4023	4032	4041

PLATE GIRDERS

Values of $2y^2$ for computing Moment of Inertia of areas about axis X-X

$(\Sigma Ay^2 = \text{Area of one flange} \times 2y^2)$

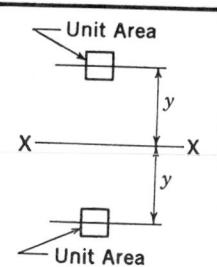

$2y$	.0	.1	.2	.3	.4	.5	.6	.7	.8	.9
90	4050	4059	4068	4077	4086	4095	4104	4113	4122	4131
91	4141	4150	4159	4168	4177	4186	4195	4204	4214	4223
92	4232	4241	4250	4260	4269	4278	4287	4297	4306	4315
93	4325	4334	4343	4352	4362	4371	4380	4390	4399	4409
94	4418	4427	4437	4446	4456	4465	4475	4484	4494	4503
95	4513	4522	4532	4541	4551	4560	4570	4579	4589	4598
96	4608	4618	4627	4637	4646	4656	4666	4675	4685	4695
97	4705	4714	4724	4734	4743	4753	4763	4773	4782	4792
98	4802	4812	4822	4831	4841	4851	4861	4871	4881	4891
99	4901	4910	4920	4930	4940	4950	4960	4970	4980	4990
100	5000	5010	5020	5030	5040	5050	5060	5070	5080	5090
101	5101	5111	5121	5131	5141	5151	5161	5171	5182	5192
102	5202	5212	5222	5233	5243	5253	5263	5274	5284	5294
103	5305	5315	5325	5335	5346	5356	5366	5377	5387	5398
104	5408	5418	5429	5439	5450	5460	5471	5481	5492	5502
105	5513	5523	5534	5544	5555	5565	5576	5586	5597	5607
106	5618	5629	5639	5650	5660	5671	5682	5692	5703	5714
107	5725	5735	5746	5757	5767	5778	5789	5800	5810	5821
108	5832	5843	5854	5864	5875	5886	5897	5908	5919	5930
109	5941	5951	5962	5973	5984	5995	6006	6017	6028	6039
110	6050	6061	6072	6083	6094	6105	6116	6127	6138	6149
111	6161	6172	6183	6194	6205	6216	6227	6238	6250	6261
112	6272	6283	6294	6306	6317	6328	6339	6351	6362	6373
113	6385	6396	6407	6418	6430	6441	6452	6464	6475	6487
114	6498	6509	6521	6532	6544	6555	6567	6578	6590	6601
115	6613	6624	6636	6647	6659	6670	6682	6693	6705	6716
116	6728	6740	6751	6763	6774	6786	6798	6809	6821	6833
117	6845	6856	6868	6880	6891	6903	6915	6927	6938	6950
118	6962	6974	6986	6997	7009	7021	7033	7045	7057	7069
119	7081	7092	7104	7116	7128	7140	7152	7164	7176	7188
120	7200	7212	7224	7236	7248	7260	7272	7284	7296	7308
121	7321	7333	7345	7357	7369	7381	7393	7405	7418	7430
122	7442	7454	7466	7479	7491	7503	7515	7528	7540	7552
123	7565	7577	7589	7601	7614	7626	7638	7651	7663	7676
124	7688	7700	7713	7725	7738	7750	7763	7775	7788	7800
125	7813	7825	7838	7850	7863	7875	7888	7900	7913	7925
126	7938	7951	7963	7976	7988	8001	8014	8026	8039	8052
127	8065	8077	8090	8103	8115	8123	8141	8154	8166	8179
128	8192	8205	8218	8230	8243	8256	8269	8282	8295	8308
129	8321	8333	8346	8359	8372	8385	8398	8411	8424	8437

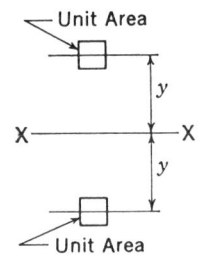

PLATE GIRDERS

Values of $2y^2$ for computing Moment of Inertia of areas about axis X-X

$(\Sigma A y^2 = $ Area of one flange $\times 2y^2)$

$2y$	.0	.1	.2	.3	.4	.5	.6	.7	.8	.9
130	8450	8463	8476	8489	8502	8515	8528	8541	8554	8567
131	8581	8594	8607	8620	8633	8646	8659	8672	8686	8699
132	8712	8725	8738	8752	8765	8778	8791	8805	8818	8831
133	8845	8858	8871	8884	8898	8911	8924	8938	8951	8965
134	8978	8991	9005	9018	9032	9045	9059	9072	9086	9099
135	9113	9126	9140	9153	9167	9180	9194	9207	9221	9234
136	9248	9262	9275	9289	9302	9316	9330	9343	9357	9371
137	8385	9398	9412	9426	9439	9453	9467	9481	9494	9508
138	9522	9536	9550	9563	9577	9591	9605	9619	9633	9647
139	9661	9674	9688	9702	9716	9730	9744	9758	9772	9786
140	9800	9814	9828	9842	9856	9870	9884	9898	9912	9926
141	9941	9955	9969	9983	9997	10011	10025	10039	10054	10068
142	10082	10096	10110	10125	10139	10153	10167	10182	10196	10210
143	10225	10239	10253	10267	10282	10296	10310	10325	10339	10354
144	10368	10382	10397	10411	10426	10440	10455	10469	10484	10498
145	10513	10527	10542	10556	10571	10585	10600	10614	10629	10643
146	10658	10673	10687	10702	10716	10731	10746	10760	10775	10790
147	10805	10819	10834	10849	10863	10878	10893	10908	10922	10937
148	10952	10967	10982	10996	11011	11026	11041	11056	11071	11086
149	11101	11115	11130	11145	11160	11175	11190	11205	11220	11235
150	11250	11265	11280	11295	11310	11325	11340	11355	11370	11385
151	11401	11416	11431	11446	11461	11476	11491	11506	11522	11537
152	11552	11567	11582	11598	11613	11628	11643	11659	11674	11689
153	11705	11720	11735	11750	11766	11781	11796	11812	11827	11842
154	11858	11873	11889	11904	11920	11935	11951	11966	11982	11997
155	12013	12028	12044	12059	12075	12090	12106	12121	12137	12152
156	12168	12184	12199	12215	12230	12246	12262	12277	12293	12309
157	12325	12340	12356	12372	12387	12403	12419	12435	12450	12466
158	12482	12498	12514	12529	12545	12561	12577	12593	12609	12625
159	12641	12656	12672	12688	12704	12720	12736	12752	12768	12784
160	12800	12816	12832	12848	12864	12880	12896	12912	12928	12944
161	12961	12977	12993	13009	13025	13041	13057	13073	13090	13106
162	13122	13138	13154	13171	13187	13203	13219	13236	13252	13268
163	13285	13301	13317	13333	13350	13366	13382	13399	13415	13432
164	13448	13464	13481	13497	13514	13530	13547	13563	13580	13596
165	13613	13629	13646	13662	13679	13695	13712	13728	13745	13761
166	13778	13795	13811	13828	13844	13861	13878	13894	13911	13927
167	13945	13961	13978	13995	14011	14028	14045	14062	14078	14095
168	14112	14129	14146	14162	14179	14196	14213	14230	14247	14264
169	14281	14297	14314	14331	14348	14365	14382	14399	14416	14433

PLATE GIRDERS
Moment of Inertia
of one plate about axis X-X

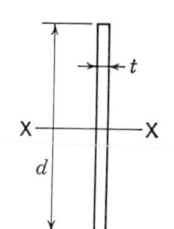

To obtain the moment of inertia for any thickness of plate not listed below, multiply the value for a plate one inch thick by the desired thickness.

Depth d Inches	Thickness, t, Inches							
	3/8	7/16	1/2	9/16	5/8	3/4	7/8	1
10	31.3	36.5	41.7	46.9	52.1	62.5	72.9	83.3
11	41.6	48.5	55.5	62.4	69.3	83.2	97.1	110.9
12	54.0	63.0	72.0	81.0	90.0	108.0	126.0	144.0
13	68.7	80.1	91.5	103.0	114.4	137.3	160.2	183.1
14	85.8	100.0	114.3	128.6	142.9	171.5	200.1	228.7
15	105.5	123.0	140.6	158.2	175.8	210.9	246.1	281.3
16	128.0	149.3	170.7	192.0	213.3	256.0	298.7	341.3
17	153.5	179.1	204.7	230.3	255.9	307.1	358.2	409.4
18	182.3	212.6	243.0	273.4	303.8	364.5	425.3	486.0
19	214.3	250.1	285.8	321.5	357.2	428.7	500.1	571.6
20	250.0	291.7	333.3	375.0	416.7	500.0	583.3	666.7
21	289.4	337.6	385.9	434.1	482.3	578.8	675.3	771.8
22	332.8	388.2	443.7	499.1	554.6	665.5	776.4	887.3
23	380.2	443.6	507.0	570.3	633.7	760.4	887.2	1013.9
24	432.0	504.0	576.0	648.0	720.0	864.0	1008.0	1152.0
25	488.3	569.7	651.0	732.4	813.8	976.6	1139.3	1302.1
26	549.3	640.8	732.3	823.9	915.4	1098.5	1281.6	1464.7
27	615.1	717.6	820.1	922.6	1025.2	1230.2	1435.2	1640.3
28	686.0	800.3	914.7	1029.0	1143.3	1372.0	1600.7	1829.3
29	762.2	889.2	1016.2	1143.2	1270.3	1524.3	1778.4	2032.4
30	843.8	984.4	1125.0	1265.6	1406.3	1687.5	1968.8	2250.0
31	931.0	1086.1	1241.3	1396.5	1551.6	1861.9	2172.3	2482.6
32	1024.0	1194.7	1365.3	1536.0	1706.7	2048.0	2389.3	2730.7
33	1123.0	1310.2	1497.4	1684.5	1871.7	2246.1	2620.4	2994.8
34	1228.3	1433.0	1637.7	1842.4	2047.1	2456.5	2865.9	3275.3
35	1339.8	1563.2	1786.5	2009.8	2233.1	2679.7	3126.3	3572.9
36	1458.0	1701.0	1944.0	2187.0	2430.0	2916.0	3402.0	3888.0
37	1582.9	1846.7	2110.5	2374.4	2638.2	3165.8	3693.4	4221.1
38	1714.8	2000.5	2286.3	2572.1	2857.9	3429.5	4001.1	4572.7
39	1853.7	2162.7	2471.6	2780.6	3089.5	3707.4	4325.3	4943.3
40	2000.0	2333.3	2666.7	3000.0	3333.3	4000.0	4666.7	5333.3
41	2153.8	2512.7	2871.7	3230.7	3589.6	4307.6	5025.5	5743.4
42	2315.3	2701.1	3087.0	3472.9	3858.8	4630.5	5402.3	6174.0
43	2484.6	2898.7	3312.8	3726.9	4141.0	4969.2	5797.4	6625.6
44	2662.0	3105.7	3549.3	3993.0	4436.7	5324.0	6211.3	7098.7
45	2847.7	3322.3	3796.9	4271.5	4746.1	5695.3	6644.5	7593.8
46	3041.8	3548.7	4055.7	4562.6	5069.6	6083.5	7097.4	8111.3
47	3244.5	3785.2	4326.0	4866.7	5407.4	6488.9	7570.4	8651.9
48	3456.0	4032.0	4608.0	5184.0	5760.0	6912.0	8064.0	9216.0
49	3676.5	4289.3	4902.0	5514.8	6127.6	7353.1	8578.6	9804.1

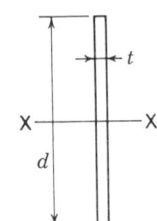

PLATE GIRDERS
Moment of Inertia
of one plate about axis X-X

To obtain the moment of inertia for any thickness of plate not listed below, multiply the value for a plate one inch thick by the desired thickness.

Depth d Inches	Thickness, t, Inches							
	3/8	7/16	1/2	9/16	5/8	3/4	7/8	1
50	3906.3	4557.3	5208.3	5859.4	6510.4	7812.5	9114.6	10417
51	4145.3	4836.2	5527.1	6218.0	6908.9	8290.7	9672.5	11054
52	4394.0	5126.3	5858.7	6591.0	7323.3	8788.0	10253.	11717
53	4652.4	5427.8	6203.2	6978.6	7754.0	9304.8	10856.	12406
54	4920.8	5740.9	6561.0	7381.1	8201.3	9841.5	11482.	13122
55	5199.2	6065.8	6932.3	7798.8	8665.4	10398	12132	13865
56	5488.0	6402.7	7317.3	8232.0	9146.7	10976	12805	14635
57	5787.3	6751.8	7716.4	8680.9	9645.5	11575	13504	15433
58	6097.3	7113.5	8129.7	9145.9	10162.	12195	14227	16259
59	6418.1	7487.8	8557.5	9627.1	10697.	12836	14976	17115
60	6750.0	7875.0	9000.0	10125	11250	13500	15750	18000
61	7093.2	8275.3	9457.5	10640	11822	14186	16551	18915
62	7447.8	8689.0	9930.3	11172	12413	14896	17378	19861
63	7814.0	9116.3	10419.	11721	13023	15628	18232	20837
64	8192.0	9557.3	10923.	12288	13653	16384	19115	21845
65	8582.0	10012	11443	12873	14303	17164	20025	22885
66	8984.3	10482	11979	13476	14974	17969	20963	23958
67	9398.8	10965	12532	14098	15665	18798	21931	25064
68	9826.0	11464	13101	14739	16377	19652	22927	26203
69	10266.	11977	13688	15399	17110	20532	23954	27376
70	10719	12505	14292	16078	17865	21438	25010	28583
72	11664	13608	15552	17496	19440	23328	27216	31104
74	12663	14774	16884	18995	21105	25327	29548	33769
76	13718	16004	18291	20577	22863	27436	32009	36581
78	14830	17301	19773	22245	24716	29660	34603	39546
80	16000	18667	21333	24000	26667	32000	37333	42667
82	17230	20102	22974	25845	28717	34461	40204	45947
84	18522	21609	24696	27783	30870	37044	43218	49392
86	19877	23190	26502	29815	33128	39754	46379	53005
88	21296	24845	28395	31944	35493	42592	49691	56789
90	22781	26578	30375	34172	37969	45563	53156	60750
92	24334	28390	32445	36501	40557	48668	56779	64891
94	25956	30282	34608	38934	43260	51912	60563	69215
96	27648	32256	36864	41472	46080	55296	64512	73728
98	29412	34314	39216	44118	49020	58825	68629	78433
100	31250	36458	41667	46875	52083	62500	72917	83333
102	33163	38690	44217	49744	55271	66326	77380	88434
104	35152	41011	46869	52728	58587	70304	82021	93739
106	37219	43422	49626	55829	62032	74439	86845	99251
108	39366	45927	52488	59049	65610	78732	91854	104976

PLATE GIRDERS
Moment of Inertia
of one plate about axis X-X

To obtain the moment of inertia for any thickness of plate not listed below, multiply the value for a plate one inch thick by the desired thickness.

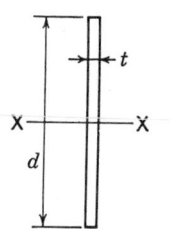

Depth d Inches	3/8	7/16	1/2	9/16	5/8	3/4	7/8	1
110	41594	48526	55458	62391	69323	83188	97052	110917
112	43904	51221	58539	65856	73173	87808	102443	117077
114	46298	54015	61731	69447	77164	92597	108029	123462
116	48778	56908	65037	73167	81297	97556	113815	130075
118	51345	59902	68460	77017	85575	102690	119804	136919
120	54000	63000	72000	81000	90000	108000	126000	144000
122	56745	66203	75660	85118	94575	113491	132406	151321
124	59582	69512	79443	89373	99303	119164	139025	158885
126	62512	72930	83349	93768	104186	125024	145861	166698
128	65536	76459	87381	98304	109227	131072	152917	174763
130	68656	80099	91542	102984	114427	137312	160198	183083
132	71874	83853	95832	107811	119790	143748	167706	191664
134	75191	87723	100254	112786	125318	150381	175445	200509
136	78608	91709	104811	117912	131013	157216	183418	209621
138	82127	95815	109503	123191	136879	164255	191630	219006
140	85750	100042	114333	128625	142917	171500	200083	228667
142	89478	104391	119304	134216	149129	178955	208781	238607
144	93312	108864	124416	139968	155520	186624	217728	248832
146	97254	113463	129672	145881	162090	194508	226927	259345
148	101306	118190	135075	151959	168843	202612	236380	270149
150	105469	123047	140625	158203	175781	210938	246094	281250
152	109744	128035	146325	164616	182907	219488	256069	292651
154	114133	133155	152178	171200	190222	228266	266311	304355
156	118638	138411	158184	177957	197730	237276	276822	316368
158	123260	143803	164346	184890	205433	246519	287606	328693
160	128000	149333	170667	192000	213333	256000	298666	341333
162	132860	155004	177147	199290	221434	265721	310007	354294
164	137842	160815	183789	206763	229737	275684	321631	367579
166	142947	166771	190596	214420	238244	285893	333542	381191
168	148176	172872	197568	222264	246960	296352	345744	395136
170	153531	179120	204708	230297	255885	307062	358240	409417

PLATE GIRDERS
Coefficients C_h for maximum allowable bending stress in hybrid girders

$$F'_b \leq C_h F_b$$

$\dfrac{A_w}{A_f}$	α = Ratio F_y (web) to F_y (flange)						
	0.9	0.8	0.7	0.6	0.5	0.4	0.3
0.3	1.00	1.00	0.99	0.99	0.99	0.98	0.97
0.4	1.00	1.00	0.99	0.99	0.98	0.97	0.96
0.5	1.00	1.00	0.99	0.98	0.98	0.97	0.96
0.6	1.00	0.99	0.99	0.98	0.98	0.96	0.95
0.7	1.00	0.99	0.99	0.98	0.97	0.95	0.94
0.8	1.00	0.99	0.99	0.98	0.97	0.95	0.93
0.9	1.00	0.99	0.98	0.97	0.96	0.94	0.93
1.0	1.00	0.99	0.98	0.97	0.96	0.94	0.92
1.1	1.00	0.99	0.98	0.97	0.96	0.93	0.91
1.2	1.00	0.99	0.98	0.97	0.95	0.93	0.91
1.3	1.00	0.99	0.98	0.96	0.95	0.92	0.90
1.4	1.00	0.99	0.98	0.96	0.95	0.92	0.89
1.5	1.00	0.99	0.98	0.96	0.94	0.91	0.89
1.6	1.00	0.99	0.97	0.96	0.94	0.91	0.88
1.7	1.00	0.99	0.97	0.95	0.94	0.90	0.88
1.8	1.00	0.99	0.97	0.95	0.93	0.90	0.87
1.9	1.00	0.99	0.97	0.95	0.93	0.89	0.86
2.0	1.00	0.99	0.97	0.95	0.93	0.89	0.86
2.2	1.00	0.99	0.97	0.94	0.92	0.88	0.85
2.4	1.00	0.98	0.97	0.94	0.92	0.88	0.84
2.6	1.00	0.98	0.96	0.94	0.91	0.87	0.83
2.8	1.00	0.98	0.96	0.93	0.91	0.86	0.82
3.0	1.00	0.98	0.96	0.93	0.90	0.86	0.81

Coefficient $C_h = \left[\dfrac{12 + (A_w/A_f)(3\alpha - \alpha^3)}{12 + 2\,(A_w/A_f)}\right]$ in Formula(1.10-6).

Note that the lower value using Formulas (1.10-5) and (1.10-6) governs for the flanges of a hybrid girder.

F_b = applicable bending stress for flange material given in Specification Sect. 1.5.1.

$F_y = 36$ ksi

PLATE GIRDERS
Allowable shear stress in webs

Tension field action neglected

$F_y = 36$ ksi

		Aspect Ratios a/h: Stiffener Spacing to Web Depth												
		0.5	0.6	0.7	0.8	0.9	1.0	1.2	1.4	1.6	1.8	2.0	2.5	3.0	over 3
Slenderness Ratios h/t: Web Depth to Web Thickness	60											14.5	14.5	14.5	14.5
	70									14.5	14.5	14.2	13.8	13.6	13.0
	80						14.5	14.1	13.4	13.0	12.6	12.4	12.0	11.9	11.4
	90				14.5	14.3	13.4	12.5	11.9	11.5	11.2	11.0	10.7	10.5	10.1
	100			14.5	13.9	12.8	12.0	11.2	10.7	10.4	10.1	9.9	9.3	9.0	8.3
	110		14.5	13.8	12.6	11.7	10.9	10.2	9.5	8.9	8.4	8.2	7.7	7.5	6.9
	120		14.3	12.7	11.6	10.7	10.0	8.8	8.0	7.5	7.1	6.9	6.5	6.3	5.8
	130	14.5	13.2	11.7	10.7	9.8	8.6	7.5	6.8	6.4	6.0	5.8	5.5	5.3	4.9
	140	14.2	12.2	10.9	9.8	8.4	7.4	6.5	5.9	5.5	5.2	5.0	4.7	4.6	4.2
	150	13.2	11.4	10.1	8.5	7.3	6.5	5.6	5.1	4.8	4.5	4.4	4.1	4.0	3.7
	160	12.4	10.7	9.1	7.5	6.4	5.7	4.9	4.5	4.2	4.0	3.9	3.6		3.2
	170	11.7	10.1	8.0	6.7	5.7	5.0	4.4	4.0	3.7	3.5	3.4			2.9
	180	11.0	9.0	7.2	5.9	5.1	4.5	3.9	3.5	3.3	3.1	3.0			2.6
	200	9.9	7.3	5.8	4.8	4.1	3.6	3.2	2.9	2.7					2.1
	220	8.2	6.1	4.8	4.0	3.4	3.0	2.6	2.4						1.7
	240	6.8	5.1	4.0	3.3	2.9	2.5								1.4
	260	5.8	4.3	3.4	2.9	2.4	2.1								1.2
	280	5.0	3.7	3.0	2.5										
	300	4.4	3.3	2.6											
	320	3.9	2.9												

Girders so proportioned that the computed shear stress is less than that given in the right-hand column do not require intermediate stiffeners.

Notes

COMPOSITE DESIGN
for building construction

NOMENCLATURE

A_c Actual area of effective concrete flange in composite design

A_s Area of steel beam in composite design

A_{sr} Area of reinforcing steel providing composite action at point of negative moment

E Modulus of elasticity of steel (29,000 kips per square inch)

E_c Modulus of elasticity of concrete

F_b Bending stress permitted in the absence of axial force

F_v Allowable shear stress

F_y Specified minimum yield stress of the type of steel being used (kips per square inch). As used in this Specification, "yield stress" denotes either the specified minimum yield point (for those steels that have a yield point) or specified minimum yield strength (for those steels that do not have a yield point).

F_{yr} Yield stress of reinforcing steel providing composite action at point of negative moment

I Moment of inertia

I_{tr} Moment of inertia of transformed composite section

K Theoretical cover plate length factor

L Span length (feet)

M Moment (kip-feet)

M_D Moment produced by dead load (loads applied before concrete has hardened)

M_L Moment produced by live load (loads applied after concrete has hardened)

N_1 Number of shear connectors equal to V_h/q or V'_h/q, as applicable

N_2 Number of shear connectors required where closer spacing is needed adjacent to point of zero moment

R Reaction or concentrated transverse load applied to beam or girder (kips)

S_{eff} Effective section modulus for incomplete composite action

S_j Section modulus of transformed composite cross-section, referred to the top of steel beam

S_s Section modulus of steel beam used in composite design, referred to the bottom flange

S_t Section modulus of transformed composite cross-section, referred to the top of concrete

S_{tr} Section modulus of transformed composite cross-section, referred to the bottom flange

S_{ts} Section modulus of steel beam used in composite design, referred to the top flange

V Statical shear on beam (kips)

V_h Total horizontal shear to be resisted by connectors under full composite action (kips)

V'_h Total horizontal shear to be resisted by connectors in providing partial composite action (kips)

b Effective width of concrete slab; actual width of stiffened and unstiffened compression elements

b_f Flange width of rolled beam or plate girder

f_b Computed bending stress

f_c Concrete working stress

f'_c Specified compression strength of concrete

n Modular ratio; equal to E/E_c

q Allowable horizontal shear to be resisted by a shear connector

t_f Flange thickness

β Ratio S_{tr}/S_s or S_{eff}/S_s

GENERAL NOTES

The AISC Specification contains provisions for designing composite steel-concrete beams as follows:

1. For totally encased unshored steel beams not requiring mechanical anchorage (shear connectors), see Sections 1.11.1 and 1.11.2.1.

2. For both shored and unshored beams with mechanically anchored slabs, design of the steel beam is based on the assumption that composite action resists the total design moment (Section 1.11.2.2). In **shored** construction, flexural stress in the concrete slab due to composite action is determined from the total moment. In **unshored** construction, flexural stress in the concrete slab due to composite action is determined from moment M_L, produced by loads imposed after the concrete has achieved 75% of its required strength. Shored construction may be used to reduce dead load deflection and **must** be used if $S_{tr} > (1.35 + 0.35\, M_L/M_D)\, S_s$.

3. For incomplete composite action, see Section 1.11.2.2.

4. For negative moment zones, see Section 1.11.2.2.

GENERAL CONSIDERATIONS

1. Composite construction is appropriate for any loading. It is most efficient with heavy loading, relatively long spans, and beams spaced as far apart as permissible.

2. For unshored construction, concrete compressive stress will seldom be critical for the beams listed in the Composite Beam Property Tables if a full width slab and $F_y = 36$ ksi steel are used. It is more likely to be critical when a narrow concrete flange or $F_y = 50$ ksi steel is used, and is frequently critical if both $F_y = 50$ ksi steel and a narrow concrete flange are used. Shored construction also increases the concrete stress.

3. Because composite construction usually involves relatively long spans and wide spacing of beams, the Specification rule that governs effective slab width is usually the provision limiting the projection beyond the edge of each beam flange to eight times the slab thickness (see Section 1.11.1).

4. Slab thicknesses of 4 to $5\frac{1}{2}$ inches will be used most often because of fireproofing considerations and because of the wide spacing of beams.

5. Steel and concrete materials of various strengths may be used.

DEFLECTION

A composite beam has much greater stiffness than a non-composite beam of equal depth, loads, and span length. Deflection of composite beams will usually be about $\frac{1}{3}$ to $\frac{1}{2}$ less than deflection of non-composite beams. In practice, shallower beams are used and deflections, particularly of the steel section alone under construction loads, should be checked.

Limiting the depth/span ratio may also prevent many deflection problems. The AISC Commentary suggests a ratio of $F_y/800$ for fully stressed beams. This yields depth/span ratios as follows:

$$1/22 \text{ for } F_y = 36 \text{ ksi}$$

$$1/16 \text{ for } F_y = 50 \text{ ksi}$$

These ratios are offered as simple guidelines; however, the intent of the Specification is that a rational calculation of deflections should be made. Such calculations often reveal that smaller depth/span ratios are satisfactory. The depth used in the above ratios is the distance from the top of concrete to the bottom of the steel section.

If it is desired to minimize the transient vibration due to pedestrian traffic when composite beams support large open floor areas free of partitions or other damping sources, the depth/span ratio of the **steel beam** should be not less than 1/20 for any grade of steel.

USE OF COVER PLATES

Bottom cover plates are an effective means of increasing the strength or reducing the depth of composite beams when deflections are not critical, but they should be used with overall economy in mind. The cost of attaching a $\frac{3}{4}$-in. thick plate is about the same as for a $\frac{1}{4}$-in. plate.

Two general guidelines for choosing between coverplated and non-coverplated sections of similar capacity are as follows:

If the coverplated section would save less than 7 lbs/ft., do not use cover plates.

If the coverplated section would save more than 12 lbs/ft., use cover plates.

Between these limits minor savings may result from either coverplated or non-coverplated sections. Note that these guidelines may vary from region to region, and should be checked locally.

OTHER CONSIDERATIONS

The AISC Specification provisions for the design of composite beams are based on ultimate load considerations, even though they are presented in terms of working stresses. Because of this, for unshored construction, actual stresses in the tension flange of the steel beam under working load are higher than calculated stresses. Formula (1.11-2) limits the tension flange stress to a value well below yield stress. This same section also provides requirements for limiting the steel beam compression flange stress under construction loading.

Adequate lateral support for the compression flange of the steel section will be provided by the concrete slab after hardening. During construction, however, lateral support must be provided or working stresses must be reduced in accordance with Section 1.5.1.4 of the Specification. Steel deck with adequate attachment to the compression flange, or properly constructed concrete forms, will usually provide the necessary lateral support for the type of construction shown in the sketches accompanying the composite beam property tables. For construction using fully encased beams, particular attention should be given to lateral support during construction.

The design of the concrete slab should conform to the ACI Building Code.

DESIGN AIDS FOR COMPOSITE CONSTRUCTION

Composite beam tables have been prepared for common conditions encountered in building design and are based on the following:

1. 3.0 ksi concrete ($n = 9$).
2. Two effective flange widths: $16t + b_f$ and $6t + b_f$, where t is the slab thickness and b_f is the compression flange width of the steel section.
3. Concrete slab thicknesses of 4, $4\frac{1}{2}$, 5 and $5\frac{1}{2}$ inches.
4. Selected steel beams ranging from 8 to 36 inches in depth. (These will generally be satisfactory for span ranges from 20 to 60 feet for girders, and longer spans for filler beams.)

For buildings, it will be found that the above conditions will be fully met in most cases. The tabulated effective flange width should be checked against flange width limits based on the given span and beam spacing, in accordance with the provisions of Section 1.11.1.

Explanation of Tables

The tables apply to composite beams having a concrete slab placed directly on a steel beam, where the two elements are connected by stud or channel shear connectors.

Data is included for both coverplated sections and sections without cover plates. This data is applicable to all grades of steel included in Section 1.4 of the AISC Specification, except that the tabulated maximum allowable web shear values, V, for coverplated beams apply only to $F_y = 36$ ksi steel.

Selection Tables

Separate composite beam selection tables are given for slab thicknesses of 4, $4\frac{1}{2}$, 5 and $5\frac{1}{2}$ inches, for 24 beams with and without cover plates, for full slab width. Beams with partial width slabs are not tabulated.

After the designer has chosen a trial section from the Selection Tables, the necessary design properties may be obtained from the Properties Tables to complete the design.

The Properties Tables also serve as selection tables for 91 beams with no cover plate, since the tabulated beam properties are listed in descending order of transformed section modulus (S_{tr}).

Properties Tables

Two sets of properties tables are provided. The first lists beams with no cover plates and the second lists beams with cover plates.

Values of effective concrete slab width, b, are tabulated for each section for use in the shear connector calculations.

Values of S_{tr}/S_t are tabulated for each section and may be used with footnote 2 of the tables to determine if concrete stress governs.

Values of S_{tr}/S_t at balanced design, below which allowable concrete stress will not be exceeded for shored construction, are listed in footnote 5 of the tables for six strengths of steel and three strengths of concrete.

Concrete stress is much more likely to control in sections with heavy cover plates, high strength steel beams or partial width slabs, but should be checked in all cases.

Values of I_{tr} and y_b are given primarily to assist the designer who may wish to check other tabular data or calculate the transformed section modulus at the top of the steel beam (S_j).

Properties Tables for Beams with Cover Plates

Tables for beams with cover plates also list average weight per foot, W_s (maximum weight per foot), K, $12\,Q/I$, and properties of the steel section alone.

The constant K is a coefficient for determining the theoretical length of the cover plate. It is exact for simply supported beams with uniformly distributed loads. The theoretical cut-off point for any type of loading occurs where the moment is equal to the maximum moment multiplied by the ratio of S_{tr} (non-coverplated) to S_{tr} (coverplated). See Example 6.

The actual required length of cover plate is the theoretical length of cover plate plus two times the extension length required by the provisions of Section 1.10.4 of the AISC Specification. For a simple span with uniformly distributed loading, $L_{cp} = KL$, where L_{cp} = theoretical length of cover plate in feet and L = span in feet.

The quantity $12Q/I$ is tabulated for use in the formula $F = (12Q/I)M$, where F = total force in kips to be developed by the cover plate end welds, and M = moment at theoretical cut-off point, in kip-ft. For development of the ends of partial length cover plates, the designer's attention is called to the provisions of Section 1.10.4 and Example 3.

The quantity $12Q/I$ may also be multiplied by $V/12$ to determine the horizontal shear in kips per linear inch of beam to be developed by intermediate welds, where V is the vertical shear in kips at the theoretical cut-off point.

Properties of the steel section alone are included for computing construction load stresses and deflections. They are also useful in interpolating for properties of a trial section when the slab width or concrete strength does not conform to the limits of the tables. For convenience they are repeated for all slab thicknesses.

Properties tables for beams with cover plates are so arranged that interpolation will usually be necessary to find the most economical coverplated section. Interpolation in $\frac{1}{8}$-in. increments of plate thickness will yield practical beam sections. Errors resulting from such interpolation or use of equivalent area cover plates are usually negligible.

Properties Tables for Partial Slab Width

Tables for partial slab widths $(b = 6t + b_f)$ are included for the selection of composite beams when the slab is present on only one side (spandrel beams) and to aid in interpolation for narrow flange composite beams (b less than in full slab tables).

Properties from these tables may also be used to estimate long term creep deflections for full slab composite beams (see discussion on Deflection Computations).

General Comments

Interpolation between the tabulated slab widths and thicknesses is considered proper. Errors resulting from such interpolation are usually negligible.

By comparing the tabulated I values for flange width $b = 16t + b_f$ and flange width $b = 6t + b_f$, it may be seen that the effect of slight changes of concrete area or b/n ratios is insignificant. Reducing the concrete area 60% results in a reduction of the moment of inertia of only 10 to 15%. For this reason, the tables may be used as a guide for determining trial sections for other concrete strengths, slab thicknesses, and effective widths. More comprehensive tables for a large range of b/n values are available from other sources.

Shear connectors must have a 1-in. minimum cover. Unless located directly over the beam web, stud diameters must not be more than 2.5 times the flange thickness (Section 1.11.4).

When shear connectors are used in combination with metal deck, the designer should consult and follow the recommendations of the manufacturer whose deck is being considered. In such cases research test data should be available to substantiate true composite action and verify design procedures. Here, as with "stay-in-place" metal forms, a determination of the "efficiency" of the concrete slab must be made and the connector welding used must provide a proper shear value per connector.

For ready reference, a list of frequently used formulas for composite design follows:

$$n = \frac{E}{E_c} = \text{modular ratio}$$

$$S_{tr} = \frac{12M}{0.66F_y}$$

$$f_b \text{ (steel)} = \frac{12M}{S_{tr}} \text{ (at bottom)}$$

$$= \frac{12M}{S_j} \text{ (at top)}$$

$$f_b \text{ (concrete)} = \frac{12M}{nS_t} \text{ (at top of slab)}$$

Max. S_{tr} (for unshored construction) $=$

$$\left(1.35 + 0.35 \frac{M_L}{M_D}\right)S_s \qquad \text{Formula (1.11-2)}$$

$$V_h = \frac{0.85 f'_c A_c}{2} \text{ (for concrete)} \qquad \text{Formula (1.11-3)}$$

$$= \frac{A_s F_y}{2} \text{ (for steel)} \qquad \text{Formula (1.11-4)}$$

$$S_{eff} = S_s + \frac{V'_h}{V_h}(S_{tr} - S_s) \qquad \text{Formula (1.11-1)}$$

$$V'_h = q \times \text{number of connectors furnished}$$

$N_1 = \dfrac{V_h}{q}$; also see Stud Coefficient tables in discussion of Shear Connector Computations.

$$N_2 = \dfrac{N_1 \times \left[\dfrac{M\beta}{M_{max}} - 1\right]}{\beta - 1}$$ Formula (1.11-6)

$F = \dfrac{12QM}{I}$ = total horizontal shear force in kips to be developed by welds at end of cover plate, where M = moment at cut-off point in kip-ft.

$\dfrac{12Q}{I} \times \dfrac{V}{12}$ = horizontal shear force, in kips per linear inch of beam, to be developed by intermediate cover plate welds, where V is the vertical shear force at cut-off, in kips.

DEFLECTION COMPUTATIONS

Deflections for simple span uniformly loaded beams at actual loads may be quickly calculated using the formula:

$$\Delta = \dfrac{ML^2}{160 S y}$$

where

Δ = deflection, in.
M = moment, kip-ft.
S = section modulus, in.^{3}
y = distance from bottom of steel section to neutral axis, in.
L = span length, ft.

For unshored beams:

Dead load deflection: $M = M_D$, $S = S_s$, and $y = y_{bs}$
Live load deflection (short term): $M = M_L$, $S = S_{tr}$, and $y = y_b$

For shored beams:

Dead load deflection: $M = M_D$, $S = S_{tr}$, and $y = y_b$
Live load deflection (short term): $M = M_L$, $S = S_{tr}$, and $y = y_b$

If it is desired to consider long term creep deflection, S_{tr} and y_b should be based on an n value double that shown in the tables. Using S_{tr} and y_b from the partial slab tables for beams with a full slab will give an estimate of this deflection.

END REACTIONS

If end reactions are not shown on the engineering drawings, they may be calculated using the formula:

$$R = \dfrac{0.33 S_{tr} F_b}{L}$$

This formula is accurate for uniformly loaded, fully stressed, simple span beams and is conservative for most other types of loading.

AMERICAN INSTITUTE OF STEEL CONSTRUCTION

SHEAR CONNECTOR COMPUTATIONS

The quantity V_h is the total horizontal shear force to be resisted by shear connectors between the points of maximum and zero moment and is computed using Formula (1.11-3) or (1.11-4) in the AISC Specification. Using Table 1.11.4 in the Specification,* the number of shear connectors required for **full** composite action is computed as follows:

$$N_1 = \frac{V_h}{q}$$

where N_1 is the number of shear connectors required between point of maximum moment and point of zero moment, q is the allowable shear load for one connector, in kips (from Table 1.11.4, or as determined by test).

The required number of shear connectors thus obtained may be spaced uniformly between the points of maximum and zero moment, except that N_2, the number of shear connectors required between a concentrated load in the area of positive bending and the nearest point of zero moment, must be not less than determined by Formula (1.11-6). The balance of the shear connectors $(N_1 - N_2)$ may be spaced uniformly between the load point and the point of maximum moment (see Example 4).

Formula (1.11-6) does not apply in negative moment areas of continuous beams where shear connectors are spaced uniformly. In this area V_h is determined from Formula (1.11-5).

The table of Stud Coefficients provided below simplifies the calculation of the value N_1. Coefficients are given for several strengths of concrete and steel combined with q values for **stud** shear connectors. To utilize the "Stud Coefficient" method, find N_1 as the lesser of the values N_c or N_s, where

N_c = number of studs required between point of maximum moment and point of zero moment based on the **concrete** section
   = A_c times the stud coefficient

N_s = number of studs required between point of maximum moment and point of zero moment based on the **steel** section
   = W_s times the stud coefficient

A_c = effective concrete flange area in square inches $(b \times t)$

W_s = weight per foot of the steel section in pounds. (For coverplated beams this is the weight per foot at the center of the beam including the plate, **not the average weight.**)

STUD COEFFICIENTS

Stud size (in.)	For computing N_s						For computing N_c		
	$F_y = 36$ ksi			$F_y = 50$ ksi			All values of F_y		
	f'_c (ksi)			f'_c (ksi)			f'_c (ksi)		
	3.0	3.5	4.0	3.0	3.5	4.0	3.0	3.5	4.0
½ × 2	1.038	0.963	0.897	1.442	1.337	1.246	0.250	0.270	0.288
⅝ × 2½	0.662	0.616	0.575	0.919	0.855	0.799	0.160	0.173	0.185
¾ × 3	0.461	0.424	0.398	0.639	0.588	0.553	0.111	0.119	0.128
⅞ × 3½	0.339	0.315	0.294	0.471	0.438	0.408	0.082	0.089	0.094

* Also see Sect. 1.11 of Supplement Nos. 1 and 2 to the 1969 AISC Specification for Table 1.11.4A

AMERICAN INSTITUTE OF STEEL CONSTRUCTION

COMPOSITE DESIGN
for building construction

EXAMPLES

EXAMPLE 1

Design a non-coverplated composite interior floor beam of an office building. There is no depth restriction. Do not use temporary shores. Limit dead load deflection to $1\frac{1}{2}$ in. and live load deflection to $L/360$.

Given: Span length, L = 36 ft. Live load = 100 lbs/ft.²
Beam spacing, s = 8 ft. Partition load = 20 lbs/ft.²
Slab thickness, t = 4 in. Ceiling load = 8 lbs/ft.²
$\left.\begin{array}{l} 3.0 \text{ ksi concrete} \\ F_y = 36 \text{ ksi steel} \end{array}\right\} n = 9$

Solution:

AISC
Specification
Reference

(a) *Bending moments:*
  1. Construction loads:
     4″ Slab = .048 kips/ft.²
     Steel (assumed) = .007
     ————
     .055 kips/ft.²

     M_D = 71.3 kip-ft.

  2. Loads applied after concrete has hardened:
     Live load = .100 kips/ft.²
     Partition load = .020
     Ceiling load = .008
     ————
     .128 kips/ft.²

     M_L = 165.9 kip-ft. $\dfrac{M_L}{M_D}$ = 2.33

  3. Maximum moment:
     $M_{max} = M_D + M_L$
     = 71.3 + 165.9 = 237.2 kip-ft.

  4. Maximum shear:
     $V = 8(.055 + .128)\dfrac{36}{2} = 26.4$ kips

(b) *Check effective width of concrete slab:*
  $b = \frac{1}{4}L = \frac{1}{4} \times 36 \times 12$ = 108 in.
  $b = s = 8 \times 12$ = 96 in. **1.11.1**
  $b = 16t + b_f = 16 \times 4 + 6.5 = 70.5$ in. (governs)

(c) *Required section moduli:*
  For M_{D+L}:
  $S_{tr} = \dfrac{12 \text{ in.} \times 237.2 \text{ kip-ft.}}{24} = 118.6$ in.³ **1.5.1.4.1**

  For M_D: $S_s = \dfrac{12 \text{ in.} \times 71.3 \text{ kip-ft.}}{24} = 35.6$ in.³

AMERICAN INSTITUTE OF STEEL CONSTRUCTION

(*d*) *Select section and determine properties:*
Enter properties table for 4-in. Slab with
$S_{tr} = 118.6$ in.[3]

Select W21 $\times$ 44 ($F_y = 36$ ksi)

$S_{tr} = 120.0 \qquad S_s = 81.6 \qquad \dfrac{S_{tr}}{S_t} = .29 \qquad y_b = 19.04$

$b = 70.5 \qquad W_s = 44 \qquad S_t = 406$

(*e*) *Check stresses:*

Concrete (unshored): $\dfrac{S_{tr}}{S_t} = .29 < .67$

Concrete stress **o.k.**

	Furnished		Required	
Steel:	Total load: 120	>	118.6	f_b **o.k.**
	Dead load: 81.6	>	35.6	f_b **o.k.**
	Web shear: 104	>	26.4	f_v **o.k.**

1.5.1.2

(*f*) *Check deflection:*

1. $\Delta_{DL} = \dfrac{M_D L^2}{160 S_s y_{bs}} = \dfrac{71 \times 36^2}{160 \times 81.6 \times 10.33}$
    $= .68 < 1\frac{1}{2}$ **o.k.**

2. $\Delta_{LL} = \dfrac{M_L L^2}{160 \, S_{tr} y_b} = \dfrac{166 \times 36^2}{160 \times 120 \times 19.04}$
    $= .59 < \dfrac{L}{360}$ **o.k.**

(Long term creep deflection not considered
significant)

(*g*) *Check Formula (1.11-2):*
$S_{tr} = [1.35 + (0.35 \times 2.33)] \times 81.6$
$= 176.7 > 120.0$ in.[3] **o.k.**

1.11.2.2

(*h*) *Shear connectors (for full composite action):*
Use: $\frac{3}{4}''\phi \times 3''$ studs.
Max. stud diameter $= 2.5 \times t_f = 2.5 \times .451$
$= 1.13 > .75$ **o.k.**

1.11.4

Using "Stud Coefficient" method (see General Notes):
$N_s = 44 \times .461 = 20.3$ (governs)
$N_c = 4 \times 70.5 \times .111 = 31.3$

Use: 42 - $\frac{3}{4}''\phi \times 3''$ studs equally spaced.
(21 each side of the point of maximum moment.)

1.11.4

EXAMPLE 2

Design the beam in Example 1 using $F_y = 50$ ksi steel.

Solution:

(a) *Required section moduli:*

For M_{D+L}: $\quad S_{tr} = \dfrac{12 \text{ in.} \times 237.2 \text{ kip-ft.}}{33.0 \text{ ksi}} = 86.2 \text{ in.}^3$

For M_D: $\quad S_s = \dfrac{12 \text{ in.} \times 71.3 \text{ kip-ft.}}{33.0 \text{ ksi}} = 25.9 \text{ in.}^3$

1.5.1.4.1

(b) *Select section and determine properties:*
Enter properties table for 4-in. slab with
$S_{tr} = 86.2 \text{ in.}^3$

Select W18 $\times$ 35 ($F_y = 50$ ksi)

$S_{tr} = 86.2 \qquad S_s = 57.9 \qquad \dfrac{S_{tr}}{S_t} = .28 \qquad y_b = 17.01$

$b = 70.0 \qquad W_s = 35 \qquad S_t = 312$

(c) *Check stresses:*

Concrete (unshored): $\dfrac{S_{tr}}{S_t} = .28 < .49$

Concrete stress **o.k.**

		Furnished		Required	
Steel:	Total load:	86.2	=	86.2	f_b **o.k.**
	Dead load:	57.9	>	25.9	f_b **o.k.**
	Web shear:	106	>	26.4	f_v **o.k.**

(d) *Check deflection:*

1. $\Delta_{DL} = \dfrac{M_D L^2}{160 S_s y_{bs}} = \dfrac{71 \times 36^2}{160 \times 57.9 \times 8.86}$
$= 1.12 < 1\frac{1}{2}$ **o.k.**

2. $\Delta_{LL} = \dfrac{M_L L^2}{160 S_{tr} y_b} = \dfrac{166 \times 36^2}{160 \times 86.2 \times 17.01}$
$= .92 < \dfrac{L}{360}$ **o.k.**

(e) *Check Formula (1.11-2):*
$S_{tr} = [1.35 + (0.35 \times 2.33)] \times 57.9$
$= 125.4 > 86.2 \text{ in.}^3$ **o.k.**

1.11.2.2

(f) *Shear connectors (for full composite action):*
Use: $\frac{3}{4}"\phi \times 3"$ **studs.**
Max. stud diameter: $\frac{3}{4}"\phi$ **o.k. by inspection**

1.11.4

Using "Stud Coefficient" method (see General Notes):
$N_s = 35 \times .640 \qquad = 22.4$ (governs)
$N_c = 4 \times 70.0 \times .111 = 31.0$

Use: 46 - $\frac{3}{4}"\phi \times 3"$ studs equally spaced.
(23 each side of the point of maximum moment.)

1.11.4

AMERICAN INSTITUTE OF STEEL CONSTRUCTION

EXAMPLE 3

Design the beam in Example 1 using a coverplated beam and $F_y = 36$ ksi steel.

Solution:

(a) *Required section moduli:*
  For M_{D+L}: $S_{tr} = 118.6$ in.³
  For M_D: S_s or $S_{ts} = 35.6$ in.³   **1.5.1.4.1**

(b) *Select section and determine properties:*
  1. Enter selection table for coverplated beams and 4-in. slab with $S_{tr} = 118.6$.
    Select W16 $\times$ 26 with $\frac{7}{8} \times 4\frac{1}{2}''$ cover plate by interpolation.
      Avg. wt. $= 35.7$ lbs/ft.

  2. From properties tables, interpolate for section properties:

$S_{tr} = 124$ $\dfrac{S_{tr}}{S_t} = .36$ $y_b = 15.08$ $K = .71$

$S_s = 80.8$ $S_{ts} = 44.9$

$W_s = 39.4$ $b = 69.5$

$y_{bs} = 5.94$ $\dfrac{12Q}{I} = 0.36$

(c) *Check stresses:*

Concrete (unshored): $\dfrac{S_{tr}}{S_t} = .36 < .67$

     Concrete stress **o.k.**

		Furnished		Required		
Steel:	Total load:	124	>	118.6	f_b **o.k.**	
	Dead load:	44.9	>	35.6	f_b **o.k.**	
	Web shear:	57	>	26.4	f_v **o.k.**	**1.5.1.2**

(d) *Check deflections:*

  1. $\Delta_{DL} = \dfrac{M_D L^2}{160\, S_s y_{bs}} = \dfrac{71 \times 36^2}{160 \times 80.8 \times 5.94}$
      $= 1.20 < 1\frac{1}{2}$ **o.k.**

  2. $\Delta_{LL} = \dfrac{M_L L^2}{160\, S_{tr} y_b} = \dfrac{166 \times 36^2}{160 \times 124 \times 15.08}$
      $= 0.72 < \dfrac{L}{360}$ **o.k.**

(e) *Check Formula (1.11-2):*
  $S_{tr} = [1.35 + (0.35 \times 2.33)] \times 80.8$ **1.11.2.2**
    $= 175.0 > 120.0$ in.³ **o.k.**

(f) *Shear connectors (for full composite action):*
  Use: $\frac{3}{4}''\phi \times 3''$ **studs**
    Max. stud diameter $= 2.5 \times t_f$
        $= 2.5 \times 0.345 = 0.86''$ **1.11.4**

Using "Stud Coefficient" method (see General Notes):

$N_s = 39.4 \times .461 \quad = 18.2$ (governs)
$N_c = 4 \times 69.5 \times .111 = 30.9$

Use: 38 - $\frac{3}{4}''\phi \times 3''$ studs equally spaced.   **1.11.4**
(19 each side of point of maximum moment.)

(g) *Cover plate length and development:*
1. Theoretical length $= KL = .71 \times 36 = 25.6$ ft.
   Distance from support to theoretical cut-off
   $$= \frac{36 - 25.6}{2} = 5.20 \text{ ft.}$$
   Moment at theoretical cut-off point $=$
   $$\frac{.183 \times 8 \times 5.20}{2} (36 - 5.20) = 117.4 \text{ kip-ft.}$$
   Force to be developed by end welds $=$
   $M(12Q/I) = 117.4 \times .36 = 42.3$ kips

2. Cover plate termination welds: **Table**
   1.17.5
   Use: $\frac{5}{16}''$ **fillet weld (min. size).**

   Capacity of $\frac{5}{16}''$ fillet (E70XX electrode)   **Table**
   $= 4.64$ kips/in.   **1.5.3**
   Weld length required by force $= \dfrac{42.3}{4.64}$ **1.10.4**
              $= 9.1$ or $5''$ each side
   Weld length required by Specification   **1.10.4**
        $= 2 \times 4\frac{1}{2}'' = 9''$ **Case 3**

   Use: **9" each side**

3. Cover plate intermediate welds:
   Use: $\frac{5}{16} \times 1\frac{1}{2}$ in. **(min. size and**   **1.17.8**
   length)
   Vertical shear (V) at cut-off
        $= 8 \times .183 (18 - 5.22) = 18.71$ kips

   Horizontal unit shear $=$

   $$\frac{V}{12} \times \frac{12Q}{I} = \frac{18.71}{12} \times .36 = .56 \text{ kips/in.}$$

   Required spacing $= \dfrac{4.64 \times 2 \times 1.5}{.56} = 24.9$ in.
   Max. spacing allowed $= 24 \, t_f$ **1.18.3.1**
        $= 24 \times .345 = 8.28$ in. (governs)

   Use: **8" spacing both sides of plate**

AMERICAN INSTITUTE OF STEEL CONSTRUCTION

4. **Use: Bottom cover plate $\frac{7}{8}'' \times 4\frac{1}{2}'' \times 27' \text{-} 0''$ welded and placed as shown below.**

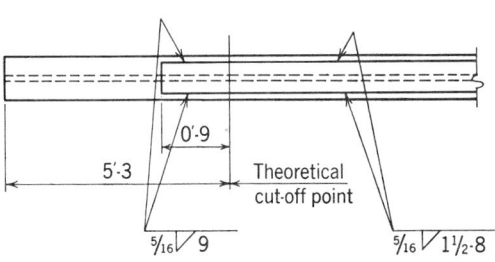

5'-3 | 0'-9 | Theoretical cut-off point

$\frac{5}{16} \diagdown 9$ $\frac{5}{16} \diagdown 1\frac{1}{2}\text{-}8$

SUMMARY (EXAMPLES 1, 2, AND 3)

Examples 1, 2, and 3 offer solutions satisfying the same design conditions. These, with two additional solutions, are summarized below:

Section	Total depth (in.)	Δ_{LL} (in.)	Δ_{DL} (in.)	Steel wt. (avg.) (lbs./ft.)	No. studs
W21×44 ($F_y = 36$ ksi)	25	0.59	0.68	44	42
W18×35 ($F_y = 50$ ksi)	22	0.92	1.12	35	46
W16×26 ($F_y = 36$ ksi) with PL $\frac{7}{8} \times 4\frac{1}{2}$	20½	0.72	1.20	36	38
W16×58 ($F_y = 36$ ksi)	20	0.72	0.77	58	36
W16×40 ($F_y = 50$ ksi)	20	0.95	1.12	40	40

If transient vibrations due to pedestrian traffic are considered objectionable, the W21 ×44 would be preferred (depth/span ratio $= 1/20.9$).

EXAMPLE 4 (SHEAR CONNECTOR SPACING FOR CONCENTRATED LOADS)

Design shear connectors for the composite beam shown below.

Given: Slab thickness, $t = 4$ in.
$F_y = 36$ ksi
$f'_c = 3.0$ ksi
$n = 10$

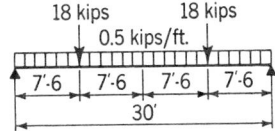

18 kips   18 kips
0.5 kips/ft.
7'-6 | 7'-6 | 7'-6 | 7'-6
30'

Solution:

(a) *Calculate moments and design the beam and shear connectors as in previous examples:*

M_{max} (at mid-span) $= 191$ kip-ft.
M (at concentrated load point) $= 177$ kip-ft.
Beam $=$ W18 ×40

$S_{tr} = 99.4;$ $S_s = 68.4;$ $\beta = \dfrac{S_{tr}}{S_s} = 1.45$

1.11.4

$N_1 = 27$ - $\frac{5}{8}''\phi \times 2\frac{1}{2}''$ studs required between the maximum and zero moment points

(b)   *Solve for N_2 (number of studs required between concentrated load and zero moment point):*

$$N_2 = \frac{N_1\left[\dfrac{M\beta}{M_{max}} - 1\right]}{\beta - 1} = \frac{27\left[\dfrac{177 \times 1.45}{191} - 1\right]}{1.45 - 1}$$
$$= 21\text{-}\tfrac{5}{8}''\phi \times 2\tfrac{1}{2}'' \text{ studs}$$

1.11.4
Formula
(1.11-6)

The stud spacing must be adjusted to place 21 studs between the concentrated load and the end of the beam (zero moment point).   The balance ($N_1 - N_2 = 6$ studs) are placed between the concentrated load and the beam center line (maximum moment point), as shown below.

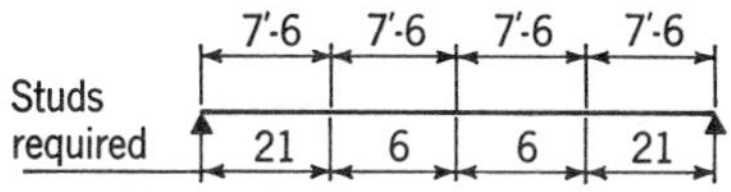

Studs required	7'-6	7'-6	7'-6	7'-6
	21	6	6	21

If the term $M\beta/M_{max}$ is less than unity, or if calculation of N_2 results in fewer shear connectors required between the concentrated load and the zero moment point than would be required by spacing N_1 uniformly between the maximum and zero moment points, then Formula (1.11-6) does not apply.

EXAMPLE 5 (INCOMPLETE COMPOSITE ACTION)

Reducing the number of shear connectors by 10 to 30% will usually reduce S_{tr} by only 3 to 10%.   Occasionally a beam selected by the designer will have a section modulus (S_{tr}) greater than required by loading conditions.   Additional economy may be achieved in this case by utilizing the incomplete composite action provisions to reduce the number of shear connectors.

Determine the minimum number of shear connectors required by AISC Specification Section 1.11.2.2, paragraph 3, for the following conditions:

Given: Uniformly loaded simple span beam.
Slab thickness, $t = 4$ in.
$F_y = 36$ ksi $f'_c = 3.0$ ksi
$n = 9$ S_{tr} (required) = 114

AISC
Specification
Reference

Solution:

(a)   *Select a composite beam and determine properties
as in Example 1:*
Select W18 ×50:
$A_s = 14.7$; $S_{tr} = 125$; $S_s = 89.1$

(b)   *Solve for V_h:*

$$V_h = \frac{14.7 \times 36}{2} = 265$$

1.11.4
Formula
(1.11-4)

(c) *Solve for required V_h':*
Rearranging Formula (1.11.1):

$$V'_h = \frac{(S_{eff} - S_s)}{(S_{tr} - S_s)} V_h$$

$$= \frac{(114 - 89.1)}{(125 - 89.1)} \ 265 = 184$$

(d) *Solve for N_1 using V'_h and $\frac{3}{4}''\phi \times 3''$ studs:*

$$N_1 = \frac{184}{11.5} = 16 \text{ studs or 32 studs per beam}$$

(e) *Solve for N_1 using V_h and $\frac{3}{4}''\phi \times 3''$ studs:*

$$N_1 = \frac{265}{11.5} = 23 \text{ studs or 46 studs per beam}$$

Use: 32 - $\frac{3}{4}''\phi \times 3''$ studs per beam

Note that incomplete composite action results in a saving of 14 studs per beam and meets all design requirements.

EXAMPLE 6 (COVER PLATE LENGTH)

Example 3 illustrates the determination of cover plate length for a simple span uniformly loaded beam, using tabular data.

The following example illustrates the calculation of cover plate length for any type of loading. The moment capacity of the beam **without** cover plate must be adequate for moments in the region from the end of the beam to the theoretical cut-off point. The moment capacity of the beam **with** cover plate must be adequate for moments required in the region between cut-off points.

Given: Span length, L = 30 ft. Slab thickness, t = 4 in.
Load P_1 = 18 kips F_y = 36 ksi
Load P_2 = 30 kips f'_c = 3.0 ksi
n = 9

(a) *Calculate moments and reactions:*

$$R_1 = \frac{18 \times 20}{30} + \frac{30 \times 10}{30} = 22 \text{ kips}$$

$$R_2 = \frac{18 \times 10}{30} + \frac{30 \times 20}{30} = 26 \text{ kips}$$

M (at load P_1) = 220 kip-ft.

M (at load P_2) = 260 kip-ft. (maximum)

$$S_{tr} \text{ (required)} = \frac{260 \times 12}{24} = 130$$

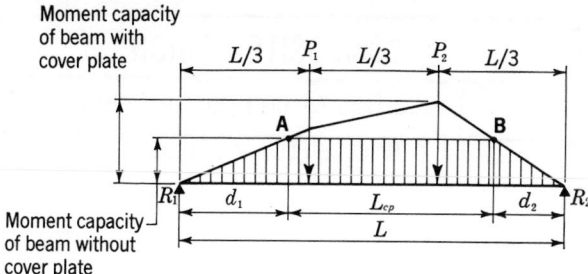

MOMENT DIAGRAM

(b) *Select a composite section from the properties tables:*
W16 ×26 with a 1″ × 4½″ cover plate:
$S_{tr} = 133 > 130$
Moment capacity of beam without cover plate:
$$M_A = M_B = S_{tr} \times \frac{F_b}{12} = 59.5 \times \frac{24}{12} = 119 \text{ kip-ft.}$$

(c) *Calculate the theoretical cut-off points:*
$$d_1 = \frac{M_A}{R_1} = \frac{119}{22} = 5.41 \text{ ft.}$$
$$d_2 = \frac{M_B}{R_2} = \frac{119}{26} = 4.58 \text{ ft.}$$

(d) *Determine the theoretical cover plate length:*
$L_{cp} = L - d_1 - d_2 = 30 - 5.41 - 4.58$
$\qquad\qquad = 20.01 \text{ ft.}$

Use: $L_{cp} = 20' \text{ - } 0''$

(e) *Determine the actual coverplate length:*
The actual required length of cover $= L_{cp}$ **plus** two times the extension length required by Specification Section 1.10.4. The calculations are similar to those in step *g* of Example 3.

4″ Slab

COMPOSITE DESIGN
Properties of composite beams
No Cover Plate—4 Inch Slab

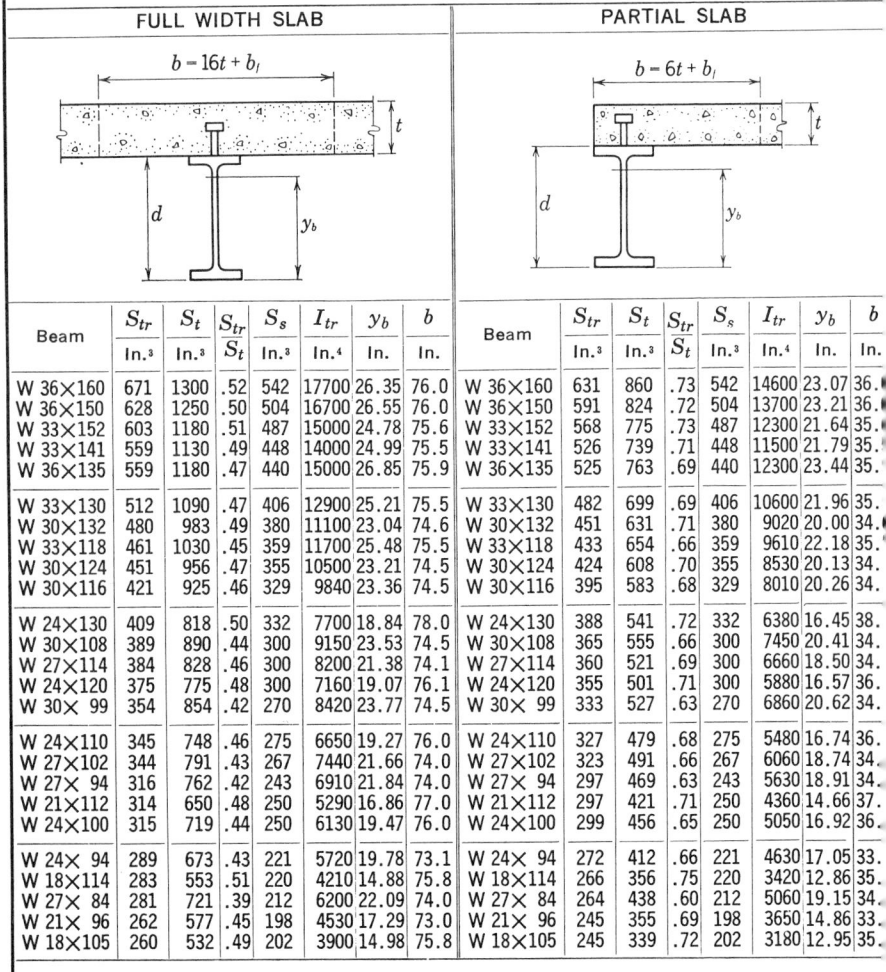

	FULL WIDTH SLAB								PARTIAL SLAB						
Beam	S_{tr}	S_t	$\frac{S_{tr}}{S_t}$	S_s	I_{tr}	y_b	b	Beam	S_{tr}	S_t	$\frac{S_{tr}}{S_t}$	S_s	I_{tr}	y_b	b
	In.³	In.³		In.³	In.⁴	In.	In.		In.³	In.³		In.³	In.⁴	In.	In.
W 36×160	671	1300	.52	542	17700	26.35	76.0	W 36×160	631	860	.73	542	14600	23.07	36.
W 36×150	628	1250	.50	504	16700	26.55	76.0	W 36×150	591	824	.72	504	13700	23.21	36.
W 33×152	603	1180	.51	487	15000	24.78	75.6	W 33×152	568	775	.73	487	12300	21.64	35.
W 33×141	559	1130	.49	448	14000	24.99	75.5	W 33×141	526	739	.71	448	11500	21.79	35.
W 36×135	559	1180	.47	440	15000	26.85	75.9	W 36×135	525	763	.69	440	12300	23.44	35.
W 33×130	512	1090	.47	406	12900	25.21	75.5	W 33×130	482	699	.69	406	10600	21.96	35.
W 30×132	480	983	.49	380	11100	23.04	74.6	W 30×132	451	631	.71	380	9020	20.00	34.
W 33×118	461	1030	.45	359	11700	25.48	75.5	W 33×118	433	654	.66	359	9610	22.18	35.
W 30×124	451	956	.47	355	10500	23.21	74.5	W 30×124	424	608	.70	355	8530	20.13	34.
W 30×116	421	925	.46	329	9840	23.36	74.5	W 30×116	395	583	.68	329	8010	20.26	34.
W 24×130	409	818	.50	332	7700	18.84	78.0	W 24×130	388	541	.72	332	6380	16.45	38.
W 30×108	389	890	.44	300	9150	23.53	74.5	W 30×108	365	555	.66	300	7450	20.41	34.
W 27×114	384	828	.46	300	8200	21.38	74.1	W 27×114	360	521	.69	300	6660	18.50	34.
W 24×120	375	775	.48	300	7160	19.07	76.1	W 24×120	355	501	.71	300	5880	16.57	36.
W 30× 99	354	854	.42	270	8420	23.77	74.5	W 30× 99	333	527	.63	270	6860	20.62	34.
W 24×110	345	748	.46	275	6650	19.27	76.0	W 24×110	327	479	.68	275	5480	16.74	36.
W 27×102	344	791	.43	267	7440	21.66	74.0	W 27×102	323	491	.66	267	6060	18.74	34.
W 27× 94	316	762	.42	243	6910	21.84	74.0	W 27× 94	297	469	.63	243	5630	18.91	34.
W 21×112	314	650	.48	250	5290	16.86	77.0	W 21×112	297	421	.71	250	4360	14.66	37.
W 24×100	315	719	.44	250	6130	19.47	76.0	W 24×100	299	456	.65	250	5050	16.92	36.
W 24× 94	289	673	.43	221	5720	19.78	73.1	W 24× 94	272	412	.66	221	4630	17.05	33.
W 18×114	283	553	.51	220	4210	14.88	75.8	W 18×114	266	356	.75	220	3420	12.86	35.
W 27× 84	281	721	.39	212	6200	22.09	74.0	W 27× 84	264	438	.60	212	5060	19.15	34.
W 21× 96	262	577	.45	198	4530	17.29	73.0	W 21× 96	245	355	.69	198	3650	14.86	33.
W 18×105	260	532	.49	202	3900	14.98	75.8	W 18×105	245	339	.72	202	3180	12.95	35.

NOTES:
1. Tables are based on specified concrete strength $f'_c = 3.0$ ksi and modular ratio $n = 9$.
2. Proper selection of S_{tr} value assures that stress in steel beam does not exceed allowable. Concrete stress due to bending does not exceed allowable under the following conditions:

$F_y = 36$ ksi	Condition	$F_y = 50$ ksi
S_{tr}/S_t	$f'_c = 3.0$ ksi	S_{tr}/S_t
$\leqslant .51$	Shored construction	$\leqslant .37$
$\leqslant 1.01$	Unshored const. with $M_L/M_D < 1.0$	$\leqslant .74$
$\leqslant .76$	Unshored const. with $M_L/M_D < 2.0$	$\leqslant .55$
$\leqslant .67$	Unshored const. with $M_L/M_D < 3.0$	$\leqslant .49$

3. For unshored construction see Sect. 1.11.2.2 of the AISC Specification.

AMERICAN INSTITUTE OF STEEL CONSTRUCTION

COMPOSITE DESIGN
Properties of composite beams
No Cover Plate—4 Inch Slab

FULL WIDTH SLAB	PARTIAL SLAB

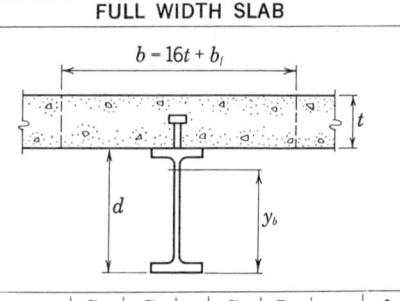

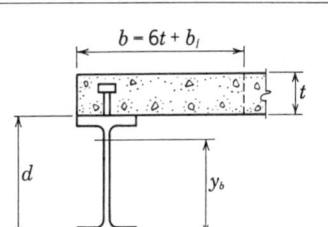

Beam	S_{tr} In.³	S_t In.³	$\frac{S_{tr}}{S_t}$	S_s In.³	I_{tr} In.⁴	y_b In.	b In.	Beam	S_{tr} In.³	S_t In.³	$\frac{S_{tr}}{S_t}$	S_s In.³	I_{tr} In.⁴	y_b In.	b In.
W 24×84	259	642	.40	197	5180	20.02	73.0	W 24×84	243	389	.63	197	4210	17.28	33.0
W 18×96	239	512	.47	185	3610	15.11	75.8	W 18×96	226	325	.70	185	2950	13.07	35.8
W 24×76	234	613	.38	176	4720	20.21	73.0	W 24×76	220	368	.60	176	3850	17.48	33.0
W 21×82	225	539	.42	169	3940	17.55	73.0	W 21×82	211	327	.64	169	3190	15.12	33.0
W 16×96	218	450	.49	166	2990	13.68	75.5	W 16×96	205	285	.72	166	2430	11.81	35.5
W 18×85	210	472	.44	157	3240	15.46	72.8	W 18×85	196	288	.68	157	2610	13.27	32.8
W 24×68	207	582	.36	153	4240	20.42	73.0	W 24×68	195	346	.56	153	3460	17.71	33.0
W 21×73	203	523	.39	151	3690	18.18	72.3	W 21×73	191	313	.61	151	2990	15.67	32.3
W 16×88	200	430	.46	151	2750	13.77	75.5	W 16×88	188	271	.69	151	2240	11.90	35.5
W 18×77	191	452	.42	142	2970	15.59	72.8	W 18×77	179	274	.65	142	2400	13.41	32.8
W 21×68	189	508	.37	140	3470	18.31	72.3	W 21×68	178	302	.59	140	2820	15.81	32.3
W 24×61	183	538	.34	130	3780	20.69	71.0	W 24×61	171	311	.55	130	3060	17.87	31.0
W 16×78	176	398	.44	128	2480	14.09	72.6	W 16×78	164	241	.68	128	1990	12.09	32.6
W 18×70	173	434	.40	129	2730	15.72	72.8	W 18×70	163	262	.62	129	2210	13.55	32.8
W 21×62	173	488	.35	127	3190	18.45	72.2	W 21×62	163	289	.56	127	2600	15.98	32.2
W 24×55	163	512	.32	114	3410	20.88	71.0	W 24×55	153	293	.52	114	2770	18.11	31.0
W 16×71	160	381	.42	116	2270	14.20	72.5	W 16×71	150	230	.65	116	1830	12.20	32.5
W 18×64	159	417	.38	118	2520	15.83	72.7	W 18×64	150	251	.60	118	2050	13.69	32.7
W 14×74	153	342	.45	112	1930	12.57	74.1	W 14×74	144	211	.68	112	1560	10.82	34.1
W 21×55	152	461	.33	110	2840	18.64	72.2	W 21×55	144	271	.53	110	2330	16.22	32.2
W 18×60	150	407	.37	108	2440	16.27	71.6	W 18×60	141	240	.58	108	1970	14.04	31.6
W 16×64	144	363	.40	104	2070	14.32	72.5	W 16×64	135	218	.62	104	1670	12.34	32.5
W 14×68	141	329	.43	103	1780	12.65	74.0	W 14×68	132	203	.65	103	1450	10.92	34.0
W 18×55	137	392	.35	98.4	2250	16.39	71.5	W 18×55	129	231	.56	98.4	1830	14.19	31.5
W 21×49	134	429	.31	93.3	2530	18.91	70.5	W 21×49	126	246	.51	93.3	2060	16.43	30.5

NOTES (Cont'd.):
4. For uniform loading: Deflection (in.) $= ML^2/160\ Sy_b$
                    End reaction (kips) $= 0.33 S_{tr} F_b/L$
                           where $M =$ kip-ft., $L =$ ft., $S =$ in.³, $y_b =$ in., $S_{tr} =$ in.³, $F_b =$ ksi
5. Ratio of S_{tr}/S_t at balanced design:

F_y (ksi)	$f'_c = 3.0$	3.75	4.0
36	.51	.59	.61
42	.44	.50	.52
45	.41	.47	.48
50	.37	.42	.44
55	.34	.38	.40
60	.31	.35	.36

4″ Slab

COMPOSITE DESIGN
Properties of composite beams
No Cover Plate—4 Inch Slab

FULL WIDTH SLAB	PARTIAL SLAB

Beam	S_{tr} In.³	S_t In.³	$\frac{S_{tr}}{S_t}$	S_s In.³	I_{tr} In.⁴	y_b In.	b In.	Beam	S_{tr} In.³	S_t In.³	$\frac{S_{tr}}{S_t}$	S_s In.³	I_{tr} In.⁴	y_b In.	b In.
W 16×58	131	348	.38	94.4	1890	14.42	72.5	W 16×58	123	208	.59	94.4	1540	12.47	32.
W 14×61	127	313	.40	92.2	1610	12.75	74.0	W 14×61	119	192	.62	92.2	1320	11.05	34.
W 18×50	125	376	.33	89.1	2060	16.52	71.5	W 18×50	118	221	.53	89.1	1690	14.37	31.
W 21×44	120	406	.29	81.6	2280	19.04	70.5	W 21×44	112	233	.48	81.6	1870	16.62	30.
W 16×50	115	331	.35	80.8	1730	15.03	71.1	W 16×50	108	195	.55	80.8	1410	13.03	31.
W 18×45	112	358	.31	79.0	1860	16.65	71.5	W 18×45	106	210	.50	79.0	1540	14.55	31.
W 14×53	110	289	.38	77.8	1430	13.00	72.1	W 14×53	103	173	.59	77.8	1160	11.25	32.
W 16×45	104	316	.33	72.5	1570	15.14	71.0	W 16×45	97.7	186	.53	72.5	1290	13.18	31.
W 14×48	99.6	276	.36	70.2	1300	13.09	72.0	W 14×48	93.7	166	.57	70.2	1070	11.38	32.
W 18×40	99.4	335	.30	68.4	1680	16.89	70.0	W 18×40	93.5	193	.48	68.4	1380	14.76	30.
W 12×50	94.3	242	.39	64.7	1100	11.64	72.1	W 12×50	88.1	145	.61	64.7	888	10.08	32.
W 16×40	92.8	300	.31	64.6	1420	15.28	71.0	W 16×40	87.5	177	.49	64.6	1170	13.39	31.
W 14×43	89.4	262	.34	62.7	1180	13.18	72.0	W 14×43	84.2	158	.53	62.7	970	11.53	32.
W 18×35	86.2	312	.28	57.9	1470	17.01	70.0	W 18×35	81.1	181	.45	57.9	1220	14.98	30.
W 12×45	85.0	229	.37	58.2	996	11.72	72.0	W 12×45	79.6	138	.57	58.2	812	10.20	32.
W 16×36	82.8	283	.29	56.5	1270	15.35	71.0	W 16×36	78.0	167	.47	56.5	1060	13.53	31.
W 14×38	80.5	253	.32	54.7	1110	13.74	70.8	W 14×38	75.5	150	.50	54.7	910	12.04	30.
W 12×40	76.3	217	.35	51.9	900	11.79	72.0	W 12×40	71.5	132	.54	51.9	739	10.33	32.
W 10×45	75.3	187	.40	49.1	758	10.06	72.0	W 10×45	69.9	113	.62	49.1	609	8.72	32.
W 14×34	72.1	239	.30	48.6	996	13.83	70.8	W 14×34	67.7	142	.48	48.6	826	12.20	30.
W 16×31	71.2	260	.27	47.2	1110	15.58	69.5	W 16×31	66.9	152	.44	47.2	921	13.77	29.
W 12×36	69.3	209	.33	46.0	845	12.19	70.6	W 12×36	64.8	124	.52	46.0	692	10.68	30.
W 10×39	65.7	173	.38	42.2	664	10.10	72.0	W 10×39	61.0	105	.58	42.2	538	8.82	32.
W 14×30	63.4	223	.28	41.9	882	13.90	70.7	W 14×30	59.6	134	.45	41.9	736	12.35	30.
W 12×31	60.1	194	.31	39.5	738	12.28	70.5	W 12×31	56.2	117	.48	39.5	610	10.85	30.

NOTES:

1. Tables are based on specified concrete strength $f'_c = 3.0$ ksi and modular ratio $n = 9$.
2. Proper selection of S_{tr} value assures that stress in steel beam does not exceed allowable. Concrete stress due to bending does not exceed allowable under the following conditions:

$F_y = 36$ ksi	Condition	$F_y = 50$ ksi
S_{tr}/S_t	$f'_c = 3.0$ ksi	S_{tr}/S_t
⩽ .51	Shored construction	⩽ .37
⩽ 1.01	Unshored const. with $M_L/M_D < 1.0$	⩽ .74
⩽ .76	Unshored const. with $M_L/M_D < 2.0$	⩽ .55
⩽ .67	Unshored const. with $M_L/M_D < 3.0$	⩽ .49

3. For unshored construction see Sect. 1.11.2.2 of the AISC Specification.

COMPOSITE DESIGN

Properties of composite beams

No Cover Plate—4 Inch Slab

FULL WIDTH SLAB	PARTIAL SLAB

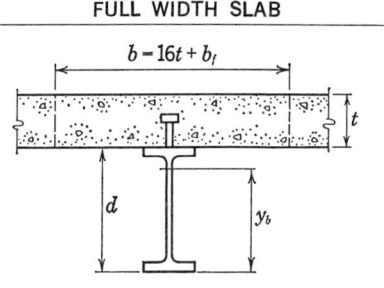

$b = 16t + b_f$

$b = 6t + b_f$

Beam	S_{tr} In.³	S_t In.³	$\dfrac{S_{tr}}{S_t}$	S_s In.³	I_{tr} In.⁴	y_b In.	b In.	Beam	S_{tr} In.³	S_t In.³	$\dfrac{S_{tr}}{S_t}$	S_s In.³	I_{tr} In.⁴	y_b In.	b In.
W 16× 26	59.5	236	.25	38.3	934	15.70	69.5	W 16× 26	55.9	139	.40	38.3	785	14.02	29.5
W 14× 26	55.0	205	.27	35.1	776	14.11	69.0	W 14× 26	51.5	121	.42	35.1	646	12.55	29.0
W 12× 27	52.5	180	.29	34.2	649	12.36	70.5	W 12× 27	49.2	109	.45	34.2	541	11.01	30.5
W 10× 29	50.2	153	.33	30.8	538	10.71	69.8	W 10× 29	46.4	91.5	.51	30.8	438	9.43	29.8
W 14× 22	46.4	187	.25	28.9	659	14.20	69.0	W 14× 22	43.4	112	.39	28.9	554	12.75	29.0
W 10× 25	43.5	142	.31	26.5	468	10.78	69.8	W 10× 25	40.3	85.2	.47	26.5	385	9.56	29.8
W 12× 22	42.6	162	.26	25.3	550	12.91	68.0	W 12× 22	39.6	95.2	.42	25.3	456	11.52	28.0
W 8× 28	42.3	118	.36	24.3	375	8.87	70.5	W 8× 28	38.8	70.7	.55	24.3	302	7.78	30.5
W 12× 19	36.8	149	.25	21.3	477	12.97	68.0	W 12× 19	34.2	88.5	.39	21.3	398	11.66	28.0
W 8× 24	36.6	109	.33	20.8	327	8.94	70.5	W 8× 24	33.7	65.7	.51	20.8	266	7.89	30.5
W 10× 21	36.6	129	.28	21.5	396	10.83	69.8	W 10× 21	33.9	77.9	.44	21.5	329	9.68	29.8
W 10× 19	33.4	124	.27	18.8	375	11.24	68.0	W 10× 19	30.8	73.4	.42	18.8	309	10.04	28.0
W12×16.5	31.7	137	.23	17.6	412	13.00	68.0	W12×16.5	29.4	81.3	.36	17.6	346	11.75	28.0
W 8× 20	31.1	102	.30	17.0	289	9.31	69.3	W 8× 20	28.6	60.7	.47	17.0	236	8.25	29.3
W 10× 17	29.5	116	.25	16.2	333	11.26	68.0	W 10× 17	27.3	68.7	.40	16.2	276	10.10	28.0
W 8× 17	26.5	93.8	.28	14.1	248	9.36	69.3	W 8× 17	24.5	55.8	.44	14.1	204	8.34	29.3

NOTES (Cont'd.):

4. For uniform loading: Deflection (in.) = $ML^2/160\,Sy_b$
   End reaction (kips) = $0.33S_{tr}F_b/L$
   where M = kip-ft., L = ft., S = in.³, y_b = in., S_{tr} = in.³, F_b = ksi

5. Ratio of S_{tr}/S_t at balanced design:

F_y (ksi)	$f'_c = 3.0$	3.75	4.0
36	.51	.59	.61
42	.44	.50	.52
45	.41	.47	.48
50	.37	.42	.44
55	.34	.38	.40
60	.31	.35	.36

AMERICAN INSTITUTE OF STEEL CONSTRUCTION

4½″ Slab

COMPOSITE DESIGN
Properties of composite beams
No Cover Plate—4½ Inch Slab

FULL WIDTH SLAB		PARTIAL SLAB	

$b = 16t + b_f$

$b = 6t + b_f$

Beam	S_{tr} In.³	S_t In.³	$\frac{S_{tr}}{S_t}$	S_s In.³	I_{tr} In.⁴	y_b In.	b In.	Beam	S_{tr} In.³	S_t In.³	$\frac{S_{tr}}{S_t}$	S_s In.³	I_{tr} In.⁴	y_b In.	b In.
W 36×160	687	1460	.47	542	18900	27.55	84.0	W 36×160	646	932	.69	542	15400	23.93	39.
W 36×150	644	1420	.45	504	17900	27.75	84.0	W 36×150	605	896	.67	504	14600	24.09	39.
W 33×152	619	1330	.47	487	16000	25.92	83.6	W 33×152	581	841	.69	487	13100	22.47	38.
W 33×141	573	1280	.45	448	15000	26.13	83.5	W 33×141	539	804	.67	448	12200	22.64	38.
W 36×135	573	1340	.43	440	16100	28.05	83.9	W 36×135	538	834	.64	440	13100	24.35	38.
W 33×130	525	1230	.43	406	13800	26.36	83.5	W 33×130	493	764	.65	406	11300	22.84	38.
W 30×132	493	1110	.44	380	11900	24.11	82.6	W 30×132	462	688	.67	380	9630	20.81	37.
W 33×118	473	1170	.40	359	12600	26.62	83.5	W 33×118	444	718	.62	359	10300	23.08	38.
W 30×124	463	1080	.43	355	11200	24.28	82.5	W 30×124	435	665	.65	355	9110	20.96	37.
W 30×116	432	1050	.41	329	10600	24.43	82.5	W 30×116	406	640	.63	329	8570	21.11	37.
W 24×130	420	918	.46	332	8280	19.73	86.0	W 24×130	398	587	.68	332	6810	17.14	41.
W 30×108	399	1010	.40	300	9830	24.60	82.5	W 30×108	375	611	.61	300	7970	21.27	37.
W 27×114	394	938	.42	300	8820	22.38	82.1	W 27×114	370	571	.65	300	7140	19.29	37.
W 24×120	386	873	.44	300	7710	19.98	84.1	W 24×120	364	546	.67	300	6300	17.28	39.
W 30× 99	364	971	.38	270	9040	24.83	82.5	W 30× 99	342	582	.59	270	7350	21.50	37.
W 24×110	355	843	.42	275	7160	20.17	84.0	W 24×110	336	524	.64	275	5860	17.47	39.
W 27×102	353	897	.39	267	8000	22.65	82.0	W 27×102	332	541	.61	267	6490	19.56	37.
W 27× 94	325	864	.38	243	7420	22.83	82.0	W 27× 94	306	517	.59	243	6040	19.74	37.
W 21×112	323	730	.44	250	5710	17.68	85.0	W 21×112	306	459	.67	250	4680	15.31	40.
W 24×100	323	811	.40	250	6590	20.37	84.0	W 24×100	307	500	.61	250	5420	17.67	39.
W 24× 94	298	762	.39	221	6170	20.70	81.1	W 24× 94	280	454	.62	221	4980	17.82	36.
W 18×114	292	621	.47	220	4570	15.63	83.8	W 18×114	275	388	.71	220	3700	13.46	38.
W 27× 84	289	819	.35	212	6660	23.06	82.0	W 27× 84	272	486	.56	212	5440	20.00	37.
W 21× 96	271	652	.42	198	4910	18.12	81.0	W 21× 96	253	391	.65	198	3940	15.56	36.
W 18×105	269	597	.45	202	4240	15.73	83.8	W 18×105	253	371	.68	202	3430	13.56	38.

NOTES:
1. Tables are based on specified concrete strength $f'_c = 3.0$ ksi and modular ratio $n = 9$.
2. Proper selection of S_{tr} value assures that stress in steel beam does not exceed allowable. Concrete stress due to bending does not exceed allowable under the following conditions:

$F_y = 36$ ksi	Condition	$F_y = 50$ ksi
S_{tr}/S_t	$f'_c = 3.0$ ksi	S_{tr}/S_t
⩽ .51	Shored construction	⩽ .37
⩽ 1.01	Unshored const. with $M_L/M_D < 1.0$	⩽ .74
⩽ .76	Unshored const. with $M_L/M_D < 2.0$	⩽ .55
⩽ .67	Unshored const. with $M_L/M_D < 3.0$	⩽ .49

3. For unshored construction see Sect. 1.11.2.2 of the AISC Specification.

COMPOSITE DESIGN

Properties of composite beams

No Cover Plate—4½ Inch Slab

FULL WIDTH SLAB		PARTIAL SLAB	

$b = 16t + b_f$

$b = 6t + b_f$

Beam	S_{tr} In.³	S_t In.³	$\dfrac{S_{tr}}{S_t}$	S_s In.³	I_{tr} In.⁴	y_b In.	b In.	Beam	S_{tr} In.³	S_t In.³	$\dfrac{S_{tr}}{S_t}$	S_s In.³	I_{tr} In.⁴	y_b In.	b In.
W 24×84	266	727	.37	197	5570	20.93	81.0	W 24×84	251	431	.58	197	4530	18.07	36.0
W 18×96	247	575	.43	185	3910	15.85	83.8	W 18×96	233	355	.65	185	3190	13.69	38.8
W 24×76	241	695	.35	176	5080	21.10	81.0	W 24×76	227	409	.55	176	4140	18.28	36.0
W 21×82	232	610	.38	169	4260	18.37	81.0	W 21×82	218	362	.60	169	3450	15.84	36.0
W 16×96	226	505	.45	166	3250	14.37	83.5	W 16×96	213	312	.68	166	2630	12.39	38.5
W 18×85	217	532	.41	157	3520	16.21	80.8	W 18×85	203	318	.64	157	2830	13.92	35.8
W 24×68	214	658	.32	153	4550	21.30	81.0	W 24×68	201	386	.52	153	3730	18.53	36.0
W 21×73	210	592	.35	151	3990	19.00	80.3	W 21×73	197	347	.57	151	3240	16.42	35.3
W 16×88	207	483	.43	151	3000	14.46	83.5	W 16×88	195	297	.65	151	2430	12.48	38.5
W 18×77	197	510	.39	142	3220	16.33	80.8	W 18×77	185	303	.61	142	2600	14.07	36.0
W 21×68	196	574	.34	140	3740	19.12	80.3	W 21×68	184	337	.55	140	3050	16.57	35.3
W 24×61	189	610	.31	130	4070	21.55	79.0	W 24×61	177	348	.51	130	3310	18.72	34.0
W 16×78	183	448	.41	128	2700	14.79	80.6	W 16×78	171	267	.64	128	2170	12.70	35.6
W 18×70	180	488	.37	129	2950	16.45	80.8	W 18×70	169	290	.58	129	2400	14.23	35.8
W 21×62	179	551	.32	127	3440	19.25	80.2	W 21×62	168	322	.52	127	2820	16.75	35.2
W 24×55	169	579	.29	114	3670	21.72	79.0	W 24×55	158	330	.48	114	3000	18.96	34.0
W 16×71	166	429	.39	116	2480	14.88	80.5	W 16×71	156	255	.61	116	2000	12.83	35.5
W 18×64	165	469	.35	118	2730	16.55	80.7	W 18×64	155	279	.56	118	2230	14.37	35.7
W 14×74	160	384	.42	112	2110	13.20	82.1	W 14×74	150	233	.64	112	1700	11.39	37.1
W 21×55	157	519	.30	110	3050	19.41	80.2	W 21×55	148	303	.49	110	2520	16.99	35.2
W 18×60	155	459	.34	108	2640	17.00	79.6	W 18×60	146	268	.54	108	2150	14.74	34.6
W 16×64	150	408	.37	104	2250	14.99	80.5	W 16×64	141	243	.58	104	1830	12.98	35.5
W 14×68	147	369	.40	103	1950	13.27	82.0	W 14×68	138	224	.62	103	1580	11.49	37.0
W 18×55	142	440	.32	98.4	2430	17.10	79.5	W 18×55	134	258	.52	98.4	1990	14.90	34.5
W 21×49	139	483	.29	93.3	2730	19.67	78.5	W 21×49	130	277	.47	93.3	2240	17.22	33.5

NOTES (Cont'd.):

4. For uniform loading: Deflection (in.) $= ML^2/160\, Sy_b$

                     End reaction (kips) $= 0.33 S_{tr} F_b/L$

                     where M = kip-ft., L = ft., S = in.³, y_b = in., S_{tr} = in.³, F_b = ksi

5. Ratio of S_{tr}/S_t at balanced design:

F_y (ksi)	$f'_c = 3.0$	3.75	4.0
36	.51	.59	.61
42	.44	.50	.52
45	.41	.47	.48
50	.37	.42	.44
55	.34	.38	.40
60	.31	.35	.36

AMERICAN INSTITUTE OF STEEL CONSTRUCTION

4½″ Slab

COMPOSITE DESIGN
Properties of composite beams
No Cover Plate—4½ Inch Slab

FULL WIDTH SLAB	PARTIAL SLAB

$b = 16t + b_f$ $b = 6t + b_f$

FULL WIDTH SLAB

Beam	S_{tr} In.³	S_t In.³	S_{tr}/S_t	S_s In.³	I_{tr} In.⁴	y_b In.	b In.
W 16×58	137	390	.35	94.4	2060	15.07	80.5
W 14×61	132	350	.38	92.2	1770	13.36	82.0
W 18×50	129	421	.31	89.1	2230	17.21	79.5
W 21×44	124	456	.27	81.6	2450	19.78	78.5
W 16×50	120	371	.32	80.8	1880	15.69	79.1
W 18×45	116	399	.29	79.0	2010	17.32	79.5
W 14×53	115	323	.36	77.8	1560	13.60	80.1
W 16×45	108	353	.31	72.5	1710	15.77	79.0
W 14×48	104	308	.34	70.2	1430	13.67	80.0
W 18×40	103	374	.28	68.4	1810	17.55	78.0
W 12×50	99.3	270	.37	64.7	1210	12.20	80.1
W 16×40	96.8	334	.29	64.6	1540	15.89	79.0
W 14×43	93.7	291	.32	62.7	1290	13.75	80.0
W 18×35	89.8	347	.26	57.9	1580	17.64	78.0
W 12×45	89.6	256	.35	58.2	1100	12.26	80.0
W 16×36	86.5	313	.28	56.5	1380	15.95	79.0
W 14×38	84.4	280	.30	54.7	1210	14.31	78.8
W 12×40	80.5	242	.33	51.9	993	12.33	80.0
W 10×45	80.1	209	.38	49.1	847	10.57	80.0
W 14×34	75.7	265	.29	48.6	1090	14.39	78.8
W 16×31	74.5	288	.26	47.2	1200	16.16	77.5
W 12×36	73.2	233	.31	46.0	932	12.73	78.6
W 10×39	69.9	194	.36	42.2	742	10.62	80.0
W 14×30	66.6	247	.27	41.9	964	14.46	78.7
W 12×31	63.5	216	.29	39.5	814	12.82	78.5

PARTIAL SLAB

Beam	S_{tr} In.³	S_t In.³	S_{tr}/S_t	S_s In.³	I_{tr} In.⁴	y_b In.	b In.
W 16×58	128	232	.55	94.4	1680	13.11	35.
W 14×61	124	213	.58	92.2	1440	11.63	37.
W 18×50	122	247	.49	89.1	1840	15.07	34.
W 21×44	117	262	.44	81.6	2030	17.41	33.
W 16×50	112	218	.52	80.8	1540	13.69	34.
W 18×45	109	235	.47	79.0	1670	15.26	34.
W 14×53	107	193	.56	77.8	1270	11.85	35.
W 16×45	102	208	.49	72.5	1410	13.85	34.
W 14×48	97.6	185	.53	70.2	1170	11.98	35.
W 18×40	97.1	217	.45	68.4	1500	15.48	33.
W 12×50	92.3	162	.57	64.7	982	10.63	35.
W 16×40	90.9	198	.46	64.6	1280	14.05	34.
W 14×43	87.7	176	.50	62.7	1060	12.12	35.
W 18×35	84.3	203	.42	57.9	1320	15.69	33.
W 12×45	83.4	154	.54	58.2	897	10.75	35.
W 16×36	81.1	187	.43	56.5	1150	14.19	34.
W 14×38	78.9	167	.47	54.7	998	12.66	33.
W 12×40	75.0	147	.51	51.9	816	10.88	35.
W 10×45	73.8	126	.58	49.1	681	9.23	35.
W 14×34	70.7	159	.44	48.6	906	12.81	33.
W 16×31	69.7	170	.41	47.2	1010	14.43	32.
W 12×36	68.0	139	.49	46.0	764	11.25	33.
W 10×39	64.5	118	.55	42.2	601	9.33	35.
W 14×30	62.3	149	.42	41.9	807	12.96	33.
W 12×31	59.0	130	.45	39.5	674	11.42	33.

NOTES:
1. Tables are based on specified concrete strength $f'_c = 3.0$ ksi and modular ratio $n = 9$.
2. Proper selection of S_{tr} value assures that stress in steel beam does not exceed allowable. Concrete stress due to bending does not exceed allowable under the following conditions:

$F_y = 36$ ksi	Condition	$F_y = 50$ ksi
S_{tr}/S_t	$f'_c = 3.0$ ksi	S_{tr}/S_t
⩽ .51	Shored construction	⩽ .37
⩽ 1.01	Unshored const. with $M_L/M_D < 1.0$	⩽ .74
⩽ .76	Unshored const. with $M_L/M_D < 2.0$	⩽ .55
⩽ .67	Unshored const. with $M_L/M_D < 3.0$	⩽ .49

3. For unshored construction see Sect. 1.11.2.2 of the AISC Specification.

COMPOSITE DESIGN

Properties of composite beams

No Cover Plate—4½ Inch Slab

FULL WIDTH SLAB	PARTIAL SLAB
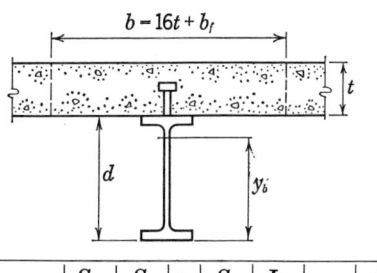	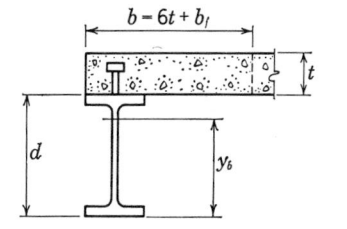

Beam	S_{tr} In.³	S_t In.³	$\dfrac{S_{tr}}{S_t}$	S_s In.³	I_{tr} In.⁴	y_b In.	b In.	Beam	S_{tr} In.³	S_t In.³	$\dfrac{S_{tr}}{S_t}$	S_s In.³	I_{tr} In.⁴	y_b In.	b In.
W 16× 26	62.4	262	.24	38.3	1010	16.27	77.5	W 16× 26	58.4	156	.37	38.3	856	14.67	32.5
W 14× 26	57.8	228	.25	35.1	849	14.67	77.0	W 14× 26	53.9	136	.40	35.1	709	13.16	32.0
W 12× 27	55.5	201	.28	34.2	716	12.91	78.5	W 12× 27	51.7	122	.42	34.2	597	11.56	33.5
W 10× 29	53.4	173	.31	30.8	600	11.24	77.8	W 10× 29	49.2	103	.48	30.8	490	9.95	32.8
W 14× 22	48.9	208	.23	28.9	721	14.76	77.0	W 14× 22	45.6	125	.37	28.9	608	13.34	32.0
W 10× 25	46.2	160	.29	26.5	523	11.31	77.8	W 10× 25	42.8	95.5	.45	26.5	431	10.07	32.8
W 12× 22	45.1	181	.25	25.3	607	13.46	76.0	W 12× 22	41.8	107	.39	25.3	505	12.09	31.0
W 8× 28	45.5	134	.34	24.3	427	9.38	78.5	W 8× 28	41.7	79.7	.52	24.3	344	8.24	33.5
W 12× 19	38.9	168	.23	21.3	527	13.52	76.0	W 12× 19	36.2	99.0	.37	21.3	441	12.20	31.0
W 8× 24	39.3	125	.32	20.8	372	9.45	78.5	W 8× 24	36.2	74.2	.49	20.8	303	8.35	33.5
W 10× 21	38.9	146	.27	21.5	443	11.37	77.8	W 10× 21	36.1	87.1	.41	21.5	368	10.18	32.8
W 10× 19	35.5	141	.25	18.8	419	11.78	76.0	W 10× 19	32.9	82.5	.40	18.8	347	10.55	31.0
W12×16.5	33.6	154	.22	17.6	455	13.55	76.0	W12×16.5	31.2	90.9	.34	17.6	383	12.28	31.0
W 8× 20	33.4	117	.29	17.0	328	9.83	77.3	W 8× 20	30.8	68.7	.45	17.0	269	8.73	32.3
W 10× 17	31.5	132	.24	16.2	372	11.80	76.0	W 10× 17	29.2	77.2	.38	16.2	310	10.61	31.0
W 8× 17	28.5	107	.27	14.1	281	9.88	77.3	W 8× 17	26.3	63.3	.42	14.1	233	8.83	32.3

NOTES (Cont'd.):

4. For uniform loading: Deflection (in.) $= ML^2/160\,Sy_b$

   End reaction (kips) $= 0.33 S_{tr}F_b/L$

   where $M =$ kip-ft., $L =$ ft., $S =$ in.³, $y_b =$ in., $S_{tr} =$ in.³, $F_b =$ ksi

5. Ratio of S_{tr}/S_t at balanced design:

F_y (ksi)	$f'_c = 3.0$	3.75	4.0
36	.51	.59	.61
42	.44	.50	.52
45	.41	.47	.48
50	.37	.42	.44
55	.34	.38	.40
60	.31	.35	.36

5″ Slab	COMPOSITE DESIGN

COMPOSITE DESIGN
Properties of composite beams
No Cover Plate—5 Inch Slab

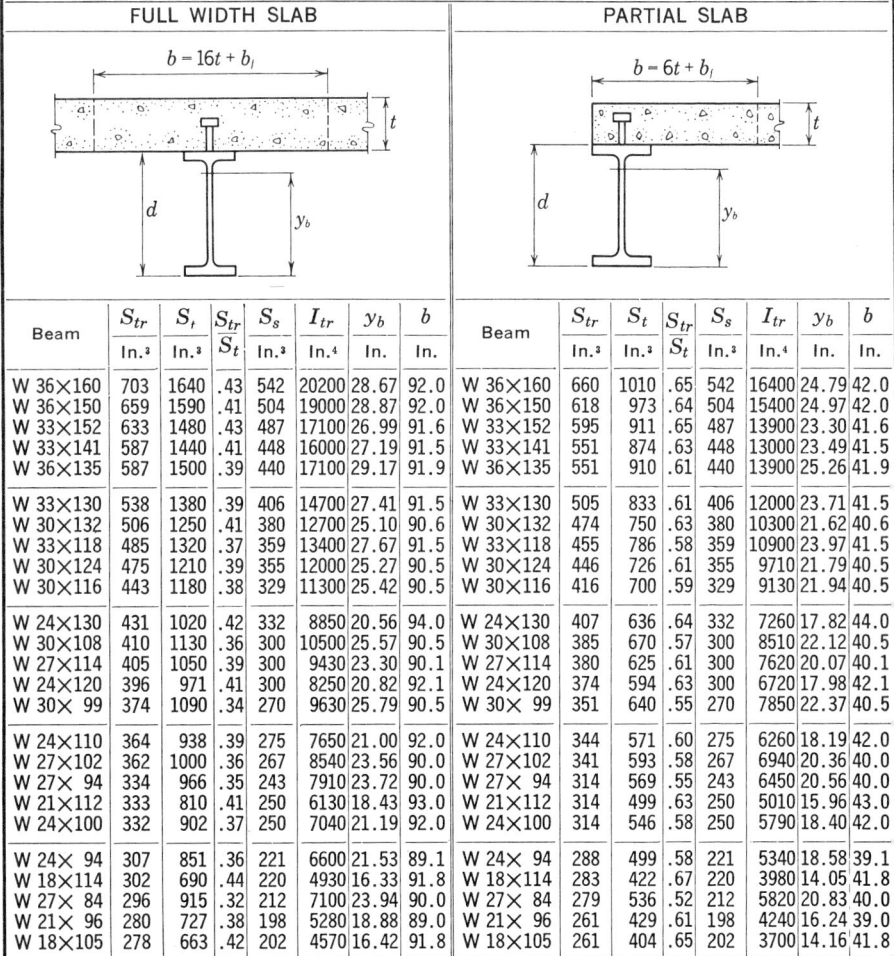

FULL WIDTH SLAB							PARTIAL SLAB						
Beam	S_{tr}	S_t	$\dfrac{S_{tr}}{S_t}$	S_s	I_{tr}	y_b	b	Beam	S_{tr}	S_t	$\dfrac{S_{tr}}{S_t}$	S_s	I_{tr}	y_b	b
	In.³	In.³		In.³	In.⁴	In.	In.		In.³	In.³		In.³	In.⁴	In.	In.
W 36×160	703	1640	.43	542	20200	28.67	92.0	W 36×160	660	1010	.65	542	16400	24.79	42.0
W 36×150	659	1590	.41	504	19000	28.87	92.0	W 36×150	618	973	.64	504	15400	24.97	42.0
W 33×152	633	1480	.43	487	17100	26.99	91.6	W 33×152	595	911	.65	487	13900	23.30	41.6
W 33×141	587	1440	.41	448	16000	27.19	91.5	W 33×141	551	874	.63	448	13000	23.49	41.5
W 36×135	587	1500	.39	440	17100	29.17	91.9	W 36×135	551	910	.61	440	13900	25.26	41.9
W 33×130	538	1380	.39	406	14700	27.41	91.5	W 33×130	505	833	.61	406	12000	23.71	41.5
W 30×132	506	1250	.41	380	12700	25.10	90.6	W 30×132	474	750	.63	380	10300	21.62	40.6
W 33×118	485	1320	.37	359	13400	27.67	91.5	W 33×118	455	786	.58	359	10900	23.97	41.5
W 30×124	475	1210	.39	355	12000	25.27	90.5	W 30×124	446	726	.61	355	9710	21.79	40.5
W 30×116	443	1180	.38	329	11300	25.42	90.5	W 30×116	416	700	.59	329	9130	21.94	40.5
W 24×130	431	1020	.42	332	8850	20.56	94.0	W 24×130	407	636	.64	332	7260	17.82	44.0
W 30×108	410	1130	.36	300	10500	25.57	90.5	W 30×108	385	670	.57	300	8510	22.12	40.5
W 27×114	405	1050	.39	300	9430	23.30	90.1	W 27×114	380	625	.61	300	7620	20.07	40.1
W 24×120	396	971	.41	300	8250	20.82	92.1	W 24×120	374	594	.63	300	6720	17.98	42.1
W 30× 99	374	1090	.34	270	9630	25.79	90.5	W 30× 99	351	640	.55	270	7850	22.37	40.5
W 24×110	364	938	.39	275	7650	21.00	92.0	W 24×110	344	571	.60	275	6260	18.19	42.0
W 27×102	362	1000	.36	267	8540	23.56	90.0	W 27×102	341	593	.58	267	6940	20.36	40.0
W 27× 94	334	966	.35	243	7910	23.72	90.0	W 27× 94	314	569	.55	243	6450	20.56	40.0
W 21×112	333	810	.41	250	6130	18.43	93.0	W 21×112	314	499	.63	250	5010	15.96	43.0
W 24×100	332	902	.37	250	7040	21.19	92.0	W 24×100	314	546	.58	250	5790	18.40	42.0
W 24× 94	307	851	.36	221	6600	21.53	89.1	W 24× 94	288	499	.58	221	5340	18.58	39.1
W 18×114	302	690	.44	220	4930	16.33	91.8	W 18×114	283	422	.67	220	3980	14.05	41.8
W 27× 84	296	915	.32	212	7100	23.94	90.0	W 27× 84	279	536	.52	212	5820	20.83	40.0
W 21× 96	280	727	.38	198	5280	18.88	89.0	W 21× 96	261	429	.61	198	4240	16.24	39.0
W 18×105	278	663	.42	202	4570	16.42	91.8	W 18×105	261	404	.65	202	3700	14.16	41.8

NOTES:
1. Tables are based on specified concrete strength $f'_c = 3.0$ ksi and modular ratio $n = 9$.
2. Proper selection of S_{tr} value assures that stress in steel beam does not exceed allowable. Concrete stress due to bending does not exceed allowable under the following conditions:

$F_y = 36$ ksi	Condition	$F_y = 50$ ksi
S_{tr}/S_t	$f'_c = 3.0$ ksi	S_{tr}/S_t
$\leqslant .51$	Shored construction	$\leqslant .37$
$\leqslant 1.01$	Unshored const. with $M_L/M_D < 1.0$	$\leqslant .74$
$\leqslant .76$	Unshored const. with $M_L/M_D < 2.0$	$\leqslant .55$
$\leqslant .67$	Unshored const. with $M_L/M_D < 3.0$	$\leqslant .49$

3. For unshored construction see Sect. 1.11.2.2 of the AISC Specification.

AMERICAN INSTITUTE OF STEEL CONSTRUCTION

COMPOSITE DESIGN

5″ Slab

Properties of composite beams

No Cover Plate—5 Inch Slab

FULL WIDTH SLAB	PARTIAL SLAB
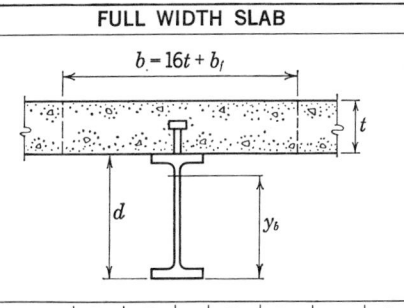	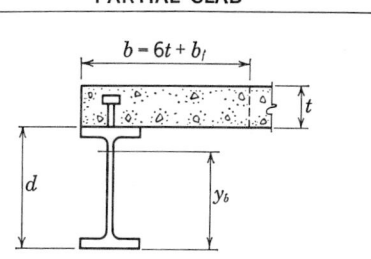

$b = 16t + b_f$ | $b = 6t + b_f$

FULL WIDTH SLAB

Beam	S_{tr} (In.³)	S_t (In.³)	$\dfrac{S_{tr}}{S_t}$	S_s (In.³)	I_{tr} (In.⁴)	y_b (In.)	b (In.)
W 24×84	274	811	.34	197	5960	21.75	89.0
W 18×96	255	637	.40	185	4220	16.54	91.8
W 24×76	248	774	.32	176	5420	21.90	89.0
W 21×82	240	678	.35	169	4580	19.11	89.0
W 16×96	235	560	.42	166	3530	15.02	91.5
W 18×85	225	592	.38	157	3800	16.90	88.8
W 24×68	220	732	.30	153	4860	22.07	89.0
W 21×73	217	658	.33	151	4280	19.74	88.3
W 16×88	215	535	.40	151	3250	15.09	91.5
W 18×77	204	565	.36	142	3480	17.01	88.8
W 21×68	202	638	.32	140	4010	19.85	88.3
W 24×61	195	679	.29	130	4350	22.32	87.0
W 16×78	190	498	.38	128	2930	15.42	88.6
W 18×70	186	541	.34	129	3180	17.11	88.8
W 21×62	185	610	.30	127	3680	19.96	88.2
W 24×55	174	643	.27	114	3910	22.47	87.0
W 16×71	173	475	.36	116	2690	15.51	88.5
W 18×64	171	518	.33	118	2940	17.20	88.7
W 14×74	167	425	.39	112	2300	13.78	90.1
W 21×55	163	573	.28	110	3270	20.10	88.2
W 18×60	161	507	.32	108	2840	17.65	87.6
W 16×64	156	451	.35	104	2440	15.60	88.5
W 14×68	154	407	.38	103	2130	13.84	90.0
W 18×55	148	485	.30	98.4	2620	17.73	87.5
W 21×49	143	533	.27	93.3	2920	20.34	86.5

PARTIAL SLAB

Beam	S_{tr} (In.³)	S_t (In.³)	$\dfrac{S_{tr}}{S_t}$	S_s (In.³)	I_{tr} (In.⁴)	y_b (In.)	b (In.)
W 24×84	258	474	.54	197	4860	18.84	39.0
W 18×96	240	388	.62	185	3430	14.31	41.8
W 24×76	233	451	.52	176	4450	19.06	39.0
W 21×82	225	398	.56	169	3720	16.53	39.0
W 16×96	220	341	.65	166	2850	12.96	41.5
W 18×85	210	349	.60	157	3060	14.56	38.8
W 24×68	207	427	.49	153	4010	19.32	39.0
W 21×73	203	383	.53	151	3490	17.15	38.3
W 16×88	202	325	.62	151	2630	13.06	41.5
W 18×77	191	334	.57	142	2820	14.72	38.8
W 21×68	190	372	.51	140	3280	17.30	38.3
W 24×61	183	387	.47	130	3560	19.52	37.0
W 16×78	177	294	.60	128	2360	13.30	38.6
W 18×70	175	320	.55	129	2600	14.88	38.8
W 21×62	174	356	.49	127	3030	17.48	38.2
W 24×55	163	367	.44	114	3230	19.76	37.0
W 16×71	161	281	.58	116	2170	13.43	38.5
W 18×64	160	307	.52	118	2410	15.02	38.7
W 14×74	156	256	.61	112	1860	11.94	40.1
W 21×55	153	336	.46	110	2710	17.72	38.2
W 18×60	151	297	.51	108	2320	15.41	37.6
W 16×64	146	268	.55	104	1980	13.59	38.5
W 14×68	143	246	.58	103	1730	12.05	40.0
W 18×55	138	285	.49	98.4	2150	15.57	37.5
W 21×49	135	308	.44	93.3	2420	17.96	36.5

NOTES (Cont'd.):

4. For uniform loading: Deflection (in.) = $ML^2/160\,Sy_b$

    End reaction (kips) = $0.33 S_{tr} F_b/L$

    where M = kip-ft., L = ft., S = in.³, y_b = in., S_{tr} = in.³, F_b = ksi

5. Ratio of S_{tr}/S_t at balanced design:

F_y (ksi)	$f'_c = 3.0$	3.75	4.0
36	.51	.59	.61
42	.44	.50	.52
45	.41	.47	.48
50	.37	.42	.44
55	.34	.38	.40
60	.31	.35	.36

5" Slab

COMPOSITE DESIGN
Properties of composite beams
No Cover Plate—5 Inch Slab

FULL WIDTH SLAB	PARTIAL SLAB

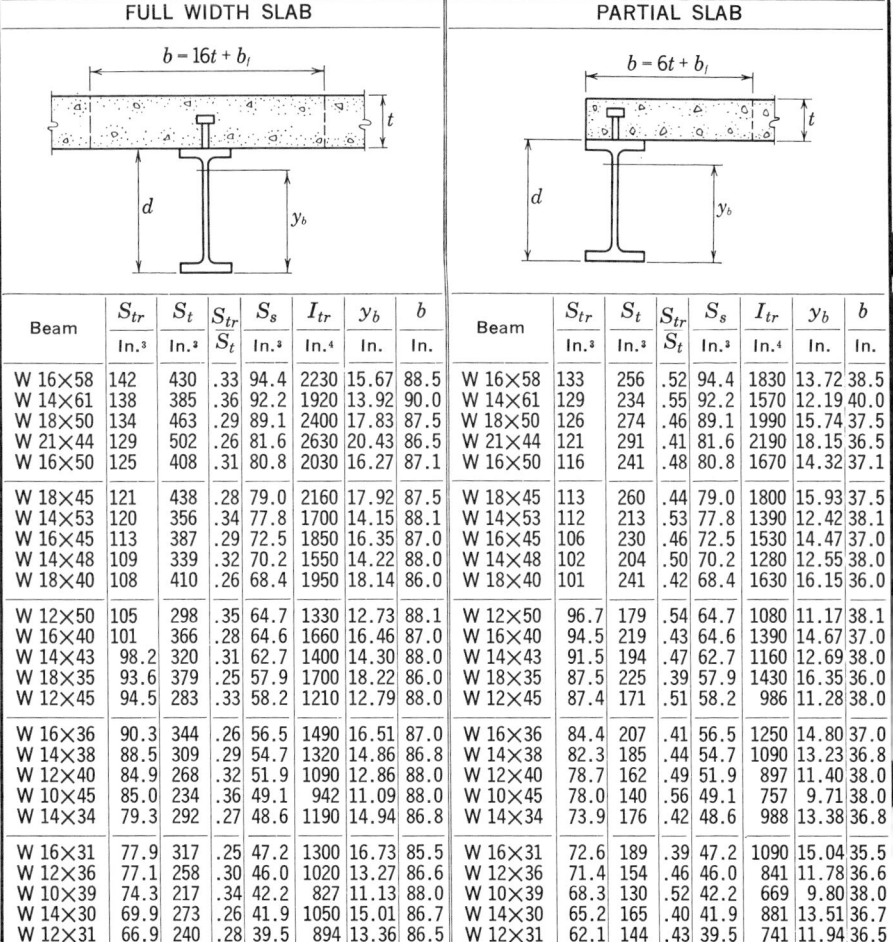

FULL WIDTH SLAB: $b = 16t + b_f$

PARTIAL SLAB: $b = 6t + b_f$

Beam	S_{tr} In.³	S_t In.³	$\frac{S_{tr}}{S_t}$	S_s In.³	I_{tr} In.⁴	y_b In.	b In.	Beam	S_{tr} In.³	S_t In.³	$\frac{S_{tr}}{S_t}$	S_s In.³	I_{tr} In.⁴	y_b In.	b In.
W 16×58	142	430	.33	94.4	2230	15.67	88.5	W 16×58	133	256	.52	94.4	1830	13.72	38.5
W 14×61	138	385	.36	92.2	1920	13.92	90.0	W 14×61	129	234	.55	92.2	1570	12.19	40.0
W 18×50	134	463	.29	89.1	2400	17.83	87.5	W 18×50	126	274	.46	89.1	1990	15.74	37.5
W 21×44	129	502	.26	81.6	2630	20.43	86.5	W 21×44	121	291	.41	81.6	2190	18.15	36.5
W 16×50	125	408	.31	80.8	2030	16.27	87.1	W 16×50	116	241	.48	80.8	1670	14.32	37.1
W 18×45	121	438	.28	79.0	2160	17.92	87.5	W 18×45	113	260	.44	79.0	1800	15.93	37.5
W 14×53	120	356	.34	77.8	1700	14.15	88.1	W 14×53	112	213	.53	77.8	1390	12.42	38.1
W 16×45	113	387	.29	72.5	1850	16.35	87.0	W 16×45	106	230	.46	72.5	1530	14.47	37.0
W 14×48	109	339	.32	70.2	1550	14.22	88.0	W 14×48	102	204	.50	70.2	1280	12.55	38.0
W 18×40	108	410	.26	68.4	1950	18.14	86.0	W 18×40	101	241	.42	68.4	1630	16.15	36.0
W 12×50	105	298	.35	64.7	1330	12.73	88.1	W 12×50	96.7	179	.54	64.7	1080	11.17	38.1
W 16×40	101	366	.28	64.6	1660	16.46	87.0	W 16×40	94.5	219	.43	64.6	1390	14.67	37.0
W 14×43	98.2	320	.31	62.7	1400	14.30	88.0	W 14×43	91.5	194	.47	62.7	1160	12.69	38.0
W 18×35	93.6	379	.25	57.9	1700	18.22	86.0	W 18×35	87.5	225	.39	57.9	1430	16.35	36.0
W 12×45	94.5	283	.33	58.2	1210	12.79	88.0	W 12×45	87.4	171	.51	58.2	986	11.28	38.0
W 16×36	90.3	344	.26	56.5	1490	16.51	87.0	W 16×36	84.4	207	.41	56.5	1250	14.80	37.0
W 14×38	88.5	309	.29	54.7	1320	14.86	86.8	W 14×38	82.3	185	.44	54.7	1090	13.23	36.8
W 12×40	84.9	268	.32	51.9	1090	12.86	88.0	W 12×40	78.7	162	.49	51.9	897	11.40	38.0
W 10×45	85.0	234	.36	49.1	942	11.09	88.0	W 10×45	78.0	140	.56	49.1	757	9.71	38.0
W 14×34	79.3	292	.27	48.6	1190	14.94	86.8	W 14×34	73.9	176	.42	48.6	988	13.38	36.8
W 16×31	77.9	317	.25	47.2	1300	16.73	85.5	W 16×31	72.6	189	.39	47.2	1090	15.04	35.5
W 12×36	77.1	258	.30	46.0	1020	13.27	86.6	W 12×36	71.4	154	.46	46.0	841	11.78	36.6
W 10×39	74.3	217	.34	42.2	827	11.13	88.0	W 10×39	68.3	130	.52	42.2	669	9.80	38.0
W 14×30	69.9	273	.26	41.9	1050	15.01	86.7	W 14×30	65.2	165	.40	41.9	881	13.51	36.7
W 12×31	66.9	240	.28	39.5	894	13.36	86.5	W 12×31	62.1	144	.43	39.5	741	11.94	36.5

NOTES:
1. Tables are based on specified concrete strength $f'_c = 3.0$ ksi and modular ratio $n = 9$.
2. Proper selection of S_{tr} value assures that stress in steel beam does not exceed allowable. Concrete stress due to bending does not exceed allowable under the following conditions:

$F_y = 36$ ksi S_{tr}/S_t	Condition $f'_c = 3.0$ ksi	$F_y = 50$ ksi S_{tr}/S_t
⩽ .51	Shored construction	⩽ .37
⩽1.01	Unshored const. with $M_L/M_D < 1.0$	⩽ .74
⩽ .76	Unshored const. with $M_L/M_D < 2.0$	⩽ .55
⩽ .67	Unshored const. with $M_L/M_D < 3.0$	⩽ .49

3. For unshored construction see Sect. 1.11.2.2 of the AISC Specification.

AMERICAN INSTITUTE OF STEEL CONSTRUCTION

COMPOSITE DESIGN

Properties of composite beams

No Cover Plate—5 Inch Slab

FULL WIDTH SLAB		PARTIAL SLAB	

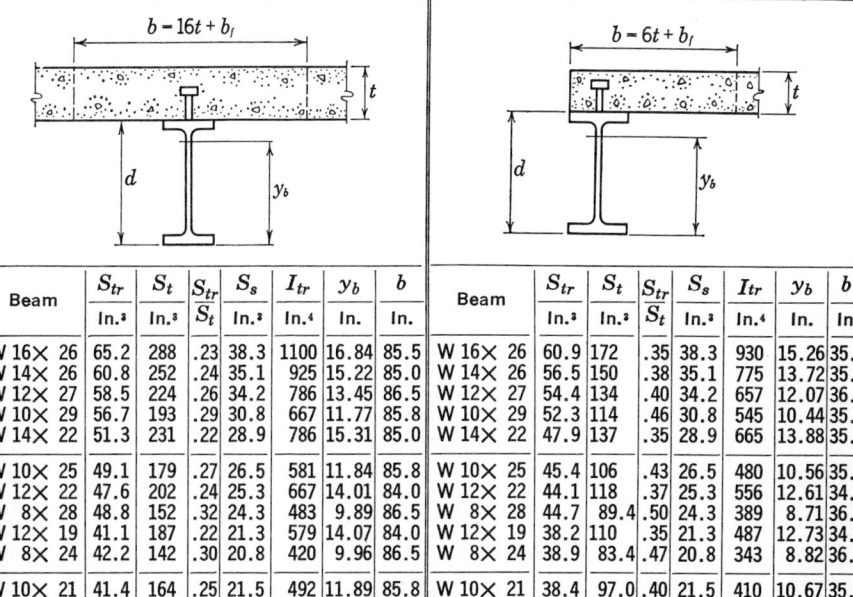

$b - 16t + b_f$ t d y_b $b - 6t + b_f$ t d y_b

Beam	S_{tr} In.³	S_t In.³	$\dfrac{S_{tr}}{S_t}$	S_s In.³	I_{tr} In.⁴	y_b In.	b In.	Beam	S_{tr} In.³	S_t In.³	$\dfrac{S_{tr}}{S_t}$	S_s In.³	I_{tr} In.⁴	y_b In.	b In.
W 16× 26	65.2	288	.23	38.3	1100	16.84	85.5	W 16× 26	60.9	172	.35	38.3	930	15.26	35.5
W 14× 26	60.8	252	.24	35.1	925	15.22	85.0	W 14× 26	56.5	150	.38	35.1	775	13.72	35.0
W 12× 27	58.5	224	.26	34.2	786	13.45	86.5	W 12× 27	54.4	134	.40	34.2	657	12.07	36.5
W 10× 29	56.7	193	.29	30.8	667	11.77	85.8	W 10× 29	52.3	114	.46	30.8	545	10.44	35.8
W 14× 22	51.3	231	.22	28.9	786	15.31	85.0	W 14× 22	47.9	137	.35	28.9	665	13.88	35.0
W 10× 25	49.1	179	.27	26.5	581	11.84	85.8	W 10× 25	45.4	106	.43	26.5	480	10.56	35.8
W 12× 22	47.6	202	.24	25.3	667	14.01	84.0	W 12× 22	44.1	118	.37	25.3	556	12.61	34.0
W 8× 28	48.8	152	.32	24.3	483	9.89	86.5	W 8× 28	44.7	89.4	.50	24.3	389	8.71	36.5
W 12× 19	41.1	187	.22	21.3	579	14.07	84.0	W 12× 19	38.2	110	.35	21.3	487	12.73	34.0
W 8× 24	42.2	142	.30	20.8	420	9.96	86.5	W 8× 24	38.9	83.4	.47	20.8	343	8.82	36.5
W 10× 21	41.4	164	.25	21.5	492	11.89	85.8	W 10× 21	38.4	97.0	.40	21.5	410	10.67	35.8
W 10× 19	37.8	158	.24	18.8	465	12.31	84.0	W 10× 19	35.0	92.1	.38	18.8	387	11.05	34.0
W12×16.5	35.5	172	.21	17.6	500	14.09	84.0	W12×16.5	33.1	101	.33	17.6	423	12.81	34.0
W 8× 20	35.8	133	.27	17.0	370	10.35	85.3	W 8× 20	33.0	77.4	.43	17.0	304	9.21	35.3
W 10× 17	33.5	148	.23	16.2	413	12.33	84.0	W 10× 17	31.1	86.4	.36	16.2	346	11.12	34.0
W 8× 17	30.5	122	.25	14.1	317	10.40	85.3	W 8× 17	28.3	71.5	.40	14.1	263	9.31	35.3

NOTES (Cont'd.):

4. For uniform loading: Deflection (in.) $= ML^2/160\, Sy_b$

    End reaction (kips) $= 0.33S_{tr}F_b/L$

    where M = kip-ft., L = ft., S = in.³, y_b = in., S_{tr} = in.³, F_b = ksi

5. Ratio of S_{tr}/S_t at balanced design:

F_y (ksi)	$f'_c = 3.0$	3.75	4.0
36	.51	.59	.61
42	.44	.50	.52
45	.41	.47	.48
50	.37	.42	.44
55	.34	.38	.40
60	.31	.35	.36

5½″ Slab

COMPOSITE DESIGN
Properties of composite beams
No Cover Plate—5½ Inch Slab

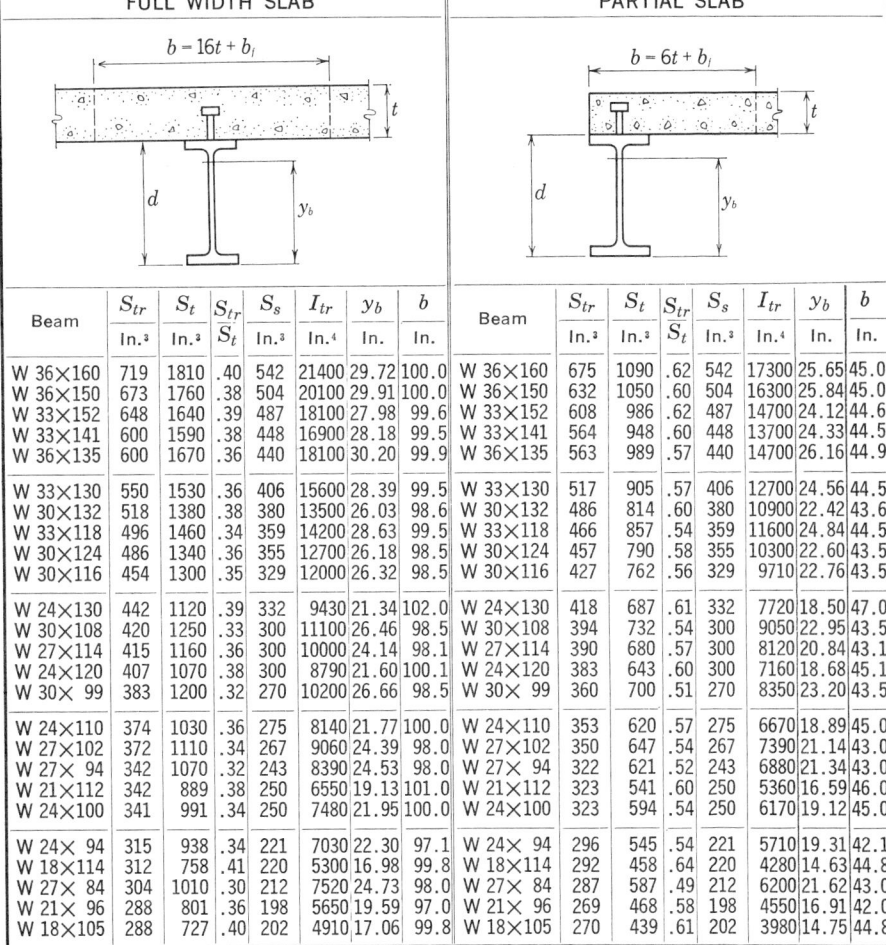

FULL WIDTH SLAB   **PARTIAL SLAB**

Beam	S_{tr} In.³	S_t In.³	$\dfrac{S_{tr}}{S_t}$	S_s In.³	I_{tr} In.⁴	y_b In.	b In.	Beam	S_{tr} In.³	S_t In.³	$\dfrac{S_{tr}}{S_t}$	S_s In.³	I_{tr} In.⁴	y_b In.	b In.
W 36×160	719	1810	.40	542	21400	29.72	100.0	W 36×160	675	1090	.62	542	17300	25.65	45.0
W 36×150	673	1760	.38	504	20100	29.91	100.0	W 36×150	632	1050	.60	504	16300	25.84	45.0
W 33×152	648	1640	.39	487	18100	27.98	99.6	W 33×152	608	986	.62	487	14700	24.12	44.6
W 33×141	600	1590	.38	448	16900	28.18	99.5	W 33×141	564	948	.60	448	13700	24.33	44.5
W 36×135	600	1670	.36	440	18100	30.20	99.9	W 36×135	563	989	.57	440	14700	26.16	44.9
W 33×130	550	1530	.36	406	15600	28.39	99.5	W 33×130	517	905	.57	406	12700	24.56	44.5
W 30×132	518	1380	.38	380	13500	26.03	98.6	W 30×132	486	814	.60	380	10900	22.42	43.6
W 33×118	496	1460	.34	359	14200	28.63	99.5	W 33×118	466	857	.54	359	11600	24.84	44.5
W 30×124	486	1340	.36	355	12700	26.18	98.5	W 30×124	457	790	.58	355	10300	22.60	43.5
W 30×116	454	1300	.35	329	12000	26.32	98.5	W 30×116	427	762	.56	329	9710	22.76	43.5
W 24×130	442	1120	.39	332	9430	21.34	102.0	W 24×130	418	687	.61	332	7720	18.50	47.0
W 30×108	420	1250	.33	300	11100	26.46	98.5	W 30×108	394	732	.54	300	9050	22.95	43.5
W 27×114	415	1160	.36	300	10000	24.14	98.1	W 27×114	390	680	.57	300	8120	20.84	43.1
W 24×120	407	1070	.38	300	8790	21.60	100.1	W 24×120	383	643	.60	300	7160	18.68	45.1
W 30× 99	383	1200	.32	270	10200	26.66	98.5	W 30× 99	360	700	.51	270	8350	23.20	43.5
W 24×110	374	1030	.36	275	8140	21.77	100.0	W 24×110	353	620	.57	275	6670	18.89	45.0
W 27×102	372	1110	.34	267	9060	24.39	98.0	W 27×102	350	647	.54	267	7390	21.14	43.0
W 27× 94	342	1070	.32	243	8390	24.53	98.0	W 27× 94	322	621	.52	243	6880	21.34	43.0
W 21×112	342	889	.38	250	6550	19.13	101.0	W 21×112	323	541	.60	250	5360	16.59	46.0
W 24×100	341	991	.34	250	7480	21.95	100.0	W 24×100	323	594	.54	250	6170	19.12	45.0
W 24× 94	315	938	.34	221	7030	22.30	97.1	W 24× 94	296	545	.54	221	5710	19.31	42.1
W 18×114	312	758	.41	220	5300	16.98	99.8	W 18×114	292	458	.64	220	4280	14.63	44.8
W 27× 84	304	1010	.30	212	7520	24.73	98.0	W 27× 84	287	587	.49	212	6200	21.62	43.0
W 21× 96	288	801	.36	198	5650	19.59	97.0	W 21× 96	269	468	.58	198	4550	16.91	42.0
W 18×105	288	727	.40	202	4910	17.06	99.8	W 18×105	270	439	.61	202	3980	14.75	44.8

NOTES:
1. Tables are based on specified concrete strength $f'_c = 3.0$ ksi and modular ratio $n = 9$.
2. Proper selection of S_{tr} value assures that stress in steel beam does not exceed allowable. Concrete stress due to bending does not exceed allowable under the following conditions:

$F_y = 36$ ksi	Condition	$F_y = 50$ ksi
S_{tr}/S_t	$f'_c = 3.0$ ksi	S_{tr}/S_t
≤ .51	Shored construction	≤ .37
≤ 1.01	Unshored const. with $M_L/M_D < 1.0$	≤ .74
≤ .76	Unshored const. with $M_L/M_D < 2.0$	≤ .55
≤ .67	Unshored const. with $M_L/M_D < 3.0$	≤ .49

3. For unshored construction see Sect. 1.11.2.2 of the AISC Specification.

COMPOSITE DESIGN

5½″ Slab

Properties of composite beams

No Cover Plate—5½ Inch Slab

FULL WIDTH SLAB	PARTIAL SLAB
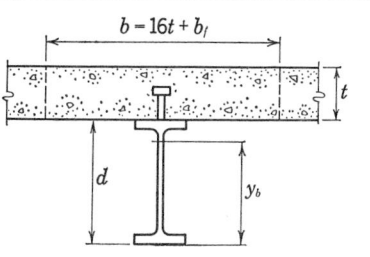	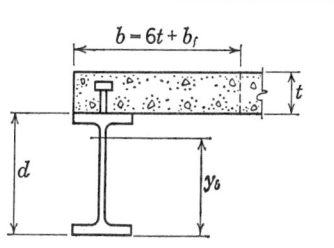
$b = 16t + b_f$	$b = 6t + b_f$

Beam	S_{tr} In.³	S_t In.³	$\dfrac{S_{tr}}{S_t}$	S_s In.³	I_{tr} In.⁴	y_b In.	b In.	Beam	S_{tr} In.³	S_t In.³	$\dfrac{S_{tr}}{S_t}$	S_s In.³	I_{tr} In.⁴	y_b In.	b In.
W 24×84	282	892	.32	197	6340	22.49	97.0	W 24×84	265	519	.51	197	5190	19.59	42.0
W 18×96	264	698	.38	185	4530	17.17	99.8	W 18×96	248	422	.59	185	3690	14.90	44.8
W 24×76	255	850	.30	176	5760	22.63	97.0	W 24×76	240	495	.48	176	4750	19.81	42.0
W 21×82	247	745	.33	169	4890	19.79	97.0	W 21×82	232	436	.53	169	3990	17.21	42.0
W 16×96	244	613	.40	166	3810	15.61	99.5	W 16×96	228	371	.61	166	3080	13.52	44.5
W 18×85	233	649	.36	157	4080	17.53	96.8	W 18×85	217	382	.57	157	3300	15.18	41.8
W 24×68	227	802	.28	153	5160	22.77	97.0	W 24×68	213	468	.46	153	4280	20.06	42.0
W 21×73	224	721	.31	151	4560	20.41	96.3	W 21×73	210	420	.50	151	3740	17.84	41.3
W 16×88	224	585	.38	151	3500	15.67	99.5	W 16×88	209	354	.59	151	2840	13.63	44.5
W 18×77	212	619	.34	142	3730	17.63	96.8	W 18×77	198	365	.54	142	3040	15.34	41.8
W 21×68	208	698	.30	140	4270	20.50	96.3	W 21×68	196	408	.48	140	3520	17.99	41.3
W 24×61	201	744	.27	130	4620	23.01	95.0	W 24×61	188	427	.44	130	3810	20.28	40.0
W 16×78	198	545	.36	128	3170	16.01	96.6	W 16×78	184	322	.57	128	2550	13.89	41.6
W 18×70	193	591	.33	129	3420	17.71	96.8	W 18×70	180	350	.52	129	2800	15.50	41.8
W 21×62	191	666	.29	127	3930	20.60	96.2	W 21×62	179	391	.46	127	3250	18.17	41.2
W 24×55	180	703	.26	114	4160	23.13	95.0	W 24×55	169	405	.42	114	3460	20.51	40.0
W 16×71	180	519	.35	116	2900	16.08	96.5	W 16×71	168	308	.54	116	2350	14.02	41.5
W 18×64	177	565	.31	116	3150	17.79	96.7	W 18×64	166	336	.49	118	2600	15.65	41.7
W 14×74	174	465	.38	112	2500	14.32	98.1	W 14×74	162	280	.58	112	2020	12.48	43.1
W 21×55	168	623	.27	110	3480	20.71	96.2	W 21×55	158	368	.43	110	2910	18.40	41.2
W 18×60	167	553	.30	108	3050	18.24	95.6	W 18×60	156	325	.48	108	2500	16.05	40.6
W 16×64	163	492	.33	104	2630	16.15	96.5	W 16×64	152	293	.52	104	2150	14.17	41.5
W 14×68	161	445	.36	103	2310	14.37	98.0	W 14×68	149	269	.55	103	1880	12.59	43.0
W 18×55	153	528	.29	98.4	2810	18.31	95.5	W 18×55	143	313	.46	98.4	2320	16.20	40.5
W 21×49	149	579	.26	93.3	3110	20.95	94.5	W 21×49	139	338	.41	93.3	2590	18.65	39.5

NOTES (Cont'd.):

4. For uniform loading: Deflection (in.) $= ML^2/160\, Sy_b$

    End reaction (kips) $= 0.33 S_{tr} F_b/L$

    where $M =$ kip-ft., $L =$ ft., $S =$ in.³, $y_b =$ in., $S_{tr} =$ in.³, $F_b =$ ksi

5. Ratio of S_{tr}/S_t at balanced design:

F_y (ksi)	$f'_c = 3.0$	3.75	4.0
36	.51	.59	.61
42	.44	.50	.52
45	.41	.47	.48
50	.37	.42	.44
55	.34	.38	.40
60	.31	.35	.36

5½″ Slab

COMPOSITE DESIGN
Properties of composite beams
No Cover Plate—5½ Inch Slab

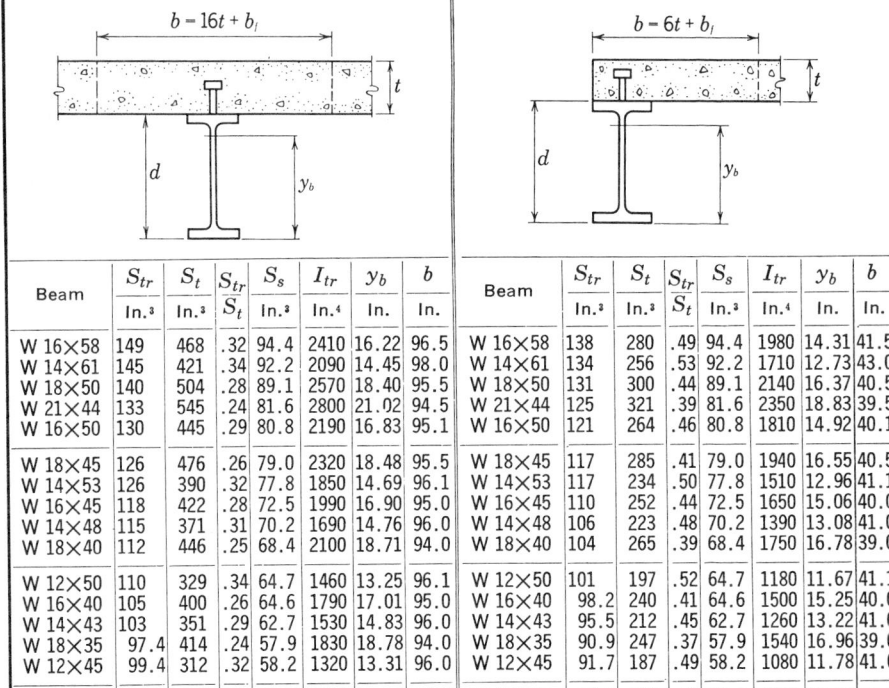

FULL WIDTH SLAB							
Beam	S_{tr} In.³	S_t In.³	$\dfrac{S_{tr}}{S_t}$	S_s In.³	I_{tr} In.⁴	y_b In.	b In.
W 16×58	149	468	.32	94.4	2410	16.22	96.5
W 14×61	145	421	.34	92.2	2090	14.45	98.0
W 18×50	140	504	.28	89.1	2570	18.40	95.5
W 21×44	133	545	.24	81.6	2800	21.02	94.5
W 16×50	130	445	.29	80.8	2190	16.83	95.1
W 18×45	126	476	.26	79.0	2320	18.48	95.5
W 14×53	126	390	.32	77.8	1850	14.69	96.1
W 16×45	118	422	.28	72.5	1990	16.90	95.0
W 14×48	115	371	.31	70.2	1690	14.76	96.0
W 18×40	112	446	.25	68.4	2100	18.71	94.0
W 12×50	110	329	.34	64.7	1460	13.25	96.1
W 16×40	105	400	.26	64.6	1790	17.01	95.0
W 14×43	103	351	.29	62.7	1530	14.83	96.0
W 18×35	97.4	414	.24	57.9	1830	18.78	94.0
W 12×45	99.4	312	.32	58.2	1320	13.31	96.0
W 16×36	94.3	376	.25	56.5	1610	17.07	95.0
W 14×38	92.7	339	.27	54.7	1430	15.41	94.8
W 12×40	89.3	295	.30	51.9	1200	13.39	96.0
W 10×45	90.1	260	.35	49.1	1040	11.60	96.0
W 14×34	83.1	321	.26	48.6	1290	15.49	94.8
W 16×31	81.3	347	.23	47.2	1410	17.28	93.5
W 12×36	81.2	285	.29	46.0	1120	13.80	94.6
W 10×39	78.7	242	.33	42.2	917	11.65	96.0
W 14×30	73.3	300	.24	41.9	1140	15.56	94.7
W 12×31	70.4	265	.27	39.5	978	13.90	94.5

PARTIAL SLAB							
Beam	S_{tr} In.³	S_t In.³	$\dfrac{S_{tr}}{S_t}$	S_s In.³	I_{tr} In.⁴	y_b In.	b In.
W 16×58	138	280	.49	94.4	1980	14.31	41.5
W 14×61	134	256	.53	92.2	1710	12.73	43.0
W 18×50	131	300	.44	89.1	2140	16.37	40.5
W 21×44	125	321	.39	81.6	2350	18.83	39.5
W 16×50	121	264	.46	80.8	1810	14.92	40.1
W 18×45	117	285	.41	79.0	1940	16.55	40.5
W 14×53	117	234	.50	77.8	1510	12.96	41.1
W 16×45	110	252	.44	72.5	1650	15.06	40.0
W 14×48	106	223	.48	70.2	1390	13.08	41.0
W 18×40	104	265	.39	68.4	1750	16.78	39.0
W 12×50	101	197	.52	64.7	1180	11.67	41.1
W 16×40	98.2	240	.41	64.6	1500	15.25	40.0
W 14×43	95.5	212	.45	62.7	1260	13.22	41.
W 18×35	90.9	247	.37	57.9	1540	16.96	39.
W 12×45	91.7	187	.49	58.2	1080	11.78	41.0
W 16×36	87.9	226	.39	56.5	1350	15.37	40.
W 14×38	86.0	203	.42	54.7	1190	13.78	39.8
W 12×40	82.6	177	.47	51.9	983	11.90	41.
W 10×45	82.5	154	.53	49.1	840	10.18	41.
W 14×34	77.3	192	.40	48.6	1070	13.91	39.
W 16×31	75.7	206	.37	47.2	1180	15.61	38.
W 12×36	75.0	169	.44	46.0	922	12.29	39.
W 10×39	72.3	144	.50	42.2	743	10.27	41.
W 14×30	68.3	180	.38	41.9	958	14.03	39.
W 12×31	65.3	158	.41	39.5	812	12.44	39.

NOTES:
1. Tables are based on specified concrete strength $f'_c = 3.0$ ksi and modular ratio $n = 9$.
2. Proper selection of S_{tr} value assures that stress in steel beam does not exceed allowable. Concrete stress due to bending does not exceed allowable under the following conditions:

$F_y = 36$ ksi	Condition	$F_y = 50$ ksi
S_{tr}/S_t	$f'_c = 3.0$ ksi	S_{tr}/S_t
≤ .51	Shored construction	≤ .37
≤ 1.01	Unshored const. with $M_L/M_D < 1.0$	≤ .74
≤ .76	Unshored const. with $M_L/M_D < 2.0$	≤ .55
≤ .67	Unshored const. with $M_L/M_D < 3.0$	≤ .49

3. For unshored construction see Sect. 1.11.2.2 of the AISC Specification.

COMPOSITE DESIGN

5½″ Slab

Properties of composite beams

No Cover Plate—5½ Inch Slab

FULL WIDTH SLAB		PARTIAL SLAB

$b = 16t + b_f$ (full width slab)

$b = 6t + b_f$ (partial slab)

Beam	S_{tr} In.³	S_t In.³	$\dfrac{S_{tr}}{S_t}$	S_s In.³	I_{tr} In.⁴	y_b In.	b In.	Beam	S_{tr} In.³	S_t In.³	$\dfrac{S_{tr}}{S_t}$	S_s In.³	I_{tr} In.⁴	y_b In.	b In.
W 16× 26	68.2	316	.22	38.3	1190	17.39	93.5	W 16× 26	63.7	188	.34	38.3	1010	15.80	38.5
W 14× 26	63.7	278	.23	35.1	1000	15.77	93.0	W 14× 26	59.3	164	.36	35.1	845	14.24	38.0
W 12× 27	61.5	247	.25	34.2	860	13.98	94.5	W 12× 27	57.3	147	.39	34.2	720	12.57	39.5
W 10× 29	60.1	215	.28	30.8	738	12.29	93.8	W 10× 29	55.4	126	.44	30.8	605	10.92	38.8
W 14× 22	53.9	254	.21	28.9	854	15.86	93.0	W 14× 22	50.3	150	.33	28.9	725	14.40	38.0
W 10× 25	52.0	200	.26	26.5	643	12.36	93.8	W 10× 25	48.2	117	.41	26.5	532	11.05	38.8
W 12× 22	50.2	224	.22	25.3	730	14.55	92.0	W 12× 22	46.6	131	.36	25.3	611	13.13	37.0
W 8× 28	52.1	172	.30	24.3	542	10.40	94.5	W 8× 28	47.9	100	.48	24.3	439	9.17	39.5
W 12× 19	43.4	207	.21	21.3	633	14.61	92.0	W 12× 19	40.4	121	.33	21.3	535	13.25	37.0
W 8× 24	45.1	160	.28	20.8	472	10.47	94.5	W 8× 24	41.6	93.4	.45	20.8	386	9.29	39.5
W 10× 21	43.9	183	.24	21.5	545	12.42	93.8	W 10× 21	40.8	108	.38	21.5	455	11.17	38.8
W 10× 19	40.0	177	.23	18.8	514	12.84	92.0	W 10× 19	37.1	103	.36	18.8	429	11.56	37.0
W 12×16.5	37.5	191	.20	17.6	548	14.63	92.0	W 12×16.5	35.0	112	.31	17.6	466	13.33	37.0
W 8× 20	38.2	149	.26	17.0	415	10.86	93.3	W 8× 20	35.4	86.8	.41	17.0	343	9.69	38.3
W 10× 17	35.5	166	.21	16.2	457	12.86	92.0	W 10× 17	33.1	96.3	.34	16.2	384	11.63	37.0
W 8× 17	32.6	138	.24	14.1	356	10.91	93.3	W 8× 17	30.3	80.3	.38	14.1	297	9.80	38.3

NOTES (Cont'd.):

4. For uniform loading: Deflection (in.) $= ML^2/160\, S y_b$

                    End reaction (kips) $= 0.33 S_{tr} F_b/L$

                    where $M =$ kip-ft., $L =$ ft., $S =$ in.³, $y_b =$ in., $S_{tr} =$ in.³, $F_b =$ ksi

5. Ratio of S_{tr}/S_t at balanced design:

F_y (ksi)	$f'_c = 3.0$	3.75	4.0
36	.51	.59	.61
42	.44	.50	.52
45	.41	.47	.48
50	.37	.42	.44
55	.34	.38	.40
60	.31	.35	.36

4″ Slab

COMPOSITE DESIGN
Properties of composite beams
With Cover Plate—4 Inch Slab

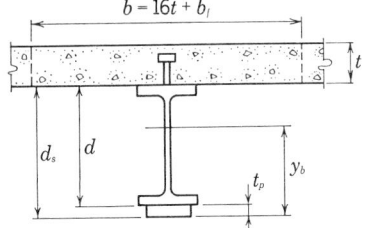

$$b = 16t + b_f$$

Beam	Cover Plate Size	Avg. Wt. per Ft.	Full Slab Transformed Section						K	W_s
			S_{tr}	S_t	$\dfrac{S_{tr}}{S_t}$	I_{tr}	y_b	$\dfrac{12Q}{I}$		
	In.	Lbs.	In.³	In.³		In.⁴	In.			Lbs.
W 36 × 170	0	170	713	1340	.53	18700	26.18	—	—	170
$b = 76.0$	½ × 10	177	872	1420	.61	22000	25.19	.07	.43	187
*$V = 357$	1½ × 10	202	1180	1540	.77	27900	23.59	.15	.63	221
W 36 × 150	0	150	628	1250	.50	16700	26.55	—	—	150
$b = 76.0$	½ × 10	158	788	1340	.59	20000	25.43	.08	.45	167
*$V = 325$	1½ × 10	184	1100	1470	.75	26000	23.64	.16	.66	201
W 36 × 135	0	135	559	1180	.47	15000	26.85	—	—	135
$b = 76.0$	½ × 10	143	720	1280	.56	18400	25.62	.08	.47	152
*$V = 308$	1½ × 10	170	1030	1410	.73	24500	23.67	.17	.68	186
W 33 × 130	0	130	512	1090	.47	12900	25.21	—	—	130
$b = 75.5$	½ × 10	138	663	1180	.56	15900	24.06	.09	.48	147
*$V = 278$	1½ × 10	165	957	1300	.74	21300	22.23	.18	.68	181
W 33 × 118	0	118	461	1030	.45	11700	25.48	—	—	118
$b = 75.5$	½ × 10	127	612	1130	.54	14800	24.22	.10	.50	135
*$V = 264$	1½ × 10	154	908	1250	.72	20200	22.26	.19	.70	169
W 30 × 108	0	108	389	890	.44	9150	23.53	—	—	108
$b = 74.5$	½ × 9	116	513	975	.53	11500	22.49	.10	.49	123
*$V = 237$	1½ × 9	140	755	1090	.69	15700	20.85	.21	.70	154
W 30 × 99	0	99	354	854	.42	8420	23.77	—	—	99
$b = 74.5$	½ × 9	107	479	944	.51	10800	22.65	.11	.51	114
*$V = 224$	1½ × 9	132	722	1060	.68	15100	20.90	.22	.71	145
W 27 × 102	0	102	344	791	.43	7440	21.66	—	—	102
$b = 74.0$	½ × 9	110	457	870	.53	9460	20.70	.12	.50	117
*$V = 203$	1½ × 9	134	678	974	.70	13000	19.20	.23	.70	148

* For steels with $F_y = 36$ ksi.

NOTES:
1. Tables are based on specified concrete strength $f'_c = 3.0$ ksi and modular ratio $n = 9$.
2. Proper selection of S_{tr} value assures that stress in steel beam does not exceed allowable. Concrete stress due to bending does not exceed allowable under the following conditions:

$F_y = 36$ ksi	Condition	$F_y = 50$ ksi
S_{tr}/S_t	$f'_c = 3.0$ ksi	S_{tr}/S_t
⩽ .51	Shored construction	⩽ .37
⩽ 1.01	Unshored const. with $M_L/M_D < 1.0$	⩽ .74
⩽ .76	Unshored const. with $M_L/M_D < 2.0$	⩽ .55
⩽ .67	Unshored const. with $M_L/M_D < 3.0$	⩽ .49

3. For unshored construction see Sect. 1.11.2.2 of the AISC Specification.

AMERICAN INSTITUTE OF STEEL CONSTRUCTION

$$10' \times 50' = 500 \text{ #}'$$

$0 \times 53.5 = 535$

$\dfrac{20}{10,700}$

$\dfrac{20}{10,000} \rightarrow WIND$

$(7)(50)(40)$

$7(2000) = 14,000 - LL$

DEAD LOAD

$\dfrac{80}{15 \text{#}/\text{#}'} = \dfrac{X}{20 \text{#}/\text{#}'}$

$1600 = 15 X$

$X = 107 \ MPH$

$\begin{array}{r} 50 \\ 40 \\ \hline 2000 \end{array}$

$\begin{array}{r} 10 \text{#} \\ 15\overline{)1600} \\ 15 \\ \hline 100 \\ 0 \end{array}$

more than $15) to be exchanged at the luncheon. If you would like to participate please complete the form below and return to Jennifer Flannery by Wednesday, November 29.

Name:

Locations where items can be left:

Hints, Ideas and Wish list:

COMPOSITE DESIGN
Properties of composite beams
With Cover Plate—4 Inch Slab

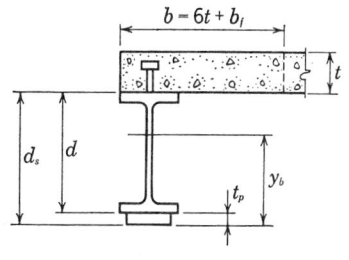
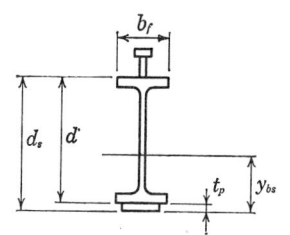

Beam	Cover Plate Size	Avg. Wt. per Ft.	Partial Slab Transformed Section						Steel Section			
			S_{tr}	S_t	$\dfrac{S_{tr}}{S_t}$	I_{tr}	y_b	$\dfrac{12Q}{I}$	S_s	S_{ts}	I	y_{bs}
	In.	Lbs.	In.³	In.³		In.⁴	In.		In.³	In.³	In.⁴	In.
W 36 × 170 $b = 36.0$	0	170	672	896	.75	15400	22.95	—	580	580	10500	18.08
	½ × 10	177	821	951	.86	17900	21.82	.07	711	609	12000	16.91
	1½ × 10	202	1110	1030	1.10	22300	20.06	.16	958	651	14600	15.23
W 36 × 150 $b = 36.0$	0	150	591	824	.72	13700	23.21	—	504	504	9030	17.92
	½ × 10	158	742	882	.84	16300	21.91	.08	634	532	10500	16.57
	1½ × 10	184	1030	963	1.10	20600	19.93	.17	881	571	12900	14.69
W 36 × 135 $b = 36.0$	0	135	525	763	.69	12300	23.44	—	440	440	7820	17.77
	½ × 10	143	676	824	.82	14900	21.99	.09	570	468	9260	16.26
	1½ × 10	170	970	905	1.10	19200	19.81	.18	814	506	11600	14.20
W 33 × 130 $b = 35.5$	0	130	482	699	.69	10600	21.96	—	406	406	6710	16.55
	½ × 10	138	624	754	.83	12800	20.58	.09	527	430	7960	15.11
	1½ × 10	165	898	829	1.10	16600	18.53	.19	754	464	9940	13.18
W 33 × 118 $b = 35.5$	0	118	433	654	.66	9610	22.18	—	359	359	5900	16.43
	½ × 10	127	576	712	.81	11900	20.66	.10	480	384	7120	14.83
	1½ × 10	154	851	787	1.10	15700	18.43	.20	705	416	9000	12.76
W 30 × 108 $b = 34.5$	0	108	365	555	.66	7450	20.41	—	300	300	4470	14.91
	½ × 9	116	482	605	.80	9200	19.11	.11	397	320	5380	13.53
	1½ × 9	140	706	670	1.10	12100	17.20	.22	579	347	6800	11.74
W 30 × 99 $b = 34.5$	0	99	333	527	.63	6860	20.62	—	270	270	4000	14.82
	½ × 9	107	450	578	.78	8640	19.20	.12	367	290	4890	13.30
	1½ × 9	132	676	644	1.10	11600	17.14	.23	548	316	6240	11.39
W 27 × 102 $b = 34.0$	0	102	323	491	.66	6060	18.74	—	267	267	3610	13.54
	½ × 9	110	430	536	.80	7530	17.52	.12	356	284	4350	12.24
	1½ × 9	134	635	595	1.10	10000	15.75	.24	520	307	5510	10.60

NOTES (Cont'd.):

4. For uniform loading: Deflection (in.) $= ML^2/160\, Sy_b$
   End reaction (kips) $= 0.33 S_{tr} F_b/L$
   where $M =$ kip-ft., $L =$ ft., $S =$ in.³, $y_b =$ in., $S_{tr} =$ in.³, $F_b =$ ksi

5. Ratio of S_{tr}/S_t at balanced design:

F_y (ksi)	$f'_c = 3.0$	3.75	4.0
36	.51	.59	.61
42	.44	.50	.52
45	.41	.47	.48
50	.37	.42	.44
55	.34	.38	.40
60	.31	.35	.36

4″ Slab

COMPOSITE DESIGN
Properties of composite beams
With Cover Plate—4 Inch Slab

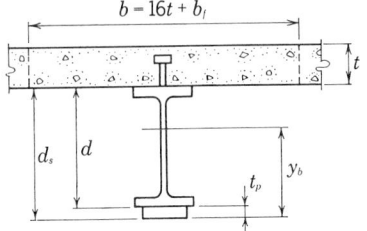

$$b = 16t + b_f$$

Beam	Cover Plate Size	Avg. Wt. per Ft.	Full Slab Transformed Section						K	W_s
			S_{tr}	S_t	$\dfrac{S_{tr}}{S_t}$	I_{tr}	y_b	$\dfrac{12Q}{I}$		
	In.	Lbs.	In.³	In.³		In.⁴	In.			Lbs.
W 27 × 94	0	94	316	762	.42	6910	21.84	—	—	94
$b = 74.0$	½ × 9	102	430	845	.51	8950	20.82	.12	.51	109
*V = 191	1½ × 9	127	652	951	.69	12500	19.23	.24	.72	139
W 27 × 84	0	84	281	721	.39	6200	22.09	—	—	84
$b = 74.0$	½ × 9	92.5	395	811	.49	8290	20.97	.13	.54	99.3
*V = 179	1½ × 9	118	619	921	.67	11900	19.26	.25	.74	130
W 24 × 68	0	68	207	582	.36	4240	20.42	—	—	68
$b = 73.0$	½ × 8	75.5	299	666	.45	5830	19.46	.16	.55	81.6
*V = 143	1½ × 8	98.7	479	767	.62	8620	17.98	.29	.75	109
W 24 × 55	0	55	163	512	.32	3410	20.88	—	—	55
$b = 71.0$	½ × 6	60.6	232	590	.39	4670	20.13	.15	.54	65.2
*V = 135	1½ × 6	77.9	367	689	.53	6960	18.95	.28	.74	85.6
W 21 × 62	0	62	173	488	.35	3190	18.45	—	—	62
$b = 72.2$	½ × 7	68.7	245	560	.44	4340	17.74	.17	.54	73.9
*V = 122	1½ × 7	88.7	385	650	.59	6400	16.64	.31	.74	97.7
W 21 × 55	0	55	152	461	.33	2840	18.64	—	—	55
$b = 72.2$	½ × 7	61.8	224	538	.42	4000	17.86	.18	.57	66.9
*V = 113	1½ × 7	82.3	365	632	.58	6080	16.68	.33	.76	90.7
W 21 × 44	0	44	120	406	.29	2280	19.04	—	—	44
$b = 70.5$	½ × 5½	49.5	176	481	.37	3250	18.42	.18	.57	53.4
*V = 104	1½ × 5½	65.6	287	574	.50	5010	17.44	.33	.76	72.1
W 18 × 50	0	50	125	376	.33	2060	16.52	—	—	50
$b = 71.5$	½ × 6	55.6	178	439	.41	2850	16.00	.20	.55	60.2
*V = 93	1½ × 6	72.9	283	521	.54	4310	15.22	.36	.75	80.6

* For steels with $F_y = 36$ ksi.

NOTES:

1. Tables are based on specified concrete strength $f'_c = 3.0$ ksi and modular ratio $n = 9$.
2. Proper selection of S_{tr} value assures that stress in steel beam does not exceed allowable. Concrete stress due to bending does not exceed allowable under the following conditions:

$F_y = 36$ ksi	Condition	$F_y = 50$ ksi
S_{tr}/S_t	$f'_c = 3.0$ ksi	S_{tr}/S_t
⩽ .51	Shored construction	⩽ .37
⩽ 1.01	Unshored const. with $M_L/M_D < 1.0$	⩽ .74
⩽ .76	Unshored const. with $M_L/M_D < 2.0$	⩽ .55
⩽ .67	Unshored const. with $M_L/M_D < 3.0$	⩽ .49

3. For unshored construction see Sect. 1.11.2.2 of the AISC Specification.

COMPOSITE DESIGN

Properties of composite beams

With Cover Plate—4 Inch Slab

4″ Slab

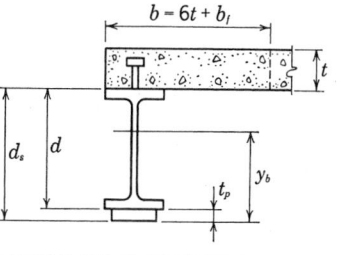

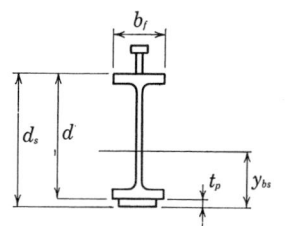

Beam	Cover Plate Size	Avg. Wt. per Ft.	Partial Slab Transformed Section						Steel Section			
			S_{tr}	S_t	$\dfrac{S_{tr}}{S_t}$	I_{tr}	y_b	$\dfrac{12Q}{I}$	S_s	S_{ts}	I	y_{bs}
	In.	Lbs.	In.³	In.³		In.⁴	In.		In.³	In.³	In.⁴	In.
W 27 × 94 $b = 34.0$	0	94	297	469	.63	5630	18.91	—	243	243	3270	13.45
	½ × 9	102	405	515	.79	7120	17.59	.13	332	260	4000	12.04
	1½ × 9	127	611	574	1.10	9590	15.70	.25	496	282	5100	10.30
W 27 × 84 $b = 34.0$	0	84	264	438	.60	5060	19.15	—	212	212	2830	13.35
	½ × 9	92.6	372	487	.76	6580	17.68	.14	301	229	3530	11.76
	1½ × 9	118	580	547	1.10	9060	15.62	.27	463	250	4570	9.88
W 24 × 68 $b = 33.0$	0	68	195	346	.56	3460	17.71	—	153	153	1820	11.86
	½ × 8	75.5	282	390	.72	4620	16.35	.17	223	166	2310	10.34
	1½ × 8	98.7	450	441	1.00	6500	14.46	.30	349	182	3010	8.63
W 24 × 55 $b = 31.0$	0	55	153	293	.52	2770	18.11	—	114	114	1340	11.77
	½ × 6	60.6	218	332	.66	3690	16.94	.16	164	125	1710	10.40
	1½ × 6	77.9	343	379	.90	5230	15.25	.30	256	138	2250	8.80
W 21 × 62 $b = 32.2$	0	62	163	289	.56	2600	15.98	—	127	127	1330	10.50
	½ × 7	68.7	231	325	.71	3440	14.91	.18	180	137	1670	9.27
	1½ × 7	88.6	360	369	.98	4830	13.41	.33	276	149	2180	7.89
W 21 × 55 $b = 32.2$	0	55	144	271	.53	2330	16.22	—	110	110	1140	10.40
	½ × 7	61.8	212	309	.68	3180	15.02	.19	163	119	1470	9.01
	1½ × 7	82.3	342	354	.97	4580	13.37	.35	257	131	1930	7.51
W 21 × 44 $b = 30.5$	0	44	112	233	.48	1870	16.62	—	81.6	81.6	843	10.33
	½ × 5½	49.5	166	268	.62	2580	15.54	.20	122	90.1	1100	8.98
	1½ × 5½	65.6	269	310	.87	3770	14.01	.35	194	100	1460	7.53
W 18 × 50 $b = 31.5$	0	50	118	221	.53	1690	14.37	—	89.1	89.1	802	9.00
	½ × 6	55.6	168	252	.67	2270	13.48	.21	128	96.1	1020	7.93
	1½ × 6	72.8	266	290	.92	3260	12.26	.38	196	105	1330	6.80

NOTES (Cont'd.):
4. For uniform loading: Deflection (in.) $= ML^2/160\, S y_b$

End reaction (kips) $= 0.33 S_{tr} F_b/L$

where $M =$ kip-ft., $L =$ ft., $S =$ in.³, $y_b =$ in., $S_{tr} =$ in.³, $F_b =$ ksi

5. Ratio of S_{tr}/S_t at balanced design:

F_y (ksi)	$f'_c = 3.0$	3.75	4.0
36	.51	.59	.61
42	.44	.50	.52
45	.41	.47	.48
50	.37	.42	.44
55	.34	.38	.40
60	.31	.35	.36

AMERICAN INSTITUTE OF STEEL CONSTRUCTION

4″ Slab

COMPOSITE DESIGN
Properties of composite beams
With Cover Plate—4 Inch Slab

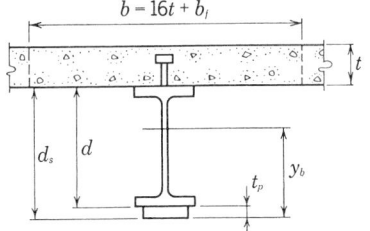

Beam	Cover Plate Size	Avg. Wt. per Ft.	Full Slab Transformed Section						K	W_s
			S_{tr}	S_t	$\dfrac{S_{tr}}{S_t}$	I_{tr}	y_b	$\dfrac{12Q}{I}$		
	In.	Lbs.	In.³	In.³		In.⁴	In.			Lbs.
W 18 × 45	0	45	112	358	.31	1860	16.65	—	—	45
$b = 71.5$	½ × 6	50.7	166	425	.39	2670	16.09	.21	.57	55.2
*V = 87	1½ × 6	68.3	271	510	.53	4130	15.25	.38	.77	75.6
W 18 × 35	0	35	86.2	312	.28	1470	17.01	—	—	35
$b = 70.0$	½ × 5	40.0	131	382	.34	2170	16.53	.22	.59	43.5
*V = 77	1½ × 5	54.9	220	468	.47	3470	15.79	.39	.78	60.5
W 16 × 40	0	40	92.8	300	.31	1420	15.28	—	—	40
$b = 71.0$	½ × 6	46.1	142	366	.39	2090	14.77	.25	.59	50.2
*V = 71	1½ × 6	64.0	238	446	.53	3330	14.02	.43	.78	70.6
W 16 × 36	0	36	82.8	283	.29	1270	15.35	—	—	36
$b = 71.0$	½ × 6	42.3	132	353	.37	1950	14.82	.27	.61	46.2
*V = 69	1¼ × 6	55.7	204	419	.49	2900	14.19	.42	.77	61.5
W 16 × 26	0	26	59.5	236	.25	934	15.70	—	—	26
$b = 69.5$	½ × 4½	30.8	96.3	305	.32	1470	15.32	.28	.62	33.7
*V = 57	1 × 4½	37.4	133	353	.38	1990	15.00	.39	.74	41.3
W 14 × 30	0	30	63.4	223	.28	882	13.90	—	—	30
$b = 70.7$	½ × 5½	35.8	104	287	.36	1400	13.50	.31	.62	39.4
*V = 54	1 × 5½	44.0	143	331	.43	1890	13.17	.44	.75	48.7
W 14 × 22	0	22	46.4	187	.25	659	14.20	—	—	22
$b = 69.0$	½ × 4	26.3	75.6	246	.31	1050	13.94	.31	.62	28.8
*V = 46	1 × 4	32.2	105	289	.36	1440	13.75	.44	.75	35.6
W 12 × 19	0	19	36.8	149	.25	477	12.97	—	—	19
$b = 68.0$	½ × 3	22.0	56.5	192	.29	727	12.88	.31	.59	24.1
*V = 42	1 × 3	26.3	75.8	227	.33	976	12.86	.46	.72	29.2

* For steels with $F_y = 36$ ksi.

NOTES:
1. Tables are based on specified concrete strength $f'_c = 3.0$ ksi and modular ratio $n = 9$.
2. Proper selection of S_{tr} value assures that stress in steel beam does not exceed allowable. Concrete stress due to bending does not exceed allowable under the following conditions:

$F_y = 36$ ksi	Condition	$F_y = 50$ ksi
S_{tr}/S_t	$f'_c = 3.0$ ksi	S_{tr}/S_t
≤ .51	Shored construction	≤ .37
≤ 1.01	Unshored const. with $M_L/M_D < 1.0$	≤ .74
≤ .76	Unshored const. with $M_L/M_D < 2.0$	≤ .55
≤ .67	Unshored const. with $M_L/M_D < 3.0$	≤ .49

3. For unshored construction see Sect. 1.11.2.2 of the AISC Specification.

AMERICAN INSTITUTE OF STEEL CONSTRUCTION

COMPOSITE DESIGN
Properties of composite beams
With Cover Plate—4 Inch Slab

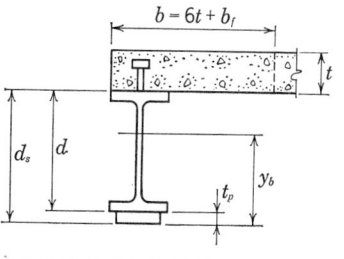
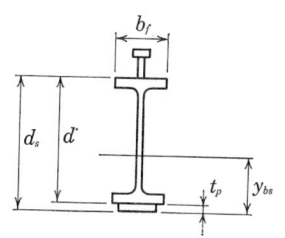

Beam	Cover Plate Size	Avg. Wt. per Ft.	Partial Slab Transformed Section						Steel Section			
			S_{tr}	S_t	$\dfrac{S_{tr}}{S_t}$	I_{tr}	y_b	$\dfrac{12Q}{I}$	S_s	S_{ts}	I	y_{bs}
	In.	Lbs.	In.³	In.³		In.⁴	In.		In.³	In.³	In.⁴	In.
W 18 × 45 $b = 31.5$	0	45	106	210	.50	1540	14.55	—	79.0	79.0	706	8.93
	½ × 6	50.7	157	242	.65	2130	13.58	.23	118	85.8	912	7.73
	1½ × 6	68.3	255	281	.91	3120	12.25	.40	186	94.1	1210	6.51
W 18 × 35 $b = 30.0$	0	35	81.1	181	.45	1220	14.98	—	57.9	57.9	513	8.85
	½ × 5	40.0	124	212	.58	1740	14.02	.24	89.7	63.9	680	7.58
	1½ × 5	54.9	207	250	.83	2630	12.69	.41	145	70.9	915	6.31
W 16 × 40 $b = 31.0$	0	40	87.5	177	.49	1170	13.39	—	64.6	64.6	517	8.00
	½ × 6	46.1	134	208	.65	1670	12.46	.26	99.6	70.3	680	6.83
	1½ × 6	64.0	223	243	.92	2500	11.21	.45	159	77.2	910	5.71
W 16 × 36 $b = 31.0$	0	36	78.0	167	.47	1060	13.53	—	56.5	56.5	447	7.92
	½ × 6	42.3	125	200	.62	1560	12.52	.28	91.1	62.0	603	6.62
	1¼ × 6	55.7	193	229	.84	2210	11.45	.44	137	67.1	769	5.63
W 16 × 26 $b = 29.5$	0	26	55.9	139	.40	785	14.02	—	38.3	38.3	300	7.82
	½ × 4½	30.8	91.3	171	.53	1200	13.13	.29	63.7	42.8	413	6.49
	1 × 4½	37.5	126	191	.66	1570	12.44	.41	86.5	45.6	497	5.75
W 14 × 30 $b = 30.7$	0	30	59.6	134	.45	736	12.35	—	41.9	41.9	290	6.93
	½ × 5½	35.9	98.0	164	.60	1130	11.48	.33	69.5	46.1	398	5.72
	1 × 5½	44.0	135	183	.74	1470	10.83	.46	94.0	48.8	478	5.08
W 14 × 22 $b = 29.0$	0	22	43.4	112	.39	554	12.75	—	28.9	28.9	198	6.86
	½ × 4	26.3	71.5	139	.51	861	12.04	.33	48.4	32.3	275	5.68
	1 × 4	32.3	99.0	157	.63	1140	11.49	.46	65.8	34.4	332	5.05
W 12 × 19 $b = 28.0$	0	19	34.2	88	.39	398	11.66	—	21.3	21.3	130	6.08
	½ × 3	22.0	52.9	110	.48	595	11.24	.33	33.9	23.9	177	5.24
	1 × 3	26.4	71.3	125	.57	779	10.92	.48	44.9	25.6	215	4.78

NOTES (Cont'd.):

4. For uniform loading: Deflection (in.) $= ML^2/160\,Sy_b$

End reaction (kips) $= 0.33 S_{tr}F_b/L$

where $M =$ kip-ft., $L =$ ft., $S =$ in.³, $y_b =$ in., $S_{tr} =$ in.³, $F_b =$ ksi

5. Ratio of S_{tr}/S_t at balanced design:

F_y (ksi)	$f'_c = 3.0$	3.75	4.0
36	.51	.59	.61
42	.44	.50	.52
45	.41	.47	.48
50	.37	.42	.44
55	.34	.38	.40
60	.31	.35	.36

4½″ Slab

COMPOSITE DESIGN
Properties of composite beams
With Cover Plate—4½ Inch Slab

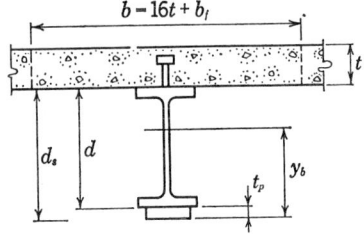

$b = 16t + b_f$

Beam	Cover Plate Size	Avg. Wt. per Ft.	Full Slab Transformed Section						K	W_s
			S_{tr}	S_t	$\dfrac{S_{tr}}{S_t}$	I_{tr}	y_b	$\dfrac{12Q}{I}$		
	In.	Lbs.	In.³	In.³		In.⁴	In.			Lbs.
W 36 × 170 $b = 84.0$ *V = 357	0 ½ × 10 1½ × 10	170 177 202	731 893 1210	1500 1600 1750	.49 .56 .69	20000 23600 30200	27.36 26.44 24.92	— .07 .14	— .43 .63	170 187 221
W 36 × 150 $b = 84.0$ *V = 325	0 ½ × 10 1½ × 10	150 158 184	644 807 1130	1420 1530 1680	.45 .53 .67	17900 21600 28200	27.75 26.71 25.02	— .07 .15	— .45 .66	150 167 201
W 36 × 135 $b = 84.0$ *V = 308	0 ½ × 10 1½ × 10	135 143 170	573 738 1060	1340 1460 1620	.43 .51 .66	16100 19900 26600	28.05 26.92 25.09	— .08 .17	— .47 .68	135 152 186
W 33 × 130 $b = 83.5$ *V = 278	0 ½ × 10 1½ × 10	130 138 165	525 679 981	1230 1340 1490	.43 .51 .66	13800 17200 23100	26.36 25.29 23.58	— .09 .18	— .48 .68	130 147 181
W 33 × 118 $b = 83.5$ *V = 264	0 ½ × 10 1½ × 10	118 127 154	473 627 930	1170 1290 1440	.40 .49 .64	12600 16000 22000	26.62 25.47 23.63	— .09 .19	— .50 .70	118 135 169
W 30 × 108 $b = 82.5$ *V = 237	0 ½ × 9 1½ × 9	108 116 140	399 526 774	1010 1110 1250	.40 .47 .62	9830 12400 17200	24.60 23.66 22.14	.10 .20	— .49 .70	108 123 154
W 30 × 99 $b = 82.5$ *V = 224	0 ½ × 9 1½ × 9	99 107 132	364 491 741	971 1080 1220	.38 .45 .60	9040 11700 16500	24.83 23.82 22.21	— .11 .21	— .51 .71	99 114 145
W 27 × 102 $b = 82.0$ *V = 203	0 ½ × 9 1½ × 9	102 110 134	353 469 696	897 993 1120	.39 .47 .62	8000 10200 14200	22.65 21.79 20.41	— .11 .22	— .50 .70	102 117 148

* For steels with $F_y = 36$ ksi.

NOTES:
1. Tables are based on specified concrete strength $f'_c = 3.0$ ksi and modular ratio $n = 9$.
2. Proper selection of S_{tr} value assures that stress in steel beam does not exceed allowable. Concrete stress due to bending does not exceed allowable under the following conditions:

$F_y = 36$ ksi	Condition	$F_y = 50$ ksi
S_{tr}/S_t	$f'_c = 3.0$ ksi	S_{tr}/S_t
⩽ .51	Shored construction	⩽ .37
⩽1.01	Unshored const. with $M_L/M_D < 1.0$	⩽ .74
⩽ .76	Unshored const. with $M_L/M_D < 2.0$	⩽ .55
⩽ .67	Unshored const. with $M_L/M_D < 3.0$	⩽ .49

3. For unshored construction see Sect. 1.11.2.2 of the AISC Specification.

COMPOSITE DESIGN

Properties of composite beams

With Cover Plate—4½ Inch Slab

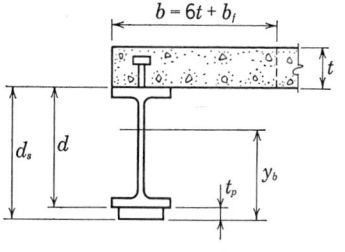

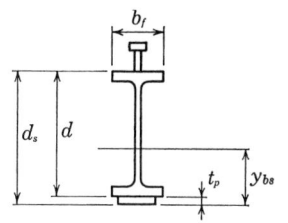

Beam	Cover Plate Size	Avg. Wt. per Ft.	Partial Slab Transformed Section						Steel Section			
			S_{tr}	S_t	$\dfrac{S_{tr}}{S_t}$	I_{tr}	y_b	$\dfrac{12Q}{I}$	S_s	S_{ts}	I	y_{bs}
	In.	Lbs.	In.³	In.³		In.⁴	In.		In.³	In.³	In.⁴	In.
◢ 36 × 170 = 39.0	0	170	687	968	.71	16300	23.79	—	580	580	10500	18.08
	½ × 10	177	839	1030	.82	19000	22.67	.07	711	609	12000	16.91
	1½ × 10	202	1140	1120	1.00	23800	20.93	.15	958	651	14600	15.23
◢ 36 × 150 = 39.0	0	150	605	896	.67	14600	24.09	—	504	504	9030	17.92
	½ × 10	158	759	961	.79	17300	22.82	.08	634	532	10500	16.57
	1½ × 10	184	1060	1050	1.00	22100	20.86	.16	881	571	12900	14.69
◢ 36 × 135 = 39.0	0	135	538	834	.64	13100	24.35	—	440	440	7820	17.77
	½ × 10	143	693	902	.77	15900	22.94	.09	570	468	9260	16.26
	1½ × 10	170	993	994	1.00	20600	20.78	.17	814	506	11600	14.20
◢ 33 × 130 = 38.5	0	130	493	764	.65	11300	22.84	—	406	406	6710	16.55
	½ × 10	138	638	826	.77	13700	21.49	.09	527	430	7960	15.11
	1½ × 10	165	919	911	1.00	17900	19.46	.19	754	464	9940	13.18
◢ 33 × 118 = 38.5	0	118	444	718	.62	10300	23.08	—	359	359	5900	16.43
	½ × 10	127	590	784	.75	12700	21.61	.10	480	384	7120	14.83
	1½ × 10	154	872	870	1.00	16900	19.40	.20	705	416	9000	12.76
◢ 30 × 108 = 37.5	0	108	375	611	.61	7970	21.27	—	300	300	4470	14.91
	½ × 9	116	494	668	.74	9890	20.01	.11	397	320	5380	13.53
	1½ × 9	140	725	743	.98	13100	18.13	.21	579	347	6800	11.74
◢ 30 × 99 = 37.5	0	99	342	582	.59	7350	21.50	—	270	270	4000	14.82
	½ × 9	107	462	641	.72	9300	20.13	.11	367	290	4890	13.30
	1½ × 9	132	694	717	.97	12600	18.11	.22	548	316	6240	11.39
◢ 27 × 102 = 37.0	0	102	332	541	.61	6490	19.56	—	267	267	3610	13.54
	½ × 9	110	441	592	.75	8110	18.38	.12	356	284	4350	12.24
	1½ × 9	134	652	660	.99	10900	16.64	.24	520	307	5510	10.60

NOTES (Cont'd.):

4. For uniform loading: Deflection (in.) = $ML^2/160\,Sy_b$

           End reaction (kips) = $0.33S_{tr}F_b/L$

               where M = kip-ft., L = ft., S = in.³, y_b = in., S_{tr} = in.³, F_b = ksi

5. Ratio of S_{tr}/S_t at balanced design:

F_y (ksi)	$f'_c = 3.0$	3.75	4.0
36	.51	.59	.61
42	.44	.50	.52
45	.41	.47	.48
50	.37	.42	.44
55	.34	.38	.40
60	.31	.35	.36

4½″ Slab

COMPOSITE DESIGN
Properties of composite beams
With Cover Plate—4½ Inch Slab

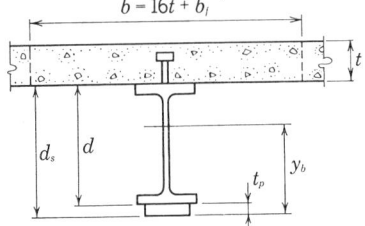

$$b = 16t + b_f$$

Beam	Cover Plate Size	Avg. Wt. per Ft.	Full Slab Transformed Section						K	W_s
			S_{tr}	S_t	$\dfrac{S_{tr}}{S_t}$	I_{tr}	y_b	$\dfrac{12Q}{I}$		
	In.	Lbs.	In.³	In.³		In.⁴	In.			Lbs.
W 27 × 94	0	94	325	864	.38	7420	22.83	—	—	94
$b = 82.0$	½ × 9	102	441	966	.46	9670	21.91	.12	.51	109
*$V = 191$	1½ × 9	127	669	1100	.61	13700	20.45	.23	.72	139
W 27 × 84	0	84	289	819	.35	6660	23.06	—	—	84
$b = 82.0$	½ × 9	92.5	405	930	.44	8950	22.07	.13	.54	99
*$V = 179$	1½ × 9	118	634	1070	.59	13000	20.51	.25	.74	130
W 24 × 68	0	68	214	658	.32	4550	21.30	—	—	68
$b = 81.0$	½ × 8	75.5	308	763	.40	6290	20.46	.15	.55	81.6
*$V = 143$	1½ × 8	98.7	492	892	.55	9420	19.15	.28	.75	109
W 24 × 55	0	55	169	579	.29	3670	21.72	—	—	55
$b = 79.0$	½ × 6	60.6	239	676	.35	5040	21.10	.15	.54	65.2
*$V = 135$	1½ × 6	77.8	377	802	.47	7580	20.10	.28	.74	85.6
W 21 × 62	0	62	179	551	.32	3440	19.25	—	—	62
$b = 80.2$	½ × 7	68.6	252	639	.39	4690	18.65	.17	.54	73.9
*$V = 122$	1½ × 7	88.7	395	754	.52	7000	17.70	.30	.74	97.7
W 21 × 55	0	55	157	519	.30	3050	19.41	—	—	55
$b = 80.2$	½ × 7	61.8	231	615	.38	4330	18.76	.18	.56	66.9
*$V = 113$	1½ × 7	82.3	375	734	.51	6650	17.74	.32	.76	90.7
W 21 × 44	0	44	124	456	.27	2450	19.78	—	—	44
$b = 78.5$	½ × 5½	49.5	182	549	.33	3500	19.28	.18	.56	53.4
*$V = 104$	1½ × 5½	65.6	295	667	.44	5460	18.48	.32	.76	72.1
W 18 × 50	0	50	129	421	.31	2230	17.21	—	—	50
$b = 79.5$	½ × 6	55.5	184	499	.37	3090	16.80	.19	.55	60.2
*$V = 93$	1½ × 6	72.8	292	603	.48	4720	16.16	.35	.75	80.6

* For steels with $F_y = 36$ ksi.

NOTES:
1. Tables are based on specified concrete strength $f'_c = 3.0$ ksi and modular ratio $n = 9$.
2. Proper selection of S_{tr} value assures that stress in steel beam does not exceed allowable. Concrete stress due to bending does not exceed allowable under the following conditions:

$F_y = 36$ ksi	Condition	$F_y = 50$ ksi
S_{tr}/S_t	$f'_c = 3.0$ ksi	S_{tr}/S_t
⩽ .51	Shored construction	⩽ .37
⩽1.01	Unshored const. with $M_L/M_D < 1.0$	⩽ .74
⩽ .76	Unshored const. with $M_L/M_D < 2.0$	⩽ .55
⩽ .67	Unshored const. with $M_L/M_D < 3.0$	⩽ .49

3. For unshored construction see Sect. 1.11.2.2 of the AISC Specification.

COMPOSITE DESIGN

4½″ Slab

Properties of composite beams

With Cover Plate—4½ Inch Slab

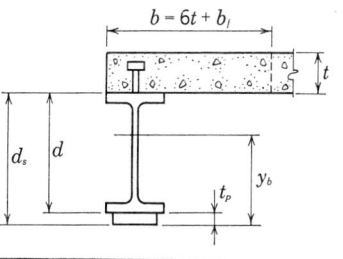

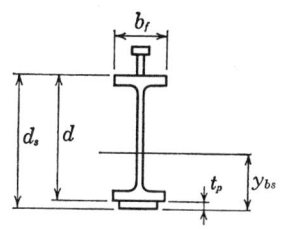

Beam	Cover Plate Size (In.)	Avg. Wt. per Ft. (Lbs.)	Partial Slab Transformed Section S_{tr} (In.³)	S_t (In.³)	$\dfrac{S_{tr}}{S_t}$	I_{tr} (In.⁴)	y_b (In.)	$\dfrac{12Q}{I}$	Steel Section S_s (In.³)	S_{ts} (In.³)	I (In.⁴)	y_{bs} (In.)
W 27 × 94 $b = 37.0$	0	94	306	517	.59	6040	19.74	—	243	243	3270	13.45
	½ × 9	102	416	571	.73	7680	18.47	.13	332	260	4000	12.04
	1½ × 9	127	628	640	.98	10400	16.61	.25	496	282	5100	10.30
W 27 × 84 $b = 37.0$	0	84	272	486	.56	5440	20.00	—	212	212	2830	13.35
	½ × 9	92.5	382	543	.70	7110	18.60	.14	301	229	3530	11.76
	1½ × 9	118	596	612	.97	9870	16.57	.26	463	250	4570	9.88
W 24 × 68 $b = 36.0$	0	68	201	386	.52	3730	18.53	—	153	153	1820	11.86
	½ × 8	75.5	291	437	.67	5010	17.24	.16	223	166	2310	10.34
	1½ × 8	98.7	463	498	.93	7130	15.40	.30	349	182	3010	8.63
W 24 × 55 $b = 34.0$	0	55	158	330	.48	3000	18.96	—	114	114	1340	11.77
	½ × 6	60.6	225	376	.60	4020	17.86	.16	164	125	1710	10.40
	1½ × 6	77.8	354	433	.82	5750	16.25	.29	256	138	2250	8.80
W 21 × 62 $b = 35.2$	0	62	168	322	.52	2820	16.75	—	127	127	1330	10.50
	½ × 7	68.6	238	365	.65	3740	15.74	.17	180	137	1670	9.27
	1½ × 7	88.6	371	418	.89	5310	14.29	.32	276	149	2180	7.89
W 21 × 55 $b = 35.2$	0	55	148	303	.49	2520	16.99	—	110	110	1140	10.40
	½ × 7	61.8	218	349	.63	3460	15.87	.19	163	119	1470	9.01
	1½ × 7	82.3	353	403	.88	5040	14.28	.34	257	131	1930	7.51
W 21 × 44 $b = 33.5$	0	44	117	262	.44	2030	17.41	—	81.6	81.6	843	10.33
	½ × 5½	49.5	171	305	.56	2810	16.42	.19	122	90.1	1100	8.98
	1½ × 5½	65.6	278	356	.78	4160	14.97	.34	194	100	1460	7.53
W 18 × 50 $b = 34.5$	0	50	122	247	.49	1840	15.07	—	89.1	89.1	802	9.00
	½ × 6	55.6	174	284	.61	2480	14.26	.20	128	96.1	1020	7.93
	1½ × 6	72.8	275	330	.83	3600	13.10	.37	196	105	1330	6.80

NOTES (Cont'd.):

4. For uniform loading: Deflection (in.) = $ML^2/160\,Sy_b$
   End reaction (kips) = $0.33S_{tr}F_b/L$
   where M = kip-ft., L = ft., S = in.³, y_b = in., S_{tr} = in.³, F_b = ksi

5. Ratio of S_{tr}/S_t at balanced design:

F_y (ksi)	$f'_c = 3.0$	3.75	4.0
36	.51	.59	.61
42	.44	.50	.52
45	.41	.47	.48
50	.37	.42	.44
55	.34	.38	.40
60	.31	.35	.36

4½″ Slab

COMPOSITE DESIGN
Properties of composite beams
With Cover Plate—4½ Inch Slab

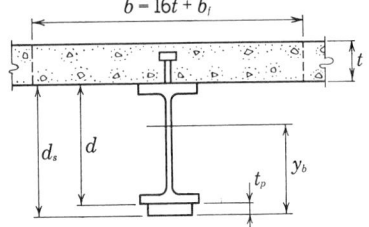

$b = 16t + b_f$

Beam	Cover Plate Size	Avg. Wt. per Ft.	Full Slab Transformed Section						K	W_s
			S_{tr}	S_t	$\dfrac{S_{tr}}{S_t}$	I_{tr}	y_b	$\dfrac{12Q}{I}$		
	In.	Lbs.	In.³	In.³		In.⁴	In.			Lbs.
W 18 × 45	0	45	116	399	.29	2010	17.32	—	—	45
$b = 79.5$	½ × 6	50.7	171	483	.35	2890	16.88	.21	.57	55.2
*V = 87	1½ × 6	68.3	279	591	.47	4530	16.20	.37	.76	75.6
W 18 × 35	0	35	89.8	347	.26	1580	17.64	—	—	35
$b = 78.0$	½ × 5	40.0	136	432	.31	2350	17.28	.22	.58	43.5
*V = 77	1½ × 5	54.8	227	541	.42	3790	16.71	.38	.78	60.5
W 16 × 40	0	40	96.8	334	.29	1540	15.89	—	—	40
$b = 79.0$	½ × 6	46.1	147	414	.35	2280	15.50	.24	.58	50.2
*V = 71	1½ × 6	63.9	246	516	.48	3660	14.91	.42	.78	70.6
W 16 × 36	0	36	86.5	313	.28	1380	15.95	—	—	36
$b = 79.0$	½ × 6	42.2	137	399	.34	2120	15.53	.26	.61	46.2
*V = 69	1¼ × 6	55.6	211	483	.44	3170	15.04	.41	.77	61.5
W 16 × 26	0	26	62.4	262	.24	1010	16.27	—	—	26
$b = 77.5$	½ × 4½	30.8	100	342	.29	1600	15.97	.27	.61	33.7
*V = 57	1 × 4½	37.4	137	401	.34	2160	15.76	.38	.74	41.3
W 14 × 30	0	30	66.6	247	.27	964	14.46	—	—	30
$b = 78.7$	½ × 5½	35.8	108	323	.33	1520	14.14	.30	.62	39.4
*V = 54	1 × 5½	43.9	149	378	.39	2060	13.90	.43	.74	48.7
W 14 × 22	0	22	48.9	208	.23	721	14.76	—	—	22
$b = 77.0$	½ × 4	26.3	79.1	274	.29	1150	14.53	.30	.62	28.8
*V = 46	1 × 4	32.2	109	327	.33	1570	14.42	.43	.74	35.6
W 12 × 19	0	19	38.9	168	.23	527	13.52	—	—	19
$b = 76.0$	½ × 3	22.0	59.4	215	.28	799	13.45	.30	.59	24.1
*V = 42	1 × 3	26.3	79.5	255	.31	1070	13.46	.44	.71	29.2

* For steels with $F_y = 36$ ksi.

NOTES:
1. Tables are based on specified concrete strength $f'_c = 3.0$ ksi and modular ratio $n = 9$.
2. Proper selection of S_{tr} value assures that stress in steel beam does not exceed allowable. Concrete stress due to bending does not exceed allowable under the following conditions:

$F_y = 36$ ksi	Condition	$F_y = 50$ ksi
S_{tr}/S_t	$f'_c = 3.0$ ksi	S_{tr}/S_t
⩽ .51	Shored construction	⩽ .37
⩽ 1.01	Unshored const. with $M_L/M_D < 1.0$	⩽ .74
⩽ .76	Unshored const. with $M_L/M_D < 2.0$	⩽ .55
⩽ .67	Unshored const. with $M_L/M_D < 3.0$	⩽ .49

3. For unshored construction see Sect. 1.11.2.2 of the AISC Specification.

AMERICAN INSTITUTE OF STEEL CONSTRUCTION

COMPOSITE DESIGN

$4\frac{1}{2}''$ Slab

Properties of composite beams
With Cover Plate—$4\frac{1}{2}$ Inch Slab

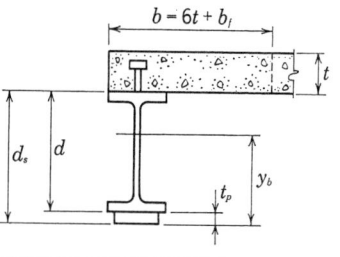

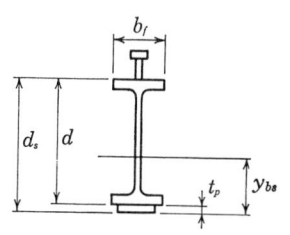

Beam	Cover Plate Size	Avg. Wt. per Ft.	Partial Slab Transformed Section						Steel Section			
			S_{tr}	S_t	$\dfrac{S_{tr}}{S_t}$	I_{tr}	y_b	$\dfrac{12Q}{I}$	S_s	S_{ts}	I	y_{bs}
	In.	Lbs.	In.³	In.³		In.⁴	In.		In.³	In.³	In.⁴	In.
W 18 × 45 $b = 34.5$	0	45	109	235	.47	1670	15.26	—	79.0	79.0	706	8.93
	½ × 6	50.7	162	274	.59	2330	14.37	.22	118	85.8	912	7.73
	1½ × 6	68.3	263	321	.82	3450	13.11	.39	186	94.1	1210	6.51
W 18 × 35 $b = 33.0$	0	35	84.3	203	.42	1320	15.69	—	57.9	57.9	513	8.85
	½ × 5	40.0	128	242	.53	1900	14.83	.23	89.7	63.9	680	7.58
	1½ × 5	54.9	214	288	.74	2910	13.60	.40	145	70.9	915	6.31
W 16 × 40 $b = 34.0$	0	40	90.9	198	.46	1280	14.05	—	64.6	64.6	517	8.00
	½ × 6	46.1	139	235	.59	1830	13.20	.25	99.6	70.3	680	6.83
	1½ × 6	64.0	231	279	.83	2780	12.03	.44	159	77.2	910	5.71
W 16 × 36 $b = 34.0$	0	36	81.1	187	.43	1150	14.19	—	56.5	56.5	447	7.92
	½ × 6	42.3	129	227	.57	1720	13.28	.27	91.1	62.0	603	6.62
	1¼ × 6	55.7	199	262	.76	2450	12.28	.43	137	67.1	769	5.63
W 16 × 26 $b = 32.5$	0	26	58.4	156	.37	856	14.67	—	38.3	38.3	300	7.82
	½ × 4½	30.8	94.6	194	.49	1310	13.89	.28	63.7	42.8	413	6.49
	1 × 4½	37.4	130	219	.59	1730	13.27	.40	86.5	45.6	497	5.75
W 14 × 30 $b = 33.7$	0	30	62.3	149	.42	807	12.96	—	41.9	41.9	290	6.93
	½ × 5½	35.8	102	186	.55	1240	12.18	.32	69.5	46.1	398	5.72
	1 × 5½	44.0	141	209	.67	1630	11.58	.45	94.0	48.8	478	5.08
W 14 × 22 $b = 32.0$	0	22	45.6	125	.37	608	13.34	—	28.9	28.9	198	6.86
	½ × 4	26.3	74.4	158	.47	947	12.73	.32	48.4	32.3	275	5.68
	1 × 4	32.2	103	181	.57	1260	12.25	.45	65.8	34.4	332	5.05
W 12 × 19 $b = 31.0$	0	19	36.2	99	.37	441	12.20	—	21.3	21.3	130	6.08
	½ × 3	22.0	55.4	125	.44	658	11.88	.32	33.9	23.9	177	5.24
	1 × 3	26.3	74.5	143	.52	865	11.62	.46	44.9	25.6	215	4.78

NOTES (Cont'd.):

4. For uniform loading: Deflection (in.) $= ML^2/160\,S y_b$

  End reaction (kips) $= 0.33 S_{tr} F_b/L$

  where $M =$ kip-ft., $L =$ ft., $S =$ in.³, $y_b =$ in., $S_{tr} =$ in.³, $F_b =$ ksi

5. Ratio of S_{tr}/S_t at balanced design:

F_y (ksi)	$f'_c = 3.0$	3.75	4.0
36	.51	.59	.61
42	.44	.50	.52
45	.41	.47	.48
50	.37	.42	.44
55	.34	.38	.40
60	.31	.35	.36

5" Slab

COMPOSITE DESIGN
Properties of composite beams
With Cover Plate—5 Inch Slab

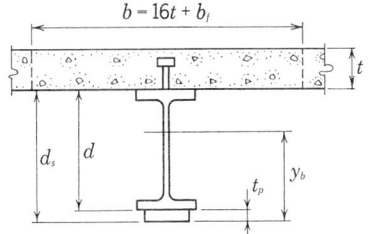

$$b = 16t + b_f$$

Beam	Cover Plate Size	Avg. Wt. per Ft.	Full Slab Transfomed Section						K	W_s
			S_{tr}	S_t	$\dfrac{S_{tr}}{S_t}$	I_{tr}	y_b	$\dfrac{12Q}{I}$		
	In.	Lbs.	In.³	In.³		In.⁴	In.			Lbs.
W 36 × 170	0	170	748	1680	.44	21300	28.48	—	—	170
$b = 92.0$	½ × 10	177	914	1800	.51	25200	27.63	.07	.43	187
*V = 357	1½ × 10	202	1240	1970	.63	32500	26.21	.14	.63	221
W 36 × 150	0	150	659	1590	.41	19000	28.87	—	—	150
$b = 92.0$	½ × 10	158	826	1720	.48	23000	27.92	.07	.45	167
*V = 325	1½ × 10	184	1150	1900	.61	30400	26.34	.15	.65	201
W 36 × 135	0	135	587	1500	.39	17100	29.17	—	—	135
$b = 92.0$	½ × 10	143	754	1640	.46	21200	28.14	.08	.47	152
*V = 308	1½ × 10	170	1080	1830	.59	28700	26.43	.16	.68	186
W 33 × 130	0	130	538	1380	.39	14700	27.41	—	—	130
$b = 91.5$	½ × 10	138	695	1510	.46	18400	26.45	.09	.48	147
*V = 278	1½ × 10	165	1000	1690	.59	24900	24.86	.17	.68	181
W 33 × 118	0	118	485	1320	.37	13400	27.67	—	—	118
$b = 91.5$	½ × 10	127	642	1460	.44	17100	26.63	.09	.49	135
*V = 264	1½ × 10	154	951	1640	.58	23700	24.93	.18	.70	169
W 30 × 108	0	108	410	1130	.36	10500	25.57	—	—	108
$b = 90.5$	½ × 9	116	539	1260	.43	13300	24.73	.10	.49	123
*V = 237	1½ × 9	140	793	1430	.56	18500	23.36	.20	.70	154
W 30 × 99	0	99	374	1090	.34	9630	25.79	—	—	99
$b = 90.5$	½ × 9	107	503	1220	.41	12500	24.89	.11	.51	114
*V = 224	1½ × 9	132	758	1400	.54	17800	23.43	.21	.71	145
W 27 × 102	0	102	362	1000	.36	8540	23.56	—	—	102
$b = 90.0$	½ × 9	110	480	1120	.43	11000	22.79	.11	.50	117
*V = 203	1½ × 9	134	713	1280	.56	15400	21.55	.22	.70	148

* For steels with $F_y = 36$ ksi.

NOTES:
1. Tables are based on specified concrete strength $f'_c = 3.0$ ksi and modular ratio $n = 9$.
2. Proper selection of S_{tr} value assures that stress in steel beam does not exceed allowable. Concrete stress due to bending does not exceed allowable under the following conditions:

$F_y = 36$ ksi	Condition	$F_y = 50$ ksi
S_{tr}/S_t	$f'_c = 3.0$ ksi	S_{tr}/S_t
$\leqslant .51$	Shored construction	$\leqslant .37$
$\leqslant 1.01$	Unshored const. with $M_L/M_D < 1.0$	$\leqslant .74$
$\leqslant .76$	Unshored const. with $M_L/M_D < 2.0$	$\leqslant .55$
$\leqslant .67$	Unshored const. with $M_L/M_D < 3.0$	$\leqslant .49$

3. For unshored construction see Sect. 1.11.2.2 of the AISC Specification.

AMERICAN INSTITUTE OF STEEL CONSTRUCTION

COMPOSITE DESIGN

Properties of composite beams
With Cover Plate—5 Inch Slab

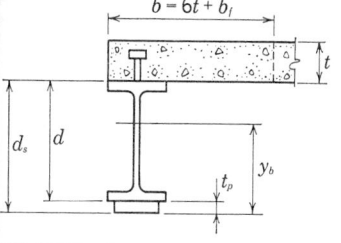
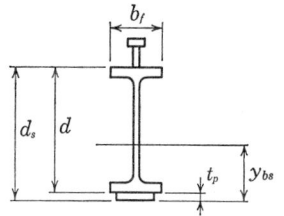

Beam	Cover Plate Size	Avg. Wt. per Ft.	Partial Slab Transformed Section						Steel Section			
			S_{tr}	S_t	$\dfrac{S_{tr}}{S_t}$	I_{tr}	y_b	$\dfrac{12Q}{I}$	S_s	S_{ts}	I	y_{bs}
	In.	Lbs.	In.³	In.³		In.⁴	In.		In.³	In.³	In.⁴	In.
₩ 36 × 170	0	170	702	1050	.67	17300	24.63	—	580	580	10500	18.08
= 42.0	½ × 10	177	857	1110	.77	20200	23.54	.07	711	609	12000	16.91
	1½ × 10	202	1160	1210	.95	25300	21.82	.15	958	651	14600	15.23
₩ 36 × 150	0	150	618	973	.64	15400	24.97	—	504	504	9030	17.92
= 42.0	½ × 10	158	776	1050	.74	18400	23.73	.08	634	532	10500	16.57
	1½ × 10	184	1080	1150	.94	23600	21.80	.16	881	571	12900	14.69
₩ 36 × 135	0	135	551	910	.61	13900	25.26	—	440	440	7820	17.77
= 42.0	½ × 10	143	709	986	.72	16900	23.89	.08	570	468	9260	16.26
	1½ × 10	170	1020	1090	.93	22100	21.77	.17	814	506	11600	14.20
₩ 33 × 130	0	130	505	833	.61	12000	23.71	—	406	406	6710	16.55
= 41.5	½ × 10	138	653	904	.72	14600	22.40	.09	527	430	7960	15.11
	1½ × 10	165	941	1000	.94	19200	20.40	.18	754	464	9940	13.18
₩ 33 × 118	0	118	455	786	.58	10900	23.97	—	359	359	5900	16.43
= 41.5	½ × 10	127	604	861	.70	13600	22.54	.10	480	384	7120	14.83
	1½ × 10	154	893	959	.93	18200	20.38	.19	705	416	9000	12.76
₩ 30 × 108	0	108	385	670	.57	8510	22.12	—	300	300	4470	14.91
= 40.5	½ × 9	116	506	735	.69	10600	20.91	.10	397	320	5380	13.53
	1½ × 9	140	743	821	.90	14200	19.07	.21	579	347	6800	11.74
₩ 30 × 99	0	99	351	640	.55	7850	22.37	—	270	270	4000	14.82
= 40.5	½ × 9	107	473	708	.67	9970	21.05	.11	367	290	4890	13.30
	1½ × 9	132	712	795	.89	13600	19.07	.22	548	316	6240	11.39
₩ 27 × 102	0	102	341	593	.58	6940	20.36	—	267	267	3610	13.54
= 40.0	½ × 9	110	453	652	.69	8700	19.23	.12	356	284	4350	12.24
	1½ × 9	134	669	731	.92	11700	17.52	.23	520	307	5510	10.60

NOTES (Cont'd.):

4. For uniform loading: Deflection (in.) $= ML^2/160\, S y_b$

   End reaction (kips) $= 0.33 S_{tr} F_b/L$

   where M = kip-ft., L = ft., S = in.³, y_b = in., S_{tr} = in.³, F_b = ksi

5. Ratio of S_{tr}/S_t at balanced design:

F_y (ksi)	$f'_c = 3.0$	3.75	4.0
36	.51	.59	.61
42	.44	.50	.52
45	.41	.47	.48
50	.37	.42	.44
55	.34	.38	.40
60	.31	.35	.36

5" Slab

COMPOSITE DESIGN
Properties of composite beams
With Cover Plate—5 Inch Slab

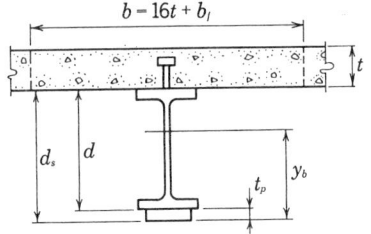

$$b - 16t + b_l$$

Beam	Cover Plate Size	Avg. Wt. per Ft.	Full Slab Transformed Section						K	W_s
			S_{tr}	S_t	$\dfrac{S_{tr}}{S_t}$	I_{tr}	y_b	$\dfrac{12Q}{I}$		
	In.	Lbs.	In.³	In.³		In.⁴	In.			Lbs.
W 27 × 94	0	94	334	966	.35	7910	23.72	—	—	94
$b = 90.0$	½ × 9	102	452	1090	.41	10400	22.91	.12	.51	109
*V = 191	1½ × 9	127	685	1250	.55	14800	21.60	.23	.72	139
W 27 × 84	0	84	296	915	.32	7100	23.94	—	—	84
$b = 90.0$	½ × 9	92.5	415	1050	.40	9580	23.06	.13	.53	99.
*V = 179	1½ × 9	118	649	1220	.53	14100	21.66	.24	.74	130
W 24 × 68	0	68	220	732	.30	4860	22.07	—	—	68
$b = 89.0$	½ × 8	75.5	316	859	.37	6740	21.36	.15	.55	81.
*V = 143	1½ × 8	98.6	504	1020	.49	10200	20.21	.27	.75	109
W 24 × 55	0	55	174	643	.27	3910	22.47	—	—	55
$b = 87.0$	½ × 6	60.6	246	760	.32	5390	21.96	.14	.54	65.
*V = 135	1½ × 6	77.8	387	916	.42	8170	21.12	.27	.74	85.
W 21 × 62	0	62	185	610	.30	3680	19.96	—	—	62
$b = 88.2$	½ × 7	68.6	259	717	.36	5040	19.46	.16	.54	73.
*V = 122	1½ × 7	88.6	406	859	.47	7580	18.66	.30	.74	97.
W 21 × 55	0	55	163	573	.28	3270	20.10	—	—	55
$b = 88.2$	½ × 7	61.8	237	689	.34	4640	19.56	.17	.56	66.
*V = 113	1½ × 7	82.2	385	838	.46	7200	18.70	.31	.76	90.
W 21 × 44	0	44	129	502	.26	2630	20.43	—	—	44
$b = 86.5$	½ × 5½	49.4	187	613	.31	3750	20.04	.17	.56	53.
*V = 104	1½ × 5½	65.5	303	760	.40	5890	19.41	.31	.76	72.
W 18 × 50	0	50	134	463	.29	2400	17.83	—	—	50
$b = 87.5$	½ × 6	55.5	190	556	.34	3330	17.51	.19	.54	60.
*V = 93	1½ × 6	72.7	301	684	.44	5120	17.02	.34	.74	80.

* For steels with $F_y = 36$ ksi.

NOTES:
1. Tables are based on specified concrete strength $f'_c = 3.0$ ksi and modular ratio $n = 9$.
2. Proper selection of S_{tr} value assures that stress in steel beam does not exceed allowable. Concrete stress due to bending does not exceed allowable under the following conditions:

$F_y = 36$ ksi	Condition	$F_y = 50$ ksi
S_{tr}/S_t	$f'_c = 3.0$ ksi	S_{tr}/S_t
$\leqslant .51$	Shored construction	$\leqslant .37$
$\leqslant 1.01$	Unshored const. with $M_L/M_D < 1.0$	$\leqslant .74$
$\leqslant .76$	Unshored const. with $M_L/M_D < 2.0$	$\leqslant .55$
$\leqslant .67$	Unshored const. with $M_L/M_D < 3.0$	$\leqslant .49$

3. For unshored construction see Sect. 1.11.2.2 of the AISC Specification.

COMPOSITE DESIGN

5″ Slab

Properties of composite beams

With Cover Plate—5 Inch Slab

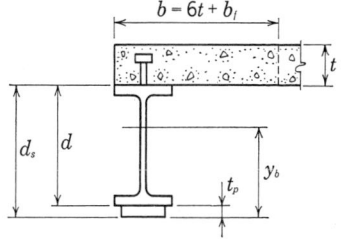 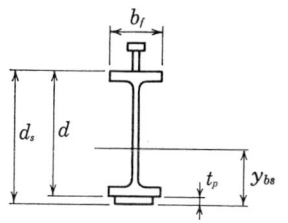

Beam	Cover Plate Size	Avg. Wt. per Ft.	Partial Slab Transformed Section						Steel Section			
			S_{tr}	S_t	$\dfrac{S_{tr}}{S_t}$	I_{tr}	y_b	$\dfrac{12Q}{I}$	S_s	S_{ts}	I	y_{bs}
	In.	Lbs.	In.³	In.³		In.⁴	In.		In.³	In.³	In.⁴	In.
W 27 × 94 ℓ = 40.0	0	94	314	569	.55	6450	20.56	—	243	243	3270	13.45
	½ × 9	102	426	630	.68	8240	19.34	.13	332	260	4000	12.04
	1½ × 9	127	644	710	.91	11300	17.52	.24	496	282	5100	10.30
W 27 × 84 ℓ = 40.0	0	84	279	536	.52	5820	20.83	—	212	212	2830	13.35
	½ × 9	92.5	392	602	.65	7640	19.49	.14	301	229	3530	11.76
	1½ × 9	118	611	683	.90	10700	17.51	.25	463	250	4570	9.88
W 24 × 68 ℓ = 39.0	0	68	207	427	.49	4010	19.32	—	153	153	1820	11.86
	½ × 8	75.5	299	487	.61	5400	18.10	.16	223	166	2310	10.34
	1½ × 8	98.6	475	559	.85	7760	16.33	.29	349	182	3010	8.63
W 24 × 55 ℓ = 37.0	0	55	163	367	.44	3230	19.76	—	114	114	1340	11.77
	½ × 6	60.6	231	421	.55	4340	18.75	.15	164	125	1710	10.40
	1½ × 6	77.8	364	489	.74	6270	17.22	.28	256	138	2250	8.80
W 21 × 62 ℓ = 38.2	0	62	174	356	.49	3030	17.48	—	127	127	1330	10.50
	½ × 7	68.6	245	406	.60	4040	16.53	.17	180	137	1670	9.27
	1½ × 7	88.6	382	470	.81	5790	15.15	.31	276	149	2180	7.89
W 21 × 55 ℓ = 38.2	0	55	153	336	.46	2710	17.72	—	110	110	1140	10.40
	½ × 7	61.8	225	389	.58	3750	16.68	.18	163	119	1470	9.01
	1½ × 7	82.2	363	454	.80	5510	15.17	.33	257	131	1930	7.51
W 21 × 44 ℓ = 36.5	0	44	121	291	.41	2190	18.15	—	81.6	81.6	843	10.33
	½ × 5½	49.5	177	342	.52	3050	17.24	.18	122	90.1	1100	8.98
	1½ × 5½	65.5	286	404	.71	4550	15.89	.33	194	100	1460	7.53
W 18 × 50 ℓ = 37.5	0	50	126	274	.46	1990	15.74	—	89.1	89.1	802	9.00
	½ × 6	55.5	180	317	.57	2690	15.00	.20	128	96.1	1020	7.93
	1½ × 6	72.8	283	372	.76	3940	13.91	.36	196	105	1330	6.80

NOTES (Cont'd.):

4. For uniform loading: Deflection (in.) $= ML^2/160\,Sy_b$

  End reaction (kips) $= 0.33 S_{tr} F_b/L$

  where M = kip-ft., L = ft., S = in.³, y_b = in., S_{tr} = in.³, F_b = ksi

5. Ratio of S_{tr}/S_t at balanced design:

F_y (ksi)	$f'_c = 3.0$	3.75	4.0
36	.51	.59	.61
42	.44	.50	.52
45	.41	.47	.48
50	.37	.42	.44
55	.34	.38	.40
60	.31	.35	.36

5" Slab

COMPOSITE DESIGN
Properties of composite beams
With Cover Plate—5 Inch Slab

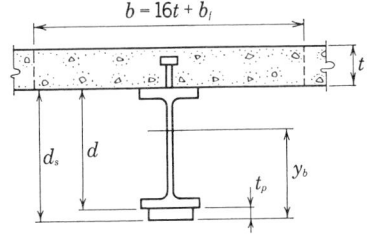

$b = 16t + b_f$

Beam	Cover Plate Size	Avg. Wt. per Ft.	Full Slab Transformed Section						K	W_s
			S_{tr}	S_t	$\dfrac{S_{tr}}{S_t}$	I_{tr}	y_b	$\dfrac{12Q}{I}$		
	In.	Lbs.	In.³	In.³		In.⁴	In.			Lbs
W 18 × 45	0	45	121	438	.28	2160	17.92	—	—	45
$b = 87.5$	½ × 6	50.6	177	537	.33	3110	17.58	.20	.56	55.2
*V = 87	1½ × 6	68.2	288	670	.43	4900	17.05	.36	.76	75.
W 18 × 35	0	35	93.6	379	.25	1700	18.22	—	—	35
$b = 86.0$	½ × 5	39.9	141	478	.29	2520	17.93	.21	.58	43.
*V = 77	1½ × 5	54.8	233	612	.38	4090	17.53	.37	.77	60.
W 16 × 40	0	40	101	366	.28	1660	16.46	—	—	40
$b = 87.0$	½ × 6	46.0	152	459	.33	2460	16.15	.23	.58	50.
*V = 71	1½ × 6	63.8	253	585	.43	3980	15.70	.41	.78	70.
W 16 × 36	0	36	90.3	344	.26	1490	16.51	—	—	36
$b = 87.0$	½ × 6	42.2	142	442	.32	2290	16.16	.25	.60	46.
*V = 69	1¼ × 6	55.5	218	545	.40	3440	15.79	.40	.76	61.
W 16 × 26	0	26	65.2	288	.23	1100	16.84	—	—	26
$b = 85.5$	½ × 4½	30.8	104	376	.28	1720	16.56	.25	.61	33.
*V = 57	1 × 4½	37.3	142	446	.32	2340	16.42	.37	.74	41.
W 14 × 30	0	30	69.9	273	.26	1050	15.01	—	—	30
$b = 86.7$	½ × 5½	35.8	113	356	.32	1660	14.71	.29	.62	39.
*V = 54	1 × 5½	43.8	154	422	.37	2240	14.54	.41	.74	48.
W 14 × 22	0	22	51.3	231	.22	786	15.31	—	—	22
$b = 85.0$	½ × 4	26.2	82.6	303	.27	1250	15.10	.29	.62	28.
*V = 46	1 × 4	32.1	113	362	.31	1700	15.02	.41	.74	35.
W 12 × 19	0	19	41.1	187	.22	579	14.07	—	—	19
$b = 84.0$	½ × 3	22.0	62.4	239	.26	874	14.01	.28	.58	24.
*V = 42	1 × 3	26.3	83.3	283	.29	1170	14.03	.42	.71	29.

* For steels with $F_y = 36$ ksi.

NOTES:
1. Tables are based on specified concrete strength $f'_c = 3.0$ ksi and modular ratio $n = 9$.
2. Proper selection of S_{tr} value assures that stress in steel beam does not exceed allowable. Concrete stress due to bending does not exceed allowable under the following conditions:

$F_y = 36$ ksi	Condition	$F_y = 50$ ksi
S_{tr}/S_t	$f'_c = 3.0$ ksi	S_{tr}/S_t
⩽ .51	Shored construction	⩽ .37
⩽ 1.01	Unshored const. with $M_L/M_D < 1.0$	⩽ .74
⩽ .76	Unshored const. with $M_L/M_D < 2.0$	⩽ .55
⩽ .67	Unshored const. with $M_L/M_D < 3.0$	⩽ .49

3. For unshored construction see Sect. 1.11.2.2 of the AISC Specification.

COMPOSITE DESIGN

Properties of composite beams

With Cover Plate—5 Inch Slab

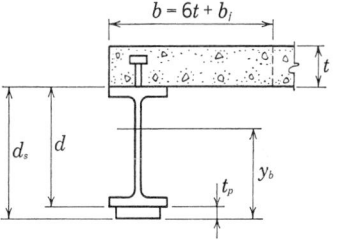
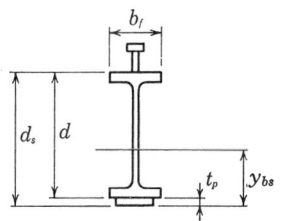

Beam	Cover Plate Size	Avg. Wt. per Ft.	Partial Slab Transformed Section						Steel Section			
			S_{tr}	S_t	$\dfrac{S_{tr}}{S_t}$	I_{tr}	y_b	$\dfrac{12Q}{I}$	S_s	S_{ts}	I	y_{bs}
	In.	Lbs.	In.³	In.³		In.⁴	In.		In.³	In.³	In.⁴	In.
18 × 45 = 37.5	0	45	113	260	.44	1800	15.93	—	79.0	79.0	706	8.93
	½ × 6	50.7	167	306	.55	2530	15.11	.21	118	85.8	912	7.73
	1½ × 6	68.2	272	363	.75	3790	13.94	.38	186	94.1	1210	6.51
18 × 35 = 36.0	0	35	87.5	225	.39	1430	16.35	—	57.9	57.9	513	8.85
	½ × 5	40.0	133	271	.49	2070	15.58	.22	89.7	63.9	680	7.58
	1½ × 5	54.8	221	327	.67	3190	14.46	.39	145	70.9	915	6.31
16 × 40 = 37.0	0	40	94.5	219	.43	1390	14.67	—	64.6	64.6	517	8.00
	½ × 6	46.1	144	263	.55	2000	13.90	.25	99.6	70.3	680	6.83
	1½ × 6	63.9	239	316	.76	3060	12.81	.42	159	77.2	910	5.71
16 × 36 = 37.0	0	36	84.4	207	.41	1250	14.80	—	56.5	56.5	447	7.92
	½ × 6	42.2	134	254	.53	1870	13.98	.26	91.1	62.0	603	6.62
	1¼ × 6	55.6	206	297	.69	2690	13.06	.42	137	67.1	769	5.63
16 × 26 = 35.5	0	26	60.9	172	.35	930	15.26	—	38.3	38.3	300	7.82
	½ × 4½	30.8	98.1	218	.45	1430	14.58	.27	63.7	42.8	413	6.49
	1 × 4½	37.4	135	248	.54	1890	14.04	.39	86.5	45.6	497	5.75
14 × 30 = 36.3	0	30	65.2	165	.40	881	13.51	—	41.9	41.9	290	6.93
	½ × 5½	35.8	106	208	.51	1360	12.83	.31	69.5	46.1	398	5.72
	1 × 5½	43.9	146	237	.62	1790	12.29	.43	94.0	48.8	478	5.08
14 × 22 = 35.0	0	22.1	47.9	137	.35	665	13.88	—	28.9	28.9	198	6.86
	½ × 4	26.3	77.5	177	.44	1040	13.37	.30	48.4	32.3	275	5.68
	1 × 4	32.2	107	204	.52	1380	12.96	.43	65.8	34.4	332	5.05
12 × 19 = 34.0	0	19	38.2	110	.35	487	12.73	—	21.3	21.3	130	6.08
	½ × 3	22.0	58.1	139	.42	724	12.45	.30	33.9	23.9	177	5.24
	1 × 3	26.3	77.7	162	.48	953	12.26	.44	44.9	25.6	215	4.78

NOTES (Cont'd.):

4. For uniform loading: Deflection (in.) = $ML^2/160\,Sy_b$

   End reaction (kips) = $0.33S_{tr}F_b/L$

   where M = kip-ft., L = ft., S = in.³, y_b = in., S_{tr} = in.³, F_b = ksi

5. Ratio of S_{tr}/S_t at balanced design:

F_y (ksi)	f'_c = 3.0	3.75	4.0
36	.51	.59	.61
42	.44	.50	.52
45	.41	.47	.48
50	.37	.42	.44
55	.34	.38	.40
60	.31	.35	.36

5½″ Slab

COMPOSITE DESIGN
Properties of composite beams
With Cover Plate—5½ Inch Slab

$b = 16t + b_f$

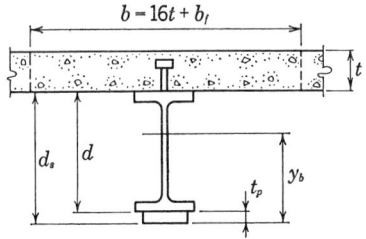

Beam	Cover Plate Size	Avg. Wt. per Ft.	Full Slab Transformed Section						K	W_s
			S_{tr}	S_t	$\dfrac{S_{tr}}{S_t}$	I_{tr}	y_b	$\dfrac{12Q}{I}$		
	In.	Lbs.	In.³	In.³		In.⁴	In.			Lbs.
W 36 × 170	0	170	765	1860	.41	22600	29.54	—	—	170
$b = 100.0$	½ × 10	177	933	2000	.47	26800	28.76	.06	.42	187
*$V = 357$	1½ × 10	202	1270	2210	.57	34700	27.44	.14	.63	221
W 36 × 150	0	150	673	1760	.38	20100	29.91	—	—	150
$b = 100.0$	½ × 10	158	843	1910	.44	24500	29.05	.07	.45	167
*$V = 325$	1½ × 10	184	1180	2130	.55	32500	27.59	.15	.65	201
W 36 × 135	0	135	600	1670	.36	18100	30.20	—	—	135
$b = 100.0$	½ × 10	143	770	1830	.42	22500	29.26	.08	.47	152
*$V = 308$	1½ × 10	170	1110	2060	.54	30600	27.70	.16	.68	186
W 33 × 130	0	130	550	1530	.36	15600	28.39	—	—	130
$b = 99.5$	½ × 10	138	709	1690	.42	19500	27.52	.08	.47	147
*$V = 278$	1½ × 10	165	1020	1900	.54	26700	26.06	.17	.68	181
W 33 × 118	0	118	496	1460	.34	14200	28.63	—	—	118
$b = 99.5$	½ × 10	127	656	1630	.40	18200	27.69	.09	.49	135
*$V = 264$	1½ × 10	154	971	1850	.52	25400	26.14	.18	.70	169
W 30 × 108	0	108	420	1250	.33	11100	26.46	—	—	108
$b = 98.5$	½ × 9	116	551	1400	.39	14200	25.72	.10	.49	123
*$V = 237$	1½ × 9	140	810	1610	.50	19800	24.48	.19	.69	154
W 30 × 99	0	99	383	1200	.32	10200	26.66	—	—	99
$b = 98.5$	½ × 9	107	514	1360	.38	13300	25.87	.10	.51	114
*$V = 224$	1½ × 9	132	774	1570	.49	19000	24.56	.20	.71	145
W 27 × 102	0	102	372	1110	.34	9060	24.39	—	—	102
$b = 98.0$	½ × 9	110	492	1250	.39	11700	23.71	.11	.49	117
*$V = 203$	1½ × 9	134	729	1440	.51	16500	22.60	.21	.70	148

* For steels with $F_y = 36$ ksi.

NOTES:

1. Tables are based on specified concrete strength $f'_c = 3.0$ ksi and modular ratio $n = 9$.

2. Proper selection of S_{tr} value assures that stress in steel beam does **not** exceed allowable. Concrete stress due to bending does not exceed allowable under the following conditions:

$F_y = 36$ ksi	Condition	$F_y = 50$ ksi
S_{tr}/S_t	$f'_c = 3.0$ ksi	S_{tr}/S_t
⩽ .51	Shored construction	⩽ .37
⩽ 1.01	Unshored const. with $M_L/M_D < 1.0$	⩽ .74
⩽ .76	Unshored const. with $M_L/M_D < 2.0$	⩽ .55
⩽ .67	Unshored const. with $M_L/M_D < 3.0$	⩽ .49

3. For unshored construction see Sect. 1.11.2.2 of the AISC Specification.

COMPOSITE DESIGN

Properties of composite beams

With Cover Plate—$5\frac{1}{2}$ Inch Slab

$5\frac{1}{2}''$ Slab

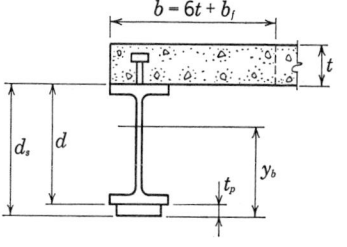

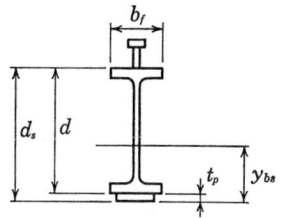

Beam	Cover Plate Size	Avg. Wt. per Ft.	Partial Slab Transformed Section						Steel Section			
			S_{tr}	S_t	$\dfrac{S_{tr}}{S_t}$	I_{tr}	y_b	$\dfrac{12Q}{I}$	S_s	S_{ts}	I	y_{bs}
	In.	Lbs.	In.³	In.³		In.⁴	In.		In.³	In.³	In.⁴	In.
36 × 170 $= 45.0$	0	170	717	1130	.64	18300	25.47	—	580	580	10500	18.08
	½ × 10	177	876	1200	.73	21400	24.42	.07	711	609	12000	16.91
	1½ × 10	202	1180	1320	.90	26900	22.72	.15	958	651	14600	15.23
36 × 150 $= 45.0$	0	150	632	1050	.60	16300	25.84	—	504	504	9030	17.92
	½ × 10	158	792	1140	.70	19500	24.64	.07	634	532	10500	16.57
	1½ × 10	184	1100	1250	.88	25100	22.74	.16	881	571	12900	14.69
36 × 135 $= 45.0$	0	135	563	989	.57	14700	26.16	—	440	440	7820	17.77
	½ × 10	143	724	1080	.67	18000	24.83	.08	570	468	9260	16.26
	1½ × 10	170	1040	1190	.87	23600	22.75	.17	814	506	11600	14.20
33 × 130 $= 44.5$	0	130	517	905	.57	12700	24.56	—	406	406	6710	16.55
	½ × 10	138	668	985	.68	15600	23.30	.09	527	430	7960	15.11
	1½ × 10	165	962	1090	.88	20500	21.35	.18	754	464	9940	13.18
33 × 118 $= 44.5$	0	118	466	857	.54	11600	24.84	—	359	359	5900	16.43
	½ × 10	127	618	942	.66	14500	23.47	.10	480	384	7120	14.83
	1½ × 10	154	913	1050	.87	19500	21.36	.19	705	416	9000	12.76
30 × 108 $= 43.5$	0	108	394	732	.54	9050	22.95	—	300	300	4470	14.91
	½ × 9	116	519	805	.64	11300	21.79	.10	397	320	5380	13.53
	1½ × 9	140	761	904	.84	15200	20.00	.21	579	347	6800	11.74
30 × 99 $= 43.5$	0	99	360	700	.51	8350	23.20	—	270	270	4000	14.82
	½ × 9	107	485	777	.62	10600	21.95	.11	367	290	4890	13.30
	1½ × 9	132	728	878	.83	14600	20.03	.21	548	316	6240	11.39
27 × 102 $= 43.0$	0	102	350	647	.54	7390	21.14	—	267	267	3610	13.54
	½ × 9	110	464	715	.65	9300	20.06	.11	356	284	4350	12.24
	1½ × 9	134	685	805	.85	12600	18.41	.23	520	307	5510	10.60

NOTES (Cont'd.):
4. For uniform loading: Deflection (in.) = $ML^2/160\,Sy_b$
   End reaction (kips) = $0.33 S_{tr} F_b / L$
   where $M =$ kip-ft., $L =$ ft., $S =$ in.³, $y_b =$ in., $S_{tr} =$ in.³, $F_b =$ ksi
5. Ratio of S_{tr}/S_t at balanced design:

F_y (ksi)	$f'_c = 3.0$	3.75	4.0
36	.51	.59	.61
42	.44	.50	.52
45	.41	.47	.48
50	.37	.42	.44
55	.34	.38	.40
60	.31	.35	.36

AMERICAN INSTITUTE OF STEEL CONSTRUCTION

5½" Slab

COMPOSITE DESIGN
Properties of composite beams
With Cover Plate—5½ Inch Slab

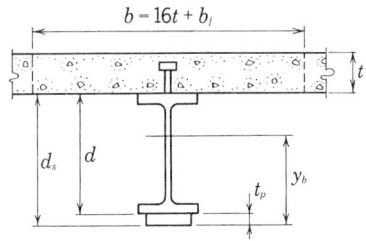

$b = 16t + b_f$

Beam	Cover Plate Size	Avg. Wt. per Ft.	Full Slab Transformed Section						K	W
			S_{tr}	S_t	$\dfrac{S_{tr}}{S_t}$	I_{tr}	y_b	$\dfrac{12Q}{I}$		
	In.	Lbs.	In.³	In.³		In.⁴	In.			Lbs
W 27 × 94 $b = 98.0$ *$V = 191$	0 ½ × 9 1½ × 9	94 102 127	342 463 701	1070 1210 1410	.32 .38 .50	8390 11000 15900	24.53 23.82 22.66	— .11 .22	— .51 .72	94 109 139
W 27 × 84 $b = 98.0$ *$V = 179$	0 ½ × 9 1½ × 9	84 92.5 118	304 425 664	1010 1170 1380	.30 .36 .48	7520 10200 15100	24.73 23.97 22.72	— .13 .24	— .53 .74	84 99 130
W 24 × 68 $b = 97.0$ *$V = 143$	0 ½ × 8 1½ × 8	68 75.5 98.6	227 324 516	802 952 1150	.28 .34 .45	5160 7180 10900	22.77 22.17 21.18	— .15 .27	— .55 .75	68 81 109
W 24 × 55 $b = 95.0$ *$V = 135$	0 ½ × 6 1½ × 6	55 60.6 77.7	180 252 396	703 840 1030	.26 .30 .39	4160 5730 8740	23.13 22.72 22.05	— .14 .26	— .54 .74	55 65 85
W 21 × 62 $b = 96.2$ *$V = 122$	0 ½ × 7 1½ × 7	62 68.6 88.5	191 267 417	666 792 963	.29 .34 .43	3930 5380 8140	20.60 20.19 19.54	— .16 .29	— .53 .74	62 73 97
W 21 × 55 $b = 96.2$ *$V = 113$	0 ½ × 7 1½ × 7	55 61.7 82.1	168 244 395	623 759 939	.27 .32 .42	3480 4950 7730	20.71 20.28 19.57	— .17 .31	— .56 .76	55 66 90
W 21 × 44 $b = 94.5$ *$V = 104$	0 ½ × 5½ 1½ × 5½	44 49.4 65.4	133 193 311	545 672 849	.24 .29 .37	2800 4000 6300	21.02 20.71 20.23	— .17 .31	— .56 .76	44 53 72
W 18 × 50 $b = 95.5$ *$V = 93$	0 ½ × 6 1½ × 6	50 55.5 72.6	140 197 310	504 611 763	.28 .32 .41	2570 3570 5510	18.40 18.15 17.79	— .18 .33	— .54 .74	50 60 80

* For steels with $F_y = 36$ ksi.

NOTES:
1. Tables are based on specified concrete strength $f'_c = 3.0$ ksi and modular ratio $n = 9$.
2. Proper selection of S_{tr} value assures that stress in steel beam does not exceed allowable. Concrete stress due to bending does not exceed allowable under the following conditions:

$F_y = 36$ ksi	Condition	$F_y = 50$ ksi
S_{tr}/S_t	$f'_c = 3.0$ ksi	S_{tr}/S_t
$\leqslant .51$	Shored construction	$\leqslant .37$
$\leqslant 1.01$	Unshored const. with $M_L/M_D < 1.0$	$\leqslant .74$
$\leqslant .76$	Unshored const. with $M_L/M_D < 2.0$	$\leqslant .55$
$\leqslant .67$	Unshored const. with $M_L/M_D < 3.0$	$\leqslant .49$

3. For unshored construction see Sect. 1.11.2.2 of the AISC Specification.

COMPOSITE DESIGN

Properties of composite beams

With Cover Plate—5½ Inch Slab

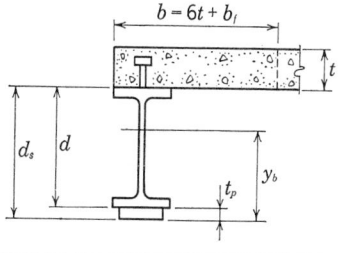

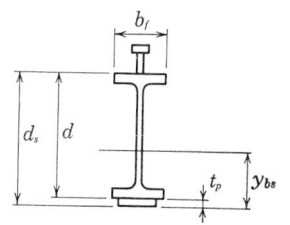

Beam	Cover Plate Size	Avg. Wt. per Ft.	Partial Slab Transformed Section						Steel Section			
			S_{tr}	S_t	$\dfrac{S_{tr}}{S_t}$	I_{tr}	y_b	$\dfrac{12Q}{I}$	S_s	S_{ts}	I	y_{bs}
	In.	Lbs.	In.³	In.³		In.⁴	In.		In.³	In.³	In.⁴	In.
W 27 × 94	0	94	322	621	.52	6880	21.34	—	243	243	3270	13.45
= 43.0	½ × 9	102	437	692	.63	8810	20.18	.12	332	260	4000	12.04
	1½ × 9	127	660	785	.84	12200	18.42	.24	496	282	5100	10.30
W 27 × 84	0	84	287	587	.49	6200	21.62	—	212	212	2830	13.35
= 43.0	½ × 9	92.5	402	663	.61	8180	20.35	.13	301	229	3530	11.76
	1½ × 9	118	626	757	.83	11500	18.44	.25	463	250	4570	9.88
W 24 × 68	0	68	213	468	.46	4280	20.06	—	153	153	1820	11.86
= 42.0	½ × 8	75.5	306	538	.57	5800	18.92	.15	223	166	2310	10.34
	1½ × 8	98.6	487	623	.78	8400	17.23	.28	349	182	3010	8.63
W 24 × 55	0	55	169	405	.42	3460	20.51	—	114	114	1340	11.77
= 40.0	½ × 6	60.6	238	468	.51	4660	19.58	.15	164	125	1710	10.40
	1½ × 6	77.8	374	548	.68	6790	18.16	.28	256	138	2250	8.80
W 21 × 62	0	62	179	391	.46	3250	18.17	—	127	127	1330	10.50
= 41.2	½ × 7	68.6	252	449	.56	4350	17.30	.16	180	137	1670	9.27
	1½ × 7	88.6	393	524	.75	6280	15.99	.31	276	149	2180	7.89
W 21 × 55	0	55	158	368	.43	2910	18.40	—	110	110	1140	10.40
= 41.2	½ × 7	61.8	231	431	.54	4030	17.45	.18	163	119	1470	9.01
	1½ × 7	82.2	373	508	.73	5980	16.03	.32	257	131	1930	7.51
W 21 × 44	0	44	125	321	.39	2350	18.83	—	81.6	81.6	843	10.33
= 39.5	½ × 5½	49.4	182	380	.48	3280	18.02	.18	122	90.1	1100	8.98
	1½ × 5½	65.5	294	454	.65	4940	16.77	.32	194	100	1460	7.53
W 18 × 50	0	50	131	300	.44	2140	16.37	—	89.1	89.1	802	9.00
= 40.5	½ × 6	55.5	185	350	.53	2910	15.70	.19	128	96.1	1020	7.93
	1½ × 6	72.7	292	416	.70	4290	14.69	.35	196	105	1330	6.80

NOTES (Cont'd.):

4. For uniform loading: Deflection (in.) $= ML^2/160\,Sy_b$

   End reaction (kips) $= 0.33 S_{tr} F_b / L$

   where $M =$ kip-ft., $L =$ ft., $S =$ in.³, $y_b =$ in., $S_{tr} =$ in.³, $F_b =$ ksi

5. Ratio of S_{tr}/S_t at balanced design:

F_y (ksi)	$f'_c = 3.0$	3.75	4.0
36	.51	.59	.61
42	.44	.50	.52
45	.41	.47	.48
50	.37	.42	.44
55	.34	.38	.40
60	.31	.35	.36

5½" Slab

COMPOSITE DESIGN
Properties of composite beams
With Cover Plate—5½ Inch Slab

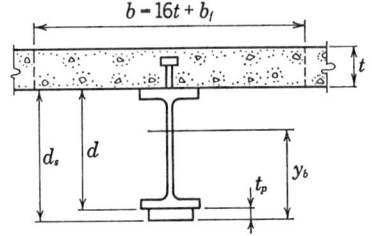

$$b = 16t + b_f$$

Beam	Cover Plate Size	Avg. Wt. per Ft.	Full Slab Transformed Section						K	W_s
			S_{tr}	S_t	$\dfrac{S_{tr}}{S_t}$	I_{tr}	y_b	$\dfrac{12Q}{I}$		
	In.	Lbs.	In.³	In.³		In.⁴	In.			Lbs.
W 18 × 45	0	45	126	476	.26	2320	18.48	—	—	45
$b = 95.5$	½ × 6	50.6	183	588	.31	3330	18.20	.19	.56	55.2
*V = 87	1½ × 6	68.1	296	748	.40	5270	17.81	.35	.76	75.6
W 18 × 35	0	35	97.4	414	.24	1830	18.78	—	—	35
$b = 94.0$	½ × 5	39.9	146	521	.28	2700	18.53	.20	.58	43.5
*V = 77	1½ × 5	54.7	240	680	.35	4390	18.26	.36	.77	60.5
W 16 × 40	0	40	105	400	.26	1790	17.01	—	—	40
$b = 95.0$	½ × 6	46.0	158	502	.31	2650	16.73	.22	.58	50.2
*V = 71	1½ × 6	63.8	261	652	.40	4290	16.42	.39	.77	70.6
W 16 × 36	0	36	94.3	376	.25	1610	17.07	—	—	36
$b = 95.0$	½ × 6	42.2	147	483	.31	2470	16.74	.24	.60	46.2
*V = 69	1¼ × 6	55.5	225	604	.37	3700	16.47	.38	.76	61.5
W 16 × 26	0	26	68.2	316	.22	1190	17.39	—	—	26
$b = 93.5$	½ × 4½	30.7	108	412	.26	1860	17.14	.25	.61	33.7
*V = 57	1 × 4½	37.3	148	489	.30	2510	17.01	.35	.73	41.3
W 14 × 30	0	30	73.3	300	.24	1140	15.56	—	—	30
$b = 94.7$	½ × 5½	35.8	117	391	.30	1790	15.28	.28	.61	39.4
*V = 54	1 × 5½	43.8	160	464	.35	2430	15.13	.40	.74	48.7
W 14 × 22	0	22	53.9	254	.21	854	15.86	—	—	22
$b = 93.0$	½ × 4	26.2	86.2	333	.26	1350	15.67	.27	.61	28.8
*V = 46	1 × 4	32.1	118	397	.30	1840	15.59	.39	.74	35.6
W 12 × 19	0	19	43.4	207	.21	633	14.61	—	—	19
$b = 92.0$	½ × 3	22.0	65.4	265	.25	952	14.56	.27	.58	24.1
*V = 42	1 × 3	26.2	87.1	313	.28	1270	14.60	.40	.71	29.2

* For steels with $F_y = 36$ ksi.

NOTES:
1. Tables are based on specified concrete strength $f'_c = 3.0$ ksi and modular ratio $n = 9$.
2. Proper selection of S_{tr} value assures that stress in steel beam does not exceed allowable. Concrete stress due to bending does not exceed allowable under the following conditions:

$F_y = 36$ ksi	Condition	$F_y = 50$ ksi
S_{tr}/S_t	$f'_c = 3.0$ ksi	S_{tr}/S_t
$\leqslant .51$	Shored construction	$\leqslant .37$
$\leqslant 1.01$	Unshored const. with $M_L/M_D < 1.0$	$\leqslant .74$
$\leqslant .76$	Unshored const. with $M_L/M_D < 2.0$	$\leqslant .55$
$\leqslant .67$	Unshored const. with $M_L/M_D < 3.0$	$\leqslant .49$

3. For unshored construction see Sect. 1.11.2.2 of the AISC Specification.

COMPOSITE DESIGN

Properties of composite beams

With Cover Plate—5½ Inch Slab

5½″ Slab

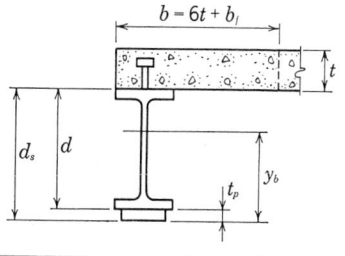

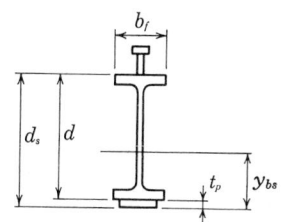

Beam	Cover Plate Size	Avg. Wt. per Ft.	Partial Slab Transformed Section						Steel Section			
			S_{tr}	S_t	$\dfrac{S_{tr}}{S_t}$	I_{tr}	y_b	$\dfrac{12Q}{I}$	S_s	S_{ts}	I	y_{bs}
	In.	Lbs.	In.³	In.³		In.⁴	In.		In.³	In.³	In.⁴	In.
W 18 × 45	0	45	117	285	.41	1940	16.55	—	79.0	79.0	706	8.93
$b = 40.5$	½ × 6	50.6	172	339	.51	2730	15.81	.21	118	85.8	912	7.73
	1½ × 6	68.2	280	407	.69	4120	14.73	.37	186	94.1	1210	6.51
W 18 × 35	0	35	90.9	247	.37	1540	16.96	—	57.9	57.9	513	8.85
$b = 39.0$	½ × 5	40.0	137	300	.46	2230	16.28	.22	89.7	63.9	680	7.58
	1½ × 5	54.8	227	368	.62	3470	15.27	.38	145	70.9	915	6.31
W 16 × 40	0	40	98.2	240	.41	1500	15.25	—	64.6	64.6	517	8.00
$b = 40.0$	½ × 6	46.1	149	291	.51	2160	14.57	.24	99.6	70.3	680	6.83
	1½ × 6	63.9	247	355	.70	3350	13.57	.41	159	77.2	910	5.71
W 16 × 36	0	36	87.9	226	.39	1350	15.37	—	56.5	56.5	447	7.92
$b = 40.0$	½ × 6	42.2	138	281	.49	2030	14.64	.26	91.1	62.0	603	6.62
	1¼ × 6	55.6	213	333	.64	2930	13.80	.40	137	67.1	769	5.63
W 16 × 26	0	26	63.7	188	.34	1010	15.80	—	38.3	38.3	300	7.82
$b = 38.5$	½ × 4½	30.8	102	241	.42	1550	15.22	.26	63.7	42.8	413	6.49
	1 × 4½	37.3	139	277	.50	2050	14.75	.37	86.5	45.6	497	5.75
W 14 × 30	0	30	68.3	180	.38	958	14.03	—	41.9	41.9	290	6.93
$b = 39.3$	½ × 5½	35.8	110	230	.48	1480	13.43	.29	69.5	46.1	398	5.72
	1 × 5½	43.9	151	264	.57	1950	12.96	.42	94.0	48.8	478	5.08
W 14 × 22	0	22	50.3	150	.33	725	14.40	—	28.9	28.9	198	6.86
$b = 38.0$	½ × 4	26.2	80.7	195	.41	1130	13.95	.29	48.4	32.3	275	5.68
	1 × 4	32.1	111	228	.49	1500	13.61	.42	65.8	34.4	332	5.05
W 12 × 19	0	19	40.4	121	.33	535	13.25	—	21.3	21.3	130	6.08
$b = 37.0$	½ × 3	22.0	61.0	153	.40	793	12.99	.29	33.9	23.9	177	5.24
	1 × 3	26.2	81.2	179	.45	1040	12.85	.43	44.9	25.6	215	4.78

NOTES (Cont'd.):

4. For uniform loading: Deflection (in.) $= ML^2/160\,Sy_b$

End reaction (kips) $= 0.33S_{tr}F_b/L$

where $M =$ kip-ft., $L =$ ft., $S =$ in.³, $y_b =$ in., $S_{tr} =$ in.³, $F_b =$ ksi

5. Ratio of S_{tr}/S_t at balanced design:

F_y (ksi)	$f'_c = 3.0$	3.75	4.0
36	.51	.59	.61
42	.44	.50	.52
45	.41	.47	.48
50	.37	.42	.44
55	.34	.38	.40
60	.31	.35	.36

4″ Slab

COMPOSITE DESIGN
Composite Beam Selection Table
4 Inch Slab (Full Width)

S_{tr}	Section		Avg. Wt. per Foot	S_{tr}	Section		Avg. Wt. per Foot
	Beam	Cover Plate			Beam	Cover Plate	
In.³		In. × In.	Lb.	In.³		In. × In.	Lb.
1180	W 36×170	1½ × 10	202	281	W 27×84	0	84
1100	W 36×150	1½ × 10	184	271	W 18×45	1½ × 6	68.3
1030	W 36×135	1½ × 10	170	245	W 21×62	½ × 7	68.7
957	W 33×130	1½ × 10	165	238	W 16×40	1½ × 6	64.0
908	W 33×118	1½ × 10	154	232	W 24×55	½ × 6	60.6
872	W 36×170	½ × 10	177	224	W 21×55	½ × 7	61.8
788	W 36×150	½ × 10	158	220	W 18×35	1½ × 5	54.9
755	W 30×108	1½ × 9	140	207	W 24×68	0	68
722	W 30× 99	1½ × 9	132	204	W 16×36	1¼ × 6	55.7
720	W 36×135	½ × 10	143	178	W 18×50	½ × 6	55.6
713	W 36×170	0	170	176	W 21×44	½ × 5½	49.5
678	W 27×102	1½ × 9	134	173	W 21×62	0	62
663	W 33×130	½ × 10	138	166	W 18×45	½ × 6	50.7
652	W 27× 94	1½ × 9	127	163	W 24×55	0	55
628	W 36×150	0	150	152	W 21×55	0	55
619	W 27× 84	1½ × 9	118	143	W 14×30	1 × 5½	44.0
612	W 33×118	½ × 10	127	142	W 16×40	½ × 6	46.1
559	W 36×135	0	135	133	W 16×26	1 × 4½	37.4
513	W 30×108	½ × 9	116	132	W 16×36	½ × 6	42.3
512	W 33×130	0	130	131	W 18×35	½ × 5	40.0
479	W 24× 68	1½ × 8	98.7	125	W 18×50	0	50
479	W 30× 99	½ × 9	107	120	W 21×44	0	44
461	W 33×118	0	118	112	W 18×45	0	45
457	W 27×102	½ × 9	110	105	W 14×22	1 × 4	32.2
430	W 27× 94	½ × 9	102	104	W 14×30	½ × 5½	35.8
395	W 27× 84	½ × 9	92.5	96.3	W 16×26	½ × 4½	30.8
389	W 30×108	0	108	92.8	W 16×40	0	40
385	W 21× 62	1½ × 7	88.7	86.2	W 18×35	0	35
367	W 24× 55	1½ × 6	77.9	82.8	W 16×36	0	36
365	W 21× 55	1½ × 7	82.3	75.8	W 12×19	1 × 3	26.3
354	W 30× 99	0	99	75.6	W 14×22	½ × 4	26.3
344	W 27×102	0	102	63.4	W 14×30	0	30
316	W 27× 94	0	94	59.5	W 16×26	0	26
299	W 24× 68	½ × 8	75.5	56.5	W 12×19	½ × 3	22.0
287	W 21× 44	1½ × 5½	65.6	46.4	W 14×22	0	22
283	W 18× 50	1½ × 6	72.9	36.8	W 12×19	0	19

COMPOSITE DESIGN
Composite Beam Selection Table

4½ Inch Slab (Full Width)

S_{tr}	Section		Avg. Wt. per Foot	S_{tr}	Section		Avg. Wt. per Foot
	Beam	Cover Plate			Beam	Cover Plate	
In.³		In. × In.	Lb.	In.³		In. × In.	Lb.
1210	W 36×170	1½ × 10	202	289	W 27×84	0	84
1130	W 36×150	1½ × 10	184	279	W 18×45	1½ × 6	68.3
1060	W 36×135	1½ × 10	170	252	W 21×62	½ × 7	68.6
981	W 33×130	1½ × 10	165	246	W 16×40	1½ × 6	63.9
930	W 33×118	1½ × 10	154	239	W 24×55	½ × 6	60.6
893	W 36×170	½ × 10	177	231	W 21×55	½ × 7	61.8
807	W 36×150	½ × 10	158	227	W 18×35	1½ × 5	54.8
774	W 30×108	1½ × 9	140	214	W 24×68	0	68
741	W 30× 99	1½ × 9	132	211	W 16×36	1¼ × 6	55.6
738	W 36×135	½ × 10	143	184	W 18×50	½ × 6	55.5
731	W 36×170	0	170	182	W 21×44	½ × 5½	49.5
696	W 27×102	1½ × 9	134	179	W 21×62	0	62
679	W 33×130	½ × 10	138	171	W 18×45	½ × 6	50.7
669	W 27× 94	1½ × 9	127	169	W 24×55	0	55
644	W 36×150	0	150	157	W 21×55	0	55
634	W 27× 84	1½ × 9	118	149	W 14×30	1 × 5½	43.9
627	W 33×118	½ × 10	127	147	W 16×40	½ × 6	46.1
573	W 36×135	0	135	137	W 16×26	1 × 4½	37.4
526	W 30×108	½ × 9	116	137	W 16×36	½ × 6	42.2
525	W 33×130	0	130	136	W 18×35	½ × 5	40.0
492	W 24× 68	1½ × 8	98.7	129	W 18×50	0	50
491	W 30× 99	½ × 9	107	124	W 21×44	0	44
473	W 33×118	0	118	116	W 18×45	0	45
469	W 27×102	½ × 9	110	109	W 14×22	1 × 4	32.2
441	W 27× 94	½ × 9	102	108	W 14×30	½ × 5½	35.8
405	W 27× 84	½ × 9	92.5	100	W 16×26	½ × 4½	30.8
399	W 30×108	0	108	96.8	W 16×40	0	40
395	W 21× 62	1½ × 7	88.7	89.8	W 18×35	0	35
377	W 24× 55	1½ × 6	77.8	86.5	W 16×36	0	36
375	W 21× 55	1½ × 7	82.3	79.5	W 12×19	1 × 3	26.3
364	W 30× 99	0	99	79.1	W 14×22	½ × 4	26.3
353	W 27×102	0	102	66.6	W 14×30	0	30
325	W 27× 94	0	94	62.4	W 16×26	0	26
308	W 24× 68	½ × 8	75.5	59.4	W 12×19	½ × 3	22.0
295	W 21× 44	1½ × 5½	65.6	48.9	W 14×22	0	22
292	W 18× 50	1½ × 6	72.8	38.9	W 12×19	0	19

5″ Slab

COMPOSITE DESIGN
Composite Beam Selection Table
5 Inch Slab (Full Width)

S_{tr}	Section		Avg. Wt. per Foot	S_{tr}	Section		Avg. Wt. per Foot
	Beam	Cover Plate			Beam	Cover Plate	
In.³		In. × In.	Lb.	In.³		In. × In.	Lb.
1240	W 36×170	1½ × 10	202	296	W 27×84	0	84
1150	W 36×150	1½ × 10	184	288	W 18×45	1½ × 6	68.2
1080	W 36×135	1½ × 10	170	259	W 21×62	½ × 7	68.6
1000	W 33×130	1½ × 10	165	253	W 16×40	1½ × 6	63.8
951	W 33×118	1½ × 10	154	246	W 24×55	½ × 6	60.6
914	W 36×170	½ × 10	177	237	W 21×55	½ × 7	61.8
826	W 36×150	½ × 10	158	233	W 18×35	1½ × 5	54.8
793	W 30×108	1½ × 9	140	220	W 24×68	0	68
758	W 30× 99	1½ × 9	132	218	W 16×36	1¼ × 6	55.5
754	W 36×135	½ × 10	143	190	W 18×50	½ × 6	55.5
748	W 36×170	0	170	187	W 21×44	½ × 5½	49.4
713	W 27×102	1½ × 9	134	185	W 21×62	0	62
695	W 33×130	½ × 10	138	177	W 18×45	½ × 6	50.6
685	W 27× 94	1½ × 9	127	174	W 24×55	0	55
659	W 36×150	0	150	163	W 21×55	0	55
649	W 27× 84	1½ × 9	118	154	W 14×30	1 × 5½	43.8
642	W 33×118	½ × 10	127	152	W 16×40	½ × 6	46.0
587	W 36×135	0	135	142	W 16×26	1 × 4½	37.3
539	W 30×108	½ × 9	116	142	W 16×36	½ × 6	42.2
538	W 33×130	0	130	141	W 18×35	½ × 5	39.9
504	W 24× 68	1½ × 8	98.6	134	W 18×50	0	50
503	W 30× 99	½ × 9	107	129	W 21×44	0	44
485	W 33×118	0	118	121	W 18×45	0	45
480	W 27×102	½ × 9	110	113	W 14×22	1 × 4	32.1
452	W 27× 94	½ × 9	102	113	W 14×30	½ × 5½	35.8
415	W 27× 84	½ × 9	92.5	104	W 16×26	½ × 4½	30.8
410	W 30×108	0	108	101	W 16×40	0	40
406	W 21× 62	1½ × 7	88.6	93.6	W 18×35	0	35
387	W 24× 55	1½ × 6	77.8	90.3	W 16×36	0	36
385	W 21× 55	1½ × 7	82.2	83.3	W 12×19	1 × 3	26.3
374	W 30× 99	0	99	82.6	W 14×22	½ × 4	26.2
362	W 27×102	0	102	69.9	W 14×30	0	30
334	W 27× 94	0	94	65.2	W 16×26	0	26
316	W 24× 68	½ × 8	75.5	62.4	W 12×19	½ × 3	22.0
303	W 21× 44	1½ × 5½	65.5	51.3	W 14×22	0	22
301	W 18× 50	1½ × 6	72.7	41.1	W 12×19	0	19

AMERICAN INSTITUTE OF STEEL CONSTRUCTION

COMPOSITE DESIGN
Composite Beam Selection Table
5½ Inch Slab (Full Width)

S_{tr}	Section Beam	Cover Plate In. × In.	Avg. Wt. per Foot Lb.	S_{tr}	Section Beam	Cover Plate In. × In.	Avg. Wt. per Foot Lb.
In.³				In.³			
1270	W 36×170	1½ × 10	202	304	W 27×84	0	84
1180	W 36×150	1½ × 10	184	296	W 18×45	1½ × 6	68.1
1110	W 36×135	1½ × 10	170	267	W 21×62	½ × 7	68.6
1020	W 33×130	1½ × 10	165	261	W 16×40	1½ × 6	63.8
971	W 33×118	1½ × 10	154	252	W 24×55	½ × 6	60.6
933	W 36×170	½ × 10	177	244	W 21×55	½ × 7	61.7
843	W 36×150	½ × 10	158	240	W 18×35	1½ × 5	54.7
810	W 30×108	1½ × 9	140	227	W 24×68	0	68
774	W 30× 99	1½ × 9	132	225	W 16×36	1¼ × 6	55.5
770	W 36×135	½ × 10	143	197	W 18×50	½ × 6	55.5
765	W 36×170	0	170	193	W 21×44	½ × 5½	49.4
729	W 27×102	1½ × 9	134	191	W 21×62	0	62
709	W 33×130	½ × 10	138	183	W 18×45	½ × 6	50.6
701	W 27× 94	1½ × 9	127	180	W 24×55	0	55
673	W 36×150	0	150	168	W 21×55	0	55
664	W 27× 84	1½ × 9	118	160	W 14×30	1 × 5½	43.8
656	W 33×118	½ × 10	127	158	W 16×40	½ × 6	46.0
600	W 36×135	0	135	148	W 16×26	1 × 4½	37.3
551	W 30×108	½ × 9	116	147	W 16×36	½ × 6	42.2
550	W 33×130	0	130	146	W 18×35	½ × 5	39.9
516	W 24× 68	1½ × 8	98.6	140	W 18×50	0	50
514	W 30× 99	½ × 9	107	133	W 21×44	0	44
496	W 33×118	0	118	126	W 18×45	0	45
492	W 27×102	½ × 9	110	118	W 14×22	1 × 4	32.1
463	W 27× 94	½ × 9	102	117	W 14×30	½ × 5½	35.8
425	W 27× 84	½ × 9	92.5	108	W 16×26	½ × 4½	30.7
420	W 30×108	0	108	105	W 16×40	0	40
417	W 21× 62	1½ × 7	88.5	97.4	W 18×35	0	35
396	W 24× 55	1½ × 6	77.7	94.3	W 16×36	0	36
395	W 21× 55	1½ × 7	82.1	87.1	W 12×19	1 × 3	26.2
383	W 30× 99	0	99	86.2	W 14×22	½ × 4	26.2
372	W 27×102	0	102	73.3	W 14×30	0	30
342	W 27× 94	0	94	68.2	W 16×26	0	26.1
324	W 24× 68	½ × 8	75.5	65.4	W 12×19	½ × 3	22.0
311	W 21× 44	1½ × 5½	65.4	53.9	W 14×22	0	22
310	W 18× 50	1½ × 6	72.6	43.4	W 12×19	0	19

BEAM DIAGRAMS AND FORMULAS
Nomenclature

E Modulus of Elasticity of steel at 29,000 ksi.

I Moment of Inertia of beam (in.^{4}).

M_{max} Maximum moment (kip in.).

M_1 Maximum moment in left section of beam (kip in.).

M_2 Maximum moment in right section of beam (kip in.).

M_3 Maximum positive moment in beam with combined end moment conditions (kip in.).

M_x Moment at distance x from end of beam (kip in.).

P Concentrated load (kips).

P_1 Concentrated load nearest left reaction (kips).

P_2 Concentrated load nearest right reaction, and of different magnitude than P_1 (kips).

R End beam reaction for any condition of symmetrical loading (kips).

R_1 Left end beam reaction (kips).

R_2 Right end or intermediate beam reaction (kips).

R_3 Right end beam reaction (kips).

V Maximum vertical shear for any condition of symmetrical loading (kips).

V_1 Maximum vertical shear in left section of beam (kips).

V_2 Vertical shear at right reaction point, or to left of intermediate reaction point of beam (kips).

V_3 Vertical shear at right reaction point, or to right of intermediate reaction point of beam (kips).

V_x Vertical shear at distance x from end of beam (kips).

W Total load on beam (kips).

a Measured distance along beam (in.).

b Measured distance along beam which may be greater or less than "a" (in.).

l Total length of beam between reaction points (in.).

w Uniformly distributed load per unit of length (kips per in.).

w_1 Uniformly distributed load per unit of length nearest left reaction (kips per in.).

w_2 Uniformly distributed load per unit of length nearest right reaction, and of different magnitude than w_1 (kips per in.).

x Any distance measured along beam from left reaction (in.).

x_1 Any distance measured along overhang section of beam from nearest reaction point (in.).

Δ_{max} Maximum deflection (in.).

Δ_a Deflection at point of load (in.).

Δ_x Deflection at any point x distance from left reaction (in.).

Δ_{x_1} Deflection of overhang section of beam at any distance from nearest reaction point (in.).

BEAM DIAGRAMS AND FORMULAS
Frequently used formulas

The formulas given below are frequently required in structural designing. They are included herein for the convenience of those engineers who have infrequent use for such formulas and hence may find reference necessary. Variation from the standard nomenclature on page 2 - 196 is noted.

BEAMS

Flexural stress at extreme fiber:

$$f = Mc/I = M/S$$

Flexural stress at any fiber:

$$f = My/I \qquad y = \text{distance from neutral axis to fiber.}$$

Average vertical shear (for maximum see below):

$$v = V/A = V/dt \text{ (for beams and girders)}$$

Horizontal shearing stress at any section A-A:

$$v = VQ/I\,b \qquad Q = \text{statical moment about the neutral axis of the entire}$$
section of that portion of the cross-section lying outside of section A-A,

$$b = \text{width at section A-A}$$

(Intensity of vertical shear is equal to that of horizontal shear acting normal to it at the same point and both are usually a maximum at mid-height of beam.)

Slope and deflection at any point:

$$EI\frac{d^2y}{dx^2} = M \qquad x \text{ and } y \text{ are abscissa and ordinate respectively of a point}$$
on the neutral axis, referred to axes of rectangular coordinates through a selected point of support.

(First integration gives slopes; second integration gives deflections. Constants of integration must be determined.)

CONTINUOUS BEAMS (THE THEOREM OF THREE MOMENTS)

Uniform load:

$$M_a\frac{l_1}{I_1} + 2M_b\left(\frac{l_1}{I_1} + \frac{l_2}{I_2}\right) + M_c\frac{l_2}{I_2} = -\frac{1}{4}\left(\frac{w_1l_1^3}{I_1} + \frac{w_2l_2^3}{I_2}\right)$$

Concentrated loads:

$$M_a\frac{l_1}{I_1} + 2M_b\left(\frac{l_1}{I_1} + \frac{l_2}{I_2}\right) + M_c\frac{l_2}{I_2} = -\frac{P_1a_1b_1}{I_1}\left(1 + \frac{a_1}{l_1}\right) - \frac{P_2a_2b_2}{I_2}\left(1 + \frac{b_2}{l_2}\right)$$

Considering any two consecutive spans in any continuous structure:

M_a, M_b, M_c = moments at left, center, and right supports respectively, of any pair of adjacent spans.

l_1 and l_2 = length of left and right spans respectively, of the pair.

I_1 and I_2 = moment of inertia of left and right spans respectively.

w_1 and w_2 = load per unit of length on left and right spans respectively.

P_1 and P_2 = concentrated loads on left and right spans respectively.

a_1 and a_2 = distance of concentrated loads from left support in left and right spans respectively.

b_1 and b_2 = distance of concentrated loads from right support in left and right spans respectively.

The above equations are for beams with moment of inertia constant in each span but differing in different spans, continuous over three or more supports. By writing such an equation for each successive pair of spans and introducing the known values (usually zero) of end moments, all other moments can be found.

BEAM DIAGRAMS AND FORMULAS
For various static loading conditions

Equivalent Tabular Load is the unifomly distributed load given in beam tables, pages **2** - 28 to **2** - 81. For meaning of symbols, see page **2** - 196.

1. SIMPLE BEAM—UNIFORMLY DISTRIBUTED LOAD

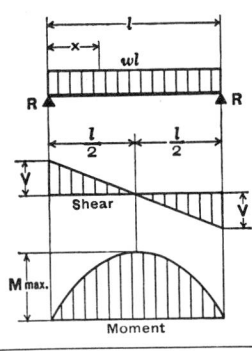

Equivalent Tabular Load . . . $= wl$

$R = V$ . . . . $= \dfrac{wl}{2}$

V_x . . . . $= w\left(\dfrac{l}{2} - x\right)$

M max. (at center) . . . . $= \dfrac{wl^2}{8}$

M_x . . . . $= \dfrac{wx}{2}(l-x)$

Δmax. (at center) . . . . $= \dfrac{5\,wl^4}{384\,EI}$

Δ_x . . . . $= \dfrac{wx}{24EI}(l^3 - 2lx^2 + x^3)$

2. SIMPLE BEAM—LOAD INCREASING UNIFORMLY TO ONE END

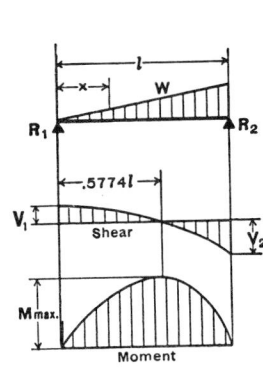

Equivalent Tabular Load . . . $= \dfrac{16W}{9\sqrt{3}} = 1.0264W$

$R_1 = V_1$ . . . . $= \dfrac{W}{3}$

$R_2 = V_2$ max. . . . . . . $= \dfrac{2W}{3}$

V_x . . . . $= \dfrac{W}{3} - \dfrac{Wx^2}{l^2}$

M max. $\left(at\ x = \dfrac{l}{\sqrt{3}} = .5774l\right)$ . . $= \dfrac{2Wl}{9\sqrt{3}} = .1283\,Wl$

M_x . . . . $= \dfrac{Wx}{3l^2}(l^2 - x^2)$

Δmax. $\left(at\ x = l\sqrt{1 - \sqrt{\dfrac{8}{15}}} = .5193l\right) = .01304\dfrac{Wl^3}{EI}$

Δ_x . . . . $= \dfrac{Wx}{180EI\ l^2}(3x^4 - 10l^2x^2 + 7l^4)$

3. SIMPLE BEAM—LOAD INCREASING UNIFORMLY TO CENTER

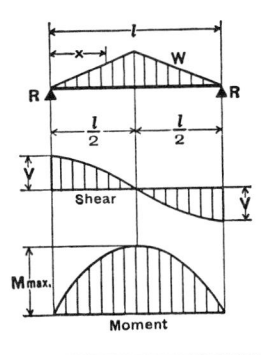

Equivalent Tabular Load . . . $= \dfrac{4W}{3}$

$R = V$ . . . . $= \dfrac{W}{2}$

V_x $\left(when\ x < \dfrac{l}{2}\right)$ . . . . $= \dfrac{W}{2l^2}(l^2 - 4x^2)$

M max. (at center) . . . . $= \dfrac{Wl}{6}$

M_x $\left(when\ x < \dfrac{l}{2}\right)$ . . . . $= Wx\left(\dfrac{1}{2} - \dfrac{2x^2}{3l^2}\right)$

Δmax. (at center) . . . . $= \dfrac{Wl^3}{60EI}$

Δ_x $\left(when\ x < \dfrac{l}{2}\right)$ . . . . $= \dfrac{Wx}{480\ EI\ l^2}(5l^2 - 4x^2)^2$

AMERICAN INSTITUTE OF STEEL CONSTRUCTION

BEAM DIAGRAMS AND FORMULAS
For various static loading conditions

For meaning of symbols, see page **2** - 196.

4. SIMPLE BEAM—UNIFORM LOAD PARTIALLY DISTRIBUTED

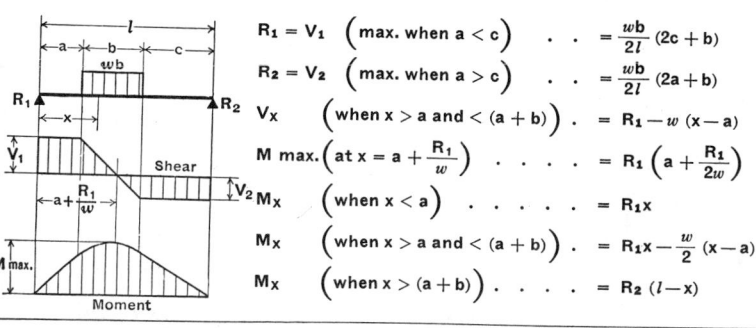

$$R_1 = V_1 \quad \left(\text{max. when } a < c\right) \quad \cdots \quad = \frac{wb}{2l}(2c+b)$$

$$R_2 = V_2 \quad \left(\text{max. when } a > c\right) \quad \cdots \quad = \frac{wb}{2l}(2a+b)$$

$$V_x \quad \left(\text{when } x > a \text{ and } < (a+b)\right) \quad = R_1 - w(x-a)$$

$$M \text{ max.} \left(\text{at } x = a + \frac{R_1}{w}\right) \quad \cdots \quad = R_1\left(a + \frac{R_1}{2w}\right)$$

$$M_x \quad \left(\text{when } x < a\right) \quad \cdots \quad = R_1 x$$

$$M_x \quad \left(\text{when } x > a \text{ and } < (a+b)\right) \quad = R_1 x - \frac{w}{2}(x-a)^2$$

$$M_x \quad \left(\text{when } x > (a+b)\right) \quad \cdots \quad = R_2(l-x)$$

5. SIMPLE BEAM—UNIFORM LOAD PARTIALLY DISTRIBUTED AT ONE END

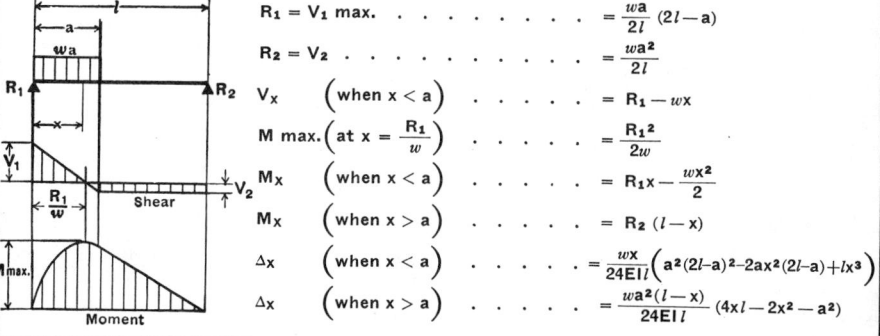

$$R_1 = V_1 \text{ max.} \quad \cdots \quad = \frac{wa}{2l}(2l-a)$$

$$R_2 = V_2 \quad \cdots \quad = \frac{wa^2}{2l}$$

$$V_x \quad \left(\text{when } x < a\right) \quad \cdots \quad = R_1 - wx$$

$$M \text{ max.} \left(\text{at } x = \frac{R_1}{w}\right) \quad \cdots \quad = \frac{R_1^2}{2w}$$

$$M_x \quad \left(\text{when } x < a\right) \quad \cdots \quad = R_1 x - \frac{wx^2}{2}$$

$$M_x \quad \left(\text{when } x > a\right) \quad \cdots \quad = R_2(l-x)$$

$$\Delta_x \quad \left(\text{when } x < a\right) \quad \cdots \quad = \frac{wx}{24EIl}\left(a^2(2l-a)^2 - 2ax^2(2l-a) + lx^3\right)$$

$$\Delta_x \quad \left(\text{when } x > a\right) \quad \cdots \quad = \frac{wa^2(l-x)}{24EIl}(4xl - 2x^2 - a^2)$$

6. SIMPLE BEAM—UNIFORM LOAD PARTIALLY DISTRIBUTED AT EACH END

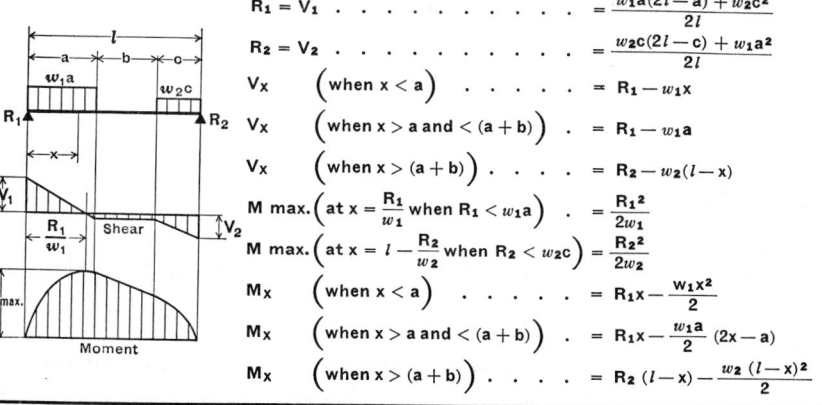

$$R_1 = V_1 \quad \cdots \quad = \frac{w_1 a(2l-a) + w_2 c^2}{2l}$$

$$R_2 = V_2 \quad \cdots \quad = \frac{w_2 c(2l-c) + w_1 a^2}{2l}$$

$$V_x \quad \left(\text{when } x < a\right) \quad \cdots \quad = R_1 - w_1 x$$

$$V_x \quad \left(\text{when } x > a \text{ and } < (a+b)\right) \quad = R_1 - w_1 a$$

$$V_x \quad \left(\text{when } x > (a+b)\right) \quad \cdots \quad = R_2 - w_2(l-x)$$

$$M \text{ max.} \left(\text{at } x = \frac{R_1}{w_1} \text{ when } R_1 < w_1 a\right) = \frac{R_1^2}{2w_1}$$

$$M \text{ max.} \left(\text{at } x = l - \frac{R_2}{w_2} \text{ when } R_2 < w_2 c\right) = \frac{R_2^2}{2w_2}$$

$$M_x \quad \left(\text{when } x < a\right) \quad \cdots \quad = R_1 x - \frac{w_1 x^2}{2}$$

$$M_x \quad \left(\text{when } x > a \text{ and } < (a+b)\right) \quad = R_1 x - \frac{w_1 a}{2}(2x-a)$$

$$M_x \quad \left(\text{when } x > (a+b)\right) \quad \cdots \quad = R_2(l-x) - \frac{w_2(l-x)^2}{2}$$

BEAM DIAGRAMS AND FORMULAS
For various static loading conditions

Equivalent Tabular Load is the uniformly distributed load given in beam tables, pages 2 - 28 to 2 - 81.
For meaning of symbols, see page 2 - 196.

7. SIMPLE BEAM—CONCENTRATED LOAD AT CENTER

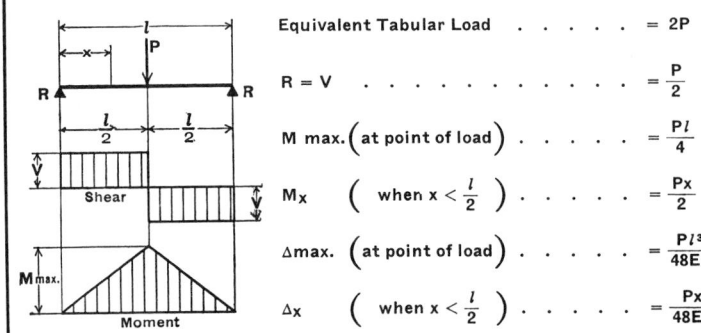

Equivalent Tabular Load . . . . . $= 2P$

$R = V$ . . . . $= \dfrac{P}{2}$

M max. $\left(\text{at point of load}\right)$ . . . . $= \dfrac{Pl}{4}$

M_x $\left(\text{when } x < \dfrac{l}{2}\right)$ . . . . $= \dfrac{Px}{2}$

Δmax. $\left(\text{at point of load}\right)$ . . . . $= \dfrac{Pl^3}{48EI}$

Δ_x $\left(\text{when } x < \dfrac{l}{2}\right)$ . . . . . $= \dfrac{Px}{48EI}(3l^2 - 4x^2)$

8. SIMPLE BEAM—CONCENTRATED LOAD AT ANY POINT

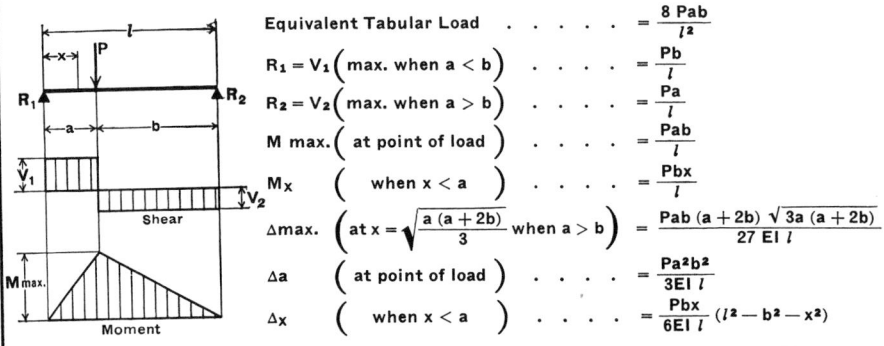

Equivalent Tabular Load . . . . $= \dfrac{8\,Pab}{l^2}$

$R_1 = V_1 \left(\text{max. when } a < b\right)$ . . . $= \dfrac{Pb}{l}$

$R_2 = V_2 \left(\text{max. when } a > b\right)$ . . . $= \dfrac{Pa}{l}$

M max. $\left(\text{at point of load}\right)$ . . . . $= \dfrac{Pab}{l}$

M_x $\left(\text{when } x < a\right)$ . . . . $= \dfrac{Pbx}{l}$

Δmax. $\left(\text{at } x = \sqrt{\dfrac{a\,(a+2b)}{3}} \text{ when } a > b\right)$ $= \dfrac{Pab\,(a+2b)\,\sqrt{3a\,(a+2b)}}{27\,EI\,l}$

Δa $\left(\text{at point of load}\right)$ . . . . $= \dfrac{Pa^2b^2}{3EI\,l}$

Δ_x $\left(\text{when } x < a\right)$ . . . . $= \dfrac{Pbx}{6EI\,l}(l^2 - b^2 - x^2)$

9. SIMPLE BEAM—TWO EQUAL CONCENTRATED LOADS SYMMETRICALLY PLACED

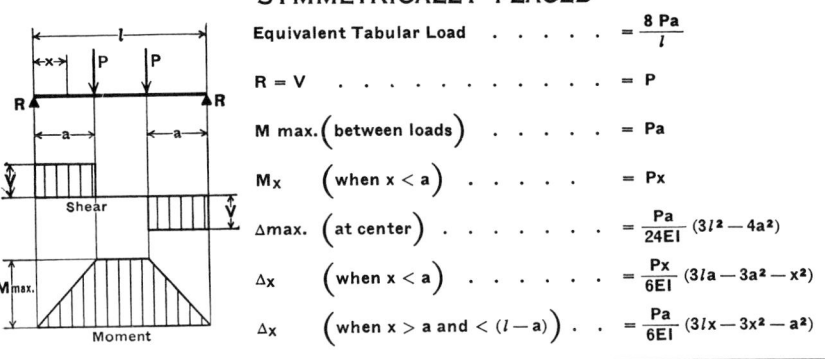

Equivalent Tabular Load . . . . . $= \dfrac{8\,Pa}{l}$

$R = V$ . . . . $= P$

M max. $\left(\text{between loads}\right)$ . . . . . $= Pa$

M_x $\left(\text{when } x < a\right)$ . . . . . $= Px$

Δmax. $\left(\text{at center}\right)$ . . . . . . $= \dfrac{Pa}{24EI}(3l^2 - 4a^2)$

Δ_x $\left(\text{when } x < a\right)$ . . . . . . $= \dfrac{Px}{6EI}(3la - 3a^2 - x^2)$

Δ_x $\left(\text{when } x > a \text{ and } < (l-a)\right)$ . . $= \dfrac{Pa}{6EI}(3lx - 3x^2 - a^2)$

BEAM DIAGRAMS AND FORMULAS
For various static loading conditions

Equivalent Tabular Load is the uniformly distributed load given in beam tables, pages **2 - 28** to **2 - 81**. For meaning of symbols, see page **2 - 196**.

10. SIMPLE BEAM—TWO EQUAL CONCENTRATED LOADS UNSYMMETRICALLY PLACED

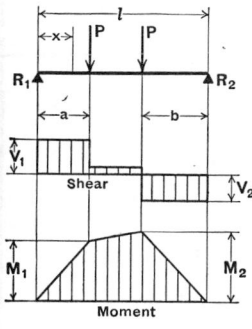

$R_1 = V_1 \left(\text{max. when } a < b \right)$ . . . . . $= \dfrac{P}{l} (l - a + b)$

$R_2 = V_2 \left(\text{max. when } a > b \right)$ . . . . . $= \dfrac{P}{l} (l - b + a)$

$V_x \quad \left(\text{when } x > a \text{ and } < (l - b) \right)$ . . $= \dfrac{P}{l} (b - a)$

$M_1 \quad \left(\text{max. when } a > b \right)$ . . . . . $= R_1 a$

$M_2 \quad \left(\text{max. when } a < b \right)$ . . . . . $= R_2 b$

$M_x \quad \left(\text{when } x < a \right)$ . . . . . . $= R_1 x$

$M_x \quad \left(\text{when } x > a \text{ and } < (l - b) \right)$ . . $= R_1 x - P (x - a)$

11. SIMPLE BEAM—TWO UNEQUAL CONCENTRATED LOADS UNSYMMETRICALLY PLACED

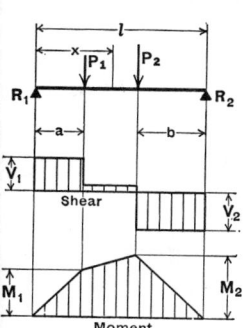

$R_1 = V_1$ . . . . $= \dfrac{P_1 (l - a) + P_2 b}{l}$

$R_2 = V_2$ . . . . $= \dfrac{P_1 a + P_2 (l - b)}{l}$

$V_x \quad \left(\text{when } x > a \text{ and } < (l - b) \right)$ . . $= R_1 - P_1$

$M_1 \quad \left(\text{max. when } R_1 < P_1 \right)$ . . . . $= R_1 a$

$M_2 \quad \left(\text{max. when } R_2 < P_2 \right)$ . . . . $= R_2 b$

$M_x \quad \left(\text{when } x < a \right)$ . . . . . . $= R_1 x$

$M_x \quad \left(\text{when } x > a \text{ and } < (l - b) \right)$ . . $= R_1 x - P_1 (x - a)$

12. BEAM FIXED AT ONE END, SUPPORTED AT OTHER— UNIFORMLY DISTRIBUTED LOAD

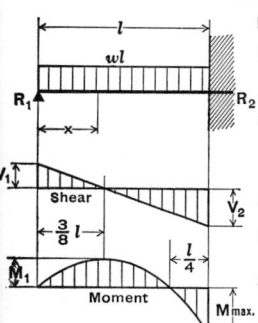

Equivalent Tabular Load . . . . . $= wl$

$R_1 = V_1$ . . . . $= \dfrac{3wl}{8}$

$R_2 = V_2$ max. . . . . $= \dfrac{5wl}{8}$

V_x . . . . $= R_1 - wx$

M max. . . . . $= \dfrac{wl^2}{8}$

$M_1 \quad \left(\text{at } x = \dfrac{3}{8} l \right)$ . . . . . . $= \dfrac{9}{128} wl^2$

M_x . . . . $= R_1 x - \dfrac{wx^2}{2}$

Δmax. $\left(\text{at } x = \dfrac{l}{16} (1 + \sqrt{33}) = .4215 l \right)$. $= \dfrac{wl^4}{185EI}$

Δ_x . . . . $= \dfrac{wx}{48EI} (l^3 - 3lx^2 + 2x^3)$

BEAM DIAGRAMS AND FORMULAS
For various static loading conditions

Equivalent Tabular Load is the uniformly distributed load given in beam tables, pages **2** - 28 to **2** - 81.
For meaning of symbols, see page **2** - 196.

13. BEAM FIXED AT ONE END, SUPPORTED AT OTHER— CONCENTRATED LOAD AT CENTER

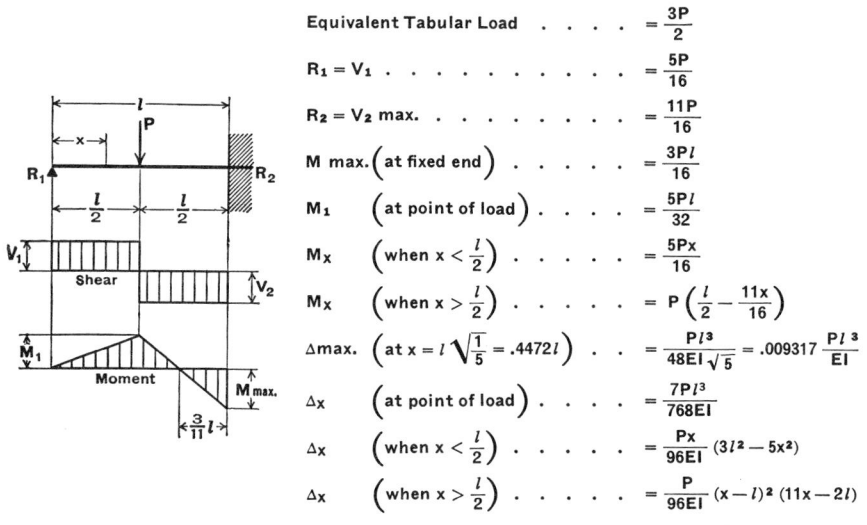

Equivalent Tabular Load $\ldots \ldots = \dfrac{3P}{2}$

$R_1 = V_1 \ldots \ldots \ldots = \dfrac{5P}{16}$

$R_2 = V_2$ max. $\ldots \ldots \ldots = \dfrac{11P}{16}$

M max. $\left(\text{at fixed end}\right) \ldots \ldots = \dfrac{3Pl}{16}$

$M_1 \left(\text{at point of load}\right) \ldots \ldots = \dfrac{5Pl}{32}$

$M_x \left(\text{when } x < \dfrac{l}{2}\right) \ldots \ldots = \dfrac{5Px}{16}$

$M_x \left(\text{when } x > \dfrac{l}{2}\right) \ldots \ldots = P\left(\dfrac{l}{2} - \dfrac{11x}{16}\right)$

Δmax. $\left(\text{at } x = l \sqrt{\dfrac{1}{5}} = .4472l\right) \ldots = \dfrac{Pl^3}{48EI\sqrt{5}} = .009317\,\dfrac{Pl^3}{EI}$

$\Delta_x \left(\text{at point of load}\right) \ldots \ldots = \dfrac{7Pl^3}{768EI}$

$\Delta_x \left(\text{when } x < \dfrac{l}{2}\right) \ldots \ldots = \dfrac{Px}{96EI}(3l^2 - 5x^2)$

$\Delta_x \left(\text{when } x > \dfrac{l}{2}\right) \ldots \ldots = \dfrac{P}{96EI}(x - l)^2(11x - 2l)$

14. BEAM FIXED AT ONE END, SUPPORTED AT OTHER— CONCENTRATED LOAD AT ANY POINT

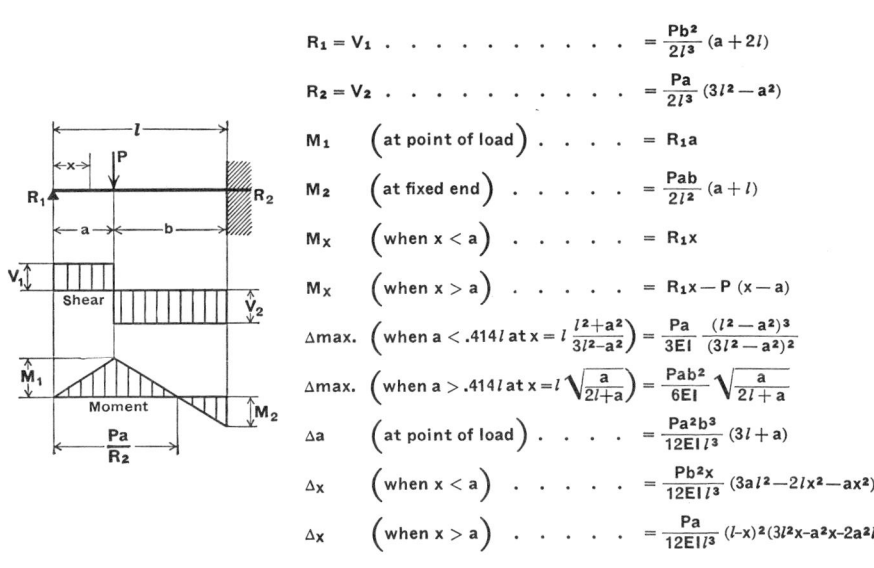

$R_1 = V_1 \ldots \ldots \ldots \ldots = \dfrac{Pb^2}{2l^3}(a + 2l)$

$R_2 = V_2 \ldots \ldots \ldots \ldots = \dfrac{Pa}{2l^3}(3l^2 - a^2)$

$M_1 \left(\text{at point of load}\right) \ldots \ldots = R_1 a$

$M_2 \left(\text{at fixed end}\right) \ldots \ldots = \dfrac{Pab}{2l^2}(a + l)$

$M_x \left(\text{when } x < a\right) \ldots \ldots = R_1 x$

$M_x \left(\text{when } x > a\right) \ldots \ldots = R_1 x - P(x - a)$

Δmax. $\left(\text{when } a < .414l \text{ at } x = l\,\dfrac{l^2 + a^2}{3l^2 - a^2}\right) = \dfrac{Pa}{3EI}\,\dfrac{(l^2 - a^2)^3}{(3l^2 - a^2)^2}$

Δmax. $\left(\text{when } a > .414l \text{ at } x = l\sqrt{\dfrac{a}{2l + a}}\right) = \dfrac{Pab^2}{6EI}\sqrt{\dfrac{a}{2l + a}}$

$\Delta_a \left(\text{at point of load}\right) \ldots \ldots = \dfrac{Pa^2 b^3}{12EI\,l^3}(3l + a)$

$\Delta_x \left(\text{when } x < a\right) \ldots \ldots = \dfrac{Pb^2 x}{12EI\,l^3}(3al^2 - 2lx^2 - ax^2)$

$\Delta_x \left(\text{when } x > a\right) \ldots \ldots = \dfrac{Pa}{12EI\,l^3}(l-x)^2(3l^2 x - a^2 x - 2a^2 l)$

BEAM DIAGRAMS AND FORMULAS
For various static loading conditions

Equivalent Tabular Load is the uniformly distributed load given in beam tables, pages 2 - 28 to 2 - 81. For meaning of symbols, see page 2 - 196.

---

15. BEAM FIXED AT BOTH ENDS—UNIFORMLY DISTRIBUTED LOADS

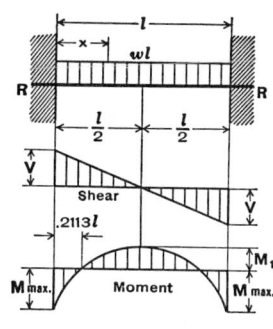

Equivalent Tabular Load . . . . . $= \dfrac{2wl}{3}$

$R = V$ . . . . $= \dfrac{wl}{2}$

V_x . . . . $= w\left(\dfrac{l}{2} - x\right)$

M max. (at ends) . . . . . $= \dfrac{wl^2}{12}$

M_1 (at center) . . . . . . $= \dfrac{wl^2}{24}$

M_x . . . . $= \dfrac{w}{12}(6lx - l^2 - 6x^2)$

Δmax. (at center) . . . . . $= \dfrac{wl^4}{384EI}$

Δ_x . . . . $= \dfrac{wx^2}{24EI}(l - x)^2$

---

16. BEAM FIXED AT BOTH ENDS—CONCENTRATED LOAD AT CENTER

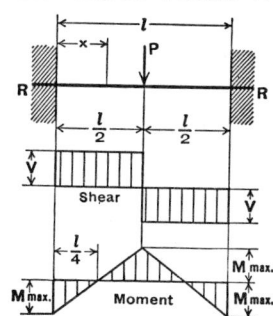

Equivalent Tabular Load . . . . . $= P$

$R = V$ . . . . $= \dfrac{P}{2}$

M max. (at center and ends) . . . $= \dfrac{Pl}{8}$

M_x (when $x < \dfrac{l}{2}$) . . . . . $= \dfrac{P}{8}(4x - l)$

Δmax. (at center) . . . . . $= \dfrac{Pl^3}{192EI}$

Δ_x (when $x < \dfrac{l}{2}$) . . . . . $= \dfrac{Px^2}{48EI}(3l - 4x)$

---

17. BEAM FIXED AT BOTH ENDS—CONCENTRATED LOAD AT ANY POINT

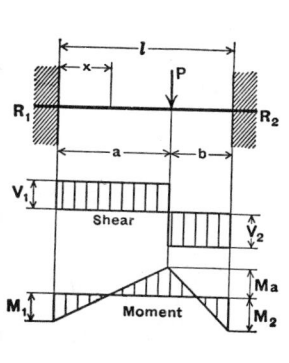

$R_1 = V_1$ (max. when $a < b$) . . . $= \dfrac{Pb^2}{l^3}(3a + b)$

$R_2 = V_2$ (max. when $a > b$) . . . $= \dfrac{Pa^2}{l^3}(a + 3b)$

M_1 (max. when $a < b$) . . . . $= \dfrac{Pab^2}{l^2}$

M_2 (max. when $a > b$) . . . . $= \dfrac{Pa^2b}{l^2}$

M_a (at point of load) . . . $= \dfrac{2Pa^2b^2}{l^3}$

M_x (when $x < a$) . . . . . $= R_1x - \dfrac{Pab^2}{l^2}$

Δmax. (when $a > b$ at $x = \dfrac{2al}{3a+b}$) . $= \dfrac{2Pa^3b^2}{3EI\,(3a+b)^2}$

Δ_a (at point of load) . . . $= \dfrac{Pa^3b^3}{3EIl^3}$

Δ_x (when $x < a$) . . . . . $= \dfrac{Pb^2x^2}{6EIl^3}(3al - 3ax - bx)$

AMERICAN INSTITUTE OF STEEL CONSTRUCTION

BEAM DIAGRAMS AND FORMULAS
For various static loading conditions

Equivalent Tabular Load is the uniformly distributed load given in beam tables, pages **2** - 28 to **2** - 81.
For meaning of symbols, see page **2** - 196.

18. CANTILEVER BEAM—LOAD INCREASING UNIFORMLY TO FIXED END

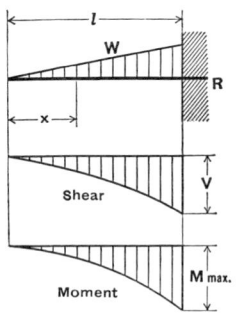

Equivalent Tabular Load . . . . $= \dfrac{8}{3} W$

$R = V$ . . . . $= W$

V_x . . . . $= W \dfrac{x^2}{l^2}$

M max. $\left(\text{at fixed end}\right)$ . . . . . $= \dfrac{Wl}{3}$

M_x . . . . $= \dfrac{Wx^3}{3l^2}$

Δmax. $\left(\text{at free end}\right)$ . . . . . $= \dfrac{Wl^3}{15EI}$

Δ_x . . . . $= \dfrac{W}{60EIl^2} (x^5 - 5l^4x + 4l^5)$

19. CANTILEVER BEAM—UNIFORMLY DISTRIBUTED LOAD

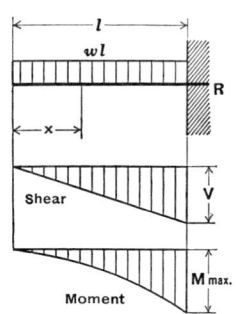

Equivalent Tabular Load . . . . $= 4wl$

$R = V$ . . . . $= wl$

V_x . . . . $= wx$

M max. $\left(\text{at fixed end}\right)$ . . . . . $= \dfrac{wl^2}{2}$

M_x . . . . $= \dfrac{wx^2}{2}$

Δmax. $\left(\text{at free end}\right)$ . . . . $= \dfrac{wl^4}{8EI}$

Δ_x . . . . $= \dfrac{w}{24EI} (x^4 - 4l^3x + 3l^4)$

20. BEAM FIXED AT ONE END, FREE TO DEFLECT VERTICALLY BUT NOT ROTATE AT OTHER—UNIFORMLY DISTRIBUTED LOAD

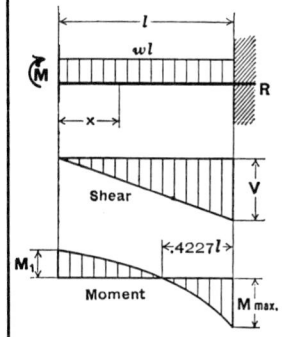

Equivalent Tabular Load . . . . $= \dfrac{8}{3} wl$

$R = V$ . . . . $= wl$

V_x . . . . $= wx$

M max. $\left(\text{at fixed end}\right)$ . . . . . $= \dfrac{wl^2}{3}$

M_1 $\left(\text{at deflected end}\right)$ . . . . $= \dfrac{wl^2}{6}$

M_x . . . . $= \dfrac{w}{6} (l^2 - 3x^2)$

Δmax. $\left(\text{at deflected end}\right)$ . . . . $= \dfrac{wl^4}{24EI}$

Δ_x . . . . $= \dfrac{w \, (l^2 - x^2)^2}{24EI}$

BEAM DIAGRAMS AND FORMULAS
For various static loading conditions

Equivalent Tabular Load is the uniformly distributed load given in beam tables, pages **2 - 28** to **2 - 81**.
For meaning of symbols, see page **2 - 196**.

21. CANTILEVER BEAM—CONCENTRATED LOAD AT ANY POINT

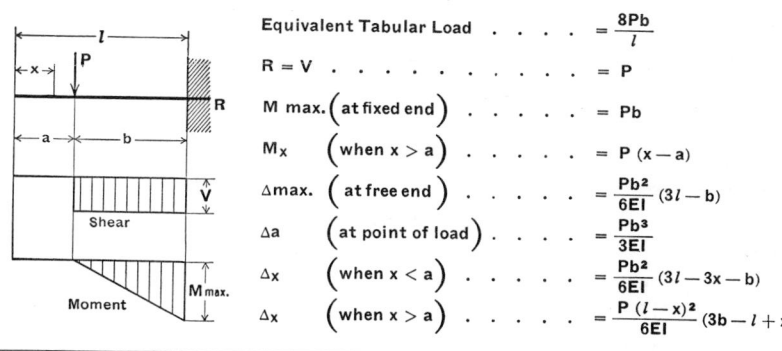

Equivalent Tabular Load . . . . $= \dfrac{8Pb}{l}$

$R = V$ . . . . $= P$

M max. $\left(\text{at fixed end}\right)$ . . . . $= Pb$

M_x $\left(\text{when } x > a\right)$ . . . . $= P\,(x - a)$

Δmax. $\left(\text{at free end}\right)$ . . . . $= \dfrac{Pb^2}{6EI}\,(3l - b)$

Δa $\left(\text{at point of load}\right)$ . . . . $= \dfrac{Pb^3}{3EI}$

Δx $\left(\text{when } x < a\right)$ . . . . . $= \dfrac{Pb^2}{6EI}\,(3l - 3x - b)$

Δx $\left(\text{when } x > a\right)$ . . . . . $= \dfrac{P\,(l - x)^2}{6EI}\,(3b - l + x)$

22. CANTILEVER BEAM—CONCENTRATED LOAD AT FREE END

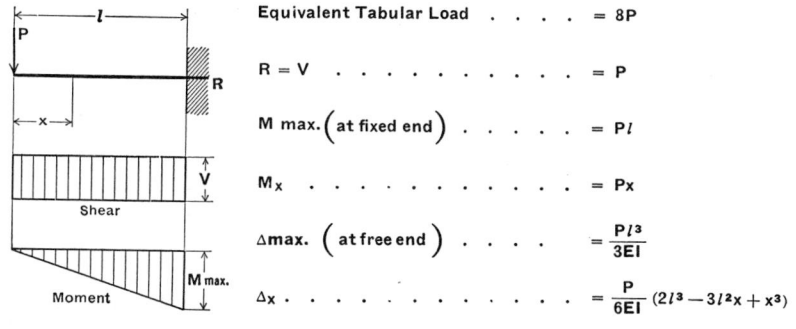

Equivalent Tabular Load . . . . $= 8P$

$R = V$ . . . . $= P$

M max. $\left(\text{at fixed end}\right)$ . . . . . $= Pl$

M_x . . . . $= Px$

Δmax. $\left(\text{at free end}\right)$ . . . . $= \dfrac{Pl^3}{3EI}$

Δx . . . . $= \dfrac{P}{6EI}\,(2l^3 - 3l^2x + x^3)$

23. BEAM FIXED AT ONE END, FREE TO DEFLECT VERTICALLY BUT NOT ROTATE AT OTHER—CONCENTRATED LOAD AT DEFLECTED END

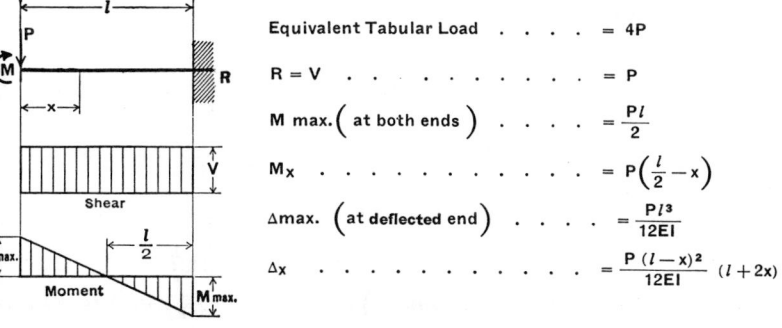

Equivalent Tabular Load . . . . $= 4P$

$R = V$ . . . . $= P$

M max. $\left(\text{at both ends}\right)$ . . . . $= \dfrac{Pl}{2}$

M_x . . . . $= P\left(\dfrac{l}{2} - x\right)$

Δmax. $\left(\text{at deflected end}\right)$ . . . . $= \dfrac{Pl^3}{12EI}$

Δx . . . . $= \dfrac{P\,(l - x)^2}{12EI}\,(l + 2x)$

BEAM DIAGRAMS AND FORMULAS
For various static loading conditions

For meaning of symbols, see page **2 - 196**.

24. BEAM OVERHANGING ONE SUPPORT—UNIFORMLY DISTRIBUTED LOAD

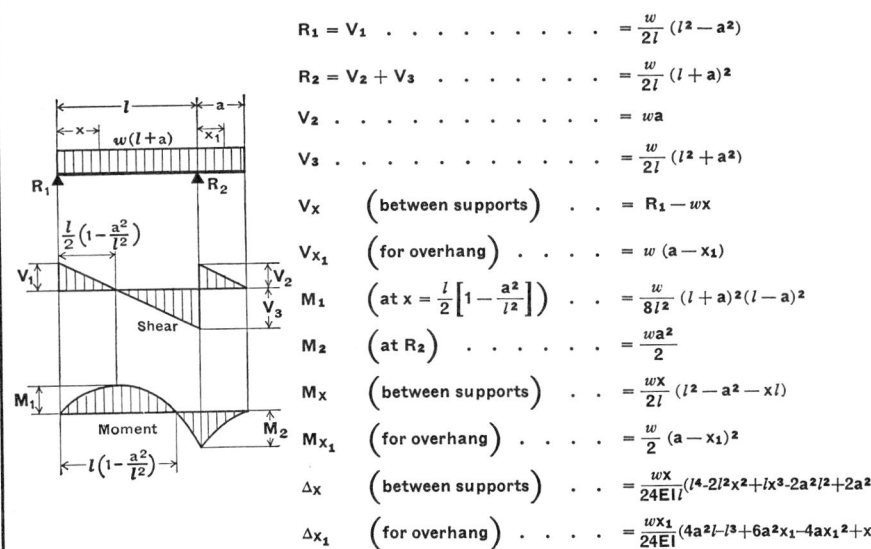

$$R_1 = V_1 \quad \ldots \quad = \frac{w}{2l}(l^2 - a^2)$$

$$R_2 = V_2 + V_3 \quad \ldots \quad = \frac{w}{2l}(l+a)^2$$

$$V_2 \quad \ldots \quad = wa$$

$$V_3 \quad \ldots \quad = \frac{w}{2l}(l^2 + a^2)$$

$$V_x \quad \left(\text{between supports}\right) \quad = R_1 - wx$$

$$V_{x_1} \quad \left(\text{for overhang}\right) \quad \ldots \quad = w(a - x_1)$$

$$M_1 \quad \left(\text{at } x = \frac{l}{2}\left[1 - \frac{a^2}{l^2}\right]\right) \quad \ldots \quad = \frac{w}{8l^2}(l+a)^2(l-a)^2$$

$$M_2 \quad \left(\text{at } R_2\right) \quad \ldots \quad = \frac{wa^2}{2}$$

$$M_x \quad \left(\text{between supports}\right) \quad \ldots \quad = \frac{wx}{2l}(l^2 - a^2 - xl)$$

$$M_{x_1} \quad \left(\text{for overhang}\right) \quad \ldots \quad = \frac{w}{2}(a - x_1)^2$$

$$\Delta_x \quad \left(\text{between supports}\right) \quad \ldots \quad = \frac{wx}{24EIl}(l^4 - 2l^2x^2 + lx^3 - 2a^2l^2 + 2a^2x)$$

$$\Delta_{x_1} \quad \left(\text{for overhang}\right) \quad \ldots \quad = \frac{wx_1}{24EI}(4a^2l - l^3 + 6a^2x_1 - 4ax_1^2 + x_1)$$

25. BEAM OVERHANGING ONE SUPPORT—UNIFORMLY DISTRIBUTED LOAD ON OVERHANG

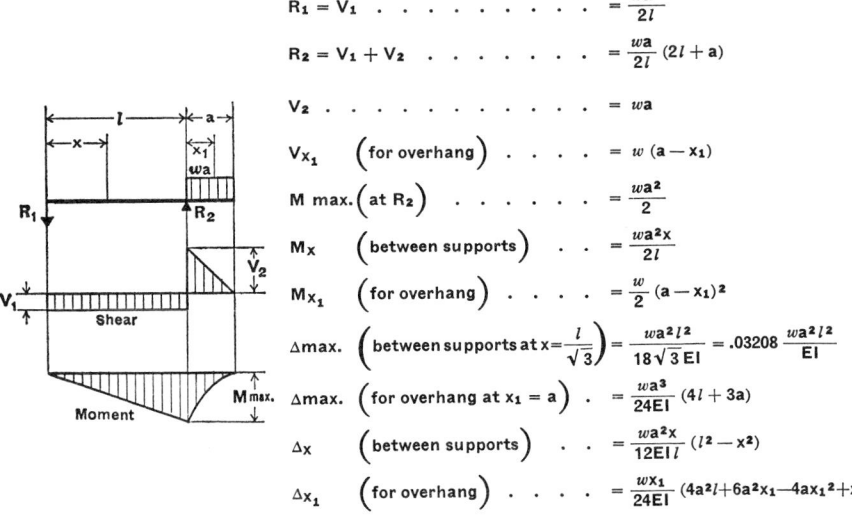

$$R_1 = V_1 \quad \ldots \quad = \frac{wa^2}{2l}$$

$$R_2 = V_1 + V_2 \quad \ldots \quad = \frac{wa}{2l}(2l + a)$$

$$V_2 \quad \ldots \quad = wa$$

$$V_{x_1} \quad \left(\text{for overhang}\right) \quad \ldots \quad = w(a - x_1)$$

$$M \text{ max.} \left(\text{at } R_2\right) \quad \ldots \quad = \frac{wa^2}{2}$$

$$M_x \quad \left(\text{between supports}\right) \quad \ldots \quad = \frac{wa^2x}{2l}$$

$$M_{x_1} \quad \left(\text{for overhang}\right) \quad \ldots \quad = \frac{w}{2}(a - x_1)^2$$

$$\Delta \text{max.} \left(\text{between supports at } x = \frac{l}{\sqrt{3}}\right) = \frac{wa^2l^2}{18\sqrt{3}\,EI} = .03208\frac{wa^2l^2}{EI}$$

$$\Delta \text{max.} \left(\text{for overhang at } x_1 = a\right) \quad . \quad = \frac{wa^3}{24EI}(4l + 3a)$$

$$\Delta_x \quad \left(\text{between supports}\right) \quad \ldots \quad = \frac{wa^2x}{12EIl}(l^2 - x^2)$$

$$\Delta_{x_1} \quad \left(\text{for overhang}\right) \quad \ldots \quad = \frac{wx_1}{24EI}(4a^2l + 6a^2x_1 - 4ax_1^2 + x_1)$$

BEAM DIAGRAMS AND FORMULAS
For various static loading conditions

Equivalent Tabular Load is the uniformly distributed load given in beam tables, pages 2 - 28 to 2 - 81. For meaning of symbols, see page 2 - 196.

26. BEAM OVERHANGING ONE SUPPORT—CONCENTRATED LOAD AT END OF OVERHANG

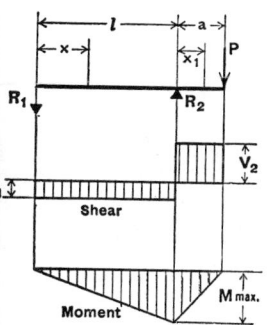

$R_1 = V_1 \quad\ldots\ldots\ldots\ldots = \dfrac{Pa}{l}$

$R_2 = V_1 + V_2 \quad\ldots\ldots\ldots = \dfrac{P}{l}(l+a)$

$V_2 \quad\ldots\ldots\ldots\ldots = P$

$M \max. \left(\text{at } R_2\right) \quad\ldots\ldots = Pa$

$M_x \quad \left(\text{between supports}\right) \quad\ldots = \dfrac{Pax}{l}$

$M_{x_1} \quad \left(\text{for overhang}\right) \quad\ldots = P(a - x_1)$

$\Delta\max. \left(\text{between supports at } x = \dfrac{l}{\sqrt{3}}\right) = \dfrac{Pal^2}{9\sqrt{3}EI} = .06415\dfrac{Pal^2}{EI}$

$\Delta\max. \left(\text{for overhang at } x_1 = a\right) \ . = \dfrac{Pa^2}{3EI}(l+a)$

$\Delta_x \quad \left(\text{between supports}\right) \quad\ldots = \dfrac{Pax}{6EIl}(l^2 - x^2)$

$\Delta_{x_1} \quad \left(\text{for overhang}\right) \quad\ldots = \dfrac{Px_1}{6EI}(2al + 3ax_1 - x_1{}^2)$

27. BEAM OVERHANGING ONE SUPPORT—UNIFORMLY DISTRIBUTED LOAD BETWEEN SUPPORTS

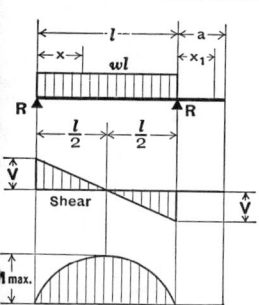

$\text{Equivalent Tabular Load} \quad\ldots\ldots = wl$

$R = V \quad\ldots\ldots\ldots\ldots = \dfrac{wl}{2}$

$V_x \quad\ldots\ldots\ldots\ldots = w\left(\dfrac{l}{2} - x\right)$

$M \max.\left(\text{at center}\right) \quad\ldots\ldots = \dfrac{wl^2}{8}$

$M_x \quad\ldots\ldots\ldots\ldots = \dfrac{wx}{2}(l - x)$

$\Delta\max.\left(\text{at center}\right) \quad\ldots\ldots = \dfrac{5wl^4}{384EI}$

$\Delta_x \quad\ldots\ldots\ldots\ldots = \dfrac{wx}{24EI}(l^3 - 2lx^2 + x^3)$

$\Delta_{x_1} \quad\ldots\ldots\ldots\ldots = \dfrac{wl^3x_1}{24EI}$

28. BEAM OVERHANGING ONE SUPPORT—CONCENTRATED LOAD AT ANY POINT BETWEEN SUPPORTS

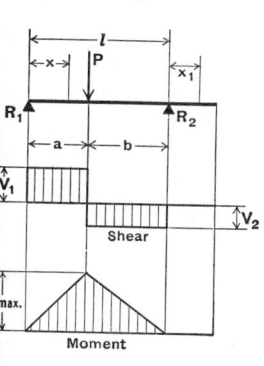

$\text{Equivalent Tabular Load} \quad\ldots\ldots = \dfrac{8Pab}{l^2}$

$R_1 = V_1 \left(\text{max. when } a < b\right) \ . \ . = \dfrac{Pb}{l}$

$R_2 = V_2 \left(\text{max. when } a > b\right) \ . \ . = \dfrac{Pa}{l}$

$M \max.\left(\text{at point of load}\right) \ . \ . = \dfrac{Pab}{l}$

$M_x \quad \left(\text{when } x < a\right) \quad\ldots = \dfrac{Pbx}{l}$

$\Delta\max.\left(\text{at } x = \sqrt{\dfrac{a(a+2b)}{3}} \text{ when } a > b\right) = \dfrac{Pab(a+2b)\sqrt{3a(a+2b)}}{27EIl}$

$\Delta a \quad \left(\text{at point of load}\right) \ . \ . = \dfrac{Pa^2b^2}{3EIl}$

$\Delta_x \quad \left(\text{when } x < a\right) \quad\ldots = \dfrac{Pbx}{6EIl}(l^2 - b^2 - x^2)$

$\Delta_x \quad \left(\text{when } x > a\right) \quad\ldots = \dfrac{Pa(l-x)}{6EIl}(2lx - x^2 - a^2)$

$\Delta_{x_1} \quad\ldots\ldots\ldots\ldots = \dfrac{Pabx_1}{6EIl}(l+a)$

BEAM DIAGRAMS AND FORMULAS
For various static loading conditions

Equivalent Tabular Load is the uniformly distributed load given in beam tables, pages 2 - 28 to 2 - 81.
For meaning of symbols, see page 2 - 196.

---

29. CONTINUOUS BEAM—TWO EQUAL SPANS—UNIFORM LOAD ON ONE SPAN

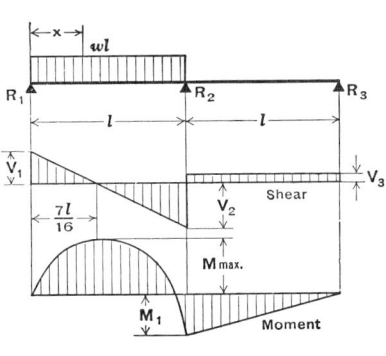

Equivalent Tabular Load . . =	$\dfrac{49}{64} wl$
$R_1 = V_1$ . . . . =	$\dfrac{7}{16} wl$
$R_2 = V_2 + V_3$ . . . . . =	$\dfrac{5}{8} wl$
$R_3 = V_3$ . . . . =	$-\dfrac{1}{16} wl$
V_2 . . . . =	$\dfrac{9}{16} wl$
M max. $\left(\text{at } x = \dfrac{7}{16} l\right)$ . . =	$\dfrac{49}{512} wl^2$
M_1 $\left(\text{at support } R_2\right)$. =	$\dfrac{1}{16} wl^2$
M_x $\left(\text{when } x < l\right)$ . . =	$\dfrac{wx}{16}(7l - 8x)$
Δ Max. (0.472 l from R_1) =	$0.0092\ wl^4/EI$

---

30. CONTINUOUS BEAM—TWO EQUAL SPANS—CONCENTRATED LOAD AT CENTER OF ONE SPAN

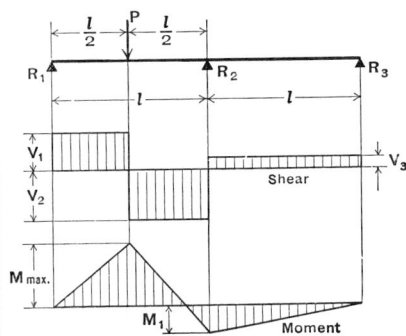

Equivalent Tabular Load . . =	$\dfrac{13}{8} P$
$R_1 = V_1$ . . . . =	$\dfrac{13}{32} P$
$R_2 = V_2 + V_3$ . . . . . =	$\dfrac{11}{16} P$
$R_3 = V_3$ . . . . =	$-\dfrac{3}{32} P$
V_2 . . . . =	$\dfrac{19}{32} P$
M max. $\left(\text{at point of load}\right)$. =	$\dfrac{13}{64} Pl$
M_1 $\left(\text{at support } R_2\right)$. =	$\dfrac{3}{32} Pl$
Δ Max. (0.480 l from R_1) =	$0.015\ Pl^3/EI$

---

31. CONTINUOUS BEAM—TWO EQUAL SPANS—CONCENTRATED LOAD AT ANY POINT

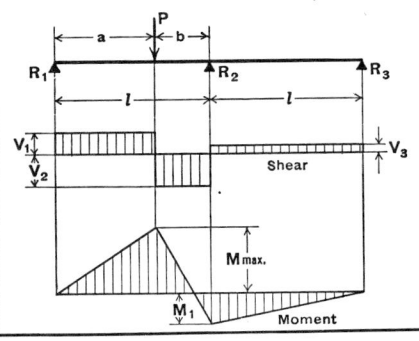

$R_1 = V_1$ . . . . =	$\dfrac{Pb}{4l^3}\left(4l^2 - a(l+a)\right)$
$R_2 = V_2 + V_3$ . . . . . =	$\dfrac{Pa}{2l^3}\left(2l^2 + b(l+a)\right)$
$R_3 = V_3$ . . . . =	$-\dfrac{Pab}{4l^3}(l+a)$
V_2 . . . . =	$\dfrac{Pa}{4l^3}\left(4l^2 + b(l+a)\right)$
M max. $\left(\text{at point of load}\right)$. =	$\dfrac{Pab}{4l^3}\left(4l^2 - a(l+a)\right)$
M_1 $\left(\text{at support } R_2\right)$. =	$\dfrac{Pab}{4l^2}(l+a)$

BEAM DIAGRAMS AND FORMULAS
For various static loading conditions

For meaning of symbols, see page 2 - 196.

---

32. BEAM—UNIFORMLY DISTRIBUTED LOAD AND VARIABLE END MOMENTS

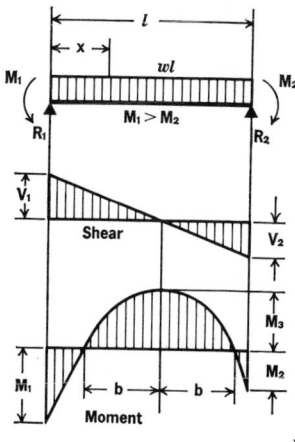

$$R_1 = V_1 = \frac{wl}{2} + \frac{M_1 - M_2}{l}$$

$$R_2 = V_2 = \frac{wl}{2} - \frac{M_1 - M_2}{l}$$

$$V_x = w\left(\frac{l}{2} - x\right) + \frac{M_1 - M_2}{l}$$

$$M_3 \left(\text{at } x = \frac{l}{2} + \frac{M_1 - M_2}{wl}\right)$$

$$= \frac{wl^2}{8} - \frac{M_1 + M_2}{2} + \frac{(M_1 - M_2)^2}{2wl^2}$$

$$M_x = \frac{wx}{2}(l - x) + \left(\frac{M_1 - M_2}{l}\right)x - M_1$$

$$b\left(\begin{array}{c}\text{To locate}\\ \text{inflection points}\end{array}\right) = \sqrt{\frac{l^2}{4} - \left(\frac{M_1 + M_2}{w}\right) + \left(\frac{M_1 - M_2}{wl}\right)^2}$$

$$\Delta_x = \frac{wx}{24EI}\left[x^3 - \left(2l + \frac{4M_1}{wl} - \frac{4M_2}{wl}\right)x^2 + \frac{12M_1}{w}x + l^3 - \frac{8M_1 l}{w} - \frac{4M_2 l}{w}\right]$$

---

33. BEAM—CONCENTRATED LOAD AT CENTER AND VARIABLE END MOMENTS

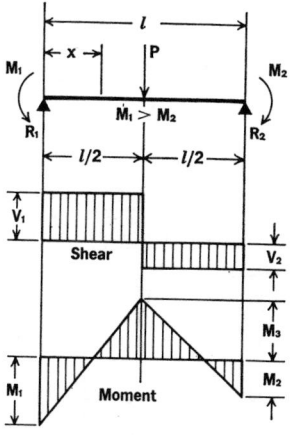

$$R_1 = V_1 = \frac{P}{2} + \frac{M_1 - M_2}{l}$$

$$R_2 = V_2 = \frac{P}{2} - \frac{M_1 - M_2}{l}$$

$$M_3 \text{ (At center)} = \frac{Pl}{4} - \frac{M_1 + M_2}{2}$$

$$M_x \left(\text{When } x < \frac{l}{2}\right) = \left(\frac{P}{2} + \frac{M_1 - M_2}{l}\right)x - M_1$$

$$M_x \left(\text{When } x > \frac{l}{2}\right) = \frac{P}{2}(l - x) + \frac{(M_1 - M_2)x}{l} - M_1$$

$$\Delta_x \left(\text{When } x < \frac{l}{2}\right) = \frac{Px}{48EI}\left(3l^2 - 4x^2 - \frac{8(l - x)}{Pl}[M_1(2l - x) + M_2(l + x)]\right)$$

BEAM DIAGRAMS AND DEFLECTIONS
For various static loading conditions

For meaning of symbols, see page **2** - 196.

---

34. CONTINUOUS BEAM—THREE EQUAL SPANS—ONE END SPAN UNLOADED

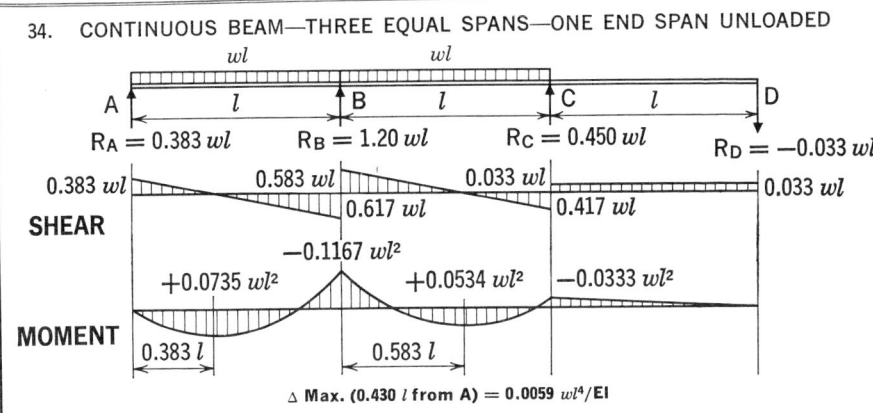

△ **Max. (0.430 l from A) = 0.0059 wl^4/EI**

---

35. CONTINUOUS BEAM—THREE EQUAL SPANS—END SPANS LOADED

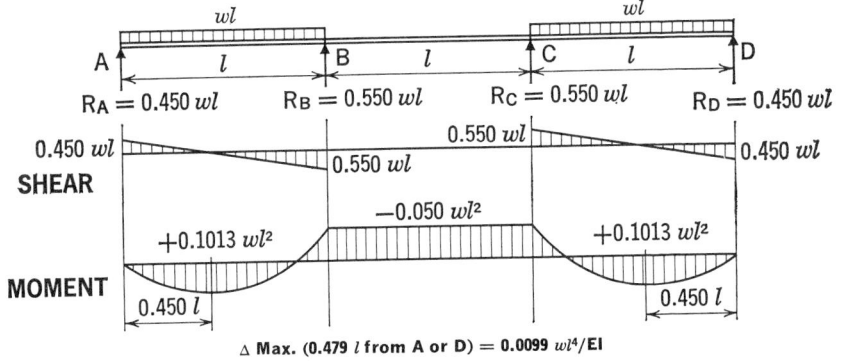

△ **Max. (0.479 l from A or D) = 0.0099 wl^4/EI**

---

36. CONTINUOUS BEAM—THREE EQUAL SPANS—ALL SPANS LOADED

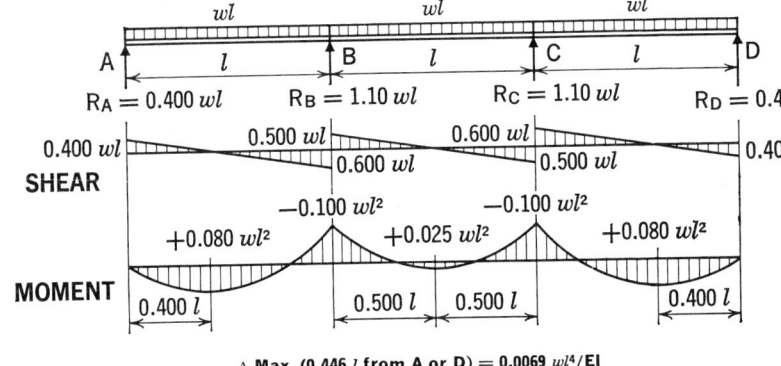

△ **Max. (0.446 l from A or D) = 0.0069 wl^4/EI**

AMERICAN INSTITUTE OF STEEL CONSTRUCTION

BEAM DIAGRAMS AND DEFLECTIONS
For various static loading conditions

For meaning of symbols, see page **2 - 196.**

---

37. CONTINUOUS BEAM—FOUR EQUAL SPANS—THIRD SPAN UNLOADED

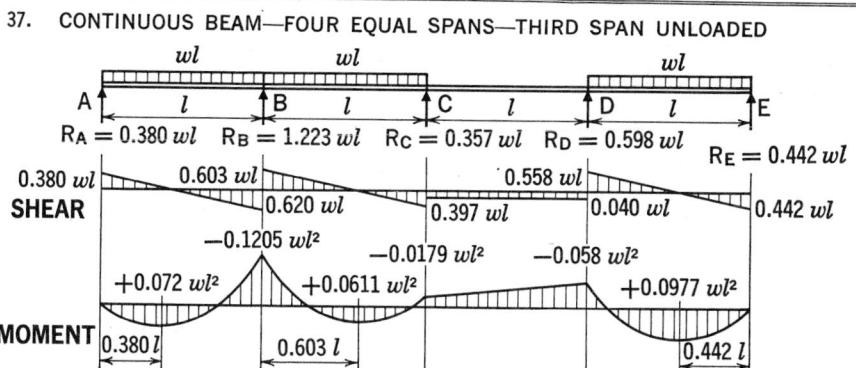

$R_A = 0.380\ wl$ $R_B = 1.223\ wl$ $R_C = 0.357\ wl$ $R_D = 0.598\ wl$

$R_E = 0.442\ wl$

SHEAR

0.380 wl   0.603 wl   0.620 wl   0.397 wl   0.558 wl   0.040 wl   0.442 wl

$-0.1205\ wl^2$ $-0.0179\ wl^2$ $-0.058\ wl^2$

$+0.072\ wl^2$ $+0.0611\ wl^2$ $+0.0977\ wl^2$

MOMENT   0.380 l   0.603 l   0.442 l

△ Max. (0.475 *l* from E) = 0.0094 wl^4/EI

---

38. CONTINUOUS BEAM—FOUR EQUAL SPANS—LOAD FIRST AND THIRD SPANS

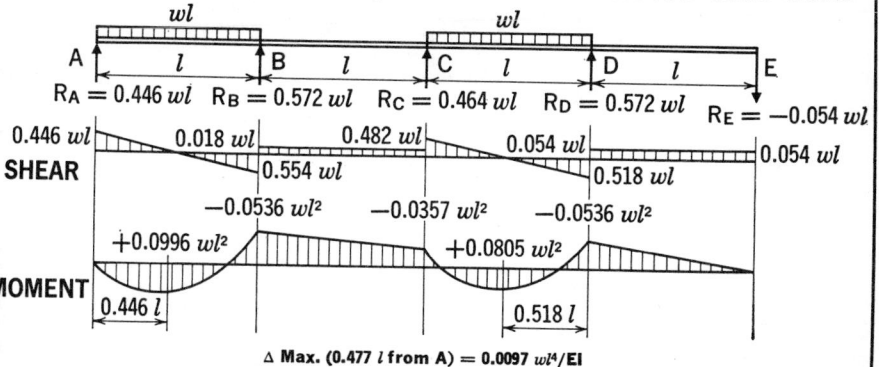

$R_A = 0.446\ wl$ $R_B = 0.572\ wl$ $R_C = 0.464\ wl$ $R_D = 0.572\ wl$

$R_E = -0.054\ wl$

SHEAR

0.446 wl   0.018 wl   0.482 wl   0.054 wl   0.054 wl   0.554 wl   0.518 wl

$-0.0536\ wl^2$ $-0.0357\ wl^2$ $-0.0536\ wl^2$

$+0.0996\ wl^2$ $+0.0805\ wl^2$

MOMENT   0.446 l   0.518 l

△ Max. (0.477 *l* from A) = 0.0097 wl^4/EI

---

39. CONTINUOUS BEAM—FOUR EQUAL SPANS—ALL SPANS LOADED

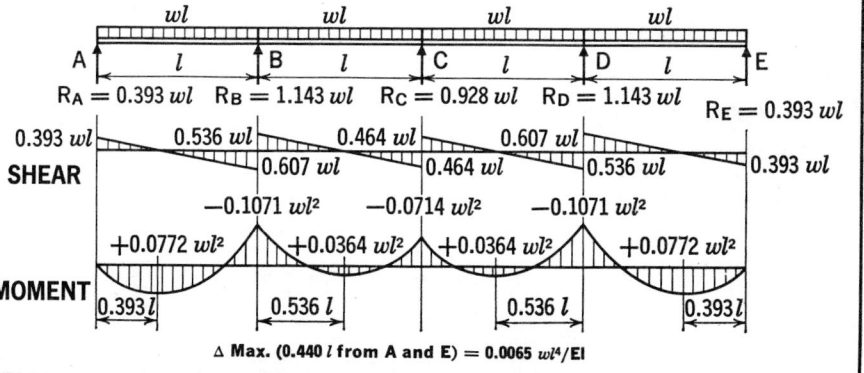

$R_A = 0.393\ wl$ $R_B = 1.143\ wl$ $R_C = 0.928\ wl$ $R_D = 1.143\ wl$

$R_E = 0.393\ wl$

SHEAR

0.393 wl   0.536 wl   0.464 wl   0.607 wl   0.607 wl   0.464 wl   0.536 wl   0.393 wl

$-0.1071\ wl^2$ $-0.0714\ wl^2$ $-0.1071\ wl^2$

$+0.0772\ wl^2$ $+0.0364\ wl^2$ $+0.0364\ wl^2$ $+0.0772\ wl^2$

MOMENT   0.393 l   0.536 l   0.536 l   0.393 l

△ Max. (0.440 *l* from A and E) = 0.0065 wl^4/EI

AMERICAN INSTITUTE OF STEEL CONSTRUCTION

BEAM DIAGRAMS AND FORMULAS
For various concentrated moving loads

The values given in these formulas do not include impact which varies according to the requirements of each case. For meaning of symbols, see page 2 - 196.

40. SIMPLE BEAM—ONE CONCENTRATED MOVING LOAD

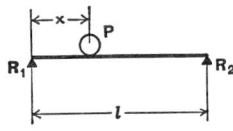

R_1 max. $= V_1$ max. $\left(\text{at } x = 0\right)$ . . . . $= P$

M max. $\left(\text{at point of load, when } x = \frac{l}{2}\right)$. $= \frac{Pl}{4}$

41. SIMPLE BEAM—TWO EQUAL CONCENTRATED MOVING LOADS

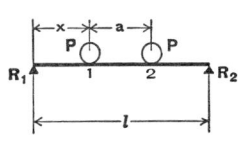

R_1 max. $= V_1$ max. $\left(\text{at } x = 0\right)$ . . . . $= P\left(2 - \frac{a}{l}\right)$

M max. $\begin{cases} \left[\begin{array}{l}\text{when } a < (2-\sqrt{2})\ l = .586l \\ \text{under load 1 at } x = \frac{1}{2}\left(l - \frac{a}{2}\right)\end{array}\right] = \frac{P}{2l}\left(l - \frac{a}{2}\right)^2 \\[2em] \left[\begin{array}{l}\text{when } a > (2-\sqrt{2})\ l = .586l \\ \text{with one load at center of span} \\ \text{(case 40)}\end{array}\right] = \frac{Pl}{4} \end{cases}$

42. SIMPLE BEAM—TWO UNEQUAL CONCENTRATED MOVING LOADS

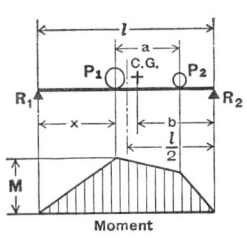

R_1 max. $= V_1$ max. $\left(\text{at } x = 0\right)$ . . . . . $= P_1 + P_2\frac{l-a}{l}$

M max. $\begin{cases} \left[\text{under } P_1, \text{ at } x = \frac{1}{2}\left(l - \frac{P_2 a}{P_1 + P_2}\right)\right] = \left(P_1 + P_2\right)\frac{x^2}{l} \\[1.5em] \left[\begin{array}{l}\text{M max. may occur with larger} \\ \text{load at center of span and other} \\ \text{load off span (case 40)}\end{array}\right] = \frac{P_1 l}{4} \end{cases}$

GENERAL RULES FOR SIMPLE BEAMS CARRYING MOVING CONCENTRATED LOADS

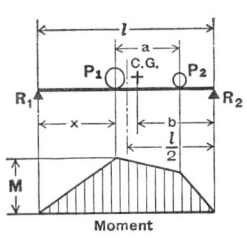

Moment

The maximum shear due to moving concentrated loads occurs at one support when one of the loads is at that support. With several moving loads, the location that will produce maximum shear must be determined by trial.

The maximum bending moment produced by moving concentrated loads occurs under one of the loads when that load is as far from one support as the center of gravity of all the moving loads on the beam is from the other support.

In the accompanying diagram, the maximum bending moment occurs under load P_1 when $x = b$. It should also be noted that this condition occurs when the center line of the span is midway between the center of gravity of loads and the nearest concentrated load.

CAMBER AND DEFLECTION
Coefficients

Given the simple span length, the depth of a beam, girder or truss, and the design unit bending stress, the center deflection in inches may be found by multiplying the span length in feet by the tabulated coefficients given in the following table.

For the unit stress values not tabulated, the deflection can be found by the equation $0.00103448 \, (L^2 f_b/d)$ where L is the span in feet, f_b is the fiber stress in kips per square inch, and d is the depth in inches.

The maximum fiber stresses listed in this table correspond to the allowable unit stresses as provided in Sections 1.5.1.4.1 and 1.5.1.4.5 of the AISC Specification for steels having yield points ranging between 36 ksi and 65 ksi when $F_b = 0.66F_y$, and between 36 ksi and 100 ksi when $F_b = 0.60F_y$.

The table values, as given, assume a uniformly distributed load. For a single load at center span multiply these factors by 0.80; for two equal concentrated loads at third points, multiply by 1.02. Likewise, for three equal concentrated loads at quarter points multiply by 0.95.

The tabulated factors are correct for beams of constant cross section; reasonably accurate for cover plated beams and girders; and approximate for trusses.

Ratio of Depth Span	Maximum Fiber Stress in Kips Per Sq. Inch												
	10.0	22.0	24.0	25.2	27.0	28.0	30.0	33.0	36.0	39.0	42.9	54.0	60.0
1/8	.0069	.0152	.0166	.0174	.0186	.0193	.0207	.0228	.0248	.0269	.0296	.0372	.0414
1/9	.0078	.0171	.0186	.0196	.0209	.0217	.0233	.0256	.0279	.0303	.0333	.0419	.0466
1/10	.0086	.0190	.0207	.0217	.0233	.0241	.0259	.0284	.0310	.0336	.0370	.0466	.0517
1/11	.0095	.0209	.0228	.0239	.0256	.0266	.0284	.0313	.0341	.0370	.0407	.0512	.0569
1/12	.0103	.0228	.0248	.0261	.0279	.0290	.0310	.0341	.0372	.0403	.0444	.0559	.0621
1/13	.0112	.0247	.0269	.0282	.0303	.0314	.0336	.0370	.0403	.0437	.0481	.0605	.0672
1/14	.0121	.0266	.0290	.0304	.0326	.0338	.0362	.0398	.0434	.0471	.0518	.0652	.0724
1/15	.0129	.0284	.0310	.0326	.0349	.0362	.0388	.0427	.0466	.0504	.0555	.0698	.0776
1/16	.0138	.0303	.0331	.0348	.0372	.0386	.0414	.0455	.0497	.0538	.0592	.0745	.0828
1/17	.0147	.0322	.0352	.0369	.0396	.0410	.0440	.0484	.0528	.0572	.0629	.0791	.0879
1/18	.0155	.0341	.0372	.0391	.0419	.0434	.0446	.0512	.0559	.0605	.0666	.0838	.0931
1/19	.0164	.0360	.0393	.0413	.0442	.0459	.0491	.0541	.0590	.0639	.0703	.0885	.0983
1/20	.0172	.0379	.0414	.0434	.0466	.0483	.0517	.0569	.0621	.0672	.0740	.0931	.1035
1/21	.0181	.0398	.0434	.0456	.0489	.0507	.0543	.0597	.0652	.0706	.0777	.0978	.1086
1/22	.0190	.0417	.0455	.0478	.0512	.0531	.0569	.0626	.0683	.0740	.0814	.1024	.1138
1/23	.0198	.0436	.0476	.0500	.0535	.0555	.0595	.0654	.0714	.0773	.0851	.1071	.1190
1/24	.0207	.0455	.0497	.0521	.0559	.0579	.0621	.0683	.0745	.0807	.0888	.1117	.1241
1/25	.0216	.0474	.0517	.0543	.0582	.0603	.0647	.0711	.0776	.0841	.0925	.1164	.1293
1/26	.0224	.0493	.0538	.0565	.0605	.0628	.0672	.0740	.0807	.0874	.0962	.1210	.1345
1/27	.0233	.0512	.0559	.0587	.0628	.0652	.0698	.0768	.0838	.0908	.0999	.1257	.1397
1/28	.0241	.0531	.0579	.0608	.0652	.0676	.0724	.0797	.0869	.0941	.1036	.1303	.1448
1/29	.0250	.0550	.0600	.0630	.0675	.0700	.0750	.0825	.0900	.0975	.1073	.1350	.1500
1/30	.0259	.0569	.0621	.0652	.0698	.0724	.0776	.0853	.0931	.1009	.1110	.1397	.1552

PART 3

Column Design

COLUMNS
General notes

COLUMN LOAD TABLES

Column load tables are presented for W, M, and S Shapes, Pipe, Structural Tubing and Double Angles. Tables of Base Plates for W, M, and S shapes are also included. Tabular loads are computed in accordance with the AISC Specification, Formulas (1.5-1) and (1.5-2), for axially loaded members having effective unsupported lengths indicated at the left of each table. The effective length KL is the actual unbraced length, in feet, multiplied by the factor K, which depends on the restraint at the ends of the unbraced length and the means available to resist lateral movements.

Table C1.8.1 in the Commentary on the AISC Specification is a guide in selecting the K-factor. Interpolation between the idealized cases is a matter of engineering judgment.

Once sections have been selected for the several framing members, Fig. C1.8.2 (given in the Commentary and reprinted below) affords a means of obtaining more precise values for K, if desired.

Load tables are provided for columns of 36 ksi yield stress steel for all shape categories. In addition, tables for W, M, and S Shapes and for Double Angles are provided for 50 ksi yield stress steel, and tables for Structural Tubing are provided for 46 ksi yield stress steel.

All loads are tabulated in kips and are for main members. The heavy horizontal lines appearing within the tables indicate $Kl/r = 120$. Load values are omitted when Kl/r exceeds 200.

Load values for Kl/r greater than 126.1 are the same for all steels with yield stress equal to, or greater than, 36 ksi. To bring this to the attention of the designer, load values in the tables are omitted when the allowable load for a shape is the same in higher strength steel as it is in 36 ksi steel. To determine these loads, refer to the equivalent 36 ksi table.

Structural tubing is available at a yield point of 46 ksi in some sizes that are not readily available at 36 ksi. Since these sizes are not shown at $F_y = 36$ ksi, load values in the 46 ksi table are extended to $Kl/r = 200$.

The Double Angle tables show loads for effective lengths about both axes. In all tables except Double Angles, allowable loads are given for effective lengths with respect to the minor axis. When the minor axis is braced at closer intervals than the major axis, the capacity of a column must be investigated with reference to both major (X-X) and minor (Y-Y) axes. The ratio r_x/r_y included in these tables provides a convenient method for investigating the strength of a column with respect to its major axis.

To obtain an effective length with respect to the minor axis equivalent in load carrying capacity to the actual effective length about the major axis, divide the major axis effective length by the r_x/r_y ratio. Compare this length with the actual effective length about the minor axis. The longer of the two lengths will control the design and the allowable load may be taken from the table opposite the longer of the two effective lengths with respect to the minor axis.

Properties useful to the designer are listed at the bottom of the column load tables. These properties, and footnotes concerning compact sections, are particularly helpful in the design of members under combined axial and bending stress as discussed below and illustrated in the design examples.

Additional notes relating specifically to the W, M, and S Shape tables, the Steel Pipe and Structural Tubing tables, and the Double Angle tables, precede each of these groups of tables.

EXAMPLE 1

Given: Design a W12 column of $F_y = 36$ ksi steel, to support a concentric load of 670 kips. The effective length with respect to its minor axis is 16 ft. The effective length with respect to its major axis is 31 ft.

Solution:

Enter Column Table I at effective length $KL = 16$ ft.:
Select W12 × 133, good for 679 kips > 670 kips. $r_x/r_y = 1.77$.
Equivalent effective length for X-X axis $= 31/1.77 = 17.5$ ft.
Since 17.5 ft. > 16 ft., X-X axis controls.
Re-enter table for lightest W12 column with effective length of 17.5 ft. to satisfy axial load of 670 kips; select W12 × 161 with $r_x/r_y = 1.78$.
By interpolation, the column is good for 800 kips.

> **Use:** **W12 × 161 column**

EXAMPLE 2

Given: Design an 11 ft. long W12 interior bay column to support a concentrated concentric axial and roof load of 540 kips. The column is rigidly framed at the top by 30 ft. long W30 × 116 girders connected to each flange. The column is braced normal to its web at top and base so that sidesway is inhibited in this plane. Use $F_y = 36$ ksi steel.

Solution:

a. Check Y-Y axis:
Assume column pin connected at top and bottom with sidesway inhibited.
From Table C1.8.1 in the Commentary for condition (d), $K = 1.0$; effective length $= 11$ ft.
Enter Table I; W12 × 99 good for 552 kips > 540 kips **o.k.**

b. Check X-X axis:
1. *Preliminary Selection:*
Assume sidesway uninhibited and pin connected at base.
*From Table C1.8.1 for condition (f), $K = 2.0$
Approximate effective length relative to the X-X axis $= 2.0 \times 11 = 22.0$ ft.
From properties section in Tables, for W12 column,
$r_x/r_y \cong 1.76$.
Corresponding effective length relative to the Y-Y axis $= \dfrac{22.0}{1.76} \cong 12.5$ ft. > 11.0 ft.
∴ Effective length for X-X axis is critical.
Enter Table I with an effective length of 12.5 ft.; W12 × 106 column, by interpolation, good for 577 kips > 540 kips **o.k.**

---

* Table C1.8.1 gives K values, in most cases, on the conservative side; therefore, final selection may be made by use of Fig. C1.8.2 when determining effective length.

2. *Final Selection:*
   Try W12 × 99

   Using Fig. C1.8.2:

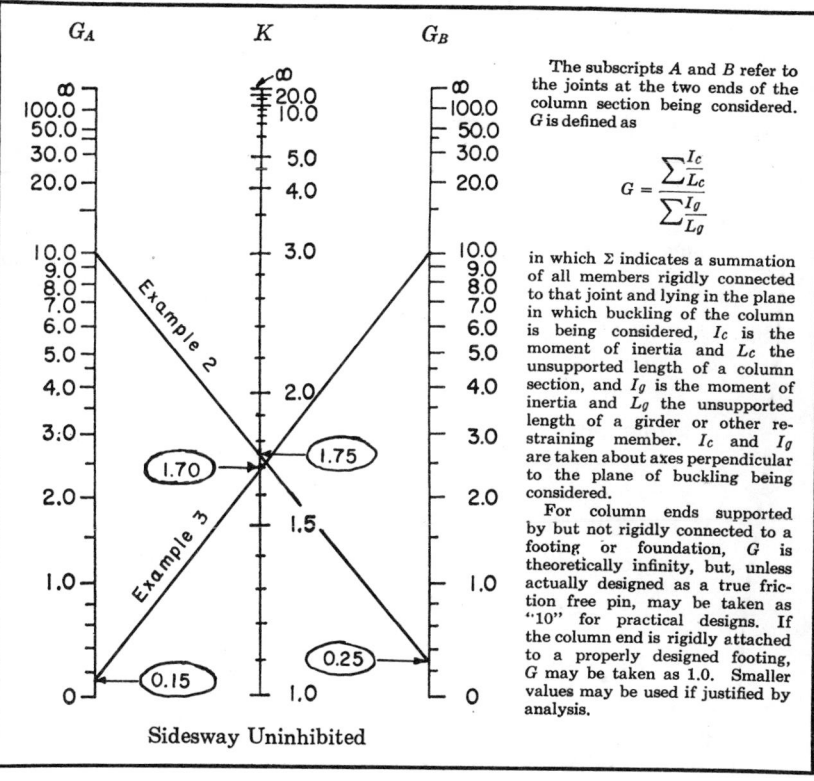

Alignment Chart for Effective Length of Columns in Continuous Frames

Fig. C1.8.2

I_x for W12 × 99 column = 859 in.[4]

I_x for W30 × 116 girder = 4930 in.[4]

G (at base) = 10 (assume supported but not rigidly connected).

G (at top) = $\dfrac{859/11}{(4930 \times 2)/30}$ = 0.238, say 0.25.

Connect points G_A = 10 and G_B = 0.25, read K = 1.75.

For W12 × 99, r_x/r_y = 1.76.

Actual effective length relative to Y-Y axis =

$\dfrac{1.75}{1.76} \times 11.0$ = 10.9 ft. < 11.0 ft.

Since effective length for Y-Y axis was critical:

Use: W12 × 99 column

EXAMPLE 3

Given: Design a 20 ft. long W12 column, using $F_y = 50$ ksi steel, with same loading and girder conditions as outlined in Example 2. However, in this case the column will be braced for its weak axis by cross bracing at top and base, and at half the length so that sidesway is inhibited in this plane.

Solution:

a. Check Y-Y axis:

Assume column pin connected at top and base, and braced at center so that sidesway is inhibited.

From Table C1.8.1, $K = 1.0$;
effective length $= 1.0 \times \frac{1}{2} \times 20 = 10.0$ ft.

Enter Table II; W12 $\times$ 72 good for 549 kips > 540 kips **o.k.**

b. Check X-X axis:

1. *Preliminary Selection:*

Assume sidesway uninhibited and pin connected at base.

*From Table C1.8.1, $K = 2.0$;
approximate effective length relative to the X-X axis $= 2.0 \times 20.0 = 40.0$ ft.

For W12 column, $r_x/r_y \cong 1.75$

Corresponding effective length relative to Y-Y axis $=$
$$\frac{40.0}{1.75} \cong 22.8 \text{ ft.} > 10.0 \text{ ft.}$$

∴ Effective length for X-X axis is critical.

Enter Table II with approximate effective length of 22.8 ft.; W12 $\times$ 106 column, by interpolation, good for
542 kips > 540 kips **o.k.**

2. *Final Selection:*

Try W12 $\times$ 99.
Using Fig. C1.8.2:

G (at base) $= 10$

$$G \text{ (at top)} = \frac{859/20}{(4930 \times 2)/30} = 0.131, \text{ say } 0.15.$$

Connect points $G_B = 10$ and $G_A = 0.15$; read $K = 1.70$.

With $r_x/r_y = 1.76$, the actual effective length relative to

$$Y\text{-}Y \text{ axis } = \frac{1.70}{1.76} \times 20 = 19.3 > 10.0 \text{ ft.}$$

∴ Effective length for X-X axis is critical.

Enter Table II with effective length of 19.3 ft.; by interpolation, W12 $\times$ 99 good for 582 kips > 540 kips.

Use: W12 × 99 column

---

* See footnote at bottom of page **3 - 4**.

SECONDARY MEMBERS

Loads shown in the column load tables are for main members. AISC Specification Section 1.5.1.3.3 permits an increase in allowable load for bracing and secondary members whose Kl/r exceeds 120. For this case, K is taken as unity.

To obtain this increased load, divide the value taken from the table by $(1.6 - l/200r)$. This increased allowable load may also be obtained by increasing the main member value by the ratio of the allowable stresses for secondary and main members, determined from Appendix A of the Specification, opposite the appropriate Kl/r value. This procedure is illustrated in Example 4.

EXAMPLE 4

Given: Using steel with a yield stress of $F_y = 36$ ksi, determine the allowable load on a W8 × 24 used as a secondary member and having an actual length of 20 ft.

Solution:

Section is to be used as a secondary member; therefore, $K = 1.0$.

Enter Table I at effective length $KL = 20$ ft.:
Allowable concentric load as a main member $= 47$ kips; $r_y = 1.61$ in.

$$l/r_y = 20 \times 12/1.61 = 149$$

Enter Appendix A, Table 1-36, AISC Specification, page 5-84:
$F_{as} = 7.87$ ksi for $l/r = 149$ (secondary members)
$F_a = 6.73$ ksi for $Kl/r = 149$ (main members)

Allowable concentric load as a secondary member equals

$$47 \text{ kips} \times 7.87/6.73 = \textbf{55 kips}$$

COMBINED AXIAL AND BENDING LOADING (INTERACTION)

Loads given in the column tables are for concentrically loaded columns. For columns subjected to both axial and bending stress, Section 1.6.1 of the AISC Specification requires that the following formulas be satisfied:

$$\frac{f_a}{F_a} + \frac{C_{mx}f_{bx}}{\left(1 - \dfrac{f_a}{F'_{ex}}\right) F_{bx}} + \frac{C_{my}f_{by}}{\left(1 - \dfrac{f_a}{F'_{ey}}\right) F_{by}} \leqslant 1.0 \quad \text{Formula (1.6-1a)}$$

$$\frac{f_a}{0.60 F_y} + \frac{f_{bx}}{F_{bx}} + \frac{f_{by}}{F_{by}} \leqslant 1.0 \qquad \text{Formula (1.6-1b)}$$

Also, when $\dfrac{f_a}{F_a} \leqslant 0.15$, Formula (1.6-2) may be used in lieu of Formulas (1.6-1a) and (1.6-1b).

$$\frac{f_a}{F_a} + \frac{f_{bx}}{F_{bx}} + \frac{f_{by}}{F_{by}} \leqslant 1.0 \qquad \text{Formula (1.6-2)}$$

Formulas for the allowable bending stress, F_b, are given in Section 1.5.1.4 of the AISC Specification and are discussed in the following paragraphs. The value of F_b depends upon width/thickness ratios and bracing intervals. To assist the designer, sections which are not compact are noted in the load tables by the symbol † and the lengths L_c and L_u are listed. Sections noted with the symbol ‡ may or may not be compact and the ratio d/t should be checked for compliance with Section 1.5.1.4.1 of the Specification. The proper value of F_b can usually be determined by inspection because:

1. All sections except W14 × 43 satisfy Section 1.9 of the Specification.
2. The majority of sections are also compact.
3. L_c and L_u are listed in the tables for ready reference.

For compact sections symmetrical about their minor axis, subject to bending about their major axis, and braced at intervals not exceeding L_c, F_b may not exceed $0.66\,F_y$. These members are limited to hot-rolled material consisting of rolled shapes, similar built-up members, and box-type profiles. Compact sections are defined in Section 1.5.1.4.1 of the Specification. When column sections (excluding box-type profiles) meet these requirements with the exception that the flange width/thickness ratio falls between $52.2/\sqrt{F_y}$ and $95.0/\sqrt{F_y}$, a value for F_b between $0.66\,F_y$ and $0.60\,F_y$ can be determined by Specification Formula (1.5-5). Specific values for this transition zone are listed in Appendix A to the Specification.

For W, M and S shapes subject to bending about their minor axis, whose flange width/thickness ratio $b_f/2t_f$ is less than $52.2/\sqrt{F_y}$, $F_b = 0.75\,F_y$. This includes all compact sections.

For box-type profiles that are not compact, but do conform to Section 1.9 of the Specification, F_b may not exceed $0.60\,F_y$. When such sections are bent about their strong axis, the compression flange must be braced at intervals not exceeding $2500/F_y$ times the flange width to qualify for this allowable stress.

For columns that do not meet the requirements of the above paragraphs, but satisfy Section 1.9 of the Specification and are symmetrical about and loaded in the plane of their web, the compressive bending stress F_b is the larger value computed by Formulas (1.5-6a), (1.5-6b), and (1.5-7), but not more than $0.60\,F_y$. Formula (1.5-6a) applies for stresses greater than $F_y/3$ and Formula (1.5-6b) applies for stresses less than $F_y/3$. Formula (1.5-7) applies to the full range of stress. The tensile bending stress F_b is limited to $0.60\,F_y$ for this case.

The allowable stress F_b for all other members is $0.60\,F_y$, provided they meet the requirements of Section 1.9 of the Specification and provided further that sections bent about their major axis have their compression flanges braced at intervals not exceeding $76\left(b_f/\sqrt{F_y}\right)$.

The bending factors B_x and B_y tabulated at the bottom of the load tables provide a convenient means of converting bending moment into equivalent axial load P', so that a trial section, capable of supporting the load $P + P'$, can be selected from the table. B_x and B_y are, respectively, equal to the area of the column divided by its appropriate section modulus. The selection is conservative, increasingly so for larger bending moments and more slender columns.

A final selection can be made using the following modified versions of the interaction Formulas (1.6-1a), (1.6-1b), and (1.6-2):

$P + P'_x + P'_y$ = required tabular load

$$= P + \left[B_x M_x C_{mx} \left(\frac{F_a}{F_{bx}} \right) \left(\frac{a_x}{a_x - P(Kl)^2} \right) \right]$$

$$+ \left[B_y M_y C_{my} \left(\frac{F_a}{F_{by}} \right) \left(\frac{a_y}{a_y - P(Kl)^2} \right) \right]$$

Modified Formula (1.6-1a)

$P + P'_x + P'_y$ = required tabular load

$$= P \left(\frac{F_a}{0.6 F_y} \right) + \left[B_x M_x \left(\frac{F_a}{F_{bx}} \right) \right] + \left[B_y M_y \left(\frac{F_a}{F_{by}} \right) \right]$$

Modified Formula (1.6-1b)

When $f_a/F_a \leqslant 0.15$

$P + P'_x + P'_y$ = required tabular load

$$= P + \left[B_x M_x \left(\frac{F_a}{F_{bx}} \right) \right] + \left[B_y M_y \left(\frac{F_a}{F_{by}} \right) \right]$$

Modified Formula (1.6-2)

In Formula (1.6-1a), for the term $(Kl)^2$, K is the effective length factor and l is the actual unbraced length in the plane of bending.

Values for the components a_x and a_y, equal to $0.149 \times 10^6 \, A r_x{}^2$ and $0.149 \times 10^6 \, A r_y{}^2$, respectively, are listed at the bottom of the load tables.

EXAMPLE 5

Given: Design a W14 column in a tier building for 18 ft. story height to support 600 kip gravity load and 190 kip-ft. maximum wind moment, as shown in sketch. Assume $K = 1$ relative to both axes and bending is about the major axis. Use $F_y = 36$ ksi.

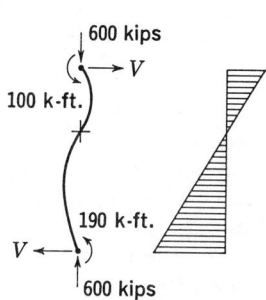

Solution:

Neglecting Wind:

From Column Table I, select W14 × 119 with allowable concentric load of 618 kips.

Including Wind:

Since the load tables do not reflect permissible one-third increase for wind, reduce given loading condition 25 percent. $P = 450$ kips; $M = 142.5$ kip-ft. $= 1,710$ kip-in.

Trial Selection:

From load table, page 3 - 15, average $B_x = 0.185$
$P + P' = 450 + (0.185 \times 1,710) = 450 + 317 = 767$ kips.
Try W14 × 142. Allowable concentric load is 750 kips, less than 767 kips. However, such trial calculations always overestimate actual requirements.

Check by Modified Formulas:

    For W14 $\times$ 142:   From Table I, section is compact.

       L_c = 16.4 < 18 ft. ∴ section not compact

       L_u = 51.8 > 18 ft.; Use F_b = 22 ksi

       r_y = 3.97 in.

       B_x = 0.185

       a_x = 249 $\times$ 10^6

    Assume C_m = 0.85

    Kl/r_y = 18 $\times$ 12/3.97 = 54.4

    From Table 1-36, Appendix A: F_a = 17.95 ksi

    $P(Kl)^2$ = 450 $\times$ $(216)^2$ = 4.50 $\times$ $(2.16)^2$ $\times$ 10^6

    Required tabular load by Modified Formula (1.6-1a):

Modified Formula (1.6-2) is not used since $\dfrac{450}{750}$ > 0.15.

$$P + P'_x = 450 + \left[0.185 \times 1710 \times 0.85 \right.$$
$$\left. \times \left(\frac{17.95}{22} \right) \left(\frac{249}{249 - (4.50 \times (2.16)^2)} \right) \right]$$

    = 690 kips

    Required tabular load by Modified Formula (1.6-1b):

$$P + P'_x = 450 \left(\frac{17.95}{22} \right) + \left[0.185 \times 1710 \left(\frac{17.95}{22} \right) \right]$$

    = 626 kips

Final Selection:

    Modified Formula (1.6-1a) requires an axial load capacity of 690
    kips. This load is greater than 600 kips required neglecting
    wind.

    Enter Column Table I and find W14 $\times$ 136 with an allowable
    concentric load equal to 707 kips, which is greater than $P + P'$
    = 690 kips.

    Use: **W14 $\times$ 136**

COLUMNS
W, M, and S Shapes
TABLES I and II

Allowable concentric loads in the tables that follow are tabulated for the effective lengths in feet KL, indicated at the left of each table. They are applicable to primary members with respect to their minor axis, in accordance with Section 1.5.1.3 of the AISC Specification. Two strengths are covered, F_y = 36 ksi in Table I and F_y = 50 ksi in Table II. Loads tabulated for the three heaviest columns in Table II are computed for F_y = 46 ksi to match the reduced yield stress furnished under ASTM A588 and are so noted in the table.

The heavy horizontal lines appearing within the tables indicate Kl/r = 120. No values are listed beyond Kl/r = 200 in Table I and no values are listed beyond Kl/r = 126.1 in Table II (see discussion in "Columns, General Notes").

All sections listed satisfy Section 1.9 of the AISC Specification with the exception of W14 $\times$ 43 at F_y = 50 ksi. For this column, Appendix C of the AISC Specification controls the design for effective column lengths, KL, from zero to approximately 4 feet. Beyond this length, the reduction in stress due to l/r permits full use of the section area.

For discussion of effective length, range of l/r, strength about the major axis, secondary members, combined axial and bending stress, and sample problems, see "Columns, General Notes".

Properties and factors are listed at the bottom of the tables for checking strength about the strong axis and for checking combined loading conditions.

$F_y = 36$ ksi		COLUMNS							

W 14 — COLUMNS — W shapes
TABLE I
Allowable axial loads in kips

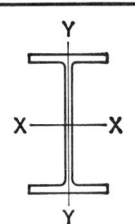

Designation			W14							
Nominal Depth and Width			14 × 16							
Weight per Foot		730	665	605	550	500	455	426	398	370
	11	4315	3928	3562	3237	2933	2670	2489	2328	2167
	12	4277	3892	3529	3206	2905	2644	2464	2304	2144
	13	4237	3855	3494	3175	2875	2616	2438	2280	2121
	14	4196	3817	3459	3142	2845	2588	2411	2255	2097
	15	4153	3777	3422	3108	2813	2559	2384	2229	2073
	16	4110	3737	3384	3073	2781	2529	2356	2202	2047
	17	4065	3695	3345	3037	2748	2498	2326	2174	2021
	18	4019	3652	3306	3000	2714	2466	2296	2146	1995
	19	3971	3608	3265	2962	2678	2433	2266	2117	1967
	20	3923	3563	3223	2923	2642	2400	2234	2087	1939
	22	3823	3469	3136	2842	2568	2330	2169	2025	1881
	24	3718	3372	3045	2758	2490	2258	2100	1960	1820
	26	3609	3270	2951	2670	2409	2182	2029	1893	1756
	28	3496	3164	2853	2579	2324	2104	1955	1823	1690
	30	3378	3055	2751	2484	2236	2022	1878	1750	1621
	32	3256	2941	2645	2386	2145	1937	1798	1674	1549
	34	3130	2823	2535	2284	2051	1849	1715	1596	1475
	36	3000	2702	2422	2179	1954	1758	1629	1515	1398
	38	2865	2576	2305	2070	1853	1664	1541	1431	1319
	40	2726	2446	2184	1958	1748	1567	1449	1344	1237
	42	2582	2312	2059	1841	1640	1466	1354	1254	1151
	44	2434	2173	1930	1721	1529	1362	1255	1161	1063
	46	2281	2030	1796	1597	1413	1254	1154	1065	974
	48	2123	1882	1659	1470	1298	1152	1060	978	895
	50	1962	1735	1529	1355	1197	1061	977	902	824

Left axis labels: r_y — with respect to least radius of gyration — $F_y = 36$ ksi — Effective length in ft. KL

Properties										
Area A (in.²)	215	196	178	162	147	134	125	117	109
I_x (in.⁴)	14400	12500	10900	9450	8250	7220	6610	6010	5450
I_y (in.⁴)	4720	4170	3680	3260	2880	2560	2360	2170	1990
Ratio r_x/r_y	1.74	1.73	1.72	1.70	1.69	1.68	1.67	1.66	1.66
r_y (in.)	4.69	4.62	4.55	4.49	4.43	4.37	4.34	4.31	4.27
L_c (ft.)	18.9	18.7	18.4	18.2	18.0	17.8	17.7	17.6	17.4
L_u (ft.)	181.6	170.3	160.2	150.4	140.3	131.6	125.5	119.4	113.6
B_x } Bending	.168	.171	.172	.174	.175	.177	.177	.179	.180
B_y } factors	.408	.416	.421	.429	.434	.441	.442	.447	.453
a_x } Multiply	2144	1864	1618	1409	1229	1079	982	896	814
a_y } values by 10⁶	705	623	549	487	430	381	351	324	296

Heavy line indicates $Kl/r = 120$.

		COLUMNS		$F_y = 36$ ksi

COLUMNS
W shapes

TABLE I

Allowable axial loads in kips

$F_y = 36$ ksi

W 14

Designation		W14								
Nominal Depth and Width		14 × 16								
Weight per Foot		342	320	314	287	264	246	237	228	219
	6	2099	1954	1917	1752	1611	1500	1446	1392	1336
	7	2082	1938	1901	1738	1597	1488	1434	1380	1324
	8	2064	1921	1885	1723	1583	1474	1421	1368	1312
	9	2045	1903	1868	1707	1568	1461	1408	1355	1300
	10	2026	1885	1850	1690	1553	1446	1394	1342	1287
	11	2006	1865	1831	1673	1537	1431	1379	1328	1273
	12	1985	1845	1812	1655	1520	1416	1364	1313	1259
	13	1963	1825	1792	1637	1503	1400	1349	1298	1245
	14	1941	1804	1771	1618	1486	1383	1333	1282	1230
	15	1918	1782	1750	1598	1467	1366	1316	1266	1214
	16	1894	1759	1728	1578	1448	1348	1299	1250	1198
	17	1870	1736	1705	1557	1429	1330	1281	1233	1182
	18	1845	1712	1682	1535	1409	1311	1263	1215	1165
	19	1819	1687	1658	1513	1389	1292	1245	1197	1148
	20	1793	1662	1634	1491	1368	1272	1226	1179	1130
	22	1738	1610	1583	1444	1324	1231	1186	1141	1093
	24	1681	1555	1530	1395	1278	1189	1145	1101	1054
	26	1621	1498	1475	1344	1231	1144	1102	1059	1014
	28	1559	1439	1417	1291	1182	1098	1057	1016	972
	30	1495	1377	1357	1235	1130	1049	1010	971	928
	32	1428	1313	1295	1178	1077	999	961	924	883
	34	1358	1247	1231	1118	1021	947	911	875	836
	36	1286	1178	1164	1056	964	893	859	824	787
	38	1212	1107	1095	992	904	837	805	772	736
	40	1135	1033	1023	926	842	779	748	718	684

Left side label: Effective length in ft. KL with respect to least radius of gyration r_y

$F_y = 36$ ksi

Properties

	342	320	314	287	264	246	237	228	219
Area A (in.²)	101	94.1	92.3	84.4	77.6	72.3	69.7	67.1	64.4
I_x (in.⁴)	4910	4140	4400	3910	3530	3230	3080	2940	2800
I_y (in.⁴)	1810	1640	1630	1470	1330	1230	1170	1120	1070
Ratio r_x/r_y	1.65	1.59	1.64	1.63	1.63	1.62	1.62	1.61	1.62
r_y (in.)	4.24	4.17	4.20	4.17	4.14	4.12	4.11	4.10	4.08
L_c (ft.)	17.3	17.7	17.2	17.1	17.0	16.9	16.8	16.8	16.8
L_u (ft.)	106.5	96.3	99.8	93.0	87.2	82.4	79.9	77.6	75.0
B_x ⎫ Bending	.181	.191	.181	.182	.182	.183	.183	.183	.183
B_y ⎭ factors	.458	.481	.460	.464	.468	.470	.471	.473	.474
a_x ⎫ Multiply	735	616	655	583	525	481	459	438	417
a_y ⎭ values by 10⁶	271	244	243	219	198	183	175	168	160

F_y = 36 ksi		COLUMNS

W 14

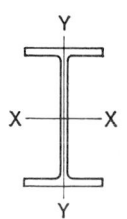

COLUMNS
W shapes

TABLE I

Allowable axial loads in kips

Designation		\multicolumn{9}{c}{W14}
Nominal Depth and Width		\multicolumn{9}{c}{14 × 16}
Weight per Foot		211	202	193	184	176	167	158	150	142
Effective length in ft. KL with respect to least radius of gyration r_y	6	1288	1232	1176	1121	1071	1017	963	914	866
	7	1277	1221	1165	1112	1062	1009	955	906	858
	8	1265	1210	1155	1102	1052	999	946	897	850
	9	1253	1198	1144	1091	1042	990	937	888	842
	10	1241	1186	1132	1080	1032	979	927	879	833
	11	1228	1174	1120	1068	1020	969	917	870	824
	12	1214	1161	1108	1056	1009	958	907	860	814
	13	1200	1147	1095	1044	997	946	896	849	804
	14	1185	1133	1081	1031	985	935	885	839	794
	15	1170	1119	1067	1018	972	923	873	828	784
	16	1155	1104	1053	1004	959	910	861	816	773
	17	1139	1089	1039	990	945	897	849	805	762
	18	1123	1073	1024	976	931	884	837	793	750
	19	1106	1057	1008	961	917	870	824	781	739
	20	1089	1040	992	946	903	857	810	768	727
	22	1053	1006	959	915	872	828	783	742	702
	24	1015	970	925	882	841	797	754	715	676
	26	976	933	889	847	807	766	724	686	648
	28	936	894	852	811	773	733	693	656	620
	30	893	853	813	774	737	699	661	625	590
	32	850	811	772	735	700	663	627	593	560
	34	804	767	731	695	661	626	592	560	528
	36	757	722	687	654	621	588	555	525	495
	38	708	675	642	610	579	548	517	489	460
	40	657	626	595	565	536	507	478	452	424

\multicolumn{11}{c}{Properties}
Area A (in.²)		62.1	59.4	56.7	54.1	51.7	49.1	46.5	44.1	41.8
I_x (in.⁴)		2670	2540	2400	2270	2150	2020	1900	1790	1670
I_y (in.⁴)		1030	980	930	883	838	790	745	703	660
Ratio r_x/r_y		1.61	1.61	1.61	1.61	1.60	1.60	1.60	1.60	1.59
r_y (in.)		4.07	4.06	4.05	4.04	4.02	4.01	4.00	3.99	3.97
L_c (ft.)		16.7	16.7	16.6	16.6	16.6	16.5	16.5	16.4	16.4
L_u (ft.)		72.6	70.2	67.5	65.0	62.4	59.6	57.1	54.5	51.8
B_x } Bending		.184	.183	.183	.183	.184	.184	.184	.184	.185
B_y } factors		.478	.480	.481	.479	.484	.487	.486	.487	.491
a_x } Multiply		398	379	358	340	320	302	284	267	249
a_y } values by 10⁶		153	146	139	132	124	118	111	105	98

Heavy line indicates $Kl/r = 120$.

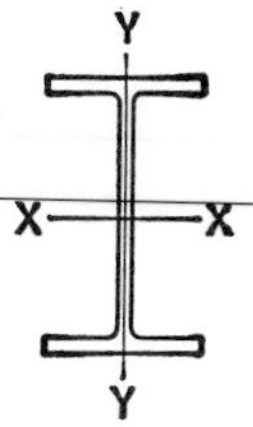

COLUMNS
W shapes

$F_y = 36$ ksi

W 14

TABLE I
Allowable axial loads in kips

Designation	W14						
Nominal Depth and Width	14 × 14½						
Weight per Foot	136	127	119	111	†103	†95	†87
$F_y = 36$ ksi — Effective length in ft. KL with respect to least radius of gyration r_y							
6	826	770	723	675	625	576	528
7	818	763	716	668	619	570	523
8	810	755	709	662	613	564	518
9	801	747	701	654	606	558	512
10	792	739	693	647	599	552	506
11	783	730	685	639	592	545	500
12	773	721	676	631	585	538	493
13	763	711	667	623	577	531	487
14	753	702	658	614	569	523	480
15	742	691	648	605	560	516	473
16	731	681	639	596	552	508	465
17	719	670	628	586	543	499	458
18	707	659	618	576	534	491	450
19	695	648	607	566	524	482	442
20	683	636	596	556	515	473	434
22	657	612	574	535	495	455	417
24	630	587	550	512	474	436	399
26	602	560	525	489	452	416	381
28	572	533	499	464	429	394	361
30	542	504	472	439	405	372	341
32	510	474	444	412	381	350	320
34	476	443	414	384	355	326	298
36	442	410	384	356	328	301	275
38	406	377	352	326	300	275	251
40	368	342	319	295	272	249	227

Properties

	136	127	119	111	†103	†95	†87
Area A (in.²)	40.0	37.3	35.0	32.7	30.3	27.9	25.6
I_x (in.⁴)	1590	1480	1370	1270	1170	1060	967
I_y (in.⁴)	568	528	492	455	420	384	350
Ratio r_x/r_y	1.67	1.67	1.67	1.67	1.67	1.66	1.66
r_y (in.)	3.77	3.76	3.75	3.73	3.72	3.71	3.70
L_c (ft.)	15.6	15.6	15.5	15.5	15.4	15.4	15.4
L_u (ft.)	49.2	46.5	43.7	41.0	38.6	35.7	33.1
B_x } Bending	.186	.185	.186	.186	.185	.185	.186
B_y } factors	.520	.520	.522	.526	.527	.529	.532
a_x } Multiply	237	220	204	189	174	158	144
a_y } values by 10^6	85	79	73	68	62	57	52

Heavy line indicates $Kl/r = 120$.

† Flange is non-compact; see discussion preceding column load tables.

$F_y = 36$ ksi
W 14

COLUMNS
W shapes
TABLE I
Allowable axial loads in kips

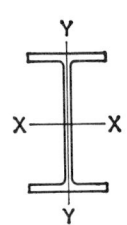

Designation		W14		W14			W14		
Nominal Depth and Width		14 × 12		14 × 10			14 × 8		
Weight per Foot		84	78	74	68	61	53	48	‡43
Effective length in ft. KL with respect to least radius of gyration r_y	6	503	466	436	400	358	302	273	244
	7	496	460	429	393	351	295	266	237
	8	489	453	421	385	345	286	258	230
	9	482	447	412	377	338	277	250	223
	10	475	439	403	369	330	268	242	215
	11	467	432	394	360	322	258	233	207
	12	458	424	384	351	314	248	224	199
	13	450	416	374	342	306	237	214	190
	14	441	408	363	332	297	226	204	181
	15	431	399	352	322	288	215	193	171
	16	422	390	341	311	278	202	182	161
	17	412	381	329	301	268	190	171	151
	18	402	371	317	289	258	177	159	140
	19	391	362	305	278	248	163	146	128
	20	381	352	292	266	237	149	133	117
	22	358	331	265	241	214	123	110	96
	24	335	309	236	214	190	104	93	81
	26	310	285	206	186	165	88	79	69
	28	284	261	177	160	142	76	68	60
	30	257	235	154	139	124	66	59	52
	32	228	209	136	123	109	58		
	34	202	185	120	109	96			
	36	180	165	107	97	86			
	38	162	148	96	87	77			
	40	146	134	87	78	70			
Properties									
Area A (in.²)		24.7	22.9	21.8	20.0	17.9	15.6	14.1	12.6
I_x (in.⁴)		928	851	797	724	641	542	485	429
I_y (in.⁴)		225	207	133	121	107	57.5	51.3	45.1
Ratio r_x/r_y		2.03	2.03	2.44	2.45	2.44	3.07	3.07	3.08
r_y (in.)		3.02	3.00	2.48	2.46	2.45	1.92	1.91	1.89
L_c (ft.)		12.7	12.7	10.7	10.6	10.6	8.6	8.5	8.5
L_u (ft.)		30.5	28.5	25.8	23.8	21.5	17.7	16.0	14.3
B_x } Bending		.189	.190	.195	.195	.195	.201	.201	.201
B_y } factors		.659	.664	.823	.830	.833	1.091	1.102	1.116
a_x } Multiply		138.3	126.5	118.9	108.0	95.4	80.9	72.1	63.6
a_y } values by 10⁶		33.6	30.7	20.0	18.0	16.0	8.6	7.7	6.7

Heavy line indicates $Kl/r = 120$. Values omitted for $Kl/r > 200$.

‡ Web may be non-compact for combined axial and bending stress; see AISC Specification Sect. 1.5.1.4.1.

AMERICAN INSTITUTE OF STEEL CONSTRUCTION

	COLUMNS	$F_y = 36$ ksi
	W shapes	W 12

TABLE I

Allowable axial loads in kips

$F_y = 36$ ksi

Designation		W12							
Nominal Depth and Width		12 × 12							
Weight per Foot		190	161	133	120	106	99	92	85
Effective length in ft. KL with respect to least radius of gyration r_y	6	1144	969	799	721	637	593	553	510
	7	1131	957	789	712	629	586	546	503
	8	1117	945	779	702	620	578	538	496
	9	1102	932	768	692	611	570	530	489
	10	1086	919	757	682	602	561	522	482
	11	1070	905	745	671	593	552	514	474
	12	1053	890	732	660	583	543	505	465
	13	1036	875	720	648	572	533	496	457
	14	1017	859	706	636	561	523	486	448
	15	999	843	693	624	550	512	476	439
	16	979	826	679	611	539	501	466	430
	17	959	809	664	597	527	490	456	420
	18	939	791	649	584	514	478	445	410
	19	918	773	634	569	502	467	434	400
	20	896	754	618	555	489	454	422	389
	22	851	715	585	525	462	429	399	367
	24	803	673	550	493	433	402	374	344
	26	753	630	514	460	404	374	347	319
	28	701	585	475	425	372	345	320	294
	30	647	537	435	388	340	314	291	267
	32	589	487	393	349	305	281	260	239
	34	530	435	350	310	271	249	231	211
	36	472	388	312	277	241	222	206	189
	38	424	349	280	248	217	200	185	169
	40	383	315	253	224	196	180	167	153

Properties									
Area A (in.²)		55.9	47.4	39.1	35.3	31.2	29.1	27.1	25.0
I_x (in.⁴)		1890	1540	1220	1070	931	859	789	723
I_y (in.⁴)		590	486	390	345	301	278	256	235
Ratio r_x/r_y		1.79	1.78	1.77	1.76	1.76	1.76	1.75	1.75
r_y (in.)		3.25	3.20	3.16	3.13	3.11	3.09	3.08	3.07
L_c (ft.)		13.4	13.3	13.1	13.1	13.0	12.9	12.9	12.8
L_u (ft.)		70.8	62.1	53.0	48.1	43.3	40.7	38.3	35.7
B_x } Bending		.213	.214	.214	.217	.216	.216	.217	.216
B_y } factors		.601	.611	.620	.631	.635	.637	.643	.643
a_x } Multiply		282.1	229.5	182.0	159.7	138.6	127.8	117.7	107.8
a_y } values by 10⁶		88.0	72.3	58.2	51.5	45.0	41.4	38.3	35.1

Heavy line indicates $Kl/r = 120$.

| $F_y = 36$ ksi
W 12 | COLUMNS
W shapes
TABLE I
Allowable axial loads in kips | | 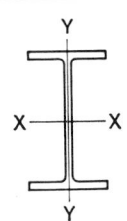 |

$F_y = 36$ ksi

Effective length in ft. KL with respect to least radius of gyration r_y

Designation	W12			W12		W12		
Nominal Depth and Width	12 × 12			12 × 10		12 × 8		
Weight per Foot	79	†72	†65	58	53	50	45	40
6	473	432	389	343	312	286	256	229
7	467	426	384	337	307	279	250	223
8	460	420	378	331	301	271	243	217
9	453	414	373	324	295	263	235	210
10	446	408	367	317	288	254	228	204
11	439	401	361	310	282	246	220	196
12	431	394	354	302	275	236	211	189
13	423	387	348	294	268	226	202	181
14	415	379	341	286	260	216	193	172
15	407	371	334	278	252	206	183	164
16	398	363	326	269	244	195	173	155
17	389	355	319	260	236	183	163	145
18	379	346	311	251	227	171	152	136
19	370	337	303	241	218	159	140	125
20	360	328	294	231	209	146	129	115
22	339	309	277	211	189	121	106	95
24	317	289	259	189	169	102	89	80
26	294	268	240	165	147	87	76	68
28	270	246	220	142	127	75	66	59
30	245	223	199	124	111	65	57	51
32	219	198	176	109	97	57	50	45
34	194	176	156	97	86			
36	173	157	139	86	77			
38	155	141	125	77	69			
40	140	127	113	70	62			

Properties

Area A (in.²)	23.2	21.2	19.1	17.1	15.6	14.7	13.2	11.8
I_x (in.⁴)	663	597	533	476	426	395	351	310
I_y (in.⁴)	216	195	175	107	96.1	56.4	50.0	44.1
Ratio r_x/r_y	1.75	1.75	1.75	2.10	2.11	2.64	2.65	2.64
r_y (in.)	3.05	3.04	3.02	2.51	2.48	1.96	1.94	1.94
L_c (ft.)	12.8	12.8	12.7	10.6	10.6	8.6	8.5	8.5
L_u (ft.)	33.4	30.5	27.8	24.4	22.2	19.8	17.9	16.1
B_x } Bending	.217	.218	.218	.219	.221	.228	.227	.228
B_y } factors	.649	.655	.657	.800	.813	1.050	1.065	1.073
a_x } Multiply	98.6	89.1	79.3	71.0	63.6	58.8	52.2	46.3
a_y } values by 10⁶	32.2	29.2	26.0	16.1	14.3	8.4	7.4	6.6

Heavy line indicates $Kl/r = 120$. Values omitted for $Kl/r > 200$.
† Flange is non-compact; see discussion preceding column load tables.

COLUMNS
W shapes

$$F_y = 36 \text{ ksi}$$

W 10

TABLE I

Allowable axial loads in kips

Designation					W10				
Nominal Depth and Width					10×10				
Weight per Foot	112	100	89	77	72	66	60	54	†49
6	663	592	527	456	426	390	355	319	289
7	653	583	519	449	419	383	350	314	284
8	642	573	510	441	412	377	343	308	279
9	630	562	501	433	404	369	337	302	273
10	618	551	491	424	396	362	330	296	268
11	605	540	480	415	387	354	323	290	262
12	592	528	470	406	378	346	315	283	255
13	578	516	458	396	369	337	307	276	249
14	564	503	447	385	359	328	299	268	242
15	549	489	435	375	349	319	291	261	235
16	534	476	422	364	339	310	282	253	228
17	518	461	409	352	328	300	273	245	221
18	502	446	396	341	317	290	264	236	213
19	485	431	382	329	306	279	254	228	205
20	468	416	368	316	294	269	244	219	197
22	432	383	339	290	270	246	224	200	180
24	393	348	308	263	244	222	202	180	161
26	353	312	275	233	217	197	178	159	142
28	310	273	240	203	188	171	155	138	123
30	270	238	209	177	164	149	135	120	107
32	238	209	184	155	144	131	118	106	94
34	210	185	163	138	128	116	105	93	83
36	188	165	145	123	114	103	94	83	74
38	168	148	130	110	102	93	84	75	67
40	152	134	117	99	92	84	76	68	60

Left axis label: Effective length in ft. KL with respect to least radius of gyration r_y

$F_y = 36$ ksi

Properties

	112	100	89	77	72	66	60	54	†49
Area A (in.²)	32.9	29.4	26.2	22.7	21.2	19.4	17.7	15.9	14.4
$_x$ (in.⁴)	719	625	542	457	421	382	344	306	273
$_y$ (in.⁴)	235	207	181	153	142	129	116	104	93
Ratio r_x/r_y	1.75	1.74	1.73	1.73	1.72	1.72	1.72	1.71	1.71
$_y$ (in.)	2.67	2.65	2.63	2.60	2.59	2.58	2.57	2.56	2.54
$_c$ (ft.)	11.0	11.0	10.9	10.8	10.8	10.7	10.7	10.6	10.6
$_u$ (ft.)	52.9	48.2	43.7	38.6	36.2	33.8	31.1	28.5	25.9
$_x$ } Bending	.262	.263	.263	.264	.265	.264	.264	.264	.264
$_y$ } factors	.728	.737	.745	.755	.760	.761	.767	.769	.775
$_x$ } Multiply	106.9	93.1	80.8	68.2	62.8	57.0	51.3	45.7	40.6
$_y$ } values by 10⁶	34.9	30.8	27.0	22.9	21.2	19.2	17.4	15.5	13.8

Heavy line indicates $Kl/r = 120$.

† Flange is non-compact; see discussion preceding column load tables.

$F_y = 36$ ksi

W 10-8

COLUMNS
W shapes
TABLE I
Allowable axial loads in kips

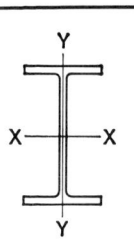

Designation		W10				W8			
Nominal Depth and Width		10 × 8				8 × 8			
Weight per Foot		45	39	†33	67	58	48	40	35	†31

Effective length in ft. KL with respect to least radius of gyration r_y

	45	39	†33	67	58	48	40	35	†31
6	257	224	189	387	336	276	231	201	178
7	251	218	184	379	328	270	225	197	174
8	245	213	179	370	320	263	220	191	169
9	237	206	173	360	312	256	213	186	164
10	230	200	167	350	303	249	207	180	159
11	222	193	161	339	293	241	200	174	154
12	214	186	155	328	283	233	193	168	148
13	206	178	149	316	273	224	186	162	142
14	197	170	142	304	263	215	178	155	136
15	188	162	135	292	251	206	170	148	130
16	178	154	127	279	240	196	162	141	123
17	168	145	120	265	228	186	153	133	117
18	158	136	112	251	216	176	144	125	110
19	147	126	103	236	203	165	135	117	102
20	136	116	95	221	190	154	125	109	95
22	113	97	78	190	162	131	105	91	79
24	95	81	66	159	136	110	88	76	66
26	81	69	56	136	116	94	75	65	57
28	70	60	48	117	100	81	65	56	49
30	61	52	42	102	87	70	57	49	42
32	53	46	37	90	76	62	50	43	37
34				79	68	55	44		

Properties

	45	39	†33	67	58	48	40	35	†31
Area A (in.²)	13.2	11.5	9.71	19.7	17.1	14.1	11.8	10.3	9.12
I_x (in.⁴)	249	210	171	272	227	184	146	126	110
I_y (in.⁴)	53.2	44.9	36.5	88.6	74.9	60.9	49.0	42.5	37.0
Ratio r_x/r_y	2.16	2.16	2.16	1.75	1.74	1.74	1.73	1.72	1.73
r_y (in.)	2.00	1.98	1.94	2.12	2.10	2.08	2.04	2.03	2.01
L_c (ft.)	8.5	8.5	8.5	8.8	8.7	8.6	8.6	8.5	8.5
L_u (ft.)	22.7	19.7	16.4	40.0	35.1	30.3	25.3	22.6	20.1
B_x ⎱ Bending	.269	.273	.278	.327	.329	.327	.333	.332	.333
B_y ⎰ factors	.993	1.027	1.061	.921	.940	.940	.976	.972	.988
a_x ⎱ Multiply	36.9	31.2	25.5	40.4	33.9	27.4	21.9	18.8	16.4
a_y ⎰ values by 10⁶	7.9	6.7	5.4	13.2	11.2	9.1	7.3	6.3	5.5

Heavy line indicates $Kl/r = 120$. Values omitted for $Kl/r > 200$.
† Flange is non-compact; see discussion preceding column load tables.

AMERICAN INSTITUTE OF STEEL CONSTRUCTION

COLUMNS
W shapes

$F_y = 36$ ksi

W 8-6

TABLE I

Allowable axial loads in kips

Designation		W8		W8		W6			W6		
Nominal Depth and Width		8 × 6½		8 × 5¼		6 × 6			6 × 4		
Weight per Foot		28	24	20	17	25	20	†15.5	16	12	†8.5
	2	172	148	122	103	153	123	95	96	72	51
	3	168	144	118	100	150	120	93	92	68	48
	4	164	141	114	96	146	117	90	87	64	45
	5	160	137	109	92	142	113	87	81	60	42
	6	155	133	104	88	137	109	84	75	55	38
	7	150	128	98	83	132	105	81	69	50	34
	8	144	123	93	78	126	100	77	62	44	30
	9	138	118	86	72	120	96	73	54	38	25
	10	132	113	79	66	114	91	69	46	31	21
	11	125	107	72	60	108	85	65	38	26	17
	12	118	101	65	53	101	80	60	32	21	14
	13	111	94	56	46	94	74	55	27	18	12
	14	103	88	49	39	86	68	50	23	16	10
	15	95	81	42	34	78	61	45	20	14	
	16	86	73	37	30	70	54	39	18		
	17	78	66	33	27	62	48	35			
	18	69	59	29	24	55	43	31			
	19	62	53	26	21	49	39	28			
	20	56	47	24	19	45	35	25			
	22	46	39			37	29	21			
	24	39	33			31	24	17			
	26	33	28								

Left margin labels: $F_y = 36$ ksi — Effective length in ft. KL with respect to least radius of gyration r_y

Properties

	28	24	20	17	25	20	†15.5	16	12	†8.5
Area A (in.²)	8.23	7.06	5.89	5.01	7.35	5.88	4.56	4.72	3.54	2.51
I_x (in.⁴)	97.8	82.5	69.4	56.6	53.3	41.5	30.1	31.7	21.7	14.8
I_y (in.⁴)	21.6	18.2	9.22	7.44	17.1	13.3	9.67	4.42	2.98	1.98
Ratio r_x/r_y	2.13	2.12	2.74	2.75	1.76	1.76	1.76	2.68	2.70	2.73
r_y (in.)	1.62	1.61	1.25	1.22	1.53	1.51	1.46	0.97	0.92	0.89
L_c (ft.)	7.0	6.9	5.6	5.6	6.5	6.4	6.4	4.3	4.3	4.2
L_u (ft.)	17.5	15.1	11.4	9.4	20.2	16.5	12.5	12.1	8.7	6.1
B_x } Bending	.339	.340	.347	.356	.441	.439	.456	.463	.489	.495
B_y } factors	1.246	1.259	1.683	1.771	1.308	1.328	1.412	2.156	2.376	2.486
a_x } Multiply	14.60	12.30	10.32	8.43	7.92	6.20	4.49	4.72	3.24	2.21
a_y } values by 10⁶	3.22	2.73	1.37	1.11	2.56	2.00	1.45	0.66	0.44	0.30

Heavy line indicates $Kl/r = 120$. Values omitted for $Kl/r > 200$.

† Flange is non-compact; see discussion preceding column load tables.

AMERICAN INSTITUTE OF STEEL CONSTRUCTION

$F_y = 36$ ksi
W 5-4
M 8-6-5-4

COLUMNS
W and M shapes
TABLE I
Allowable axial loads in kips

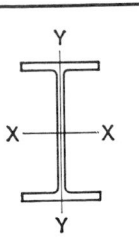

Designation		W5		W4	M8		M6		M5	M4
Nominal Depth and Width		5 × 5		4 × 4	8 × 8		6 × 6		5 × 5	4 × 4
Weight per Foot		18.5	16	13	34.3	32.6	22.5	20	18.9	13
Effective length in ft. KL with respect to least radius of gyration r_y	2	112	97	78	212	201	137	122	114	77
	3	109	94	74	208	198	134	119	111	74
	4	105	91	71	204	194	130	116	106	70
	5	101	87	66	200	190	125	112	102	65
	6	97	83	62	195	185	120	107	96	60
	7	92	79	57	190	180	115	103	91	54
	8	86	74	51	184	175	109	98	85	48
	9	81	69	45	178	170	103	92	78	42
	10	75	64	39	172	164	96	87	71	35
	11	68	58	32	165	158	89	81	64	29
	12	62	52	27	158	151	82	74	56	24
	13	54	46	23	151	144	74	68	48	21
	14	47	39	20	143	137	66	61	42	18
	15	41	34	17	135	130	57	53	36	15
	16	36	30	15	127	122	50	47	32	
	17	32	27		118	114	45	41	28	
	18	28	24		109	106	40	37	25	
	19	26	21		100	98	36	33	23	
	20	23	19		91	89	32	30		
	22				75	73	27	25		
	24				63	62				
	26				54	52				
	28				46	45				
	30				40	39				

Properties

	W5		W4	M8		M6		M5	M4
Area A (in.²)	5.43	4.70	3.82	10.1	9.58	6.62	5.89	5.55	3.81
I_x (in.⁴)	25.4	21.3	11.3	116	114	41.2	39.0	24.1	10.5
I_y (in.⁴)	8.89	7.51	3.76	34.9	34.1	12.4	11.6	7.86	3.36
Ratio r_x/r_y	1.69	1.69	1.74	1.83	1.82	1.82	1.84	1.75	1.77
r_y (in.)	1.28	1.26	.99	1.86	1.89	1.37	1.40	1.19	0.94
L_c (ft.)	5.4	5.3	4.3	8.5	8.4	6.4	6.3	5.3	4.2
L_u (ft.)	19.1	16.7	15.6	21.3	21.1	17.8	17.5	19.3	17.0
B_x } Bending	.547	.551	.701	.348	.338	.484	.454	.577	.728
B_y } factors	1.534	1.567	2.065	1.157	1.117	1.623	1.511	1.768	2.229
a_x } Multiply	3.77	3.18	1.68	17.40	16.89	6.12	5.80	3.58	1.56
a_y } values by 10⁶	1.33	1.11	0.56	5.21	5.10	1.85	1.72	1.17	1.50

Heavy line indicates $Kl/r = 120$. Values omitted for $Kl/r > 200$.

$F_y = 36$ ksi

COLUMNS
S shapes

$F_y = 36$ ksi

S 6-5-4-3

TABLE I
Allowable axial loads in kips

$F_y = 36$ ksi

Effective length in ft. KL with respect to least radius of gyration r_y

Designation		S6		S5		S4		S3	
Nominal Depth and Width		$6 \times 3\frac{3}{8}$		5×3		$4 \times 2\frac{5}{8}$		$3 \times 2\frac{3}{8}$	
Weight per Foot		17.25	12.5	14.75	10	9.5	7.7	7.5	5.7
	2	99	72	84	57	53	43	41	31
	3	92	67	76	52	48	39	36	28
	4	83	61	68	47	41	34	31	23
	5	73	54	58	41	34	28	24	18
	6	61	47	47	34	26	22	17	13
	7	49	38	35	26	19	16	12	10
	8	37	30	27	20	15	12	10	7
	9	30	23	21	16	12	10		
	10	24	19	17	13				
	11	20	16						

Properties

	S6		S5		S4		S3	
Area A (in.^{2})	5.07	3.67	4.34	2.94	2.79	2.26	2.21	1.67
I_x (in.^{4})	26.3	22.1	15.2	12.3	6.79	6.08	2.93	2.52
I_y (in.^{4})	2.31	1.82	1.67	1.22	.903	.764	.586	.455
Ratio r_x/r_y	3.38	3.48	3.02	3.19	2.74	2.82	2.23	2.36
r_y (in.)	.67	.70	.62	.64	.57	.58	.52	.52
r_c (ft.)	3.8	3.6	3.5	3.2	3.0	2.9	2.7	2.5
L_u (ft.)	9.9	9.3	10.0	9.1	9.5	9.1	10.1	9.4
B_x ⎫ Bending	.579	.498	.713	.598	.824	.744	1.134	.995
B_y ⎭ factors	3.901	3.367	4.298	3.635	4.319	3.938	4.723	4.283
a_x ⎫ Multiply	3.927	3.282	2.261	1.841	1.012	.906	.435	.376
a_y ⎭ values by 10^6	.344	.272	.249	.181	.135	.114	.088	.068

Heavy line indicates $Kl/r = 120$.   Values omitted for $Kl/r > 200$.

$F_y = 50$ ksi

W 14

COLUMNS
W shapes

TABLE II

Allowable axial loads in kips

Designation		W14								
Nominal Depth and Width		14 × 16								
Weight per Foot		*730	*665	*605	550	500	455	426	398	370
Effective length in ft. KL with respect to least radius of gyration r_y	11	5443	4953	4490	4411	3995	3635	3388	3168	2947
	12	5384	4898	4439	4357	3945	3589	3344	3126	2908
	13	5324	4842	4387	4301	3893	3540	3298	3083	2868
	14	5261	4784	4333	4243	3840	3490	3251	3039	2826
	15	5196	4724	4277	4183	3784	3439	3203	2993	2782
	16	5130	4662	4219	4121	3727	3386	3153	2946	2738
	17	5061	4598	4160	4057	3668	3331	3101	2897	2692
	18	4991	4532	4099	3992	3608	3275	3048	2847	2644
	19	4919	4465	4037	3925	3546	3217	2994	2795	2596
	20	4845	4396	3972	3856	3482	3158	2938	2743	2546
	22	4691	4253	3839	3713	3350	3035	2822	2633	2442
	24	4530	4103	3700	3564	3211	2906	2700	2518	2333
	26	4363	3946	3555	3407	3066	2771	2573	2397	2220
	28	4188	3784	3403	3244	2915	2630	2440	2272	2101
	30	4007	3614	3246	3074	2757	2483	2302	2141	1977
	32	3818	3438	3082	2897	2594	2331	2158	2004	1848
	34	3623	3256	2912	2714	2423	2171	2008	1862	1713
	36	3420	3066	2736	2522	2245	2006	1852	1714	1573
	38	3210	2870	2553	2324	2061	1834	1689	1560	1427
	40	2992	2666	2363	2117	1870	1659	1526	1409	1288
	42	2766	2455	2166	1920	1696	1504	1384	1278	1168
	44	2533	2241	1974	1749	1545	1371	1261	1164	1065
	46	2318	2050	1806	1601	1414				
	48	2129	1883							

Properties

	*730	*665	*605	550	500	455	426	398	370
Area A (in.²)	215	196	178	162	147	134	125	117	109
I_x (in.⁴)	14400	12500	10900	9450	8250	7220	6610	6010	5450
I_y (in.⁴)	4720	4170	3680	3260	2880	2560	2360	2170	1990
Ratio r_x/r_y	1.74	1.73	1.72	1.70	1.69	1.68	1.67	1.66	1.66
r_y (in.)	4.69	4.62	4.55	4.49	4.43	4.37	4.34	4.31	4.27
L_c (ft.)	16.8	16.5	16.3	15.5	15.3	15.1	15.0	14.9	14.8
L_u (ft.)	142.1	133.3	125.4	108.3	101.1	94.7	90.4	86.0	81.4
B_x ⎱ Bending	.168	.171	.172	.174	.175	.177	.177	.179	.180
B_y ⎰ factors	.408	.416	.421	.429	.434	.441	.442	.447	.453
a_x ⎱ Multiply	2144	1864	1618	1409	1229	1079	982	896	814
a_y ⎰ values by 10⁶	705	623	549	487	430	381	351	324	296

Heavy line indicates $Kl/r = 120$. Values omitted are same as for $F_y = 36$ ksi.
* Allowable loads are tabulated for $F_y = 46$ ksi (available under ASTM A588).

$$F_y = 50 \text{ ksi}$$

COLUMNS
W shapes

TABLE II

Allowable axial loads in kips

W 14

$F_y = 50$ ksi

Designation				W14					
Nominal Depth and Width				14×16					
Weight per Foot	342	320	314	287	264	246	237	228	219
6	2890	2689	2639	2412	2217	2065	1990	1916	1838
7	2860	2662	2612	2387	2194	2043	1969	1895	1818
8	2829	2632	2584	2361	2169	2020	1947	1874	1798
9	2797	2601	2554	2333	2144	1996	1924	1852	1776
10	2763	2569	2522	2304	2117	1971	1899	1828	1753
11	2728	2536	2490	2274	2089	1945	1874	1803	1730
12	2692	2501	2456	2243	2060	1917	1848	1778	1705
13	2654	2464	2421	2210	2029	1889	1820	1751	1679
14	2614	2427	2384	2177	1998	1860	1792	1724	1653
15	2574	2388	2347	2142	1966	1829	1763	1696	1626
16	2532	2348	2308	2106	1933	1798	1732	1667	1597
17	2489	2307	2268	2069	1898	1766	1701	1636	1568
18	2444	2265	2227	2031	1863	1733	1669	1606	1538
19	2399	2221	2185	1992	1827	1699	1636	1574	1507
20	2352	2177	2141	1952	1790	1664	1602	1541	1476
22	2255	2084	2051	1869	1712	1591	1532	1473	1410
24	2153	1986	1957	1782	1631	1515	1458	1402	1341
26	2047	1885	1858	1690	1546	1435	1381	1327	1269
28	1935	1778	1755	1595	1457	1352	1301	1249	1194
30	1819	1667	1647	1495	1365	1265	1216	1168	1115
32	1698	1551	1535	1391	1268	1174	1128	1083	1033
34	1572	1430	1418	1283	1167	1079	1037	994	947
36	1441	1304	1296	1170	1062	981	941	902	857
38	1304	1175	1169	1054	955	881	846	810	770
40	1177	1061	1055	951	862	795	763	731	695

Effective length in ft. KL with respect to least radius of gyration r_y

Properties									
Area A (in.²)	101	94.1	92.3	84.4	77.6	72.3	69.7	67.1	64.4
I_x (in.⁴)	4910	4140	4400	3910	3530	3230	3080	2940	2800
I_y (in.⁴)	1810	1640	1630	1470	1330	1170	1120	1120	1070
Ratio r_x/r_y	1.65	1.59	1.64	1.63	1.63	1.62	1.62	1.61	1.62
r_y (in.)	4.24	4.17	4.20	4.17	4.14	4.12	4.11	4.10	4.08
L_c (ft.)	14.7	15.0	14.6	14.5	14.4	14.3	14.3	14.3	14.2
L_u (ft.)	76.7	69.4	71.9	67.0	62.8	59.4	57.5	55.9	54.0
B_x } Bending	.181	.191	.181	.182	.182	.183	.183	.183	.183
B_y } factors	.458	.481	.460	.464	.468	.470	.471	.473	.474
a_x } Multiply	735	616	655	583	525	481	459	438	417
a_y } values by 10⁶	271	244	243	219	198	183	175	168	160

$F_y = 50$ ksi

W 14

I

COLUMNS
W shapes

TABLE II

Allowable axial loads in kips

Designation		W14								
Nominal Depth and Width		14 × 16								
Weight per Foot		211	202	193	184	176	167	158	150	142
	6	1772	1695	1618	1543	1474	1400	1326	1257	1191
	7	1753	1677	1600	1526	1458	1385	1311	1243	1178
	8	1733	1657	1582	1509	1441	1368	1296	1228	1164
	9	1712	1637	1562	1490	1423	1351	1279	1213	1149
	10	1690	1616	1542	1471	1405	1334	1263	1197	1134
	11	1667	1594	1521	1451	1385	1315	1245	1180	1118
	12	1643	1571	1499	1430	1365	1296	1227	1163	1101
	13	1619	1547	1476	1408	1344	1276	1208	1145	1084
	14	1593	1523	1453	1385	1322	1255	1188	1126	1066
	15	1566	1497	1428	1362	1300	1234	1168	1107	1048
	16	1539	1471	1403	1338	1277	1212	1147	1087	1028
	17	1511	1444	1377	1313	1253	1189	1125	1066	1009
	18	1482	1416	1351	1288	1228	1165	1103	1045	989
	19	1452	1388	1323	1261	1203	1141	1080	1023	968
	20	1422	1358	1295	1234	1177	1117	1056	1001	946
	22	1358	1297	1237	1179	1123	1065	1008	954	902
	24	1291	1233	1175	1120	1067	1011	956	905	855
	26	1222	1166	1111	1058	1007	955	903	854	806
	28	1149	1096	1044	994	945	896	846	801	755
	30	1072	1023	974	927	881	834	788	745	702
	32	993	947	901	856	813	770	726	686	646
	34	910	867	824	783	742	702	662	625	588
	36	823	783	744	707	669	632	595	562	527
	38	739	703	668	634	600	567	534	504	473
	40	667	635	603	572	542	512	482	455	427

Left axis: r_y — KL with respect to least radius of gyration — Effective length in ft. $F_y = 50$ ksi

Properties										
Area A (in.²)		62.1	59.4	56.7	54.1	51.7	49.1	46.5	44.1	41.8
I_x (in.⁴)		2670	2540	2400	2270	2150	2020	1900	1790	1670
I_y (in.⁴)		1030	980	930	883	838	790	745	703	660
Ratio r_x/r_y		1.61	1.61	1.61	1.61	1.60	1.60	1.60	1.60	1.59
r_y (in.)		4.07	4.06	4.05	4.04	4.02	4.02	4.00	3.99	3.97
L_c (ft.)		14.2	14.2	14.1	14.1	14.1	14.0	14.0	13.9	13.9
L_u (ft.)		52.3	50.6	48.6	46.8	44.9	43.0	41.1	39.3	37.3
B_x } Bending		.184	.183	.183	.183	.184	.184	.184	.184	.185
B_y } factors		.478	.480	.481	.479	.484	.487	.486	.487	.491
a_x } Multiply		398	379	358	340	320	302	284	267	249
a_y } values by 10⁶		153	146	139	132	124	118	111	105	98

Heavy line indicates $Kl/r = 120$.

$$F_y = 50 \text{ ksi}$$

COLUMNS
W shapes

W 14

TABLE II

Allowable axial loads in kips

$F_y = 50$ ksi

Designation				W14			
Nominal Depth and Width				14 × 14½			
Weight per Foot	136	127	†119	†111	†103	†95	†87
Effective length in ft. KL with respect to least radius of gyration r_y — 6	1136	1059	993	928	860	791	726
7	1122	1046	981	917	849	782	717
8	1108	1033	969	905	838	771	708
9	1093	1019	955	892	826	761	698
10	1077	1004	942	879	814	749	687
11	1060	988	927	865	801	738	676
12	1043	972	912	851	788	725	665
13	1025	956	896	836	774	713	653
14	1007	938	880	821	760	699	641
15	988	921	863	805	745	686	629
16	968	902	846	789	730	672	616
17	948	883	828	772	714	657	602
18	927	863	809	754	698	642	589
19	905	843	790	737	682	627	574
20	883	823	771	718	665	611	560
22	837	780	730	680	629	578	530
24	789	734	688	640	592	544	498
26	738	687	643	598	552	507	464
28	685	637	596	553	511	469	429
30	629	585	547	507	468	429	392
32	571	530	495	458	423	387	354
34	510	473	442	408	376	344	314
36	455	422	394	364	336	307	280
38	408	379	353	327	301	276	252

Properties

Area A (in.²)	40.0	37.3	35.0	32.7	30.3	27.9	25.6
I_x (in.⁴)	1590	1480	1370	1270	1170	1060	967
I_y (in.⁴)	568	528	492	455	420	384	350
Ratio r_x/r_y	1.67	1.67	1.67	1.67	1.67	1.66	1.66
r_y (in.)	3.77	3.76	3.75	3.73	3.72	3.71	3.70
L_c (ft.)	13.3	13.2	13.2	13.1	13.1	13.1	13.0
L_u (ft.)	35.5	33.5	31.5	29.5	27.8	25.7	23.9
B_x } Bending	.186	.185	.186	.186	.185	.185	.186
B_y } factors	.520	.520	.522	.526	.527	.529	.532
a_x } Multiply	237	220	204	189	174	158	144
a_y } values by 10⁶	85	79	73	68	62	57	52

Heavy line indicates $Kl/r = 120$. Values omitted are same as for $F_y = 36$ ksi.
† Flange is non-compact; see discussion preceding column load tables.

AMERICAN INSTITUTE OF STEEL CONSTRUCTION

$F_y = 50$ ksi

W 14

COLUMNS
W shapes
TABLE II
Allowable axial loads in kips

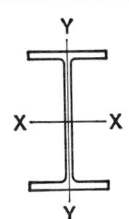

Designation	W14		W14			W14		
Nominal Depth and Width	14 × 12		14 × 10			14 × 8		
Weight per Foot	†84	†78	74	68	††61	‡53	‡48	††*43
6	689	638	595	545	487	408	369	329
7	677	627	581	533	476	395	356	317
8	665	616	567	519	464	380	343	305
9	652	604	552	505	452	364	329	292
10	639	592	536	491	439	348	313	279
11	625	578	520	475	425	330	298	264
12	610	565	502	459	410	312	281	249
13	595	550	484	443	395	293	263	233
14	579	536	465	425	379	273	245	216
15	563	520	446	407	363	251	226	199
16	546	504	426	388	346	229	206	181
17	528	488	405	368	328	206	185	162
18	510	471	383	348	310	184	165	144
19	491	453	360	327	291	165	148	129
20	472	435	337	305	272			
22	432	398	287	259	230			
24	389	358	241	218	193			
26	344	315						
28	298	273						
30	260	237						

Effective length in ft. KL with respect to least radius of gyration r_y

Properties

Area A (in.²)	24.7	22.9	21.8	20.0	17.9	15.6	14.1	12.6
I_x (in.⁴)	928	851	797	724	641	542	485	429
I_y (in.⁴)	225	207	133	121	107	57.5	51.3	45.1
Ratio r_x/r_y	2.03	2.03	2.44	2.45	2.44	3.07	3.07	3.08
r_y (in.)	3.02	3.00	2.48	2.46	2.45	1.92	1.91	1.89
L_c (ft.)	10.8	10.8	9.1	9.0	9.0	7.3	7.2	7.2
L_u (ft.)	22.0	20.5	18.6	17.1	15.5	12.7	11.5	10.3
B_x } Bending	.189	.190	.195	.195	.195	.201	.201	.201
B_y } factors	.659	.664	.823	.830	.833	1.091	1.102	1.11
a_x } Multiply	138.3	126.5	118.9	108.0	95.4	80.9	72.1	63.6
a_y } values by 10⁶	33.6	30.7	20.0	18.0	16.0	8.6	7.7	6.7

Heavy line indicates $Kl/r = 120$. Values omitted are same as for $F_y = 36$ ksi.

† Flange is non-compact; see discussion preceding column load tables.

‡ Web may be non-compact for combined axial and bending stress; see AISC Specification Sect. 1.5.1.4.1.

* Web exceeds AISC Specification Sect. 1.9. See discussion preceding Tables I and II.

COLUMNS
W shapes

$$F_y = 50 \text{ ksi}$$

W 12

TABLE II

Allowable axial loads in kips

$F_y = 50$ ksi

Designation		W12						
Nominal Depth and Width		12×12						
Weight per Foot		190	161	133	120	106	99	92	†85
Effective length in ft. KL with respect to least radius of gyration r_y	6	1569	1329	1095	987	872	813	757	698
	7	1546	1308	1078	972	858	800	745	687
	8	1521	1287	1060	956	844	786	732	675
	9	1495	1264	1041	938	828	772	718	662
	10	1468	1241	1021	920	812	756	704	649
	11	1439	1216	1000	901	795	740	689	635
	12	1409	1190	979	881	777	724	673	621
	13	1378	1163	956	860	759	706	657	606
	14	1346	1136	933	839	740	688	640	590
	15	1313	1107	908	817	720	670	623	574
	16	1279	1077	883	794	699	650	605	557
	17	1243	1046	857	770	678	630	586	540
	18	1207	1014	831	746	656	610	567	522
	19	1169	981	803	720	634	589	547	503
	20	1130	948	775	694	611	567	526	484
	22	1049	877	715	640	562	521	484	445
	24	963	803	653	583	511	473	438	403
	26	873	724	586	522	457	421	390	358
	28	778	641	516	457	399	368	340	312
	30	680	559	450	398	348	320	296	271
	32	598	492	395	350	306			

Properties

	190	161	133	120	106	99	92	†85
Area A (in.²)	55.9	47.4	39.1	35.3	31.2	29.1	27.1	25.0
I_x (in.⁴)	1890	1540	1220	1070	931	859	789	723
I_y (in.⁴)	590	486	390	345	301	278	256	235
Ratio r_x/r_y	1.79	1.78	1.77	1.76	1.76	1.76	1.75	1.75
r_y (in.)	3.25	3.20	3.16	3.13	3.11	3.09	3.08	3.07
L_c (ft.)	11.4	11.3	11.1	11.1	11.0	11.0	10.9	10.9
L_u (ft.)	51.0	44.7	38.1	34.7	31.2	29.3	27.6	25.7
B_x ⎰ Bending	.213	.214	.214	.217	.216	.216	.217	.216
B_y ⎱ factors	.601	.611	.620	.631	.635	.637	.643	.643
a_x ⎰ Multiply	282.1	229.5	182.0	159.7	138.6	127.8	117.7	107.8
a_y ⎱ values by 10⁶	88.0	72.3	58.2	51.5	45.0	41.4	38.3	35.1

Heavy line indicates $Kl/r = 120$. Values omitted are same as for $F_y = 36$ ksi.
† Flange is non-compact; see discussion preceding column load tables.

AMERICAN INSTITUTE OF STEEL CONSTRUCTION

$F_y = 50$ ksi	COLUMNS	
W 12	**W shapes**	
	TABLE II	
	Allowable axial loads in kips	

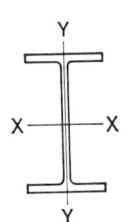

$F_y = 50$ ksi

Designation		W12			W12		W12		
Nominal Depth and Width		12 × 12			12 × 10		12 × 8		
Weight per Foot		†79	†72	†65	†58	†53	50	45	†‡40
Effective length in ft. KL with respect to least radius of gyration r_y	6	647	591	533	467	425	386	346	310
	7	637	582	524	457	416	374	335	299
	8	626	571	514	446	406	360	322	288
	9	614	561	504	434	395	346	309	277
	10	601	549	494	422	384	331	296	264
	11	588	537	483	409	372	315	281	251
	12	575	525	472	396	360	298	266	238
	13	561	512	460	382	347	281	250	223
	14	546	498	448	368	333	262	233	208
	15	531	484	435	353	319	243	216	193
	16	515	470	422	337	305	223	197	176
	17	499	455	408	321	289	202	178	159
	18	482	440	394	304	274	181	159	142
	19	465	424	380	287	258	162	143	128
	20	447	408	365	269	241			
	22	410	373	334	231	206			
	24	371	337	301	194	173			
	26	329	299	266					
	28	285	259	230					
	30	249	226	201					

Properties

	†79	†72	†65	†58	†53	50	45	†‡40
Area A (in.²)	23.2	21.2	19.1	17.1	15.6	14.7	13.2	11.8
I_x (in.⁴)	663	597	533	476	426	395	351	310
I_y (in.⁴)	216	195	175	107	96	56.4	50.0	44.1
Ratio r_x/r_y	1.75	1.75	1.75	2.10	2.11	2.64	2.65	2.64
r_y (in.)	3.05	3.04	3.02	2.51	2.48	1.96	1.94	1.94
L_c (ft.)	10.9	10.8	10.8	9.0	9.0	7.3	7.3	7.2
L_u (ft.)	24.0	22.0	20.0	17.6	16.0	14.2	12.9	11.6
B_x } Bending	.217	.218	.218	.219	.221	.228	.227	.228
B_y } factors	.649	.655	.657	.800	.813	1.050	1.065	1.073
a_x } Multiply	98.6	89.1	79.3	71.0	63.6	58.8	52.2	46.3
a_y } values by 10⁶	32.2	29.2	26.0	16.1	14.3	8.4	7.4	6.6

Heavy line indicates $Kl/r = 120$. Values omitted are same as for $F_y = 36$ ksi.

† Flange is non-compact; see discussion preceding column load tables.

‡ Web may be non-compact for combined axial and bending stress; see AISC Specification Sect. 1.5.1.4.1.

$F_y = 50$ ksi

COLUMNS
W shapes

W 10

TABLE II

Allowable axial loads in kips

Designation		W10								
Nominal Depth and Width		10 × 10								
Weight per Foot		112	100	89	77	72	66	60	†54	†49
$F_y = 50$ ksi — Effective length in ft. KL with respect to least radius of gyration r_y	6	905	808	720	623	581	532	485	435	394
	7	887	792	705	610	569	521	475	426	385
	8	868	775	689	596	556	509	464	416	376
	9	848	756	673	581	543	496	452	406	367
	10	826	737	655	566	528	483	440	395	357
	11	804	717	637	550	513	469	427	383	346
	12	781	696	618	533	497	454	414	371	335
	13	756	674	598	516	481	439	400	359	324
	14	731	651	578	497	464	423	386	346	312
	15	704	627	556	479	446	407	370	332	299
	16	677	602	534	459	427	390	355	318	286
	17	649	577	511	439	408	372	339	303	273
	18	620	550	487	417	388	354	322	288	259
	19	589	523	462	396	368	335	305	273	245
	20	558	494	437	373	347	316	287	256	230
	22	492	435	383	326	302	275	249	222	198
	24	422	372	326	276	256	232	210	188	167
	26	360	317	278	235	218	198	179	160	143

Properties										
Area A (in.²)		32.9	29.4	26.2	22.7	21.2	19.4	17.7	15.9	14.4
I_x (in.⁴)		719	625	542	457	421	382	344	306	273
I_y (in.⁴)		235	207	181	153	142	129	116	104	93.0
Ratio r_x/r_y		1.75	1.74	1.73	1.73	1.72	1.72	1.72	1.71	1.71
r_y (in.)		2.67	2.65	2.63	2.60	2.59	2.58	2.57	2.56	2.54
L_c (ft.)		9.4	9.3	9.3	9.2	9.2	9.1	9.1	9.0	9.0
L_u (ft.)		38.1	34.7	31.5	27.8	26.1	24.4	22.4	20.5	18.7
B_x } Bending		.262	.263	.263	.264	.265	.264	.264	.264	.264
B_y } factors		.728	.737	.745	.755	.760	.761	.767	.769	.775
a_x } Multiply		106.9	93.1	80.8	68.2	62.8	57.0	51.3	45.7	40.6
a_y } values by 10⁶		34.9	30.8	27.0	22.9	21.2	19.2	17.4	15.5	13.8

Heavy line indicates $Kl/r = 120$. Values omitted are same as for $F_y = 36$ ksi.
† Flange is non-compact; see discussion preceding column load tables.

AMERICAN INSTITUTE OF STEEL CONSTRUCTION

$F_y = 50$ ksi

W 10-8

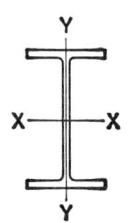

COLUMNS
W shapes
TABLE II
Allowable axial loads in kips

Designation		W10			W8					
Nominal Depth and Width		10 × 8			8 × 8					
Weight per Foot		45	†39	†33	67	58	48	40	†35	†31
	6	348	303	255	525	455	375	312	272	241
	7	337	293	246	510	442	363	303	264	233
	8	326	283	237	494	428	352	293	255	225
	9	313	272	228	477	413	339	282	246	217
	10	300	260	217	459	397	326	270	236	208
	11	286	248	207	440	380	312	258	225	198
	12	271	235	196	420	363	297	246	214	188
	13	256	221	184	399	344	282	233	202	178
	14	240	207	171	378	325	266	219	190	167
	15	224	193	159	355	305	249	204	177	155
	16	206	177	145	331	284	232	189	164	143
	17	188	161	131	307	263	214	174	150	131
	18	169	144	117	281	240	195	157	136	118
	19	152	130	105	254	217	175	141	122	106
	20	137	117		230	196	158	127	110	96

$F_y = 50$ ksi — Effective length in ft. KL with respect to least radius of gyration r_y

Properties

	45	†39	†33	67	58	48	40	†35	†31
Area A (in.²)	13.2	11.5	9.71	19.7	17.1	14.1	11.8	10.3	9.12
I_x (in.⁴)	249	210	171	272	227	184	146	126	110
I_y (in.⁴)	53.2	44.9	36.5	88.6	74.9	60.9	49.0	42.5	37.0
Ratio r_x/r_y	2.16	2.16	2.16	1.75	1.74	1.74	1.73	1.72	1.73
r_y (in.)	2.00	1.98	1.94	2.12	2.10	2.08	2.04	2.03	2.01
L_c (ft.)	7.2	7.2	7.2	7.5	7.4	7.3	7.3	7.2	7.2
L_u (ft.)	16.4	14.2	11.8	28.8	25.3	21.8	18.3	16.3	14.5
B_x } Bending	.269	.273	.278	.327	.329	.327	.333	.332	.333
B_y } factors	.993	1.027	1.061	.921	.940	.940	.976	.972	.988
a_x } Multiply	36.9	31.2	25.5	40.4	33.9	27.4	21.9	18.8	16.4
a_y } values by 10⁶	7.9	6.7	5.4	13.2	11.2	9.1	7.3	6.3	5.5

Heavy line indicates $Kl/r = 120$. Values omitted are same as for $F_y = 36$ ksi.
† Flange is non-compact; see discussion preceding column load tables.

AMERICAN INSTITUTE OF STEEL CONSTRUCTION

COLUMNS
W shapes

$F_y = 50$ ksi

W 8-6

TABLE II

Allowable axial loads in kips

$F_y = 50$ ksi

Designation	W8		W8		W6			W6		
Nominal Depth and Width	8 × 6½		8 × 5¼		6 × 6			6 × 4		
Weight per Foot	28	†24	20	†17	25	†20	†15.5	16	12	†8.5
2	237	203	167	142	211	169	131	131	98	69
3	231	198	161	136	205	164	127	124	92	65
4	224	192	153	130	198	158	122	115	85	60
5	216	185	145	123	191	152	117	106	77	54
6	207	178	136	115	182	145	112	95	68	47
7	198	169	126	106	173	138	105	83	59	40
8	188	161	116	97	163	130	99	70	48	32
9	177	152	104	86	153	121	92	57		
10	166	142	92	76	142	112	85			
11	154	131	79	64	130	103	77			
12	141	120	66	54	118	93	68			
13	128	109			105	82	60			
14	114	97			91	71	51			
15	100	84			79	62				
16	87	74								

Effective length in ft. KL with respect to least radius of gyration r_y

$F_y = 50$ ksi

Properties

	28	†24	20	†17	25	†20	†15.5	16	12	†8.5
Area A (in.²)	8.23	7.06	5.89	5.01	7.35	5.88	4.56	4.72	3.54	2.51
x (in.⁴)	97.8	82.5	69.4	56.6	53.3	41.5	30.1	31.7	21.7	14.8
y (in.⁴)	21.6	18.2	9.22	7.44	17.1	13.3	9.67	4.42	2.98	1.98
Ratio r_x/r_y	2.13	2.12	2.74	2.75	1.76	1.76	1.76	2.68	2.70	2.73
y (in.)	1.62	1.61	1.25	1.22	1.53	1.51	1.46	.97	.92	.89
c (ft.)	5.9	5.9	4.8	4.8	5.5	5.4	5.4	3.7	3.6	3.6
u (ft.)	12.6	10.9	8.2	6.8	14.5	11.9	9.0	8.7	6.2	4.4
B_x } Bending	.339	.340	.347	.356	.441	.439	.456	.463	.489	.495
B_y } factors	1.246	1.259	1.683	1.771	1.308	1.328	1.412	2.156	2.376	2.486
x } Multiply	14.60	12.30	10.32	8.43	7.92	6.20	4.49	4.72	3.24	2.21
y } values by 10⁶	3.22	2.73	1.37	1.11	2.56	2.00	1.45	.66	.44	.30

Heavy line indicates $Kl/r = 120$.   Values omitted are same as for $F_y = 36$ ksi.
† Flange is non-compact; see discussion preceding column load tables.

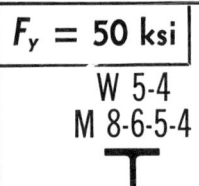

$F_y = 50$ ksi

W 5-4
M 8-6-5-4

COLUMNS
W and M shapes
TABLE II
Allowable axial loads in kips

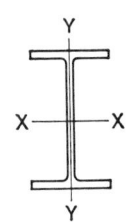

Designation	W5		W4	M8		M6		M5	M4
Nominal Depth and Width	5 × 5		4 × 4	8 × 8		6 × 6		5 × 5	4 × 4
Weight per Foot	18.5	16	13	†34.3	†32.6	†22.5	†20	18.9	13
2	154	133	106	293	278	189	168	157	105
3	149	128	101	287	272	183	163	151	99
4	142	123	94	279	265	175	157	143	92
5	135	116	86	271	258	167	150	135	84
6	127	109	78	263	250	159	142	126	75
7	118	101	69	253	241	149	134	116	65
8	109	93	59	243	232	139	125	105	54
9	98	84	48	233	222	127	115	93	43
10	88	74		222	212	116	105	81	
11	76	64		210	201	103	94	67	
12	64	54		197	189	89	83	57	
13	55			184	177	76	71		
14				170	165				
15				156	151				
16				141	137				
17				125	123				
18				112	110				

Left label: $F_y = 50$ ksi — Effective length in ft. KL with respect to least radius of gyration r_y

Properties

	W5 18.5	W5 16	W4 13	M8 †34.3	M8 †32.6	M6 †22.5	M6 †20	M5 18.9	M4 13
Area A (in.²)	5.43	4.70	3.82	10.1	9.58	6.62	5.89	5.55	3.81
I_x (in.⁴)	25.4	21.3	11.3	116	114	41.2	39.0	24.1	10.5
I_y (in.⁴)	8.89	7.51	3.76	34.90	34.10	12.40	11.60	7.86	3.3
Ratio r_x/r_y	1.69	1.69	1.74	1.83	1.82	1.82	1.84	1.75	1.77
r_y (in.)	1.28	1.26	.99	1.86	1.89	1.37	1.40	1.19	.94
L_c (ft.)	4.6	4.5	3.7	7.2	7.2	5.5	5.4	4.5	3.6
L_u (ft.)	13.8	12.0	11.3	15.3	15.2	12.8	12.6	13.9	12.3
B_x } Bending	.547	.551	.701	.348	.338	.484	.454	.577	.72
B_y } factors	1.534	1.567	2.065	1.157	1.117	1.623	1.511	1.768	2.22
a_x } Multiply	3.77	3.18	1.68	17.40	16.89	6.12	5.80	3.58	1.56
a_y } values by 10^6	1.33	1.11	0.56	5.21	5.10	1.85	1.72	1.17	0.50

Heavy line indicates $Kl/r = 120$. Values omitted are same as for $F_y = 36$ ksi.
† Flange is non-compact; see discussion preceding column load tables.

COLUMNS
S shapes

$F_y = 50$ ksi

S 6-5-4-3

TABLE II

Allowable axial loads in kips

Designation		S6		S5		S4		S3	
Nominal Depth and Width		6 × 3⅜		5 × 3		4 × 2⅝		3 × 2⅜	
Weight per Foot		17.25	12.5	14.75	10	9.5	7.7	7.5	5.7
Effective length in ft. KL with respect to least radius of gyration r_y	2	134	98	113	77	71	58	55	42
	3	121	89	100	69	62	51	46	35
	4	105	78	85	59	51	42	36	28
	5	87	66	67	48	37	32		19
	6	67	52	48	35				
	7		39						

Properties

Area A (in.²)		5.07	3.67	4.34	2.94	2.79	2.26	2.21	1.67
(in.⁴)		26.3	22.1	15.2	12.3	6.79	6.08	2.93	2.52
(in.⁴)		2.31	1.82	1.67	1.22	.903	.764	.586	.455
ratio r_x/r_y		3.38	3.48	3.02	3.19	2.74	2.82	2.23	2.36
(in.)		.67	.70	.62	.64	.57	.58	.52	.52
(ft.)		3.2	3.0	3.0	2.7	2.6	2.4	2.3	2.1
(ft.)		7.2	6.7	7.2	6.6	6.9	6.5	7.3	6.8
Bending		.579	.498	.713	.598	.824	.744	1.134	.995
factors		3.901	3.367	4.298	3.635	4.319	3.938	4.723	4.283
Multiply		3.927	3.282	2.261	1.841	1.012	.906	.435	.376
values by 10⁶		.344	.272	.249	.181	.135	.114	.088	.068

Heavy line indicates $Kl/r = 120$.   Values omitted are same as for $F_y = 36$ ksi.

$F_y = 50$ ksi

Notes

COLUMNS
Steel Pipe and Structural Tubing
TABLES III, IV, and V

Allowable concentric loads in the tables that follow are tabulated for the effective lengths in feet KL, indicated at the left of each table. They are applicable to primary members with respect to their minor axis in accordance with Section 1.5.1.3 of the AISC Specification.

For discussion of effective length, range of l/r, strength about the major axis, secondary members, combined axial and bending stress, and sample problems, see "Columns, General Notes".

Properties and factors are listed at the bottom of the tables for checking strength about the strong axis and for checking combined loading conditions.

STEEL PIPE COLUMNS (TABLE III)

Allowable loads for unfilled pipe columns are tabulated for $F_y = 36$ ksi. Steel pipe manufactured to ASTM A501 furnishes $F_y = 36$ ksi and ASTM A53, Types E or S, Grade B furnishes $F_y = 35$ ksi and may be designed at stresses allowed for $F_y = 36$ ksi steel.

The heavy horizontal lines within the table indicate $Kl/r = 120$. No values are listed beyond $Kl/r = 200$.

STRUCTURAL TUBING COLUMNS (TABLES IV AND V)

Allowable loads for square and rectangular structural tubing columns are tabulated for two strengths, $F_y = 36$ ksi and $F_y = 46$ ksi. As listed in Section 1.4.1 of the AISC Specification, structural tubing is manufactured to $F_y = 36$ ksi under ASTM A501, to $F_y = 46$ ksi under ASTM A500, Grade B, and to $F_y = 50$ ksi under ASTM A618.

All tubes listed in the column load tables satisfy Section 1.9 of the AISC Specification.

The heavy horizontal lines appearing within the tables indicate $Kl/r = 120$. No values are listed beyond $Kl/r = 200$. Load values for Kl/r above 126.1 are the same for all steels with yield stresses equal to, or greater than, 36 ksi. Load values are therefore omitted in the table for $F_y = 46$ ksi when a column has the same allowable load for both $F_y = 36$ ksi and $F_y = 46$ ksi, and is available at the lesser yield stress.

Some structural tubing is available at a yield stress of 46 ksi in sizes not readily available at 36 ksi. Since these sizes are not included at $F_y = 36$ ksi, load values for these sizes are shown to $Kl/r = 200$ in the 46 ksi table.

$F_y = 36$ ksi

COLUMNS
Standard steel pipe
TABLE III
Allowable concentric loads in kips

Nominal Dia.		12	10	8	6	5	4	3½	3
Wall Thickness		.375	.365	.322	.280	.258	.237	.226	.216
Weight per Foot		49.56	40.48	28.55	18.97	14.62	10.79	9.11	7.58
	6	303	246	171	110	83	59	48	38
	7	301	243	168	108	81	57	46	36
	8	299	241	166	106	78	54	44	34
	9	296	238	163	103	76	52	41	31
	10	293	235	161	101	73	49	38	28
	11	291	232	158	98	71	46	35	25
	12	288	229	155	95	68	43	32	22
	13	285	226	152	92	65	40	29	19
	14	282	223	149	89	61	36	25	16
	15	278	220	145	86	58	33	22	14
	16	275	216	142	82	55	29	19	12
	17	272	213	138	79	51	26	17	11
	18	268	209	135	75	47	23	15	10
	19	265	205	131	71	43	21	14	9
	20	261	201	127	67	39	19	12	
	22	254	193	119	59	32	15	10	
	24	246	185	111	51	27	13		
	26	238	176	102	43	23			
	28	229	167	93	37	20			
	30	220	158	83	32	17			
	32	211	148	73	29				
	34	201	137	65	25				
	36	192	127	58	23				
	38	181	115	52					
	40	171	104	47					

Effective length in feet KL with respect to radius of gyration

Properties									
Area A (in.²)		14.6	11.9	8.40	5.58	4.30	3.17	2.68	2.23
I (in.⁴)		279.	161.	72.5	28.1	15.2	7.23	4.79	3.02
r (in.)		4.38	3.67	2.94	2.25	1.88	1.51	1.34	1.16
B (Bending factor)		.333	.398	.500	.657	.789	.987	1.12	1.29
a (Multiply values by 10⁶)		41.7	23.9	10.8	4.21	2.26	1.08	.717	.44

Heavy line indicates $Kl/r = 120$. Values omitted for $Kl/r > 200$.
For dimensions and properties, see Part 1.

COLUMNS

Extra strong steel pipe

TABLE III

Allowable concentric loads in kips

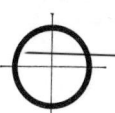

$$F_y = 36 \text{ ksi}$$

Nominal Dia.	12	10	8	6	5	4	3½	3
Wall Thickness	.500	.500	.500	.432	.375	.337	.318	.300
Weight per Foot	65.42	54.74	43.39	28.57	20.78	14.98	12.50	10.25

Effective length in feet KL with respect to radius of gyration	12	10	8	6	5	4	3½	3
6	400	332	259	166	118	81	66	52
7	397	328	255	162	114	78	63	48
8	394	325	251	159	111	75	59	45
9	390	321	247	155	107	71	55	41
10	387	318	243	151	103	67	51	37
11	383	314	239	146	99	63	47	33
12	379	309	234	142	95	59	43	28
13	375	305	229	137	91	54	38	24
14	371	301	224	132	86	49	33	21
15	367	296	219	127	81	44	29	18
16	363	291	214	122	76	39	25	16
17	358	286	209	116	71	34	23	14
18	353	281	203	111	65	31	20	12
19	349	276	197	105	59	28	18	11
20	344	271	191	99	54	25	16	
22	334	260	179	86	44	21		
24	323	248	166	73	37	17		
26	312	236	152	62	32			
28	301	224	137	54	27			
30	289	211	122	47	24			
32	277	197	107	41				
34	264	183	95	36				
36	251	168	85	32				
38	237	152	76					
40	223	137	69					

Properties

	12	10	8	6	5	4	3½	3
Area A (in.²)	19.2	16.1	12.8	8.40	6.11	4.41	3.68	3.02
(in.⁴)	362.	212.	106.	40.5	20.7	9.61	6.28	3.89
(in.)	4.33	3.63	2.88	2.19	1.84	1.48	1.31	1.14
(Bending factor)	.339	.408	.521	.688	.822	1.03	1.17	1.36
(Multiply values by 10⁶)	53.6	31.6	15.8	6.00	3.08	1.44	.941	.585

Heavy line indicates $Kl/r = 120$. Values omitted for $Kl/r > 200$.
For dimensions and properties, see Part 1.

$F_y = 36$ ksi

COLUMNS
Double-extra strong steel pipe
TABLE III
Allowable concentric loads in kips

Nominal Dia.	8	6	5	4	3
Wall Thickness	.875	.864	.750	.674	.600
Weight per Foot	72.42	53.16	38.55	27.54	18.58
6	431	306	216	147	91
7	424	299	209	140	84
8	417	292	202	133	77
9	410	284	195	126	69
10	403	275	187	118	60
11	395	266	178	109	51
12	387	257	170	100	43
13	378	247	160	91	37
14	369	237	151	81	32
15	360	227	141	70	28
16	351	216	130	62	24
17	341	205	119	55	22
18	331	193	108	49	
19	321	181	97	44	
20	310	168	87	40	
22	288	142	72	33	
24	264	119	61		
26	240	102	52		
28	213	88	44		
30	187	76			
32	164	67			
34	145	60			
36	130				
38	116				
40	105				

Effective length in feet KL with respect to radius of gyration

Properties

	8	6	5	4	3
Area A (in.²)	21.3	15.6	11.3	8.10	5.47
I (in.⁴)	162.	66.3	33.6	15.3	5.99
r (in.)	2.76	2.06	1.72	1.37	1.05
B (Bending factor)	.567	.781	.938	1.19	1.60
a (Multiply values by 10⁶)	24.2	9.86	4.98	2.27	.899

Heavy line indicates $Kl/r = 120$. Values omitted for $Kl/r > 200$.
For dimensions and properties, see Part 1.

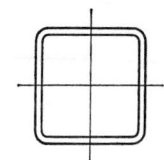

COLUMNS
Square structural tubing
Allowable concentric loads in kips
TABLE IV

$F_y = 36$ ksi

Nominal Size		10 × 10					8 × 8			
Wall Thickness	5⁄8	1⁄2	3⁄8	5⁄16	1⁄4	5⁄8	1⁄2	3⁄8	5⁄16	1⁄4
Weight per Foot	73.98	60.95	47.03	39.74	†32.23	56.98	47.35	36.83	31.24	25.44
6	450	370	285	242	196	341	283	220	187	153
7	446	366	283	240	195	336	279	217	185	151
8	441	363	280	238	193	331	275	214	183	149
9	436	359	277	235	191	326	271	211	180	147
10	431	355	274	233	189	321	267	208	177	145
11	426	351	271	230	187	315	262	205	174	142
12	421	347	268	228	185	309	257	201	171	140
13	415	342	265	225	182	303	252	197	168	137
14	410	338	261	222	180	296	247	193	165	135
15	404	333	258	219	178	290	242	189	162	132
16	397	328	254	216	175	283	237	185	158	129
17	391	323	250	213	173	276	231	181	155	127
18	385	318	246	209	170	269	225	177	151	124
19	378	312	242	206	167	261	219	172	148	121
20	371	307	238	203	165	253	213	168	144	118
22	357	295	230	195	159	237	200	158	136	111
24	342	284	221	188	153	220	187	148	127	104
26	326	271	211	180	147	202	173	137	119	97
28	310	258	202	172	140	184	158	126	109	90
30	293	245	191	164	133	164	142	115	100	82
32	275	231	181	155	126	144	126	102	89	74
34	257	216	170	146	119	128	111	91	79	66
36	238	201	159	136	111	114	99	81	71	59
38	218	185	147	126	104	102	89	73	63	53
40	198	168	134	116	95	92	81	66	57	47

Effective length in feet KL with respect to radius of gyration

$F_y = 36$ ksi

Properties										
Area A (in.²)	21.8	17.9	13.8	11.7	9.48	16.8	13.9	10.8	9.19	7.48
I (in.⁴)	304	260	208	179	148	142	124	102	88.1	73.4
r (in.)	3.74	3.81	3.88	3.92	3.95	2.91	2.99	3.06	3.10	3.13
B { Bending factor	.359	.344	.332	.327	.320	.473	.448	.424	.417	.408
a { Multiply values by 10⁶	45.4	38.7	31.0	26.8	22.0	21.2	18.5	15.1	13.2	10.9

Heavy line indicates $Kl/r = 120$.
† Flange is non-compact for bending; see discussion preceding column load tables.

AMERICAN INSTITUTE OF STEEL CONSTRUCTION

F_y = 36 ksi

COLUMNS
Square structural tubing
Allowable concentric loads in kips
TABLE IV

F_y = 36 ksi — Effective length in feet KL with respect to radius of gyration

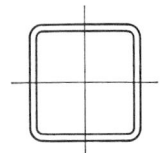

Nominal Size	7 × 7				6 × 6			
Wall Thickness	½	⅜	5⁄16	¼	½	⅜	5⁄16	¼
Weight per Foot	40.55	31.73	26.99	22.04	34.48	27.04	23.02	18.82
6	239	188	160	131	199	157	134	110
7	235	185	158	129	195	154	132	108
8	231	182	155	127	191	151	129	106
9	227	178	152	125	186	147	126	103
10	222	175	149	122	181	144	123	101
11	217	171	146	120	176	140	120	98
12	212	168	143	117	170	136	116	95
13	207	164	140	115	165	131	113	93
14	201	160	137	112	159	127	109	90
15	196	155	133	109	153	122	105	87
16	190	151	129	106	146	118	101	83
17	184	146	126	103	140	113	97	80
18	178	142	122	100	133	108	93	77
19	171	137	118	97	126	102	88	73
20	165	132	114	93	118	97	84	69
22	151	122	105	86	103	85	74	62
24	136	111	96	79	87	73	64	54
26	121	99	86	71	74	62	54	46
28	105	87	76	63	64	54	47	39
30	91	75	66	55	56	47	41	34
32	80	66	58	49	49	41	36	30
34	71	59	52	43	43	36	32	27
36	63	52	46	38	39	32	28	24
38	57	47	41	34			25	21
40	51	42	37	31				

Properties

Area A (in.²)	11.9	9.33	7.94	6.48	10.1	7.95	6.77	5.54
I (in.⁴)	79.2	65.6	57.4	48.1	48.6	40.5	35.5	29.9
r (in.)	2.58	2.65	2.69	2.72	2.19	2.26	2.29	2.32
B Bending factor	.526	.498	.484	.472	.623	.589	.572	.556
a Multiply values by 10^6	11.8	9.76	8.56	7.14	7.22	6.05	5.29	4.44

Heavy line indicates $Kl/r = 120$. Values omitted for $Kl/r > 200$.

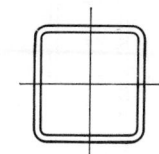

COLUMNS
Square structural tubing
Allowable concentric loads in kips
TABLE IV

Nominal Size		5 × 5				4 × 4		
Wall Thickness	½	⅜	⁵⁄₁₆	¼	½	⅜	⁵⁄₁₆	¼
Weight per Foot	27.68	21.94	18.77	15.42	20.88	16.84	14.52	12.02
2	171	135	116	95	127	103	89	74
3	168	133	114	94	124	100	87	72
4	164	130	112	92	120	98	84	70
5	160	127	109	90	116	94	82	68
6	156	124	107	88	111	91	79	66
7	151	121	104	86	106	87	76	63
8	147	117	101	83	101	83	72	60
9	141	113	98	81	95	79	69	57
10	136	109	94	78	88	74	65	54
11	130	105	91	75	82	69	61	51
12	124	101	87	72	75	64	57	48
13	118	96	83	69	68	59	52	44
14	111	91	79	66	60	53	47	40
15	104	86	75	62	52	47	42	36
16	97	81	70	59	46	42	37	32
17	90	75	66	55	41	37	33	29
18	82	69	61	51	36	33	30	25
19	74	63	56	47	33	29	27	23
20	67	57	51	43	29	27	24	21
22	55	47	42	35	24	22	20	17
24	46	40	35	30		18	17	14
26	40	34	30	25				
28	34	29	26	22				
30		25	22	19				

Effective length in feet KL with respect to radius of gyration

$F_y = 36$ ksi

Properties

Area A (in.²)	8.14	6.45	5.52	4.54	6.14	4.95	4.27	3.54
I (in.⁴)	25.7	22.0	19.5	16.6	11.4	10.2	9.23	8.00
r (in.)	1.78	1.85	1.88	1.91	1.36	1.44	1.47	1.50
B { Bending factor	.792	.733	.708	.684	1.08	.971	.925	.885
a { Multiply values by 10⁶	3.84	3.29	2.91	2.47	1.69	1.53	1.37	1.19

Heavy line indicates $Kl/r = 120$. Values omitted for $Kl/r > 200$.

$F_y = 36$ ksi

COLUMNS
Rectangular structural tubing
Allowable concentric loads in kips
TABLE IV

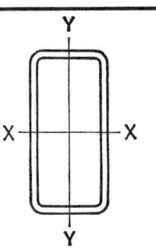

Nominal Size	12 × 6			10 × 8				10 × 6			
Wall Thickness	½	⅜	5⁄16	½	⅜	5⁄16	¼	½	⅜	5⁄16	¼
Weight per Foot	54.15	41.93	†35.49	54.15	41.93	35.49	†28.83	47.35	36.83	31.24	†25.44
6	318	247	208	324	251	213	173	277	216	184	150
7	312	242	205	320	248	210	171	272	212	180	147
8	306	238	201	316	245	207	169	266	208	177	144
9	299	233	197	311	242	205	167	260	204	173	141
10	292	228	193	307	238	202	165	254	199	169	138
11	285	222	188	302	234	199	162	248	194	165	135
12	278	217	184	297	230	195	160	241	189	161	132
13	270	211	179	291	226	192	157	234	184	157	128
14	262	205	174	286	222	189	154	227	178	152	125
15	253	199	169	280	218	185	151	219	173	148	121
16	245	192	163	274	213	181	148	211	167	143	117
17	236	186	158	268	209	177	145	203	161	138	113
18	226	179	152	262	204	174	142	195	154	133	109
19	217	172	146	255	199	170	139	186	148	127	105
20	207	164	140	249	194	165	135	177	141	122	100
22	186	149	127	235	184	157	129	158	127	110	91
24	164	133	114	220	173	148	121	138	112	98	81
26	141	115	100	205	162	138	114	118	96	85	71
28	121	100	86	189	150	128	106	102	83	73	61
30	106	87	75	172	137	118	97	89	72	64	53
32	93	76	66	155	124	107	89	78	64	56	47
34	82	67	58	137	110	96	79	69	56	49	41
36	73	60	52	122	98	85	71	62	50	44	37
38	66	54	47	110	88	76	64	55	45	40	33
40	59	49	42	99	80	69	57		41	36	30

Left axis: Effective length in feet KL with respect to least radius of gyration
$F_y = 36$ ksi

Properties											
Area A (in.²)	15.9	12.3	10.4	15.9	12.3	10.4	8.48	13.9	10.8	9.19	7.48
I_x (in.⁴)	271	220	190	215	174	150	124	170	139	120	100
I_y (in.⁴)	92.0	75.0	65.1	153	123	107	88.4	76.9	63.1	55.0	45.1
Ratio r_x/r_y	1.72	1.71	1.70	1.18	1.19	1.18	1.19	1.49	1.49	1.48	1.48
r_y (in.)	2.40	2.47	2.50	3.10	3.16	3.20	3.23	2.35	2.41	2.45	2.48
B_x ⎰ Bending	.352	.335	.328	.370	.353	.347	.342	.409	.388	.383	.374
B_y ⎱ factors	.518	.492	.479	.416	.400	.389	.384	.542	.513	.501	.489
a_x ⎰ Multiply	40.4	32.6	28.1	31.9	25.8	22.3	18.5	25.2	20.6	17.9	14.9
a_y ⎱ values by 10⁶	13.6	11.2	9.68	22.8	18.3	15.9	13.2	11.4	9.35	8.22	6.8

Heavy line indicates $Kl/r = 120$. Values omitted for $Kl/r > 200$.

† Flange is non-compact for weak axis bending; see discussion preceding column load tables.

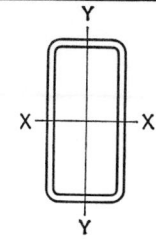

COLUMNS
Rectangular structural tubing
Allowable concentric loads in kips

TABLE IV

$F_y = 36$ ksi

Nominal Size	8 × 6				8 × 4			
Wall Thickness	½	⅜	⁵⁄₁₆	¼	½	⅜	⁵⁄₁₆	¼
Weight per Foot	40.55	31.73	26.99	22.04	34.48	27.04	23.02	18.82
6	236	186	158	129	188	149	127	105
7	231	182	155	127	181	144	123	101
8	226	178	152	124	173	138	118	98
9	221	174	149	122	165	132	114	94
10	215	170	145	119	157	126	108	89
11	210	166	142	116	148	119	103	85
12	203	161	138	113	138	112	97	80
13	197	156	134	110	129	105	91	76
14	191	152	130	107	118	97	85	71
15	184	146	126	103	107	89	78	65
16	177	141	121	100	96	81	71	60
17	169	136	117	96	85	72	64	54
18	162	130	112	92	76	64	57	48
19	154	124	107	88	68	58	51	43
20	146	118	102	84	61	52	46	39
22	129	105	92	76	51	43	38	32
24	110	92	80	67	43	36	32	27
26	94	78	69	58		31	27	23
28	81	68	59	50				
30	71	59	52	43				
32	62	52	46	38				
34	55	46	40	34				
36	49	41	36	30				
38		37	32	27				
40				24				

Effective length in feet KL with respect to least radius of gyration

Properties

	½	⅜	⁵⁄₁₆	¼	½	⅜	⁵⁄₁₆	¼
Area A (in.²)	11.9	9.33	7.94	6.48	10.1	7.95	6.77	5.54
I_x (in.⁴)	96.2	79.7	69.7	58.4	71.6	59.9	52.6	44.2
I_y (in.⁴)	61.7	51.2	44.8	37.6	23.7	20.1	17.7	15.0
Ratio r_x/r_y	1.25	1.25	1.24	1.24	1.74	1.72	1.72	1.72
r_y (in.)	2.27	2.34	2.38	2.41	1.53	1.59	1.62	1.65
B_x ⎱ Bending	.495	.468	.456	.444	.564	.531	.515	.501
B_y ⎰ factors	.579	.547	.532	.517	.852	.791	.765	.739
a_x ⎱ Multiply	14.3	11.9	10.4	8.69	10.6	8.89	7.85	6.61
a_y ⎰ values by 10⁶	9.14	7.61	6.70	5.61	3.52	2.99	2.65	2.25

Heavy line indicates $Kl/r = 120$. Values omitted for $Kl/r > 200$.

COLUMNS
Rectangular structural tubing
Allowable concentric loads in kips
TABLE IV

$F_y = 36$ ksi

$F_y = 36$ ksi

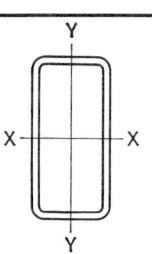

Nominal Size		7 × 5				6 × 4			
Wall Thickness		½	⅜	⁵⁄₁₆	¼	½	⅜	⁵⁄₁₆	¼
Weight per Foot		34.48	27.04	23.02	18.82	27.68	21.94	18.77	15.42
Effective length in feet KL with respect to least radius of gyration	6	196	154	132	108	150	120	103	85
	7	191	150	128	105	144	116	99	82
	8	185	146	125	103	138	111	95	79
	9	179	142	121	100	131	106	91	76
	10	173	137	117	96	124	100	87	72
	11	166	132	113	93	116	94	82	68
	12	160	127	109	90	108	88	77	64
	13	152	122	105	86	99	82	72	60
	14	145	116	100	82	90	75	66	56
	15	137	110	95	79	81	68	60	51
	16	129	104	90	75	71	61	54	46
	17	120	98	85	70	63	54	48	41
	18	112	91	79	66	56	48	43	37
	19	102	85	74	62	51	43	39	33
	20	93	77	68	57	46	39	35	30
	22	77	64	56	47	38	32	29	25
	24	65	54	47	40	32	27	24	21
	26	55	46	40	34			21	18
	28	47	40	35	29				
	30	41	34	30	26				
	32		30	27	22				
Properties									
Area A (in.²)		10.1	7.95	6.77	5.54	8.14	6.45	5.52	4.54
I_x (in.⁴)		60.8	50.7	44.4	37.4	33.4	28.6	25.4	21.6
I_y (in.⁴)		35.9	30.0	26.4	22.3	17.6	15.2	13.5	11.5
Ratio r_x/r_y		1.30	1.30	1.30	1.30	1.37	1.38	1.37	1.37
r_y (in.)		1.88	1.94	1.97	2.00	1.47	1.53	1.56	1.59
B_x ⎫ Bending		.581	.549	.534	.518	.731	.677	.652	.631
B_y ⎬ factors		.703	.663	.641	.621	.925	.849	.818	.790
a_x ⎫ Multiply		9.03	7.52	6.61	5.58	4.95	4.28	3.77	3.21
a_y ⎭ values by 10⁶		5.32	4.46	3.91	3.30	2.62	2.25	2.00	1.71

Heavy line indicates $Kl/r = 120$. Values omitted for $Kl/r > 200$.

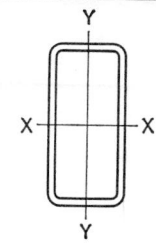

COLUMNS
Rectangular structural tubing
Allowable concentric loads in kips
TABLE IV

$F_y = 36$ ksi

$F_y = 36$ ksi

Nominal Size	6 × 3				5 × 3			
Wall Thickness	½	⅜	⁵⁄₁₆	¼	½	⅜	⁵⁄₁₆	¼
Weight per Foot	24.28	19.39	16.65	13.72	20.88	16.84	14.52	12.02
Effective length in feet KL with respect to least radius of gyration								
2	146	117	101	83	125	102	88	73
3	141	113	98	81	121	98	85	70
4	135	109	94	78	115	94	81	68
5	128	103	90	74	109	89	78	65
6	120	98	85	71	102	84	73	61
7	112	92	80	67	95	79	69	58
8	103	85	74	62	87	73	64	54
9	93	78	69	58	78	66	59	50
10	83	71	63	53	69	60	53	45
11	72	63	56	48	59	52	47	40
12	61	54	49	42	50	45	41	35
13	52	46	42	36	42	38	35	30
14	45	40	36	31	37	33	30	26
15	39	35	31	27	32	29	26	23
16	34	31	28	24	28	25	23	20
17	30	27	24	21	25	22	20	18
18	27	24	22	19		20	18	16
19		22	20	17			16	14
20				15				

Properties

Area A (in.²)	7.14	5.70	4.90	4.04	6.14	4.95	4.27	3.54
I_x (in.⁴)	25.8	22.7	20.3	17.4	15.5	14.0	12.6	11.0
I_y (in.⁴)	8.44	7.51	6.79	5.88	6.86	6.21	5.65	4.93
Ratio r_x/r_y	1.74	1.73	1.73	1.72	1.50	1.50	1.50	1.49
r_y (in.)	1.09	1.15	1.18	1.21	1.06	1.12	1.15	1.18
B_x ⎰ Bending	.830	.753	.724	.697	.990	.884	.847	.805
B_y ⎱ factors	1.27	1.14	1.08	1.03	1.34	1.20	1.13	1.08
a_x ⎰ Multiply	3.84	3.36	3.04	2.60	2.31	2.08	1.88	1.63
a_y ⎱ values by 10⁶	1.26	1.12	1.02	.881	1.03	.925	.841	.734

Heavy line indicates $Kl/r = 120$. Values omitted for $Kl/r > 200$.

$F_y = 46$ ksi

COLUMNS
Square structural tubing
Allowable concentric loads in kips
TABLE V

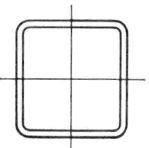

Nominal Size				10 × 10			8 × 8			
Wall Thickness				½	⅜	⁵⁄₁₆	½	⅜	⁵⁄₁₆	¼
Weight per Foot				60.95	47.03	†39.74	47.35	36.83	31.24	†25.44
			6	469	362	307	358	278	237	193
			7	464	358	304	352	274	234	190
			8	459	354	301	346	270	230	187
			9	453	350	297	340	265	226	184
			10	447	345	293	333	260	222	181
			11	440	341	289	326	255	217	177
			12	434	336	285	319	249	213	174
			13	427	331	281	311	244	208	170
			14	420	325	276	304	238	203	166
			15	413	320	272	295	232	198	162
			16	405	314	267	287	225	193	158
			17	398	308	262	278	219	188	153
			18	390	302	257	269	212	182	149
			19	381	296	252	260	205	176	144
			20	373	290	247	251	198	170	140
			22	356	277	236	231	183	158	130
			24	337	263	224	210	168	145	119
			26	318	249	212	188	151	131	108
			28	298	234	200	164	134	117	96
			30	277	218	187	143	117	102	84
			32	255	201	173				
			34	232	184	159				
			36	208	166	144				
			38	187	149	129				
			40		135	117				

Left side labels: $F_y = 46$ ksi; Effective length in feet KL with respect to radius of gyration

Properties										
Area A (in.²)				17.9	13.8	11.7	13.9	10.8	9.19	7.48
I (in.⁴)				260	208	179	124	102	88.1	73.4
r (in.)				3.81	3.88	3.92	2.99	3.06	3.10	3.13
B { Bending factor				.344	.332	.327	.448	.424	.417	.408
a { Multiply values by 10⁶				38.7	31.0	26.8	18.5	15.1	13.2	10.9

Heavy line indicates $Kl/r = 120$. Values omitted are same as for $F_y = 36$ ksi.
† Flange is non-compact for bending; see discussion preceding column load tables.

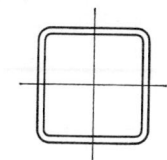

COLUMNS
Square structural tubing
Allowable concentric loads in kips
TABLE V

$F_y = 46$ ksi

$F_y = 46$ ksi

Nominal Size		7 × 7					6 × 6				
Wall Thickness		½	⅜	⁵⁄₁₆	¼	³⁄₁₆	½	⅜	⁵⁄₁₆	¼	³⁄₁₆
Weight per Foot		40.55	31.73	26.99	22.04	†16.85	34.48	27.04	23.02	18.82	†14.41
Effective length in feet KL with respect to radius of gyration	6	302	237	202	165	127	251	198	169	139	106
	7	296	233	198	162	124	244	193	165	135	104
	8	289	228	194	159	122	237	188	161	132	101
	9	283	223	190	156	119	230	183	156	128	98
	10	276	218	186	152	117	223	177	151	124	96
	11	268	212	181	148	114	215	171	146	120	93
	12	260	206	176	144	111	206	165	141	116	89
	13	252	200	171	140	108	197	158	136	112	86
	14	244	194	166	136	105	188	151	130	107	83
	15	235	187	161	132	102	179	144	124	103	79
	16	226	181	155	127	98	169	137	118	98	75
	17	217	174	149	123	95	159	129	112	92	72
	18	208	166	143	118	91	148	121	105	87	68
	19	198	159	137	113	87	137	113	98	82	64
	20	187	151	131	108	84	126	104	91	76	59
	22	166	135	117	97	76	104	87	76	64	50
	24	143	118	103	86	67					42
	26	122	101	88	74	58					36
	28					50					31
	30					44					27
	32					38					24
	34					34					21
	36					30					19
	38					27					17
	40					24					
Properties											
Area A (in.²)		11.9	9.33	7.94	6.48	4.96	10.1	7.95	6.77	5.54	4.24
I (in.⁴)		79.2	65.6	57.4	48.1	37.7	48.6	40.5	35.5	29.9	23.5
r (in.)		2.58	2.65	2.69	2.72	2.76	2.19	2.26	2.29	2.32	2.35
B { Bending factor		.526	.498	.484	.472	.460	.623	.589	.572	.556	.541
a { Multiply values by 10⁶		11.8	9.76	8.56	7.14	5.63	7.22	6.05	5.29	4.44	3.49

Heavy line indicates $Kl/r = 120$.

Values omitted are same as for $F_y = 36$ ksi; values for sections not listed in Table IV omitted for $Kl/r > 200$.

† Flange is non-compact for bending; see discussion preceding column load tables.

AMERICAN INSTITUTE OF STEEL CONSTRUCTION

$F_y = 46$ ksi

COLUMNS
Square structural tubing
Allowable concentric loads in kips
TABLE V

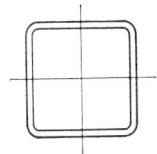

Nominal Size		5 × 5					4 × 4			
Wall Thickness		½	⅜	⁵⁄₁₆	¼	³⁄₁₆	⅜	⁵⁄₁₆	¼	³⁄₁₆
Weight per Foot		27.68	21.94	18.77	15.42	11.86	16.84	14.52	12.02	9.31
	6	195	155	133	110	85	112	97	81	63
	7	188	150	129	107	82	107	93	77	60
	8	180	145	124	103	80	100	87	73	57
	9	172	139	120	99	77	94	82	69	54
	10	164	133	114	95	73	87	76	64	51
	11	155	126	109	90	70	79	70	59	47
	12	146	119	103	86	67	71	63	54	43
	13	136	112	97	81	63	63	56	48	39
	14	126	104	91	76	59	54	49	42	34
	15	115	96	84	70	55		43	37	30
	16	104	88	77	65	51				26
	17	93	79	70	59	47				23
	18	83	71	62	53	43				21
	19				48	38				19
	20					34				17
	22					28				14
	24					24				12
	26					20				
	28					18				
	30					15				
	32					13				

$F_y = 46$ ksi — Effective length in feet KL with respect to radius of gyration

Properties										
Area A (in.²)		8.14	6.45	5.52	4.54	3.49	4.95	4.27	3.54	2.74
I (in.⁴)		25.7	22.0	19.5	16.6	13.2	10.2	9.23	8.00	6.47
r (in.)		1.78	1.85	1.88	1.91	1.95	1.44	1.47	1.50	1.54
B { Bending factor		.792	.733	.708	.684	.661	.971	.925	.885	.847
a { Multiply values by 10⁶		3.84	3.29	2.91	2.47	1.98	1.53	1.37	1.19	.968

Heavy line indicates $Kl/r = 120$.
Values omitted are same as for $F_y = 36$ ksi; values for sections not listed in Table IV omitted for $Kl/r > 200$.

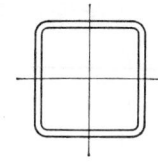

COLUMNS
Square structural tubing
Allowable concentric loads in kips
TABLE V

$F_y = 46$ ksi

$F_y = 46$ ksi

Nominal Size		$3\frac{1}{2} \times 3\frac{1}{2}$		3×3	
Wall Thickness		$\frac{1}{4}$	$\frac{3}{16}$	$\frac{1}{4}$	$\frac{3}{16}$
Weight per Foot		10.50	8.14	8.80	6.86
Effective length in feet KL with respect to radius of gyration	2	81	63	67	52
	3	78	61	64	50
	4	75	59	61	48
	5	72	56	57	45
	6	68	53	53	42
	7	64	50	48	38
	8	59	47	44	35
	9	55	43	38	31
	10	49	39	32	27
	11	44	35	27	22
	12	38	31	23	19
	13	33	26	19	16
	14	28	23	17	14
	15	24	20	14	12
	16	21	17	13	10
	17	19	15	11	9
	18	17	14	10	8
	19	15	12		
	20	14	11		
	22		9		
Properties					
Area A (in.²)		3.09	2.39	2.59	2.02
I (in.⁴)		5.29	4.29	3.16	2.60
r (in.)		1.31	1.34	1.10	1.13
B { Bending factor		1.02	.975	1.23	1.17
a { Multiply values by 10⁶		.790	.639	.467	.384

Heavy line indicates $Kl/r = 120$. Values omitted for $Kl/r > 200$.

$F_y = 46$ ksi

COLUMNS
Rectangular structural tubing
Allowable concentric loads in kips
TABLE V

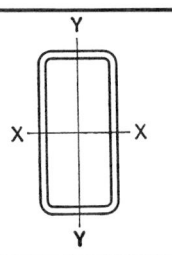

Nominal Size		12 × 8		12 × 6		10 × 8		
Wall Thickness		½	⅜	½	⅜	½	⅜	5/16
Weight per Foot		60.95	†47.03	54.15	†41.93	54.15	41.93	†35.49
	6	463	358	400	311	410	318	269
	7	456	353	391	304	404	313	265
	8	449	347	382	297	398	308	261
	9	442	342	372	290	391	303	257
	10	434	336	362	282	384	298	252
	11	426	330	351	274	376	292	248
	12	417	323	339	266	368	286	243
	13	409	317	327	257	360	280	238
	14	399	310	315	247	352	274	232
	15	390	303	302	238	343	267	227
	16	380	295	288	228	334	260	221
	17	370	288	274	218	324	253	216
	18	359	280	260	207	315	246	210
	19	349	272	245	196	305	239	203
	20	338	263	229	184	295	231	197
	22	314	246	197	160	273	215	184
	24	290	228	165	135	251	198	170
	26	264	209			227	180	155
	28	237	188			202	161	139
	30	209	167			176	142	123
	32	183	147					108
	34	162	130					
	36	145	116					
	38	130	104					
	40	117	94					

(Left side vertical label: Effective length in feet KL with respect to least radius of gyration)

(Left margin vertical label: $F_y = 46$ ksi)

Properties								
Area A (in.²)		17.9	13.8	15.9	12.3	15.9	12.3	10.4
I_x (in.⁴)		337	270	271	220	215	174	150
I_y (in.⁴)		181	145	92.0	75.0	153	123	107
Ratio r_x/r_y		1.36	1.36	1.72	1.71	1.18	1.19	1.18
r_y (in.)		3.18	3.24	2.40	2.47	3.10	3.16	3.20
B_x } Bending		.319	.307	.352	.335	.370	.353	.347
B_y } factors		.396	.381	.519	.492	.416	.400	.389
a_x (Multiply		50.2	40.2	40.4	32.6	31.9	25.8	22.3
a_y } values by 10⁶		27.0	21.6	13.6	11.2	22.8	18.3	15.9

Heavy line indicates $Kl/r = 120$. Values omitted are same as for $F_y = 36$ ksi.
† Flange is non-compact for weak axis bending; see discussion preceding column load tables.

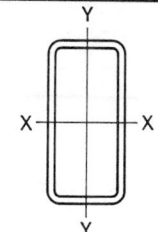

COLUMNS
Rectangular structural tubing
Allowable concentric loads in kips
TABLE V

$F_y = 46$ ksi

$F_y = 46$ ksi

Nominal Size		10 × 6			8 × 6			
Wall Thickness		½	⅜	⁵⁄₁₆	½	⅜	⁵⁄₁₆	¼
Weight per Foot		47.35	36.83	†31.24	40.55	31.73	26.99	†22.04
Effective length in feet KL with respect to least radius of gyration	6	349	272	231	297	234	199	163
	7	341	266	226	290	228	195	159
	8	333	260	221	282	223	190	155
	9	324	253	216	274	216	185	151
	10	314	246	210	265	210	180	147
	11	304	239	204	257	203	174	143
	12	294	231	197	247	196	168	138
	13	283	223	191	237	189	162	133
	14	272	214	184	227	182	156	128
	15	260	206	176	217	174	150	123
	16	248	197	169	206	165	143	118
	17	235	187	161	194	157	136	112
	18	222	177	153	183	148	128	106
	19	209	167	145	170	139	121	100
	20	195	157	136	158	130	113	94
	22	165	135	118	131	109	96	81
	24	139	113	99			81	

Properties

Area A (in.²)		13.9	10.8	9.19	11.9	9.33	7.94	6.48
I_x (in.⁴)		170	139	120	96.2	79.7	69.7	58.4
I_y (in.⁴)		76.9	63.1	55.0	61.7	51.2	44.8	37.6
Ratio r_x/r_y		1.49	1.49	1.48	1.25	1.25	1.24	1.24
r_y (in.)		2.35	2.41	2.45	2.27	2.34	2.38	2.41
B_x \ Bending		.409	.388	.383	.495	.468	.456	.444
B_y / factors		.542	.513	.501	.579	.547	.532	.517
a_x \ Multiply		25.2	20.6	17.9	14.3	11.9	10.4	8.69
a_y / values by 10⁶		11.4	9.35	8.22	9.14	7.61	6.70	5.61

Heavy line indicates $Kl/r = 120$. Values omitted are same as for $F_y = 36$ ksi.
†Flange is non-compact for weak axis bending; see discussion preceding column load tables.

COLUMNS
Rectangular structural tubing
Allowable concentric loads in kips
TABLE V

$F_y = 46$ ksi

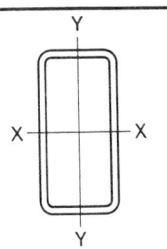

Nominal Size		8 × 4				7 × 5				
Wall Thickness		½	⅜	⁵⁄₁₆	¼	½	⅜	⁵⁄₁₆	¼	³⁄₁₆
Weight per Foot		34.48	27.04	23.02	†18.82	34.48	27.04	23.02	18.82	†14.41
	6	233	185	159	130	245	193	165	135	104
	7	222	177	152	125	237	187	160	131	101
	8	211	169	145	119	229	181	155	127	98
	9	199	160	137	113	220	174	149	123	95
	10	185	150	129	107	210	167	143	118	91
	11	172	140	121	100	200	159	137	113	87
	12	157	129	112	93	189	152	130	108	83
	13	141	117	102	86	178	143	123	102	79
	14	125	105	92	78	167	135	116	96	75
	15	109	93	82	69	154	126	109	90	71
	16			72	61	142	116	101	84	66
	17					128	106	93	77	61
	18					115	96	84	71	56
	19					103	86	75	64	51
	20						78			46
	22									38
	24									32
	26									27
	28									23
	30									20
	32									18
	34									16

Effective length in feet KL with respect to least radius of gyration

Properties

	½	⅜	⁵⁄₁₆	¼	½	⅜	⁵⁄₁₆	¼	³⁄₁₆
Area A (in.²)	10.1	7.95	6.77	5.54	10.1	7.95	6.77	5.54	4.24
I_x (in.⁴)	71.6	59.9	52.6	44.2	60.8	50.7	44.4	37.4	29.4
I_y (in.⁴)	23.7	20.1	17.7	15.0	35.9	30.0	26.4	22.3	17.6
Ratio r_x/r_y	1.74	1.72	1.72	1.72	1.30	1.30	1.30	1.30	1.29
r_y (in.)	1.53	1.59	1.62	1.65	1.88	1.94	1.97	2.00	2.04
B_x ⎰ Bending	.564	.531	.515	.501	.581	.549	.534	.518	.505
B_y ⎱ factors	.852	.791	.765	.739	.703	.663	.641	.621	.602
a_x ⎰ Multiply	10.6	8.89	7.85	6.61	9.03	7.52	6.61	5.58	4.37
a_y ⎱ values by 10⁶	3.52	2.99	2.65	2.25	5.32	4.46	3.91	3.30	2.63

Heavy line indicates $Kl/r = 120$.
Values omitted are same as for $F_y = 36$ ksi; values for sections not listed in Table IV omitted for $Kl/r > 200$.
† Flange is non-compact for weak axis bending; see discussion preceding column load tables.

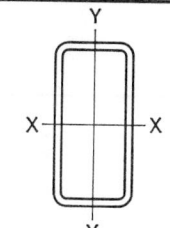

COLUMNS
Rectangular structural tubing
Allowable concentric loads in kips
TABLE V

$F_y = 46$ ksi

$F_y = 46$ ksi (with respect to least radius of gyration — Effective length in feet KL)

Nominal Size		6 × 4					6 × 3		
Wall Thickness	½	⅜	⁵⁄₁₆	¼	³⁄₁₆	⅜	⁵⁄₁₆	¼	³⁄₁₆
Weight per Foot	27.68	21.94	18.77	15.42	†11.86	19.39	16.65	13.72	†10.58
2	215	171	146	121	93	148	128	106	81
3	209	166	143	117	90	142	123	102	78
4	202	161	138	114	88	135	117	97	75
5	194	155	133	110	85	128	111	92	71
6	186	149	128	106	82	119	104	86	67
7	177	142	122	101	78	110	96	80	63
8	167	135	116	96	75	100	87	74	58
9	156	127	110	91	71	89	79	66	52
10	145	118	103	86	67	77	69	59	47
11	133	110	95	80	62	65	58	51	41
12	120	100	88	74	58			43	34
13	107	90	79	67	53				29
14	93	80	71	60	48				25
15		70	62	53	42				22
16					37				19
17					33				17
18					29				15
19					26				14
20					24				12
22					20				
24					16				
26					14				

Properties

Area A (in.²)	8.14	6.45	5.52	4.54	3.49	5.70	4.90	4.04	3.11
I_x (in.⁴)	33.4	28.6	25.4	21.6	17.2	22.7	20.3	17.4	14.0
I_y (in.⁴)	17.6	15.2	13.5	11.5	9.20	7.51	6.79	5.88	4.76
Ratio r_x/r_y	1.37	1.38	1.37	1.37	1.37	1.73	1.73	1.72	1.71
r_y (in.)	1.47	1.53	1.56	1.59	1.62	1.15	1.18	1.21	1.24
B_x ⎰ Bending	.731	.677	.652	.631	.609	.753	.724	.697	.666
B_y ⎱ factors	.925	.849	.818	.790	.759	1.14	1.08	1.03	.980
u_x ⎰ Multiply	4.95	4.28	3.77	3.21	2.56	3.36	3.04	2.60	2.08
u_y ⎱ values by 10⁶	2.62	2.25	2.00	1.71	1.36	1.12	1.02	.881	.713

Heavy line indicates $Kl/r = 120$.

Values omitted are same as for $F_y = 36$ ksi; values for sections not listed in Table IV omitted for $Kl/r > 200$.

† Flange is non-compact for weak axis bending; see discussion preceding column load tables.

AMERICAN INSTITUTE OF STEEL CONSTRUCTION

COLUMNS
Rectangular structural tubing
Allowable concentric loads in kips

TABLE V

$F_y = 46$ ksi

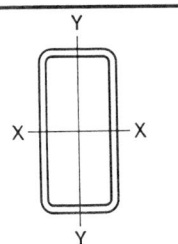

Nominal Size	5 × 3				4 × 3		4 × 2		3 × 2	
Wall Thickness	⅜	⁵⁄₁₆	¼	³⁄₁₆	¼	³⁄₁₆	¼	³⁄₁₆	¼	³⁄₁₆
Weight per Foot	16.84	14.52	12.02	9.31	10.50	8.14	8.80	6.86	7.10	5.59
2	129	111	92	72	80	62	65	51	52	41
3	123	107	89	69	77	60	60	47	48	38
4	117	101	85	66	73	57	54	43	43	34
5	110	96	80	62	69	54	48	38	37	30
6	102	89	75	59	65	51	41	33	31	26
7	94	82	69	54	60	47	32	27	24	21
8	85	75	63	50	54	43	25	21	19	16
9	75	67	57	45	48	38	20	16	15	12
10	64	58	50	40	42	34	16	13	12	10
11	53	48	42	34	35	29	13	11	10	8
12				29	29	24	11	9	8	7
13				25	25	20		8		
14				21	22	18				
15				18	19	15				
16				16	17	13				
17				14	15	12				
18				13	13	11				
19				12	12	10				
20				10						

Effective length in feet KL with respect to least radius of gyration

Properties

Area A (in.²)	4.95	4.27	3.54	2.74	3.09	2.39	2.59	2.02	2.09	1.64
I_x (in.⁴)	14.0	12.6	11.0	8.87	6.45	5.23	4.69	3.87	2.21	1.86
I_y (in.⁴)	6.21	5.65	4.93	4.02	4.10	3.34	1.54	1.29	1.15	.977
Ratio r_x/r_y	1.50	1.50	1.49	1.49	1.26	1.25	1.75	1.73	1.39	1.37
r_y (in.)	1.12	1.15	1.18	1.21	1.15	1.18	.770	.798	.742	.771
B_x ⎫ Bending	.884	.847	.805	.772	.958	.914	1.10	1.04	1.42	1.32
B_y ⎭ factors	1.20	1.13	1.08	1.02	1.13	1.07	1.68	1.57	1.82	1.68
a_x ⎱ Multiply	2.08	1.88	1.63	1.32	.968	.780	.703	.573	.330	.275
a_y ⎰ values by 10⁶	.925	.841	.734	.598	.609	.496	.229	.192	.171	.145

Heavy line indicates $Kl/r = 120$.
Values omitted are same as for $F_y = 36$ ksi; values for sections not listed in Table IV omitted for $Kl/r > 200$.

Notes

COLUMNS
Double-Angles
TABLES VI AND VII

In designing members fabricated of two angles connected to opposite faces of a gusset plate, Section 1.15.3 of the AISC Specification states that eccentricity between the gage lines and gravity axis **may** be neglected. In the following tables, eccentricity is neglected.

Tabulated loads are based on the assumption that intermittent fillers have been provided according to Section 1.18.2.4 of the AISC Specification.

Angle sizes tabulated do not exceed width-thickness ratios stipulated in Specification Section 1.9.1.2.

Allowable concentric loads in the following tables are for primary members opposite the effective length in feet (KL) with respect to both major and minor axes in accordance with Section 1.5.1.3 of the Specification. Discussion under Section 1.8 of the Specification Commentary points out that, for trusses, it is usual practice to take K equal to 1.0. Each angle size is tabulated, with respect to the X-X and Y-Y axes, for a different set of lengths than its neighbor in order:

1. To locate more precisely the length at which the Kl/r ratio equals 120.
2. To facilitate accurate interpolation for lengths not shown.

Two strengths are covered, $F_y = 36$ ksi in Table VI and $F_y = 50$ ksi in Table VII.

Double angles are often used as struts for bracing and secondary members. When Kl/r exceeds 120 for such members, the allowable load may be increased as illustrated in the discussion of secondary members, see "Columns, General Notes". For this case, K is taken as unity.

The tabulated loads for double angles referred to the Y-Y axis assume gusset plates $\frac{3}{8}$ in. thick. These values are conservative when thicker gussets are used. Example 6 illustrates a method for determining the allowable load when a thicker gusset plate is used.

For discussion of effective length, range of Kl/r, secondary members, sample problems, etc., see "Columns, General Notes".

EXAMPLE 6

Given: Using $F_y = 36$ ksi steel, determine the maximum allowable concentric load with respect to Y-Y axis on a double angle member of $8 \times 8 \times 1$ angles with an effective length equal to 12 ft., and connected to a $\frac{3}{4}$ in. thick gusset plate.

Solution:

r_y = 3.53 in. (from Table VI for 2 L 8 $\times$ 8 $\times$ 1 with $\frac{3}{8}$ in. plate).
r_y' = 3.67 in. (from Table of Two Equal Angles, Properties, 2 L 8 $\times$ 8 $\times$ 1 with $\frac{3}{4}$ in. plate).

$$\frac{r_y}{r_y'} = \frac{3.53}{3.67} = 0.962$$

Equivalent Length = 0.962 × 12 ft. = 11.5 ft.

Enter Table VI for 2 L 8 × 8 × 1 with reference to Y-Y axis for effective lengths between 10 and 15 ft., read 590 and 548 kips, respectively.

$$\text{Equivalent allowable load} = 590 - \left[(590 - 548) \times \frac{11.5 - 10}{15 - 10} \right]$$
$$= \textbf{577 kips.}$$

SINGLE-ANGLE STRUTS

Allowable loads on single angle struts are not tabulated in this Manual because it is virtually impossible to load such struts concentrically. In theory, concentric loading could be accomplished by milling the ends of an angle and loading it through bearing plates. However, in practice, the actual eccentricity of loading is relatively large; and, its neglect in design may lead to a dangerously underdesigned member.

An approximate procedure for determining the allowable load on a single angle strut is to compute the bending stress from the actual eccentricity as scaled from a sketch on which the principal axes Z-Z and W-W are drawn. Information on determining the properties of a single-angle with respect to these axes is given in Properties of Geometric Sections, Part 6 of this Manual. The angle of the Z-Z axis with respect to the Y-Y axis, and the value for r_z may be found in Tables of Properties of Angles.

The design of a single angle strut must meet the provisions of Section 1.6.1 of the AISC Specification. When bending occurs about both principal axes and Formula (1.6-1a) is critical, Formula (1.6-1a) may be expressed as follows:

$$\frac{f_a}{F_a} + \frac{M_w}{S_w F_b \left(1 - \dfrac{f_a}{F_{ew}{'}} \right)} + \frac{M_z}{S_z F_b \left(1 - \dfrac{f_a}{F_{ez}{'}} \right)} \leq 1.0$$

in which the allowable axial stress F_a is with respect to the Z-Z axis, and the bending components are with respect to the W-W and Z-Z axes.

Complete analysis of the torsional effects caused by twist buckling of single angle compression members is beyond the scope of this Manual. If a more accurate theoretical analysis is required, refer to appropriate technical publications.

$F_y = 36$ ksi

COLUMNS
Double angles

Allowable concentric loads in kips

TABLE VI

Equal legs

⅜ in. back to back of angles

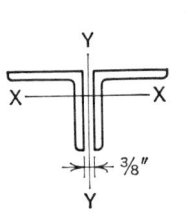

Properties of 2 Angles — ⅜ in. Back to Back

8 × 8

Thickness	1⅛	1	⅞	¾	⅝
Weight per Foot	113.8	102.0	90.0	77.8	65.4

X - X AXIS (Effective length KL in feet)

KL	113.8	102.0	90.0	77.8	65.4
0	724	648	572	495	415
10	616	553	489	423	355
14	552	496	439	381	320
18	479	431	382	332	280
22	395	357	317	277	234
23	373	337	300	262	222
24	349	317	282	247	209
25	325	296	263	231	196
28	260	236	210	185	157
32	199	181	161	141	121
36	157	143	127	112	95
40	127	116	103	91	77
41				86	73

Y - Y AXIS

KL	113.8	102.0	90.0	77.8	65.4
0	724	648	572	495	415
10	659	590	520	449	376
15	613	548	483	417	349
20	559	499	440	379	317
25	497	444	390	336	281
30	429	382	335	288	240
34	368	327	287	246	204
35	353	313	274	234	195
40	274	242	212	181	150
45	216	191	167	143	118
50	175	155	135	116	96
55	145	128	112	96	79
56	140	124	108	92	76
57	135	119	104	89	74
58	130	115	101	86	
59	126				

Properties	113.8	102.0	90.0	77.8	65.4
Area A (in.²)	33.5	30.0	26.5	22.9	19.2
r_x (in.)	2.42	2.44	2.45	2.47	2.49
r_y (in.)	3.55	3.53	3.51	3.49	3.47

6 × 6

Thickness	1	⅞	¾	⅝	9/16	½
Weight per Foot	74.8	66.2	57.4	48.4	43.8	39.2

X - X AXIS

KL	74.8	66.2	57.4	48.4	43.8	39.2
0	475	421	365	307	279	248
8	397	353	306	258	235	209
10	369	328	285	240	219	195
12	338	300	262	221	201	180
14	304	270	236	199	182	163
16	267	238	209	176	161	145
18	226	202	179	151	139	125
22	153	137	121	103	95	85
26	109	98	87	74	68	61
30	82	74	65	55	51	46
31						43

Y - Y AXIS

KL	74.8	66.2	57.4	48.4	43.8	39.2
0	475	421	365	307	279	248
10	415	367	318	267	242	216
12	398	352	304	255	232	206
14	380	336	290	243	221	196
16	361	318	275	230	209	186
18	340	299	258	216	196	174
20	318	280	241	201	182	162
22	295	259	223	186	168	149
24	270	236	203	169	153	136
26	244	213	182	151	137	121
27	230	201	172	142	128	114
30	189	164	140	116	104	92
34	147	128	109	90	81	72
38	118	102	87	72	65	58
42	96	84	71	59	53	47
43	92	80	68	56	51	45
44	88	76	65	54	49	43
45	84	73				

Properties	74.8	66.2	57.4	48.4	43.8	39.2
Area A (in.²)	22.0	19.5	16.9	14.2	12.9	11.5
r_x (in.)	1.80	1.81	1.83	1.84	1.85	1.8
r_y (in.)	2.73	2.70	2.68	2.66	2.65	2.6

Heavy line indicates $Kl/r = 120$. Values omitted for $Kl/r > 200$.

COLUMNS
Double angles

Allowable concentric loads in kips
TABLE VI
Equal legs
3/8 in. back to back of angles

$F_y = 36$ ksi

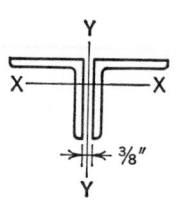

$F_y = 36$ ksi with respect to indicated axis. Effective length in feet KL with respect to indicated axis.

5 × 5 — X-X AXIS

Thickness	7/8	3/4	5/8	1/2	7/16
Weight per Foot	54.4	47.2	40.0	32.4	28.6
0	346	300	253	205	181
6	296	258	217	177	156
8	272	237	200	163	144
10	245	214	181	148	131
12	214	188	160	131	116
14	181	160	136	112	100
15	163	145	123	102	91
18	114	101	87	72	64
21	84	75	64	53	47
24	64	57	49	41	36
25		53	45	37	33

5 × 5 — Y-Y AXIS

Thickness	7/8	3/4	5/8	1/2	7/16
0	346	300	253	205	181
6	318	276	232	188	166
8	305	264	222	180	159
10	291	252	211	171	151
12	275	238	200	162	142
14	258	223	187	151	133
16	239	207	173	140	123
18	220	190	158	128	112
20	199	171	142	115	100
22	176	151	126	101	88
23	165	141	117	93	81
25	140	120	99	79	69
28	112	96	79	63	55
31	91	78	64	51	45
34	76	65	54	43	37
37	64	55	45	36	32
38	61	52			

4 × 4 — X-X AXIS

Thickness	3/4	5/8	1/2	7/16	3/8	5/16
Weight per Foot	37.0	31.4	25.6	22.6	19.6	16.4
0	235	199	162	143	124	104
4	209	177	144	128	110	93
6	189	161	131	116	100	85
8	167	142	116	103	89	75
10	140	120	99	88	76	64
11	126	108	89	80	69	58
12	110	95	79	71	61	52
14	82	70	59	53	46	39
16	63	54	45	41	35	30
18	49	42	36	32	28	24
19	44	38	32	29	25	21
20		34	29	26	22	19

4 × 4 — Y-Y AXIS

Thickness	3/4	5/8	1/2	7/16	3/8	5/16
0	235	199	162	143	124	104
6	211	178	144	127	110	92
8	199	168	136	120	103	87
10	186	157	127	112	96	81
12	171	144	116	102	88	74
14	156	131	105	92	79	66
15	147	123	99	87	75	62
16	139	116	93	81	70	58
17	129	108	86	75	65	54
18	120	100	79	69	59	49
20	100	83	65	57	49	40
22	83	68	54	47	40	33
24	69	57	45	39	34	28
26	59	49	39	34	29	24
28	51	42	33	29	25	21
29	48	39	31	27	23	19
30	44	37	29	25	22	

Properties of 2 Angles—3/8 in. Back to Back

	5 × 5					4 × 4					
Area A (in.²)	16.0	13.9	11.7	9.50	8.37	10.9	9.22	7.50	6.62	5.72	4.80
r_x (in.)	1.49	1.51	1.52	1.54	1.55	1.19	1.20	1.22	1.23	1.23	1.24
r_y (in.)	2.30	2.28	2.26	2.24	2.23	1.88	1.86	1.83	1.82	1.81	1.80

Heavy line indicates $Kl/r = 120$. Values omitted for $Kl/r > 200$.

$F_y = 36$ ksi

COLUMNS
Double angles

Allowable concentric loads in kips
TABLE VI
Equal legs
3⁄8 in. back to back of angles

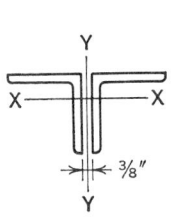

$F_y = 36$ ksi
Effective length in feet KL with respect to indicated axis

Size: 3½ × 3½

Axis	KL	½ (22.2)	7⁄16 (19.6)	3⁄8 (17.0)	5⁄16 (14.4)
X-X	0	140	124	107	90
X-X	2	133	117	102	86
X-X	4	122	108	93	79
X-X	6	108	96	83	70
X-X	8	92	82	71	60
X-X	10	73	65	57	48
X-X	12	53	47	41	35
X-X	14	39	35	30	26
X-X	16	30	27	23	20
X-X	17	26	24	20	17
X-X	18				16
Y-Y	0	140	124	107	90
Y-Y	6	123	108	93	79
Y-Y	8	114	100	87	73
Y-Y	10	104	92	79	66
Y-Y	12	94	82	71	59
Y-Y	14	82	72	62	52
Y-Y	16	69	60	52	43
Y-Y	18	55	48	41	34
Y-Y	20	45	39	33	28
Y-Y	22	37	32	28	23
Y-Y	24	31	27	23	19
Y-Y	26	26	23	20	16
Y-Y	27	25	21		

Size: 3 × 3

Axis	KL	½ (18.8)	7⁄16 (16.6)	3⁄8 (14.4)	5⁄16 (12.2)	¼ (9.8)
X-X	0	119	105	91	77	62
X-X	2	111	98	85	72	58
X-X	4	99	88	76	64	52
X-X	5	92	82	71	60	49
X-X	6	84	75	65	55	45
X-X	7	76	68	59	50	41
X-X	8	66	59	52	44	36
X-X	9	56	51	44	38	31
X-X	10	46	41	36	31	26
X-X	12	32	29	25	22	18
X-X	14	23	21	19	16	13
X-X	15		18	16	14	11
Y-Y	0	119	105	91	77	62
Y-Y	2	114	101	88	74	60
Y-Y	4	108	96	83	70	56
Y-Y	6	101	89	77	65	52
Y-Y	8	92	81	70	59	48
Y-Y	9	87	77	66	56	45
Y-Y	10	82	72	62	52	42
Y-Y	11	77	67	58	49	39
Y-Y	12	71	62	54	45	36
Y-Y	13	65	57	49	41	33
Y-Y	14	59	51	44	37	29
Y-Y	15	52	45	39	32	26
Y-Y	16	46	40	34	28	23
Y-Y	18	36	31	27	22	18
Y-Y	20	29	25	22	18	14
Y-Y	22	24	21	18	15	12
Y-Y	23	22	19	16	14	11

Properties of 2 Angles—3⁄8 in. Back to Back

	3½ × 3½ ½	7⁄16	3⁄8	5⁄16	3 × 3 ½	7⁄16	3⁄8	5⁄16	¼
Area A (in.²)	6.50	5.74	4.97	4.18	5.50	4.87	4.22	3.55	2.88
r_x (in.)	1.06	1.07	1.07	1.08	.898	.905	.913	.922	.93⏝
r_y (in.)	1.63	1.62	1.61	1.60	1.43	1.42	1.41	1.40	1.39

Heavy line indicates $Kl/r = 120$. Values omitted for $Kl/r > 200$.

F_y = 36 ksi

COLUMNS

Double angles

Allowable concentric loads in kips

TABLE VI

Equal legs

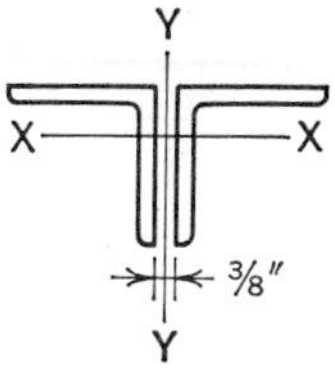

⅜ in. back to back of angles

Effective length in feet KL with respect to indicated axis

ize		2½ × 2½			
hickness		½	⅜	5/16	¼
eight per Foot		15.4	11.8	10.0	8.2
X-X AXIS	0	97	75	63	51
	2	89	69	58	47
	3	83	64	54	44
	4	76	59	50	41
	5	68	53	45	37
	6	60	47	40	33
	7	50	40	34	28
	8	40	32	27	23
	9	31	25	22	18
	10	25	20	18	15
	11	21	17	15	12
	12	18	14	12	10
Y-Y AXIS	0	97	75	63	51
	2	93	72	60	49
	4	87	67	56	46
	6	79	61	51	41
	7	75	57	48	39
	8	70	54	45	36
	9	65	50	42	34
	10	60	45	38	31
	11	55	41	34	27
	12	49	36	30	24
	13	42	31	26	21
	14	37	27	22	18
	15	32	23	19	16
	17	25	18	15	12
	19	20	15	12	10
	20	18	13	11	

		2 × 2			
		⅜	5/16	¼	3/16
		9.4	7.84	6.38	4.88
X-X AXIS	0	59	50	41	31
	2	52	44	36	28
	3	47	40	33	25
	4	42	35	29	22
	5	35	30	25	19
	6	27	24	20	15
	7	20	18	15	12
	8	16	13	11	9
	9	12	11	9	7
	10		9	7	6
Y-Y AXIS	0	59	50	41	31
	2	55	47	38	29
	4	50	43	35	26
	5	48	40	33	25
	6	44	37	30	23
	7	41	34	28	21
	8	37	31	25	19
	9	33	27	22	17
	10	28	24	19	14
	11	24	20	16	12
	12	20	17	13	10
	13	17	14	11	8
	14	15	12	10	7
	15	13	11	8	6
	16	11	9	7	6
	17				

		1¾ × 1¾	
		¼	3/16
		5.54	4.24
X-X AXIS	0	35	27
	2	31	23
	3	27	21
	4	23	18
	5	18	14
	6	13	10
	7	10	8
	8	7	6
	9		
Y-Y AXIS	0	35	27
	2	33	25
	4	29	22
	5	27	21
	6	25	19
	7	22	17
	8	19	15
	9	16	12
	10	13	10
	11	11	8
	12	9	7
	13	8	6
	14	7	5

Properties of 2 Angles—⅜ in. Back to Back

	2½ × 2½ ½	⅜	5/16	¼	2 × 2 ⅜	5/16	¼	3/16	1¾ × 1¾ ¼	3/16
rea A (in.²)	4.50	3.47	2.93	2.38	2.72	2.30	1.88	1.43	1.63	1.24
(in.)	.739	.753	.761	.769	.594	.601	.609	.617	.529	.537
(in.)	1.24	1.21	1.20	1.19	1.01	1.00	.989	.977	.890	.877

Heavy line indicates $Kl/r = 120$. Values omitted for $Kl/r > 200$.

$F_y = 36$ ksi

COLUMNS
Double angles
Allowable concentric loads in kips
TABLE VI
Equal legs

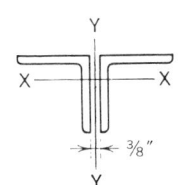

⅜ in. back to back of angles

Size	1½ × 1½				1¼ × 1¼				1 × 1		
Thickness	¼	3/16	⅛		¼	3/16	⅛		¼	3/16	1/…
Weight per Foot	4.38	3.60	2.46		3.84	2.96	2.02		2.98	2.32	1.

$F_y = 36$ ksi — Effective length in feet KL with respect to indicated axis

1½ × 1½ — X-X AXIS

KL	¼	3/16	⅛
0	30	23	16
2	25	19	13
3	21	16	11
4	17	13	9
5	12	9	6
6	8	6	4
7	6	5	3

1½ × 1½ — Y-Y AXIS

KL	¼	3/16	⅛
0	30	23	16
2	27	21	14
3	26	20	13
4	24	18	12
5	22	16	11
6	19	15	10
7	17	13	8
8	14	10	7
9	11	8	5
10	9	7	4
11	7	5	4
12	6	5	3
13	5		

1¼ × 1¼ — X-X AXIS

KL	¼	3/16	⅛
0	24	19	13
1	22	17	12
2	19	15	10
3	15	12	8
4	10	8	6
5	6	5	4
6	4	4	3

1¼ × 1¼ — Y-Y AXIS

KL	¼	3/16	⅛
0	24	19	13
2	22	17	12
3	21	16	11
4	19	14	10
5	17	13	8
6	14	11	7
7	12	9	6
8	9	7	4
9	7	5	3
10	6	4	3
11	5	3	2

1 × 1 — X-X AXIS

KL	¼	3/16	⅛
0	19	15	1…
1	17	13	
2	13	10	
3	8	7	
4	5	4	
5			

1 × 1 — Y-Y AXIS

KL	¼	3/16	⅛
0	19	15	1…
2	17	13	
3	15	12	
4	13	10	
5	11	9	
6	9	7	
7	7	5	
8	5	4	
9	4	3	
10	3		

Properties of 2 Angles—⅜ in. Back to Back

	¼	3/16	⅛		¼	3/16	⅛		¼	3/16	…
Area A (in.²)	1.38	1.05	.719		1.13	.867	.594		.875	.680	.
r_x (in.)	.449	.457	.465		.369	.377	.385		.290	.297	.
r_y (in.)	.793	.779	.766		.696	.682	.668		.601	.586	.

Heavy line indicates $Kl/r = 120$. Values omitted for $Kl/r > 200$.

COLUMNS

Double angles

$F_y = 36$ ksi

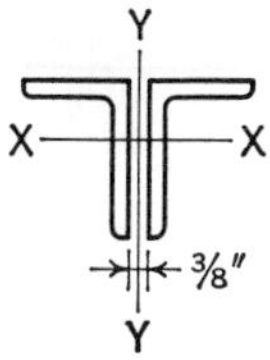

Allowable concentric loads in kips

TABLE VI

Unequal leg angles

Long legs 3/8 in. back to back of angles

ze			9 × 4		
hickness			1	7/8	3/4
'eight per Foot			81.6	72.2	62.6
Effective length in feet *KL* with respect to indicated axis	X-X AXIS	0	518	458	397
		10	456	403	351
		12	439	388	338
		14	420	372	324
		16	400	355	309
		18	379	336	293
		20	356	316	276
		22	332	295	258
		25	294	262	229
		28	253	226	198
		29	238	213	187
		32	196	176	155
		35	164	147	129
		38	139	125	110
		41	119	107	94
		44	104	93	82
		47	91	81	72
		48			69
	Y-Y AXIS	0	518	458	397
		6	448	394	341
		8	414	363	314
		10	375	328	283
		12	333	289	248
		14	285	246	210
		15	260	223	189
		18	185	157	133
		21	136	115	97
		24	104	88	75
		25	96	81	69

		8 × 6			
		1	7/8	3/4	5/8
		88.4	78.2	67.6	57.0
X-X AXIS	0	562	497	430	361
	10	481	426	370	310
	12	459	407	353	296
	15	421	374	325	273
	18	379	337	293	247
	21	333	297	259	218
	24	283	254	222	187
	25	266	238	209	176
	26	247	222	195	165
	29	199	179	157	133
	32	163	147	129	109
	35	136	123	108	91
	38	116	104	91	77
	41	99	89	79	66
	42			75	63
Y-Y AXIS	0	562	497	430	361
	10	483	426	368	308
	12	460	406	351	293
	15	423	373	322	269
	18	382	336	289	242
	21	337	296	254	212
	24	288	252	216	179
	25	271	236	202	167
	29	204	177	151	125
	33	157	137	117	96
	37	125	109	93	77
	40	107	93	79	66
	41	102	89	76	62
	42	97			

		8 × 4			
		1	7/8	3/4	5/8
		74.8	66.2	57.4	48.4
X-X AXIS	0	475	421	365	307
	10	408	362	314	265
	12	389	346	300	253
	14	369	328	285	240
	16	347	308	268	226
	18	324	288	251	212
	20	299	266	232	196
	22	272	242	212	179
	25	229	204	179	153
	26	214	191	168	143
	28	185	165	145	124
	30	161	144	127	108
	32	141	126	111	95
	34	125	112	99	84
	36	112	100	88	75
	39	95	85	75	64
	42	82	73	65	55
Y-Y AXIS	0	475	421	365	307
	6	414	365	315	264
	8	384	338	291	244
	10	351	308	264	221
	12	314	274	234	195
	14	273	237	201	166
	15	251	217	183	151
	16	229	196	164	135
	20	148	126	105	86
	24	103	88	73	60
	25	95	81	67	55
	26	87	75		

Properties of 2 Angles—3/8 in. Back to Back

	9 × 4, 1	7/8	3/4	8 × 6, 1	7/8	3/4	5/8	8 × 4, 1	7/8	3/4	5/8
rea *A* (in.²)	24.0	21.2	18.4	26.0	23.0	19.9	16.7	22.0	19.5	16.9	14.2
(in.)	2.84	2.86	2.88	2.49	2.51	2.53	2.54	2.52	2.53	2.55	2.57
(in.)	1.55	1.52	1.50	2.52	2.50	2.48	2.46	1.61	1.58	1.55	1.53

Heavy line indicates $Kl/r = 120$. Values omitted for $Kl/r > 200$.

COLUMNS
Double angles

Allowable concentric loads in kips
TABLE VI
Unequal leg angles

Long legs ⅜ in. back to back of angles

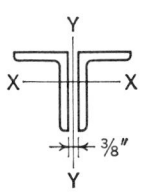

$F_y = 36$ ksi

$F_y = 36$ ksi — Effective length in feet KL with respect to indicated axis

Size	7 × 4					6 × 4						6×3½
Thickness	⅞	¾	⅝	⁹⁄₁₆		⅞	¾	⅝	⁹⁄₁₆	½		½
Weight per Foot	60.4	52.4	44.2	40.0		54.4	47.2	40.0	36.2	32.4		30.6

X-X AXIS

KL	⅞	¾	⅝	⁹⁄₁₆	KL	⅞	¾	⅝	⁹⁄₁₆	½	KL	½
0	382	333	281	253	0	363	300	253	229	205	0	194
8	334	291	246	222	8	306	254	214	194	174	8	165
10	318	277	234	211	10	285	237	200	181	163	10	155
12	299	261	221	199	12	263	219	185	168	151	12	143
14	279	244	207	186	14	238	198	168	153	137	14	130
16	257	225	191	172	16	211	177	150	136	123	16	117
18	234	205	175	157	18	182	153	131	118	107	18	102
20	209	184	157	141	19	166	140	120	109	99	19	94
22	182	161	138	124	20	151	127	110	99	90	20	86
24	154	137	117	106	22	125	105	90	82	74	22	71
26	131	116	100	90	24	105	88	76	69	62	24	60
28	113	100	86	78	26	89	75	65	59	53	26	51
30	99	87	75	68	28	77	65	56	51	46	28	44
33	82	72	62	56	30	67	57	49	44	40	30	38
36	69	61	52	47	31	63	53	46	41	37	32	34
37		57	49	44								

Y-Y AXIS

KL	⅞	¾	⅝	⁹⁄₁₆	KL	⅞	¾	⅝	⁹⁄₁₆	½	KL	½
					0	363	300	253	229	205	0	194
0	382	333	281	253	6	320	264	222	200	179	4	177
6	334	290	244	219	8	299	246	207	187	167	6	164
8	311	270	226	203	10	276	227	190	171	153	8	150
10	285	246	206	185	12	250	205	171	154	137	10	133
12	256	221	184	165	14	222	181	151	135	120	12	114
14	224	193	159	142	16	191	155	129	114	102	13	104
15	207	177	146	130	17	174	142	117	103	92	14	94
16	189	162	132	118	18	157	127	104	92	82	16	72
19	137	116	94	84	21	116	93	77	68	60	18	57
22	102	87	70	63	24	88	71	59	52	46	20	46
25	79	67	55	48	27	70	56	46	41	36	22	38
26	73	62	50	45	28	65	53				23	35
27	68	57										

Properties of 2 Angles—⅜ in. Back to Back

	⅞	¾	⅝	⁹⁄₁₆		⅞	¾	⅝	⁹⁄₁₆	½		½
Area A (in.²)	17.7	15.4	13.0	11.7		16.0	13.9	11.7	10.6	9.50		9.00
r_x (in.)	2.20	2.22	2.24	2.24		1.86	1.88	1.90	1.90	1.91		1.92
r_y (in.)	1.64	1.62	1.59	1.58		1.71	1.69	1.67	1.65	1.64		1.41

Heavy line indicates $Kl/r = 120$. Values omitted for $Kl/r > 200$.

COLUMNS
Double angles

$F_y = 36$ ksi

Allowable concentric loads in kips
TABLE VI
Unequal leg angles

Long legs ⅜ in. back to back of angles

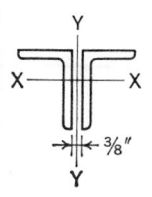

Effective length in feet KL with respect to indicated axis

Size 5 × 3½ — X-X AXIS

Thickness	¾	⅝	½	7/16
Weight per Foot	39.6	33.6	27.2	24.0
KL				
0	251	213	173	152
4	231	196	159	140
6	216	184	150	132
8	200	170	139	123
10	181	154	126	112
12	161	137	113	100
14	138	118	97	86
15	126	108	89	79
16	113	97	81	72
18	89	77	64	57
20	72	62	52	46
22	60	51	43	38
24	50	43	36	32
25	46	40	33	30
26		37	31	27

Size 5 × 3 — X-X AXIS

Thickness	½	7/16
Weight per Foot	25.6	22.6
KL		
0	162	143
2	157	138
4	149	132
6	141	124
8	130	115
10	119	105
12	106	94
14	92	82
15	84	75
16	76	68
18	61	54
20	49	44
22	41	36
24	34	31
26	29	26

Size 4 × 3½ — X-X AXIS

Thickness	⅝	½	7/16	⅜	5/16
Weight per Foot	29.4	23.8	21.2	18.2	15.4
KL					
0	186	151	133	115	97
2	177	144	128	110	93
4	165	135	119	103	87
6	151	123	109	94	79
8	133	109	97	84	71
10	113	93	83	72	61
12	91	75	67	59	50
14	68	56	50	44	38
16	52	43	38	34	29
18	41	34	30	27	23
20	33	27	25	22	18
21					17

Size 5 × 3½ — Y-Y AXIS

KL	¾	⅝	½	7/16
0	251	213	173	152
4	230	195	158	139
6	216	183	148	130
8	199	168	136	119
10	180	152	122	107
12	159	133	107	93
14	136	113	90	78
15	123	102	81	70
16	110	91	72	62
18	87	72	57	49
20	70	58	46	39
22	58	48	38	33
24	49	40	32	27
25	45	37		

Size 5 × 3 — Y-Y AXIS

KL	½	7/16
0	162	143
2	155	137
4	145	128
6	132	117
8	118	104
10	101	89
12	82	72
14	62	54
16	47	41
18	38	33
20	30	26

Size 4 × 3½ — Y-Y AXIS

KL	⅝	½	7/16	⅜	5/16
0	186	151	133	115	97
2	179	146	129	111	94
4	171	139	123	106	89
6	161	131	116	100	84
8	150	121	107	92	77
10	137	111	97	84	70
12	122	98	87	74	62
14	106	85	75	64	53
15	97	78	68	58	49
16	88	70	61	53	44
18	70	56	49	42	35
20	57	45	39	34	28
22	47	37	33	28	23
24	40	31	27	23	19
25	36	29	25	22	18
26	34	27	23	20	

Properties of 2 Angles—⅜ in. Back to Back

	5 × 3½				5 × 3		4 × 3½				
rea A (in.²)	11.6	9.84	8.00	7.05	7.50	6.62	8.59	7.00	6.18	5.34	4.49
(in.)	1.55	1.56	1.58	1.59	1.59	1.60	1.22	1.23	1.24	1.25	1.26
(in.)	1.53	1.51	1.49	1.47	1.25	1.24	1.60	1.58	1.57	1.56	1.55

Heavy line indicates $Kl/r = 120$. Values omitted for $Kl/r > 200$.

$F_y = 36$ ksi

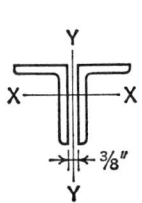

COLUMNS
Double angles

Allowable concentric loads in kips
TABLE VI
Unequal leg angles

Long legs ⅜ in. back to back of angles

$F_y = 36$ ksi

Effective length in feet KL with respect to indicated axis

X - X AXIS

Size	4 × 3						3½ × 3					3½ × 2½		
Thickness	⅝	½	⁷⁄₁₆	⅜	⁵⁄₁₆		½	⁷⁄₁₆	⅜	⁵⁄₁₆		½	⁷⁄₁₆	⅜
Weight per Ft.	27.2	22.2	19.6	17.0	14.4		20.4	18.2	15.8	13.2		18.8	16.6	14.4
0	172	140	124	107	90	0	130	114	99	84	0	119	105	91
2	164	134	119	103	86	2	123	108	94	79	2	113	100	86
4	154	126	111	96	81	4	113	100	87	73	4	104	92	80
6	140	115	101	88	74	6	100	89	77	65	6	93	82	71
8	124	102	90	78	66	8	85	76	66	56	8	79	70	61
10	106	88	77	67	57	10	68	61	54	46	10	64	57	50
12	85	71	63	55	47	11	59	53	46	40	11	56	49	43
14	64	54	47	42	36	12	49	45	39	34	12	47	42	37
16	49	41	36	32	27	14	36	33	29	25	14	35	31	27
18	39	33	29	25	22	16	28	25	22	19	16	26	23	21
20	31	26	23	20	17	17	25	22	20	17	17	23	21	18
21				19	16	18		20	17	15	18	21	19	16

Y - Y AXIS

Size	4 × 3						3½ × 3					3½ × 2½		
0	172	140	124	107	90	0	130	114	99	84	0	119	105	91
2	165	135	119	103	86	2	125	110	95	80	2	113	100	87
4	156	127	112	97	81	4	118	104	90	76	4	105	92	80
6	144	117	103	89	75	6	109	96	83	70	6	94	83	72
8	130	105	93	80	67	8	99	87	75	63	8	82	72	62
10	115	92	81	70	58	10	87	77	66	55	10	68	59	50
12	97	77	68	58	48	12	75	65	56	47	11	60	52	44
13	88	69	61	52	43	13	68	59	51	42	12	51	44	37
14	78	61	53	45	37	14	60	52	45	37	14	38	32	28
16	60	47	41	35	29	16	46	40	34	29	16	29	25	21
18	47	37	32	27	23	18	37	32	27	23	18	23	20	17
20	38	30	26	22	18	20	30	26	22	18				
21	35	27	24	20	17	22	24	21	18	15				
22	32	25	21			23	22							

Properties of 2 Angles—⅜ in. Back to Back

	4 × 3						3½ × 3					3½ × 2½		
Area A (in.²)	7.97	6.50	5.74	4.97	4.18		6.00	5.30	4.59	3.87		5.50	4.87	4.22
r_x (in.)	1.23	1.25	1.25	1.26	1.27		1.07	1.08	1.09	1.10		1.09	1.09	1.10
r_y (in.)	1.36	1.33	1.32	1.31	1.30		1.38	1.37	1.36	1.35		1.14	1.12	1.11

Heavy line indicates $Kl/r = 120$. Values omitted for $Kl/r > 200$.

COLUMNS
Double angles

$F_y = 36$ ksi

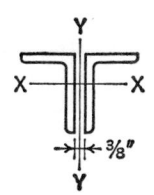

Allowable concentric loads in kips
TABLE VI
Unequal leg angles

Long legs ⅜ in. back to back of angles

X - X AXIS

Effective length in feet KL with respect to indicated axis

Size	3 × 2½						3 × 2						2½ × 2		
Thickness	½	7/16	⅜	5/16	¼		½	7/16	⅜	5/16	¼		⅜	5/16	¼
Weight per Ft.	17.0	15.2	13.2	11.2	9.0		15.4	13.6	11.8	10.0	8.2		10.6	9.0	7.2
0	108	96	83	70	57	0	97	86	75	63	51	0	67	57	46
2	101	90	78	66	53	2	91	81	70	59	48	2	61	52	42
4	91	80	70	59	48	3	87	77	67	57	46	3	58	49	40
5	84	75	65	55	45	4	82	73	63	54	44	4	53	45	37
6	77	69	60	51	41	5	76	68	59	50	41	5	48	41	34
7	70	62	54	46	38	6	70	62	55	46	38	6	42	36	30
8	62	55	48	41	34	7	63	57	50	42	34	7	36	31	26
9	53	47	41	35	29	8	56	50	44	38	31	8	30	26	21
10	43	39	34	29	24	9	48	43	38	33	27	9	23	20	17
11	36	32	28	24	20	10	40	36	32	27	23	10	19	16	14
12	30	27	24	20	17	11	33	30	26	23	19	11	16	14	11
14	22	20	17	15	12	12	28	25	22	19	16	12	13	11	9
15	19	17	15	13	11	15	18	16	14	12	10	13			8
						16									

Y - Y AXIS

Size	3 × 2½						3 × 2						2½ × 2		
	½	7/16	⅜	5/16	¼		½	7/16	⅜	5/16	¼		⅜	5/16	¼
0	108	96	83	70	57	0	97	86	75	63	51	0	67	57	46
2	103	91	79	67	54	2	91	81	70	59	48	2	63	53	43
4	96	85	73	62	50	3	87	77	67	56	46	3	60	51	41
5	91	81	70	59	48	4	82	73	63	53	43	4	57	48	39
6	87	77	66	56	45	5	77	68	59	49	40	5	53	45	36
7	82	72	62	52	42	6	71	62	54	45	36	6	49	41	33
8	76	67	58	48	39	7	65	57	49	41	33	7	45	38	30
9	70	62	53	44	36	8	57	50	43	36	28	8	40	34	27
10	64	56	48	40	32	9	50	43	37	30	24	9	35	29	23
11	57	50	43	36	28	10	42	36	30	25	20	10	30	24	19
12	50	44	37	31	24	11	34	30	25	20	16	11	24	20	16
13	43	37	32	26	21	12	29	25	21	17	14	12	21	17	13
14	37	32	27	23	18	13	25	21	18	15	12	13	18	14	11
16	28	25	21	17	14	14	21	18	15	13	10	14	15	12	10
18	22	19	17	14	11	15	19	16	13	11		15	13	11	9
19	20	17	15	12								16	12		

Properties of 2 Angles—⅜ in. Back to Back

	3 × 2½						3 × 2						2½ × 2		
Area A (in.²)	5.00	4.43	3.84	3.24	2.63		4.50	3.99	3.47	2.93	2.38		3.09	2.62	2.13
(in.)	.913	.920	.928	.937	.945		.924	.932	.940	.948	.957		.768	.776	.784
(in.)	1.18	1.17	1.16	1.15	1.13		.945	.931	.917	.903	.891		.961	.948	.935

Heavy line indicates $Kl/r = 120$. Values omitted for $Kl/r > 200$.

$F_y = 36$ ksi

COLUMNS
Double angles

Allowable concentric loads in kips
TABLE VI
Unequal leg angles

Long legs ⅜ in. back to back of angles

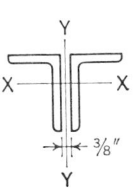

Size	2½ × 1½			2 × 1½			2 × 1¼			1¾ × 1	
Thickness	5⁄16	¼		¼	3⁄16		¼	3⁄16		¼	3...
Weight per Foot	7.84	6.38		5.54	4.24		5.10	3.92		4.68	3...

Effective length in feet KL with respect to indicated axis

X-X AXIS

2½ × 1½

KL	5⁄16	¼
0	50	41
2	46	37
3	43	35
4	40	33
5	36	30
6	32	27
7	28	23
8	23	19
9	18	15
10	15	12
11	12	10
12	10	9
13	9	7

2 × 1½

KL	¼	3⁄16
0	35	27
2	31	24
3	29	22
4	26	20
5	22	17
6	18	14
7	13	10
8	10	8
9	8	6
10	7	5

2 × 1¼

KL	¼	3⁄16
0	32	25
2	29	22
3	27	20
4	24	18
5	20	16
6	17	13
7	13	10
8	10	8
9	8	6
10	6	5

1¾ × 1

KL	¼
0	30
2	26
3	23
4	20
5	16
6	12
7	9
8	7
9	5

Y-Y AXIS

2½ × 1½

KL	5⁄16	¼
0	50	41
2	45	37
3	42	34
4	38	31
5	34	28
6	30	24
7	24	19
8	19	15
9	15	12
10	12	10
11	10	8

2 × 1½

KL	¼	3⁄16
0	35	27
2	32	24
3	30	23
4	28	21
5	25	19
6	22	16
7	18	14
8	14	11
9	11	8
10	9	7
11	8	6
12	6	5

2 × 1¼

KL	¼	3⁄16
0	32	25
2	29	22
3	26	20
4	24	18
5	20	15
6	16	12
7	12	9
8	9	7
9	7	5
10	6	4

1¾ × 1

KL	¼
0	30
2	27
3	25
4	22
5	19
6	16
7	12
8	9
9	7
10	6

Properties of 2 Angles—⅜ in. Back to Back

	2½ × 1½			2 × 1½			2 × 1¼			1¾ × 1	
Area A (in.²)	2.30	1.88		1.63	1.24		1.50	1.15		1.38	1...
r_x (in.)	.785	.794		.623	.632		.628	.636		.543	
r_y (in.)	.713	.699		.740	.726		.624	.609		.644	

Heavy line indicates $Kl/r = 120$. Values omitted for $Kl/r > 200$.

COLUMNS
Double angles

$$F_y = 36 \text{ ksi}$$

Allowable concentric loads in kips
TABLE VI
Unequal legs

Short legs ⅜ in. back to back of angles

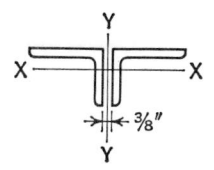

$F_y = 36$ ksi — Effective length in feet KL with respect to indicated axis

9 × 4

Thickness	1	⅞	¾
Weight per Foot	81.6	72.2	62.6
X-X AXIS KL			
0	518	458	397
4	445	394	342
6	389	345	301
8	323	288	252
10	247	222	195
12	173	156	138
14	127	114	101
16	97	88	78
17			69
Y-Y AXIS KL			
0	518	458	397
16	458	404	351
20	437	386	334
24	414	365	316
28	389	343	296
32	362	319	275
36	333	293	253
40	302	265	229
44	269	236	203
45	261	228	196
46	252	220	189
48	234	204	175
52	200	174	149
56	172	150	129
60	150	131	112
64	132	115	99
68	117	102	87
72	104	91	78
76	94	82	70
77	91	79	

8 × 6

Thickness	1	⅞	¾	⅝
Weight per Foot	88.4	78.2	67.6	57.0
X-X AXIS KL				
0	562	497	430	361
8	464	411	357	300
12	390	346	302	254
16	300	267	235	198
17	275	246	216	183
18	249	223	197	167
20	202	181	160	136
24	140	125	111	94
28	103	92	82	69
29		86	76	65
Y-Y AXIS KL				
0	562	497	430	361
12	503	444	384	322
16	475	420	363	304
20	444	392	339	283
24	410	362	312	261
28	373	328	283	236
32	332	292	251	209
36	288	253	217	180
37	277	243	208	172
40	241	211	180	149
44	199	174	149	123
48	167	146	125	103
52	142	125	107	88
56	123	108	92	76
60	107	94	80	66
61	104	91	78	64
62	100	88	75	
63	97			

8 × 4

Thickness	1	⅞	¾	⅝
Weight per Foot	74.8	66.2	57.4	48.4
X-X AXIS KL				
0	475	421	365	307
4	410	364	316	267
6	362	322	280	237
8	304	272	237	202
10	237	213	187	162
12	168	152	134	117
14	123	112	99	86
16	95	85	75	66
17	84	76	67	58
Y-Y AXIS KL				
0	475	421	365	307
12	430	381	330	277
16	410	363	314	263
20	387	342	296	248
24	361	319	276	231
28	333	294	254	212
32	303	267	230	192
36	270	238	205	171
39	244	214	184	153
40	235	206	177	147
44	198	173	148	123
48	166	145	125	103
52	142	124	106	88
56	122	107	92	76
60	107	93	80	66
64	94	82	70	58
66	88	77	66	55
67	85	75	64	53
68	83			

Properties of 2 Angles—⅜ in. Back to Back

	9 × 4			8 × 6				8 × 4			
Area A (in.²)	24.0	21.2	18.4	26.0	23.0	19.9	16.7	22.0	19.5	16.9	14.2
r_x (in.)	1.00	1.01	1.02	1.73	1.74	1.76	1.77	1.03	1.04	1.05	1.07
r_y (in.)	4.66	4.63	4.60	3.78	3.76	3.74	3.71	4.10	4.07	4.05	4.02

Heavy line indicates $Kl/r = 120$. Values omitted for $Kl/r > 200$.

COLUMNS
Double angles

$F_y = 36$ ksi

Allowable concentric loads in kips
TABLE VI
Unequal legs

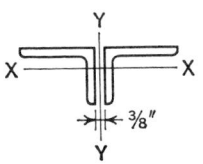

Short legs ⅜ in. back to back of angles

Size	7 × 4					6 × 4						6×3½
Thickness	⅞	¾	⅝	9⁄16		⅞	¾	⅝	9⁄16	½		½
Weight per Foot	60.4	52.4	44.2	40.0		54.4	47.2	40.0	36.2	32.4		30.6

$F_y = 36$ ksi — Effective length in feet KL with respect to indicated axis

X - X AXIS

7 × 4:

KL	⅞	¾	⅝	9⁄16
0	382	333	281	253
4	333	290	246	221
6	296	259	220	198
8	252	222	189	171
10	201	180	153	140
11	173	156	134	122
12	146	132	113	104
14	107	97	83	76
16	82	74	64	58
17	73	66	56	52
18		59	50	46

6 × 4:

KL	⅞	¾	⅝	9⁄16	½
0	346	300	253	229	205
4	303	264	222	202	181
6	271	236	200	181	163
8	234	204	173	158	142
10	191	168	142	130	118
11	167	147	126	115	105
12	142	126	108	99	90
14	104	92	79	73	66
16	80	71	61	56	51
18	63	56	48	44	40
19				40	36

6×3½:

KL	½
0	194
4	166
6	144
8	118
9	104
10	88
12	61
14	45
16	34

Y - Y AXIS

7 × 4:

KL	⅞	¾	⅝	9⁄16
0	382	333	281	253
8	356	310	261	235
12	338	294	248	223
16	318	276	232	209
20	294	255	215	193
24	268	232	195	175
28	240	207	174	156
32	209	180	151	135
34	192	165	138	124
35	184	158	132	118
36	175	150	125	112
40	142	122	101	91
44	117	100	84	75
48	99	84	70	63
52	84	72	60	54
56	73	62	52	46
57	70	60	50	45
58	68	58		

6 × 4:

KL	⅞	¾	⅝	9⁄16	½
0	346	300	253	229	205
8	316	275	231	209	187
12	296	256	215	195	175
15	278	241	202	183	164
18	258	223	187	169	152
21	237	204	171	155	138
24	214	184	154	139	124
27	189	162	135	122	109
28	180	154	128	116	103
29	171	146	122	110	98
30	162	138	115	103	92
34	127	108	89	81	72
38	101	86	72	64	57
42	83	71	59	53	47
46	69	59	49	44	39
47	66	56	47	42	38
48	64	54	45	40	36
49	61	52			

6×3½:

KL	½
0	194
8	178
12	166
14	160
16	153
18	145
20	137
22	129
24	120
26	111
28	101
29	96
30	91
33	76
36	64
39	5
42	4
45	4
48	3
49	3

Properties of 2 Angles—⅜ in. Back to Back

	⅞	¾	⅝	9⁄16		⅞	¾	⅝	9⁄16	½		½
Area A (in.²)	17.7	15.4	13.0	11.7		16.0	13.9	11.7	10.6	9.50		9.0
r_x (in.)	1.07	1.09	1.10	1.11		1.11	1.12	1.13	1.14	1.15		.9
r_y (in.)	3.52	3.49	3.47	3.46		2.97	2.94	2.92	2.91	2.90		2.9

Heavy line indicates $Kl/r = 120$. Values omitted for $Kl/r > 200$.

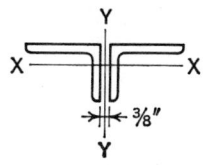

COLUMNS
Double angles

$$F_y = 36 \text{ ksi}$$

Allowable concentric loads in kips
TABLE VI
Unequal legs

Short legs ⅜ in. back to back of angles

Size		5 × 3½					5 × 3			4 × 3½				
Thickness		¾	⅝	½	⁷⁄₁₆		½	⁷⁄₁₆		⅝	½	⁷⁄₁₆	⅜	⁵⁄₁₆
Weight per Foot		39.6	33.6	27.2	24.0		25.6	22.6		29.4	23.8	21.2	18.2	15.4

$F_y = 36$ ksi — Effective length in feet KL with respect to indicated axis

X - X AXIS

KL (5×3½)	¾	⅝	½	⁷⁄₁₆	KL (5×3)	½	⁷⁄₁₆	KL (4×3½)	⅝	½	⁷⁄₁₆	⅜	⁵⁄₁₆
0	251	213	173	152	0	162	143	0	186	151	133	115	97
2	236	200	163	144	2	150	133	2	175	143	126	109	92
4	214	182	149	131	4	132	117	4	160	131	116	100	84
6	186	159	130	115	6	109	97	6	141	116	102	89	75
8	153	132	109	96	8	82	73	8	119	97	87	75	64
9	135	116	97	85	10	53	48	10	93	77	69	60	51
10	115	100	84	74	12	37	33	12	66	55	49	43	37
12	80	70	59	52	13	32	28	14	48	40	36	32	27
14	59	51	43	38	14			16	37	31	28	24	21
16	45	39	33	29				17	33	27	24	22	18

Y - Y AXIS

KL (5×3½)	¾	⅝	½	⁷⁄₁₆	KL (5×3)	½	⁷⁄₁₆	KL (4×3½)	⅝	½	⁷⁄₁₆	⅜	⁵⁄₁₆
0	251	213	173	152	0	162	143	0	186	151	133	115	97
8	224	189	154	135	8	145	128	4	174	142	125	108	91
10	215	181	147	130	10	139	123	6	167	135	119	103	87
12	204	173	140	123	12	132	117	8	158	128	113	97	82
14	193	163	132	116	14	125	110	10	148	120	105	91	76
16	181	153	124	109	16	118	104	12	137	110	97	84	70
18	169	142	115	101	18	110	97	14	125	100	88	76	64
20	155	130	105	92	20	101	89	16	111	89	79	67	56
22	141	118	95	83	22	92	81	18	97	78	68	58	49
23	133	111	89	78	23	87	77	19	90	71	62	53	44
24	126	105	84	73	24	82	72	20	82	65	57	48	40
26	109	91	72	63	25	77	68	21	74	59	51	44	37
28	94	78	62	55	26	72	63	22	68	54	47	40	33
32	72	60	48	42	28	62	54	24	57	45	39	34	28
36	57	47	38	33	32	47	42	26	49	38	34	29	24
39	49	40	32	28	36	38	33	28	42	33	29	25	21
40	46	38	31	27	40	30	27	30	36	29	25	22	18
41	44				41	29	25	31	34	27	24	20	17

Properties of 2 Angles—⅜ in. Back to Back

	¾	⅝	½	⁷⁄₁₆		½	⁷⁄₁₆		⅝	½	⁷⁄₁₆	⅜	⁵⁄₁₆
Area A (in.²)	11.6	9.84	8.00	7.05		7.50	6.62		8.59	7.00	6.18	5.34	4.49
r_x (in.)	.977	.991	1.01	1.01		.829	.837		1.03	1.04	1.05	1.06	1.07
r_y (in.)	2.48	2.45	2.43	2.42		2.50	2.49		1.92	1.89	1.88	1.87	1.86

Heavy line indicates $Kl/r = 120$.   Values omitted for $Kl/r > 200$.

COLUMNS
Double angles
Allowable concentric loads in kips
TABLE VI
Unequal legs

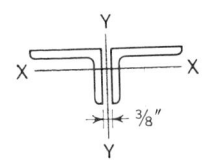

Short legs ⅜ in. back to back of angles

Fₓ = 36 ksi

4 × 3 — X-X AXIS

KL	⅝	½	⁷⁄₁₆	⅜	⁵⁄₁₆
Weight per Ft.	27.2	22.2	19.6	17.0	14.4
0	172	140	124	107	90
2	160	131	115	100	84
4	142	116	103	89	75
6	118	97	86	75	64
8	90	75	67	59	50
9	74	62	56	49	42
10	60	50	45	40	34
12	41	35	31	28	24
14	30	26	23	20	17

4 × 3 — Y-Y AXIS

KL	⅝	½	⁷⁄₁₆	⅜	⁵⁄₁₆
0	172	140	124	107	90
4	162	132	117	101	85
6	155	126	112	96	81
8	147	120	106	91	77
10	139	113	99	86	72
12	129	104	92	79	67
14	118	96	84	73	61
16	107	86	76	65	55
18	95	76	66	57	48
19	88	70	62	53	44
20	81	65	56	48	40
22	68	54	47	40	33
24	57	45	39	34	28
26	48	38	33	29	24
28	42	33	29	25	21
30	36	29	25	22	18
32	32	25	22	19	16
33	30				

3½ × 3 — X-X AXIS

KL	½	⁷⁄₁₆	⅜	⁵⁄₁₆
Weight per Ft.	20.4	18.2	15.8	13.2
0	130	114	99	84
2	121	107	93	78
4	108	95	83	70
6	91	81	70	60
8	71	63	55	47
9	59	53	47	40
10	48	43	38	33
12	34	30	27	23
14	25	22	20	17
15				15

3½ × 3 — Y-Y AXIS

KL	½	⁷⁄₁₆	⅜	⁵⁄₁₆
0	130	114	99	84
4	120	106	92	77
6	114	100	87	73
8	107	94	81	68
10	98	86	75	63
12	89	78	67	56
14	79	69	59	50
16	68	59	50	42
17	62	53	46	38
18	55	48	41	34
20	45	39	33	28
22	37	32	27	23
24	31	27	23	19
26	27	23	20	16
27	25	21	18	15

3½ × 2½ — X-X AXIS

KL	½	⁷⁄₁₆	⅜	⁵⁄₁₆
Weight per Ft.	18.8	16.6	14.4	12.2
0	119	105	91	77
2	108	96	83	70
4	91	81	71	60
6	70	62	55	47
7	57	51	45	39
8	44	40	35	30
10	28	26	23	19
11	23	21	19	16
12				14

3½ × 2½ — Y-Y AXIS

KL	½	⁷⁄₁₆	⅜	⁵⁄₁₆
0	119	105	91	77
4	111	98	85	71
6	105	93	81	68
8	99	87	75	63
10	92	81	70	59
12	84	74	63	53
14	75	66	57	47
16	65	57	49	41
17	60	52	45	38
18	55	48	41	34
20	45	39	33	28
22	37	32	27	23
24	31	27	23	19
26	26	23	20	16
27	25	21	18	15
28	23	20	17	14

Effective length in feet KL with respect to indicated axis — Fₓ = 36 ksi

Properties of 2 Angles—⅜ in. Back to Back

	4 × 3					3½ × 3				3½ × 2½			
Area A (in.²)	7.97	6.50	5.74	4.97	4.18	6.00	5.30	4.59	3.87	5.50	4.87	4.22	3.58
r_x (in.)	.849	.864	.871	.879	.887	.881	.889	.897	.905	.704	.711	.719	.72
r_y (in.)	1.99	1.96	1.95	1.94	1.93	1.70	1.68	1.67	1.66	1.77	1.75	1.74	1.73

Heavy line indicates $Kl/r = 120$. Values omitted for $Kl/r > 200$.

COLUMNS
Double angles

Allowable concentric loads in kips
TABLE VI
Unequal legs

Short legs ⅜ in. back to back of angles

$F_y = 36$ ksi

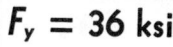

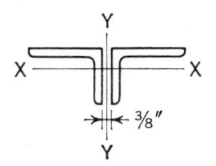

$r_y = 36$ ksi

Effective length in feet KL with respect to indicated axis

Size		3 × 2½						3 × 2						2½ × 2		
Thickness		½	7/16	⅜	5/16	¼		½	7/16	⅜	5/16	¼		⅜	5/16	¼
Weight per Ft.		17.0	15.2	13.2	11.2	9.0		15.4	13.6	11.8	10.0	8.2		10.6	9.0	7.2

X - X AXIS

	3×2½						3×2						2½×2		
0	108	96	83	70	57	0	97	86	75	63	51	0	67	57	46
2	99	87	76	64	52	2	85	75	66	56	45	2	59	50	41
3	92	82	71	60	49	3	76	68	59	50	41	3	53	45	37
4	84	75	65	55	45	4	65	58	51	43	36	4	46	40	32
5	75	67	58	50	40	5	53	47	42	36	30	5	39	33	27
6	65	58	51	43	36	6	39	35	31	27	23	6	30	26	21
7	54	49	43	37	30	7	28	26	23	20	17	7	22	19	16
8	42	38	34	29	24	8	22	20	18	15	13	8	17	14	12
10	27	24	22	19	15	9	17	16	14	12	10	9	13	11	10
12	19	17	15	13	11										

Y - Y AXIS

	3×2½						3×2						2½×2		
						0	97	86	75	63	51	0	67	57	46
0	108	96	83	70	57	2	94	83	72	61	50	2	64	54	44
2	104	92	80	67	55	4	90	79	69	58	47	4	60	51	41
4	99	88	76	64	52	6	84	75	65	55	44	6	55	46	38
6	93	82	71	60	48	8	78	69	60	50	41	7	52	44	36
8	85	75	65	55	44	10	71	63	54	45	37	8	49	41	33
10	77	68	58	49	40	11	67	59	51	43	35	9	46	39	31
11	72	64	55	46	37	12	63	56	48	40	32	10	42	36	29
12	67	59	51	43	34	13	59	52	45	37	30	11	39	32	26
13	62	55	47	39	32	14	54	48	41	34	28	12	35	29	23
14	57	50	43	36	29	15	50	44	38	31	25	13	31	25	20
15	51	45	38	32	25	16	45	39	34	28	22	14	27	22	18
16	46	40	34	28	22	17	40	35	30	25	20	15	23	19	15
17	40	35	30	25	20	18	36	31	27	22	18	16	21	17	13
18	36	31	27	22	18	20	29	25	22	18	14	17	18	15	12
20	29	25	22	18	14	22	24	21	18	15	12	18	16	13	11
22	24	21	18	15	12	24	20	17	15	12	10	19	15	12	10
24	20	18	15	12	10	25	18	16	14	11	9	20	13	11	9
25	19					26	17	15				21	12	10	

Properties of 2 Angles—⅜ in. Back to Back

	3 × 2½						3 × 2						2½ × 2		
Area A (in.²)	5.00	4.43	3.84	3.24	2.63		4.50	3.99	3.47	2.93	2.38		3.09	2.62	2.13
r_x (in.)	.722	.729	.736	.744	.753		.546	.553	.559	.567	.574		.577	.584	.592
r_y (in.)	1.50	1.49	1.47	1.46	1.45		1.57	1.56	1.55	1.53	1.52		1.28	1.26	1.25

Heavy line indicates $Kl/r = 120$. Values omitted for $Kl/r > 200$.

$F_y = 36$ ksi

COLUMNS
Double angles
Allowable concentric loads in kips
TABLE VI
Unequal legs

Short legs ⅜ in. back to back of angles

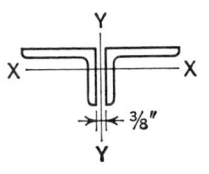

Size	2½ × 1½			2 × 1½			2 × 1¼			1¾ × 1¼	
Thickness	5/16	¼		¼	3/16		¼	3/16		¼	3/16
Weight per Foot	7.84	6.38		5.54	4.24		5.10	3.92		4.68	3.60

X - X AXIS (Effective length in feet KL with respect to indicated axis)

KL	2½×1½ 5/16	2½×1½ ¼	KL	2×1½ ¼	2×1½ 3/16	KL	2×1¼ ¼	2×1¼ 3/16	KL	1¾×1¼ ¼	1¾×1¼ 3/16
0	50	41	0	35	27	0	32	25	0	30	23
1	46	38	2	29	22	1	29	23	1	27	21
2	40	33	3	24	19	2	25	19	2	23	18
3	33	27	4	19	15	3	19	15	3	18	14
4	24	20	5	13	10	4	12	9	4	11	9
5	16	13	6	9	7	5	7	6	5	7	6
6	11	9	7	6	5				6		

Y - Y AXIS

KL	2½×1½ 5/16	2½×1½ ¼	KL	2×1½ ¼	2×1½ 3/16	KL	2×1¼ ¼	2×1¼ 3/16	KL	1¾×1¼ ¼	1¾×1¼ 3/16
0	50	41	0	35	27	0	32	25	0	30	23
2	48	39	2	33	25	2	31	24	2	28	21
4	45	37	4	31	23	4	28	22	4	25	19
6	41	34	5	29	22	5	27	21	5	24	18
7	39	32	6	27	20	6	25	19	6	22	17
8	37	30	7	25	19	7	24	18	7	20	15
9	35	29	8	23	17	8	22	16	8	18	13
10	33	27	9	21	15	9	20	15	9	16	12
11	30	25	10	18	14	10	17	13	10	13	10
12	28	22	11	15	11	11	15	11	11	11	8
13	25	20	12	13	10	12	13	10	12	9	7
14	22	18	13	11	8	13	11	8	13	8	6
15	19	15	14	10	7	14	9	7	14	7	5
16	17	13	15	8	6	15	8	6	15	6	4
17	15	12	16	7	5	16	7	5			
18	13	11	17	6	5	17	6	5			
19	12	10				18	6	4			
20	11	9									
21	10	8									
22	9	7									

Properties of 2 Angles—⅜ in. Back to Back

	2½×1½ 5/16	2½×1½ ¼		2×1½ ¼	2×1½ 3/16		2×1¼ ¼	2×1¼ 3/16		1¾×1¼ ¼	1¾×1¼ 3/16
Area A (in.²)	2.30	1.88		1.63	1.24		1.50	1.15		1.38	1.05
r_x (in.)	.408	.415		.432	.440		.344	.351		.352	.35
r_y (in.)	1.34	1.33		1.05	1.04		1.09	1.08		.958	.94

Heavy line indicates $Kl/r = 120$. Values omitted for $Kl/r > 200$.

COLUMNS
Double angles

$F_y = 50$ ksi

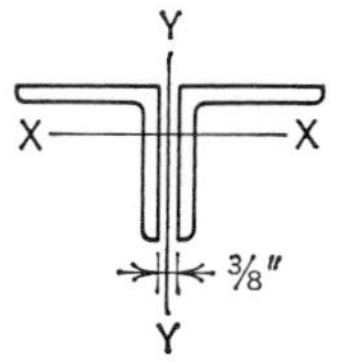

Allowable concentric loads in kips
TABLE VII
Equal legs

⅜ in. back to back of angles

$F_y = 50$ ksi

Effective length in feet KL with respect to indicated axis

X - X AXIS

Size		8 × 8					6 × 6				
Thickness		1⅛	1	⅞	¾		1	⅞	¾	⅝	⁹⁄₁₆
Weight per Foot		113.8	102.0	90.0	77.8		74.8	66.2	57.4	48.4	43.8
0		1005	900	795	687	0	660	585	507	426	387
10		818	734	649	563	8	524	465	405	341	310
14		705	634	562	488	10	474	421	367	310	282
18		573	518	459	400	12	418	372	326	275	251
22		420	383	341	299	14	357	318	280	237	216
23		385	350	312	274	16	289	259	229	194	178
24		353	322	286	252	18	228	204	181	154	141
25		326	296	264	232	22					
28											

Y - Y AXIS

Size		8 × 8					6 × 6				
Thickness		1⅛	1	⅞	¾		1	⅞	¾	⅝	⁹⁄₁₆
0		1005	900	795	687	0	660	585	507	426	387
10		893	799	705	609	10	556	491	425	356	323
15		812	726	640	552	12	526	465	402	336	305
20		716	639	563	485	14	494	436	376	315	285
25		606	540	474	407	16	459	404	349	292	264
30		482	427	374	320	18	422	371	319	267	241
34		379	335	293	250	20	382	335	288	240	217
35		357	316	276	236	22	340	297	254	211	191
40						24	295	256	219	181	163
						26	252	218	186	154	139
						27	233	202	173	143	129
						30					

Properties of 2 Angles—⅜ in. Back to Back

		1⅛	1	⅞	¾		1	⅞	¾	⅝	⁹⁄₁₆
Area A (in.²)		33.5	30.0	26.5	22.9		22.0	19.5	16.9	14.2	12.9
r_x (in.)		2.42	2.44	2.45	2.47		1.80	1.81	1.83	1.84	1.85
r_y (in.)		3.55	3.53	3.51	3.49		2.73	2.70	2.68	2.66	2.65

Heavy line indicates $Kl/r = 120$. Values omitted are same as for $F_y = 36$ ksi.

AMERICAN INSTITUTE OF STEEL CONSTRUCTION

COLUMNS
Double angles

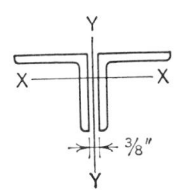

$F_y = 50$ ksi

Allowable concentric loads in kips
TABLE VII
Equal legs

⅜ in. back to back of angles

$F_y = 50$ ksi — Effective length in feet KL with respect to indicated axis

Properties of 2 Angles—⅜ in. Back to Back

X - X AXIS

Size	5 × 5					4 × 4				
Thickness	⅞	¾	⅝	½		¾	⅝	½	⁷⁄₁₆	⅜
Weight per Foot	54.4	47.2	40.0	32.4		37.0	31.4	25.6	22.6	19.6
0	480	417	351	285	**0**	327	277	225	199	172
6	394	343	290	236	**4**	281	238	194	172	149
8	351	307	259	212	**6**	247	209	172	152	131
10	302	266	225	185	**8**	206	175	145	128	111
12	248	219	186	154	**10**	158	136	113	101	87
14	188	168	143	119	**11**	132	114	96	86	74
15	164	146	125	104	**12**	111	96	80	72	62
18					**14**					

Y - Y AXIS

Size	5 × 5					4 × 4				
Thickness	⅞	¾	⅝	½		¾	⅝	½	⁷⁄₁₆	⅜
Weight per Foot	54.4	47.2	40.0	32.4		37.0	31.4	25.6	22.6	19.6
0	480	417	351	285	**0**	327	277	225	199	172
6	432	375	315	255	**6**	284	240	194	171	148
8	409	355	298	242	**8**	264	222	180	158	137
10	384	333	279	226	**10**	240	202	163	144	124
12	356	308	258	209	**12**	215	180	145	127	109
14	326	281	235	190	**14**	186	156	124	109	93
16	293	252	211	170	**15**	171	142	113	99	85
18	257	221	184	147	**16**	155	129	102	89	76
20	219	187	155	124	**17**	138	114	90	79	67
22	181	155	128	102	**18**	123	102	80	70	60
23	166	142	117	93	**20**					
25										

Properties of 2 Angles—⅜ in. Back to Back

	⅞	¾	⅝	½		¾	⅝	½	⁷⁄₁₆	⅜
Area A (in.²)	16.0	13.9	11.7	9.50		10.9	9.22	7.50	6.62	5.72
r_x (in.)	1.49	1.51	1.52	1.54		1.19	1.20	1.22	1.23	1.23
r_y (in.)	2.30	2.28	2.26	2.24		1.88	1.86	1.83	1.82	1.81

Heavy line indicates $Kl/r = 120$. Values omitted are same as for $F_y = 36$ ksi.

AMERICAN INSTITUTE OF STEEL CONSTRUCTION

COLUMNS
Double angles

$$F_y = 50 \text{ ksi}$$

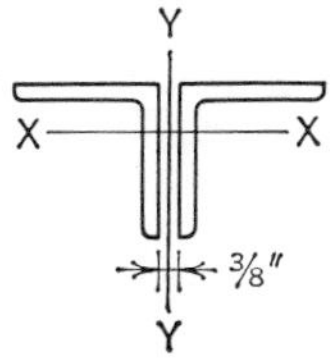

Allowable concentric loads in kips
TABLE VII
Equal legs

⅜ in. back to back of angles

$F_y = 50$ ksi — Effective length in feet KL with respect to indicated axis

Size 3½ × 3½

Thickness	½	7/16	⅜
Weight per Foot	22.2	19.6	17.0

X - X AXIS

KL	½	7/16	⅜
0	195	172	149
2	182	161	139
4	163	144	125
6	139	123	107
8	109	98	84
10	76	68	59
12			

Y - Y AXIS

KL	½	7/16	⅜
0	195	172	149
6	164	145	125
8	149	131	113
10	132	116	100
12	112	99	85
14	91	79	68
15	80	69	59
16	70	61	52
18			

Size 3 × 3

Thickness	½	7/16	⅜	5/16
Weight per Foot	18.8	16.6	14.4	12.2

X - X AXIS

KL	½	7/16	⅜	5/16
0	165	146	127	106
2	152	134	116	98
4	131	116	101	85
5	118	105	92	78
6	104	93	81	69
7	89	80	70	59
8	72	65	57	49
9	57	51	45	39
10				

Y - Y AXIS

KL	½	7/16	⅜	5/16
0	165	146	127	106
2	157	139	121	102
4	147	130	112	94
6	134	118	102	86
8	118	104	90	75
9	109	96	83	69
10	100	88	76	63
11	90	79	68	57
12	80	70	60	50
13	69	60	51	43
14	60	52	44	37
15	52			
16				

Properties of 2 Angles—⅜ in. Back to Back

	½	7/16	⅜		½	7/16	⅜	5/16
Area A (in.²)	6.50	5.74	4.97		5.50	4.87	4.22	3.55
r_x (in.)	1.06	1.07	1.07		.898	.905	.913	.922
r_y (in.)	1.63	1.62	1.61		1.43	1.42	1.41	1.40

Heavy line indicates $Kl/r = 120$. Values omitted are same as for $F_y = 36$ ksi.

AMERICAN INSTITUTE OF STEEL CONSTRUCTION

$F_y = 50$ ksi

COLUMNS
Double angles

Allowable concentric loads in kips
TABLE VII
Equal legs

⅜ in. back to back of angles

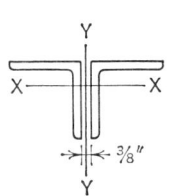

Size		2½ × 2½					2 × 2					1¾ × 1¾	
Thickness		½	⅜	⁵⁄₁₆	¼		⅜	⁵⁄₁₆	¼	³⁄₁₆		¼	³⁄₁₆
Weight per Foot		15.4	11.8	10.0	8.2		9.4	7.84	6.38	4.88		5.54	4.2

X - X AXIS ($F_y = 50$ ksi, Effective length in feet KL with respect to indicated axis)

KL	2½×2½ (½)	(⅜)	(⁵⁄₁₆)	(¼)	KL	2×2 (⅜)	(⁵⁄₁₆)	(¼)	(³⁄₁₆)	KL	1¾×1¾ (¼)	(³⁄₁₆)
0	135	104	88	71	0	82	69	56	43	0	49	37
2	121	93	79	64	2	70	59	49	37	2	41	31
3	110	86	73	59	3	62	52	43	33	3	35	27
4	98	77	65	53	4	51	44	36	28	4	27	21
5	84	66	56	46	5	39	34	28	22	5	19	15
6	69	54	47	38	6	28	24	20	16	6		
7	52	42	36	30	7							
8				23								
9												

Y - Y AXIS

KL	2½×2½ (½)	(⅜)	(⁵⁄₁₆)	(¼)	KL	2×2 (⅜)	(⁵⁄₁₆)	(¼)	(³⁄₁₆)	KL	1¾×1¾ (¼)	(³⁄₁₆)
					0	82	69	56	43	0	49	37
					2	76	64	52	40	2	45	34
0	135	104	88	71	4	67	57	46	35	4	39	29
2	128	98	83	67	5	62	52	42	32	5	35	26
4	117	90	76	61	6	56	47	38	29	6	31	23
6	104	79	67	54	7	50	42	34	25	7	26	19
7	96	73	61	50	8	43	36	29	22	8	21	15
8	88	66	56	45	9	36	29	24	17	9	17	12
9	79	59	50	40	10	29	24	19	14	10		
10	69	52	43	35	11							
11	59	44	36	29								
12	50	37	30	24								
13	42											
14												

Properties of 2 Angles—⅜ in. Back to Back

	2½×2½ (½)	(⅜)	(⁵⁄₁₆)	(¼)		2×2 (⅜)	(⁵⁄₁₆)	(¼)	(³⁄₁₆)		1¾×1¾ (¼)	(³⁄₁₆)
Area A (in.²)	4.50	3.47	2.93	2.38		2.72	2.30	1.88	1.43		1.63	1.2
r_x (in.)	.739	.753	.761	.769		.594	.601	.609	.617		.529	.5
r_y (in.)	1.24	1.21	1.20	1.19		1.01	1.00	.989	.977		.890	.8

Heavy line indicates $Kl/r = 120$. Values omitted are same as for $F_y = 36$ ksi.

COLUMNS
Double angles

$F_y = 50$ ksi

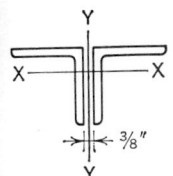

Allowable concentric loads in kips
TABLE VII
Equal legs

⅜ in. back to back of angles

e / Thickness / Weight per Foot	1½ × 1½			1¼ × 1¼				1 × 1		
ckness	¼	³⁄₁₆		¼	³⁄₁₆	⅛		¼	³⁄₁₆	⅛
ight per Foot	4.38	3.60		3.84	2.96	2.02		2.98	2.32	1.60

X-X AXIS

KL	¼	³⁄₁₆	KL	¼	³⁄₁₆	⅛	KL	¼	³⁄₁₆	⅛
0	41	31	0	34	26	18	0	26	20	14
2	33	25	1	30	23	16	1	22	18	12
3	26	20	2	25	19	13	2	16	13	9
4	18	14	3	17	14	10	3	8	7	5
5			4			6	4			
			5							

Y-Y AXIS

KL	¼	³⁄₁₆	KL	¼	³⁄₁₆	⅛	KL	¼	³⁄₁₆	⅛
0	41	31					0	26	20	14
2	37	28	0	34	26	18	2	23	17	12
3	35	26	2	30	23	16	3	20	15	10
4	31	24	3	27	21	14	4	17	13	9
5	27	21	4	24	18	12	5	13	10	6
6	23	17	5	20	15	10	6	9	7	4
7	18	13	6	16	12	8	7			
8	14	10	7	12	9	6				
9			8							

Effective length in feet KL with respect to indicated axis

Properties of 2 Angles—⅜ in. Back to Back

	1½ × 1½			1¼ × 1¼				1 × 1		
ea A (in.²)	1.38	1.05		1.13	.867	.594		.875	.680	.469
(in.)	.449	.457		.369	.377	.385		.290	.297	.304
(in.)	.793	.779		.696	.682	.668		.601	.586	.571

Heavy line indicates $Kl/r = 120$. Values omitted are same as for $F_y = 36$ ksi.

AMERICAN INSTITUTE OF STEEL CONSTRUCTION

COLUMNS
Double angles

$F_y = 50$ ksi

Allowable concentric loads in kips
TABLE VII
Unequal legs

Long legs ⅜ in. back to back of angles

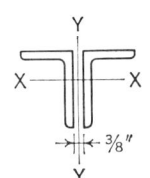

Size	9 × 4			8 × 6				8 × 4		
Thickness	1	⅞		1	⅞	¾		1	⅞	¾
Weight per Foot	81.6	72.2		88.4	78.2	67.6		74.8	66.2	57.

X - X AXIS

KL	9×4: 1	⅞	KL	8×6: 1	⅞	¾	KL	8×4: 1	⅞	¾
0	720	636	0	780	690	597	0	660	585	50
10	612	542	10	640	568	492	10	544	483	41
12	582	515	12	600	533	462	12	510	453	39
14	549	486	15	533	474	412	14	474	421	36
16	513	455	18	458	409	357	16	435	387	33
18	475	422	21	375	336	294	18	393	349	30
20	434	386	24	290	261	229	20	347	310	27
22	391	348	25	267	240	211	22	299	267	23
25	321	287	26	247	222	195	25	232	207	18
28	256	229	29				26	214	191	16
29	239	214					28			
32										

Y - Y AXIS

KL	9×4: 1	⅞	KL	8×6: 1	⅞	¾	KL	8×4: 1	⅞	¾
			0	780	690	597				
			10	643	567	490				
0	720	636	12	603	532	459	0	660	585	50
6	597	525	15	537	473	407	6	553	488	42
8	537	470	18	464	407	349	8	501	440	37
10	469	408	21	382	334	285	10	442	386	33
12	391	337	24	297	259	220	12	375	325	27
14	305	259	25	274	239	203	14	301	258	21
15	266	226	29				15	263	224	18
18							16	231	197	16
							20			

Effective length in feet KL with respect to indicated axis

Properties of 2 Angles—⅜ in. Back to Back

	9×4			8×6				8×4		
Area A (in.²)	24.0	21.2		26.0	23.0	19.9		22.0	19.5	16.
r_x (in.)	2.84	2.86		2.49	2.51	2.53		2.52	2.53	2.
r_y (in.)	1.55	1.52		2.52	2.50	2.48		1.61	1.58	1.

Heavy line indicates $Kl/r = 120$. Values omitted are same as for $F_y = 36$ ksi.

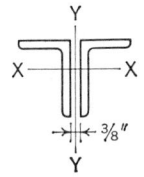

COLUMNS
Double angles

Allowable concentric loads in kips
TABLE VII
Unequal legs

$$F_y = 50 \text{ ksi}$$

Long legs ⅜ in. back to back of angles

$F_y = 50$ ksi — Effective length in feet KL with respect to indicated axis

Size		7 × 4			6 × 4			
Thickness		⅞	¾		⅞	¾	⅝	⁹⁄₁₆
Weight per Foot		60.4	52.4		54.4	47.2	40.0	36.2
X - X AXIS	0	531	462	0	504	417	351	318
	8	448	391	8	405	336	284	257
	10	418	365	10	368	307	259	235
	12	385	337	12	328	274	232	210
	14	349	306	14	283	237	202	183
	16	310	272	16	234	198	169	153
	18	268	236	18	186	157	135	122
	20	222	197	19	167	141	121	110
	22	184	163	20				
	24							
Y - Y AXIS				0	504	417	351	318
	0	531	462	6	429	354	297	268
	6	447	388	8	393	323	271	244
	8	406	352	10	351	288	241	217
	10	360	311	12	305	250	208	186
	12	308	265	14	254	206	170	151
	14	250	213	16	199	161	132	117
	15	219	186	17	176	142	117	104
	16	193	164	18				
	19							

Properties of 2 Angles—⅜ in. Back to Back

		7 × 4			6 × 4			
Area A (in.²)		17.7	15.4		16.0	13.9	11.7	10.6
r_x (in.)		2.20	2.22		1.86	1.88	1.90	1.90
r_y (in.)		1.64	1.62		1.71	1.69	1.67	1.65

Heavy line indicates $Kl/r = 120$. Values omitted are same as for $F_y = 36$ ksi.

AMERICAN INSTITUTE OF STEEL CONSTRUCTION

COLUMNS
Double angles

Allowable concentric loads in kips

TABLE VII

Unequal legs

Long legs ⅜ in. back to back of angles

$F_y = 50$ ksi

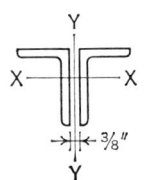

Size	5 × 3½				5 × 3		4 × 3½			
Thickness	¾	⅝	½		½		⅝	½	⁷⁄₁₆	⅜
Weight per Foot	39.6	33.6	27.2		25.6		29.4	23.8	21.2	18.

$F_y = 50$ ksi — Effective length in feet KL with respect to indicated axis

X-X AXIS

5 × 3½

KL	¾	⅝	½
0	348	295	240
4	314	266	217
6	289	245	200
8	260	221	181
10	226	193	158
12	189	162	134
14	147	127	106
15	128	110	92
16	113	97	81
18			

5 × 3

KL	½
0	225
2	216
4	203
6	188
8	170
10	149
12	126
14	100
15	87
16	77
18	

4 × 3½

KL	⅝	½	⁷⁄₁₆	⅜
0	258	210	185	16
2	243	198	175	15
4	223	182	161	13
6	197	161	142	12
8	166	136	121	10
10	130	107	95	8
12	92	76	68	6
14				

Y-Y AXIS

5 × 3½

KL	¾	⅝	½
0	348	295	240
4	313	265	215
6	288	243	197
8	258	217	176
10	224	188	151
12	186	155	124
14	144	119	94
15	125	103	82
16	110		
18			

5 × 3

KL	½
0	225
2	213
4	195
6	173
8	147
10	117
12	84
14	

4 × 3½

KL	⅝	½	⁷⁄₁₆	⅜
0	258	210	185	16
2	247	201	178	15
4	233	190	167	14
6	216	175	154	13
8	195	158	139	12
10	172	139	122	10
12	145	117	102	8
14	116	92	81	6
15	101	81	70	6
16	89	71	62	5
18				

Properties of 2 Angles—⅜ in. Back to Back

	¾	⅝	½		½		⅝	½	⁷⁄₁₆	⅜
Area A (in.²)	11.6	9.84	8.00		7.50		8.59	7.00	6.18	5.
r_x (in.)	1.55	1.56	1.58		1.59		1.22	1.23	1.24	1.
r_y (in.)	1.53	1.51	1.49		1.25		1.60	1.58	1.57	1.

Heavy line indicates $Kl/r = 120$. Values omitted are same as for $F_y = 36$ ksi.

AMERICAN INSTITUTE OF STEEL CONSTRUCTION

COLUMNS
Double angles

Allowable concentric loads in kips
TABLE VII
Unequal legs

Long legs ⅜ in. back to back of angles

$F_y = 50$ ksi

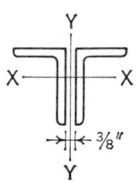

Size	4 × 3					3½ × 3				3½ × 2½		
Thickness	⅝	½	⁷⁄₁₆	⅜		½	⁷⁄₁₆	⅜		½	⁷⁄₁₆	⅜
Weight per Foot	27.2	22.2	19.6	17.0		20.4	18.2	15.8		18.8	16.6	14.4

$F_y = 50$ ksi — Effective length in feet KL with respect to indicated axis

X-X AXIS

4 × 3:

KL	⅝	½	⁷⁄₁₆	⅜
0	239	195	172	149
2	226	184	163	141
4	207	169	150	130
6	183	150	133	115
8	155	128	113	98
10	122	102	90	78
12	87	73	65	57
14				

3½ × 3:

KL	½	⁷⁄₁₆	⅜
0	180	159	138
2	168	149	129
4	151	134	116
6	129	114	99
8	102	91	80
10	71	64	57
11	59	53	47
12			

3½ × 2½:

KL	½	⁷⁄₁₆	⅜
0	165	146	127
2	154	137	119
4	139	123	107
6	119	105	92
8	95	84	74
10	68	60	53
11	56	50	44
12			

Y-Y AXIS

4 × 3:

KL	⅝	½	⁷⁄₁₆	⅜
0	239	195	172	149
2	227	185	164	142
4	211	171	151	131
6	190	154	136	117
8	166	133	117	101
10	138	110	96	82
12	106	83	72	61
13	90	71	61	52
14	78			
16				

3½ × 3:

KL	½	⁷⁄₁₆	⅜
0	180	159	138
2	171	151	131
4	159	140	122
6	144	127	110
8	126	111	96
10	106	92	79
12	82	72	61
13	70	61	52
14	60	53	45
16			

3½ × 2½:

KL	½	⁷⁄₁₆	⅜
0	165	146	127
2	155	137	119
4	140	124	107
6	122	107	92
8	100	87	75
10	74	63	54
11	61	52	45
12			

Properties of 2 Angles—⅜ in. Back to Back

	4 × 3					3½ × 3			3½ × 2½		
Area A (in.²)	7.97	6.50	5.74	4.97		6.00	5.30	4.59	5.50	4.87	4.22
r_x (in.)	1.23	1.25	1.25	1.26		1.07	1.08	1.09	1.09	1.09	1.10
r_y (in.)	1.36	1.33	1.32	1.31		1.38	1.37	1.36	1.14	1.12	1.11

Heavy line indicates $Kl/r = 120$. Values omitted are same as for $F_y = 36$ ksi.

COLUMNS
Double angles

$F_y = 50$ ksi

Allowable concentric loads in kips
TABLE VII
Unequal legs

Long legs ⅜ in. back to back of angles

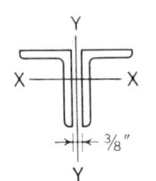

Size	3 × 2½					3 × 2					2½ × 2		
Thickness	½	7/16	3/8	5/16		½	7/16	3/8	5/16		3/8	5/16	¼
Weight per Foot	17.0	15.2	13.2	11.2		15.4	13.6	11.8	10.0		10.6	9.0	7.2

Effective length in feet KL with respect to indicated axis

X - X AXIS

3 × 2½:

KL (ft)	½	7/16	3/8	5/16
0	150	133	115	97
2	138	122	106	90
4	120	106	92	78
5	109	97	84	71
6	96	86	75	64
7	83	74	65	55
8	67	61	53	46
9	53	48	42	36
10				

3 × 2:

KL (ft)	½	7/16	3/8	5/16
0	135	120	104	88
2	124	110	96	81
3	117	104	90	77
4	108	96	84	71
5	98	88	77	65
6	87	78	68	58
7	75	67	59	51
8	62	56	49	42
9	49	44	39	34
10				

2½ × 2:

KL (ft)	3/8	5/16	¼
0	93	79	64
2	83	71	58
3	77	65	53
4	69	59	48
5	60	51	42
6	50	43	35
7	39	33	28
8	30	26	21
9			

Y - Y AXIS

3 × 2½:

KL (ft)	½	7/16	3/8	5/16
0	150	133	115	97
2	141	125	108	91
4	129	114	98	83
5	121	107	92	78
6	113	99	86	72
7	104	91	79	66
8	94	82	71	59
9	83	73	62	52
10	72	62	53	44
11	60	52	44	37
12	50	44	37	31
13				

3 × 2:

KL (ft)	½	7/16	3/8	5/16
0	135	120	104	88
2	125	110	96	81
3	117	104	90	76
4	109	96	83	70
5	100	88	76	63
6	89	78	67	56
7	77	67	58	48
8	65	56	47	39
9	51	44	37	31
10				

2½ × 2:

KL (ft)	3/8	5/16	¼
0	93	79	64
2	86	73	59
3	81	68	55
4	75	64	51
5	69	58	47
6	62	52	42
7	54	45	36
8	46	38	30
9	37	30	24
10	30		
11			

Properties of 2 Angles—⅜ in. Back to Back

	3 × 2½					3 × 2					2½ × 2		
Area A (in.²)	5.00	4.43	3.84	3.24		4.50	3.99	3.47	2.93		3.09	2.62	2.13
r_x (in.)	.913	.920	.928	.937		.924	.932	.940	.948		.768	.776	.784
r_y (in.)	1.18	1.17	1.16	1.15		.945	.931	.917	.903		.961	.948	.93⅜

Heavy line indicates $Kl/r = 120$. Values omitted are same as for $F_y = 36$ ksi.

COLUMNS
Double angles

Allowable concentric loads in kips
TABLE VII
Unequal legs

$F_y = 50$ ksi

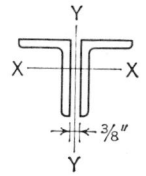

Long legs ⅜ in. back to back of angles

Fy = 50 KSI

Effective length in feet KL with respect to indicated axis

Size	2½ × 1½			2 × 1½			2 × 1¼			1¾ × 1¼	
Thickness	⁵⁄₁₆	¼		¼	³⁄₁₆		¼	³⁄₁₆		¼	³⁄₁₆
Weight per Foot	7.84	6.38		5.54	4.24		5.10	3.92		4.68	3.60

X-X AXIS

KL	2½ × 1½ ⁵⁄₁₆	2½ × 1½ ¼	KL	2 × 1½ ¼	2 × 1½ ³⁄₁₆	KL	2 × 1¼ ¼	2 × 1¼ ³⁄₁₆	KL	1¾ × 1¼ ¼	1¾ × 1¼ ³⁄₁₆
0	69	56	0	49	37	0	45	34	0	41	31
2	62	51	2	42	32	2	39	30	2	35	27
4	52	43	3	38	29	3	35	27	3	30	23
5	45	37	4	32	25	4	30	23	4	24	18
6	38	32	5	25	20	5	24	18	5	17	13
7	30	25	6	18	14	6	17	13	6		
8	23	19	7			7					
9											

Y-Y AXIS

KL	2½ × 1½ ⁵⁄₁₆	2½ × 1½ ¼	KL	2 × 1½ ¼	2 × 1½ ³⁄₁₆	KL	2 × 1¼ ¼	2 × 1¼ ³⁄₁₆	KL	1¾ × 1¼ ¼	1¾ × 1¼ ³⁄₁₆
0	69	56	0	49	37	0	45	34	0	41	31
2	61	50	2	44	33	2	39	30	2	36	27
4	49	40	3	40	30	3	35	26	3	32	24
5	42	34	4	36	27	4	29	22	4	28	21
6	33	26	5	31	23	5	23	17	5	22	17
7	25	19	6	25	18	6	17	12	6	16	12
8			7	19	14	7			7		
			8								

Properties of 2 Angles—⅜ in. Back to Back

	2½ × 1½ ⁵⁄₁₆	2½ × 1½ ¼		2 × 1½ ¼	2 × 1½ ³⁄₁₆		2 × 1¼ ¼	2 × 1¼ ³⁄₁₆		1¾ × 1¼ ¼	1¾ × 1¼ ³⁄₁₆
Area A (in.²)	2.30	1.88		1.63	1.24		1.50	1.15		1.38	1.05
(in.)	.785	.794		.623	.632		.628	.636		.543	.551
(in.)	.713	.699		.740	.726		.624	.609		.644	.630

Heavy line indicates $Kl/r = 120$. Values omitted are same as for $F_y = 36$ ksi.

$F_y = 50$ ksi

COLUMNS
Double angles

Allowable concentric loads in kips
TABLE VII
Unequal legs

Short legs ⅜ in. back to back of angles

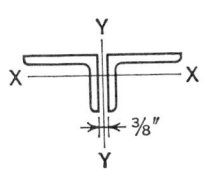

Size	9 × 4			8 × 6				8 × 4		
Thickness	1	⅞		1	⅞	¾		1	⅞	¾
Weight per Foot	81.6	72.2		88.4	78.2	67.6		74.8	66.2	57.4

X - X AXIS

KL	9×4 (1)	9×4 (⅞)	KL	8×6 (1)	8×6 (⅞)	8×6 (¾)	KL	8×4 (1)	8×4 (⅞)	8×4 (¾)
0	720	636	0	780	690	597	0	660	585	507
4	592	524	8	610	541	470	4	547	486	423
6	494	439	12	477	424	371	6	461	411	358
8	375	336	16	315	282	250	8	357	321	281
10	249	224	17	279	250	221	10	242	219	193
12			18	249	223	197	12			
			20							

Y - Y AXIS

KL	9×4 (1)	9×4 (⅞)	KL	8×6 (1)	8×6 (⅞)	8×6 (¾)	KL	8×4 (1)	8×4 (⅞)	8×4 (¾)
0	720	636	0	780	690	597	0	660	585	507
16	616	543	12	679	600	518	12	583	516	447
20	579	510	16	630	556	480	16	546	483	418
24	538	474	20	575	507	438	20	505	446	386
28	493	434	24	514	453	390	24	460	406	350
32	445	390	28	447	393	338	28	410	361	311
36	392	344	32	373	327	280	32	355	312	268
40	336	294	36	297	260	223	36	296	258	222
44	279	243	37	281	246	211	39	252	220	189
45	267	233	40				40	240	209	180
46	255	223					44			
48	235	205								
52										

Effective length in feet KL with respect to indicated axis

$F_y = 50$ ksi

Properties of 2 Angles—⅜ in. Back to Back

	9×4 (1)	9×4 (⅞)		8×6 (1)	8×6 (⅞)	8×6 (¾)		8×4 (1)	8×4 (⅞)	8×4 (¾)
Area A (in.²)	24.0	21.2		26.0	23.0	19.9		22.0	19.5	16.9
r_x (in.)	1.00	1.01		1.73	1.74	1.76		1.03	1.04	1.
r_y (in.)	4.66	4.63		3.78	3.76	3.74		4.10	4.07	4.

Heavy line indicates $Kl/r = 120$. Values omitted are same as for $F_y = 36$ ksi.

COLUMNS
Double angles

$F_y = 50$ ksi

Allowable concentric loads in kips
TABLE VII
Unequal legs

Short legs ⅜ in. back to back of angles

Size			7 × 4			6 × 4			
Thickness			⅞	¾		⅞	¾	⅝	9/16
Weight per Foot			60.4	52.4		54.4	47.2	40.0	36.2
Effective length in feet KL with respect to indicated axis	X - X AXIS	0	531	462	0	480	417	351	318
		4	445	389	4	406	353	298	271
		6	379	334	6	350	305	258	235
		8	301	267	8	283	248	211	192
		10	210	190	10	204	181	155	143
		11	174	157	11	169	149	128	118
		12			12				
	Y - Y AXIS	0	531	462	0	480	417	351	318
		8	486	423	8	430	373	313	284
		12	455	395	12	393	341	286	259
		16	418	363	15	362	313	262	237
		20	377	326	18	327	282	236	214
		24	330	285	21	288	248	207	187
		28	279	240	24	246	211	176	158
		32	222	190	27	201	171	142	128
		34	197	168	28	187	159	132	119
		35	186	159	29	174	148	123	111
		36	175	150	30	163	138	115	103
		40			34				

Properties of 2 Angles—⅜ in. Back to Back

			7 × 4			6 × 4			
Area A (in.²)			17.7	15.4		16.0	13.9	11.7	10.6
r_x (in.)			1.07	1.09		1.11	1.12	1.13	1.14
r_y (in.)			3.52	3.49		2.97	2.94	2.92	2.91

Heavy line indicates $Kl/r = 120$. Values omitted are same as for $F_y = 36$ ksi.

$F_y = 50$ ksi

AMERICAN INSTITUTE OF STEEL CONSTRUCTION

COLUMNS
Double angles

Allowable concentric loads in kips
TABLE VII
Unequal legs

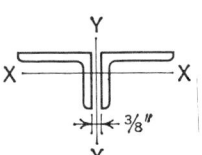

$F_y = 50$ ksi

Short legs ⅜ in. back to back of angles

X - X AXIS

Size	5 × 3½				5 × 3		4 × 3½			
Thickness	¾	⅝	½		½		⅝	½	⁷⁄₁₆	⅜
Weight per Foot	39.6	33.6	27.2		25.6		29.4	23.8	21.2	18.2
KL 0	348	295	240	0	225	0	258	210	185	160
2	322	274	223	2	205	2	240	196	173	150
4	284	242	198	4	173	4	214	175	155	134
6	235	201	166	6	132	6	180	148	131	114
8	175	152	127	8	84	8	140	115	103	90
9	142	124	104	10		10	95	79	71	62
10	115	100	85			12				
12										

Y - Y AXIS

KL	5 × 3½ ¾	5 × 3½ ⅝	5 × 3½ ½	KL	5 × 3 ½	KL	4 × 3½ ⅝	4 × 3½ ½	4 × 3½ ⁷⁄₁₆	4 × 3½ ⅜
0	348	295	240	0	225	0	258	210	185	160
8	302	255	207	8	195	4	238	194	171	148
10	285	241	196	10	185	6	225	183	161	139
12	267	226	183	12	173	8	209	170	149	129
14	248	209	169	14	161	10	191	155	136	117
16	226	190	154	16	147	12	172	138	122	105
18	204	171	137	18	133	14	150	120	106	91
20	179	149	120	20	117	16	126	100	88	75
22	153	127	101	22	100	18	101	80	70	60
23	140	116	93	23	92	19	91	72	63	54
24	128	106	85	24	84	20	82			
26	109			25	78	21				
28				26	72					
				28						

Properties of 2 Angles—⅜ in. Back to Back

	5 × 3½ ¾	5 × 3½ ⅝	5 × 3½ ½	5 × 3 ½	4 × 3½ ⅝	4 × 3½ ½	4 × 3½ ⁷⁄₁₆	4 × 3½ ⅜
Area A (in.²)	11.6	9.84	8.00	7.50	8.59	7.00	6.18	5.34
r_x (in.)	.977	.991	1.01	.829	1.03	1.04	1.05	1.06
r_y (in.)	2.48	2.45	2.43	2.50	1.92	1.89	1.88	1.87

Heavy line indicates $Kl/r = 120$. Values omitted are same as for $F_y = 36$ ksi.

Effective length in feet KL with respect to indicated axis

COLUMNS
Double angles

Allowable concentric loads in kips
TABLE VII
Unequal legs

Short legs ⅜ in. back to back of angles

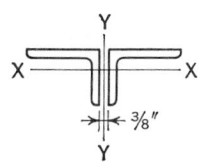

$F_y = 50$ ksi

$F_y = 50$ ksi — Effective length in feet KL with respect to indicated axis

Size	4 × 3					3½ × 3				3½ × 2½		
Thickness	⅝	½	7⁄16	⅜		½	7⁄16	⅜		½	7⁄16	⅜
Weight per Foot	27.2	22.2	19.6	17.0		20.4	18.2	15.8		18.8	16.6	14.4

X - X AXIS

KL	⅝	½	7⁄16	⅜	KL	½	7⁄16	⅜	KL	½	7⁄16	⅜
0	239	195	172	149	0	180	159	138	0	165	146	127
2	218	178	158	137	2	165	146	126	2	146	130	113
4	186	153	135	117	4	142	126	109	4	117	104	91
6	144	119	106	93	6	112	100	87	6	78	70	62
8	93	79	71	62	8	75	68	60	7	58	52	46
9		62	56	49	9	60	54	47	8			
10					10							

Y - Y AXIS

KL	⅝	½	7⁄16	⅜	KL	½	7⁄16	⅜	KL	½	7⁄16	⅜
0	239	195	172	149	0	180	159	138	0	165	146	127
4	222	181	160	138	4	164	145	125	4	151	134	116
6	210	171	151	130	6	153	135	117	6	142	125	108
8	196	159	140	121	8	140	123	106	8	130	115	99
10	181	146	129	111	10	125	110	95	10	117	103	89
12	163	132	116	100	12	108	95	81	12	103	90	78
14	144	116	102	88	14	90	78	67	14	87	76	65
16	124	99	86	74	16	70	61	52	16	70	60	52
18	101	80	70	60	17	62	54	46	17	62	54	46
19	91	72	63	54	18				18	55	48	41
20	82	65	57	48					20			
22												

Properties of 2 Angles—⅜ in. Back to Back

	⅝	½	7⁄16	⅜		½	7⁄16	⅜		½	7⁄16	⅜
Area A (in.²)	7.97	6.50	5.74	4.97		6.00	5.30	4.59		5.50	4.87	4.22
r_x (in.)	.849	.864	.871	.879		.881	.889	.897		.704	.711	.719
r_y (in.)	1.99	1.96	1.95	1.94		1.70	1.68	1.67		1.77	1.75	1.74

Heavy line indicates $Kl/r = 120$. Values omitted are same as for $F_y = 36$ ksi.

$F_y = 50$ ksi

COLUMNS
Double angles

Allowable concentric loads in kips
TABLE VII
Unequal legs

Short legs ⅜ in. back to back of angles

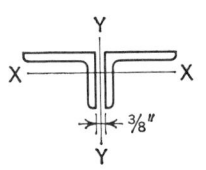

$F_y = 50$ ksi — Effective length in feet KL with respect to indicated axis

X - X AXIS

KL (3 × 2½)	½	7/16	⅜	5/16	KL (3 × 2)	½	7/16	⅜	5/16	KL (2½ × 2)	⅜	5/16	¼
0	150	133	115	97	0	135	120	104	88	0	93	79	64
2	134	119	103	87	2	114	101	88	75	2	79	67	55
3	122	108	94	80	3	98	87	76	65	3	69	59	48
4	108	96	84	71	4	78	70	62	53	4	57	49	40
5	92	82	72	61	5	56	51	45	39	5	43	37	31
6	74	66	58	50	6					6	30	26	22
7	55	50	44	38						7			
8													

Y - Y AXIS

KL (3 × 2½)	½	7/16	⅜	5/16	KL (3 × 2)	½	7/16	⅜	5/16	KL (2½ × 2)	⅜	5/16	¼
0	150	133	115	97	0	135	120	104	88	0	93	79	64
2	144	127	110	93	2	129	115	100	84	2	88	74	60
4	135	119	103	87	4	122	108	94	79	4	81	68	55
6	123	109	94	79	6	112	100	86	73	6	72	61	49
8	110	97	84	70	8	101	90	78	65	7	67	56	46
10	95	84	72	60	10	89	78	68	57	8	62	52	42
11	87	76	65	55	11	82	72	62	52	9	56	47	38
12	78	69	58	49	12	75	66	57	47	10	50	41	33
13	69	60	51	42	13	67	59	51	42	11	43	36	29
14	60	52	44	37	14	59	51	44	36	12	36	30	24
15	52	45	38	32	15	51	45	38	32	13	31	26	20
16					16	45	39	34	28	14			
					17								

Properties of 2 Angles—⅜ in. Back to Back

	½	7/16	⅜	5/16		½	7/16	⅜	5/16		⅜	5/16	¼
Area A (in.²)	5.00	4.43	3.84	3.24		4.50	3.99	3.47	2.93		3.09	2.62	2.13
r_x (in.)	.722	.729	.736	.744		.546	.553	.559	.567		.577	.584	.592
r_y (in.)	1.50	1.49	1.47	1.46		1.57	1.56	1.55	1.53		1.28	1.26	1.25

Heavy line indicates $Kl/r = 120$. Values omitted are same as for $F_y = 36$ ksi.

COLUMNS
Double angles

Allowable concentric loads in kips
TABLE VII
Unequal legs

$F_y = 50$ ksi

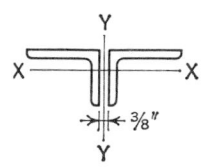 

Short legs ⅜ in. back to back of angles

$F_y = 50$ ksi — Effective length in feet KL with respect to indicated axis

Size		2½ × 1½			2 × 1½			2 × 1¼			1¾ × 1¼	
Thickness		5/16	1/4		1/4	3/16		1/4	3/16		1/4	3/16
Weight per Foot		7.84	6.38		5.54	4.24		5.10	3.92		4.68	3.60

X-X AXIS

KL	2½ × 1½ 5/16	2½ × 1½ 1/4	KL	2 × 1½ 1/4	2 × 1½ 3/16	KL	2 × 1¼ 1/4	2 × 1¼ 3/16	KL	1¾ × 1¼ 1/4	1¾ × 1¼ 3/16
0	69	56	0	49	37	0	45	34	0	41	31
1	63	51	1	45	34	1	40	31	1	37	28
2	53	43	2	38	29	2	31	24	2	29	23
3	40	33	3	30	23	3	20	16	3	20	15
4	25	21	4	20	16	4			4		
5			5								

Y-Y AXIS

KL	2½ × 1½ 5/16	2½ × 1½ 1/4	KL	2 × 1½ 1/4	2 × 1½ 3/16	KL	2 × 1¼ 1/4	2 × 1¼ 3/16	KL	1¾ × 1¼ 1/4	1¾ × 1¼ 3/16
0	69	56	0	49	37	0	45	34	0	41	31
2	66	54	2	46	35	2	42	32	2	38	29
4	61	50	4	41	31	4	38	29	4	34	25
6	55	45	5	38	29	5	35	27	5	31	23
7	51	42	6	35	26	6	32	25	6	28	21
8	47	39	7	31	23	7	29	22	7	24	18
9	43	35	8	27	20	8	26	20	8	20	15
10	39	32	9	23	17	9	22	17	9	16	12
11	35	28	10	19	14	10	18	14	10	13	
12	30	24	11	15		11	15	11	11		
13	25	20	12			12					
14	22										
15											

Properties of 2 Angles—⅜ in. Back to Back

	2½ × 1½ 5/16	2½ × 1½ 1/4		2 × 1½ 1/4	2 × 1½ 3/16		2 × 1¼ 1/4	2 × 1¼ 3/16		1¾ × 1¼ 1/4	1¾ × 1¼ 3/16
Area A (in.²)	2.30	1.88		1.63	1.24		1.50	1.15		1.38	1.05
x (in.)	.408	.415		.432	.440		.344	.351		.352	.359
y (in.)	1.34	1.33		1.05	1.04		1.09	1.08		.958	.945

Heavy line indicates $Kl/r = 120$. Values omitted are same as for $F_y = 36$ ksi.

AMERICAN INSTITUTE OF STEEL CONSTRUCTION

Notes

COLUMN BASE PLATES
Design procedure

Steel base plates are generally used under columns for distributing the column loads over a sufficient area of concrete support. The method of design, immediately following, was employed in preparing the tables of column base plate sizes and is recommended for use when a given load and column combination is not covered by the tables.

The following method of design is recommended:

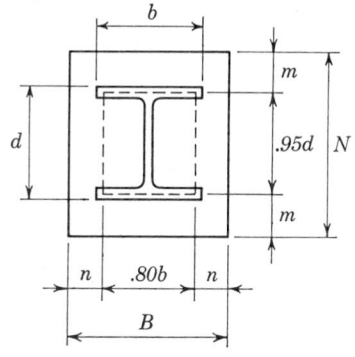

P = Total column load, kips

A = $B \times N$ = Area of plate, square inches

F_b = Allowable bending stress in base plate, ksi

F_p = Allowable bearing pressure on support, ksi

f_p = Actual bearing pressure

f'_c = Compressive strength of concrete, ksi or psi

t = Thickness of plate, inches

The column load, P, is assumed to be uniformly distributed over the base plate within a rectangle whose dimensions are $.95d$ and $.80b$. The base plate is assumed to distribute this load uniformly to the concrete support. The allowable bearing strength, F_p, of the concrete depends on f'_c and the percent of support area occupied by the base plate. From AISC Specification, Sect. 1.5.5, $F_p = .25f'_c$ when the entire area of a concrete support is covered, and $F_p = .375f'_c$ when only one third of the area is covered.

1. Establish bearing value of concrete, F_p, ksi
2. Determine the required area, $A = P/F_p$
3. Establish B and N, preferably rounded to full inches, so that m and n are approximately equal, and $B \times N \geq A$
4. Determine $m = (N - .95d)/2$ and $n = (B - .80b)/2$
5. Determine actual bearing pressure on concrete, $f_p = P/(B \times N)$
6. Use the larger of the values, m or n, to solve for t by whichever is the applicable formula:

$$t = \sqrt{\frac{3f_p\, m^2}{F_b}} \quad \text{or} \quad t = \sqrt{\frac{3f_p\, n^2}{F_b}}$$

EXAMPLE

A W14×95 column ($d = 14.12$; $b = 14.545$) has a reaction of 480 kips, and rests on a base plate fully covering a concrete support. f'_c of the concrete is specified to be 3000 psi at 28 days. Using $F_y = 36.0$ ksi material with $F_b = 27.0$ ksi, (AISC Spec. Sect. 1.5.1.4.3), design a base plate for this column.

F_p (allow.) = $.25 \times 3000$ psi = .750 ksi

A (req.) = $480/.750$ = 640 sq. in.

Assume $N = 26$ in.; then $B = 640/26$
   = 24.62 in.; use 25 in.

$m = [26 - (.95 \times 14.12)]/2 = 6.3$ in.

$n = [25 - (.80 \times 14.545)]/2 = 6.7$ in. (use)

f_p (actual) = $480/(25 \times 26)$
   = .738 ksi

$t = \sqrt{(3 \times .738 \times 6.7^2)/27.0}$
   = 1.92 in.; use 2 in.

Use: Base plate 2 × 25 × 2'-2

COLUMN BASE PLATES
Finishing

Rolled steel plates are extensively used for column bases. In order that they may function properly in transmitting loads to masonry supports, finishing is regulated by specification.

In AISC Specification, Sect. 1.21.3, it is stated:

"Column bases shall be finished in accordance with the following requirements:

1. Rolled steel bearing plates, 2 inches or less in thickness, may be used without planing, provided a satisfactory contact bearing is obtained; rolled steel bearing plates over 2 inches but not over 4 inches in thickness may be straightened by pressing; or, if presses are not available, by planing for all bearing surfaces (except as noted under requirement 3 of this Section), to obtain a satisfactory contact bearing; rolled steel bearing plates over 4 inches in thickness shall be planed for all bearing surfaces (except as noted under requirement 3 of this Section).

2. Column bases other than rolled steel bearing plates shall be planed for all bearing surfaces (except as noted under requirement 3 of this Section).

3. The bottom surfaces of bearing plates and column bases which are grouted to insure full bearing contact on foundations need not be planed."

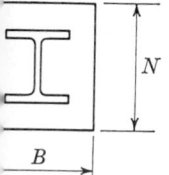

COLUMN BASE PLATES

Dimensions for maximum column loads

Base plates, $F_b = 27$ ksi to 8″ thick
Base plates, $F_b = 24$ ksi over 8″ thick
Concrete, $f'_c = 3000$ psi

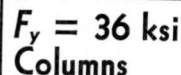

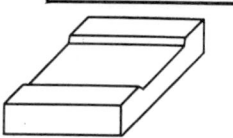

$F_y = 36$ ksi Columns

Column		Unit Pressure on Support $F_p = 0.25 f'_c = 750$ psi						Unit Pressure on Support $F_p = 0.375 f'_c = 1125$ psi					
signation	Max. Load	Dimensions		Thickness of Plate			Gross Wt.	Dimensions		Thickness of Plate			Gross Wt.
		B	N	Calc.	Fin.	Rolled		B	N	Calc.	Fin.	Rolled	
	Kips	In.	In.	In.	In.	In.	Lb.	In.	In.	In.	In.	In.	Lb.
14 × 730	4315	72	80	8.98	9	9½	15502	59	65	8.38	8½	9	9778
665	3928	69	76	8.48	8½	9	13371	56	63	7.46	7½	8	7996
605	3562	66	72	7.52	7½	8	10770	54	59	7.06	7	7½	6769
550	3237	62	70	7.31	7¼	7¾	9529	51	57	6.64	6¾	7¼	5971
500	2933	60	66	6.79	6¾	7¼	8134	49	54	6.21	6¼	6¾	5060
455	2670	57	63	6.45	6½	7	7121	47	51	5.90	5⅞	6¼	4244
14 × 426	2489	55	61	6.21	6¼	6¾	6416	45	50	5.65	5⅝	6	3825
398	2328	54	58	5.85	5⅞	6¼	5546	44	48	5.38	5⅜	5¾	3440
370	2167	52	56	5.60	5⅝	6	4950	42	46	5.11	5⅛	5½	3010
342	2099	51	55	5.52	5½	5⅞	4669	41	46	5.15	5⅛	5½	2939
314	1917	49	53	5.25	5¼	5⅝	4138	40	43	4.75	4¾	5⅛	2497
287	1752	47	50	4.91	4⅞	5¼	3495	38	41	4.44	4½	4⅞	2152
264	1611	45	48	4.65	4⅝	5	3060	36	40	4.29	4¼	4⅝	1887
246	1500	43	47	4.53	4½	4⅞	2791	35	39	4.12	4⅛	4½	1740
237	1446	43	45	4.36	4⅜	4¾	2604	34	38	4.00	4	4	1464
228	1392	42	45	4.26	4¼	4⅝	2476	34	37	3.82	3⅞	3⅞	1381
219	1336	41	44	4.15	4⅛	4½	2300	33	36	3.70	3¾	3¾	1262
211	1288	40	43	4.04	4⅛	4½	2193	33	35	3.58	3⅝	3⅝	1186
202	1232	40	42	3.91	3⅞	3⅞	1844	32	35	3.52	3½	3½	1111
193	1176	39	41	3.78	3¾	3¾	1699	31	34	3.39	3⅜	3⅜	1008
184	1121	38	40	3.65	3⅝	3⅝	1561	31	33	3.22	3¼	3¼	942
176	1071	37	39	3.52	3½	3½	1431	30	32	3.08	3⅛	3⅛	850
167	1017	36	38	3.40	3⅜	3⅜	1308	29	32	3.08	3⅛	3⅛	822
158	963	35	37	3.27	3¼	3¼	1192	29	30	2.90	2⅞	2⅞	709
150	914	34	36	3.15	3⅛	3⅛	1084	28	30	2.76	2¾	2¾	654
142	866	33	35	3.03	3	3	982	27	29	2.63	2⅝	2⅝	582
4 × 320	1954	50	53	5.30	5¼	5⅝	4223	40	44	4.92	4⅞	5¼	2618
4 × 136	826	32	35	3.00	3	3	952	26	29	2.61	2⅝	2⅝	561
127	770	31	34	2.86	2⅞	2⅞	858	25	28	2.47	2½	2½	496
119	723	30	33	2.74	2¾	2¾	771	24	27	2.33	2⅜	2⅜	436
111	675	30	30	2.64	2⅝	2⅝	669	24	25	2.18	2¼	2¼	382
103	625	28	30	2.37	2⅜	2⅜	565	23	25	1.99	2	2	326
95	576	27	29	2.23	2¼	2¼	499	22	24	1.84	1⅞	1⅞	280
87	528	26	28	2.09	2⅛	2⅛	438	21	23	1.69	1¾	1¾	239
4 × 84	503	24	28	2.09	2⅛	2⅛	405	19	24	1.84	1⅞	1⅞	242
78	466	23	28	2.08	2⅛	2⅛	388	19	22	1.65	1¾	1¾	207
4 × 74	436	22	27	1.99	2	2	337	17	23	1.68	1¾	1¾	194
68	400	21	26	1.85	1⅞	1⅞	290	16	23	1.67	1¾	1¾	182
61	358	20	24	1.73	1¾	1¾	238	16	20	1.41	1½	1½	136
4 × 53	302	17	24	1.54	1⅝	1⅝	188	13	21	1.36	1⅜	1⅜	106
48	273	16	23	1.42	1½	1½	156	12	21	1.37	1⅜	1⅜	98
43	244	15	22	1.29	1⅜	1⅜	129	12	19	1.04	1⅛	1⅛	73

te: Rolled plate thicknesses above 4 inches are based on finished thickness plus suggested allowances for finishing one side, and may be modified to suit fabricating plant practice. When it is required to finish both surfaces of base plates, additional allowance must be made.

COLUMN BASE PLATES
Dimensions for maximum column loads

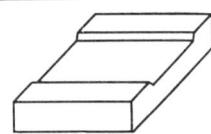

Base plates, F_b = 27 ksi to 8″ thick
Base plates, F_b = 24 ksi over 8″ thick
Concrete, f'_c = 3000 psi

$F_y = 36$ ksi
Columns

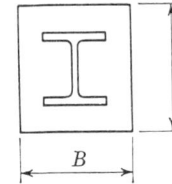

B

Column Designation	Max. Load	Unit Pressure on Support $F_p = 0.25 f'_c = 750$ psi						Unit Pressure on Support $F_p = 0.375 f'_c = 1125$ psi					
		Dimensions		Thickness of Plate			Gross Wt.	Dimensions		Thickness of Plate			Gr. W
		B	N	Calc.	Fin.	Rolled		B	N	Calc.	Fin.	Rolled	
	Kips	In.	In.	In.	In.	In.	Lb.	In.	In.	In.	In.	In.	L
W 12 × 190	1144	38	41	3.98	4	4	1766	30	34	3.59	3⅝	3⅝	1C
161	969	34	38	3.58	3⅝	3⅝	1327	28	31	3.17	3¼	3¼	7
133	799	31	35	3.19	3¼	3¼	999	25	29	2.85	2⅞	2⅞	F
120	721	30	32	2.91	3	3	816	24	27	2.55	2⅝	2⅝	L
106	637	28	31	2.68	2¾	2¾	676	23	25	2.32	2⅜	2⅜	
99	593	27	30	2.55	2⅝	2⅝	602	22	24	2.16	2¼	2¼	
92	553	26	29	2.43	2½	2½	534	21	24	2.09	2⅛	2⅛	
85	510	25	28	2.29	2⅜	2⅜	471	20	23	1.95	2	2	
79	473	24	27	2.17	2¼	2¼	413	20	22	1.79	1⅞	1⅞	
72	432	23	26	2.03	2⅛	2⅛	360	19	21	1.62	1⅝	1⅝	
65	389	22	24	1.79	1⅞	1⅞	280	18	20	1.47	1½	1½	
W 12 × 58	343	20	23	1.73	1¾	1¾	228	16	20	1.45	1½	1½	
53	312	19	22	1.58	1⅝	1⅝	192	15	19	1.32	1⅜	1⅜	
W 12 × 50	286	17	23	1.63	1⅝	1⅝	180	14	19	1.30	1⅜	1⅜	
45	256	16	22	1.50	1½	1½	150	13	18	1.14	1¼	1¼	
40	229	15	21	1.37	1⅜	1⅜	123	12	17	1.00	1	1	
W 10 × 112	663	29	31	2.96	3	3	764	23	26	2.67	2¾	2¾	
100	592	27	30	2.77	2¾	2¾	631	22	24	2.42	2½	2½	
89	527	26	28	2.52	2½	2½	516	21	23	2.22	2¼	2¼	
77	456	24	26	2.27	2¼	2¼	398	19	22	2.07	2⅛	2⅛	
72	426	23	25	2.16	2¼	2¼	367	19	20	1.92	2	2	
66	390	22	24	2.03	2⅛	2⅛	318	18	20	1.76	1¾	1⅝	
60	355	21	23	1.90	2	2	274	17	19	1.62	1¾	1⅝	
54	319	20	22	1.76	1¾	1¾	218	16	18	1.47	1½	1½	
49	289	19	21	1.63	1⅝	1⅝	184	16	17	1.37	1⅜	1⅜	
W 10 × 45	257	17	21	1.61	1⅝	1⅝	164	14	17	1.31	1⅜	1⅜	
39	224	16	19	1.37	1⅜	1⅜	118	13	16	1.14	1¼	1¼	
33	189	14	18	1.26	1¼	1¼	89	12	14	.99	1	1	
W 8 × 67	387	22	24	2.20	2¼	2¼	337	18	20	1.98	2	2	
58	336	20	23	2.09	2⅛	2⅛	277	16	19	1.87	1⅞	1⅞	
48	276	18	21	1.84	1⅞	1⅞	201	15	17	1.55	1⅝	1⅝	
40	231	17	19	1.57	1⅝	1⅝	149	14	15	1.32	1⅜	1⅜	
35	201	16	17	1.37	1⅜	1⅜	106	13	14	1.15	1¼	1¼	
31	178	15	16	1.23	1¼	1¼	85	12	14	1.10	1⅛	1⅛	
W 8 × 28	172	14	17	1.32	1⅜	1⅜	93	11	14	1.12	1⅛	1⅛	
24	148	13	16	1.19	1¼	1¼	74	11	12	1.02	1⅛	1⅛	
W 8 × 20	122	11	15	1.04	1⅛	1⅛	53	9	13	.90	1	1	
17	103	10	14	.91	1	1	40	8	12	.76	⅞	⅞	

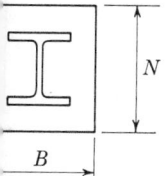

COLUMN BASE PLATES
Dimensions for maximum column loads

Base plates, F_b = 27 ksi to 8″ thick
Base plates, F_b = 24 ksi over 8″ thick
Concrete, f'_c = 3000 psi

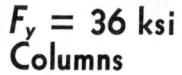
F_y = 36 ksi
Columns

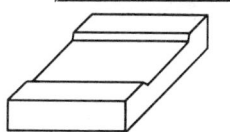

Column Designation	Max. Load	Unit Pressure on Support $F_p = 0.25 f'_c = 750$ psi						Unit Pressure on Support $F_p = 0.375 f'_c = 1125$ psi					
		Dimensions		Thickness of Plate			Gross Wt.	Dimensions		Thickness of Plate			Gross Wt.
		B	N	Calc.	Fin.	Rolled		B	N	Calc.	Fin.	Rolled	
	Kips	In.	In.	In.	In.	In.	Lb.	In.	In.	In.	In.	In.	Lb.
6 × 25	153	14	15	1.30	1⅜	1⅜	82	11	13	1.20	1¼	1¼	51
20	123	12	14	1.16	1¼	1¼	59	10	11	.91	1	1	31
15.5	95	11	12	.89	1	1	37	9	10	.74	¾	¾	19
6 × 16	96	10	13	1.01	1⅛	1⅛	41	8	11	.88	⅞	⅞	22
12	72	9	11	.82	⅞	⅞	25	7	10	.73	¾	¾	15
8.5	51	7	10	.63	¾	¾	15	6	8	.49	½	½	7
5 × 18.5	112	12	13	1.15	1¼	1¼	55	10	10	1.05	1⅛	1⅛	32
16	97	11	12	1.04	1⅛	1⅛	42	9	10	.91	1	1	25
4 × 13	78	10	11	.99	1	1	31	8	9	.88	⅞	⅞	18
8 × 34.3	212	16	18	1.49	1½	1½	122	13	15	1.29	1⅜	1⅜	76
32.6	201	16	17	1.38	1⅜	1⅜	106	13	14	1.16	1¼	1¼	64
5 × 22.5	137	13	15	1.30	1⅜	1⅜	76	11	12	1.07	1⅛	1⅛	42
20	122	12	14	1.18	1¼	1¼	59	10	11	.93	1	1	31
5 × 18.9	114	12	13	1.18	1¼	1¼	55	10	11	1.06	1⅛	1⅛	35
4 × 13	77	10	11	1.00	1	1	31	8	9	.90	1	1	20
5 × 17.25	99	10	14	1.16	1¼	1¼	50	8	11	.94	1	1	25
12.5	72	8	12	.91	1	1	27	7	10	.73	¾	¾	15
5 × 14.75	84	10	12	1.03	1⅛	1⅛	38	8	10	.92	1	1	23
10	57	8	10	.79	⅞	⅞	20	6	9	.73	¾	¾	11
4 × 9.5	53	8	9	.82	⅞	⅞	18	6	8	.74	¾	¾	10
7.7	43	7	9	.72	¾	¾	13	5	8	.73	¾	¾	8
3 × 7.5	41	7	8	.73	¾	¾	12	6	7	.68	¾	¾	9
5.7	31	6	7	.59	⅝	⅝	7	5	6	.53	⅝	⅝	5

Notes

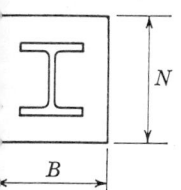

COLUMN BASE PLATES
Dimensions for maximum column loads

Base plates, F_b = 27 ksi to 8″ thick
Base plates, F_b = 24 ksi over 8″ thick
Concrete, f'_c = 3000 psi

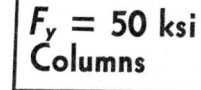
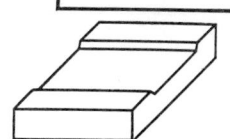

Column		Unit Pressure on Support $F_p = 0.25 f'_c = 750$ psi						Unit Pressure on Support $F_p = 0.375 f'_c = 1125$ psi					
	Max. Load	Dimensions		Thickness of Plate			Gross Wt.	Dimensions		Thickness of Plate			Gross Wt.
Designation		B	N	Calc.	Fin.	Rolled		B	N	Calc.	Fin.	Rolled	
	Kips	In.	In.	In.	In.	In.	Lb.	In.	In.	In.	In.	In.	Lb.
14 × 730*	5443	82	89	10.33	10¼	10¾	22226	66	74	9.83	9¾	10¼	14182
665*	4953	78	85	9.84	9¾	10¼	19252	63	70	9.26	9¼	9¾	12181
605*	4490	74	81	9.34	9¼	9¾	16573	60	67	8.80	8¾	9¼	10535
550	4411	74	80	9.27	9¼	9¾	16352	60	66	8.72	8¾	9¼	10377
500	3995	71	76	8.73	8¾	9¼	14140	57	63	7.80	7¾	8¼	8393
455	3635	67	73	8.31	8¼	8¾	12137	54	60	7.40	7½	8	7343
14 × 426	3388	65	70	7.51	7½	8	10312	53	57	7.00	7	7½	6419
398	3168	63	68	7.25	7¼	7¾	9406	51	56	6.78	6¾	7¼	5866
370	2947	60	66	7.04	7	7½	8414	49	54	6.50	6½	7	5247
342	2890	60	65	6.93	7	7½	8287	49	53	6.39	6½	7	5150
314	2639	58	61	6.48	6½	7	7016	47	50	6.01	6	6½	4327
287	2412	55	59	6.18	6¼	6¾	6205	45	48	5.65	5⅝	6	3672
264	2217	53	56	5.81	5⅞	6¼	5255	43	46	5.35	5⅜	5¾	3222
246	2065	51	54	5.57	5⅝	6	4681	42	44	5.15	5⅛	5½	2879
237	1990	50	54	5.54	5½	5⅞	4494	41	44	5.02	5	5⅜	2747
228	1916	49	53	5.41	5⅜	5¾	4230	40	43	4.89	4⅞	5¼	2558
219	1838	48	52	5.28	5¼	5⅝	3978	39	42	4.75	4¾	5⅛	2378
211	1772	47	51	5.16	5⅛	5½	3735	39	41	4.62	4⅝	5	2265
202	1695	47	49	4.92	4⅞	5¼	3425	38	40	4.47	4½	4⅞	2099
193	1618	45	48	4.80	4⅞	5¼	3213	37	39	4.31	4⅜	4¾	1942
184	1543	44	47	4.66	4⅝	5	2929	36	39	4.26	4¼	4⅝	1840
176	1474	43	46	4.53	4½	4⅞	2732	35	38	4.13	4⅛	4½	1696
167	1400	42	45	4.39	4⅜	4¾	2543	34	37	3.98	4	4	1426
158	1326	41	44	4.25	4¼	4⅝	2364	33	36	3.83	3⅞	3⅞	1304
150	1257	40	42	4.02	4	4	1904	33	34	3.63	3⅝	3⅝	1152
142	1191	39	41	3.88	3⅞	3⅞	1755	32	34	3.49	3½	3½	1079
14 × 320	2689	58	62	6.64	6¾	7¼	7386	47	51	6.18	6¼	6¾	4584
14 × 136	1136	38	40	3.78	3¾	3¾	1615	31	33	3.37	3⅜	3⅜	978
127	1059	37	39	3.60	3⅝	3⅝	1482	30	32	3.19	3¼	3¼	884
119	993	35	38	3.49	3½	3½	1319	29	31	3.03	3	3	764
111	928	34	37	3.34	3⅜	3⅜	1203	28	30	2.86	2⅞	2⅞	684
103	860	33	35	3.08	3⅛	3⅛	1023	27	29	2.70	2¾	2¾	610
95	791	32	33	2.94	3	3	897	26	28	2.53	2⅝	2⅝	541
87	726	31	32	2.77	2¾	2¾	773	25	26	2.36	2⅜	2⅜	437
14 × 84	689	28	33	2.81	2⅞	2⅞	753	23	27	2.38	2⅜	2⅜	418
78	638	28	31	2.63	2⅝	2⅝	645	22	26	2.23	2¼	2¼	365
14 × 74	595	26	31	2.57	2⅝	2⅝	599	21	26	2.25	2¼	2¼	348
68	545	24	31	2.52	2½	2½	527	20	25	2.08	2⅛	2⅛	301
61	487	23	29	2.25	2¼	2¼	425	19	23	1.94	2	2	248
14 × 53	408	20	28	2.10	2⅛	2⅛	337	16	23	1.71	1¾	1¾	182
48	369	19	26	1.86	1⅞	1⅞	262	15	22	1.57	1⅝	1⅝	152
43	329	18	25	1.71	1¾	1¾	223	14	21	1.41	1½	1½	125

Note: Rolled plate thicknesses above 4 inches are based on finished thickness plus suggested allowances for finishing one side, and may be modified to suit fabricating plant practice. When it is required to finish both surfaces of base plates, additional allowance must be made.
* Available under ASTM A588 at F_y = 46 ksi.

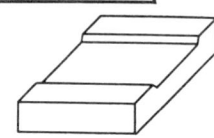

F_y = 50 ksi Columns

COLUMN BASE PLATES
Dimensions for maximum column loads

Base plates, F_b = 27 ksi to 8″ thick
Base plates, F_b = 24 ksi over 8″ thick
Concrete, f'_c = 3000 psi

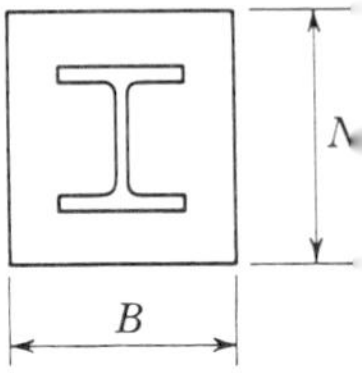

Column Designation	Max. Load	Unit Pressure on Support $F_p = 0.25 f'_c = 750$ psi						Unit Pressure on Support $F_p = 0.375 f'_c = 1125$ psi					
		Dimensions B	N	Thickness of Plate Calc.	Fin.	Rolled	Gross Wt.	Dimensions B	N	Thickness of Plate Calc.	Fin.	Rolled	Gross Wt.
	Kips	In.	In.	In.	In.	In.	Lb.	In.	In.	In.	In.	In.	Lb.
W 12 × 190	1569	44	48	4.93	5	5⅜	3216	35	40	4.65	4⅝	5	198
161	1329	41	44	4.43	4½	4⅞	2491	33	36	4.05	4⅛	4½	15
133	1095	37	40	3.91	3⅞	3⅞	1625	30	33	3.56	3⅝	3⅝	10
120	987	35	38	3.67	3¾	3¾	1413	29	31	3.34	3⅜	3⅜	8
106	872	33	36	3.39	3⅜	3⅜	1136	27	29	3.03	3	3	6
99	813	32	34	3.21	3¼	3¼	1002	26	28	2.86	2⅞	2⅞	5
92	757	31	33	3.05	3⅛	3⅛	906	25	27	2.70	2¾	2¾	5
85	698	30	32	2.89	2⅞	2⅞	782	24	26	2.52	2½	2½	4
79	647	28	31	2.77	2¾	2¾	676	23	25	2.36	2⅜	2⅜	3
72	591	27	30	2.61	2⅝	2⅝	602	22	24	2.18	2¼	2¼	3
65	533	26	28	2.35	2⅜	2⅜	490	21	23	2.01	2	2	2
W 12 × 58	467	24	26	2.31	2⅜	2⅜	420	19	22	1.94	2	2	2
53	425	22	26	2.09	2⅛	2⅛	344	18	22	1.82	1⅞	1⅞	2
W 12 × 50	386	20	26	2.07	2⅛	2⅛	313	16	22	1.82	1⅞	1⅞	1
45	346	19	25	1.93	2	2	269	15	21	1.67	1¾	1¾	1
40	310	18	23	1.68	1¾	1¾	205	14	20	1.52	1⅝	1⅝	1
W 10 × 112	905	33	37	3.76	3¾	3¾	1297	27	30	3.38	3⅜	3⅜	7
100	808	31	35	3.52	3½	3½	1076	26	28	3.11	3⅛	3⅛	6
89	720	30	32	3.14	3⅛	3⅛	850	24	27	2.93	3	3	5
77	623	28	30	2.86	2⅞	2⅞	684	23	25	2.59	2⅝	2⅝	4
72	581	27	29	2.73	2¾	2¾	610	22	24	2.45	2½	2½	3
66	532	26	28	2.58	2⅝	2⅝	541	21	23	2.30	2⅜	2⅜	3
60	485	24	27	2.49	2½	2½	459	20	22	2.15	2⅛	2⅛	2
54	435	24	25	2.27	2¼	2¼	382	19	21	1.98	2	2	2
49	394	22	24	2.09	2⅛	2⅛	318	18	20	1.83	1⅞	1⅞	1
W 10 × 45	348	20	24	2.04	2⅛	2⅛	289	16	20	1.81	1⅞	1⅞	1
39	303	19	22	1.79	1⅞	1⅞	222	15	18	1.52	1⅝	1⅝	1
33	255	17	20	1.55	1⅝	1⅝	157	14	17	1.33	1⅜	1⅜	
W 8 × 67	525	25	28	2.81	2⅞	2⅞	570	21	23	2.51	2½	2½	3
58	455	24	26	2.52	2½	2½	442	19	22	2.38	2⅜	2⅜	2
48	375	22	23	2.22	2¼	2¼	323	18	19	2.01	2	2	1
40	312	20	21	1.94	2	2	238	16	18	1.76	1¾	1¾	1
35	272	18	21	1.88	1⅞	1⅞	201	15	17	1.60	1⅝	1⅝	1
31	241	17	19	1.64	1⅝	1⅝	149	14	16	1.45	1½	1½	
W 8 × 28	237	17	19	1.68	1¾	1¾	160	14	16	1.50	1½	1½	
24	203	16	17	1.56	1⅝	1⅝	125	13	14	1.37	1⅜	1⅜	
W 8 × 20	167	14	16	1.41	1½	1½	95	11	14	1.18	1¼	1¼	
17	142	12	16	1.20	1¼	1¼	68	10	13	1.01	1⅛	1⅛	

Note: Rolled plate thicknesses above 4 inches are based on finished thickness plus suggested allowances for finishing one side, and may be modified to suit fabricating plant practice. When it is required to finish both surfaces of base plates, additional allowance must be made.

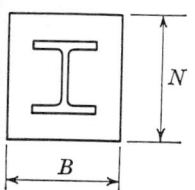

COLUMN BASE PLATES
Dimensions for maximum column loads

Base plates, $F_b = 27$ ksi to 8″ thick
Base plates, $F_b = 24$ ksi over 8″ thick
Concrete, $f'_c = 3000$ psi

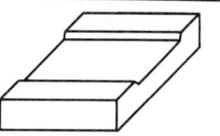

Column							Unit Pressure on Support $F_p = 0.25\,f'_c = 750$ psi						Unit Pressure on Support $F_p = 0.375\,f'_c = 1125$ psi					
Designation	Max. Load	Dimensions		Thickness of Plate			Gross Wt.	Dimensions		Thickness of Plate			Gross Wt.
		B	N	Calc.	Fin.	Rolled		B	N	Calc.	Fin.	Rolled	
	Kips	In.	In.	In.	In.	In.	Lb.	In.	In.	In.	In.	In.	Lb.
W 6 × 25	211	16	18	1.70	1¾	1¾	143	13	15	1.55	1⅝	1⅝	90
20	169	15	16	1.42	1½	1½	102	12	13	1.25	1¼	1¼	55
15.5	131	13	14	1.17	1¼	1¼	64	10	12	1.10	1⅛	1⅛	38
W 6 × 16	131	12	15	1.29	1⅜	1⅜	70	9	13	1.25	1¼	1¼	41
12	98	11	12	1.12	1⅛	1⅛	42	8	11	.93	1	1	25
8.5	69	9	11	.81	⅞	⅞	25	7	9	.67	¾	¾	13
W 5 × 18.5	154	14	15	1.45	1½	1½	89	12	12	1.38	1⅜	1⅜	56
16	133	13	14	1.32	1⅜	1⅜	71	11	11	1.22	1¼	1¼	43
W 4 × 13	106	12	12	1.25	1¼	1¼	51	9	11	1.22	1¼	1¼	35
M 8 × 34.3	293	19	21	1.91	2	2	226	16	17	1.66	1¾	1¾	135
32.6	278	19	20	1.80	1⅞	1⅞	202	15	17	1.64	1⅝	1⅝	117
M 6 × 22.5	189	15	17	1.62	1⅝	1⅝	117	12	14	1.47	1½	1½	71
20	168	14	16	1.49	1½	1½	95	12	13	1.26	1¼	1¼	55
M 5 × 18.9	157	14	15	1.48	1½	1½	89	11	13	1.44	1½	1½	61
M 4 × 13	105	12	12	1.26	1¼	1¼	51	9	11	1.24	1¼	1¼	35
S 6 × 17.25	134	12	15	1.34	1⅜	1⅜	70	10	12	1.26	1¼	1¼	42
12.5	98	10	14	1.16	1¼	1¼	50	8	11	.94	1	1	25
S 5 × 14.75	113	11	14	1.32	1⅜	1⅜	60	9	12	1.24	1¼	1¼	38
10	77	9	12	1.02	1⅛	1⅛	34	7	10	.92	1	1	20
S 4 × 9.5	71	9	11	1.02	1⅛	1⅛	32	8	8	1.01	1⅛	1⅛	20
7.7	58	8	10	.88	⅞	⅞	20	7	8	.83	⅞	⅞	14
S 3 × 7.5	55	8	10	.99	1	1	23	7	7	.88	⅞	⅞	12
5.7	42	7	8	.74	¾	¾	12	6	7	.69	¾	¾	9

PART 4
Connections

RIVETS AND THREADED FASTENERS
Tension
Allowable loads in kips

Unfinished Bolts and Threaded Parts
Tension on tensile stress area

ASTM Designation or Yield Stress		Allowable Tensile Stress F_t ksi	Nominal Diameter, in.							
			5/8	3/4	7/8	1	1 1/8	1 1/4	1 3/8	1 1/2
			Tensile Stress Area, sq. in.							
			0.2260	0.3345	0.4617	0.6057	0.7633	0.9691	1.1549	1.4053
A307 Bolts		20.0	4.52	6.69	9.23	12.11	15.27	19.38	23.10	28.11
Threaded Parts F_u, ksi	36	22.0	4.97	7.36	10.16	13.33	16.79	21.32	25.41	30.92
	42	25.2	5.70	8.41	11.64	15.27	19.23	24.42	29.23	35.53
	45	27.0	6.10	9.03	12.47	16.35	20.61	26.17	31.18	37.94
	50	30.0	6.78	10.04	13.85	18.17	22.90	29.07	34.65	42.16
	55	33.0	7.46	11.04	15.24	19.99	25.19	31.98	38.11	46.37
	60	36.0	8.14	12.04	16.62	21.81	—	—	—	—

The definition of tensile stress area is given in the AISC Specification, Section 1.5.2.1. Values are based on UNC thread dimensions.

Nuts must meet specifications compatible with threaded parts.

For Upset Rods see AISC Specification, Section 1.5.2.1.

Rivets and High Strength Bolts
Tension on gross (nominal) area

ASTM Designation		Allowable Tensile Stress F_t ksi	Nominal Diameter, in.							
			5/8	3/4	7/8	1	1 1/8	1 1/4	1 3/8	1 1/2
			Gross (Nominal) Area, sq. in.							
			0.3068	0.4418	0.6013	0.7854	0.9940	1.2272	1.4849	1.7671
Rivets	A502-1	20.0	6.14	8.84	12.03	15.71	19.88	24.54	29.70	35.34
	A502-2	27.0	8.28	11.93	16.24	21.21	26.84	33.13	40.09	47.71
Bolts	A325	40.0	12.27	17.67	24.05	31.42	39.76	49.09	59.40	70.68
	A490	54.0[a]	16.57[a]	23.86[a]	32.47[a]	42.41[a]	53.68[a]	66.27[a]	80.18[a]	95.42[a]

[a] For static loading only.

For allowable combined shear and tension loads, see AISC Specification, Section 1.6.3.

RIVETS AND THREADED FASTENERS
Shear
Allowable loads in kips

Power Driven Shop and Field Rivets

Diam. — Area	⅝ in. — 0.3068 sq. in.		¾ in. — 0.4418 sq. in.	
ASTM Designation	A502-1	A502-2	A502-1	A502-2
Shear F_v, ksi	15.0	20.0	15.0	20.0
Single Shear, kips	4.60	6.14	6.63	8.84
Double Shear, kips	9.20	12.27	13.25	17.67

Unfinished Bolts, ASTM A307, and Threaded Parts, $F_y = 36$ ksi[a]

Diam. — Area	⅝ in. — 0.3068 sq. in.		¾ in. — 0.4418 sq. in.	
ASTM Designation or Yield Stress, ksi	A307	$F_y = 36$	A307	$F_y = 36$
Shear F_v, ksi	10.0	10.8[a]	10.0	10.8[a]
Single Shear, kips	3.07	3.31	4.42	4.77
Double Shear, kips	6.14	6.63	8.84	9.54

High Strength Bolts in Friction Type Connections and in Bearing Type Connections with Threads in Shear Planes

Diam. — Area	⅝ in. — 0.3068 sq. in.			¾ in. — 0.4418 sq. in.		
[b]ASTM Designation	A325-F A325-N	A490-F	A490-N	A325-F A325-N	A490-F	A490-N
Shear F_v, ksi	15.0	20.0	22.5	15.0	20.0	22.5
Single Shear, kips	4.60	6.14	6.90	6.63	8.84	9.94
Double Shear, kips	9.20	12.27	13.81	13.25	17.67	19.88

High Strength Bolts in Bearing Type Connections with Threads Excluded from Shear Planes

Diam. — Area	⅝ in. — 0.3068 sq. in.		¾ in. — 0.4418 sq. in.	
[b]ASTM Designation	A325-X	A490-X	A325-X	A490-X
Shear F_v, ksi	22.0	32.0	22.0	32.0
Single Shear, kips	6.75	9.82	9.72	14.14
Double Shear, kips	13.50	19.64	19.44	28.28

[a] For threaded parts of material other than $F_y = 36$ ksi steel, use $F_v = 0.30 F_y$.
[b] The letter suffixes following the ASTM Designations A325 and A490 represent the following:
   F: Friction type connection
   N: Bearing type connection with threads **included** in shear plane
   X: Bearing type connection with threads **excluded** from shear plane

AMERICAN INSTITUTE OF STEEL CONSTRUCTION

RIVETS AND THREADED FASTENERS
Bearing
Allowable loads in kips
All rivets and bolts in bearing type connections

Diam., in.	5/8								3/4							
F_y, ksi	36	42	45	50	55	60	65	100	36	42	45	50	55	60	65	100
Bearing F_p, ksi	48.6	56.7	60.8	67.5	74.3	81.0	87.8	135	48.6	56.7	60.8	67.5	74.3	81.0	87.8	135
1/8	3.80	4.43	4.75	5.27	5.80	6.33	6.86	10.5	4.56	5.31	5.70	6.33	6.97	7.59	8.23	12.7
3/16	5.70	6.64	7.13	7.91	8.71	9.49	10.3	15.8	6.83	7.97	8.55	9.49	10.4	11.4	12.3	19.0
1/4	7.59	8.86	9.50	10.6	11.6	12.7	13.7	21.1	9.11	10.6	11.4	12.7	13.9	15.2	16.5	25.3
5/16	9.49	11.1	11.9	13.2	14.5	15.8	17.1	26.4	11.4	13.3	14.3	15.8	17.4	19.0	20.6	31.6
3/8	11.4	13.3	14.3	15.8	17.4	19.0	20.6	31.6	13.7	15.9	17.1	19.0	20.9	22.8	24.7	38.0
7/16	13.3	15.5	16.6	18.5	20.3	22.1		36.9	15.9	18.6	19.9	22.1	24.4	26.6	28.8	44.3
1/2	15.2	17.7	19.0	21.1				42.2	18.2	21.3	22.8	25.3	27.9	30.4		50.6
9/16	17.1	19.9	21.4					47.5	20.5	23.9	25.7	28.5	31.3			57.0
5/8	19.0							52.7	22.8	26.6	28.5					63.3
11/16	20.9							58.0	25.1	29.2						69.6
3/4								63.3	27.3							75.9
13/16								68.6	29.6							82.3
7/8								73.8								88.6
15/16								79.1								94.9
1	30.4	35.4	38.0	42.2	46.4	50.6	54.9	84.4	36.5	42.5	45.6	50.6	55.7	60.8	65.9	101

MATERIAL THICKNESS

This table not applicable to fasteners in friction type connections.

F_y is the yield stress of the connected material; see AISC Specification, Sect. 1.5.2.2.

F_p, the unit bearing stress, applies equally to conditions of single shear and enclosed bearing.

Values for thicknesses not listed may be obtained by multiplying the unlisted thickness by the value given for a 1" thickness in the appropriate F_y column.

Values for F_y's not listed may be obtained by multiplying the value given for $F_y = 100$ ksi by the unlisted F_y and dividing by 100.

RIVETS AND THREADED FASTENERS
Shear
Allowable loads in kips

Power Driven Shop and Field Rivets

Diam. — Area	7/8 in. — 0.6013 sq. in.		1 in. — 0.7854 sq. in.	
ASTM Designation	A502-1	A502-2	A502-1	A502-2
Shear F_v, ksi	15.0	20.0	15.0	20.0
Single Shear, kips Double Shear, kips	9.02 18.04	12.03 24.05	11.78 23.56	15.71 31.42

Unfinished Bolts, ASTM A307, and Threaded Parts, $F_y = 36$ ksi[a]

Diam. — Area	7/8 in. — 0.6013 sq. in.		1 in. — 0.7854 sq. in.	
ASTM Designation or Yield Stress, ksi	A307	$F_y = 36$	A307	$F_y = 36$
Shear F_v, ksi	10.0	10.8[a]	10.0	10.8[a]
Single Shear, kips Double Shear, kips	6.01 12.03	6.49 12.99	7.85 15.71	8.48 16.96

High Strength Bolts in Friction Type Connections and in Bearing Type Connections with Threads in Shear Planes

Diam. — Area	7/8 in. — 0.6013 sq. in.			1 in. — 0.7854 sq. in.		
[b]ASTM Designation	A325-F A325-N	A490-F	A490-N	A325-F A325-N	A490-F	A490-N
Shear F_v, ksi	15.0	20.0	22.5	15.0	20.0	22.5
Single Shear, kips Double Shear, kips	9.02 18.04	12.03 24.05	13.53 27.06	11.78 23.56	15.71 31.42	17.67 35.34

High Strength Bolts in Bearing Type Connections with Threads Excluded from Shear Planes

Diam. — Area	7/8 in. — 0.6013 sq. in.		1 in. — 0.7854 sq. in.	
[b]ASTM Designation	A325-X	A490-X	A325-X	A490-X
Shear F_v, ksi	22.0	32.0	22.0	32.0
Single Shear, kips Double Shear, kips	13.23 26.46	19.24 38.48	17.28 34.56	25.13 50.27

[a] For threaded parts of material other than $F_y = 36$ ksi steel, use $F_v = 0.30\, F_y$.
[b] The letter suffixes following the ASTM Designations A325 and A490 represent the following:
    F: Friction type connection
    N: Bearing type connection with threads **included** in shear plane
    X: Bearing type connection with threads **excluded** from shear plane

RIVETS AND THREADED FASTENERS
Bearing

Allowable loads in kips
All rivets and bolts in bearing type connections

Diam., in.	7/8								1							
F_y, ksi	36	42	45	50	55	60	65	100	36	42	45	50	55	60	65	100
Bearing F_p, ksi	48.6	56.7	60.8	67.5	74.3	81.0	87.8	135	48.6	56.7	60.8	67.5	74.3	81.0	87.8	135
1/8	5.32	6.20	6.65	7.38	8.13	8.86	9.60	14.8	6.08	7.09	7.60	8.44	9.29	10.1	11.0	16.9
3/16	7.97	9.30	9.98	11.1	12.2	13.3	14.4	22.1	9.11	10.6	11.4	12.7	13.9	15.2	16.5	25.3
1/4	10.6	12.4	13.3	14.8	16.3	17.7	19.2	29.5	12.2	14.2	15.2	16.9	18.6	20.3	22.0	33.8
5/16	13.3	15.5	16.6	18.5	20.3	22.1	24.0	36.9	15.2	17.7	19.0	21.1	23.2	25.3	27.4	42.2
3/8	15.9	18.6	20.0	22.1	24.4	26.6	28.8	44.3	18.2	21.3	22.8	25.3	27.9	30.4	32.9	50.6
7/16	18.6	21.7	23.3	25.8	28.4	31.0	33.6	51.7	21.3	24.8	26.6	29.5	32.5	35.4	38.4	59.1
1/2	21.3	24.8	26.6	29.5	32.5	35.4	38.4	59.1	24.3	28.4	30.4	33.8	37.2	40.5	43.9	67.5
9/16	23.9	27.9	29.9	33.2	36.6	39.9	43.2	66.4	27.3	31.9	34.2	38.0	41.8	45.6	49.4	75.9
5/8	26.6	31.0	33.3	36.9	40.6			73.8	30.4	35.4	38.0	42.2	46.4	50.6	54.9	84.4
11/16	29.2	34.1	36.6	40.6				81.2	33.4	39.0	41.8	46.4	51.1			92.8
3/4	31.9	37.2	39.9					88.6	36.5	42.5	45.6	50.6				101
13/16	34.6	40.3						96.0	39.5	46.1	49.4					110
7/8	37.2							103	42.5	49.6	53.2					118
15/16	39.9							111	45.6	53.2						127
1	42.5	49.6	53.2	59.1	65.0	70.9	76.8	118	48.6	56.7	60.8	67.5	74.3	81.0	87.8	135
1 1/16								126	51.6							143

This table not applicable to fasteners in friction type connections.

F_y is the yield stress of the connected material; see AISC Specification, Sect. 1.5.2.2.

F_p, the unit bearing stress, applies equally to conditions of single shear and enclosed bearing.

Values for thicknesses not listed may be obtained by multiplying the unlisted thickness by the value given for a 1″ thickness in the appropriate F_y column.

Values for F_y's not listed may be obtained by multiplying the value given for $F_y = 100$ ksi by the unlisted F_y and dividing by 100.

RIVETS AND THREADED FASTENERS
Shear
Allowable loads in kips

Power Driven Shop and Field Rivets				
Diam. — Area	1⅛ in. — 0.9940 sq. in.		1¼ in. — 1.2272 sq. in.	
ASTM Designation	A502-1	A502-2	A502-1	A502-2
Shear F_v, ksi	15.0	20.0	15.0	20.0
Single Shear, kips Double Shear, kips	14.91 29.82	19.88 39.76	18.41 36.82	24.54 49.09

Unfinished Bolts, ASTM A307, and Threaded Parts, $F_y = 36$ ksi[a]				
Diam. — Area	1⅛ in. — 0.9940 sq. in.		1¼ in. — 1.2272 sq. in.	
ASTM Designation or Yield Stress, ksi	A307	$F_y = 36$	A307	$F_y = 36$
Shear F_v, ksi	10.0	10.8[a]	10.0	10.8[a]
Single Shear, kips Double Shear, kips	9.94 19.88	10.74 21.47	12.27 24.54	13.25 26.51

High Strength Bolts in Friction Type Connections and in Bearing Type Connections with Threads in Shear Planes						
Diam. — Area	1⅛ in. — 0.9940 sq. in.			1¼ in. — 1.2272 sq. in.		
[b]ASTM Designation	A325-F A325-N	A490-F	A490-N	A325-F A325-N	A490-F	A490-N
Shear F_v, ksi	15.0	20.0	22.5	15.0	20.0	22.5
Single Shear, kips Double Shear, kips	14.91 29.82	19.88 39.76	22.37 44.73	18.41 36.82	24.54 49.09	27.61 55.22

High Strength Bolts in Bearing Type Connections with Threads Excluded from Shear Planes				
Diam. — Area	1⅛ in. — 0.9940 sq. in.		1¼ in. — 1.2272 sq. in.	
[b]ASTM Designation	A325-X	A490-X	A325-X	A490-X
Shear F_v, ksi	22.0	32.0	22.0	32.0
Single Shear, kips Double Shear, kips	21.87 43.74	31.81 63.62	27.00 54.00	39.27 78.54

[a] For threaded parts of material other than $F_y = 36$ ksi steel, use $F_v = 0.30\ F_y$.
[b] The letter suffixes following the ASTM Designations A325 and A490 represent the following:
    F: Friction type connection
    N: Bearing type connection with threads **included** in shear plane
    X: Bearing type connection with threads **excluded** from shear plane

RIVETS AND THREADED FASTENERS
Bearing

Allowable loads in kips
All rivets and bolts in bearing type connection

Diam., in.	1⅛								1¼							
F_y, ksi	36	42	45	50	55	60	65	100	36	42	45	50	55	60	65	100
Bearing F_p, ksi	48.6	56.7	60.8	67.5	74.3	81.0	87.8	135	48.6	56.7	60.8	67.5	74.3	81.0	87.8	135
⅛	6.83	7.97	8.55	9.49	10.4	11.4	12.3	19.0	7.59	8.86	9.50	10.6	11.6	12.7	13.7	21.1
3/16	10.2	12.0	12.8	14.2	15.7	17.1	18.5	28.5	11.4	13.3	14.3	15.8	17.4	19.0	20.6	31.6
¼	13.7	15.9	17.1	19.0	20.9	22.8	24.7	38.0	15.2	17.7	19.0	21.1	23.2	25.3	27.4	42.2
5/16	17.1	19.9	21.4	23.7	26.1	28.5	30.9	47.5	19.0	22.1	23.7	26.4	29.0	31.6	34.3	52.7
⅜	20.5	23.9	25.7	28.5	31.3	34.2	37.0	57.0	22.8	26.6	28.5	31.6	34.8	38.0	41.2	63.3
7/16	23.9	27.9	29.9	33.2	36.6	39.9	43.2	66.4	26.6	31.0	33.3	36.9	40.6	44.3	48.0	73.8
½	27.3	31.9	34.2	38.0	41.8	45.6	49.4	75.9	30.4	35.4	38.0	42.2	46.4	50.6	54.9	84.4
9/16	30.8	35.9	38.5	42.7	47.0	51.3	55.6	85.4	34.2	39.9	42.7	47.5	52.2	57.0	61.7	94.9
⅝	34.2	39.9	42.7	47.5	52.2	57.0	61.7	94.9	38.0	44.3	47.5	52.7	58.1	63.3	68.6	105
11/16	37.6	43.9	47.0	52.2	57.5	62.6	67.9	104	41.8	48.7	52.5	58.0	63.9	69.6	75.5	116
¾	41.0	47.8	51.3	57.0	62.7	68.3		114	45.6	53.2	57.0	63.3	69.7	75.9	82.3	127
13/16	44.4	51.8	55.6	61.7	67.9			123	49.4	57.6	61.7	68.6	75.5	82.3		137
⅞	47.8	55.8	59.9	66.4				133	53.2	62.0	66.5	73.8	81.3			148
15/16	51.3	59.8	64.1					142	57.0	66.4	71.3	79.1				158
1	54.7	63.8	68.4	75.9	83.6	91.1	98.8	152	60.8	70.9	76.0	84.4	92.9	101	110	169
1 1/16	58.1							161	64.5	75.3	80.7					179
1⅛	61.5							171	68.3	79.7						190
1 3/16	64.9							180	72.1							200
1¼									75.9							211
1 5/16									79.7							221

MATERIAL THICKNESS

This table not applicable to fasteners in friction type connections.

F_y is the yield stress of the connected material; see AISC Specification, Sect. 1.5.2.2.

F_p, the unit bearing stress, applies equally to conditions of single shear and enclosed bearing.

Values for thicknesses not listed may be obtained by multiplying the unlisted thickness by the value given for a 1″ thickness in the appropriate F_y column.

Values for F_y's not listed may be obtained by multiplying the value given for $F_y = 100$ ksi by the unlisted F_y and dividing by 100.

RIVETS AND THREADED FASTENERS
Shear
Allowable load in kips

Power Driven Shop and Field Rivets

Diam. — Area	1⅜ in. — 1.4849 sq. in.		1½ in. — 1.7671 sq. in.	
ASTM Designation	A502-1	A502-2	A502-1	A502-2
Shear F_v, ksi	15.0	20.0	15.0	20.0
Single Shear, kips	22.27	29.70	26.51	35.34
Double Shear, kips	44.55	59.40	53.01	70.68

Unfinished Bolts, ASTM A307, and Threaded Parts, $F_y = 36$ ksi[a]

Diam. — Area	1⅜ in. — 1.4849 sq. in.		1½ in. — 1.7621 sq. in.	
ASTM Designation or Yield Stress, ksi	A307	$F_y = 36$	A307	$F_y = 36$
Shear F_v, ksi	10.0	10.8[a]	10.0	10.8[a]
Single Shear, kips	14.85	16.04	17.67	19.08
Double Shear, kips	29.70	32.07	35.34	38.17

High Strength Bolts in Friction Type Connections and in Bearing Type Connections with Threads in Shear Planes

Diam. — Area	1⅜ in. — 1.4849 sq. in.			1½ in. — 1.7671 sq. in.		
[b]ASTM Designation	A325-F A325-N	A490-F	A490-N	A325-F A325-N	A490-F	A490-N
Shear F_v, ksi	15.0	20.0	22.5	15.0	20.0	22.5
Single Shear, kips	22.27	29.70	33.41	26.51	35.34	39.76
Double Shear, kips	44.55	59.40	66.82	53.01	70.68	79.52

High Strength Bolts in Bearing Type Connections with Threads Excluded from Shear Planes

Diam. — Area	1⅜ in. — 1.4849 sq. in.		1½ in. — 1.7671 sq. in.	
[b]ASTM Designation	A325-X	A490-X	A325-X	A490-X
Shear F_v, ksi	22.0	32.0	22.0	32.0
Single Shear, kips	32.67	47.52	38.88	56.55
Double Shear, kips	65.34	95.03	77.75	113.09

[a] For threaded parts of material other than $F_y = 36$ ksi steel, use $F_v = 0.30\ F_y$.
[b] The letter suffixes following the ASTM Designations A325 and A490 represent the following:
   F: Friction type connection
   N: Bearing type connection with threads **included** in shear plane
   X: Bearing type connection with threads **excluded** from shear plane

RIVETS AND THREADED FASTENERS
Bearing

Allowable loads in kips
All rivets and bolts in bearing type connections

1⅜-1½

Diam., in.	1⅜								1½							
F_y, ksi	36	42	45	50	55	60	65	100	36	42	45	50	55	60	65	100
Bearing F_p, ksi	48.6	56.7	60.8	67.5	74.3	81.0	87.8	135	48.6	56.7	60.8	67.5	74.3	81.0	87.8	135
⅛	8.35	9.75	10.5	11.6	12.8	13.9	15.1	23.2	9.11	10.6	11.4	12.7	13.9	15.2	16.5	25.3
3⁄16	12.5	14.6	15.7	17.4	19.2	20.9	22.6	34.8	13.7	15.9	17.1	19.0	20.9	22.8	24.7	38.0
¼	16.7	19.5	20.9	23.2	25.5	27.8	30.2	46.4	18.2	21.3	22.8	25.3	27.9	30.4	32.9	50.6
5⁄16	20.9	24.4	26.1	29.0	31.9	34.8	37.7	58.0	22.8	26.6	28.5	31.6	34.8	38.0	41.2	63.3
⅜	25.1	29.2	31.3	34.8	38.3	41.8	45.3	69.6	27.3	31.9	34.2	38.0	41.8	45.6	49.4	75.9
7⁄16	29.2	34.1	36.6	40.6	44.7	48.7	52.8	81.2	31.9	37.2	39.9	44.3	48.8	53.2	57.6	88.6
½	33.4	39.0	41.8	46.4	51.1	55.7	60.4	92.8	36.5	42.5	45.6	50.6	55.7	60.8	65.9	101
9⁄16	37.6	43.9	47.0	52.2	57.5	62.6	67.9	104	41.0	47.8	51.3	57.0	62.7	68.3	74.1	114
⅝	41.8	48.7	52.3	58.0	63.9	69.6	75.5	116	45.6	53.2	57.0	63.3	69.7	75.9	82.3	127
11⁄16	45.9	53.6	57.5	63.8	70.2	76.6	83.0	128	50.1	58.5	62.7	69.6	76.6	83.5	90.5	139
¾	50.1	58.5	62.7	69.6	76.6	83.5	90.5	139	54.7	63.8	68.4	75.9	83.6	91.1	98.8	152
13⁄16	54.3	63.3	67.9	75.4	83.0	90.5	98.1	151	59.2	69.1	74.1	82.3	90.6	98.7	107	165
⅞	58.5	68.2	73.1	81.2	89.4	97.5		162	63.8	74.4	79.8	88.6	97.5	106	115	177
15⁄16	62.7	73.1	78.4	87.0	95.8			174	68.3	79.7	85.5	94.9	104	114		190
1	66.8	78.0	83.6	92.8	102	111	121	186	72.9	85.1	91.2	101	111	122	132	203
1 1⁄16	71.0	82.8	88.8	98.6				197	77.5	90.4	96.9	108	118			215
1⅛	75.2	87.7	94.1					209	82.0	95.7	103	114				228
1 3⁄16	79.4	92.6	99.3					220	86.6	101	108					240
1¼	83.5	97.5						232	91.1	106	114					253
1 5⁄16	87.7							244	95.7	112						266
1⅜	91.9							255	100	117						278
1 7⁄16	96.1							267	105							291
1½									109							304
1 9⁄16									114							316

MATERIAL THICKNESS

This table not applicable to fasteners in friction type connections.

F_y is the yield stress of the connected material; see AISC Specification, Sect. 1.5.2.2.

F_p, the unit bearing stress, applies equally to conditions of single shear and enclosed bearing.

Values for thicknesses not listed may be obtained by multiplying the unlisted thickness by the value given for a 1″ thickness in the appropriate F_y column.

Values for F_y's not listed may be obtained by multiplying the value given for $F_y = 100$ ksi by the unlisted F_y and dividing by 100.

FRAMED BEAM CONNECTIONS
and
HEAVY FRAMED BEAM CONNECTIONS
Bolted or Riveted

TABLES I and II

BEAM REACTIONS

For economical connections, the beam reactions should be shown on the contract drawings. If these reactions are not shown, connections shall be selected to support half the total uniform load capacity shown in Tables for Allowable Loads on Beams for the given shape, span and steel specified. The effect of concentrated loads must be accounted for.

Beam reactions must be shown on contract drawings for composite beam construction and continuous beam framing.

TYPE OF CONNECTION

Tables are developed for allowable reactions from simple beam (Type 2) framing. No eccentricity or moment resistance is considered in determining tabulated values. Inherent rigidity of the connections is a factor the designer should be aware of and consider where critical.

FASTENERS

Bolts and rivets are listed in AISC Specification Sect. 1.4.4, Bolts, and Sect. 1.4.3, Rivets. Applications should comply with Sect. 1.5.2, Rivets, Bolts and Threaded Parts, and Sect. 1.15.12, Field Connections.

Type of high strength bolt is indicated as follows:

A 325-F and A 490-F: Friction type connection
A 325-N and A 490-N: Bearing type connections with threads included in shear plane
A 325-X and A 490-X: Bearing type connections with threads excluded from shear plane

TABLE I-A AND TABLE II-A

These tables give allowable connection capacities based on:

(a) Vertical shear capacity of the fastener group
(b) Bearing capacity of F_y = 36 ksi steel framing angles of the listed thickness, shear or capacity on the longitudinal gross area of the F_y = 36 ksi framing angles
(c) An arbitrary thickness limitation of $5/8''$ for framing angles to assure flexibility

TABLE I-B AND TABLE II-B

These capacities are based on the bearing capacity for the specific group of fasteners in the designated steel for 1″ thickness. Bearing capacity of a beam web can be determined by using the web thickness of the supported beam as a multiplier with the appropriate tabular load. Bearing values for unlisted values of F_y may be obtained by multiplying the value given for F_y = 100 ksi by the unlisted yield strength divided by 100.

DETAILS

(a) Connection angle lengths vary from a maximum equal to the T dimension to a minimum equal to half the T dimension of the supported beam.

(b) Vertical fastener spacing is arbitrarily chosen as 3″ for these tables. This may be varied, providing requirements for shear in the connection angles and for Specification Sect. 1.16.4, Minimum Pitch, are met.

(c) Edge distance at ends of framing angles is set at $1\frac{1}{4}$″ as permitted in Sect. 1.16.5 of the AISC Specification for sizes of fasteners included.

(d) Standard gage for the supporting column should be followed when practical with the angle gage selected to meet requirements of Sect. 1.16.4, Minimum Pitch, and Sect. 1.16.5, Minimum Edge Distance.

(f) Clearance for assembly is essential in all cases.

COMBINATION OF WELDED AND BOLTED FRAMED BEAM CONNECTION

Either the bolted framing angle connection to the supported beam web or the outstanding leg bolted connection may be used with the appropriate welded connection. See FRAMED BEAM CONNECTIONS—WELDED.

OTHER FRAMED CONNECTIONS

These tables are not intended to preclude the use of other designed adequate connections.

EXAMPLES

The purpose of the following examples is to illustrate the primary use of Tables I and II. This primary use is to provide shear and bearing values along with minimum connection angle thickness for selected groups of fasteners.

(a) **Given:** *Beam:*   W 36 × 230, t_w = 0.761″

                               ASTM A572 grade 45 steel (F_y = 45 ksi)

            Bolts: 1″ ϕ high-strength ASTM A490-X

                               (Bearing type—threads excluded)

      Reaction: 320 kips

Solution, design: Table I-A7 gives a shear value of 352 kips with the use of $\frac{5}{8}$″ thick angles for 1″ϕ A490 bolts in a bearing type connection with no threads in the shear plane. This is for seven fasteners, permitted for all W 36 beams.

Conditions affecting the bearing value from Table I-B7 are F_y = 45 ksi and seven 1″ ϕ bolts. These correspond to a value from the table of 425 kips for 1″ thick, F_y = 45 ksi steel. The web thickness of 0.761″ governs the bearing conditions and gives a bearing value of 0.761 × 425 = 323 kips.

Solution, detail: A quick check for clearance and edge distance indicates a 4″ leg will be adequate for attachment to the beam web and is compatible with the suggested $2\frac{1}{2}''$ gage shown. It will be sufficient for the outstanding legs. A minimum gage for outstanding legs is developed as follows:

Angle thickness required:	$\frac{5}{8}''$
Washer thickness (web bolt):	$\frac{3}{16}''$
Nut thickness (web bolt):	$1''$
Bolt projection (web bolts):	$\frac{1}{4}''$
Impact wrench clearance:	$1\frac{7}{16}''$
	$3\frac{1}{2}''$

A minimum leg gage of $3\frac{1}{2}''$ allows bolts in both legs to be plac on the same horizontal rows and also gives sufficient clearance f the impact wrench. AISC Specification Table 1.16.5 specifies minimum edge distance of $1\frac{1}{4}''$ for $1''\phi$ bolts. Thus, the minimu angle leg width for the outstanding legs will be $3\frac{1}{2}'' + 1\frac{1}{4}''$ $4\frac{3}{4}''$. Use either $6 \times 4 \times \frac{5}{8}'' \times 1'$-$8\frac{1}{2}''$ angles or $5 \times 5 \times \frac{5}{8}$ $\times 1'$-$8\frac{1}{2}''$ angles.

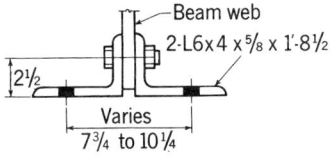

Beam web
2-L6x4 x⅝ x 1'-8½
$2\frac{1}{2}$
Varies
$7\frac{3}{4}$ to $10\frac{1}{4}$

Detail for Example (a)
Angles of $F_y = 36$ ksi material

The use of two $6 \times 4 \times \frac{5}{8}''$ angles gives a slightly greater option for gage on the outstanding legs. The minimum needed is $(2 \times 3\frac{1}{2}'') + \frac{3}{4}''$ web $= 7\frac{3}{4}''$. The maximum that may be used is $(2 \times 6'') + \frac{3}{4}''$ web $- (2 \times 1\frac{1}{4}''$ edge distance$) = 10\frac{1}{4}''$. The gage chosen may be anywhere between these two limits; selection may be dependent upon gage lines established in the connecting member.

(b) Given: *Beam:*   W 12 $\times$ 14, $t_w = 0.198''$
                        ASTM A36 steel $(F_y = 36$ ksi$)$
       Bolts: $\frac{3}{4}''\phi$ ASTM A307
       Reaction: 20 kips

Solution, design: A glance at the shear values in Table I-A3 indi- cates that the end reaction can be satisfied by using a single vertical row containing three $\frac{3}{4}''\phi$ A307 bolts. This group has a shear value of 26.5 kips and the table also shows a minimum thickness angle of $\frac{1}{4}''$. A compatibility check indicates a three bolt group will provide a suitable angle length for use with a W12 shape.

Conditions governing the bearing value found in Table I-B3 are $F_y = 36$ ksi and three $\frac{3}{4}''\phi$ bolts. This table shows a value of 109 kips for $1''$ thick steel under these conditions. The W 12×14 has a $0.198''$ web thickness. The bearing value for the group is then $0.198 \times 109 = 21.6$ kips.

The allowable shear and bearing values of 26.5 kips and 21.6 kips are each greater than the reaction of 20 kips and the selected connection is satisfactory.

Solution, detail:

(1) Consider that the W 12 × 14 is to frame into the flange of a W 8 × 28. From AISC Manual Part 1, the usual gage for this flange is $3\frac{1}{2}''$. Using the $3\frac{1}{2}''$ gage in the column flange will result in a gage of $(\frac{1}{2} \times 3\frac{1}{2}) - \frac{1}{8}$ (for $\frac{1}{2}$ the web thickness) $= 1\frac{5}{8}''$. AISC Specification Table 1.16.5 requires a minimum edge distance of $1''$, making the minimum width of angle $1\frac{5}{8}'' + 1 = 2\frac{5}{8}''$. The outstanding angle leg width chosen would then be $3''$. If a $3''$ web leg is used it will not allow enough edge distance with the suggested $2\frac{1}{4}''$ gage shown in the sketch accompanying Table I-A3 and there will be insufficient clearance. Increase the angle size; choose two angles $3\frac{1}{2} \times 3 \times \frac{1}{4}'' \times 0'\text{-}8\frac{1}{2}''$.

(2) Consider that the W 12 × 14 is to frame into the flange of a W 8 × 31, which has a usual gage of $5\frac{1}{2}''$. This will result in a gage of $(\frac{1}{2} \times 5\frac{1}{2}) - \frac{1}{8} = 2\frac{5}{8}''$. The edge distance of $1''$ still prevails and gives a minimum leg width of $2\frac{5}{8} + 1 = 3\frac{5}{8}''$. Use $4 \times 3\frac{1}{2} \times \frac{1}{4}'' \times 0'\text{-}8\frac{1}{2}''$ angles to adequately satisfy this condition. The $2\frac{1}{4}''$ gage is still satisfactory for the web legs.

(1)	$3\frac{1}{2}$	2-L3½x3x¼ x 8½"
(2)	$5\frac{1}{2}$	2-L4x3½x¼ x 8½"

Detail for Example (b)
Beam and angles of $F_y = 36$ ksi material

(c) Given: *Beam:* W 18 × 60, $t_w = 0.416''$
ASTM A572 grade 50 steel ($F_y = 50$ ksi)
Bolts: $\frac{7}{8}''\phi$ ASTM A325-X (Bearing type—threads excluded)
Reaction: 150 kips

Solution, design: Table I-A5 gives a shear value of 132 kips for five bolts and Table I-A6 shows 159 kips for six bolts. However, consulting the limit of sections indicated for Table I-A6, it is seen that six horizontal rows of fasteners cannot be used without reducing the $3''$ fastener spacing or going to a heavy framed (double vertical row) connection. A third solution would be to increase the size of fasteners; in most instances this would be undesirable. Arbitrarily, use the heavy framed connection. Table II-A4 gives a value of 159 kips using four horizontal rows and a total of six $\frac{7}{8}''\phi$ A325 bolts. It also indicates that a minimum angle thickness of $\frac{1}{2}''$ is needed to maintain this shear value.

Conditions affecting the bearing value selected from Table II-B4 are $F_y = 50$ ksi and six $\frac{7}{8}''$ ϕ bolts. These correspond to a value from the table of 354 kips for $1''$ steel, $F_y = 50$ ksi. The web thickness of $0.416''$ governs the bearing condition and gives a bearing value of $0.416 \times 354 = 147$ kips. Use a seven bolt group.

Table II does not include a seven fastener connection; however, the five row, eight fastener tables can be used, and one fastener dropped, provided the shear and bearing check and the symmetry of the connection is maintained. Table II-A5 gives a shear value of 212 kips for eight $\frac{7}{8}''\phi$ A325-X bolts: for seven bolts the shear will be $212 \times \frac{7}{8} = 186$ kips. The angle thickness required for eight bolts is $\frac{9}{16}''$. In the interest of economy this may be revised, using $t_{min} = R \div (F_v \times L \times 2)$, where F_v is the allowable shear stress in the angle (A36 steel) and L is the length of the angle: $t_{min} = 150 \div (14.5 \times 14\frac{1}{2} \times 2) = 0.357''$, or a $\frac{3}{8}''$ angle. From Table II-B5, 473 kips is allowed for $1''$ of $F_y = 50$ ksi beam web material using eight fasteners. With seven fasteners and a web of $0.416''$, the permissible bearing is $473 \times 0.416 \times \frac{7}{8} = 172$ kips. The bearing in the two $\frac{3}{8}''$ angles (A36 steel) is not critical.

Solution, detail: Using the $2\frac{1}{4}''$-$2\frac{1}{2}''$ gages shown on the sketch for Table II-A5, the connection for the angle legs attaching to the web will require an additional edge distance of $1\frac{1}{8}''$. This gives a minimum width of leg $2\frac{1}{4}'' + 2\frac{1}{2}'' + 1\frac{1}{8}'' = 5\frac{7}{8}''$ or $6''$. A minimum gage for the outstanding legs is developed as follows:

Angle thickness required:	$\frac{3}{8}''$
Washer thickness (web bolt):	$\frac{3}{16}''$
Nut thickness (web bolt):	$\frac{7}{8}''$
Bolt projection (web bolt):	$\frac{1}{4}''$
Impact wrench clearance:	$1\frac{3}{8}''$
	$3\frac{1}{16}''$

A minimum leg gage of $3\frac{1}{16}''$ to the first bolt allows bolts in both legs to be placed on the same horizontal rows and also gives sufficient clearance for the impact wrench. The minimum edge distance per AISC Specification Table 1.16.5 is $1\frac{1}{8}''$ for $\frac{7}{8}''\phi$ bolts. Thus, the minimum angle leg width for the outstanding leg will be $3\frac{1}{16} + 2\frac{1}{2} + 1\frac{1}{8} = 6\frac{11}{16}''$.

Since a $6''$ leg must be used with the web and at least $6\frac{11}{16}''$ is needed on the outstanding legs, use two angles $8 \times 6 \times \frac{7}{16}'' \times 1'$-$2\frac{1}{2}''$. (This size angle is not rolled in a $\frac{3}{8}''$ thickness; therefore, a $\frac{7}{16}''$ angle is selected.) The minimum inside gage that may be used across the outstanding legs is $2 \times (3\frac{1}{16} + \frac{1}{16}) + \frac{7}{16}$ beam web $= 6\frac{11}{16}''$. The maximum inside gage that may be used across the outstanding legs is $(2 \times 8) + \frac{7}{16}$ web $- 2\,(2\frac{1}{2}''$ gage $+ 1\frac{1}{8}''$ edge distance$) = 9\frac{3}{16}''$. The gage chosen may be anywhere between these two values and is the option of the detailer.

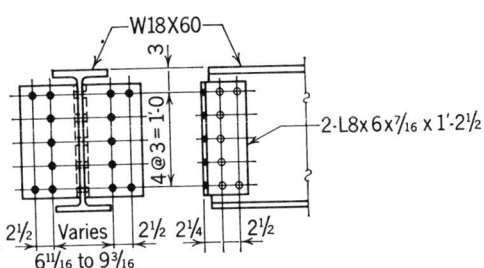

Detail for Example (c)
Angle material: $F_y = 36$ ksi
Beam material: $F_y = 50$ ksi

FRAMED BEAM CONNECTIONS
Bolted or riveted
TABLE I Allowable loads in kips

10 ROWS

W 36

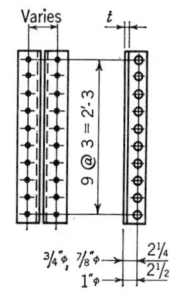

Varies t

$9 @ 3 = 2'\text{-}3$

$\frac{3}{4}"\phi, \frac{7}{8}"\phi$ $\frac{2\frac{1}{4}}{2\frac{1}{2}}$
$1"\phi$

TABLE I-A10 Total Shear, kips

[a]Fastener Designation	F_v ksi	Fastener Diameter					
		$\frac{3}{4}$		$\frac{7}{8}$		1	
		Load	t^b	Load	t^b	Load	t^b
A307	10.0	88.4	$\frac{1}{4}$	120	$\frac{1}{4}$	157	$\frac{1}{4}$
A325-F A325-N A502-1	15.0	133	$\frac{1}{4}$	180	$\frac{1}{4}$	236	$\frac{5}{16}$
A490-F A502-2	20.0	177	$\frac{1}{4}$	241	$\frac{5}{16}$	314	$\frac{3}{8}$
A325-X	22.0	194	$\frac{5}{16}$	265	$\frac{5}{16}$	346	$\frac{7}{16}$
A490-N	22.5	199	$\frac{5}{16}$	271	$\frac{3}{8}$	353	$\frac{7}{16}$
A490-X	32.0	283	$\frac{7}{16}$	385	$\frac{1}{2}$	503	$\frac{5}{8}$

TABLE I-B10 Total Bearing,[c] kips, 10 fasteners on 1" thick material

	F_y	36	42	45	50	55	60	65	100
Fastener Diameter	$\frac{3}{4}$	365	425	456	506	557	608	658	1010
	$\frac{7}{8}$	425	496	532	591	650	709	768	1180
	1	486	567	608	675	743	810	878	1350

9 ROWS

W 36, 33

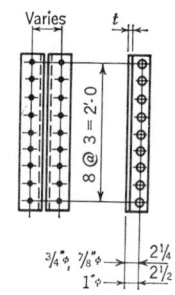

Varies t

$8 @ 3 = 2'\text{-}0$

$\frac{3}{4}"\phi, \frac{7}{8}"\phi$ $\frac{2\frac{1}{4}}{2\frac{1}{2}}$
$1"\phi$

TABLE I-A9 Total Shear, kips

[a]Fastener Designation	F_v ksi	Fastener Diameter					
		$\frac{3}{4}$		$\frac{7}{8}$		1	
		Load	t^b	Load	t^b	Load	t^b
A307	10.0	79.6	$\frac{1}{4}$	108	$\frac{1}{4}$	141	$\frac{1}{4}$
A325-F A325-N A502-1	15.0	119	$\frac{1}{4}$	162	$\frac{1}{4}$	212	$\frac{5}{16}$
A490-F A502-2	20.0	159	$\frac{1}{4}$	216	$\frac{5}{16}$	283	$\frac{3}{8}$
A325-X	22.0	175	$\frac{5}{16}$	238	$\frac{5}{16}$	311	$\frac{7}{16}$
A490-N	22.5	179	$\frac{5}{16}$	244	$\frac{3}{8}$	318	$\frac{7}{16}$
A490-X	32.0	255	$\frac{7}{16}$	346	$\frac{1}{2}$	452	$\frac{5}{8}$

TABLE I-B9 Total Bearing,[c] kips, 9 fasteners on 1" thick material

	F_y	36	42	45	50	55	60	65	100
Fastener Diameter	$\frac{3}{4}$	328	383	410	456	501	547	592	911
	$\frac{7}{8}$	383	447	478	532	585	638	691	1060
	1	437	510	547	608	668	729	790	1220

[a] For description of fastener designation see page 4-12.
[b] Thickness t based on connection angles of $F_y = 36$ ksi material.
[c] Use decimal thickness of enclosed web material as multiplying factor for these values.

AMERICAN INSTITUTE OF STEEL CONSTRUCTION

FRAMED BEAM CONNECTIONS
Bolted or riveted
TABLE I   Allowable loads in kips

8 ROWS

W 36, 33, 30

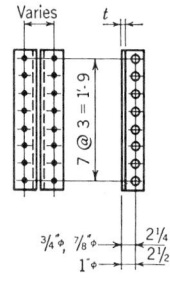

3/4"ϕ, 7/8"ϕ → 2¼
1"ϕ → 2½

TABLE I-A8   Total Shear, kips

^aFastener Designation	F_v ksi	Fastener Diameter					
		3/4		7/8		1	
		Load	t^b	Load	t^b	Load	t^b
A307	10.0	70.7	¼	96.2	¼	126	¼
A325-F A325-N A502-1	15.0	106	¼	144	¼	188	5/16
A490-F A502-2	20.0	141	¼	192	5/16	251	3/8
A325-X	22.0	156	5/16	212	5/16	276	7/16
A490-N	22.5	159	5/16	216	3/8	283	7/16
A490-X	32.0	226	7/16	308	½	402	5/8

TABLE I-B8   Total Bearing,^c kips, 8 fasteners on 1" thick material

	F_y	36	42	45	50	55	60	65	100
Fastener Diameter	3/4	292	340	364	405	446	486	527	810
	7/8	340	397	425	472	520	567	614	945
	1	389	454	486	540	594	648	702	1080

7 ROWS

W 36, 33, 30, 27, 24
S 24*

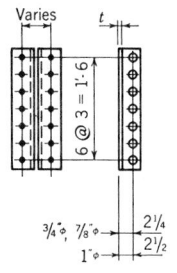

3/4"ϕ, 7/8"ϕ → 2¼
1"ϕ → 2½

TABLE I-A7   Total Shear, kips

^aFastener Designation	F_v ksi	Fastener Diameter					
		3/4		7/8		1	
		Load	t^b	Load	t^b	Load	t^b
A307	10.0	61.9	¼	84.2	¼	110	¼
A325-F A325-N A502-1	15.0	92.8	¼	126	¼	165	5/16
A490-F A502-2	20.0	124	¼	168	5/16	220	3/8
A325-X	22.0	136	5/16	185	5/16	242	7/16
A490-N	22.5	139	5/16	189	3/8	247	7/16
A490-X	32.0	198	7/16	269	½	352	5/8

TABLE I-B7   Total Bearing,^c kips, 7 fasteners on 1" thick material

	F_y	36	42	45	50	55	60	65	100
Fastener Diameter	3/4	255	298	319	354	390	425	461	709
	7/8	298	347	372	413	455	496	537	827
	1	340	397	425	473	520	567	614	945

^{a.} For description of fastener designation see page 4-12.
^b Thickness t based on connection angles of $F_y = 36$ ksi material.
^c Use decimal thickness of enclosed web material as multiplying factor for these values.
* Limited to S 24 × 79.9, 90, 100.

AMERICAN INSTITUTE OF STEEL CONSTRUCTION

FRAMED BEAM CONNECTIONS
Bolted or riveted
TABLE I   Allowable loads in kips

6 ROWS

W 36, 33, 30, 27, 24, 21
S 24

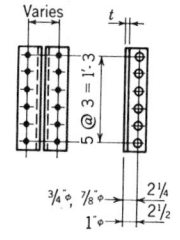

3/4"ø, 7/8"ø, 1"ø   2¼   2½

TABLE I-A6   Total Shear, kips

[a]Fastener Designation	F_v ksi	Fastener Diameter					
		¾		⅞		1	
		Load	t^b	Load	t^b	Load	t^b
A307	10.0	53.0	¼	72.2	¼	94.3	¼
A325-F A325-N A502-1	15.0	79.5	¼	108	¼	141	5⁄16
A490-F A502-2	20.0	106	¼	144	5⁄16	189	⅜
A325-X	22.0	117	5⁄16	159	⅜	207	7⁄16
A490-N	22.5	119	5⁄16	162	⅜	212	7⁄16
A490-X	32.0	170	7⁄16	231	½	302	⅝

TABLE I-B6   Total Bearing,[c] kips, 6 fasteners on 1″ thick material

	F_y	36	42	45	50	55	60	65	100
Fastener Diameter	¾	219	255	273	304	334	365	395	608
	⅞	255	298	319	354	390	425	461	709
	1	292	340	365	405	446	486	527	810

5 ROWS

W 30, 27, 24, 21, 18
S 24, 20, 18
MC 18

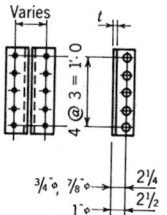

3/4"ø, 7/8"ø, 1"ø   2¼   2½

TABLE I-A5   Total Shear, kips

[a]Fastener Designation	F_v ksi	Fastener Diameter					
		¾		⅞		1	
		Load	t^b	Load	t^b	Load	t^b
A307	10.0	44.2	¼	60.2	¼	78.6	¼
A325-F A325-N A502-1	15.0	66.3	¼	90.2	¼	118	5⁄16
A490-F A502-2	20.0	88.4	¼	120	5⁄16	157	⅜
A325-X	22.0	97.2	5⁄16	132	⅜	173	7⁄16
A490-N	22.5	99.4	5⁄16	135	⅜	177	7⁄16
A490-X	32.0	141	7⁄16	192	½	251	⅝

TABLE I-B5   Total Bearing,[c] kips, 5 fasteners on 1″ thick material

	F_y	36	42	45	50	55	60	65	100
Fastener Diameter	¾	182	213	228	253	278	304	329	506
	⅞	213	248	266	295	325	354	384	591
	1	243	284	304	338	371	405	439	675

[a] For description of fastener designation see page 4-12.
[b] Thickness t based on connection angles of $F_y = 36$ ksi material.
[c] Use decimal thickness of enclosed web material as multiplying factor for these values.

FRAMED BEAM CONNECTIONS
Bolted or riveted
TABLE I Allowable loads in kips

4 ROWS

W 24, 21, 18, 16
M 14
S 24, 20, 18, 15
C 15; MC 18

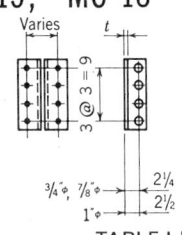

Varies

3 @ 3 = 9

3/4" φ, 7/8" φ 2 1/4
1" φ 2 1/2

TABLE I-A4 Total Shear, kips

[a]Fastener Designation	F_v ksi	Fastener Diameter					
		3/4		7/8		1	
		Load	t^b	Load	t^b	Load	t^b
A307	10.0	35.4	1/4	48.1	1/4	62.8	1/4
A325-F A325-N A502-1	15.0	53.0	1/4	72.2	1/4	94.2	5/16
A490-F A502-2	20.0	70.7	1/4	96.2	5/16	126	7/16
A325-X	22.0	77.8	5/16	106	3/8	138	7/16
A490-N	22.5	79.5	5/16	108	3/8	141	7/16
A490-X	32.0	113	7/16	154	1/2	201	5/8

TABLE I-B4 Total Bearing,[c] ksi, 4 fasteners on 1" thick material

	F_y	36	42	45	50	55	60	65	100
Fastener Diameter	3/4	146	170	182	203	223	243	263	405
	7/8	170	198	213	236	260	284	307	473
	1	194	227	243	270	297	324	351	540

3 ROWS

W 18, 16, 14, 12, 10*
M 14, 12
S 18, 15, 12
C 15, 12, 10*
MC 12, 10

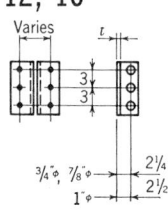

Varies

3/4" φ, 7/8" φ 2 1/4
1" φ 2 1/2

TABLE I-A3 Total Shear, kips

[a]Fastener Designation	F_v ksi	Fastener Diameter					
		3/4		7/8		1	
		Load	t^b	Load	t^b	Load	t^b
A307	10.0	26.5	1/4	36.1	1/4	47.1	1/4
A325-F A325-N A502-1	15.0	39.8	1/4	54.1	1/4	70.7	5/16
A490-F A502-2	20.0	53.0	1/4	72.2	5/16	94.3	7/16
A325-X	22.0	58.3	5/16	79.4	3/8	104	7/16
A490-N	22.5	59.6	5/16	81.2	3/8	106	7/16
A490-X	32.0	84.8	7/16	115	1/2	151	5/8

TABLE I-B3 Total Bearing,[c] kips, 3 fasteners on 1" thick material

	F_y	36	42	45	50	55	60	65	100
Fastener Diameter	3/4	109	128	137	152	167	182	197	304
	7/8	128	149	159	177	195	213	230	354
	1	146	170	182	203	223	243	263	405

[a] For description of fastener designation see page 4-12.
[b] Thickness t based on connection angles of $F_y = 36$ ksi material.
[c] Use decimal thickness of enclosed web material as multiplying factor for these values.
* Limited to W 10 × 11.5, 15, 17, 19, 21, 25, 29; C 10 × 15.3, 20, 25, 30.

FRAMED BEAM CONNECTIONS
Bolted or riveted
TABLE I Allowable loads in kips

2 ROWS

W 12, 10, 8
S 12, 10, 8
C 12, 10, 9, 8

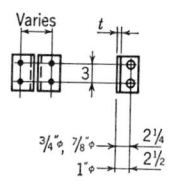

TABLE I-A2 Total Shear, kips

^{a}Fastener Designation	F_v ksi	Fastener Diameter					
		3/4		7/8		1	
		Load	t^b	Load	t^b	Load	t^b
A307	10.0	17.7	1/4	24.1	1/4	31.4	1/4
A325-F A325-N A502-1	15.0	26.5	1/4	36.1	1/4	47.1	5/16
A490-F A502-2	20.0	35.3	1/4	48.1	5/16	62.8	7/16
A325-X	22.0	38.9	5/16	52.9	3/8	69.1	7/16
A490-N	22.5	39.8	5/16	54.1	3/8	70.7	1/2
A490-X	32.0	56.6	7/16	77.0	1/2	99.7*	5/8

TABLE I-B2 Total Bearing,^{c} kips, 2 fasteners on 1″ thick material

	F_y	36	42	45	50	55	60	65	100
Fastener Diameter	3/4	72.9	85.1	91.1	101	111	122	132	203
	7/8	85.1	99.2	106	118	130	142	154	236
	1	97.2	113	122	135	149	162	176	270

1 ROW

W 6, 5
M 6, 5
S 8, 7, 6, 5
C 7, 6, 5

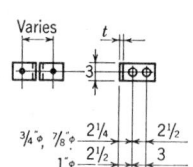

TABLE I-A1 Total Shear, kips

^{a}Fastener Designation	F_v ksi	Fastener Diameter					
		3/4		7/8		1	
		Load	t^b	Load	t^b	Load	t^b
A307	10.0	8.8	1/4	12.0	1/4	15.7	1/4
A325-F A325-N A502-1	15.0	13.3	1/4	18.0	1/4	23.6	5/16
A490-F A502-2	20.0	17.7	1/4	24.1	5/16	31.4	3/8
A325-X	22.0	19.4	5/16	26.5	5/16	34.6	7/16
A490-N	22.5	19.9	5/16	27.1	3/8	35.3	7/16
A490-X	32.0	28.3	7/16	38.5	1/2	50.3	5/8

TABLE I-B1 Total Bearing,^{cd} kips, on 1″ thick material

	F_y	36	42	45	50	55	60	65	100
Fastener Diameter	3/4	72.9	85.1	91.1	101	111	122	132	203
	7/8	85.1	99.2	106	118	130	142	154	236
	1	97.2	113	122	135	149	162	176	270

^{a} For description of fastener designation see page 4-12.
^{b} Thickness t based on connection angles of $F_y = 36$ ksi material.
^{c} Use decimal thickness of enclosed web material as multiplying factor for these values.
^{d} Values shown are for 1 bolt in each outstanding leg or 2 bolts in web leg.
* Indicates shear values are limited by shear capacity of 5/8″ angle of $F_y = 36$ ksi material (arbitrary limit for flexibility), and length of angle assumed to be c/c outside fasteners plus 2½″.

AMERICAN INSTITUTE OF STEEL CONSTRUCTION

HEAVY FRAMED BEAM CONNECTIONS
Bolted or riveted
TABLE II Allowable loads in kips

10 ROWS

W 36

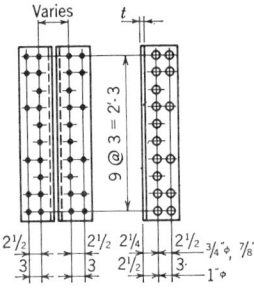

TABLE II-A10 Total Shear, kips, 16 fasteners

| ^aFastener Designation | F_v ksi | Fastener diameter | | | | | |
| | | 3/4 | | 7/8 | | 1 | |
		Load	t^b	Load	t^b	Load	t^b
A325-F A325-N A502-1	15.0	212	1/4	289	3/8	377	1/2
A490-F A502-2	20.0	283	3/8	385	1/2	503	5/8
A325-X	22.0	311	3/8	423	1/2	535*	5/8
A490-N	22.5	318	3/8	433	9/16		
A490-X	32.0	452	9/16	535*	5/8		

TABLE II-B10 Total Bearing,^c kips, 16 fasteners on 1" thick material

	F_y	36	42	45	50	55	60	65	100
Fastener Diameter	3/4	583	680	729	810	891	972	1050	1620
	7/8	680	794	851	945	1040	1130	1230	1890
	1	778	907	972	1080	1190	1300	1400	2160

9 ROWS

W 36, 33

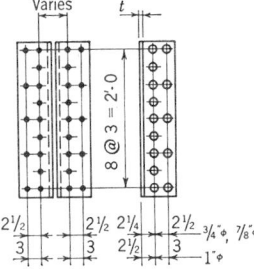

TABLE II-A9 Total Shear, kips, 14 fasteners

| ^aFastener Designation | F_v ksi | Fastener diameter | | | | | |
| | | 3/4 | | 7/8 | | 1 | |
		Load	t^b	Load	t^b	Load	t^b
A325-F A325-N A502-1	15.0	186	1/4	253	3/8	330	7/16
A490-F A502-2	20.0	247	3/8	337	1/2	440	5/8
A325-X	22.0	272	3/8	370	1/2	480*	5/8
A490-N	22.5	278	3/8	379	1/2		
A490-X	32.0	396	9/16	480*	5/8		

TABLE II-B9 Total Bearing,^c kips, 14 fasteners on 1" thick material

	F_y	36	42	45	50	55	60	65	100
Fastener Diameter	3/4	510	595	638	709	780	851	921	1420
	7/8	595	695	744	827	910	992	1080	1650
	1	680	794	851	945	1040	1130	1230	1890

^a For description of fastener designation see page 4-12.
^b Thickness t based on connection angles of $F_y = 36$ ksi material.
^c Use decimal thickness of enclosed web material as multiplying factor for these values.
* Indicates shear values are limited by shear capacity of 5/8" angle of $F_y = 36$ ksi material (arbitrary limit for flexibility), and length of angle assumed to be c/c outside fasteners plus 2½".

HEAVY FRAMED BEAM CONNECTIONS
Bolted or riveted
TABLE II   Allowable loads in kips

8 ROWS
W 36, 33, 30

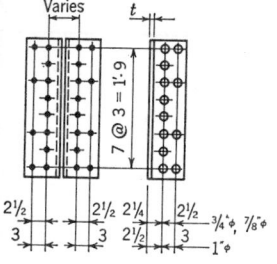

TABLE II-A8   Total Shear, kips, 12 fasteners

[a]Fastener Designation	F_v ksi	Fastener diameter					
		3/4		7/8		1	
		Load	t^b	Load	t^b	Load	t^b
A325-F A325-N A502-1	15.0	159	1/4	216	3/8	283	7/16
A490-F A502-2	20.0	212	5/16	289	7/16	377	9/16
A325-X	22.0	233	3/8	318	1/2	415	5/8
A490-N	22.5	239	3/8	325	1/2	426*	5/8
A490-X	32.0	339	1/2	426*	5/8		

TABLE II-B8   Total Bearing,[c] kips, 12 fasteners on 1″ thick material

	F_y	36	42	45	50	55	60	65	100
Fastener Diameter	3/4	437	510	547	608	668	729	790	1220
	7/8	510	595	638	709	780	851	921	1420
	1	583	680	729	810	891	972	1050	1620

7 ROWS
W 36, 33, 30, 27, 24
S 24**

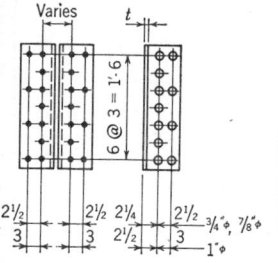

TABLE II-A7   Total Shear, kips, 11 fasteners

[a]Fastener Designation	F_v ksi	Fastener diameter					
		3/4		7/8		1	
		Load	t^b	Load	t^b	Load	t^b
A325-F A325-N A502-1	15.0	146	1/4	198	3/8	259	1/2
A490-F A502-2	20.0	194	3/8	265	1/2	346	5/8
A325-X	22.0	214	3/8	291	1/2	372*	5/8
A490-N	22.5	219	3/8	298	9/16		
A490-X	32.0	311	9/16	372*	5/8		

TABLE II-B7   Total Bearing,[c] kips, 11 fasteners on 1″ thick material

	F_y	36	42	45	50	55	60	65	100
Fastener Diameter	3/4	401	468	501	557	613	668	724	1110
	7/8	468	546	585	650	715	780	845	1300
	1	535	624	668	743	817	891	965	1490

[a] For description of fastener designation see page 4-12.
[b] Thickness t based on connection angles of $F_y = 36$ ksi material.
[c] Use decimal thickness of enclosed web material as multiplying factor for these values.
* Indicates shear values limited by shear capacity of 5/8″ angle of $F_y = 36$ ksi material (arbitrary limit for flexibility), and length of angle assumed to be c/c of outside fasteners plus 2½″.
** Limited to S 24 × 79.9, 90, 100.

HEAVY FRAMED BEAM CONNECTIONS
Bolted or riveted
TABLE II   Allowable loads in kips

6 ROWS

W 36, 33, 30, 27, 24, 21
S 24

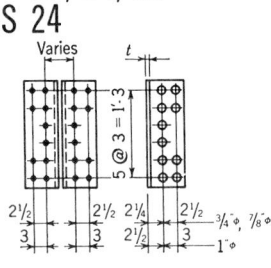

TABLE II-A6   Total Shear, kips, 10 fasteners

[a]Fastener Designation	F_v ksi	Fastener diameter					
		3/4		7/8		1	
		Load	t^b	Load	t^b	Load	t^b
A325-F A325-N A502-1	15.0	133	5/16	180	3/8	236	1/2
A490-F A502-2	20.0	177	3/8	241	1/2	314	5/8
A325-X	22.0	194	7/16	265	9/16	317*	5/8
A490-N	22.5	199	7/16	271	9/16		
A490-X	32.0	283	9/16	317*	5/8		

TABLE II-B6   Total Bearing,[c] kips, 10 fasteners on 1″ thick material

	F_y	36	42	45	50	55	60	65	100
Fastener Diameter	3/4	365	425	456	506	557	608	658	1010
	7/8	425	496	532	591	650	709	768	1180
	1	486	567	608	675	743	810	878	1350

5 ROWS

W 30, 27, 24, 21, 18
S 24, 20, 18
MC 18

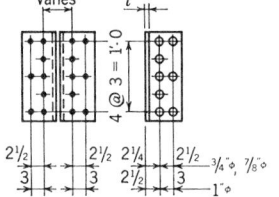

TABLE II-A5   Total Shear, kips, 8 fasteners

[a]Fastener Designation	F_v ksi	Fastener diameter					
		3/4		7/8		1	
		Load	t^b	Load	t^b	Load	t^b
A325-F A325-N A502-1	15.0	106	5/16	144	3/8	188	1/2
A490-F A502-2	20.0	141	3/8	192	1/2	251	5/8
A325-X	22.0	156	3/8	212	9/16	263*	5/8
A490-N	22.5	159	7/16	216	9/16		
A490-X	32.0	226	9/16	263*	5/8		

TABLE II-B5   Total Bearing,[c] kips, 8 fasteners on 1″ thick material

	F_y	36	42	45	50	55	60	65	100
Fastener Diameter	3/4	292	340	365	405	446	486	527	810
	7/8	340	397	425	473	520	567	614	945
	1	389	454	486	540	594	648	702	1080

[a] For description of fastener designation see page 4-12.
[b] Thickness t based on connection angles of $F_y = 36$ ksi material.
[c] Use decimal thickness of enclosed web material as multiplying factor for these values.
* Indicates shear values limited by shear capacity of 5/8″ angle of $F_y = 36$ ksi material (arbitrary limit for flexibility), and length of angle assumed to be c/c of outside fasteners plus 2½″.

HEAVY FRAMED BEAM CONNECTIONS
Bolted or riveted
TABLE II   Allowable loads in kips

4 ROWS

W 24, 21, 18, 16
M 14
S 24, 20, 18, 15
C 15;   MC 18

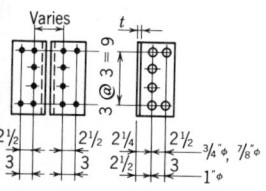

$2\frac{1}{2}$ | $2\frac{1}{2}$ $2\frac{1}{4}$ | $2\frac{1}{2}$ $\frac{3}{4}$"ϕ, $\frac{7}{8}$"ϕ
3 | 3 $2\frac{1}{2}$ | 3
1"ϕ

TABLE II-A4   Total Shear, kips, 6 fasteners

[a]Fastener Designation	F_v ksi	Fastener diameter					
		$\frac{3}{4}$		$\frac{7}{8}$		1	
		Load	t^b	Load	t^b	Load	t^b
A325-F A325-N A502-1	15.0	79.5	$\frac{1}{4}$	108	$\frac{3}{8}$	141	$\frac{7}{16}$
A490-F A502-2	20.0	106	$\frac{3}{8}$	144	$\frac{7}{16}$	189	$\frac{5}{8}$
A325-X	22.0	117	$\frac{3}{8}$	159	$\frac{1}{2}$	207	$\frac{5}{8}$
A490-N	22.5	119	$\frac{3}{8}$	162	$\frac{1}{2}$	208*	$\frac{5}{8}$
A490-X	32.0	170	$\frac{9}{16}$	208*	$\frac{5}{8}$		

TABLE II-B4   Total Bearing,[c] kips, 6 fasteners on 1″ thick material

	F_y	36	42	45	50	55	60	65	100
Fastener Diameter	$\frac{3}{4}$	219	255	273	304	334	365	395	608
	$\frac{7}{8}$	255	298	319	354	390	425	461	709
	1	292	340	365	405	446	486	527	810

3 ROWS

W 18, 16, 14, 12, 10**
M 14, 12
S 18, 15, 12
C 15, 12;   MC 12, 10

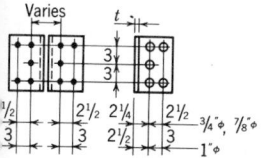

$\frac{1}{2}$ | $2\frac{1}{2}$ $2\frac{1}{4}$ | $2\frac{1}{2}$ $\frac{3}{4}$", $\frac{7}{8}$"ϕ
3 | 3 $2\frac{1}{2}$ | 3
1"ϕ

TABLE II-A3   Total Shear, kips, 5 fasteners

[a]Fastener Designation	F_v ksi	Fastener diameter					
		$\frac{3}{4}$		$\frac{7}{8}$		1	
		Load	t^b	Load	t^b	Load	t^b
A325-F A325-N A502-1	15.0	66.3	$\frac{5}{16}$	90.2	$\frac{3}{8}$	118	$\frac{1}{2}$
A490-F A502-2	20.0	88.4	$\frac{3}{8}$	120	$\frac{1}{2}$	154*	$\frac{5}{8}$
A325-X	22.0	97.2	$\frac{7}{16}$	132	$\frac{9}{16}$		
A490-N	22.5	99.4	$\frac{7}{16}$	135	$\frac{9}{16}$		
A490-X	32.0	141	$\frac{5}{8}$	154*	$\frac{5}{8}$		

TABLE II-B3   Total Bearing,[c] kips, 5 fasteners on 1″ thick material

	F_y	36	42	45	50	55	60	65	100
Fastener Diameter	$\frac{3}{4}$	182	213	228	253	278	304	329	506
	$\frac{7}{8}$	213	248	266	295	325	354	384	591
	1	243	284	304	338	371	405	439	675

[a] For description of fastener designation see page 4-12.
[b] Thickness t based on connection angles of $F_y = 36$ ksi material.
[c] Use decimal thickness of enclosed web material as multiplying factor for these values.
* Indicates shear values limited by shear capacity of $\frac{5}{8}$″ angle of $F_y = 36$ ksi material (arbitrary limit for flexibility), and length of angle assumed to be c/c of outside fasteners plus $2\frac{1}{2}$″.
** Limited to W 10 × 11.5, 15, 17, 19, 21, 25, 29.

HEAVY FRAMED BEAM CONNECTIONS
Bolted or riveted
TABLE II   Allowable loads in kips

2 ROWS

W 12, 10, 8
S 12, 10, 8
C 12, 10, 9, 8

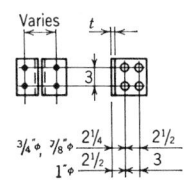

TABLE II-A2   Total Shear, kips, 4 fasteners

[a]Fastener Designation	F_v ksi	Fastener Diameter					
		3/4		7/8		1	
		Load	t^b	Load	t^b	Load	t^b
A325-F A325-N A502-1	15.0	26.5	1/4	36.1	1/4	47.1	5/16
A490-F A502-2	20.0	35.4	1/4	48.1	5/16	62.8	7/16
A325-X	22.0	38.9	1/4	52.9	3/8	69.2	7/16
A490-N	22.5	39.8	1/4	54.1	3/8	70.7	1/2
A490-X	32.0	56.6	3/8	77.0	1/2	100*	5/8

TABLE II-B2   Total Bearing,[cd] kips, on 1" thick material

	F_y	36	42	45	50	55	60	65	100
Fastener Diameter	3/4	146	170	182	203	223	243	263	405
	7/8	170	198	213	236	260	284	307	473
	1	194	227	243	270	297	324	351	540

[a] For description of fastener designation see page 4-12.
[b] Thickness t based on connection angles of $F_y = 36$ ksi material.
[c] Use decimal thickness of enclosed web material as multiplying factor for these values.
[d] Values shown are for 2 bolts in each outstanding leg or 4 bolts in web legs.
* Indicates shear values limited by shear capacity of 5/8" angle of $F_y = 36$ ksi material (arbitrary limit for flexibility), and length of angle assumed to be c/c of outside fasteners plus 2½".

Notes

FRAMED BEAM CONNECTIONS
Welded—E70XX electrodes
for combination with Table I connections

TABLE III

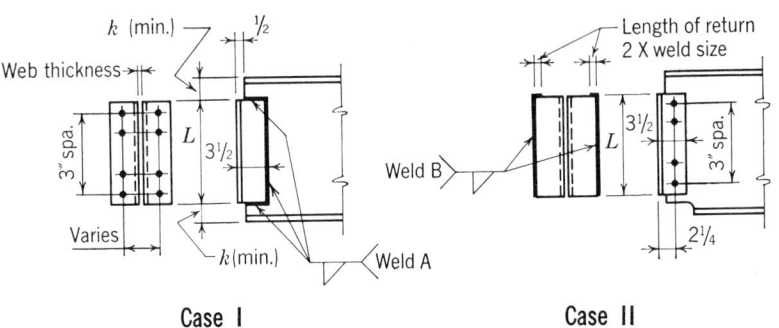

Case I

Case II

Table III is arranged to permit substitution of welds for rivets or bolts in the connections shown in Table I which fall within the weld capacities. Welds **A** replace fasteners in the beam web legs (Case I). Welds **B** replace fasteners in the outstanding legs (Case II).

To accommodate usual gages, angle leg widths will generally be 4 × $3\frac{1}{2}$″, with the 4″ leg outstanding. Width of web legs in Case I may be reduced optionally from $3\frac{1}{2}$″ to 3″. Width of outstanding legs in Case II may be reduced optionally from 4″ to 3″ for values of $L = 5\frac{1}{2}$″ through $1'-5\frac{1}{2}$″. When 3″ legs are used, tabular capacities of welds **A** and **B** are conservative.

Angle thickness is equal to weld size plus $\frac{1}{16}$″, or thickness of angle from applicable Table I-A, whichever is greater.

Angle length L must be as tabulated in Table III.

Holes for erection bolts may be placed as required in legs to be field welded (optional).

When rivets or bolts in bearing type connections are used in outstanding legs, investigate bearing capacity of supporting member.

Although it is permissible to use welds **A** and **B** in combination to obtain all-welded connections, it is recommended that such connections be chosen from Table IV. This table will usually provide greater economy and allow increased flexibility in selection of angle lengths and connection capacities.

EXAMPLES   CASE I

(a) **Given:**   *Beam:*   W36 × 150; $t_w = 0.625$

   $F_y = 36$ ksi; $F_v = 14.5$ ksi

   Reaction: 200 kips

   Bolts: $\frac{7}{8}''\phi$, ASTM A325-X

   Welds: E70XX

Solution: Enter Table III under Weld **A** and note that the value most nearly satisfying the reaction is 217 kips. This requires $\frac{5}{16}$ in. welds and 1'-11½" long angles. Use $\frac{3}{8}''$ thick angles to meet the weld requirement stipulated in AISC Specification Sect. 1.17.6. The 0.625" web thickness exceeds the minimum required 0.54", so no reduction in capacity is necessary.

   Note in Table I-A8 that the angle length is compatible for the 36" deep beam and that 8 rows of $\frac{7}{8}''$ ϕ ASTM A325-X bolts have a capacity of 212 kips. The $\frac{5}{16}''$ required angle thickness is less than the $\frac{3}{8}''$ angle thickness required due to Weld **A**.

Detail Data: Two L 4 × 3½ × $\frac{3}{8}$ × 1'-11½"

   $F_y = 36$ ksi

   Sixteen $\frac{7}{8}''$ ϕ ASTM A325-X bolts (threads excluded from shear plane)

   $\frac{5}{16}$ in. fillet weld, E70XX

(b) **Given:**   *Beam:*   W16 × 26; $t_w = 0.25$

   $F_y = 36$ ksi; $F_v = 14.5$ ksi

   Reaction: 48 kips

   Bolts: $\frac{7}{8}''$ ϕ ASTM A307

   Welds: E70XX

Solution: See Table I-A4 and note 4 rows of bolts with 11½" long angles are compatible with a 16" deep section. Capacity of the $\frac{7}{8}''$ ϕ ASTM A307 bolts with $\frac{1}{4}''$ thick angles is 48.1 kips.

   Note in Table III that 59.4 kips capacity is designated for $\frac{3}{16}$ in. Weld **A** and 11½" long angles. The 0.25" web thickness is less than the minimum 0.29" listed. The reduced capacity is 0.25/0.29 times 59.4 kips, or 51.2 kips. The $\frac{1}{4}''$ angle thickness required for bolts is satisfactory for the $\frac{3}{16}$ in. weld.

Detail Data: Two L 4 × 3½ × $\frac{1}{4}$ × 0'-11½"

   $F_y = 36$ ksi

   Eight $\frac{7}{8}''$ ϕ ASTM A307 bolts

   $\frac{3}{16}$ in. fillet weld, E70XX

EXAMPLES   CASE II

(c) **Given:** *Beam:* W36 × 150; $t_w = 0.625''$
$F_y = 36$ ksi; $F_v = 14.5$ ksi
Reaction: 150 kips
Bolts: $\frac{7}{8}''$ φ ASTM A490-F (friction type)
Welds: E70XX

Solution: Enter Table III under Weld **B** and note that the value most nearly satisfying the reaction is 152 kips. This requires $\frac{3}{8}$ in. Weld **B** and 1'-5$\frac{1}{2}$" long $\frac{7}{16}$" thick angles. However, Table I-A6 shows a bolt capacity for this connection of 144 kips, which is less than the 150 kips required. Therefore a 1'-8$\frac{1}{2}$" long angle is selected from Table III. This angle requires a $\frac{5}{16}$ in. Weld **B** and $\frac{3}{8}$" thick angles with a capacity of 156 kips.

Note in Table I-A7 that 7 rows of $\frac{7}{8}$" φ ASTM A490-F bolts have a capacity of 168 kips. The $\frac{5}{16}$" angle thickness required is less than the thickness required by Weld **B**. Bearing on the web need not be checked since a friction-type connection is used.

Detail Data: Two L 4 × 3$\frac{1}{2}$ × $\frac{3}{8}$ × 1'-8$\frac{1}{2}$"
$F_y = 36$ ksi
Seven $\frac{7}{8}$" φ ASTM A490-F bolts
$\frac{5}{16}$ in. fillet weld, E70XX

(d) **Given:** *Beam:* W16 × 31; $t_w = 0.275''$
$F_y = 50$ ksi; $F_v = 20$ ksi
Reaction: 39 kips
Bolts: $\frac{3}{4}''$ φ ASTM A325-N (threads included in shear plane)
Welds: E70XX

Solution: Enter Table III under Weld **B** and note that the value most nearly satisfying the reaction is 40.3 kips. This requires $\frac{5}{16}$ in. Weld **B** and 8$\frac{1}{2}$" long, $\frac{3}{8}$" thick angles.

Enter Table I-A3 for 3 rows of fasteners and note that the angle length is compatible with beam size. Capacity of three $\frac{3}{4}$" φ ASTM A325 bolts acting in bearing is 39.8 kips. Check web bearing on bolts. Bearing capacity for 1" material from Table I-B3 is 152 kips. For this beam, web capacity = 152 × 0.275 = 41.8 kips.

Detail Data: Two L 4 × 3$\frac{1}{2}$ × $\frac{3}{8}$ × 0'-8$\frac{1}{2}$"
$F_y = 36$ ksi
Three $\frac{3}{4}$" φ ASTM A325-N bolts
$\frac{5}{16}$ in. fillet weld, E70XX

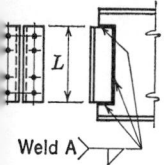

FRAMED BEAM CONNECTIONS
Welded—E70XX electrodes
for combination with Table I connections
TABLE III   Allowable loads in kips

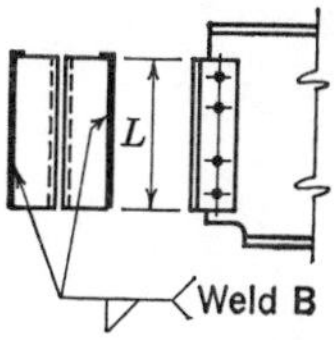

Weld A⟩   ⟨Weld B

| Weld A | | Weld B | | Angle Length L | [a]Minimum Web Thickness for Welds A | | Number of Fasteners in One Vertical Row (Table I) |
Capacity Kips	[b]Size In.	[c]Capacity Kips	[b]Size In.		$F_y = 36$ ksi $F_v = 14.5$ ksi	$F_y = 50$ ksi $F_v = 20$ ksi	
276	5/16	296	3/8	2'- 5½	.56	.41	
221	¼	247	5/16	2'- 5½	.46	.33	10
166	3/16	197	¼	2'- 5½	.34	.25	
246	5/16	261	3/8	2'- 2½	.55	.40	
197	¼	217	5/16	2'- 2½	.45	.32	9
148	3/16	173	¼	2'- 2½	.33	.24	
217	5/16	223	3/8	1'-11½	.54	.39	
173	¼	186	5/16	1'-11½	.44	.32	8
130	3/16	149	¼	1'-11½	.33	.24	
186	5/16	187	3/8	1'- 8½	.53	.39	
149	¼	156	5/16	1'- 8½	.43	.31	7
112	3/16	125	¼	1'- 8½	.32	.23	
157	5/16	152	3/8	1'- 5½	.52	.38	
125	¼	126	5/16	1'- 5½	.42	.30	6
94.1	3/16	101	¼	1'- 5½	.31	.23	
128	5/16	115	3/8	1'- 2½	.50	.36	
102	¼	95.7	5/16	1'- 2½	.41	.29	5
76.6	3/16	76.6	¼	1'- 2½	.30	.22	
99.0	5/16	80.1	3/8	11½	.48	.35	
79.2	¼	66.9	5/16	11½	.39	.28	4
59.4	3/16	53.4	¼	11½	.29	.21	
71.2	5/16	48.2	3/8	8½	.46	.33	
57.0	¼	40.3	5/16	8½	.37	.27	3
42.8	3/16	32.2	¼	8½	.28	.20	
44.9	5/16	21.9	3/8	5½	.44	.32	
35.9	¼	18.3	5/16	5½	.35	.25	2
27.0	3/16	14.6	¼	5½	.26	.19	

[a] When the beam web thickness is less than the minimum, multiply the connection capacity furnished by Weld A by the ratio of the actual web thickness to the tabulated minimum thickness. Thus, if 5/16 in. Weld A, with a connection capacity of 128 kips and a 1'-2½" long angle, is considered for a beam of web thickness of 0.375" with $F_y = 36$ ksi, the connection capacity must be multiplied by 0.375/0.50, giving 96.0 kips.

[b] Should the thickness of material to which connection angles are welded exceed the limits set by AISC Specifications, Sect. 1.17.5, for weld sizes specified, increase the weld size as required, but not to exceed the angle thickness.

[c] When welds are used on outstanding legs, connection capacity may be limited by the shear capacity of the supporting member as stipulated by AISC Specification Sect. 1.17.6. See Examples (d) and (e), pages 4 - 34 and 4 - 35.

Note 1: Connection Angles: Two L 4 × 3½ × Thickness × L; $F_y = 36$ ksi. See page 4 - 28 for limiting values of thickness and optional width of legs.

Note 2: Capacities shown in this table apply only when the material welded is $F_y = 36$ ksi c[?] $F_y = 50$ ksi steel.

AMERICAN INSTITUTE OF STEEL CONSTRUCTION

Notes

FRAMED BEAM CONNECTIONS
Welded—E70XX electrodes

TABLE IV

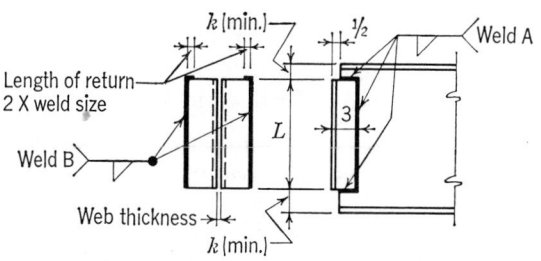

Table IV lists capacities and connection details for angle connections welded to both the beam web and the supporting member.

Holes for erection bolts may be placed as required in legs to be field welded (optional).

EXAMPLES

(a) **Given:** *Beam:* W36 × 150; $t_w = 0.625''$; $T = 32\frac{1}{8}''$
  $F_y = 36$ ksi; $F_v = 14.5$ ksi
  Weld: E70XX
  Reaction: 180 kips

Solution: Enter Table IV and select a Weld **A** capacity of 181 kips (weld size = $\frac{3}{16}$ in.). Weld **B** has a capacity of 217 kips and is satisfactory. The angle length (32″) is slightly less than T for the W36 × 150 and is satisfactory. The beam web thickness (0.625″) exceeds the minimum web thickness (0.34″), so no reduction in Weld **A** capacity is required.

Detail Data: Two L 4 × 3 × $\frac{5}{16}$ × 2′-8″; $F_y = 36$ ksi;
  Weld **A** = $\frac{3}{16}''$; Weld **B** = $\frac{1}{4}''$; E70XX

(b) **Given:** Same data as Example (a) except the reaction is 144 kips.

Solution: Enter Table IV and select a Weld **A** capacity of 144 kips (weld size = $\frac{5}{16}''$). Weld **B** has a capacity of 148 kips and is satisfactory. The angle length (16″) is less than T and is satisfactory. The beam web thickness (0.625″) exceeds the minimum web thickness (0.51″), so no reduction in Weld **A** capacity is required.

Unless framing details require this short angle length, longer angles with less deposited weld metal may be desirable. The 26″ long angles with Weld **A** capacity of 145 kips (weld size = $\frac{3}{16}$ in.) and Weld **B** capacity of 169 kips are also satisfactory and may be selected.

Detail Data: Two L 4 × 3 × $\frac{5}{16}$ × 2′-2″; $F_y = 36$ ksi;
  Weld **A** = $\frac{3}{16}$ in.; Weld **B** = $\frac{1}{4}$ in.; E70XX

AMERICAN INSTITUTE OF STEEL CONSTRUCTION

(c) **Given:** *Beam:* W 16 × 26; $t_w = 0.25''$; $T = 13\frac{3}{4}''$;

$F_y = 50$ ksi; $F_v = 20$ ksi

Weld: E70XX

Reaction: 35 kips

Solution: Enter Table IV and select a Weld **B** capacity of 35.5 kips (weld size = $\frac{1}{4}''$). Angle length (8″) is less than T and is satisfactory. Weld **A** has a capacity of 40.0 kips and is satisfactory. The beam web thickness (0.25″) exceeds the minimum web thickness (0.20″), so no reduction in Weld **A** capacity is required.

Note: Had this beam been of $F_y = 36$ ksi steel, the beam web thickness (0.25″) would have been less than the minimum web thickness and the capacity of Weld **A** would have to be reduced. Multiplying 40 kips by 0.25/0.28 gives a reduced capacity of 35.7 kips, which would still be adequate for this reaction. (See note (a) below Table IV.)

Detail Data: Two L 3 × 3 × $\frac{5}{16}$ × 0′-8″; $F_y = 36$ ksi;
Weld **A** = $\frac{3}{16}$ in.; Weld **B** = $\frac{1}{4}$ in.; E70XX

WELDS TO SUPPORTING MEMBERS

Selection of connections tabulated herein is based on and limited by the requirement that Welds **B** will be applied in accordance with AISC Specification Sect. 1.17.5, which stipulates minimum welds for various material thicknesses.

With respect to Welds **B** it should be noted that supporting members with limited shear capacity, or which support opposed connections, may be subject to a reduction in connection capacity. See AISC Specification, Sect. 1.17.6.

EXAMPLES

(d) **Given:** Weld **B** = $\frac{5}{16}$ in. fillet weld, E70XX, fully loaded on one side of $\frac{1}{4}''$ thick supporting member web of $F_y = 36$ ksi steel.

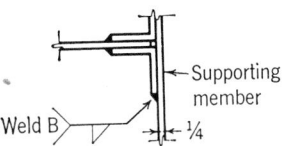

Solution: Shear value of one $\frac{5}{16}$ in. fillet weld = 0.3125″ × 0.707 × 21.0 ksi = 4.64 kips/lin. inch. Shear value of $\frac{1}{4}''$ thick web = 0.25″ × 14.5 ksi = 3.63 kips/lin. inch.

Because of this deficiency in web shear capacity, the total capacity selected from the Weld **B** column for $\frac{5}{16}$ in. weld size must be multiplied by the ratio 3.63/4.64.

(e) **Given:** Two floor beams with end reactions of 15.0 kips each are to be supported by a beam of $F_y = 36$ ksi steel with a $\frac{5}{16}''$ thick web.

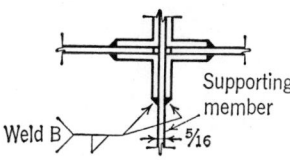

Supporting
member

Weld B

$\frac{5}{16}$

Solution: $\frac{1}{4}$ in. Weld **B** with 5″ long angles has a capacity of 15.7 kips and would be almost fully stressed. Maximum shear developed in the two $\frac{1}{4}$ in. fillet Welds **B** on opposite sides of the supporting beam web = $2 \times 0.25 \times 0.707 \times 21.0 \times 15/15.7 = 7.09$ kips/lin. inch. Shear capacity of $\frac{5}{16}''$ web = $0.3125 \times 14.5 = 4.53$ kips/lin. inch. A longer connection is required to reduce the web shear. Required Weld **B** capacity is 15.7 kips $\times$ 7.09/4.53 = 24.6. Two 7″ long angles with $\frac{1}{4}$ in. Weld **B** have a tabulated capacity of 28.3 kips and are adequate.

FRAMED BEAM CONNECTIONS
Welded—E70XX electrodes
TABLE IV

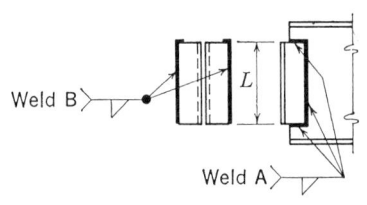

Weld B

L

Weld A

Weld **A**		Weld **B**		Angle Length *L* In.	Angle Size $F_y = 36$ ksi	[a]Minimum Web Thickness for Weld **A**	
Capacity Kips	[b]Size In.	[c]Capacity Kips	[b]Size In.			$F_y = 36$ ksi $F_v = 14.5$ ksi	$F_y = 50$ ksi $F_v = 20$ ksi
302	5/16	326	3/8	32	4 × 3 × 7/16	.57	.42
242	1/4	271	5/16	32	4 × 3 × 3/8	.46	.33
181	3/16	217	1/4	32	4 × 3 × 5/16	.34	.25
282	5/16	302	3/8	30	4 × 3 × 7/16	.57	.41
226	1/4	251	5/16	30	4 × 3 × 3/8	.46	.33
169	3/16	201	1/4	30	4 × 3 × 5/16	.34	.25
262	5/16	278	3/8	28	4 × 3 × 7/16	.56	.41
210	1/4	231	5/16	28	4 × 3 × 3/8	.45	.33
157	3/16	185	1/4	28	4 × 3 × 5/16	.34	.24
242	5/16	254	3/8	26	4 × 3 × 7/16	.55	.40
194	1/4	211	5/16	26	4 × 3 × 3/8	.45	.32
145	3/16	169	1/4	26	4 × 3 × 5/16	.33	.24
221	5/16	230	3/8	24	4 × 3 × 7/16	.55	.40
178	1/4	191	5/16	24	4 × 3 × 3/8	.44	.32
133	3/16	153	1/4	24	4 × 3 × 5/16	.33	.24
202	5/16	206	3/8	22	4 × 3 × 7/16	.54	.39
162	1/4	171	5/16	22	4 × 3 × 3/8	.44	.31
121	3/16	137	1/4	22	4 × 3 × 5/16	.32	.24
182	5/16	181	3/8	20	4 × 3 × 7/16	.53	.39
146	1/4	152	5/16	20	4 × 3 × 3/8	.43	.31
110	3/16	121	1/4	20	4 × 3 × 5/16	.32	.23
162	5/16	157	3/8	18	4 × 3 × 7/16	.52	.38
130	1/4	131	5/16	18	4 × 3 × 3/8	.42	.30
97.7	3/16	105	1/4	18	4 × 3 × 5/16	.31	.23
144	5/16	148	3/8	16	3 × 3 × 7/16	.51	.37
114	1/4	123	5/16	16	3 × 3 × 3/8	.41	.30
85.9	3/16	98.8	1/4	16	3 × 3 × 5/16	.31	.22
123	5/16	124	3/8	14	3 × 3 × 7/16	.50	.36
98.8	1/4	103	5/16	14	3 × 3 × 3/8	.40	.29
74.0	3/16	82.5	1/4	14	3 × 3 × 5/16	.30	.22
104	5/16	99.6	3/8	12	3 × 3 × 7/16	.48	.35
83.2	1/4	83.1	5/16	12	3 × 3 × 3/8	.39	.28
62.5	3/16	66.5	1/4	12	3 × 3 × 5/16	.29	.21

For footnotes, see pg. **4** - 37.

FRAMED BEAM CONNECTIONS
Welded—E70XX electrodes

TABLE IV

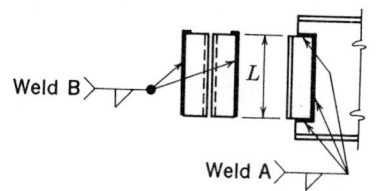

Weld B

L

Weld A

Weld **A**		Weld **B**		Angle Length L In.	Angle Size $F_y = 36$ ksi	[a]Minimum Web Thickness for Weld **A**	
Capacity Kips	[b]Size In.	[c]Capacity Kips	[b]Size In.			$F_y = 36$ ksi $F_v = 14.5$ ksi	$F_y = 50$ ksi $F_v = 20$ ksi
85.1	5/16	75.9	3/8	10	3 × 3 × 7/16	.47	.34
68.1	1/4	63.3	5/16	10	3 × 3 × 3/8	.38	.27
51.0	3/16	50.5	1/4	10	3 × 3 × 5/16	.28	.21
75.9	5/16	64.3	3/8	9	3 × 3 × 7/16	.46	.34
60.6	1/4	53.7	5/16	9	3 × 3 × 3/8	.38	.27
45.5	3/16	42.9	1/4	9	3 × 3 × 5/16	.28	.20
66.7	5/16	53.2	3/8	8	3 × 3 × 7/16	.46	.33
53.3	1/4	44.4	5/16	8	3 × 3 × 3/8	.37	.27
40.0	3/16	35.5	1/4	8	3 × 3 × 5/16	.28	.20
57.8	5/16	42.5	3/8	7	3 × 3 × 7/16	.45	.32
46.3	1/4	35.5	5/16	7	3 × 3 × 3/8	.36	.26
34.7	3/16	28.3	1/4	7	3 × 3 × 5/16	.27	.19
49.2	5/16	32.6	3/8	6	3 × 3 × 7/16	.44	.32
39.3	1/4	27.1	5/16	6	3 × 3 × 3/8	.36	.26
29.5	3/16	21.7	1/4	6	3 × 3 × 5/16	.27	.19
40.8	5/16	23.4	3/8	5	3 × 3 × 7/16	.43	.32
32.6	1/4	19.5	5/16	5	3 × 3 × 3/8	.35	.25
24.5	3/16	15.7	1/4	5	3 × 3 × 5/16	.26	.19
32.7	5/16	15.4	3/8	4	3 × 3 × 7/16	.43	.31
26.2	1/4	12.9	5/16	4	3 × 3 × 3/8	.35	.25
19.7	3/16	10.4	1/4	4	3 × 3 × 5/16	.26	.19

[a] When the beam web thickness is less than the minimum, multiply the connection capacity furnished by Welds **A** by the ratio of the actual thickness to the tabulated minimum thickness. Thus, if 5/16 in. Weld **A**, with a connection capacity of 66.7 kips and an 8″ long angle, is considered for a beam of web thickness 0.305″ and $F_y = 36$ ksi, the connection capacity must be multiplied by 0.305/0.46, giving 44.2 kips.

[b] Should the thickness of material to which connection angles are welded exceed the limits set by AISC Specification Sect. 1.17.5 for weld sizes specified, increase the weld size as required, but not to exceed the angle thickness.

[c] For welds on outstanding legs, connection capacity may be limited by the shear capacity of the supporting members, as stipulated by AISC Specification Sect. 1.17.6. See Examples (d) and (e), pages 4-34, 4-35.

Note 1: Capacities shown in this table apply only when connection angles are $F_y = 36$ ksi steel and the material to which they are welded is either $F_y = 36$ ksi or $F_y = 50$ ksi steel.

SPECIAL FRAMED BEAM CONNECTIONS

In designing framed beam connections there may be cases where Tables I–VIII will not apply. This may occur when bearing governs over single shear or the length of connection angles is limited by framing conditions. The following example outlines the design method recommended when tabulated connections are not applicable.

EXAMPLE 1

Given: Design a connection for a W21 ×55 with a 100 kip end reaction. Beam and connection are F_y = 36 ksi steel. Use $\frac{7}{8}$" diam. ASTM A502 Gr 1 rivets in beam web leg, and $\frac{7}{8}$" diam. ASTM A325 Friction Type bolts in outstanding leg. The depth of angle is limited to 12 in.

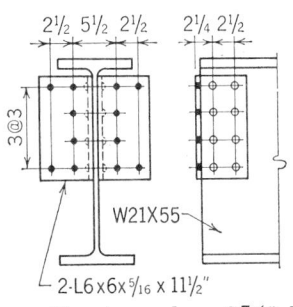

2½ 5½ 2½   2¼ 2½

3@3

W21X55

2-L6x6x⁵⁄₁₆ x 11½"

Solution:

1. *Outstanding legs:*
   Single shear value of $\frac{7}{8}$" diam. A325-F bolt from shear load tables = 9.02 kips.

   No. req'd. $= \dfrac{100}{9.02} = 11.1$ **Use: 12 bolts**

2. *Web legs:*
   Double shear value of $\frac{7}{8}$" diam. A502 Gr 1 rivets from shear load tables = 18.04 kips.

Bearing value of $\frac{7}{8}$" diam. A502 Gr 1 rivets in 0.375 in. web from bearing tables = 0.375 × 42.5 = 15.9 kips.

Bearing governs. No. req'd. $= \dfrac{100}{15.9} = 6.3$ **Use: 8 rivets**

3. *Angle size:*
   Use 2 angles 6 x 6 x t x 11½"
   t required by bearing at 42.5 kips per inch thick material

   $= \dfrac{9.02}{42.5} = 0.21$ in.

   t required by gross shear in vertical section $= \dfrac{100}{11.5 \times 14.5 \times 2}$

   $= 0.30$ in. (governs)

Use: 2 angles 6 x 6 x $\frac{5}{16}$ x 11½"

EXAMPLE 2

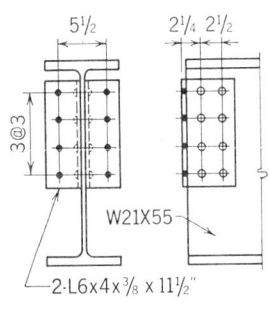

5½   2¼ 2½

3@3

W21X55

2-L6x4x³⁄₈ x 11½"

Given: Same as Example 1 except use $\frac{7}{8}$" diam. A325-X Bearing Type bolts (with threads excluded from the shear planes) in the outstanding legs. Web t is $\frac{5}{16}$" (ASTM A36).

Solution:

1. *Outstanding legs:*
   Supporting girder web is $\frac{5}{16}$" thick A36
   Bearing value of $\frac{5}{16}$" web with $\frac{7}{8}$" fasteners = 13.3 kips.

Single shear value of $\frac{7}{8}$" diam. A325-X bolts from shear load tables = 13.23 kips (governs).

$$\text{No. req'd.} = \frac{100}{13.23} = 7.6 \qquad \textbf{Use:} \quad \textbf{8 bolts}$$

2. *Web legs:* Same as Example 1
3. *Angle size:* Use: **2 angles 6 x 4 x $\frac{3}{8}$ x 11$\frac{1}{2}$".**

Another case where the tables may not apply is when beams of different depths are framed opposite. Example 3 outlines one design method recommended when tabulated connections are not applicable.

EXAMPLE 3

Given: Design connections for a W12 × 27 with a 27 kip end reaction and a W24 × 68 with an 82 kip end reaction framed opposite to a girder with a $\frac{1}{4}$" web. Beams, girder and connections are F_y = 36 ksi steel. Use $\frac{7}{8}$" diam. A502 Gr 1 rivets in beam web and $\frac{7}{8}$" diam. ASTM A325 Bearing Type Bolts, with threads in shear planes in girder web.

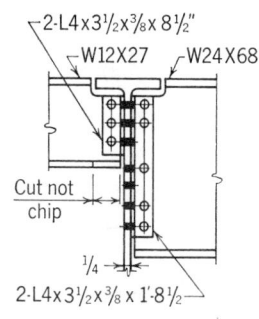

Solution:

1. *Web legs:*

    Double shear value of $\frac{7}{8}$" diam. A502 Gr 1 rivets from shear load tables = 18.04 kips. Bearing value of $\frac{7}{8}$" diam. A502 Gr 1 rivets in 0.24 in. web (W12 × 27) from bearing tables = 0.237 × 42.5 = 10.1 kips; bearing value in 0.416 in. web (W24 × 68) = 0.416 × 42.5 = 17.7 kips. Bearing governs in both beams.

W12 × 27: No. req'd. $= \dfrac{27}{10.1} = 2.6$ Use: **3 rivets**

W24 × 68: No. req'd. $= \dfrac{82}{17.7} = 4.6$ Use: **Minimum of 5 rivets**

2. *Outstanding legs:*

    The fasteners in the outstanding legs are governed by two criteria. Where the beams are framed opposite, the fasteners are governed by double shear or bearing on the web, while fasteners that are not framed opposite are governed by single shear or bearing on the web.

    Double shear value of $\frac{7}{8}$" diam. ASTM A325 bolts (with threads in shear planes) from allowable load tables = 18.04 kips; single shear = 9.02 kips. Bearing value of $\frac{7}{8}$" diam. A325-N bolts in 0.25 in. girder web, from allowable load tables = 0.25 × 42.5 = 10.6 kips. Bearing governs for bolts framed opposite.

    The three-row web pattern of the W12 × 27 makes convenient a 6 bolt connection to the girder, each bolt in girder web being loaded at 27/6 = 4.5 kips. With total allowable bearing at 10.6 kips, girder web capacity available for supporting the W24 × 68 is 10.6 − 4.5 = 6.1 kips per bolt, which is less than single shear and therefore governs. Assuming that all bolts will transmit loads equally to the girder web, the 82 kip load for the W24 × 68 will require 82/6.1 = 13.4.

    Use: **14 bolts.**

3. *Angle size:*

    Use: **Two angles 4 x 3$\frac{1}{2}$ x $\frac{3}{8}$ x 8$\frac{1}{2}$" for W12 × 27**
    Use: **Two angles 4 x 3$\frac{1}{2}$ x $\frac{3}{8}$ x 1'-8$\frac{1}{2}$" for W24 × 68**

SEATED BEAM CONNECTIONS
Bolted or riveted
TABLE V

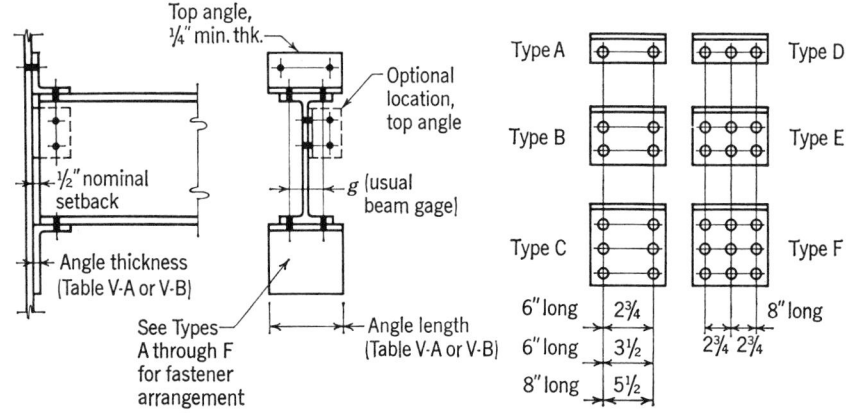

Seat Angle Types

Seated connections should be used only when the beam is supported by a top angle placed as shown above, or in the optional location as indicated.

Nominal beam setback is $\frac{1}{2}''$. Allowable loads in Tables V-A and V-B are based on $\frac{3}{4}''$ setback, which provides for possible mill underrun in beam length.

ASTM A307 bolts may be used in seated connections, provided the stipulations of AISC Specification, Sect. 1.15.12, are observed.

Allowable loads in Table V-A are based on F_y = 36 ksi steel in both beam and seat angle. These values will be conservative when used with beams of F_y greater than 36 ksi. For beams with F_y equal to or greater than 50 ksi, use Table V-B.

Allowable loads in Table V-B are based on F_y = 36 ksi steel in the seat angle and F_y = 50 ksi steel in the beams. For beams with F_y greater than 50 ksi, these values will be conservative.

Vertical spacing of fasteners and gages in seat angles may be arranged to suit conditions, provided they conform to AISC Specification, Sects. 1.16.4 and 1.16.5, with regard to minimum pitch and minimum edge distances. Where thick angles are used, driving clearances may require an increase in the outstanding leg gage and tabulated width.

In the event the thin web of a supporting member limits its bearing capacity, it may be necessary to reduce values listed in Table V-C.

For the most economical seated connection, the reaction values of the beams should be shown on the contract drawings. If the reactions are not shown, the connections shall be selected to support half the total uniform load capacity shown in tables of Allowable Loads on Beams for the given shape, span, and steel specified for the beam in question. The effect of concentrated loads near an end connection must also be considered.

AMERICAN INSTITUTE OF STEEL CONSTRUCTION

EXAMPLES

(a) **Given:** *Beam:* W16 × 36 (⁵⁄₁₆″ web)
  F_y = 36 ksi material
  Reaction: 25 kips
  Bolts: ⅞″ φ A325-N
  Column gage: 5½″ in column web

Solution: Enter Table V-A under 8″ angle length, for a ⁵⁄₁₆″ beam web; select a ¾″ angle thickness (capacity = 26.5 kips). Enter Table V-C opposite ⅞″φ A325-N; note that a Type D connection (capacity = 27.1 kips) is required. From Table V-D, with a Type D connection, a 4 × 4 angle is available in ¾″ thickness.

Detail Data: Seat: One L 4 × 4 × ¾ × 0′-8 with three ⅞″φ A325-N bolts. Top or side support, if required, to be chosen to suit conditions.

(b) **Given:** Same as Example (a) except connect to a column flange with column gage = 5½″.

Solution: As in Example (a), a ¾″ angle thickness is adequate. Enter Table V-C opposite ⅞″φ A325-N; note that a Type B connection (capacity = 36.1 kips) is required. From Table V-D, with a Type B connection, a 6 × 4 angle is available in ¾″ thickness.

Detail Data: Seat: One L 6 × 4 × ¾ × 0′-8 (4″ OSL) with four ⅞″φ A325-N bolts. Top or side support, if required, to be chosen to suit conditions.

SEATED BEAM CONNECTIONS
Bolted or riveted
TABLE V   Allowable loads in kips

TABLE V-A   Outstanding Leg Capacity, kips (based on OSL = 4 inches)

Angle Material		$F_y = 36$ ksi										
Angle Length		6 inches						8 inches				
Angle Thickness, In.		⅜	½	⅝	¾	⅞	1	⅜	½	⅝	¾	⅞	1
Beam Web Thickness (in.) $F_y = 36$ ksi	3⁄16	7.50	10.3	13.1	15.9	18.7	18.8	8.44	11.5	14.6	17.7	18.8	18.8
	¼	9.57	13.0	16.3	19.7	23.1	26.2	10.6	14.4	18.1	21.8	25.5	26.2
	5⁄16	11.3	16.3	20.3	24.2	28.1	32.0	13.1	17.9	22.2	26.5	30.8	34.7
	⅜	12.4	19.3	24.3	28.7	33.2	37.6	14.3	21.5	26.3	31.2	36.1	40.9
	7⁄16	13.4	21.1	28.8	33.7	38.7	43.6	15.5	23.8	30.9	36.3	41.7	47.1
	½	14.3	22.8	31.6	39.2	44.6	50.0	16.5	25.7	35.1	41.8	47.7	53.6
	9⁄16	15.2	24.4	34.0	43.8	51.0	56.9	17.5	27.5	37.8	47.8	54.1	60.5

TABLE V-B   Outstanding Leg Capacity, kips (based on OSL = 4 inches)

Angle Material		$F_y = 36$ ksi										
Angle Length		6 inches						8 inches				
Angle Thickness, In.		⅜	½	⅝	¾	⅞	1	⅜	½	⅝	¾	⅞	1
Beam Web Thickness (in.) $F_y = 50$ ksi	3⁄16	9.14	12.6	16.1	19.5	23.0	26.2	10.2	14.1	17.9	21.7	25.5	26.2
	¼	11.9	16.1	20.3	24.5	28.7	32.9	13.1	17.7	22.4	27.0	31.6	36.2
	5⁄16	13.3	20.7	25.6	30.5	35.5	40.4	15.4	22.4	27.8	33.2	38.6	43.9
	⅜	14.6	23.3	31.1	36.7	42.3	47.9	16.9	26.3	33.4	39.5	45.6	51.7
	7⁄16	15.8	25.5	35.8	43.5	50.0	56.1	18.3	28.8	39.6	46.4	53.2	60.0
	½	16.9	27.7	39.0	50.6	57.9	64.8	19.5	31.1	43.2	53.9	61.4	68.8
	9⁄16	17.9	29.7	42.2	55.0	66.8	74.3	20.7	33.3	46.6	60.1	70.3	78.4

TABLE V-C   Fastener Capacity, kips

[a]Fastener Specification	Fastener Diameter in.	Connection Type					
		A	B	C	D	E	F
A307	¾	8.8	17.7	26.5	13.3	26.5	39.8
	⅞	12.0	24.0	36.1	18.0	36.1	54.1
	1	15.7	31.4	47.1	23.6	47.1	70.7
A325-F A325-N A502-1	¾	13.3	26.5	39.8	19.9	39.8	59.7
	⅞	18.0	36.1	54.1	27.1	54.1	81.2
	1	23.6	47.1	70.7	35.3	70.7	—
A490-F A502-2	¾	17.7	35.4	53.0	26.5	53.0	79.6
	⅞	24.1	48.1	72.2	36.1	72.2	—
	1	31.4	62.8	94.3	47.1	94.3	—
A325-X	¾	19.4	38.9	58.3	29.2	58.3	87.5
	⅞	26.5	52.9	79.4	39.7	79.4	—
	1	34.6	69.1	—	51.8	—	—
A490-N	¾	19.9	39.8	59.6	29.8	59.6	89.5
	⅞	27.1	54.1	81.2	40.6	81.2	—
	1	35.3	70.7	—	53.0	—	—
A490-X	¾	28.3	56.6	84.8	42.4	84.8	127
	⅞	38.5	77.0	—	57.7	—	—
	1	50.3	101	—	75.4	—	—

[a] A325-F and A490-F: Friction type connections.
A325-N and A490-N: Bearing type connections with threads included in shear plane.
A325-X and A490-X: Bearing type connections with threads excluded from shear plane.

TABLE V-D   Available Seat Angle and Thickness Range

Type	Angle Size In.	t In.
A, D	4 × 3	⅜– ⅝
	4 × 3½	⅜– ⅝
	4 × 4	⅜– ¾
B, E	6 × 4	⅜– ⅞
	7 × 4	⅜– ⅞
	8 × 4	½–1
C, F	[b]8 × 4	½–1
	9 × 4	½–1

[b] Suitable for use with ¾" and ⅞" fasteners only.

SEATED BEAM CONNECTIONS
Welded—E70XX Electrodes
TABLE VI

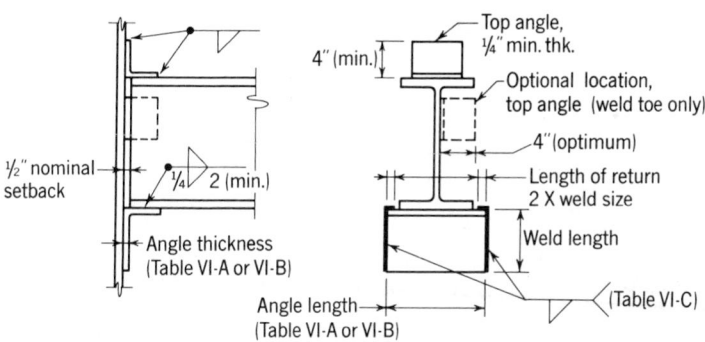

Seated connections should be used only when the beam is supported by a top angle placed as shown above, or in the optional location as indicated.

Allowable loads in Table VI are based on the use of E70XX electrodes. The table may be used for other electrodes provided the tabular values are adjusted for the electrodes used (e.g., for E60XX electrodes, multiply tabular values by $18\!/\!21$, or 0.86, etc.) and the welds and base metal meet the provisions of AISC Specification Sect. 1.5.3.

Welds attaching beams to seat or top angles may be replaced by bolts or rivets, provided the limitations on the use of ASTM A307 bolts stipulated in AISC Specification Sect. 1.15.12 are observed.

In addition to the welds shown, temporary erection bolts may be used to attach beams to seats (optional).

Nominal beam setback is $\frac{1}{2}''$. Allowable loads in Tables VI-A and VI-B are based on $\frac{3}{4}''$ setback, which provides for possible mill underrun in beam length.

Allowable loads in Table VI-A are based on F_y = 36 ksi material in both beam and seat angle. These values will be conservative when used for beams with F_y greater than 36 ksi. For beams with F_y equal to or greater than 50 ksi, use Table VI-B.

Allowable loads in Table VI-B are based on F_y = 36 ksi material in the seat angle with beam material of F_y = 50 ksi. These values will be conservative when used with beams of F_y greater than 50 ksi.

Should combinations of material thickness and weld size selected from Tables VI-A or VI-B and VI-C exceed the limits set by AISC Specification Sects. 1.17.5 and 1.17.6, increase the weld size or material thickness as required.

No reduction of the tabulated weld capacity is required when unstiffened seats line up on opposite sides of the supporting web.

For the most economical seated connection, the reaction values of the beams should be shown on the contract drawings. If the reactions are not shown, the connections shall be selected to support half the total uniform load capacity shown in the tables for Allowable Loads on Beams for the given shape, span, and steel specified for the beam in question. The effect of concentrated loads near an end connection shall also be considered.

AMERICAN INSTITUTE OF STEEL CONSTRUCTION

EXAMPLE

Given: *Beam:* W21 ×62 ($\frac{3}{8}$″ web).
Attach beam flange to seat with bolts.
F_y = 36 ksi material
Reaction: 35 kips
Welds: E70XX electrodes
Column: Column web will permit use of 8″ long seat angle.

Solution: Enter Table VI-A opposite $\frac{3}{8}$″ web thickness; under 8″ angle length, read 36.1 kips. Note that a $\frac{7}{8}$″ angle thickness is required. Enter Table VI-C and note that satisfactory weld capacities appear under 6 through 9 inch leg angles, all of which are shown to be available in $\frac{7}{8}$″ thickness. In this case the 6 × 4 angle is ruled out because of the rather heavy $\frac{7}{16}$″ weld required. The 9 × 4 angle is ruled out because the 8 × 4 angle can provide adequate capacity. Angles 8 × 4 (capacity = 35.6 kips, $\frac{1}{4}$″ weld) and 7 × 4 (capacity = 35.6 kips, $\frac{5}{16}$″ weld) are equally suitable. Angle 7 × 4 is chosen because the material savings will usually offset the cost differential between welds of $\frac{1}{16}$″ thickness differential provided that each weld can be made with the same number of passes ($\frac{5}{16}$″ welds and smaller are single pass welds).

Detail Data: One L 7 × 4 × $\frac{7}{8}$ × 0′-8, with $\frac{5}{16}$ welds (E70XX). Top or side angle, if required, to be chosen with the same welds.

Had it been required to weld the beam to the seat, the $\frac{7}{8}$″ seat angle thickness would dictate a $\frac{5}{16}$″ weld (see AISC Specification Sect. 1.17.5), which is compatible with the $\frac{5}{8}$″ beam flange thickness (see Sect. 1.17.6). Block beam flange to permit welding to the 8″ seat angle or use a longer seat angle if space permits.

SEATED BEAM CONNECTIONS
Welded—E70XX electrodes
TABLE VI Allowable loads in kips

TABLE VI-A Outstanding Leg Capacity, kips (based on OSL = 3½ or 4 inches)

Angle Material		F_y = 36 ksi										
Angle Length		6 inches						8 inches				
Angle Thickness, In.		⅜	½	⅝	¾	⅞	1	⅜	½	⅝	¾	⅞	1
Beam Web Thickness (in.) F_y = 36 ksi	³⁄₁₆	7.50	10.3	13.1	15.9	18.7	18.8	8.44	11.5	14.6	17.7	18.8	18.8
	¼	9.57	13.0	16.3	19.7	23.1	26.2	10.6	14.4	18.1	21.8	25.5	26.2
	⁵⁄₁₆	11.3	16.3	20.3	24.2	28.1	32.0	13.1	17.9	22.2	26.5	30.8	34.7
	⅜	12.4	19.3	24.3	28.7	33.2	37.6	14.3	21.5	26.3	31.2	36.1	40.9
	⁷⁄₁₆	13.4	21.1	28.8	33.7	38.7	43.6	15.5	23.8	30.9	36.3	41.7	47.1
	½	14.3	22.8	31.6	39.2	44.6	50.0	16.5	25.7	35.1	41.8	47.7	53.6
	⁹⁄₁₆	15.2	24.4	34.0	43.8	51.0	56.9	17.5	27.5	37.8	47.8	54.1	60.5

Note: Values above heavy lines apply only for 4-inch outstanding legs.

TABLE VI-B Outstanding Leg Capacity, kips (based on OSL = 3½ or 4 inches)

Angle Material		F_y = 36 ksi										
Angle Length		6 inches						8 inches				
Angle Thickness, In.		⅜	½	⅝	¾	⅞	1	⅜	½	⅝	¾	⅞	1
Beam Web Thickness (in.) F_y = 50 ksi	³⁄₁₆	9.14	12.6	16.1	19.5	23.0	26.2	10.2	14.1	17.9	21.7	25.5	26.2
	¼	11.9	16.1	20.3	24.5	28.7	32.9	13.1	17.7	22.4	27.0	31.6	36.2
	⁵⁄₁₆	13.3	20.7	25.6	30.5	35.5	40.4	15.4	22.4	27.8	33.2	38.6	43.9
	⅜	14.6	23.3	31.1	36.7	42.3	47.9	16.9	26.3	33.4	39.5	45.6	51.7
	⁷⁄₁₆	15.8	25.5	35.8	43.5	50.0	56.1	18.2	28.8	39.6	46.4	53.2	60.0
	½	16.9	27.7	39.0	50.6	57.9	64.8	19.5	31.1	43.2	53.9	61.4	68.8
	⁹⁄₁₆	17.9	29.7	42.2	55.0	66.8	74.3	20.7	33.3	46.6	60.1	70.3	78.4

Note: Values above heavy lines apply only for 4-inch outstanding legs.

TABLE VI-C Weld Capacity, kips

Weld Size In.	E70XX Electrodes					
	Seat Angle Size (long leg vertical)					
	4 × 3½	5 × 3½	6 × 4	7 × 4	8 × 4	9 × 4
¼	11.5	17.2	21.8	28.5	35.6	43.0
⁵⁄₁₆	14.3	21.5	27.3	35.6	44.5	53.8
⅜	17.2	25.8	32.7	42.7	53.4	64.6
⁷⁄₁₆	20.1	30.1	38.2	49.8	62.3	75.3
½	22.9	34.4	43.6	56.9	71.2	86.1
⅝	—	43.0	54.5	71.2	89.0	—
¹¹⁄₁₆	—	47.3	60.0	78.3	—	—
¾	—	—	65.4	85.4	—	—
Range of available seat angle thicknesses						
Minimum	⅜	⅜	⅜	⅜	½	½
Maximum	⅝	¾	⅞	⅞	1	1

AMERICAN INSTITUTE OF STEEL CONSTRUCTION

Notes

STIFFENED SEATED BEAM CONNECTIONS
Bolted or Riveted
TABLE VII

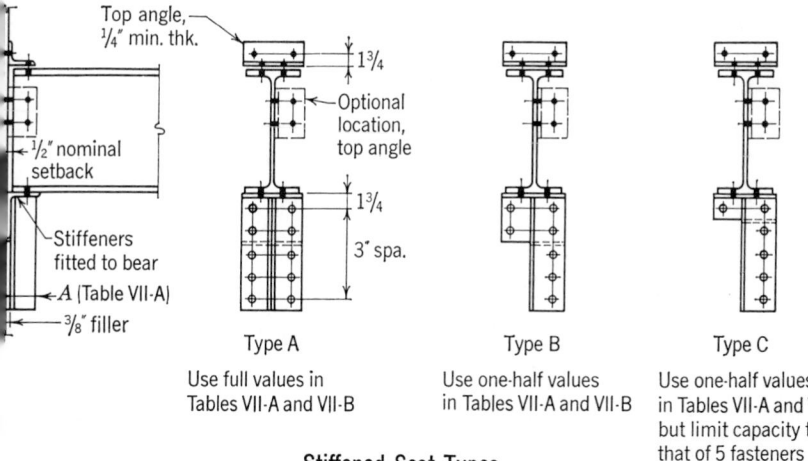

Type A	Type B	Type C
Use full values in Tables VII-A and VII-B	Use one-half values in Tables VII-A and VII-B	Use one-half values in Tables VII-A and VII-B but limit capacity to that of 5 fasteners through stiffeners of $3\frac{1}{2}''$ max. OSL.

Stiffened Seat Types

Seated connections should be used only when the beam is supported by a top angle placed as shown above, or in the optional location as indicated.

Allowable capacities in Table VII-A are based on allowable bearing using steel of $F_y = 36$ ksi or $F_y = 50$ ksi in the stiffener angles. Capacities of fastener groups in Table VII-B are based on single shear. Capacity of the connection is based on the lesser of these two values in conjunction with the web crippling value of the supported beam.

Effective length of stiffener bearing is assumed $\frac{1}{2}''$ less than length of outstanding leg.

Maximum gage in legs of stiffeners connected to columns is $4\frac{3}{4}''$.

ASTM A307 bolts may be used in seated connections, providing the stipulations of AISC Specification Sect. 1.15.12 are observed.

Vertical spacing of fasteners in stiffener angles may be arranged to suit conditions, provided they conform to Sections 1.16.4 and 1.16.5 with respect to minimum pitch and minimum edge distances.

Paired stiffener angles shown in contact may be separated to accommodate column gages, but should not exceed $2 \times (k - \text{stiffener thickness})$, with a minimum opening of $1''$, where the k value is for the supported beam (see tables of dimensions, Part 1 of this Manual). If it is not required to paint the connection parts, the $1''$ minimum may be ignored.

To permit selection of the most economical seated beam connection, the beam reactions should be shown on the contract drawings. If they are not shown, the connections should be selected to support half the total uniform load capacity shown in the beam load tables for the given shape, span, and steel of the beam in question. The effect of concentrated loads near an end connection must also be considered.

For loads in excess of tabulated capacities it is necessary to design special seated connections.

EXAMPLE

Given: Design a stiffened seated beam connection of F_y = 36 ksi steel to support a W30 × 99, also F_y = 36 ksi, with an end reaction of 85 kips. Use $\frac{7}{8}''\phi$ ASTM A325-F bolts to attach the seat to a column web with a $5\frac{1}{2}''$ gage. Assume that a top angle is required.

Solution:

1. From the F_y = 36 ksi beam load tables, under W 30 × 99, note that R = 70 kips and R_i = 14.1 kips. Required length of bearing is:

$$3.5 + \frac{85 - 70}{14.1} = 4.56''$$

From Table VII-A, under F_y = 36 ksi, it will be seen that a 4.56″ length of bearing requires that 5″ OSL stiffener angles be used. In the outstanding leg column under "5 in.", note that the 85 kip reaction requires stiffener angles of $\frac{5}{16}''$ thickness. Use a seat angle of $\frac{3}{8}''$ thickness extending beyond the stiffener angle; this requires a 6″ leg outstanding.

2. In Table VII-B for a $\frac{7}{8}''\phi$ A325-F fastener, 5 rows of bolts with a capacity of 90.2 kips will be required for an 85 kip reaction.

Detail Data: Steps 1 and 2 indicate the use of a Type A connection with 5 rows of $\frac{7}{8}''\phi$ A325-F bolts. Assuming it is possible to employ the suggested spacing of fasteners, detail material will be as follows:

Steel:	F_y = 36 ksi
2 Stiffeners:	L 5 × 5 × $\frac{5}{16}$ × 1′-2$\frac{5}{8}$
1 Seat Angle:	L 6 × 6 × $\frac{3}{8}$ × 0′-10
1 Filler:	PL $\frac{3}{8}$ × 8$\frac{3}{4}$ × 0′-10
1 Top Angle:	L 4 × 3 × $\frac{1}{4}$ × 0′-8 (4″ OSL)

Had the reaction been 45 kips, and all other conditions the same, a $3\frac{1}{2}''$ OSL of stiffener and a 6 × 4 × $\frac{3}{8}''$ seat angle would have been adequate. Using a Type B connection, enter Table VII-A with two times the reaction (or 90 kips) and select $\frac{1}{2}''$ stiffeners. From Table VII-B, 5 fasteners per row is still required for $\frac{7}{8}''\phi$ A325-F bolts (capacity = 90.2 kips).

Components of a Type B connection with 5 rows of $\frac{7}{8}''\phi$ A325-F bolts are as follows:

Steel:	F_y = 36 ksi
1 Stiffener:	L 4 × 3$\frac{1}{2}$ × $\frac{1}{2}$ × 1′-2$\frac{5}{8}$ (3$\frac{1}{2}''$ OSL)
1 Seat Angle:	L 6 × 4 × $\frac{3}{8}$ × 0′-8 (4″ OSL)
1 Filler:	PL $\frac{3}{8}$ × 4 × 0′-8$\frac{3}{4}$
1 Top Angle:	L 4 × 3 × $\frac{1}{4}$ × 0′-8 (4″ OSL)

STIFFENED SEATED BEAM CONNECTIONS
Bolted or riveted
TABLE VII

TABLE VII-A   Stiffener Angle Capacity, kips

Stiffener Material		$F_y = 36$ ksi ($F_p = 33$ ksi)			$F_y = 50$ ksi ($F_p = 45$ ksi)		
Stiffener Outstanding Leg, A, In.		3½	4	5	3½	4	5
Max. Length Beam Bearing, In.		3½	4¼	5¼	3½	4¼	5¼
Thickness of Stiffener Outstanding Legs In.	5⁄16	61.9	72.2	92.8	84.4	98.4	127
	3⁄8	74.3	86.6	111	101	118	152
	7⁄16	86.6	101	130	118	138	177
	½	99.0	116	149	135	158	203
	5⁄8	124	144	186	169	197	253
	¾	149	173	223	203	236	304

Use 3⁄8" thick seat angles with vertical legs wide enough to accommodate fastener pattern, and with outstanding legs wide enough to extend beyond outstanding legs of stiffener.

TABLE VII-B   Fastener Capacity, kips

[a]Fastener Specification	Fastener Diameter In.	Number of Fasteners in One Vertical Row				
		3	4	5	6	7
A307	¾	26.5	35.4	44.2	53.0	61.9
	⅞	36.1	48.1	60.2	72.2	84.2
	1	47.1	62.8	78.6	94.3	110
A325-F A325-N A502-1	¾	39.8	53.0	66.3	79.5	92.8
	⅞	54.1	72.2	90.2	108	126
	1	70.7	94.2	118	141	165
A490-F A502-2	¾	53.0	70.7	88.4	106	124
	⅞	72.2	96.2	120	144	168
	1	94.3	126	157	189	220
A325-X	¾	58.3	77.8	97.2	117	136
	⅞	79.4	106	132	159	185
	1	104	138	173	207	242
A490-N	¾	59.6	79.8	99.4	119	139
	⅞	81.2	108	135	162	189
	1	106	141	177	212	247
A490-X	¾	84.8	113	141	170	198
	⅞	115	154	192	231	269
	1	151	201	251	302	352

[a] A325-F and A490-F: Friction type connections.
  A325-N and A490-N: Bearing type connections with threads included in shear plane.
  A325-X and A490-X: Bearing type connections with threads excluded from shear plane.

STIFFENED SEATED BEAM CONNECTIONS
Welded—E70XX Electrodes

TABLE VIII

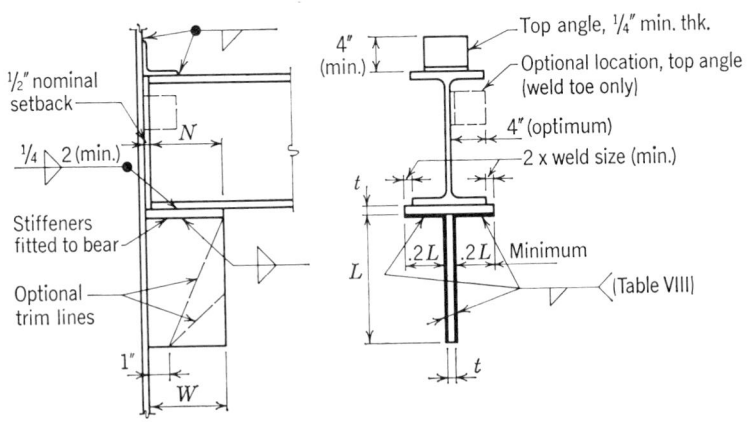

Seated connections should be used only when the beam is supported by a top angle placed as shown above, or in the optional location as indicated.

Allowable loads in Table VIII are based on the use of E70XX electrodes. The table may be used for other electrodes, provided that the tabular values are adjusted for the electrodes used (e.g., for E60XX electrodes, multiply tabular values by $18/21$, or 0.86, etc.) and the welds and base metal meet the provisions of AISC Specification Sect. 1.5.3.

Based on F_y = 36 ksi bracket material, minimum stiffener plate thickness, t, for supported beams with unstiffened webs should not be less than the supported beam web thickness for F_y = 36 ksi beams, and not less than 1.4 times the beam web thickness for beams with F_y = 50 ksi. Based on bracket material of F_y = 50 ksi or greater, the minimum stiffener plate thickness, t, for supported beams with unstiffened webs should be the beam web thickness multiplied by the ratio of F_y of the beam to F_y of the bracket [e.g., F_y (beam) = 65 ksi; F_y (bracket) = 50 ksi; $t = t_w$ (beam) $\times$ 65/50, minimum]. The minimum stiffener plate thickness, t, should be at least two times the required E70XX weld size when F_y of bracket is 36 ksi, and should be at least 1.5 times the required E70XX weld size when F_y of the bracket is 50 ksi.

Thickness, t, of the horizontal seat plate, or flange of tee, should not be less than the thickness of the stiffener.

If seat and stiffener are separate plates, fit stiffener to bear against seat. Welds connecting the two plates should have a strength equal to, or greater than, the horizontal welds to the support under the seat plate.

Welds attaching beam to seat may be replaced by bolts or rivets, providing the limitations on the use of ASTM A307 bolts, stipulated in AISC Specification Sect. 1.15.12, are observed.

For stiffener seats in line on opposite sides of a column web of $F_y = 36$ ksi material, select E70XX weld size no greater than 0.50 of column web thickness. For column web of $F_y = 50$ ksi, select E70XX weld size no greater than 0.67 of column web thickness.

Should combinations of material thickness and weld size selected from Table VIII exceed the limits set by AISC Specification Sects. 1.17.5 and 1.17.6, increase the weld size or material thickness as required.

In addition to the welds shown, temporary erection bolts may be used to attach beams to seats (optional).

To permit selection of the most economical seated connection, the reaction values should be given on the contract drawings. If the reaction values are not given, the connections should be selected to support half the total load capacity tabulated in the beam load tables for the given shape, span, and steel specification of the beam in question. The effect of concentrated loads near an end connection must also be considered.

EXAMPLES

(**a**) **Given:** *Beam:*   W30 × 116 (flange = 10.5″ × 0.85″; web = 0.564″)

ASTM A36 steel ($F_y = 36$ ksi)

Welds: E70XX

Reaction: 100 kips

Design a two-plate welded stiffener seat.

Solution: From the $F_y = 36$ ksi beam load tables: $R = 78$ kips and $R_i = 15.2$ kips.

Required length of bearing: $N = 3.5 + \dfrac{100 - 78}{15.2} = 4.94''$

Stiffener width: $W = 4.94 + 0.5$ (setback) $= 5.44''$

Use: $W = 6''$

Table VIII with $W = 6''$ and a reaction of 100 kips; select a $\frac{5}{16}''$ weld with $L = 15''$, which has a capacity of 103 kips. From this, the minimum length of weld between seat plate and support is $2 \times 0.2L = 6''$. This also establishes the minimum weld between the seat plate and the stiffener as 6″ total, or 3″ on each side of stiffener.

Stiffener plate thickness, t, to develop welds $= 2 \times \frac{5}{16} = \frac{5}{8}''$, or 0.625″. This is greater than the beam web thickness of 0.564″; thus, the stiffener plate thickness need not be increased.

Use: $\frac{5}{8}''$ **plates for the seat and the stiffener.**

Welds attaching the beam flange to the seat must be increased from $\frac{1}{4}''$ to $\frac{5}{16}''$ to conform to AISC Specification Sect. 1.17.5, due to the 0.85″ flange thickness of the W30 × 116 beam.

Seat plate width to permit field welding of beam to seat = flange width + 4 × weld size = $10.5 + 4 (5/16) = 11.75''$.

Use: $12''$

This width is also adequate for the required minimum weld length, horizontal plate to the support.

Detail Data:

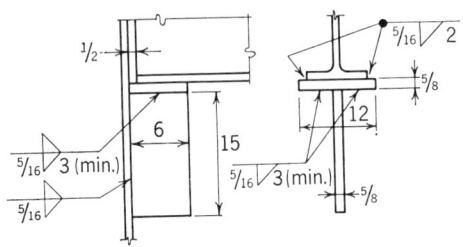

Use: L 4 × 4 × 3/8 × 0'-4 top angle (F_y = 36 ksi) with 5/16 in. welds along toes of angle only (if required).

(b) Given: *Beam:* W 21 × 68 (flange = 8.27″ × 0.685″; web = 0.43″)
ASTM A572, Grade 50 steel (F_y = 50 ksi)
Welds: E70XX electrodes
Reaction: 83 kips

Design a two-plate welded stiffener seat using ASTM A36 steel.

Solution: From the F_y = 50 ksi beam load tables, R = 78 kips and R_i = 16.1 kips.

Required length of bearing;

$$N = 3.5 + \frac{83 - 78}{16.1} = 3.80″$$

Stiffener width:
W = 3.9 + 0.5 (setback) = 4.4″

Use: $W = 5″$

Enter Table VIII with W = 5″ and a reaction of 83 kips; satisfying these requirements are a 5/16 in. weld, L = 13″ (91.3 kips) or a 3/8 in. weld, L = 11″ (83.3 kips), or an even larger weld size. Generally, the 5/16 in. weld is the better selection as this can be made in one pass using manual welding. Select 5/16 in. weld. From this, the minimum length of 5/16 in. weld between seat plate and support is 2 × 0.2L = 5.2″.

Use: **6″.** This also establishes the minimum weld between the seat plate and the stiffener as 6″ total, or 3″ on each side.

Stiffener plate thickness, t, to develop welds = 2 × 5/16 = 5/8 or 0.625″. The minimum thickness, t, for a bracket of F_y = 36 ksi with a beam of F_y = 50 ksi is 1.4 times the beam web thickness = 1.4 × 0.43 = 0.602″.

Use: 5/8″ plates for both the stiffener and the seat.

Welds attaching the beam flange to the seat can be $\frac{1}{4}$ in. for a flange of 0.685″ as per AISC Specification Sect. 1.17.5.

Seat plate width, to permit field welding of beam to seat = flange width + 4 × weld size = 8.27 + (4 × $\frac{1}{4}$) = 9.27″.

Use: 10″. This width is also adequate for the required minimum weld length, horizontal plate to the support.

Detail Data:

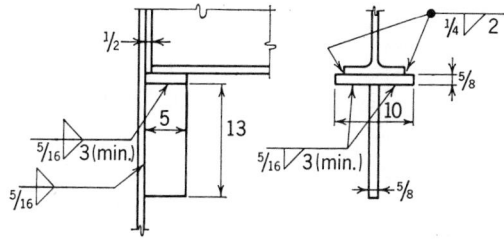

Use: L 4 × 4 × $\frac{3}{8}$ × 0′-4 top angle (F_y = 36 ksi) with $\frac{5}{16}$ in. welds along toes of angle only (if required).

STIFFENED SEATED BEAM CONNECTIONS
Welded—E70XX electrodes
TABLE VIII   Allowable loads in kips

L In.	Width of Seat, W, inches											
	4				5				6			
	Weld Size, inches				Weld Size, inches				Weld Size, inches			
	¼	⁵⁄₁₆	⅜	⁷⁄₁₆	⁵⁄₁₆	⅜	⁷⁄₁₆	½	⁵⁄₁₆	⅜	⁷⁄₁₆	½
6	22.7	28.4	34.0	39.7	23.5	28.1	32.8	37.5	19.9	23.9	27.9	31.
7	29.9	37.4	44.9	52.4	31.2	37.5	43.7	50.0	26.7	32.0	37.3	42.
8	37.8	47.2	56.7	66.1	39.8	47.8	55.8	63.7	34.3	41.1	48.0	54.
9	46.1	57.6	69.2	80.7	49.1	59.0	68.8	78.6	42.5	51.1	59.6	68.
10	54.9	68.6	82.3	96.0	59.0	70.8	82.6	94.4	51.4	61.7	72.0	82.
11	63.9	79.8	95.8	112	69.4	83.3	97.1	111	60.9	73.1	85.2	97
12	73.1	91.4	110	128	80.2	96.2	112	128	70.8	85.0	99.2	113
13	82.5	103	124	144	91.3	110	128	146	81.1	97.4	114	130
14	92.0	115	138	161	103	123	144	164	91.9	110	129	147
15	101	127	152	178	114	137	160	183	103	123	144	165
16	111	139	167	195	126	151	176	202	115	138	160	183
17	121	151	181	212	138	165	193	221	126	151	176	201
18	131	163	196	229	150	180	210	240	137	164	192	219
19	140	175	211	246	162	194	227	259	149	179	208	238
20	150	188	225	263	174	209	243	278	161	193	225	257
21	160	200	240	280	189	223	260	298	173	207	242	276
22	169	212	254	296	198	238	277	317	185	221	258	295
23	179	224	269	313	210	252	294	336	197	236	275	315
24	189	236	283	330	222	267	311	356	209	250	292	334
25	198	248	297	347	234	281	328	375	221	265	309	353
26	208	260	312	364	247	296	345	394	233	279	326	373
27	217	272	326	380	259	310	362	414	245	294	343	392

Note: Loads shown are for E70XX electrodes. For E60XX electrodes, multiply tabular loads by 0.86, or enter table with 1.17 times the given reaction. For E80XX electrodes, multiply tabular loads by 1.14, or enter table with 87.5% of the given reaction.

STIFFENED SEATED BEAM CONNECTIONS
Welded—E70XX electrodes
TABLE VIII   Allowable loads in kips

L In.	Width of Seat, W, inches											
	7				8				9			
	Weld Size, inches				Weld Size, inches				Weld Size, inches			
	5/16	3/8	7/16	1/2	5/16	3/8	1/2	5/8	5/16	3/8	1/2	5/8
11	54.0	64.8	75.6	86.3	48.4	58.0	77.3	96.6	43.7	52.4	69.9	87.4
12	63.1	75.7	88.4	101	56.7	68.1	90.7	113	51.4	61.7	82.2	103
13	72.7	87.2	102	117	65.5	78.7	105	131	59.6	71.5	95.3	119
14	82.6	99.1	116	132	74.8	89.8	120	149	68.2	81.8	109	136
15	92.9	112	130	149	84.4	101	135	169	77.2	92.6	123	154
16	104	124	145	166	94.4	113	151	189	86.5	104	138	173
17	114	137	160	183	105	126	167	209	96.2	115	154	192
18	126	151	176	201	115	138	184	230	106	127	170	212
19	137	164	192	219	126	151	202	252	117	140	186	233
20	148	178	208	237	137	165	219	274	127	152	203	254
21	160	192	224	256	148	178	237	296	138	165	220	276
22	172	206	240	274	159	192	255	319	149	178	238	297
23	183	220	257	293	171	205	274	342	160	192	256	320
24	195	234	274	312	183	219	292	365	171	205	274	342
25	207	249	290	331	195	233	311	389	182	219	292	365
26	219	263	307	351	206	248	330	412	194	233	310	388
27	231	278	324	370	218	262	349	436	206	247	329	411
28	243	292	341	389	230	276	368	460	217	261	348	435
29	256	307	358	409	242	291	387	484	229	275	367	458
30	268	321	375	428	254	305	406	508	241	289	386	482
31	280	336	392	447	266	319	426	532	253	303	405	506
32	292	350	409	467	278	334	445	556	265	318	424	530

Note: Loads shown are for E70XX electrodes. For E60XX electrodes, multiply tabular loads by 0.86, or enter table with 1.17 times the given reaction. For E80XX electrodes, multiply tabular loads by 1.14, or enter table with 87.5% of the given reaction.

Notes

END PLATE SHEAR CONNECTIONS
TABLE IX

This type of connection consists of a plate, less than the beam depth in length, perpendicular to the longitudinal axis of the beam, welded to the beam web with fillet welds each side of the beam web. The end plate connection compares favorably to the double angle connection and for like thicknesses, gage lines and length of connection will furnish end rotation capacity and strength of connection closely approximating that of the double angle framing connection, within the range listed in the table.

Fabrication of this type of connection requires close control in cutting the beam to length and adequate consideration must be given to squaring the beam ends such that both end plates are parallel and the effect of beam camber does not result in out-of-square end plates which makes erection and field fit-up difficult. Shims may be required on runs of beams to compensate for mill and shop tolerances.

For adequate end rotation capacity, it is suggested that end plates be designed for a plate thickness range of $\frac{1}{4}''$ to $\frac{3}{8}''$ inclusive. To develop full capacity of the fasteners and welds, the end plate and web thicknesses must equal or exceed the values listed in the table. If the material thickness supplied by either the plate or the web is less than required, the fastener or weld capacity must be reduced by the ratio of thickness supplied to thickness required.

The gage, g, should be $3\frac{1}{2}''$ to $5\frac{1}{2}''$ for average plate thicknesses, with an edge distance of $1\frac{1}{4}''$. Lesser values of edge distance increase bolt prying and should it become necessary to reduce edge distance, it may be necessary to investigate prying action. Plates $\frac{1}{4}''$ thick of $F_y = 36$ ksi steel and a gage of $3''$ should provide adequate end rotation capacity in the connection. All end plate material thicknesses listed in the table are for $F_y = 36$ ksi. Use of higher values of F_y should be based on engineering investigation that confirms that adequate end rotation capacity is available.

Weld values listed are for two fillet welds and are based on the use of E70XX electrodes. These weld values have been reduced by considering the effective weld length equal to the plate length minus twice the weld size. Welds should not be returned across the web at the top or bottom of the end plates.

EXAMPLE 1

Given: Select an end plate connection for a W14 × 30 beam
$F_y = 36$ ksi and end reaction = 24 kips.

Solution: Beam web thickness: 0.270″
Usual gage: $3\frac{1}{2}''$

From Table IX for beam depth limits 12″ through 18″, select a plate length of $8\frac{1}{2}''$ with three $\frac{3}{4}''$ diameter A307 bolts per vertical row, with a listed capacity of 26.5 kips and a required minimum plate thickness of $t = 0.121''$.

Select a $\frac{1}{4}''$ plate: 0.250 > 0.121 in. **o.k.**

From Table IX:
Weld Capacity: $8\frac{1}{2}''$ of $\frac{3}{16}$ in. fillet $= 45.2$ kips
Minimum web thickness $= 0.389''$

$$\frac{0.270}{0.389} \times 45.2 = 31.4 > 24 \text{ kips \textbf{o.k.}}$$

Use: End plate 6" wide x $8\frac{1}{2}''$ long x $\frac{1}{4}''$ thick with six $\frac{3}{4}''$ diameter A307 bolts on $3\frac{1}{2}''$ gage. Weld the plate to the beam web with $\frac{3}{16}$ in. fillet welds on each side of the web.

EXAMPLE 2

Given: Select an end plate connection for two W12 × 58 beams framing into both sides of a W30 × 190 girder. Beam reaction $= 34$ kips for each of the W12 × 58 beams and $F_y = 50$ ksi for both beams and girder.

Solution: Beam web thickness: $0.359''$
Usual gage: $5\frac{1}{2}''$
Girder web thickness: $0.710''$

From Table IX for beam depth limits 8" through 12", select a plate length of $5\frac{1}{2}''$ with two $\frac{3}{4}''$ diameter A325 bolts per vertical row, with a listed capacity of 38.9 kips and minimum $t = 0.267''$.
Try a $\frac{1}{4}''$ end plate thickness:

$$\frac{0.250}{0.267} \times 38.9 = 36.4 > 34 \text{ kips \textbf{o.k.}}$$

From Table IX:
Weld Capacity: $5\frac{1}{2}''$ of $\frac{1}{4}$ in. fillet $= 37.1$ kips
Minimum web $t = 0.370''$

$$\frac{0.359}{0.370} \times 37.1 = 36.0 > 34 \text{ kips \textbf{o.k.}}$$

Since the connection bolts are common to both beams through the girder web, the required girder web thickness must be twice the minimum value shown in the table.
Check girder web:

$$\frac{0.710}{0.740} \times (2 \times 36.4) = 69.8 > 64 \text{ kips \textbf{o.k.}}$$

Use: End plate 8" wide x $5\frac{1}{2}''$ long x $\frac{1}{4}''$ thick with four $\frac{3}{4}''$ diameter A325 bolts on $5\frac{1}{2}''$ gage. Weld the plate to the beam web with $\frac{1}{4}$ in. fillet welds on each side of the web.

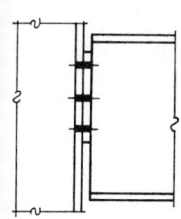

END PLATE SHEAR CONNECTIONS
Welded—E70XX electrodes
TABLE IX

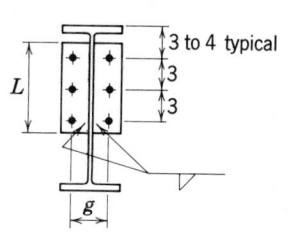

Fasteners per Vertical Line	Fastener	¾″ Diam.		⅞″ Diam.		Plate Length (L) Ft-In.	Beam Depth Limits In.
		Total Capacity Kips	Min. Plate Thickness (t) In.	Total Capacity Kips	Min. Plate Thickness (t) In.		
1	ASTM A307 Bolts	8.8	.121	12.0	.141		
	*a*ASTM A325 HS Bolts	13.3	.182	18.0	.212	3	5–8
	*b*ASTM A325 HS Bolts	19.4	.267	26.5	.311		
2	ASTM A307 Bolts	17.7	.121	24.0	.141		
	*a*ASTM A325 HS Bolts	26.5	.182	36.1	.212	5½	8–12
	*b*ASTM A325 HS Bolts	38.9	.267	52.9	.311		
3	ASTM A307 Bolts	26.5	.121	36.1	.141		
	*a*ASTM A325 HS Bolts	39.8	.182	54.1	.212	8½	12–18
	*b*ASTM A325 HS Bolts	58.3	.267	79.4	.311		
4	ASTM A307 Bolts	35.4	.121	48.1	.141		
	*a*ASTM A325 HS Bolts	53.0	.182	72.2	.212	11½	15–24
	*b*ASTM A325 HS Bolts	77.8	.267	105.8	.311		
5	ASTM A307 Bolts	44.2	.121	60.1	.141		
	*a*ASTM A325 HS Bolts	66.3	.182	90.2	.212	1′–2½	18–30
	*b*ASTM A325 HS Bolts	97.2	.267	132.3	.311		
6	ASTM A307 Bolts	53.0	.121	72.1	.141		
	*a*ASTM A325 HS Bolts	79.6	.182	108.2	.212	1′–5½	21–36
	*b*ASTM A325 HS Bolts	116.6	.267	158.8	.311		

a Friction type connection, or bearing type with threads in shear planes.
b Bearing type connection; threads excluded from shear planes.

WELD CAPACITY

Weld Size	Minimum Web Thickness, In.		Weld Capacity, Kips (2 Fillet Welds)					
	$F_y = 36$	$F_y = 50$	3	5½	8½	11½	1′–2½	1′–5½
³⁄₁₆	.389	.280	14.7	28.5	45.2	61.9	78.7	95.2
¼	.514	.370	18.6	37.1	59.4	81.6	103.9	126.1
⁵⁄₁₆	.646	.465	22.1	45.3	73.1	101.0	128.8	156.7
⅜	.771	.555	25.1	52.9	86.3	119.8	153.4	186.6

AMERICAN INSTITUTE OF STEEL CONSTRUCTION

ECCENTRIC LOADS ON FASTENER GROUPS
TABLES X—XIII

When a group of fasteners supports an eccentric load, as in Fig. 1, the several fasteners in such a group are not equally stressed. Each supports an equal share of the vertical load P, and each supports additional force due to moment, which is proportional to its distance from the center of gravity of the group. The total force on one fastener is the resultant of the components.

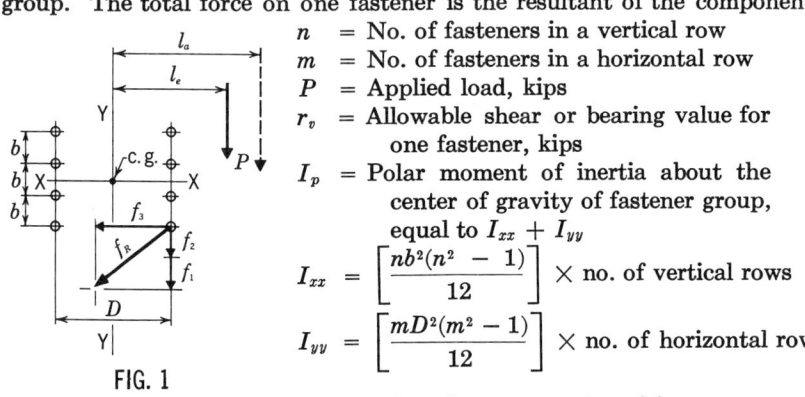

n = No. of fasteners in a vertical row
m = No. of fasteners in a horizontal row
P = Applied load, kips
r_v = Allowable shear or bearing value for one fastener, kips
I_p = Polar moment of inertia about the center of gravity of fastener group, equal to $I_{xx} + I_{yy}$

$$I_{xx} = \left[\frac{nb^2(n^2 - 1)}{12}\right] \times \text{no. of vertical rows}$$

$$I_{yy} = \left[\frac{mD^2(m^2 - 1)}{12}\right] \times \text{no. of horizontal rows}$$

FIG. 1

$l_a = l_{\text{actual}}$ = Actual arm between P and center gravity of fastener group
$l_e = l_{\text{eff.}}$ = Effective arm between P and center gravity of fastener group
$= l_a - [(1 + n)/2]$

$$f_1 = \frac{P}{mn} \qquad f_2 = \frac{(Pl_e)D}{2 I_p} \qquad f_3 = \frac{(Pl_e)(n - 1)b}{2 I_p} \qquad \text{(See Fig. 1)}$$

$f_R = \sqrt{(f_3)^2 + (f_1 + f_2)^2}$ and $f_R = r_v$

EXAMPLE 1

Given: Find the maximum load that can be supported by the bracket shown in Fig. 2. Column and bracket are $F_y = 36$ ksi. Use $\frac{7}{8}''$ ASTM A502 Gr 1 rivets, and assume that the column flange and bracket are at least $\frac{1}{4}''$ thick so that shear will govern. $n = 6, m = 2, b = 3, D = 5\frac{1}{2}, l_a = 16$.

Solution:

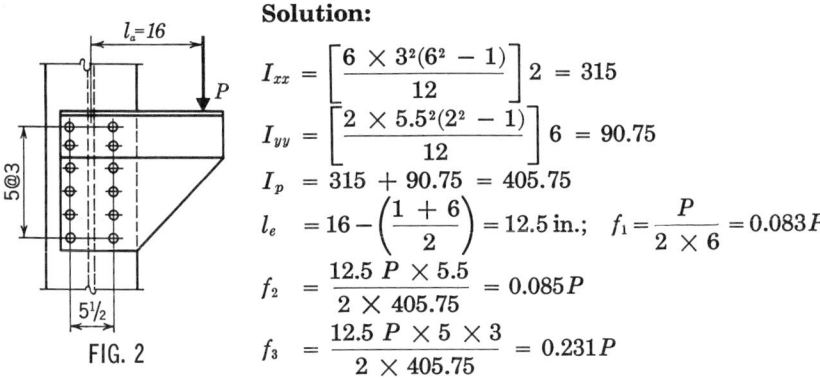

$$I_{xx} = \left[\frac{6 \times 3^2(6^2 - 1)}{12}\right] 2 = 315$$

$$I_{yy} = \left[\frac{2 \times 5.5^2(2^2 - 1)}{12}\right] 6 = 90.75$$

$$I_p = 315 + 90.75 = 405.75$$

$$l_e = 16 - \left(\frac{1 + 6}{2}\right) = 12.5 \text{ in.}; \quad f_1 = \frac{P}{2 \times 6} = 0.083P$$

$$f_2 = \frac{12.5\, P \times 5.5}{2 \times 405.75} = 0.085P$$

$$f_3 = \frac{12.5\, P \times 5 \times 3}{2 \times 405.75} = 0.231P$$

FIG. 2

$f_R = P\sqrt{(0.231)^2 + (0.083 + 0.085)^2} = 0.285P; \quad P = f_R/0.285 = 3.51\, f_R$
A502 Gr 1 rivets, single shear $r_v = 9.02$ kips.
Since f_R equals r_v, $P = 3.51 \times 9.02 = $ **31.7 kips.**

For any fastener group and any given lever arm of applied load a coefficient C times the allowable value of one fastener equals the total load P permissible on the connection. Thus, $P = C \times r_v$ or, knowing P, and dividing by the allowable fastener value r_v, the necessary coefficient C is obtained, and a fastener group must be employed for which the coefficient is of that magnitude or greater. The coefficients for several fastener groups are given in Tables X to XIII Part 4 of this Manual.

EXAMPLE 2

Given: Using tables, find the maximum load that was found in Example 1 by using the equations given above. $n = 6, b = 3, D = 5\frac{1}{2}, l_a = 16$.

Solution:

$$l_e = 16 - \left(\frac{1 + 6}{2}\right) = 12.5 \text{ in.}$$

From Table XII, with $n = 6$ and $l_e = 12.5$ by interpolating, $C = 3.51$.

Using $r_v = 9.02$ kips,
$$P = 3.51 \times 9.02 = \textbf{31.7 kips.}$$

EXAMPLE 3

Given: Investigate the rivets in the outer legs of the bracket shown in Fig. 3 for a load P of 29 kips, with $l_a = 12$ in., $b = 3$ in., and using $\frac{3}{4}$ in. ASTM A502 Gr 1 rivets.

For brackets subjected to eccentric loading as shown, the moment produces a varying amount of tension in the rivets above the neutral axis, coupled with bearing pressure below the neutral axis. There is no definite basis for locating the neutral axis. It lies below the center line of the connection. Example 3 illustrates a simple conservative solution, which is reasonably economical in the case of relatively small brackets, by assuming that the neutral axis is at the centroid of the rivet group, and that the bearing pressure distribution is the same as the tensile stress distribution above the neutral axis.

Solution:

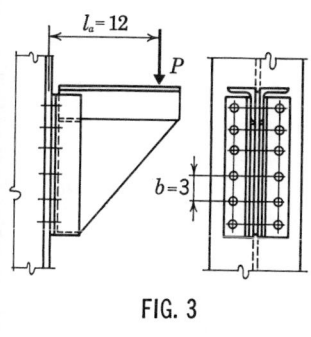

FIG. 3

Moment of Inertia of rivets about the assumed centroid of group =

$$\sum A d^2 = 0.4418 \times 4(1.5^2 + 4.5^2 + 7.5^2)$$
$$= 139 \text{ in.}^4$$

$$f_v = \frac{29}{12 \times 0.4418} = 5.47 \text{ ksi}$$

$$F_t = 28.0 - 1.6 f_v \leq 20.0 \text{ (Spec. Sect. 1.6.3)}$$
$$= 28.0 - (1.6 \times 5.47) = 19.25 \text{ ksi}$$

$$f_t = \frac{P \times l_a \times d_{\max}}{\sum A d^2} = \frac{29 \times 12 \times 7.5}{139}$$
$$= 18.78 < 19.25 \text{ ksi \textbf{o.k.}}$$

Note: The thickness of the bracket connection angles should be ample to resist the bending moment. See page 4 - 80.

AMERICAN INSTITUTE OF STEEL CONSTRUCTION

ECCENTRIC LOADS ON FASTENER GROUPS

TABLE X   Coefficients C

Required minimum $C = \dfrac{P}{r_v}$

$P = C \times r_v$

n = Total number of fasteners in the vertical row

P = Permissible load acting with effective lever arm l_{eff}

r_v = Permissible load on one fastener by Specification

$l_{eff} = l_{actual} - \left(\dfrac{1 + 2n}{4}\right)$

C = Coefficients tabulated below.

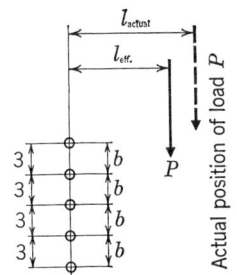

l_{eff} In.	n										
	2	3	4	5	6	7	8	9	10	11	12
1½	1.41	2.40	3.43	4.47	5.51	6.55	7.59	8.62	9.65	10.7	11.7
2	1.20	2.12	3.12	4.16	5.21	6.26	7.31	8.36	9.40	10.4	11.5
2½	1.03	1.87	2.83	3.84	4.88	5.94	7.00	8.05	9.10	10.2	11.2
3	.89	1.66	2.56	3.54	4.56	5.60	6.66	7.72	8.78	9.85	10.9
3½	.79	1.49	2.32	3.25	4.24	5.27	6.31	7.37	8.44	9.50	10.6
4	.70	1.34	2.12	3.00	3.95	4.95	5.98	7.03	8.09	9.15	10.2
4½	.63	1.22	1.94	2.77	3.68	4.65	5.66	6.69	7.74	8.80	9.86
5	.57	1.11	1.79	2.57	3.44	4.37	5.35	6.36	7.40	8.45	9.51
5½	.53	1.03	1.66	2.39	3.22	4.12	5.07	6.05	7.07	8.11	9.16
6	.49	.95	1.54	2.24	3.02	3.88	4.80	5.76	6.76	7.78	8.82
6½	.45	.88	1.44	2.10	2.84	3.67	4.55	5.49	6.46	7.46	8.45
7	.42	.82	1.35	1.97	2.68	3.47	4.33	5.23	6.18	7.16	8.17
7½	.39	.77	1.26	1.86	2.54	3.29	4.12	4.99	5.91	6.87	7.86
8	.37	.73	1.19	1.76	2.40	3.13	3.92	4.77	5.67	6.60	7.57
8½	.35	.69	1.13	1.66	2.28	2.98	3.74	4.56	5.43	6.34	7.29
9	.33	.65	1.07	1.58	2.17	2.84	3.58	4.37	5.21	6.10	7.03
10	.30	.59	.97	1.44	1.98	2.60	3.28	4.02	4.82	5.66	6.5
11	.27	.54	.89	1.32	1.82	2.39	3.03	3.72	4.47	5.27	6.1
12	.25	.49	.82	1.21	1.68	2.21	2.81	3.46	4.17	4.92	5.7
14	.21	.42	.70	1.05	1.46	1.92	2.45	3.03	3.66	4.33	5.0
16	.19	.37	.62	.92	1.28	1.70	2.17	2.68	3.25	3.86	4.5
18	.17	.33	.55	.82	1.15	1.52	1.94	2.41	2.92	3.48	4.0
20	.15	.30	.50	.74	1.03	1.37	1.76	2.18	2.65	3.16	3.7
22	.14	.27	.45	.68	.94	1.25	1.60	1.99	2.43	2.89	3.4
24	.12	.25	.41	.62	.87	1.15	1.47	1.84	2.23	2.67	3.1

In general, $C = \dfrac{n}{\sqrt{\left[\dfrac{6l_{eff}}{(n+1)b}\right]^2 + 1}}$

ECCENTRIC LOADS ON FASTENER GROUPS
TABLE XI   Coefficients C

Required minimum $C = \dfrac{P}{r_v}$

$P = C \times r_v$

n = Total number of fasteners in any one vertical row

P = Permissible load acting with effective lever arm l_{eff}

r_v = Permissible load on one fastener by Specification

$l_{\text{eff}} = l_{\text{actual}} - \left(\dfrac{1+n}{2}\right)$

C = Coefficients tabulated below.

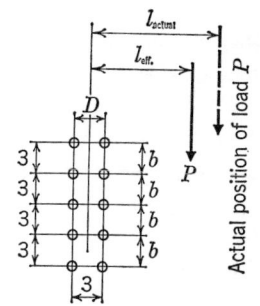

in.	\(n\) 1	2	3	4	5	6	7	8	9	10	11	12
½	1.00	2.53	4.33	6.30	8.36	10.4	12.5	14.6	16.7	18.8	20.9	23.0
	.86	2.23	3.88	5.75	7.74	9.80	11.9	14.0	16.1	18.2	20.3	22.4
½	.75	1.99	3.50	5.24	7.16	9.17	11.2	13.3	15.5	17.6	19.7	21.8
	.67	1.79	3.17	4.80	6.62	8.56	10.6	12.7	14.8	16.9	19.0	21.1
½	.60	1.63	2.89	4.41	6.13	8.00	9.97	12.0	14.1	16.2	18.3	20.5
	.55	1.49	2.66	4.07	5.69	7.48	9.39	11.4	13.4	15.5	17.6	19.8
½	.50	1.37	2.45	3.77	5.30	7.01	8.85	10.8	12.8	14.8	16.9	19.0
	.46	1.27	2.28	3.51	4.96	6.58	8.34	10.2	12.2	14.2	16.3	18.4
½	.43	1.19	2.12	3.28	4.64	6.19	7.88	9.70	11.6	13.6	15.6	17.7
	.40	1.11	1.99	3.07	4.37	5.84	7.46	9.21	11.1	13.0	15.0	17.0
½	.37	1.04	1.87	2.89	4.12	5.52	7.08	8.76	10.6	12.4	14.4	16.4
	.35	.98	1.76	2.73	3.89	5.23	6.72	8.35	10.1	11.9	13.8	15.8
½	.33	.93	1.66	2.58	3.69	4.97	6.40	7.96	9.64	11.4	13.3	15.2
	.32	.88	1.58	2.45	3.50	4.72	6.10	7.61	9.23	11.0	12.8	14.6
½	.30	.84	1.50	2.33	3.33	4.50	5.82	7.28	8.85	10.5	12.3	14.1
	.29	.80	1.43	2.22	3.18	4.30	5.57	6.97	8.49	10.1	11.8	13.6
	.26	.73	1.30	2.03	2.91	3.94	5.12	6.43	7.85	9.38	11.0	12.7
	.24	.67	1.20	1.87	2.68	3.64	4.73	5.95	7.29	8.73	10.3	11.9
	.22	.62	1.11	1.73	2.48	3.38	4.40	5.54	6.80	8.16	9.61	11.2
	.19	.54	.97	1.50	2.16	2.95	3.85	4.86	5.98	7.19	8.51	9.91
	.17	.48	.86	1.33	1.92	2.61	3.41	4.32	5.32	6.42	7.61	8.88
	.15	.43	.77	1.19	1.72	2.34	3.07	3.88	4.79	5.79	6.88	8.04
	.14	.39	.70	1.08	1.56	2.12	2.78	3.53	4.36	5.27	6.26	7.34
	.13	.36	.64	.99	1.42	1.94	2.54	3.23	3.99	4.83	5.75	6.74
	.12	.33	.59	.91	1.31	1.79	2.34	2.98	3.68	4.46	5.31	6.23

In general, $C = \dfrac{n}{\sqrt{\left[\dfrac{l_{\text{eff}}\,(n-1)b}{D^2 + \frac{1}{3}(n^2-1)b^2}\right]^2 + \left[\dfrac{l_{\text{eff}}\,D}{D^2 + \frac{1}{3}(n^2-1)b^2} + \frac{1}{2}\right]^2}}$

ECCENTRIC LOADS ON FASTENER GROUPS

TABLE XII Coefficients C

Required minimum $C = \dfrac{P}{r_v}$

$P = C \times r_v$

n = Total number of fasteners in any one vertical row

P = Permissible load acting with effective lever arm l_{eff}

r_v = Permissible load on one fastener by Specification

$l_{eff} = l_{actual} - \left(\dfrac{1+n}{2}\right)$

C = Coefficients tabulated below.

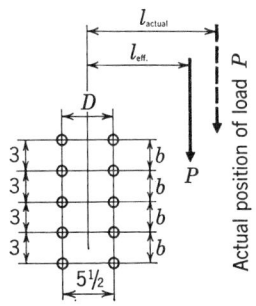

l_{eff} In.						n						
	1	2	3	4	5	6	7	8	9	10	11	12
1½	1.29	2.78	4.46	6.29	8.24	10.3	12.3	14.4	16.5	18.5	20.6	22.7
2	1.16	2.52	4.07	5.81	7.68	9.64	11.7	13.7	15.8	17.9	20.0	22.1
2½	1.05	2.29	3.74	5.37	7.15	9.06	11.0	13.1	15.2	17.2	19.3	21.4
3	.96	2.11	3.45	4.98	6.67	8.51	10.4	12.4	14.5	16.6	18.7	20.8
3½	.88	1.95	3.20	4.63	6.24	7.99	9.87	11.8	13.8	15.9	18.0	20.1
4	.81	1.81	2.98	4.32	5.84	7.52	9.33	11.2	13.2	15.2	17.3	19.4
4½	.76	1.69	2.78	4.05	5.49	7.09	8.83	10.7	12.6	14.6	16.6	18.7
5	.71	1.59	2.61	3.80	5.17	6.70	8.37	10.2	12.0	14.0	16.0	18.6
5½	.67	1.49	2.46	3.58	4.88	6.34	7.94	9.67	11.5	13.4	15.4	17.4
6	.63	1.41	2.32	3.39	4.62	6.01	7.55	9.22	11.0	12.8	14.8	16.8
6½	.59	1.34	2.20	3.21	4.38	5.71	7.19	8.80	10.5	12.3	14.2	16.2
7	.56	1.27	2.09	3.05	4.16	5.44	6.86	8.40	10.1	11.8	13.7	15.6
7½	.54	1.21	1.99	2.90	3.96	5.18	6.55	8.04	9.65	11.4	13.2	15.6
8	.51	1.15	1.90	2.77	3.78	4.95	6.26	7.70	9.26	10.9	12.7	14.6
8½	.49	1.10	1.81	2.64	3.62	4.74	6.00	7.39	8.90	10.5	12.2	14.6
9	.47	1.06	1.74	2.53	3.46	4.54	5.76	7.10	8.56	10.1	11.8	13.
10	.43	.98	1.60	2.33	3.19	4.19	5.32	6.57	7.94	9.42	11.0	12.
11	.40	.91	1.48	2.16	2.96	3.88	4.94	6.11	7.40	8.80	10.3	11.
12	.37	.85	1.38	2.01	2.75	3.62	4.61	5.71	6.92	8.24	9.65	11.
14	.33	.75	1.22	1.77	2.42	3.18	4.06	5.04	6.12	7.30	8.58	9.
16	.29	.67	1.09	1.58	2.16	2.84	3.62	4.50	5.48	6.55	7.70	8.
18	.26	.60	.98	1.42	1.94	2.56	3.26	4.06	4.95	5.92	6.98	8.
20	.24	.55	.89	1.29	1.77	2.33	2.97	3.70	4.51	5.41	6.38	7.
22	.22	.51	.82	1.19	1.62	2.13	2.73	3.40	4.14	4.97	5.87	6.
24	.21	.47	.76	1.10	1.50	1.97	2.52	3.14	3.83	4.59	5.43	6.

In general,
$$C = \frac{n}{\sqrt{\left[\dfrac{l_{eff}(n-1)b}{D^2 + \frac{1}{3}(n^2-1)b^2}\right]^2 + \left[\dfrac{l_{eff}\,D}{D^2 + \frac{1}{3}(n^2-1)b^2} + \frac{1}{2}\right]^2}}$$

AMERICAN INSTITUTE OF STEEL CONSTRUCTION

ECCENTRIC LOADS ON FASTENER GROUPS

TABLE XIII   Coefficients C

Required minimum $C = \dfrac{P}{r_v}$

$P = C \times r_v$

n = Total number of fasteners in any
    one vertical row

P = Permissible load acting with
    effective lever arm l_{eff}

r_v = Permissible load on one fastener
    by Specification

$l_{\text{eff}} = l_{\text{actual}} - \left(\dfrac{1+n}{2} \right)$

C = Coefficients tabulated below.

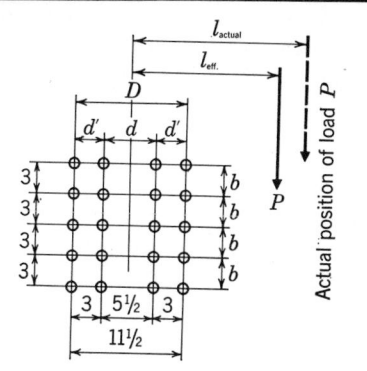

| l_{eff} n. | \multicolumn{12}{c}{n} |
	1	2	3	4	5	6	7	8	9	10	11	12
½	2.81	5.77	8.96	12.4	16.0	19.8	23.8	27.8	31.9	36.0	40.1	44.2
	2.55	5.28	8.25	11.5	15.0	18.6	22.5	26.4	30.5	34.6	38.7	42.8
½	2.34	4.86	7.63	10.7	14.0	17.5	21.3	25.1	29.1	33.2	37.3	41.4
	2.16	4.50	7.10	9.97	13.1	16.5	20.1	23.9	27.8	31.8	35.9	40.0
½	2.01	4.20	6.63	9.35	12.3	15.6	19.1	22.7	26.6	30.5	34.5	38.6
	1.88	3.93	6.22	8.79	11.6	14.8	18.1	21.7	25.4	29.2	33.2	37.2
½	1.76	3.69	5.86	8.29	11.0	14.0	17.2	20.6	24.3	28.0	31.9	35.9
	1.66	3.48	5.53	7.84	10.4	13.3	16.4	19.7	23.2	26.9	30.7	34.6
½	1.56	3.29	5.24	7.44	9.91	12.6	15.6	18.8	22.2	25.8	29.6	33.4
	1.48	3.12	4.98	7.08	9.43	12.1	14.9	18.0	21.3	24.8	28.5	32.2
½	1.41	2.97	4.74	6.74	9.00	11.5	14.3	17.3	20.5	23.9	27.4	31.1
	1.34	2.83	4.52	6.44	8.60	11.0	13.7	16.6	19.7	23.0	26.4	30.1
½	1.28	2.71	4.33	6.16	8.24	10.6	13.1	15.9	18.9	22.1	25.5	29.0
	1.22	2.59	4.14	5.91	7.90	10.1	12.6	15.3	18.2	21.3	24.6	28.1
½	1.17	2.49	3.98	5.67	7.59	9.74	12.1	14.7	17.6	20.6	23.8	27.2
	1.13	2.39	3.82	5.45	7.30	9.37	11.7	14.2	16.9	19.9	23.0	26.3
	1.04	2.22	3.55	5.06	6.78	8.71	10.9	13.2	15.8	18.6	21.6	24.7
	.97	2.07	3.31	4.72	6.33	8.14	10.2	12.4	14.8	17.5	20.3	23.3
	.91	1.93	3.10	4.42	5.93	7.63	9.53	11.6	13.9	16.4	19.1	21.9
	.81	1.72	2.75	3.93	5.27	6.78	8.48	10.4	12.4	14.7	17.1	19.7
	.72	1.54	2.47	3.53	4.73	6.10	7.63	9.33	11.2	13.3	15.5	17.8
	.66	1.40	2.25	3.21	4.30	5.54	6.93	8.48	10.2	12.1	14.1	16.3
	.60	1.28	2.06	2.94	3.94	5.07	6.35	7.77	9.34	11.1	12.9	14.9
	.55	1.18	1.90	2.71	3.63	4.67	5.85	7.17	8.62	10.2	11.9	13.8
	.51	1.10	1.76	2.51	3.37	4.33	5.43	6.65	8.00	9.48	11.1	12.8

In general, $C = \dfrac{n}{\sqrt{\left[\dfrac{l_{\text{eff}}\,(n-1)b}{d^2 + D^2 + \frac{2}{3}(n^2-1)b^2} \right]^2 + \left[\dfrac{l_{\text{eff}}\,D}{d^2 + D^2 + \frac{2}{3}(n^2-1)b^2} + \frac{1}{4} \right]^2}}$

ECCENTRIC LOADS ON WELD GROUPS

TABLES XIV–XXI

The solution of eccentric loading of weld groups is similar to the method employed for fastener groups, except that for computation of properties, the weld is considered a line coincident with the edge to be fillet welded.

P = Permissible load, kips

A = Distance from vertical weld to P, inches $= l(a + x)$

l = Length of vertical weld, inches

kl = Length of horizontal weld, inches

L = Total length of weld, inches $= l(1 + 2k)$

xl = Distance from vertical weld to center of gravity of weld group, in inches

$$= \frac{(kl)^2}{L} \text{ or } x = \frac{k^2}{(1 + 2k)}$$

I_p = Polar moment of inertia, inches[4]

$$= l^3 \left[\frac{(1 + 2k)^3}{12} - \frac{k^2(1 + k)^2}{(1 + 2k)} \right]$$

D = Number of sixteenths of an inch in weld size

$0.928D$ = Value of E70XX weld per sixteenth inch of weld per lineal inch, kips

f_1 = Stress on weld at **B** due to vertical load

$$= P/(l + 2kl) = P/l(1 + 2k)$$

f_2 = Vertical stress on weld at **B** due to moment

$$= \frac{Pal(kl - xl)}{I_p} = \frac{Pal^2(k - x)}{I_p}$$

f_3 = Horizontal stress on weld at **B** due to moment

$$= \frac{Pal(l/2)}{I_p} = \frac{Pal^2}{2 I_p}$$

f_R = Resultant of stresses on weld at **B**

$$= \sqrt{(f_1 + f_2)^2 + (f_3)^2}$$

and

f_R = $0.928D$ (for E70XX electrodes)

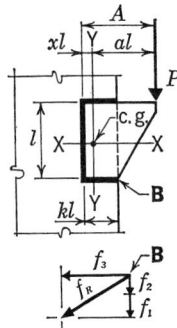

FORCES AT **B**
(most highly stressed point of weld)

FIG. 1

EXAMPLE

Given: Weld group shown in Fig. 1 with $l = 10''$, $kl = 5''$ and $A = 10''$. Find the maximum allowable load P for a $\frac{3}{8}''$ weld using E70XX electrodes: (a) with formulas and (b) by using Table XVI, page 4 - 70.

Solution:

(a) $k = \dfrac{kl}{l} = \dfrac{5}{10} = 0.5$

$x = \dfrac{k^2}{1 + 2k} = \dfrac{(0.5)^2}{1 + 2(0.5)} = 0.125$

$xl = (0.125)(10) = 1.25$

$al = A - xl = 10 - 1.25 = 8.75 \qquad a = 0.875$

$I_p = (10)^3 \left[\dfrac{(1 + 1)^3}{12} - \dfrac{(0.5)^2(1.5)^2}{(1 + 1)} \right] = 385$

$f_1 = \dfrac{P}{l(1 + 2k)} = \dfrac{P}{10(1 + 2x.5)} = \dfrac{P}{20} = 0.05P$

$f_2 = \dfrac{Pal^2(k - x)}{I_p} = \dfrac{P(.875)(10^2)(0.5 - 0.125)}{385} = 0.085P$

$f_3 = \dfrac{Pal^2}{2I_p} = \dfrac{P(0.875)(10^2)}{2(385)} = 0.114P$

$f_R = \sqrt{(0.05P + 0.085P)^2 + (0.114P)^2} = 0.177P$

Using $\frac{3}{8}''$ welds (E70XX electrodes):

$f_R = 0.928D = 0.928 \times 6 = 5.568$. Since f_R also equals $0.177P$,

$P = \dfrac{5.568}{0.177} = $ **31.5 kips**

(b) $l = 10$, $kl = 5$, $k = 0.5$, $A = 10$

Enter Table XVI, page 4 - 70, for $k = 0.5$: $x = 0.125$

$xl = (0.125)(10) = 1.25$

$al = A - xl = 8.75 \qquad a = 0.875$

Interpolating between $a = 0.8$ and $a = 0.9$ for $k = 0.5$, $C = 0.527$

Using $\frac{3}{8}''$ welds, $D = 6$

$C_1 = 1.0$ for E70XX electrodes (see below)

$P = C_1CDl = (1.0)(0.527)(6)(10) = $ **31.6 kips**

Tables XIV through XXI are based on welds made with E70XX electrodes. Multiply by C_1 values tabulated in table below:

Electrode	E60	E70	E80	E90	E100	E110
F_v(ksi)	18.0	21.0	24.0	27.0	30.0	33.0
C_1	0.857	1.0	1.14	1.29	1.43	1.57

ECCENTRIC LOADS ON WELD GROUPS

TABLE XIV Coefficients C

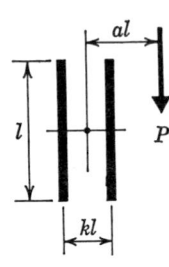

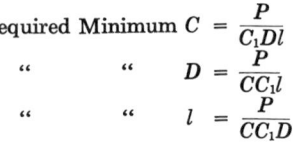

Required Minimum $C = \dfrac{P}{C_1 D l}$

"   " $D = \dfrac{P}{C C_1 l}$

"   " $l = \dfrac{P}{C C_1 D}$

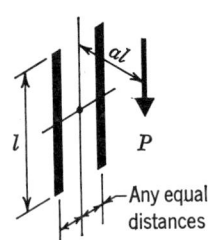

P = Permissible eccentric load in kips.
l = Length of each weld in inches.
D = Number of sixteenths of an inch in fillet weld size.
C = Coefficients tabulated below.
C_1 = Coefficient for electrode used (see Table on page 4-67).
= 1.0 for E70XX electrodes.

$$P = C C_1 D l$$

— Any equal distances

SPECIAL CASE*
(Load not in plane of weld group.)

Use C-values given in column headed $k = 0$.

a	k															
	0	0.1	0.2	0.3	0.4	0.5	0.6	0.7	0.8	0.9	1.0	1.2	1.4	1.6	1.8	2.
0.1	1.59	1.54	1.51	1.50	1.51	1.52	1.54	1.55	1.57	1.59	1.60	1.63	1.65	1.67	1.68	1.7
0.2	1.19	1.15	1.15	1.16	1.20	1.23	1.27	1.30	1.33	1.36	1.39	1.44	1.48	1.51	1.54	1.5
0.3	.901	.881	.892	.923	.966	1.01	1.06	1.11	1.15	1.19	1.22	1.28	1.33	1.38	1.41	1.4
0.4	.714	.704	.721	.756	.803	.854	.906	.956	1.00	1.05	1.09	1.16	1.21	1.26	1.31	1.3
0.5	.587	.583	.601	.637	.683	.734	.787	.839	.887	.933	.975	1.05	1.11	1.17	1.21	1.2
0.6	.497	.495	.514	.548	.593	.642	.694	.745	.794	.840	.883	.960	1.03	1.08	1.13	1.1
0.7	.430	.430	.449	.481	.523	.570	.620	.669	.717	.763	.806	.883	.951	1.01	1.06	1.1
0.8	.379	.380	.397	.428	.467	.512	.559	.607	.654	.698	.741	.818	.885	.945	.998	1.0
0.9	.338	.340	.357	.385	.422	.464	.509	.555	.600	.644	.685	.761	.828	.888	.941	.9
1.0	.305	.308	.323	.350	.384	.424	.467	.511	.554	.596	.637	.711	.778	.837	.891	.9
1.2	.255	.258	.272	.296	.326	.362	.401	.441	.481	.520	.558	.629	.693	.751	.804	.8
1.4	.219	.222	.235	.256	.283	.316	.351	.387	.424	.460	.496	.563	.625	.681	.732	.7
1.6	.192	.195	.206	.225	.250	.280	.312	.345	.379	.413	.446	.509	.568	.622	.672	.7
1.8	.171	.174	.184	.201	.224	.251	.280	.311	.343	.374	.405	.465	.521	.573	.621	.6
2.0	.154	.157	.166	.182	.203	.227	.255	.283	.313	.342	.371	.428	.481	.531	.577	.6
2.2	.140	.143	.152	.166	.185	.208	.233	.260	.287	.315	.342	.396	.447	.494	.539	.5
2.4	.129	.131	.139	.153	.170	.192	.215	.240	.266	.292	.318	.369	.417	.463	.505	.5
2.6	.119	.121	.129	.141	.158	.178	.200	.223	.247	.272	.296	.345	.391	.435	.476	.5
2.8	.110	.112	.120	.131	.147	.166	.186	.208	.231	.254	.278	.324	.368	.410	.449	.4
3.0	.103	.105	.112	.123	.138	.155	.174	.195	.217	.239	.261	.305	.347	.388	.426	.4

* Valid only when the connection material between the welds is solid and does not bend in the plane of the welds.

ECCENTRIC LOADS ON WELD GROUPS

TABLE XV Coefficients C

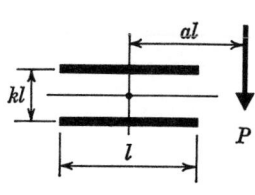

P = Permissible eccentric load in kips.
l = Length of each weld in inches.
D = Number of sixteenths of an inch in fillet weld size.
C = Coefficients tabulated below.
C_1 = Coefficient for electrode used (see Table on page 4-67).
= 1.0 for E70XX electrodes.

$$P = CC_1Dl$$

Required Minimum $C = \dfrac{P}{C_1Dl}$

" " $D = \dfrac{P}{CC_1l}$

" " $l = \dfrac{P}{CC_1D}$

a	k															
	0	0.1	0.2	0.3	0.4	0.5	0.6	0.7	0.8	0.9	1.0	1.2	1.4	1.6	1.8	2.0
0.1	1.16	1.17	1.21	1.25	1.31	1.37	1.43	1.48	1.53	1.57	1.60	1.66	1.70	1.73	1.75	1.77
0.2	.844	.856	.891	.944	1.01	1.08	1.15	1.22	1.28	1.34	1.39	1.48	1.55	1.60	1.64	1.67
0.3	.663	.674	.707	.756	.818	.887	.959	1.03	1.10	1.16	1.22	1.33	1.41	1.48	1.54	1.58
0.4	.546	.556	.585	.630	.687	.752	.820	.890	.958	1.02	1.09	1.20	1.29	1.37	1.44	1.50
0.5	.464	.473	.499	.540	.592	.652	.716	.782	.848	.913	.975	1.09	1.19	1.28	1.35	1.41
0.6	.404	.412	.435	.473	.520	.575	.635	.698	.760	.822	.883	.996	1.10	1.19	1.27	1.33
0.7	.357	.364	.386	.420	.464	.515	.571	.629	.688	.748	.806	.917	1.02	1.11	1.19	1.26
0.8	.320	.327	.347	.378	.418	.466	.518	.572	.629	.685	.741	.848	.948	1.04	1.12	1.19
0.9	.290	.296	.315	.343	.381	.425	.474	.525	.578	.632	.685	.788	.886	.975	1.06	1.13
1.0	.265	.271	.288	.315	.350	.391	.436	.485	.535	.586	.637	.736	.830	.919	1.00	1.07
1.2	.226	.231	.246	.270	.300	.337	.377	.420	.465	.511	.558	.649	.737	.821	.900	.973
1.4	.197	.202	.215	.236	.263	.296	.332	.371	.412	.453	.496	.580	.662	.741	.816	.887
1.6	.175	.179	.191	.210	.234	.264	.296	.332	.369	.407	.446	.524	.601	.675	.746	.814
1.8	.157	.161	.172	.189	.211	.238	.268	.300	.334	.369	.405	.477	.549	.619	.686	.751
2.0	.143	.146	.156	.171	.192	.217	.244	.274	.306	.338	.371	.438	.505	.571	.635	.696
2.2	.131	.134	.143	.157	.176	.199	.224	.252	.281	.312	.342	.405	.468	.530	.590	.649
2.4	.121	.123	.132	.145	.163	.184	.208	.233	.261	.289	.318	.377	.436	.494	.551	.607
2.6	.112	.115	.122	.135	.151	.171	.193	.217	.243	.269	.296	.352	.407	.463	.517	.570
2.8	.104	.107	.114	.126	.141	.160	.180	.203	.227	.252	.278	.330	.383	.435	.487	.537
3.0	.0977	.100	.107	.118	.132	.150	.169	.191	.213	.237	.261	.311	.361	.410	.460	.508

ECCENTRIC LOADS ON WELD GROUPS

TABLE XVI   Coefficients C

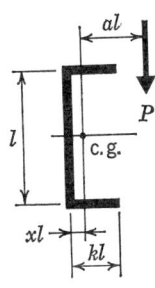

P = Permissible eccentric load in kips.
l = Length of weld parallel to load P in inches.
D = Number of sixteenths of an inch in fillet weld size.
C = Coefficients tabulated below.
C_1 = Coefficient for electrode used (see Table on page 4-67).
= 1.0 for E70XX electrodes.
xl = Distance from vertical weld to center of gravity of weld group.

$$P = CC_1Dl$$

Required Minimum $C = \dfrac{P}{C_1Dl}$

      "   " $D = \dfrac{P}{CC_1l}$

      "   " $l = \dfrac{P}{CC_1D}$

a	\multicolumn{16}{c}{k}
	0	0.1	0.2	0.3	0.4	0.5	0.6	0.7	0.8	0.9	1.0	1.2	1.4	1.6	1.8	2.•
0.1	.796	.951	1.09	1.23	1.38	1.52	1.66	1.81	1.96	2.11	2.27	2.58	2.90	3.23	3.56	3.9
0.2	.594	.758	.889	1.01	1.13	1.25	1.37	1.50	1.63	1.76	1.89	2.16	2.45	2.74	3.05	3.3
0.3	.451	.608	.730	.840	.946	1.05	1.16	1.27	1.38	1.50	1.61	1.86	2.11	2.38	2.66	2.9
0.4	.357	.499	.611	.711	.807	.901	.997	1.09	1.19	1.30	1.40	1.62	1.86	2.10	2.35	2.6
0.5	.293	.421	.523	.614	.701	.786	.872	.960	1.05	1.14	1.24	1.44	1.65	1.88	2.11	2.3
0.6	.248	.362	.455	.539	.618	.695	.774	.854	.937	1.02	1.11	1.29	1.49	1.70	1.91	2.1
0.7	.215	.317	.402	.479	.551	.623	.695	.769	.844	.922	1.00	1.17	1.35	1.55	1.75	1.9
0.8	.189	.282	.360	.430	.498	.564	.630	.698	.768	.840	.915	1.07	1.24	1.42	1.61	1.8
0.9	.169	.254	.326	.391	.453	.514	.576	.639	.704	.772	.841	.988	1.15	1.31	1.49	1.6
1.0	.153	.230	.297	.358	.416	.473	.530	.589	.650	.713	.778	.916	1.06	1.22	1.39	1.5
1.2	.128	.194	.252	.306	.356	.407	.458	.510	.563	.619	.676	.798	.929	1.07	1.22	1.3
1.4	.110	.168	.219	.267	.312	.357	.402	.449	.496	.546	.598	.707	.825	.952	1.09	1.2
1.6	.096	.148	.194	.236	.277	.318	.359	.400	.444	.489	.536	.635	.742	.857	.981	1.1
1.8	.086	.132	.174	.212	.249	.286	.323	.362	.401	.442	.485	.576	.674	.780	.893	1.
2.0	.077	.119	.157	.192	.226	.260	.295	.330	.366	.404	.443	.527	.617	.715	.820	.
2.2	.070	.109	.143	.176	.207	.239	.270	.303	.336	.371	.408	.485	.570	.660	.758	.
2.4	.064	.100	.132	.162	.191	.220	.250	.280	.311	.344	.378	.450	.529	.613	.705	.
2.6	.059	.092	.122	.150	.178	.205	.232	.260	.290	.320	.352	.419	.493	.573	.658	.
2.8	.055	.086	.113	.140	.166	.191	.217	.243	.271	.299	.329	.393	.462	.537	.618	.
3.0	.051	.080	.107	.131	.155	.179	.203	.228	.254	.281	.309	.369	.435	.505	.582	.
x	0	.008	.029	.056	.089	.125	.164	.204	.246	.289	.333	.424	.516	.610	.704	.

ECCENTRIC LOADS ON WELD GROUPS

TABLE XVII   Coefficients C

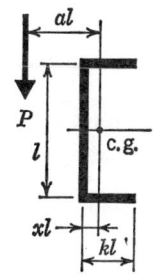

P = Permissible eccentric load in kips.
l = Length of weld parallel to load P in inches.
D = Number of sixteenths of an inch in fillet weld size.
C = Coefficients tabulated below.
C_1 = Coefficient for electrode used (see Table on page 4-67).
= 1.0 for E70XX electrodes.
xl = Distance from vertical weld to center of gravity of weld group.

$$P = CC_1Dl$$

Required Minimum $C = \dfrac{P}{C_1Dl}$

"   " $D = \dfrac{P}{CC_1l}$

"   " $l = \dfrac{P}{CC_1D}$

a	\multicolumn{16}{c}{k}
	0	0.1	0.2	0.3	0.4	0.5	0.6	0.7	0.8	0.9	1.0	1.2	1.4	1.6	1.8	2.0
0.1	.796	1.01	1.19	1.37	1.53	1.69	1.85	2.01	2.17	2.33	2.48	2.80	3.12	3.45	3.78	4.12
0.2	.594	.823	1.01	1.18	1.34	1.49	1.64	1.78	1.92	2.07	2.21	2.49	2.78	3.08	3.38	3.69
0.3	.451	.659	.841	1.01	1.16	1.30	1.44	1.57	1.71	1.84	1.97	2.23	2.50	2.77	3.05	3.33
0.4	.357	.539	.704	.857	1.00	1.14	1.27	1.40	1.52	1.64	1.76	2.01	2.26	2.51	2.77	3.03
0.5	.293	.451	.599	.739	.873	1.00	1.12	1.24	1.36	1.48	1.59	1.82	2.05	2.29	2.53	2.78
0.6	.248	.386	.518	.646	.770	.890	1.01	1.12	1.23	1.34	1.45	1.66	1.88	2.10	2.33	2.57
0.7	.215	.337	.455	.572	.686	.798	.907	1.01	1.12	1.22	1.32	1.53	1.73	1.94	2.16	2.38
0.8	.189	.298	.405	.512	.617	.722	.824	.925	1.02	1.12	1.22	1.41	1.61	1.81	2.01	2.22
0.9	.169	.267	.364	.462	.560	.658	.754	.849	.943	1.04	1.13	1.31	1.50	1.69	1.88	2.08
1.0	.153	.242	.331	.421	.513	.604	.694	.784	.873	.961	1.05	1.22	1.40	1.58	1.76	1.95
1.2	.128	.203	.279	.357	.437	.518	.599	.679	.759	.839	.918	1.08	1.24	1.40	1.57	1.74
1.4	.110	.175	.241	.310	.380	.452	.525	.598	.671	.744	.816	.962	1.11	1.26	1.41	1.57
1.6	.096	.153	.212	.273	.335	.398	.465	.534	.600	.667	.734	.868	1.00	1.14	1.29	1.43
1.8	.086	.137	.189	.242	.295	.350	.408	.468	.531	.599	.666	.790	.916	1.05	1.18	1.32
2.0	.077	.123	.170	.217	.264	.312	.363	.416	.471	.531	.593	.725	.843	.963	1.09	1.22
2.2	.070	.112	.154	.196	.239	.282	.327	.374	.424	.476	.532	.654	.780	.893	1.01	1.13
2.4	.064	.103	.141	.179	.217	.257	.297	.340	.385	.432	.482	.591	.714	.832	.941	1.05
2.6	.059	.095	.130	.165	.200	.236	.273	.311	.352	.395	.440	.540	.651	.775	.882	.989
2.8	.055	.088	.121	.153	.185	.218	.252	.287	.325	.364	.406	.496	.598	.711	.830	.931
3.0	.051	.082	.112	.142	.172	.203	.234	.267	.301	.338	.376	.459	.553	.657	.773	.880
∞	0	.008	.029	.056	.089	.125	.164	.204	.246	.289	.333	.424	.516	.610	.704	.800

ECCENTRIC LOADS ON WELD GROUPS

TABLE XVIII Coefficients C

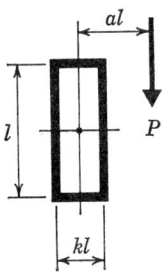

P = Permissible eccentric load in kips.
l = Length of longer welds in inches.
D = Number of sixteenths of an inch in fillet weld size.
C = Coefficients tabulated below.
C_1 = Coefficient for electrode used (see Table on page 4-67).
= 1.0 for E70XX electrodes.

$$P = CC_1Dl$$

Required Minimum $C = \dfrac{P}{C_1Dl}$

" " $D = \dfrac{P}{CC_1l}$

" " $l = \dfrac{P}{CC_1D}$

Note: When load P is perpendicular to longer side l use table on facing page.

a	\multicolumn{11}{c}{k}
---	0	0.1	0.2	0.3	0.4	0.5	0.6	0.7	0.8	0.9	1.0
0.1	1.59	1.76	1.92	2.08	2.23	2.39	2.55	2.71	2.87	3.04	3.20
0.2	1.19	1.38	1.55	1.72	1.87	2.03	2.18	2.33	2.48	2.63	2.78
0.3	.901	1.09	1.26	1.43	1.58	1.73	1.87	2.02	2.16	2.30	2.45
0.4	.714	.881	1.04	1.20	1.35	1.49	1.63	1.77	1.90	2.04	2.17
0.5	.586	.736	.884	1.03	1.17	1.30	1.44	1.57	1.69	1.82	1.95
0.6	.497	.629	.764	.898	1.03	1.16	1.28	1.40	1.52	1.65	1.77
0.7	.430	.548	.671	.795	.916	1.04	1.15	1.27	1.38	1.50	1.61
0.8	.379	.485	.598	.712	.825	.937	1.05	1.16	1.27	1.37	1.48
0.9	.338	.435	.538	.644	.750	.855	.959	1.06	1.17	1.27	1.37
1.0	.305	.394	.489	.588	.687	.786	.884	.982	1.08	1.18	1.27
1.2	.255	.331	.414	.499	.587	.675	.763	.851	.939	1.03	1.12
1.4	.219	.286	.358	.434	.512	.592	.671	.751	.831	.911	.991
1.6	.192	.251	.315	.384	.454	.526	.598	.671	.745	.818	.892
1.8	.171	.224	.282	.344	.408	.473	.540	.607	.674	.742	.810
2.0	.154	.202	.255	.311	.370	.430	.492	.553	.616	.679	.742
2.2	.140	.184	.232	.284	.338	.394	.451	.509	.567	.626	.685
2.4	.129	.169	.213	.261	.312	.364	.417	.471	.525	.580	.636
2.6	.119	.156	.197	.242	.289	.338	.387	.438	.489	.540	.593
2.8	.110	.145	.184	.225	.269	.315	.362	.409	.457	.506	.555
3.0	.103	.135	.172	.211	.252	.295	.339	.384	.430	.476	.522

ECCENTRIC LOADS ON WELD GROUPS

TABLE XIX   Coefficients C

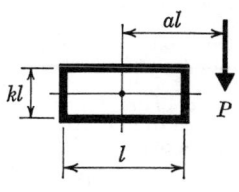

P = Permissible eccentric load in kips.
l = Length of longer welds in inches.
D = Number of sixteenths of an inch in fillet weld size.
C = Coefficients tabulated below.
C_1 = Coefficient for electrode used (see Table on page 4-67).
 = 1.0 for E70XX electrodes.

$$P = CC_1Dl$$

Required Minimum $C = \dfrac{P}{C_1Dl}$

"   " $D = \dfrac{P}{CC_1l}$

"   " $l = \dfrac{P}{CC_1D}$

Note: When load P is parallel to longer side l use table on facing page.

a	k										
	0	0.1	0.2	0.3	0.4	0.5	0.6	0.7	0.8	0.9	1.0
0.1	1.16	1.36	1.57	1.78	1.98	2.19	2.39	2.59	2.80	3.00	3.20
0.2	.844	1.02	1.21	1.40	1.59	1.79	1.99	2.18	2.38	2.58	2.78
0.3	.663	.819	.984	1.15	1.33	1.51	1.69	1.88	2.07	2.25	2.45
0.4	.546	.683	.829	.982	1.14	1.30	1.47	1.64	1.82	1.99	2.17
0.5	.464	.585	.716	.854	.998	1.15	1.30	1.46	1.62	1.78	1.95
0.6	.404	.512	.630	.755	.887	1.02	1.16	1.31	1.46	1.61	1.77
0.7	.357	.455	.562	.677	.798	.924	1.05	1.19	1.33	1.47	1.61
0.8	.320	.410	.508	.613	.725	.841	.962	1.09	1.21	1.35	1.48
0.9	.290	.373	.463	.561	.664	.772	.885	1.00	1.12	1.24	1.37
1.0	.265	.341	.426	.516	.613	.714	.819	.927	1.04	1.15	1.27
1.2	.226	.293	.366	.446	.530	.619	.712	.809	.908	1.01	1.12
1.4	.197	.256	.321	.392	.468	.547	.630	.716	.805	.897	.991
1.6	.175	.228	.286	.350	.418	.490	.565	.643	.724	.807	.892
1.8	.157	.205	.258	.316	.378	.444	.512	.583	.657	.732	.810
2.0	.143	.186	.235	.288	.345	.405	.468	.533	.601	.671	.742
2.2	.131	.171	.216	.265	.317	.373	.431	.491	.554	.618	.685
2.4	.121	.158	.199	.245	.294	.345	.399	.456	.514	.574	.636
2.6	.112	.146	.185	.228	.273	.322	.372	.425	.479	.535	.593
2.8	.104	.137	.173	.213	.256	.301	.348	.398	.449	.501	.555
3.0	.098	.128	.162	.200	.240	.283	.327	.374	.422	.471	.522

ECCENTRIC LOADS ON WELD GROUPS

TABLE XX   Coefficients C

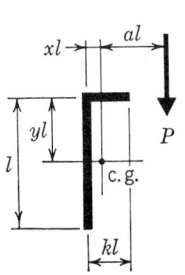

P = Permissible eccentric load in kips.
l = Length of weld parallel to load P in inches.
D = Number of sixteenths of an inch in fillet weld size.
C = Coefficients tabulated below.
C_1 = Coefficient for electrode used (see Table on page 4-67).
= 1.0 for E70XX electrodes.
xl = Distance from vertical weld to center of gravity of weld group.
yl = Distance from horizontal weld to center of gravity of weld group.

$$P = CC_1Dl$$

Required Minimum $C = \dfrac{P}{C_1Dl}$

"   " $D = \dfrac{P}{CC_1l}$

"   " $l = \dfrac{P}{CC_1D}$

a	k															
	0.0	0.1	0.2	0.3	0.4	0.5	0.6	0.7	0.8	0.9	1.0	1.2	1.4	1.6	1.8	2.0
0.1	.796	.854	.900	.944	.990	1.04	1.09	1.15	1.22	1.29	1.36	1.52	1.69	1.86	2.04	2.22
0.2	.594	.671	.715	.748	.780	.815	.855	.900	.951	1.01	1.07	1.20	1.35	1.51	1.68	1.85
0.3	.451	.521	.580	.611	.638	.666	.698	.736	.778	.826	.879	.998	1.13	1.27	1.42	1.58
0.4	.357	.415	.466	.513	.537	.562	.589	.621	.658	.700	.746	.851	.970	1.10	1.24	1.38
0.5	.294	.342	.384	.427	.463	.485	.509	.537	.570	.607	.648	.742	.850	.967	1.09	1.23
0.6	.248	.290	.326	.362	.402	.426	.448	.473	.502	.536	.573	.658	.756	.864	.980	1.10
0.7	.215	.251	.282	.313	.348	.380	.400	.423	.449	.479	.513	.591	.680	.780	.888	1.00
0.8	.189	.221	.248	.276	.306	.342	.361	.382	.406	.433	.464	.536	.619	.711	.811	.91
0.9	.169	.198	.222	.246	.273	.305	.329	.348	.370	.396	.424	.490	.567	.653	.747	.84
1.0	.153	.178	.200	.222	.246	.275	.302	.320	.340	.364	.390	.452	.524	.604	.692	.78
1.2	.128	.149	.168	.186	.206	.229	.257	.275	.293	.314	.337	.391	.454	.525	.603	.68
1.4	.110	.128	.144	.160	.177	.197	.221	.241	.257	.275	.296	.344	.401	.464	.535	.61
1.6	.096	.113	.126	.140	.155	.172	.193	.215	.229	.246	.264	.307	.358	.416	.480	.54
1.8	.086	.100	.112	.124	.138	.153	.171	.193	.207	.222	.238	.278	.324	.377	.436	.49
2.0	.077	.090	.101	.112	.124	.138	.154	.174	.188	.202	.217	.253	.296	.345	.399	.45
2.2	.070	.082	.092	.102	.113	.125	.140	.158	.173	.185	.200	.233	.272	.317	.368	.42
2.4	.064	.075	.084	.093	.103	.115	.128	.144	.160	.171	.185	.216	.252	.294	.341	.39
2.6	.059	.070	.078	.086	.095	.106	.118	.133	.148	.159	.172	.201	.235	.274	.318	.36
2.8	.055	.065	.072	.080	.088	.098	.110	.124	.139	.149	.160	.188	.220	.257	.298	.34
3.0	.052	.060	.068	.075	.083	.092	.103	.115	.130	.140	.150	.176	.206	.241	.280	.32
x	.000	.005	.017	.035	.057	.083	.113	.144	.178	.213	.250	.327	.408	.492	.579	.66
y	.500	.455	.417	.385	.357	.333	.313	.294	.278	.264	.250	.227	.308	.192	.179	.16

ECCENTRIC LOADS ON WELD GROUPS

TABLE XXI Coefficients C

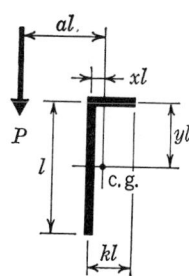

P = Permissible eccentric load in kips.
l = Length of weld parallel to load P in inches.
D = Number of sixteenths of an inch in fillet weld size.
C = Coefficients tabulated below.
C_1 = Coefficient for electrode used (see Table on page 4-67).
  = 1.0 for E70XX electrodes.
xl = Distance from vertical weld to center of gravity of weld group.
yl = Distance from horizontal weld to center of gravity of weld group.

$$P = CC_1Dl$$

Required Minimum $C = \dfrac{P}{C_1Dl}$

"　　　"　$D = \dfrac{P}{CC_1l}$

"　　　"　$l = \dfrac{P}{CC_1D}$

| a | \multicolumn{17}{c}{k} |
	0	0.1	0.2	0.3	0.4	0.5	0.6	0.7	0.8	0.9	1.0	1.2	1.4	1.6	1.8	2.0
0.1	.796	.886	.964	1.04	1.11	1.18	1.26	1.33	1.41	1.49	1.58	1.75	1.92	2.09	2.27	2.45
0.2	.594	.674	.739	.798	.857	.920	.987	1.06	1.14	1.21	1.29	1.46	1.63	1.81	1.98	2.16
0.3	.451	.517	.570	.619	.669	.723	.782	.847	.917	.991	1.07	1.23	1.40	1.57	1.74	1.91
0.4	.357	.412	.456	.497	.539	.585	.638	.695	.759	.827	.899	1.05	1.21	1.38	1.54	1.71
0.5	.294	.340	.377	.412	.448	.489	.535	.586	.643	.705	.771	.913	1.06	1.22	1.38	1.54
0.6	.248	.289	.320	.351	.382	.418	.459	.504	.556	.612	.672	.804	.945	1.09	1.24	1.39
0.7	.215	.250	.278	.305	.333	.364	.401	.442	.488	.539	.595	.716	.848	.987	1.13	1.27
0.8	.189	.221	.245	.269	.294	.323	.356	.393	.435	.482	.533	.645	.769	.899	1.03	1.17
0.9	.169	.197	.219	.241	.264	.289	.319	.353	.392	.435	.482	.587	.702	.825	.953	1.08
1.0	.152	.178	.198	.218	.239	.262	.290	.321	.357	.396	.440	.537	.646	.762	.884	1.01
1.2	.128	.149	.166	.183	.200	.221	.244	.271	.302	.336	.374	.460	.556	.660	.770	.884
1.4	.110	.128	.143	.157	.173	.190	.211	.234	.261	.292	.325	.401	.487	.581	.681	.786
1.6	.096	.112	.125	.138	.152	.167	.185	.206	.230	.257	.287	.356	.434	.519	.611	.707
1.8	.086	.100	.111	.123	.135	.149	.165	.184	.206	.230	.257	.320	.391	.469	.553	.642
2.0	.077	.090	.101	.111	.122	.134	.149	.166	.186	.208	.233	.290	.355	.428	.506	.588
2.2	.070	.082	.092	.101	.111	.122	.136	.152	.170	.190	.213	.265	.326	.393	.465	.542
2.4	.064	.075	.084	.093	.102	.112	.125	.139	.156	.175	.196	.244	.301	.363	.431	.503
2.6	.059	.069	.078	.085	.094	.104	.115	.129	.144	.162	.182	.227	.279	.338	.401	.469
2.8	.055	.065	.072	.079	.087	.097	.107	.120	.134	.151	.169	.211	.260	.315	.375	.440
3.0	.052	.060	.067	.074	.082	.090	.100	.112	.126	.141	.158	.198	.244	.296	.353	.413
x	.000	.005	.017	.035	.057	.083	.113	.144	.178	.213	.250	.327	.408	.492	.579	.667
y	.500	.455	.417	.385	.357	.333	.313	.294	.278	.263	.250	.227	.208	.192	.179	.167

ONE-SIDED CONNECTIONS

In designing a one-sided connection it is customary to consider vertical shear or bearing in all fasteners and the effect of eccentricity in the outstanding leg fasteners. Shown below is a table of coefficients for one-sided framed beam connections and an example of its use.

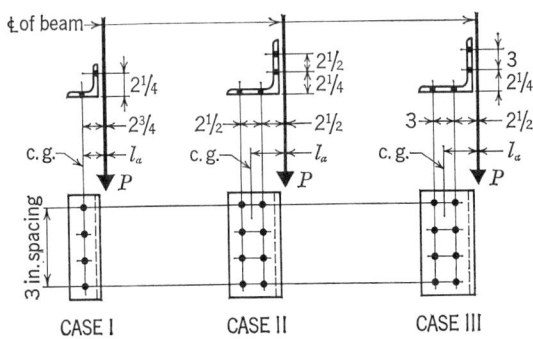

n	Coefficient C			
	Case I	Case II	Case III
1	...	0.63	0.67
2	1.41	2.05	1.99
3	2.68	4.10	3.88
4	3.92	6.64	6.31
5	5.00	9.32	8.97
6	6.00	11.83	11.60
7	7.00	14.00	14.00
8	8.00	16.00	16.00
9	9.00	18.00	18.00
10	10.00	20.00	20.00

$P = Cr_v$ or $C = P/r_v$
n = Total number of fasteners in one vertical row
C = Coefficient
P = Permissible load, kips
r_v = Allowable shear or bearing value for one fastener, kips
$l_a = l_{actual}$ = Actual arm between center line of beam and center of gravity of fasteners
$l_e = l_{eff.}$ = Effective arm between center line of beam and center of gravity of fasteners

In computation of coefficients C the actual moment arm l_a is corrected to l_e using the empirical formulas, $l_e = l_a - \left(\dfrac{1 + 2n}{4}\right)$ for single gage and $l_e = l_a - \left(\dfrac{1 + n}{2}\right)$ for double gage.

Do not exceed gages shown for web leg. Pattern of web leg fasteners may vary to suit required number of fasteners. For outstanding leg gages, other than those shown, coefficients may be interpolated from Tables X to XII, Part 4 of the Manual. Select angle thickness to provide sufficient gross shear capacity, or limit connection capacity to permissible shear value of angle used. Use minimum angle thickness of $\frac{3}{8}''$ for $\frac{3}{4}''$ diam. and $\frac{7}{8}''$ diam. fasteners, and $\frac{1}{2}''$ for $1''$ diam. fasteners. It will be permissible to design a connection using combinations of leg widths as well as fastener specification and diameters.

EXAMPLE 1

Given: Select a one-sided connection for a W18 × 50, $F_y = 36$ ksi with an end reaction of 50 kips. Use $\frac{7}{8}''$ diam. ASTM A502 Gr 1 rivets in the beam web leg and $\frac{7}{8}''$ diam. ASTM A325 friction type bolts in the outstanding leg.

Solution:

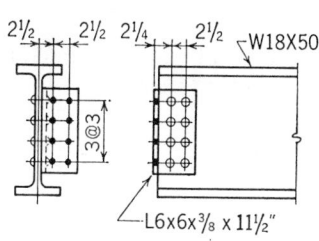

1. *Outstanding leg:*
   Single shear value of $\frac{7}{8}''$ diam. A325 bolt, from shear allowable load tables = 9.02 kips.

$$C = \frac{50}{9.02} = 5.54$$

The next larger value of C in the table above requires six A325 bolts in Case I or eight A325 bolts in Case II. Since the beam depth will not allow Case I to be used, **use 8 bolts as shown.**

2. *Web leg:*
   Single shear value of $\frac{7}{8}''$ diam. A502 Gr 1 rivets from shear allowable load tables = 9.02 kips.

   Bearing value of $\frac{7}{8}''$ diam. rivet in 0.358″ thick web, from bearing allowable load tables = $0.358 \times 42.5 = 15.2$ kips.

   Single shear at 9.02 kips governs, requiring $50/9.02 = 5.54$ rivets.

   Use: 8 rivets arranged in pattern dictated by outstanding leg.

3. *Angle size:* Try $6 \times 6 \times \frac{3}{8} \times 11\frac{1}{2}''$ angle. Allowable load = $11.5 \times \frac{3}{8} \times 14.5 = 62.5 > 50$ kips **o.k. Use: $6 \times 6 \times \frac{3}{8} \times 11\frac{1}{2}''$ angle.**

EXAMPLE 2

Given: Same as Example 1 except weld the web leg of the connection.

Solution:

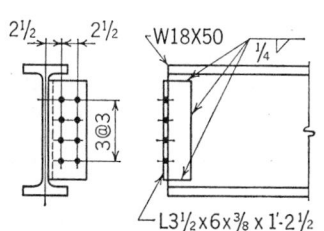

1. *Outstanding leg:* Same as Example 1.

2. *Web leg:* The required weld may be determined from Framed Beam Connections, Welded, E70XX electrodes, Table III, page 4 - 31.

   Since the capacities shown in Table III are for two angles, it will be convenient to double the given reaction and select weld sizes directly from the tables, and angle lengths directly or by interpolation.

Since $R = 50$ kips, the tabular capacity needed is 100 kips.

From Table III, which covers $F_y = 36$ ksi connections and E70XX electrodes, the capacity of Weld A at $\frac{1}{4}$ in. on a $1'\text{-}2\frac{1}{2}''$ angle is 102 kips.

Check beam web thickness: $0.358 > 0.41/2$ **o.k.**

Use: E70XX $\frac{1}{4}$ in. weld (as shown).

3. *Angle size:* Use 6″ for outstanding leg and $3\frac{1}{2}''$ for web leg. The required thickness of $\frac{3}{8}''$ for the web leg is the same as required for the outstanding leg and will accept the $\frac{1}{4}$ in. weld.

   Use: $6 \times 3\frac{1}{2} \times \frac{3}{8} \times 1'\text{-}2\frac{1}{2}''$ angle.

ECCENTRIC CONNECTIONS

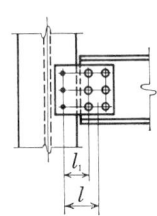

BEAM TO COLUMN CONNECTION To avoid moment in the column full eccentricity in the fasteners connecting plate to beam should be figured. Lever arm l should be used. A coefficient for this fastener group, for ordinary cases, can be found in the tables on pages 4 - 62 to 4 - 65.

Field fasteners connecting plate to column should be used (least number) if beam can be erected and if there are no interfering details in the web of the column. The plate should figure for a moment with lever arm l_1. See page 4 - 79 for table of Net Section Moduli of Bracket Plates.

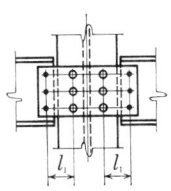

SYMMETRICAL BEAM TO COLUMN CONNECTIONS A single plate across the column may be used. If the reactions of the two beams are equal there is no eccentricity to figure on either beams or columns. The case of live load on one beam only must, however, be considered. Where for this or other reason the beam reactions are unequal, figure the fasteners in the column for the sum of the reactions and the difference of the moments, taken to the center of the connection. See page 4 - 60.

Plate should figure for greater moment with lever arm l_1. See page 4 - 79 for table of Net Section Moduli of Bracket Plates.

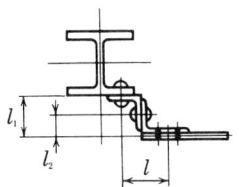

ZEE CONNECTIONS In general use for light loads only. Eccentricity in fasteners connecting connection angle to the beam should be figured, using the lever arm l. Eccentricity in fasteners connecting connection angle to column, with a lever arm of l_1, should be figured. The thickness of the angle should be ample to resist the bending moment. See page 4 - 80.

Eccentricity in fasteners connecting the two connection angles should be figured if the lever arm l_2 is $2\frac{1}{2}''$ or more. The connection should be designed so field work is at a minimum. There can be many variations of this type of connection depending on the length of l_1. The eccentricity should be considered in all cases.

TRUSS CONNECTION

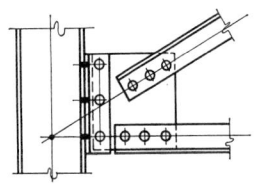

The intersection of the working lines should be located to hold the effect of moment on connection and column to a minimum.

BRACKET PLATES
Net Section Moduli

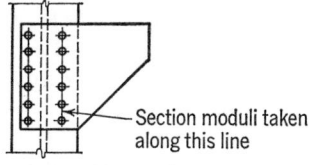

Diameter of holes assumed ⅛ in. larger than nominal diameter of fastener

Section moduli taken along this line

Fasteners spaced 3 in. vertically

No. of Fasteners in One Vertical Line	Depth of Plate in Inches	¾ in. Fasteners					⅞ in. Fasteners					1 in. Fasteners				
		Thickness of Plate, In.					Thickness of Plate, In.					Thickness of Plate, In.				
		¼	⅜	½	⅝	¾	⅜	½	⅝	¾	⅞	½	⅝	¾	⅞	1
2	6	1.2	1.8	2.3	2.9	3.5	1.7	2.3	2.9	3.4	4.0	2.2	2.7	3.2	3.8	4.3
3	9	2.5	3.8	5.0	6.3	7.5	3.6	4.8	5.9	7.1	8.3	4.5	5.6	6.8	7.9	9.0
4	12	4.4	6.3	8.7	11	13	6.2	8.2	10	12	14	7.8	9.7	12	14	16
5	15	6.8	10	14	17	20	10	13	16	19	22	12	15	18	21	24
6	18	9.6	15	19	24	29	14	18	23	27	32	17	21	26	30	34
7	21	13	20	26	33	39	19	25	31	37	43	23	29	35	41	47
8	24	17	26	34	43	51	24	32	40	48	56	30	38	45	53	61
9	27	22	32	43	54	65	31	41	51	61	71	38	48	57	67	77
10	30	27	40	53	67	80	38	50	63	75	88	47	59	71	83	94
12	36	38	58	77	96	115	54	72	90	108	126	68	85	102	119	136
14	42	52	78	104	130	157	74	98	123	147	172	92	115	138	161	184
16	48	68	102	136	170	204	96	128	160	192	224	120	150	180	211	241
18	54	86	129	172	215	259	122	162	203	243	284	152	190	228	266	304
20	60	106	160	213	266	319	150	200	250	300	350	188	235	282	329	376
22	66	129	193	257	322	386	182	242	303	363	424	227	284	341	398	454
24	72	153	230	306	383	459	216	288	360	432	504	270	338	406	473	541
26	78	180	270	359	449	539	254	338	423	507	592	317	397	476	555	634
28	84	208	313	417	521	625	294	392	490	588	686	368	460	552	644	736
30	90	240	359	478	598	718	338	450	563	675	788	422	528	633	739	845
32	96	272	408	544	680	816	384	512	640	768	896	480	600	721	841	961
34	102	308	461	614	768	922	434	578	723	867	1012	542	678	813	949	1085
36	108	344	517	689	861	1033	486	648	810	972	1134	608	760	912	1064	1216

Interpolate for intermediate thickness of plates.

General equation for net section modulus of bracket plates:

$$S_{net} = \frac{t_p\, d^2}{6} - \frac{b^2 n(n^2 - 1)\,[t_p \times (\text{Bolt Diam.} + 0.125)]}{6d}$$

where

t_p = Plate thickness, inches
d = Plate depth, inches
n = Number of fasteners in one vertical row
b = Fastener spacing vertically, inches

HANGER TYPE CONNECTIONS
Fasteners loaded in tension

In the design of hanger type connections, prying action must be considered. It will usually increase the tension in the fasteners transmitting tension force through the flange of a tee or the outstanding leg of angles and it will introduce additional bending stresses in the steel fitting.

The following table is useful for making a rapid selection of a trial fitting using $F_y = 36$ ksi. The fitting must then be checked for bending stresses due to prying force Q and possible increase in size.

STRUCTURAL TEE OR DOUBLE ANGLE HANGERS
Loads in kips per linear inch for trial section

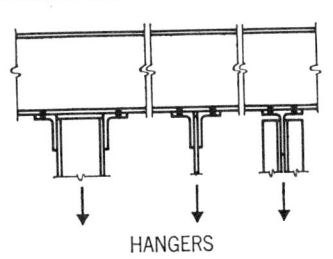

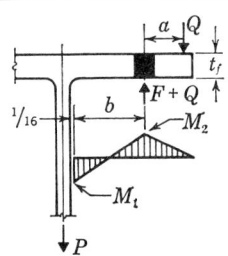

HANGERS

b in.	Thickness of angle or flange of tee, t_f, inches															
	5/16	3/8	7/16	1/2	9/16	5/8	11/16	3/4	13/16	7/8	15/16	1	1 1/16	1 1/8	1 3/16	1 1/4
1	1.76	2.53	3.45	4.50	5.70	7.03	8.51	10.13	11.88	13.78	15.82	18.00	20.32	22.78	25.38	28.1
1 1/4	1.41	2.03	2.76	3.60	4.56	5.63	6.81	8.10	9.51	11.03	12.66	14.40	16.26	18.23	20.31	22.
1 1/2	1.17	1.69	2.30	3.00	3.80	4.69	5.67	6.75	7.92	9.19	10.55	12.00	13.55	15.19	16.92	18.
1 3/4	1.00	1.45	1.97	2.57	3.25	4.02	4.86	5.79	6.79	7.88	9.04	10.29	11.61	13.02	14.50	16.
2	0.88	1.27	1.72	2.25	2.85	3.52	4.25	5.06	5.94	6.89	7.91	9.00	10.16	11.39	12.69	14.
2 1/4	0.78	1.13	1.53	2.00	2.53	3.13	3.78	4.50	5.28	6.13	7.03	8.00	9.03	10.13	11.28	12.
2 1/2	0.70	1.01	1.38	1.80	2.28	2.81	3.40	4.05	4.75	5.51	6.33	7.20	8.13	9.11	10.15	11.
2 3/4	0.64	0.92	1.25	1.64	2.07	2.56	3.09	3.68	4.32	5.01	5.75	6.55	7.39	8.28	9.23	10.
3	0.59	0.84	1.15	1.50	1.90	2.34	2.84	3.38	3.96	4.59	5.27	6.00	6.77	7.59	8.46	9.
3 1/4	0.54	0.78	1.06	1.38	1.75	2.16	2.62	3.12	3.66	4.24	4.87	5.54	6.25	7.01	7.81	8.

For the above table, the points of critical moment are assumed at the fastener line and at a point one-sixteenth of an inch from the near face of the outstanding leg of the angle or tee.

$$M = \frac{P}{2} \times \frac{b}{2} = \frac{27t_f^2}{6}; \quad P = \frac{18t_f^2}{b}$$

where

P = Allowable load on two angles or structural tee, in kips per linear inch, using maximum allowable bending stress of 27.0 ksi

b = Distance from fastener line to near face of outstanding leg of angle or structural tee less $1/16''$ ($b/2$ is the lever arm used to determine the assumed moment)

t_f = Thickness of angle or flange of tee

AMERICAN INSTITUTE OF STEEL CONSTRUCTION

The table is based upon the simplifying approximation that the moments M_1 and M_2 are equal in magnitude and opposite in direction; that the geometry of the fittings is such that $a \cong b/2$; and that the prying force, Q, therefore, is equal to F, the applied force per fastener. A tentative selection of required fitting thickness can be made from the values tabulated, and a fastener size assumed. The corresponding prying force, Q, can then be determined for connections assembled with high strength bolts, and any necessary adjustment made in fitting thickness to satisfy the calculated prying force.

In the case of connections assembled with rivets or A307 bolts, for which formulas similar to those for high strength bolts are not available, an assumed value of Q equal to $F/2$ will generally provide a conservative design.

PRYING ACTION

Precise evaluation of the prying effect in a given connection involves complex analysis. Research* on test joints reported to date (1969) has resulted in the following empirical formulas:

For connections using A325 bolts:

$$Q = F \left[\frac{100b(d_b)^2 - 18w(t_f)^2}{70a(d_b)^2 + 21w(t_f)^2} \right]$$

For connections using A490 bolts:

$$Q = F \left[\frac{100b(d_b)^2 - 14w(t_f)^2}{62a(d_b)^2 + 21w(t_f)^2} \right]$$

where

Q = Prying force per fastener, kips
F = Externally applied load per fastener = $wP/2$, kips
w = Length of flange tributary to each bolt, in.
d_b = Nominal bolt diameter, in.
a = Distance from fastener line to edge of flange, not to exceed $2t_f$, in.

The adequacy of the fasteners must be checked against the total tension due to external loading and prying action. The adequacy of the fitting flange must be checked against the bending stress due to the prying action moment, and the adequacy of the tee stem or outstanding angle leg must be checked against the tensile stress due to external loading P.

EXAMPLE

Select a tee-section hanger using A36 steel and fasteners to support 44 kips suspended from bottom flange of a W36 × 160.

Given:

Fasteners to be located on 4″ beam gage
Fitting length: 9″
Fasteners: Four A325 bolts

Solution:

1. Trial section:

$44/9 = 4.9$ kips per lin. inch of fitting

* *Behavior of Bolts in Tee-Connections Subject to Prying Action*, Structural Research Series No. 353, University of Illinois, Sept. 1969.

Distance b is estimated at $1\frac{3}{4}''$ on the basis of a $4''$ gage. From hanger table, on the $b = 1\frac{3}{4}''$ line and in the $\frac{3}{4}'' t_f$ column, the next larger P value is 5.79 kips per lin. in. Therefore, try a $9''$ length of tee cut from $W 18 \times 70$; $t_f = 0.751''$

Note that t_f for supporting member is $1.02 > 0.751''$.

2. *Trial fasteners:*

External load per bolt: $F = 44/4 = 11.0$ kips (assuming 4 bolts)

Try prying ratio Q/F of 0.5; then $Q = 5.5$ kips

Total trial load per bolt $= 11.0 + 5.5 = 16.5$ kips

Allowable tensile load per bolt, $\frac{3}{4}''$ diam. A325 $= 17.67$ kips

3. *Compute Q:*

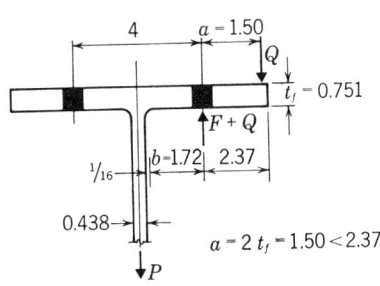

$a = 2 t_f = 1.50 < 2.37$

$$Q = F \left[\frac{100b(d_b)^2 - 18w(t_f)^2}{70a(d_b)^2 + 21w(t_f)^2} \right]$$

$$= F \left[\frac{100 \times 1.72 \times (\frac{3}{4})^2 - 18 \times 4.5 \times (0.751)^2}{70 \times 1.50 \times (\frac{3}{4})^2 + 21 \times 4.5(0.751)^2} \right]$$

$$= 0.455 \ F$$

Since $F = \dfrac{wP}{2}$,

$$Q = \frac{0.455 \times 4.5 \times 4.9}{2} = 5.0 \text{ kips}$$

4. *Check fastener load:*

Total tension on $\frac{3}{4}''$ diam. A325 $= F + Q = 11.0 + 5.0 = 16.0$ kips

Allowable tensile load $= 17.67$ kips, $\therefore$ bolts are **o.k.**

Check bending strength of flange:

Moment $M_2 = Qa = 5.0 \times 1.50 = 7.5$ kip-in.

Moment $M_1 = (F + Q)b - Q(a + b)$
$= 16.0 \times 1.72 - 5.0 \times 3.22$
$= 27.5 - 16.1 = 11.4$ kip-in. (governs)

$$f_b = \frac{11.4}{\dfrac{4.5 \times (0.751)^2}{6}} = 27.0 \text{ ksi} = \text{allowable } 27.0 \text{ ksi}$$

$\therefore$ tee cut from $W 18 \times 70$, $9''$ long, is **o.k.**

Notes

TENSION MEMBERS
Net Areas

Angle Designation	TWO ANGLES—NET AREA											
	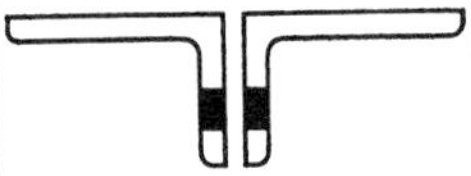 2 Holes out				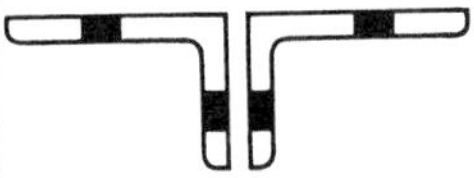 4 Holes out				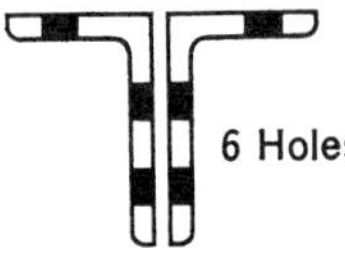 6 Holes out			
	Fastener Diam., In.				Fastener Diam., In.				Fastener Diam., In.			
	¾	⅞	1	1⅛	¾	⅞	1	1⅛	¾	⅞	1	1⅛
L 9 × 4 × 1	22.3	22.0	21.8	21.5	20.5	20.0	19.5	19.0	18.8	18.0	17.3	16.5
⅞	19.7	19.5	19.3	19.0	18.2	17.7	17.3	16.8	16.6	16.0	15.3	14.7
¾	17.1	16.9	16.7	16.5	15.8	15.4	15.0	14.6	14.4	13.9	13.3	12.8
⅝	14.4	14.2	14.1	13.9	13.3	13.0	12.7	12.3	12.2	11.7	11.2	10.8
⁹⁄₁₆	13.0	12.9	12.7	12.6	12.0	11.8	11.5	11.2	11.1	10.6	10.2	9.78
½	11.6	11.5	11.4	11.3	10.8	10.5	10.3	10.0	9.88	9.50	9.12	8.75
L 8 × 8 × 1⅛	31.5	31.2	30.9	30.7	29.5	29.0	28.4	27.8	27.6	26.7	25.9	25.0
1	28.3	28.0	27.8	27.5	26.5	26.0	25.5	25.0	24.8	24.0	23.3	22.5
⅞	24.9	24.7	24.5	24.3	23.4	23.0	22.5	22.1	21.9	21.2	20.6	19.9
¾	21.6	21.4	21.2	21.0	20.3	19.9	19.5	19.1	18.9	18.4	17.8	17.3
⅝	18.1	18.0	17.8	17.7	17.0	16.7	16.4	16.1	15.9	15.5	15.0	14.5
⁹⁄₁₆	16.4	16.2	16.1	16.0	15.4	15.1	14.8	14.6	14.4	14.0	13.6	13.2
½	14.6	14.5	14.4	14.3	13.8	13.5	13.3	13.0	12.9	12.5	12.1	11.8
L 8 × 6 × 1	24.3	24.0	23.8	23.5	22.5	22.0	21.5	21.0	20.8	20.0	19.3	18.5
⅞	21.4	21.2	21.0	20.8	19.9	19.5	19.0	18.6	18.4	17.7	17.1	16.4
¾	18.6	18.4	18.2	18.0	17.3	16.9	16.5	16.1	15.9	15.4	14.8	14.3
⅝	15.6	15.5	15.3	15.2	14.5	14.2	13.9	13.6	13.4	13.0	12.5	12.0
⁹⁄₁₆	14.1	14.0	13.9	13.7	13.2	12.9	12.6	12.3	12.2	11.8	11.3	10.9
½	12.6	12.5	12.4	12.3	11.8	11.5	11.3	11.0	10.9	10.5	10.1	9.75
⁷⁄₁₆	11.1	11.0	10.9	10.8	10.3	10.1	9.89	9.67	9.56	9.24	8.91	8.58
L 8 × 4 × 1	20.3	20.0	19.8	19.5	18.5	18.0	17.5	17.0	16.8	16.0	15.3	14.5
⅞	17.9	17.7	17.5	17.3	16.4	16.0	15.5	15.1	14.9	14.2	13.6	12.9
¾	15.6	15.4	15.2	15.0	14.3	13.9	13.5	13.1	12.9	12.4	11.8	11.3
⅝	13.1	13.0	12.8	12.7	12.0	11.7	11.4	11.1	10.9	10.5	10.0	9.53
⁹⁄₁₆	11.9	11.7	11.6	11.5	11.0	10.6	10.3	10.1	9.90	9.50	9.09	8.64
½	10.6	10.5	10.4	10.3	9.75	9.50	9.25	9.00	8.87	8.50	8.13	7.75
⁷⁄₁₆	9.35	9.24	9.14	9.03	8.59	8.37	8.15	7.93	7.83	7.50	7.18	6.84
L 7 × 4 × ⅞	16.2	16.0	15.8	15.5	14.7	14.2	13.8	13.3	13.1	12.5	—	—
¾	14.1	13.9	13.7	13.5	12.8	12.4	12.0	11.6	11.4	10.9	—	—
⅝	11.9	11.7	11.6	11.4	10.8	10.5	10.2	9.84	9.70	9.23	—	—
⁹⁄₁₆	10.8	10.6	10.5	10.3	9.77	9.49	9.21	8.93	8.78	8.38	—	—
½	9.62	9.50	9.37	9.25	8.75	8.50	8.25	8.00	7.87	7.50	—	—
⁷⁄₁₆	8.47	8.36	8.26	8.15	7.71	7.49	7.27	7.05	6.95	6.62	—	—
⅜	7.32	7.23	7.14	7.04	6.67	6.48	6.27	6.08	6.01	5.73	—	—
L 6 × 6 × 1	20.3	20.0	19.8	19.5	18.5	18.0	17.5	17.0	16.8	16.0	—	—
⅞	17.9	17.7	17.5	17.3	16.4	16.0	15.5	15.1	14.9	14.2	—	—
¾	15.6	15.4	15.2	15.0	14.3	13.9	13.5	13.1	12.9	12.4	—	—
⅝	13.1	13.0	12.8	12.7	12.0	11.7	11.4	11.1	10.9	10.5	—	—
⁹⁄₁₆	11.9	11.7	11.6	11.5	10.9	10.9	10.3	10.1	9.91	9.49	—	—
½	10.6	10.5	10.4	10.3	9.75	9.50	9.25	9.00	8.87	8.50	—	—
⁷⁄₁₆	9.35	9.24	9.14	9.03	8.59	8.37	8.15	7.93	7.82	7.50	—	—
⅜	8.06	7.97	7.88	7.78	7.41	7.22	7.03	6.84	6.75	6.47	—	—

Net areas are computed in accordance with AISC Specification, Section 1.14.5.

TENSION MEMBERS
Net Areas

Angle Designation	2 Holes out				4 Holes out				6 Holes out			
	Fastener Diam., In.				Fastener Diam., In.				Fastener Diam., In.			
	¾	⅞	1	1⅛	¾	⅞	1	1⅛	¾	⅞	1	1⅛
L 6 × 4 × ⅞	14.4	14.2	14.0	13.8	12.9	12.5	12.0	11.6	11.4	—	—	—
¾	12.6	12.4	12.2	12.0	11.3	10.9	10.5	10.1	9.94	—	—	—
⅝	10.6	10.5	10.3	10.2	9.53	9.22	8.91	8.60	8.44	—	—	—
9/16	9.64	9.49	9.35	9.21	8.65	8.37	8.09	7.81	7.67	—	—	—
½	8.62	8.50	8.37	8.25	7.75	7.50	7.25	7.00	6.88	—	—	—
7/16	7.59	7.48	7.38	7.27	6.83	6.61	6.39	6.17	6.06	—	—	—
⅜	6.56	6.47	6.38	6.28	5.91	5.72	5.53	5.34	5.25	—	—	—
L 5 × 5 × ⅞	14.4	14.2	14.0	13.8	12.9	12.5	12.0	11.6	—	—	—	—
¾	12.6	12.4	12.2	12.0	11.3	10.9	10.5	10.1	—	—	—	—
⅝	10.6	10.5	10.3	10.2	9.53	9.22	8.91	8.59	—	—	—	—
½	8.62	8.50	8.37	8.25	7.75	7.50	7.25	7.00	—	—	—	—
7/16	7.59	7.48	7.38	7.27	6.83	6.61	6.39	6.17	—	—	—	—
⅜	6.56	6.47	6.38	6.28	5.91	5.72	5.53	5.34	—	—	—	—
L 6 × 3½ × ½	8.12	8.00	7.87	—	7.25	7.00	—	—	6.38	—	—	—
⅜	6.18	6.09	6.00	—	5.53	5.34	—	—	4.87	—	—	—
5/16	5.19	5.11	5.04	—	4.65	4.49	—	—	4.10	—	—	—
L 5 × 3½ × ¾	10.3	10.1	9.93	—	8.99	8.62	—	—	—	—	—	—
⅝	8.75	8.59	8.43	—	7.65	7.34	—	—	—	—	—	—
½	7.12	7.00	6.87	—	6.25	6.00	—	—	—	—	—	—
7/16	6.29	6.18	6.08	—	5.53	5.31	—	—	—	—	—	—
⅜	5.44	5.35	5.25	—	4.79	4.60	—	—	—	—	—	—
5/16	4.57	4.49	4.42	—	4.03	3.87	—	—	—	—	—	—
L 5 × 3 × ½	6.62	6.50	—	—	5.75	5.50	—	—	—	—	—	—
⅜	5.06	4.97	—	—	4.41	4.22	—	—	—	—	—	—
5/16	4.25	4.17	—	—	3.71	3.55	—	—	—	—	—	—
L 4 × 4 × ¾	9.57	9.38	9.19	9.00	8.26	7.88	—	—	—	—	—	—
⅝	8.13	7.97	7.81	7.66	7.03	6.72	—	—	—	—	—	—
½	6.62	6.50	6.37	6.25	5.75	5.50	—	—	—	—	—	—
7/16	5.85	5.74	5.64	5.53	5.09	4.87	—	—	—	—	—	—
⅜	5.06	4.97	4.88	4.78	4.41	4.22	—	—	—	—	—	—
5/16	4.25	4.17	4.10	4.02	3.71	3.55	—	—	—	—	—	—
L 4 × 3½ × ⅝	7.51	7.35	7.19	—	6.42	6.10	—	—	—	—	—	—
½	6.12	6.00	5.87	—	5.25	5.00	—	—	—	—	—	—
7/16	5.41	5.30	5.20	—	4.65	4.43	—	—	—	—	—	—
⅜	4.68	4.59	4.50	—	4.03	3.84	—	—	—	—	—	—
5/16	3.95	3.87	3.80	—	3.41	3.25	—	—	—	—	—	—
L 4 × 3 × ⅝	6.87	6.71	—	—	5.77	5.46	—	—	—	—	—	—
½	5.62	5.50	—	—	4.75	4.50	—	—	—	—	—	—
7/16	4.97	4.86	—	—	4.21	3.99	—	—	—	—	—	—
⅜	4.30	4.21	—	—	3.65	3.46	—	—	—	—	—	—
5/16	3.63	3.55	—	—	3.09	2.93	—	—	—	—	—	—
¼	2.94	2.88	—	—	2.50	2.38	—	—	—	—	—	—

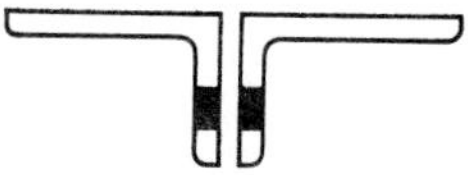

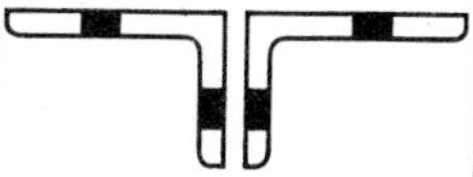

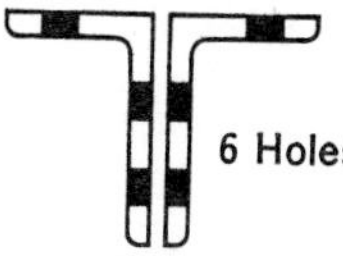

Net areas are computed in accordance with AISC Specification, Section 1.14.5.

REDUCTION OF AREA FOR BOLT AND RIVET HOLES

Area in square inches = assumed diameter of hole by thickness of metal. For computation purposes holes shall be taken as the nominal diameter of fastener plus ⅛ inch

Thickness of Metal Inches	Diameter of Hole, Inches					
	¾	⅞	1	1⅛	1¼	1⅜
³⁄₁₆	.141	.164	.188	.211	.234	.258
¼	.188	.219	.250	.281	.313	.344
⁵⁄₁₆	.234	.273	.313	.352	.391	.430
⅜	.281	.328	.375	.422	.469	.516
⁷⁄₁₆	.328	.383	.438	.492	.547	.602
½	.375	.438	.500	.563	.625	.688
⁹⁄₁₆	.422	.492	.563	.633	.703	.773
⅝	.469	.547	.625	.703	.781	.859
¹¹⁄₁₆	.516	.602	.688	.773	.859	.945
¾	.563	.656	.750	.844	.938	1.031
¹³⁄₁₆	.609	.711	.813	.914	1.016	1.117
⅞	.656	.766	.875	.984	1.094	1.203
¹⁵⁄₁₆	.703	.820	.938	1.055	1.172	1.289
1	.750	.875	1.000	1.125	1.250	1.375
¹⁄₁₆	.797	.930	1.063	1.195	1.328	1.461
⅛	.844	.984	1.125	1.266	1.406	1.547
³⁄₁₆	.891	1.039	1.188	1.336	1.484	1.633
¼	.938	1.094	1.250	1.406	1.563	1.719
⁵⁄₁₆	.984	1.148	1.313	1.477	1.641	1.805
⅜	1.031	1.203	1.375	1.547	1.719	1.891
⁷⁄₁₆	1.078	1.258	1.438	1.617	1.797	1.977
½	1.125	1.313	1.500	1.688	1.875	2.063
⁹⁄₁₆	1.172	1.367	1.563	1.758	1.953	2.148
⅝	1.219	1.422	1.625	1.828	2.031	2.234
¹¹⁄₁₆	1.266	1.477	1.688	1.898	2.109	2.320
¾	1.313	1.531	1.750	1.969	2.188	2.406
¹³⁄₁₆	...	1.586	1.813	2.039	2.266	2.492
⅞	...	1.641	1.875	2.109	2.344	2.578
¹⁵⁄₁₆	...	1.695	1.938	2.180	2.422	2.664
2	...	1.750	2.000	2.250	2.500	2.750
¹⁄₁₆	...	1.805	2.063	2.320	2.578	2.836
⅛	...	1.859	2.125	2.391	2.656	2.922
³⁄₁₆	...	1.914	2.188	2.461	2.734	3.008
¼	...	1.969	2.250	2.531	2.813	3.094
⁵⁄₁₆	...	2.023	2.313	2.602	2.891	3.180
⅜	...	2.078	2.375	2.672	2.969	3.266
⁷⁄₁₆	...	2.133	2.438	2.742	3.047	3.352
½	...	2.188	2.500	2.813	3.125	3.438
⅝	...	2.297	2.625	2.953	3.281	3.609
¾	...	2.406	2.750	3.094	3.438	3.781
⅞	...	2.516	2.875	3.234	3.594	3.953
3	...	2.625	3.000	3.375	3.750	4.125

AMERICAN INSTITUTE OF STEEL CONSTRUCTION

NET SECTION OF TENSION MEMBERS

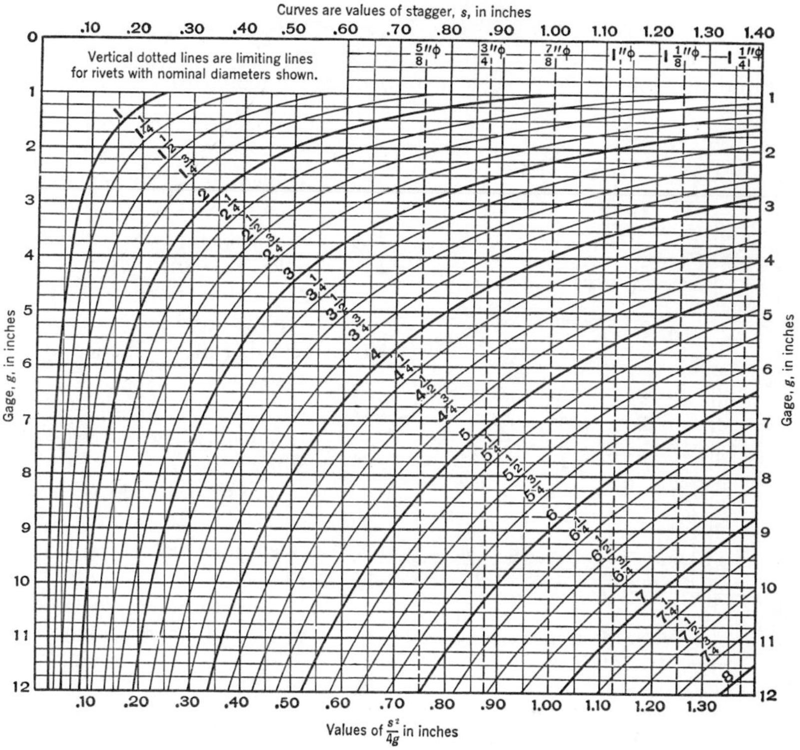

Curves are values of stagger, *s*, in inches

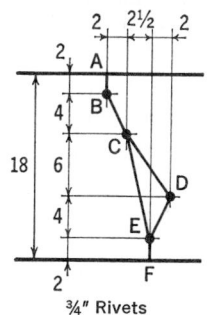

The above chart will simplify the application of the rule for net width, Sections 1.14.3 and 1.14.4 of the AISC Specification. Entering the chart at left or right with the gage *g* and proceeding horizontally to intersection with the curve for the pitch *s*, thence vertically to top or bottom, the value of $s^2/4g$ may be read directly.

Step 1 of the example below illustrates the application of the rule and the use of the chart. Step 2 illustrates the application of the 85% of gross area limitation.

Step 1: Chain A B C E F
Deduct for 3 holes @ (¾ + ⅛) = −2.625
BC, *g* = 4, *s* = 2; add $s^2/4g$ = +0.25
CE, *g* = 10, *s* = 2½; add $s^2/4g$ = +0.16

Total Deduction = −2.215″

Chain A B C D E F
Deduct for 4 holes @ (¾ + ⅛) = −3.50
BC, as above, add = +0.25
CD, *g* = 6, *s* = 4½; add $s^2/4g$ = +0.85
DE, *g* = 4, *s* = 2; add $s^2/4g$ = +0.25

Total Deduction = −2.15″
Net Width = 18.0 − 2.215 = 15.785″.

Step 2: Net width = 18.0 × 0.85 = 15.3″
(Governs in this example)

¾″ Rivets

In comparing the path CDE with the path CE, it is seen that if the sum of the two values of $s^2/4g$ for CD and DE exceed the single value of $s^2/4g$ for CE, by more than the deduction for one hole, then the path CDE is not critical as compared with CE.

Evidently if the value of $s^2/4g$ for one leg CD of the path CDE is greater than the deduction for one hole, the path CDE cannot be critical as compared with CE. The vertical dotted lines in the chart serve to indicate, for the respective rivet diameters noted at the top thereof, that any value of $s^2/4g$ to the right of such line is derived from a non-critical chain which need not be further considered.

AMERICAN INSTITUTE OF STEEL CONSTRUCTION

MOMENT CONNECTIONS
Welded

Many connections in Type 3 "semi-rigid framing" must be designed to develop specified resisting moments. The following method is recommended for design of such a connection subjected to gravity loading.

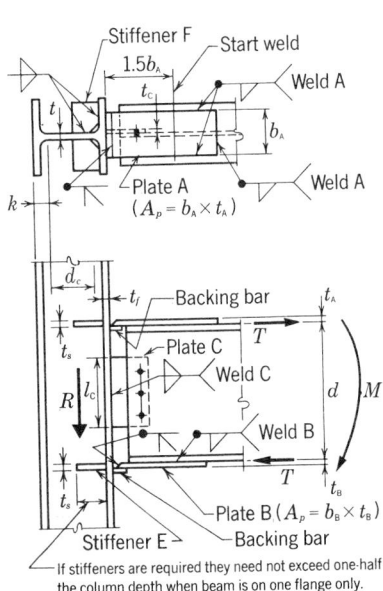

If stiffeners are required they need not exceed one-half the column depth when beam is on one flange only.

M = Connection moment, kip-ft.
R = End reaction of beam, kips
r_v = Allowable shear or bearing value for one fastener, kips
F_{vp} = Allowable shear in plate, ksi
F_{vw} = Allowable shear in welds, ksi
F_t = Allowable tension stress in plates and groove weld, ksi
D = Number of $\frac{1}{16}$ inches in weld size
$0.928D$ = Value of E70XX weld per lineal inch of fillet weld, kips
T = Horizontal force top and bottom of beam, kips
A_p = Area of plate, top or bottom
A_{st} = Area of stiffeners
A_{bc} = Planar area of web at beam-to-column connection
C_1 = Ratio of beam flange yield stress to column yield stress
C_2 = Ratio of column yield stress to stiffener yield stress.

The moment is assumed to be resisted by plates "A" and "B" welded to the top and bottom of beam and to the column. The shear is assumed to be transferred to the column by a vertical side plate, using fasteners in the beam web and shop welds on the column. A length of the top plate, equal to 1.5 times the width b_A, is kept free of weld to allow the elongation under load that is necessary to obtain the desired semi-rigid connection action.

AISC
Specification
Reference

1. Determine horizontal force $T = \dfrac{M \times 12}{d}$

2. Design top plate A; determine length and size of weld A.

$$A_p = \frac{T}{F_t}$$

Length of weld $= \dfrac{T}{0.928D}$ (for E70XX electrodes)

3. Select bottom plate B and determine length and size of weld B. Area plate B should be $\geqslant$ area plate A.

4. Determine number of fasteners in vertical plate C and size of weld between plate and column.

AMERICAN INSTITUTE OF STEEL CONSTRUCTION

No. of fasteners $= \dfrac{R}{r_v}$; select l_C and assume weld full length.

Min. $t_C = \dfrac{R}{F_{vp} \times l_C}$

Min. $D = \dfrac{R}{2 \times 0.928 \times l_C}$ (E70XX electrodes, welded full length both sides)

If intermittent or less than full length welds are used, min. t_C and min. D must be adjusted to satisfy Specification Sects. 1.5.3 and 1.17.6

5. Investigate column web shear.

1.5.1.2

Column web reinforcement required if

$t_w < \dfrac{32M}{A_{bc}F_y}$

Commentary
1.5.1.2

6. Check column for web crippling. Column web stiffeners are required:

1.15.5

At compression flange if $t < \dfrac{C_1 A_p}{t_B + 5k}$ or when $t \leqslant \dfrac{d_C \sqrt{F_y}}{180}$

Formulas
(1.15-1)
and (1.15-2)

At tension flange if $t_f < 0.4\sqrt{C_1 A_p}$

Formula
(1.15-3)

If required, bearing area of stiffeners

$A_{st} \geqslant [C_1 A_p - t(t_B + 5k)]C_2$

Formula
(1.15-4)

Check stiffener width-thickness ratio.
Fillet weld stiffener full length to column web.

1.9.1.2

Min. $D = \dfrac{(t \text{ or } t_s) F_{vp}}{2 \times 0.928}$ (E70XX electrodes)

Total length of weld against column tension flange.

$l = \dfrac{A_{st} F_y}{0.928D \times 1.65}$

EXAMPLE

Given: Design a semi-rigid connection for a W18 × 50 ($t = 0.358$) framed to one side of a W10 × 49 column ($t = 0.340$; $k = 1.12$). The end moment is 100 kip-ft. and end reaction is 26 kips. Beam and connection material are $F_y = 36$ ksi steel with $F_t = 22.0$ ksi. The column is $F_y = 50$ ksi steel. Use ASTM A325 bolts in a bearing type connection and E70XX electrodes, with $0.928D$ value per lineal inch of weld. Stiffeners, if required, to be $F_y = 36$ ksi steel.

1. $T = \dfrac{100 \times 12}{18} = 66.7$ kips

2. $A_p = \dfrac{66.7}{22.0} = 3.03$ in.^{2}

   Use: $\frac{1}{2} \times 6''$ **for top Plate A with** $\frac{5}{16}$ **in. Weld A.**

   $l = \dfrac{66.7}{5 \times 0.928} = 14.4''$

   Use: $6''$ **across end and** $4\frac{1}{2}''$ **each side.**

3. **Use:** $\frac{3}{8} \times 9''$ **for bottom Plate B.**

   $A_p = 3.38 > 3.03$ in.^{2}

   Use: $\frac{5}{16}$ **in. Weld B;** $7\frac{1}{2}''$ **each side.**

4. Try $\frac{3}{4}''$ diam. A325 bolts in a bearing type connection, with threads excluded from shear planes.

   Bearing on web $r_v = 0.358 \times 0.75 \times 48.6 = 13.1$ kips

   Single shear $r_v = 9.72$ kips (governs). See pg. **4-4.**

   No. of bolts $= \dfrac{26}{9.72} = 2.67$

   Use: Three bolts and $8\frac{1}{2}''$ **long vertical Plate C.**

   Min. $t_C = \dfrac{26}{14.5 \times 8.5} = 0.21''$; try $\frac{1}{4} \times 4 \times 8\frac{1}{2}''$ plate.

   Bearing on plate $= \dfrac{26}{3 \times 0.25 \times 0.75}$

   $\qquad\qquad\qquad = 46.3 < 48.6$ ksi **o.k.**

   $t_f = 0.558''$ for W10 $\times$ 49; min. weld size is $\frac{1}{4}$ in.

   Minimum length of weld to avoid overstressing base metal of plate:

   $l = \dfrac{26}{0.25 \times 14.5} = 7.2 < 8.5''$ **o.k.**

   Min. $D = \dfrac{26}{2 \times 0.928 \times 8.5} = 1.65 < 4$ **o.k.**

   Use: $\frac{1}{4} \times 4 \times 8\frac{1}{2}''$ **plate with** $\frac{1}{4}$ **in. Weld C for full length each side.**

5. Investigate column web shear.

   $A_{bc} = (18.00 + \frac{1}{2} + \frac{3}{8})(10.00) = 189$ in.^{2}

   $\dfrac{32M}{A_{bc}F_y} = \dfrac{32 \times 100}{189 \times 50} = 0.339 < t_w = 0.34$

   $\therefore$ Column web need not be reinforced.

1.5.2
and
Appendix A
(1.5.2)

1.17.5

1.5.1.2
and
Commentary
1.5.1.2

AMERICAN INSTITUTE OF STEEL CONSTRUCTION

6. Stiffener E (compression flange): **1.15.5**

$$C_1 = \frac{36}{50} = 0.72$$

$$\frac{0.72 \times 3.03}{0.375 + (5 \times 1.12)} = 0.365 > t = 0.34''$$

∴ Stiffeners required.

Formula
(1.15-1)

Stiffener F (tension flange):

$$0.4 \sqrt{0.72 \times 3.03} = 0.59 > t_f = 0.558''$$

∴ Stiffeners required.

Formula
(1.15-3)

$$C_2 = \frac{50}{36} = 1.39$$

$$A_{st} = [0.72 \,(3.03) - 0.34 \,(0.375 + 5 \times 1.12)]\,1.39$$

$$= 0.21 \text{ in.}^2 \text{ or } 0.105 \text{ in.}^2 \text{ per stiffener}$$

Formula
(1.15-4)

As a practical solution stiffeners requiring such small area may be omitted. However, if stiffeners are demanded:

Assume total stiffener width $b = 6''$.

Try: 3″ wide stiffeners, with clipped corners and 2½″ bearing width.

Min. $t_s = \dfrac{3.0}{15.8} = 0.19''$;   use ¼ in.

1.9.1.2
and
Appendix A
(**1.9.1**)

Min. $D = \dfrac{¼ \times 14.5}{2 \times 0.928} = 1.95$

$\frac{3}{16}$ in. weld permissible at web of column; ¼ in. weld at column flange.

1.17.5

$$= \frac{0.21 \times 36}{0.928 \times 3 \times 1.65} = 1.64'' \text{ total} = 0.82'' \text{ per stiffener}$$

(for ¼ in. weld, min. $l = 1.23''$)

Use: **Two plates ¼ × 3 × 4½″ at both tension and compression flanges with two $\frac{3}{16}$ × 4″ welds against column web and two ¼ × 2½″ welds against column flange opposite beam tension flange.**

MOMENT CONNECTIONS
Shop welded—field bolted

Many framing systems are designed as Type 1 (rigid-frame) and the connections must be designed to develop the inherent frame moments. The following example illustrates the design of a moment connection that may be used in rigid-frame construction. For nomenclature, see "Moment Connections, Welded".

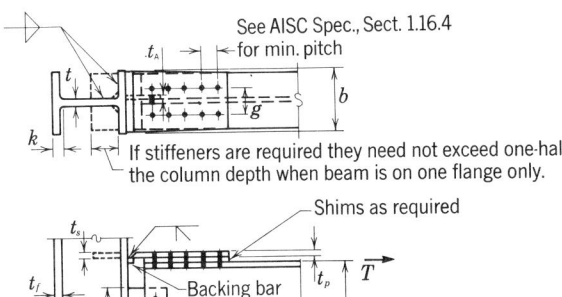

The moment is assumed to be resisted by the flange plates shop welded to the column and field fastened to the beam flanges. The shear is assumed to be transferred to the column by a vertical plate shop welded to the column and field fastened to the beam web.

AISC
Specification
Reference

1. Determine flange area reduction for fastener holes.   **1.10.1**

2. Determine horizontal force $T = \dfrac{M \times 12}{d}$

3. Design flange plates: $A_p = \dfrac{T}{F_t}$;

   $b = \dfrac{A_p}{t_p} + \text{Diam. of fastener holes deducted}$

4. Determine the number of fasteners required to develop the horizontal force in the flanges.

   No. of fasteners $= \dfrac{T}{r_v}$

AMERICAN INSTITUTE OF STEEL CONSTRUCTION

5. Determine number of fasteners in vertical plate A, size of
   weld, and size of plate.

   No. of fasteners $= \dfrac{R}{r_v};$ select l

   Min. $t_A = \dfrac{R}{F_{vp} \times l}$

   Welds to be full length of plate and on both sides.

   Min. weld $D = \dfrac{R}{2 \times 0.928 \times l}$ (E70XX electrodes)

6. Check column web shear.

   Column web reinforcement required where

   $t_w < \dfrac{32M}{A_{bc}F_y}$

   Commentary
   1.5.1.2

7. Check column for web crippling.

   1.15.5

   Column web stiffeners are required:

   At compression flange, if $t < \dfrac{C_1 A_p}{t_p + 5k}$ or $t \leqslant \dfrac{d_c\sqrt{F_y}}{180}$

   Formulas
   (1.15-1 & -2)

   At tension flange, if $t_f < 0.4\sqrt{C_1 A_p}$

   Formula
   (1.15-3)

   Determine area of stiffeners, if required:

   $A_{st} \geqslant [C_1 A_p - t(t_p + 5k)]C_2$

   Formula
   (1.15-4)

   Check width-thickness ratio.

   1.9.1.2

   For stiffener welds see Step 6 of example for "Moment
   Connections, Welded."

XAMPLE

   Given: Design a moment connection for a W18 × 55
eam framed to a W12 × 99 column. The design moment is
63 kip-ft. and the end reaction is 35 kips. All material is
STM A36 steel with $F_t = 22.0$ ksi (for beam, $F_b = 24.0$ ksi).
se ASTM A325 bolts in a bearing type connection and
70XX electrodes.

   $M = 163$ kip-ft.; $S_{req} = \dfrac{163 \times 12}{24.0} = 81.5$ in.^{3}

   Assuming $\frac{7}{8}''$ diam. A325 bolts in a bearing type connection, threads excluded from shear plane (2 rows):

   A_f (gross) $= 7.532 \times 0.630 = 4.75$ in.^{2}

   A_f (net) $= 4.75 - 2(0.875 + 0.125)(0.63) = 3.49$ in.^{2}

   1.14.5

   $\dfrac{4.75 - 3.49}{4.75}(100) = 26.5\%$

   1.10.1

   $\underline{\hphantom{xxxx} - 15.0\%}$

   $\overline{11.5\%}$ excess

$$I \text{ (net)} = 891 - \left[2 \times 0.115 \times 4.75 \left(\frac{18.12 - 0.63}{2} \right)^2 \right]$$

$$= 807.5 \text{ in.}^4$$

1.10.1

$$S \text{ (net)} = \frac{807.5}{9.06} = 89 > 81.5 \text{ in.}^3 \text{ o.k.}$$

2. $T = \dfrac{163(12)}{18.12} = 108 \text{ kips}$

3. $F_t = 22 \text{ ksi};\ A_p = 108/22 = 4.9 \text{ in.}^2 \text{ (net)}$

   Try $\frac{7}{8}''$ plate thickness: $t_p = 0.875 \text{ in.}$

   $b \text{ (gross)} = \dfrac{4.9}{0.875} + 2(0.875 + 0.125) = 7.6''$

1.14.5

   Use: $\frac{7}{8} \times 8''$ **flange plates.**

4. Flange connection:

   Bearing on beam flange $r_v = 0.63 \times 0.875 \times 48.6$
   $\qquad\qquad\qquad\qquad\qquad = 26.8 \text{ kips. See pg. 4-7.}$

   Single shear $r_v = 13.23 \text{ kips (governs). See pg. 4-6.}$

   No. of bolts $= \dfrac{108}{13.23} = 8.2$ **Use 10 bolts**

5. Web connection:
   Assume $\frac{7}{8}''$ diam. A325 bolts in a bearing type connection with threads in shear plane.
   Try $\frac{1}{4}''$ plate:
   Bearing on $\frac{1}{4}''$ plate $r_v = 10.6 \text{ kips. See pg. 4-7.}$
   Single shear $r_v = 9.02 \text{ kips (governs). See pg. 4-6.}$

   No. of bolts $= \dfrac{35}{9.02} = 3.88$ **Use 4 bolts**

   At $3''$ pitch and $1\frac{1}{2}$ in. edge distance, the plate length is 12 in.

   Min. t_A for shear $= \dfrac{35}{14.5 \times 12} = 0.20 < 0.25'' \text{ o.k.}$

   Use: $\frac{1}{4} \times 4 \times 1'\text{-}0''$ **plate for web connection.**

   Weld A connecting web plate to column flange:

   $t_f = 0.921''$ for W12 $\times$ 99; minimum weld size is $\frac{5}{16}$ in.

1.17.5

   Weld plate full length on each side.

   Min. $D = \dfrac{35}{2 \times 0.928 \times 12} = 1.57 < 5 \text{ o.k.}$

   Use: $\frac{5}{16}$ **in. weld, full length, each side.**

6. Column web shear:

$$A_{bc} = [18.12 + (2 \times 0.875)] \times 12.75 = 253 \text{ in.}^2$$

$$\frac{32M}{A_{bc}F_y} = \frac{32 \times 163}{253 \times 36} = 0.573 < t = 0.582 \text{ in.}$$

Commentary
1.5.1.2

∴ Column web need not be reinforced.

7. Column web stiffeners:

1.15.5

Req'd. $A_p(\text{net}) = 4.9 \text{ in.}^2$ (See Step 3.)

At compression flange: $t = 0.582$ in.

$$\frac{C_1 A_p}{t_p + 5k} = \frac{4.9}{0.875 + (5 \times 1.625)} = 0.544 < 0.582 \text{ in.}$$
o.k.

Formula
(1.15-1)

$$\frac{d_c \sqrt{F_y}}{180} = \frac{9.5\sqrt{36}}{180} = 0.317 < 0.582 \text{ in. } \textbf{o.k.}$$

Formula
(1.15-2)

∴ Stiffeners not required at compression flange.

At tension flange: $t_f = 0.921$ in.

$$0.4\sqrt{C_1 A_p} = 0.4\sqrt{4.9} = 0.885 < 0.921 \text{ in. } \textbf{o.k.}$$

Formula
(1.15-3)

∴ Stiffeners not required at tension flange

MOMENT CONNECTIONS
End plate

DESIGN EXAMPLE

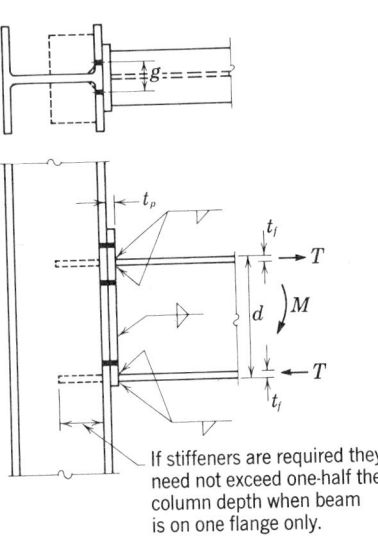

If stiffeners are required they need not exceed one-half the column depth when beam is on one flange only.

Given: A beam having an end reaction of 30 kips and a fixed-end negative moment of 120 kip-ft. framed to a W14 × 184 column. The beam-to-column connection is to be an end plate type connection using ASTM A325 bolts. F_y = 36 ksi steel is used for all members. The end plate is to be shop welded to the beam with **E70XX** electrodes. The moment has been reduced in accordance with Specification Sect. 1.5.1.4.1 for members rigidly framed to columns.

Solution: Select the beam and assume its flanges are stressed to the full allowable stress. Based on the beam and column dimensions and normal gage lines, an end plate size with bolts is then selected. Use fillet welds between the beam flanges and end plate capable of developing the necessary flange force. The beam web will be attached with fillet welds as necessary to resist the end shear and moment equivalent to the web. The fillet welds must also satisfy Sect. 1.17.5 of the AISC Specification. Alternatively, if beam ends are milled or saw-cut to bear, welds are not required between the end plate and the compression flange.

	AISC Specification or Manual Reference
A. Beam selection:	
1. Required section modulus: $S = \dfrac{120 \times 12}{24} = 60$ in.^{3}	
Use: W16 × 40 ($S = 64.6 > 60$ in.^{3})	pg. 2 - 10
Dimensions:	Properties tables (Part 1)

Dimensions:

Depth d	=	16.0"
Flange width b_f	=	7.00"
Flange t_f	=	0.503"
Web t	=	0.307"

$T = 24.0 \times 7.00 \times 0.503 = 84.5$ kips

Revised 6/73

4 - 97

AISC
Specification
or Manual
Reference

B. *Trial end plate size:*

1. Assume four 1″ diam. bolts at top flange of beam.

2. Determine size of weld required to develop top flange between flange and end plate:

$$l = 2b_f - t = (2 \times 7.00) - 0.307 = 13.69″$$

$$D = \frac{84.5}{0.928 \times 13.69} = 6.65;$$ **Use: $\frac{7}{16}$ in. fillet weld.**   Specification Table 1.5.3

3. Trial width for end plate (W):

   Column $b_f = 15.66″$; column $g = 5\frac{1}{2}″$
   Try $W = 9″$ (see sketch below).

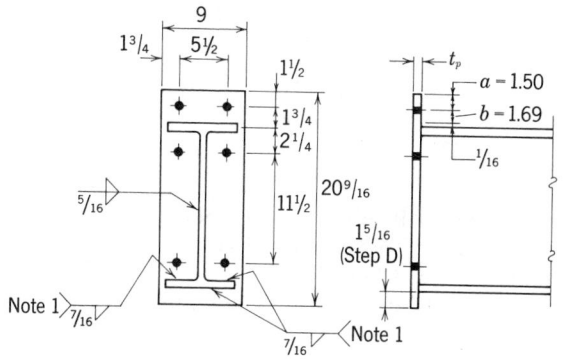

   Note 1: Typ. top and
   bottom flange.

1.16.5

4. Determine thickness of end plate, including effect of prying action:

   Determine b-distance; where b is distance from cen-   Commentary
   ter line of bolts to top flange of beam minus $\frac{1}{16}″$.   **1.5.2.1**
   (See "Hanger Type Connections", Part 4.)

   Minimum clearance for installing a 1″ diam. bolt
   = $1\frac{5}{16}″$. (See "Threaded Fasteners, Erection
   Clearances", Part 4.)

   $b = 1\frac{5}{16} + \frac{7}{16} - \frac{1}{16} = 1\frac{11}{16}″$; Use: $b = \mathbf{1.69″}$
   Trial thickness of end plate, t_p: $F_b = 27$ ksi

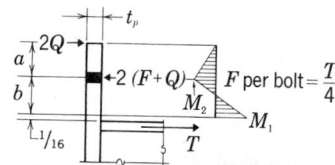

1.5.1.4.3

For trial assume $Q = 0$ and $M_2 = 0$.

Let $M_1 = 2F \times b = Tb/2 = S \times$ allowable F_b, where

$$S = \frac{t_p^2 W}{6}$$

W = width of end plate

$\therefore$ Req'd $t_p = \sqrt{\dfrac{3Tb}{WF_b}} = \sqrt{\dfrac{3(84.5)(1.69)}{9(27)}} = 1.33''$

Try $1\frac{5}{16}''$ plate.

C. *Check trial end plate:*

1. Compute prying force assuming $1''$ diam. bolts. See "Hanger Type Connections", Part 4.

$$\frac{Q}{F} = \frac{100b(d_b)^2 - 18w(t_p)^2}{70a(d_b)^2 + 21w(t_p)^2} \text{ (for A325 bolts),}$$

where

Q = Prying force per bolt, kips
F = Externally applied load per bolt, kips
d_b = Nominal diameter of bolt, in.
a = Distance from bolt line to edge of plate, but not more than $2t_p$
w = Width of plate tributary to each bolt, in.
= $W/2$ for this example

$$\frac{Q}{F} = \frac{100(1.69)(1)^2 - 18(4.5)(1.313)^2}{70(1.5)(1)^2 + 21(4.5)(1.313)^2} = 0.11$$

$F = \dfrac{84.5}{4} = 21.1$ kips; $Q = 21.1 \times 0.11 = 2.32$ kips

Total load per bolt = $21.1 + 2.3 = 23.4$ kips (tension)

Allowable load for $1''$ diam. bolt = 31.4 kips. See pg. 4-3.

2. Check bending stress in plate:

$M_2 = 2(2.32)1.5 = 6.96$ kip-in.

$M_1 = 2(21.1 + 2.32)(1.69) - 2(2.32)(1.5 + 1.69)$
   $= 64.3$ kip-in.

Section modulus of plate $= \dfrac{(9)(1.313)^2}{6} = 2.59$ in.^{3}

Max. bending stress $f_b = \dfrac{64.3}{2.59} = 24.8 < 27$ ksi **o.k.**

1.5.1.4.3

Revised 6/73.

4 - 99

AISC
Specification
or Manual
Reference

3. Check shear and tension on bolts:

Assume six 1″ diam. bolts.

$$f_v = \frac{30}{6(0.7854)} = 6.37 \text{ ksi} < F_v = 15 \text{ ksi } \textbf{o.k.}$$

If considered as a friction type connection, the inter-action equation in Sect. 1.6.3 need not be checked (see Fig. 2a and discussion of that figure in Sect. C4, *Specification for Structural Joints Using ASTM A325 or A490 Bolts.*

Assume bolts to be in a bearing type connection:
Allowable tensile stress $F_t = 50 - 1.6(6.37)$
  $= 39.8 > 23.4/0.7854 = \textbf{29.8 ksi (Step C1) o.k.}$

Use: Six 1″ diam. A325 bolts.

4. Welding:

As bottom flange is not considered in bearing, flange welds have been determined to be $\frac{7}{16}$ in. fillet welds (Step B2).

Min. size fillet weld is $\frac{5}{16}$ in. for web.

Min. length to avoid overstressing base metal of web
in shear $= \dfrac{30}{0.307 \times 14.5} = 6.73''$

Since allowable bending stress of 0.66 F_y was used for the compact beam, the web must be capable of bending to this stress throughout its entire depth.   Therefore, weld web both sides entire depth.

Required weld to develop web to $0.66F_y$:

$$D = \frac{(0.307)(0.66F_y)}{2(0.928)} = 3.9 < 5 \therefore \frac{5}{16}'' \text{ weld } \textbf{o.k.}$$

Column web stiffeners and reinforcement.

Check column web as in previous moment connection examples.   Note that by extending the end plate $1\frac{5}{16}''$ below the beam flange and assuming a stress flow through the end plate on a 1:1 slope, $(t_b + 5k + 2t_p)$ may be conservatively used in lieu of $(t_b + 5k)$ in Formula (1.15-1).   In this example stiffeners were not required opposite the beam compression flange;   due to the spacing of bolts at the tension flange, stiffeners were also not required at the tension flange.

Use: $1\frac{5}{16} \times 9 \times 1'\text{-}8\frac{9}{16}''$ end plate without column web stiffeners.

Notes

SUGGESTED DETAILS
Beam framing

etails on this and succeeding pages are suggested treatments only, and are not intended to limit the use of other similar connections not illustrated.

SKEWED AND SLOPED CONNECTIONS

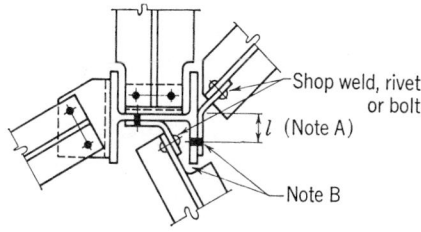

Shop weld, rivet or bolt

l (Note A)

Note B

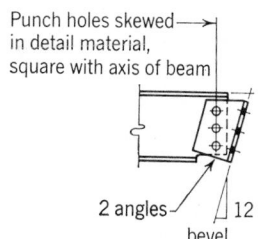

Punch holes skewed in detail material, square with axis of beam

2 angles — ⌐12 bevel

Note A: For bent plate connection, size of plate should be checked using arm l, and eccentricity in fasteners checked using tables of Eccentric Loads on Fastener Groups.

Note B: If a combination of several connections occur at one level, provide field and driving clearance.

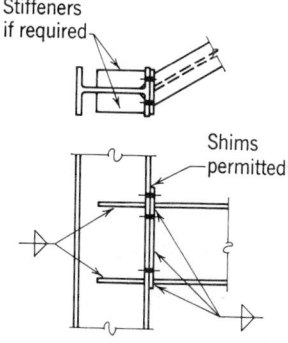

Stiffeners if required

Shims permitted

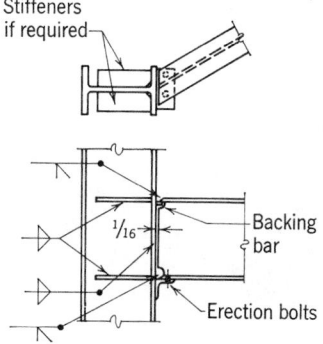

Stiffeners if required

$1/16$

Backing bar

Erection bolts

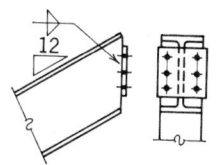

12

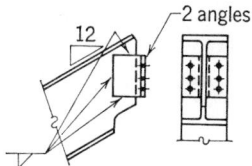

12

2 angles

SUGGESTED DETAILS
Beam framing

MOMENT CONNECTIONS

Wind bracing connections, or connections designed to resist bending moments, are usual[ly]
made with angles, structural tees or plates.

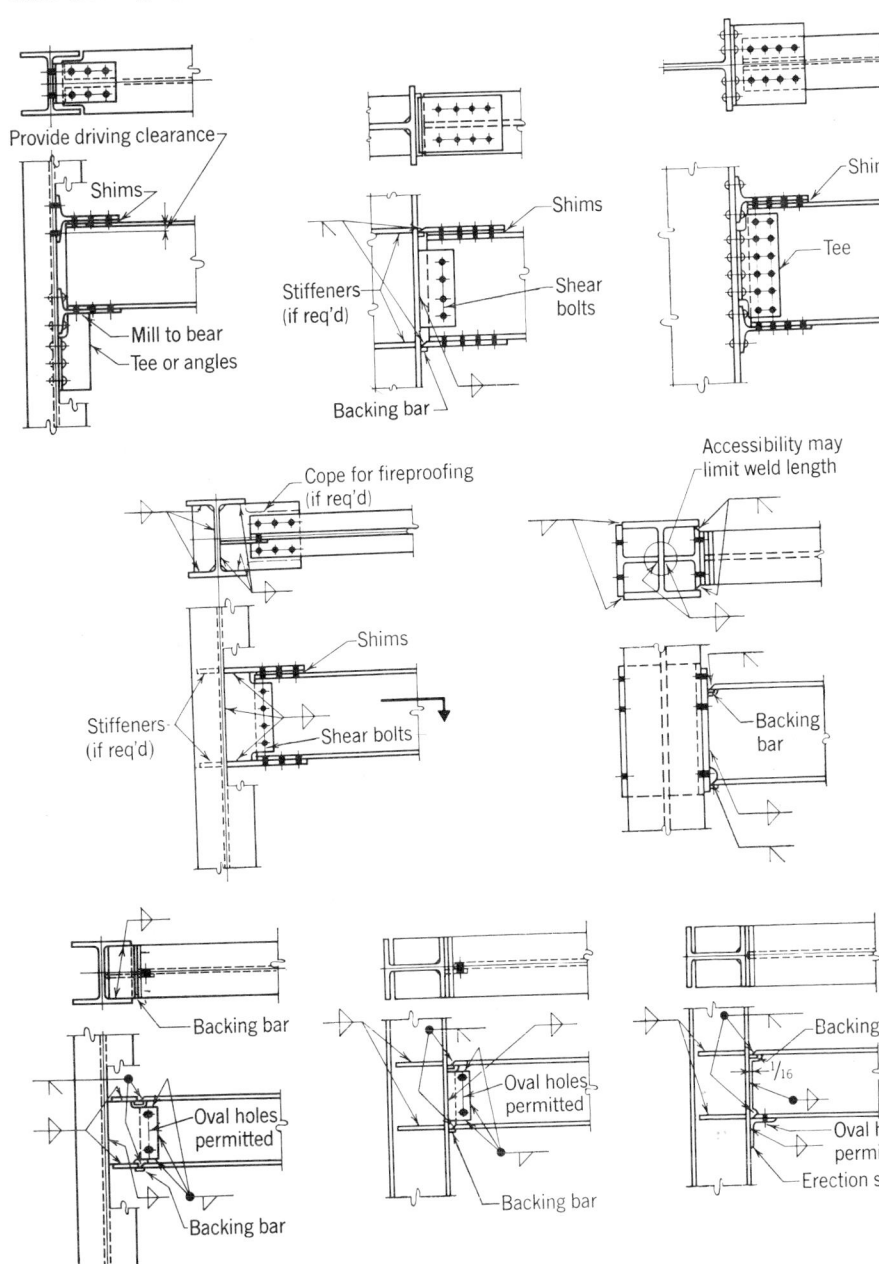

SUGGESTED DETAILS
Beam framing

SHEAR CONNECTIONS

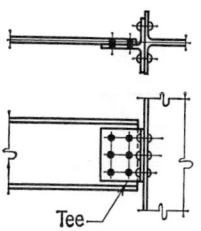

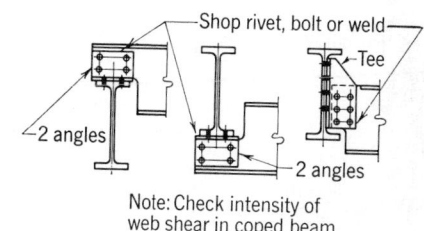

Shop rivet, bolt or weld

Tee

2 angles

2 angles

Tee

Note: Check intensity of
web shear in coped beam

SHEAR SPLICES

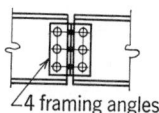

4 framing angles

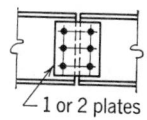

1 or 2 plates

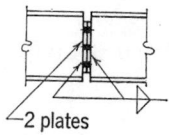

2 plates

Note: Of the above types, 4 framing angles is most flexible.

BOLTED MOMENT SPLICES

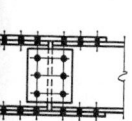

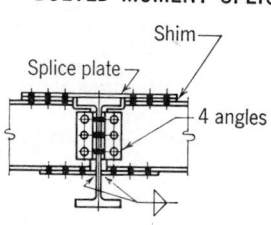

Shim

Splice plate

4 angles

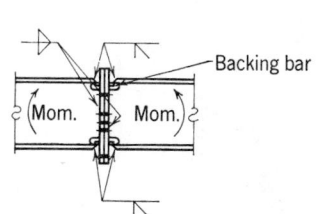

Backing bar

Mom.   Mom.

SUGGESTED DETAILS
Beam Framing

WELDED MOMENT SPLICES

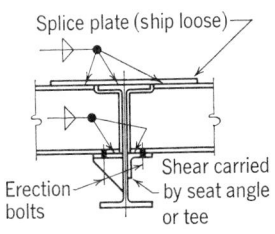

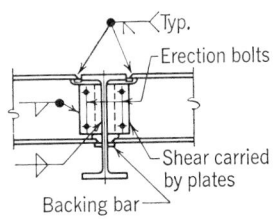

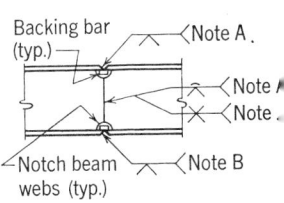

Note A: Joint preparation depends on thickness of material, and welding process.
Note B: Invert this joint preparation if beam cannot be turned over.

MOMENT SPLICE AT RIDGE
(FIELD BOLTED)

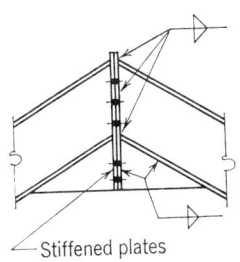

*BEAM OVER COLUMN
(WITH CONTINUITY)

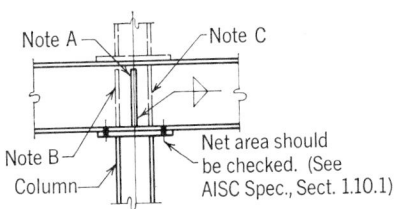

Note A: Two stiffeners, effective only if deck or slab prevents rotation of top flange.
Note B: Optional location of 2 stiffeners over supporting column flanges.
Note C: If column above, use 4 fitted stiffeners.

* For Plastic Design see Spec. Sects. 1.15.5 and 2.6.

SUGGESTED DETAILS
Column base plates

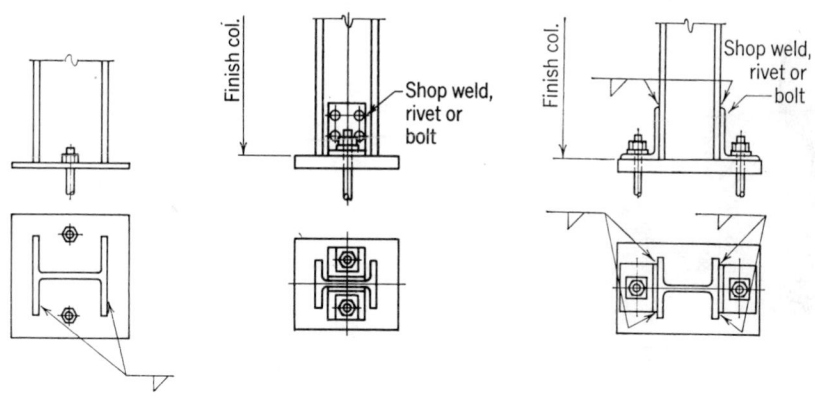

Base plate detailed and shipped separately when required.

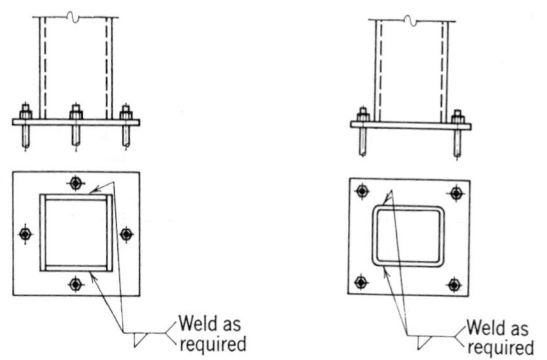

Note: Anchor bolts should be spread as far as practical for safety during erection.

AMERICAN INSTITUTE OF STEEL CONSTRUCTION

SUGGESTED DETAILS
Column base plates

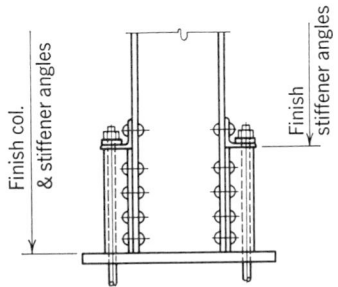

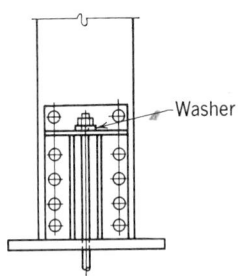

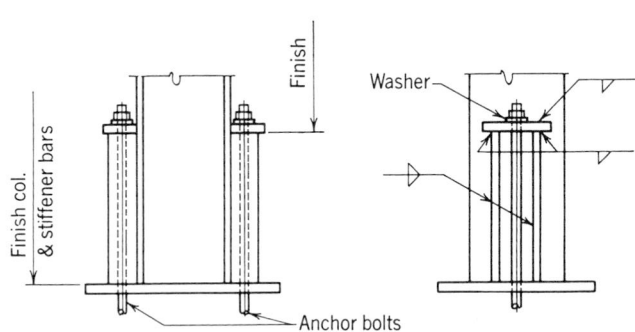

Note: Anchor bolts should be spread as far as practical for safety during erection. Base plate detailed and shipped separately when required.

AMERICAN INSTITUTE OF STEEL CONSTRUCTION

SUGGESTED DETAILS
Column splices
Riveted and bolted

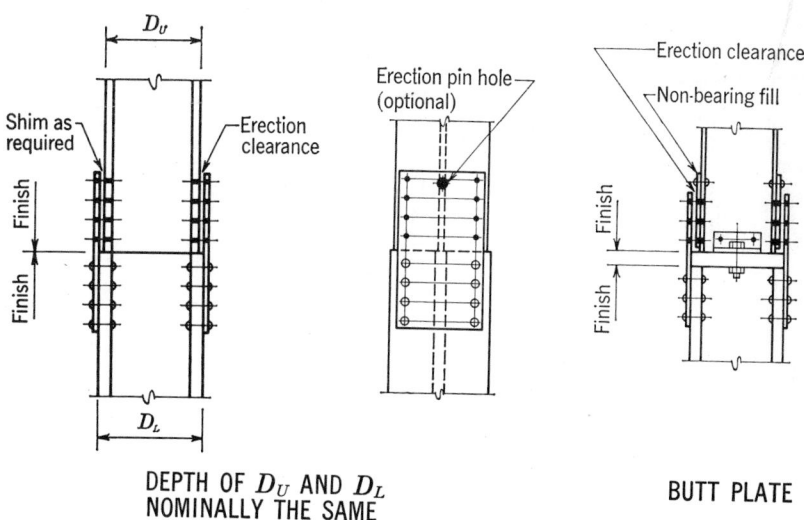

Shim as required

Finish

Finish

D_U

Erection clearance

D_L

DEPTH OF D_U AND D_L NOMINALLY THE SAME

Erection pin hole (optional)

Erection clearance

Non-bearing fill

Finish

Finish

BUTT PLATE

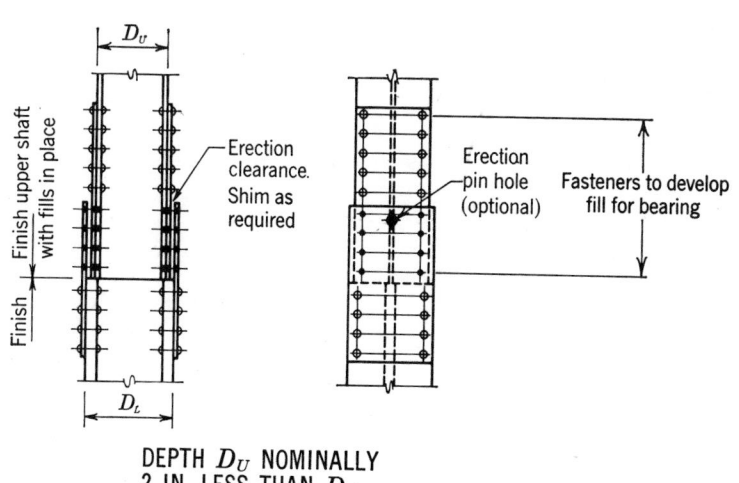

D_U

Finish upper shaft with fills in place

Finish

Erection clearance. Shim as required

D_L

Erection pin hole (optional)

Fasteners to develop fill for bearing

DEPTH D_U NOMINALLY 2 IN. LESS THAN D_L

Note: Erection clearance = ⅛ in.

AMERICAN INSTITUTE OF STEEL CONSTRUCTION

SUGGESTED DETAILS
Column splices
Welded

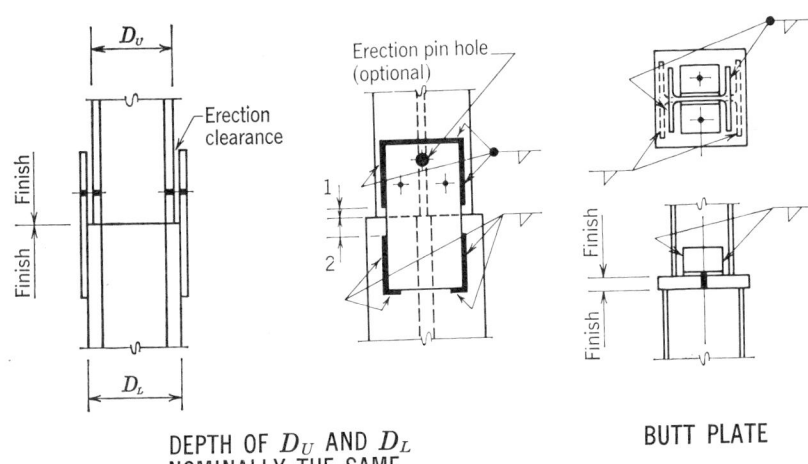

**DEPTH OF D_U AND D_L
NOMINALLY THE SAME**

BUTT PLATE

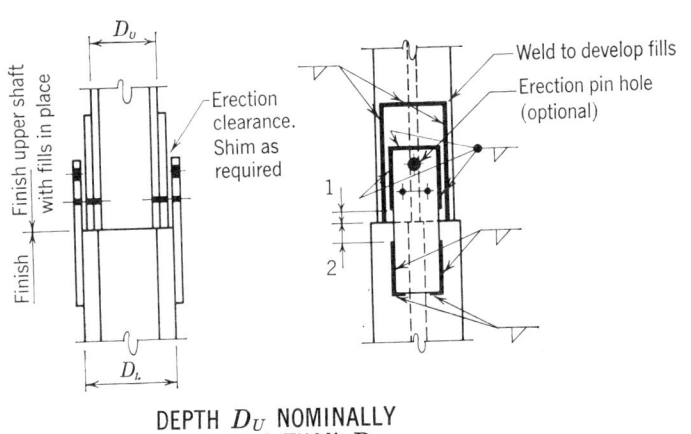

**DEPTH D_U NOMINALLY
2 IN. LESS THAN D_L**

Note 1: Erection clearance = $\frac{1}{16}$ in.
Note 2: When D_U and D_L are nominally the same and thin fills are required, shop may atta
splice plate to upper section and provide field clearance over lower section.

AMERICAN INSTITUTE OF STEEL CONSTRUCTION

SUGGESTED DETAILS
Column splices

Welded

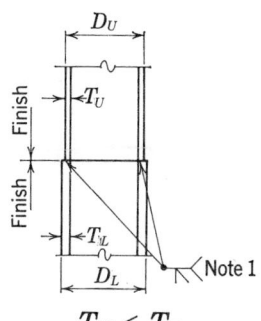

$T_U \leq T_L$

DEPTH OF D_U AND D_L
NOMINALLY THE SAME

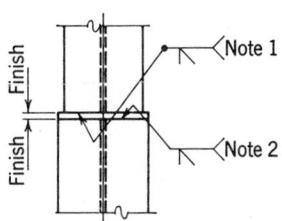

BUTT PLATE

DEPTH D_U NOMINALLY
2 IN. LESS THAN D_L

Box columns

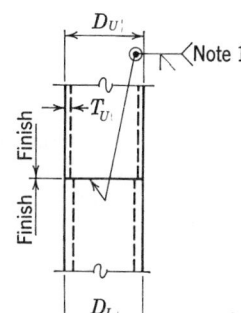

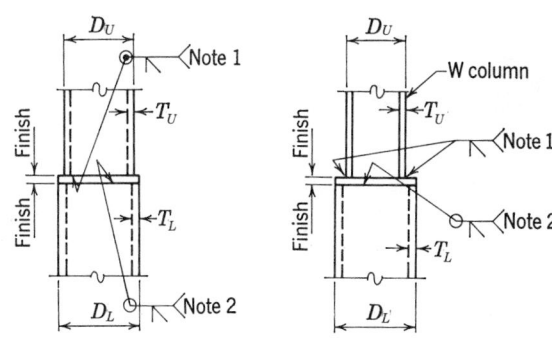

DEPTH OF D_U AND D_L
NOMINALLY THE SAME

BUTT PLATE

DEPTH D_U NOMINALLY
2 IN. LESS THAN D_L

Note 1: Weld size based on T_U.
Note 2: Weld size based on T_L.

AMERICAN INSTITUTE OF STEEL CONSTRUCTION

SUGGESTED DETAILS
Miscellaneous
STRUCTURAL TUBING AND PIPE
BEAM-TO-COLUMN CONNECTIONS

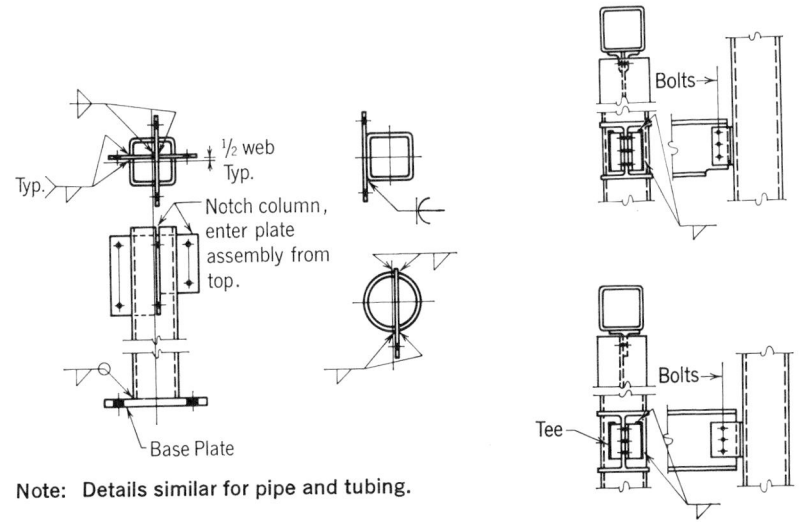

Note: Details similar for pipe and tubing.

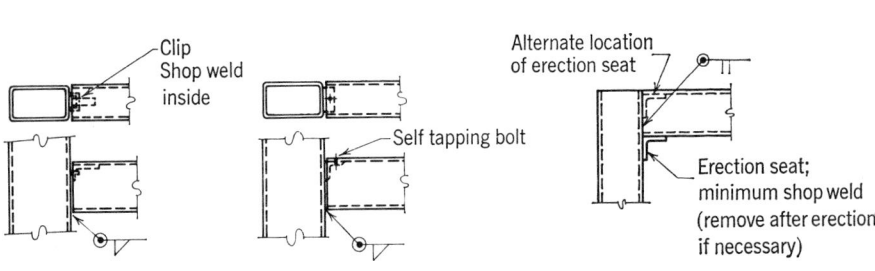

PURLIN CONNECTIONS

GIRT CONNECTIONS

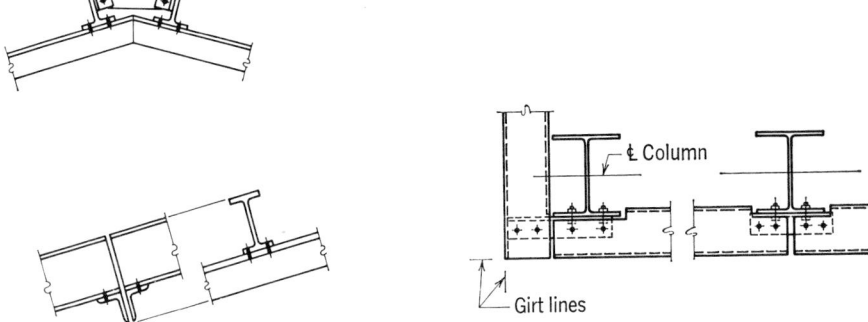

AMERICAN INSTITUTE OF STEEL CONSTRUCTION

SUGGESTED DETAILS
Miscellaneous

SHELF ANGLES WITH ADJUSTMENT

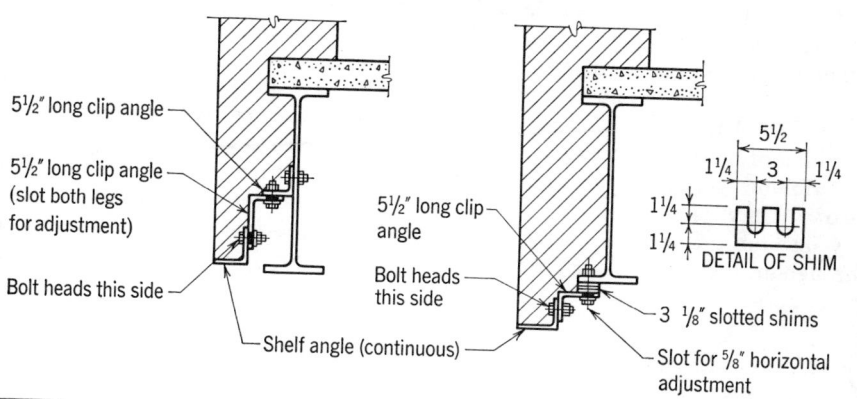

5½" long clip angle

5½" long clip angle (slot both legs for adjustment)

Bolt heads this side

5½" long clip angle

Bolt heads this side

Shelf angle (continuous)

3 ⅛" slotted shims

Slot for ⅝" horizontal adjustment

DETAIL OF SHIM

Note: Horizontal adjustment is made by slotted holes; vertical adjustment may be made by slotted holes or by shims.
For tolerance allowance in alignment, see AISC Code of Standard Practice.

TIE RODS AND ANCHORS

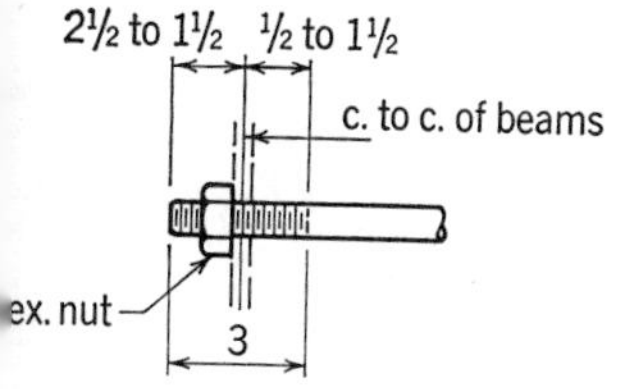

2½ to 1½   ½ to 1½

c. to c. of beams

Hex. nut

3

Length of rod o. to o. should be specified in multiples of 3 in.

Tie Rods

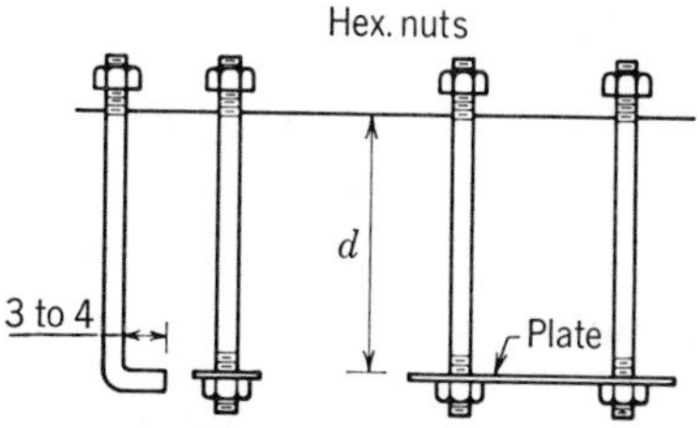

Hex. nuts

d

3 to 4

Plate

Note: Dimension d should be based on design req't for uplift

Anchor Bolts

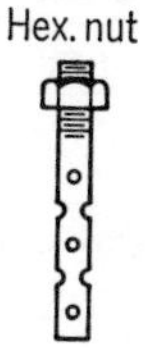

Hex. nut

Swedge Bolts

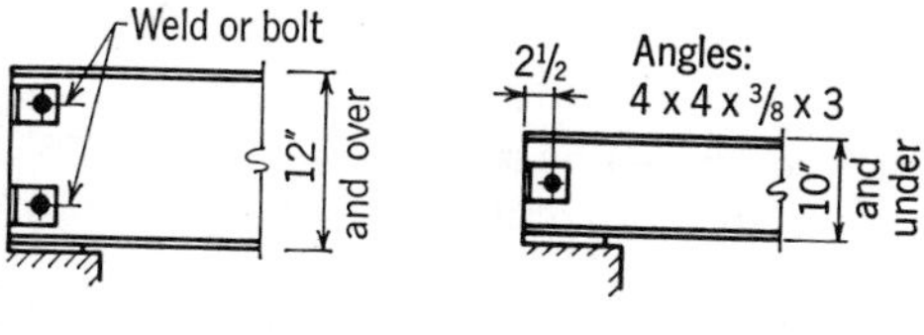

Weld or bolt

12" and over

Angle Wall Anchors

2½   Angles: 4 x 4 x ⅜ x 3

10" and under

2

3⅜

7   1'–6

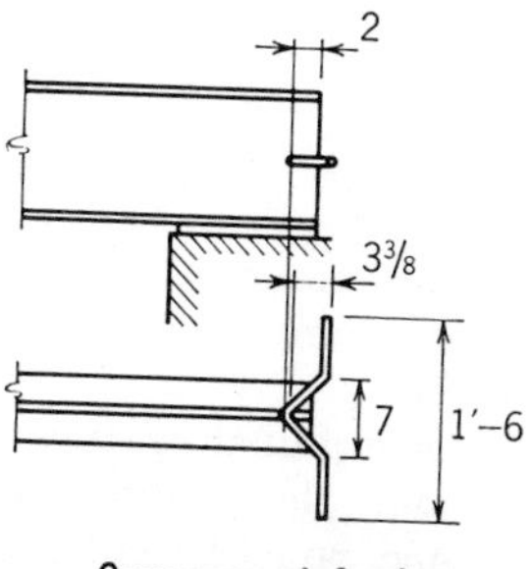

Government Anchor

DETAILING PRACTICE
Bolted and riveted connections

Maximum efficiency in the fabrication of structural steel by modern shops is entirely dependent upon close cooperation between designing office, drafting room and shop. Designs should be favorable to, the drafting room should recognize and call for, and the shop should adapt its equipment to, the use of recurrent details which have been standardized.

Consideration should be given to duplication of details and multiple punching or drilling. Utilization of standard jigs and machine set-ups eliminates unnecessary handling of material and aids drilling or punching holes in groups.

Column gage lines should conform to the standard machine set-ups illustrated below. Once determined they should be duplicated as far as possible throughout any one job. Gages on an individual member if possible should not be varied throughout the length of that member.

DRILL GAGES

Keep gages and longitudinal spacing alike, if possible, as drilling can be done simultaneously in both flanges.

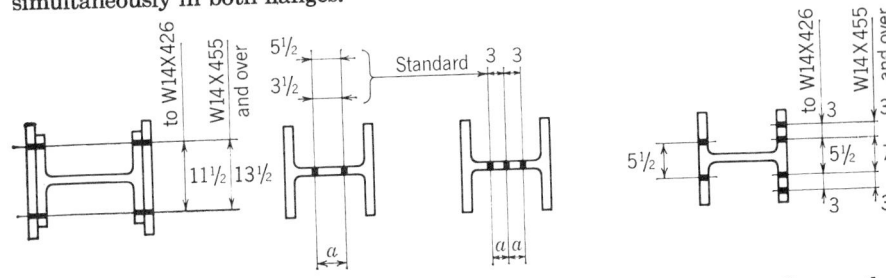

Minimum a = 3 in.; maximum a controlled by size of member. Gages other than standard should be multiples of 3 in.

PUNCH GAGES

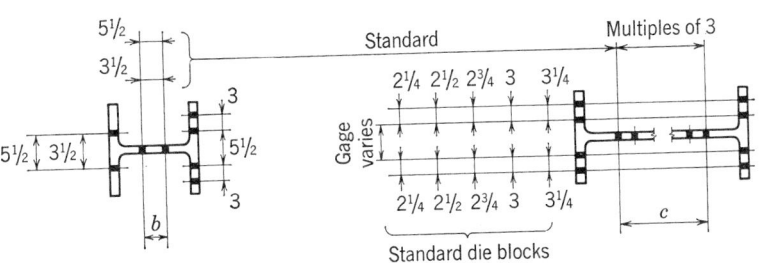

Minimum b = $2\frac{1}{4}$ in.; maximum b controlled by size of member. Gages other than standard should be multiples of 3 in. Maximum c controlled by size member.

Longitudinal spacing of holes for both punched and drilled work should be in. or multiples of 3 in. The adoption of such spacing facilitates the use of multiple drills and punches and makes possible the use of the Framed Beam Connection given on pages 4 - 17 to 4 - 26.

AMERICAN INSTITUTE OF STEEL CONSTRUCTION

In general the principles governing the selection of gages and longitudinal spacing of holes in beam webs and flanges are identical with those for columns. Sketches and notes for "Punch Gages" apply to all sections. Minimum gages are tabulated under "Dimensions for Detailing" in Part 1. See page 4 - 115 for information and dimensions pertaining to clearance requirements.

Beams are connected to columns or other beams by framed, heavy framed or seated connections. The need of providing for wind or bending requires a specially designed moment connection. Typical examples of seated and wind bracing connections are illustrated on page 4 - 102.

Heavy Framed Beam Connections, page 4 - 22, should be used only when the capacities of Framed Beam Connections are exceeded. Stiffened beam seats, page 4 - 47, should be used only when the capacities of unstiffened beam seats are exceeded.

Copes, blocks and cuts

C

| Note 1 | "Cut not chip" |
| Note 2 | "Cut and chip" |

Note 1: Preferred
Note 2: Use if surface C must be flush with web

All re-entrant corners shall be shaped, notch free, to a radius of at least ½ in.

These sketches indicate standard methods of providing clearance for beams connecting to beams or columns. Where possible, a minimum clearance of ½ in. to be provided. Fabricators may vary in designation and dimensions of copes and blocks. Some fabricators designate all of the operations pictured above by the term "cuts."

For economy, coping or blocking of beams should be avoided if possible. When construction will permit, the elevation of the top of filler beams should be established a sufficient distance below the top of girders to clear the girder fillet. Unusually long or deep copes and blocks, or blocks in beams with thin webs, may materially affect the capacity of the beam. Such beams must be investigated for both shear and moment at lines A and B and, when necessary, adequate reinforcement provided.

RIVETS AND THREADED FASTENERS

Erection clearances

BOLT IMPACT WRENCHES

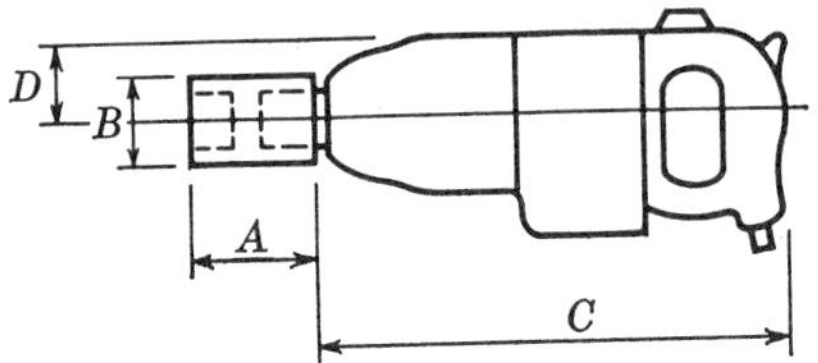

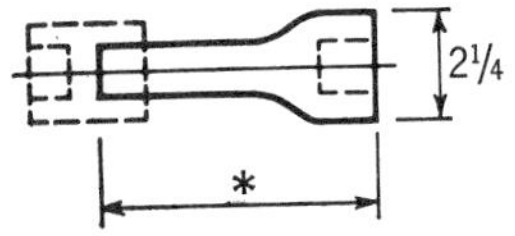

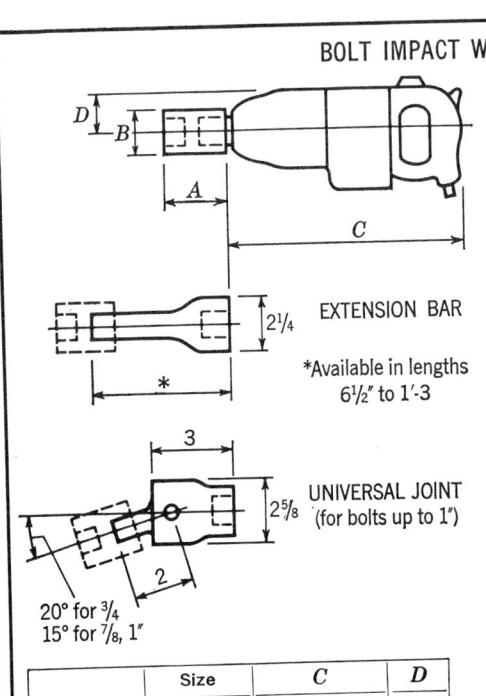

EXTENSION BAR

*Available in lengths 6½″ to 1′-3

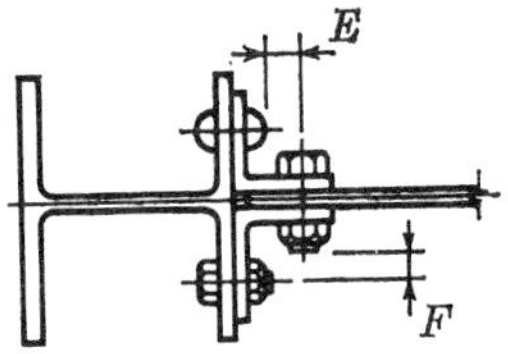

MINIMUM CLEARANCES

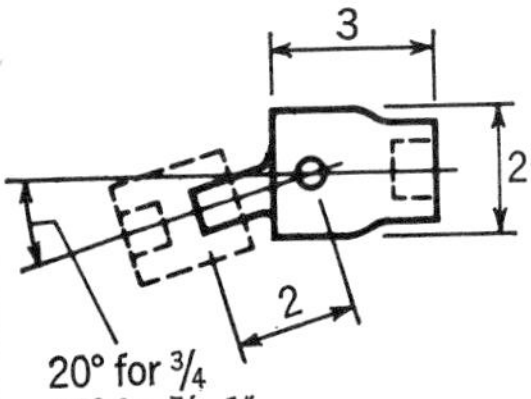

UNIVERSAL JOINT (for bolts up to 1″)

20° for ¾
15° for ⅞, 1″

	Size	C	D
Light Wrenches	⅝ to 1	1-1¼ to 1-2	2⅛
Heavy Wrenches	1 to 1½	1-2¾ to 1-5¼	2½

Sockets			Min. Clear.	
Bolt Size	A	B	E	F
⅝	2⅝	1¾		
¾	3	2¼	1⅛	1¼
⅞	3¼	2½	1¼	1⅜
1	3½	2⅝	1 5/16	1 7/16
1⅛	3¾	2⅞	1 7/16	1 9/16
1¼	4	3⅛	1 9/16	1 11/16
1⅜	4¼	3¼	1⅝	1¾
1½	4⅜	4¼	2⅛	2¼

RIVET GUNS

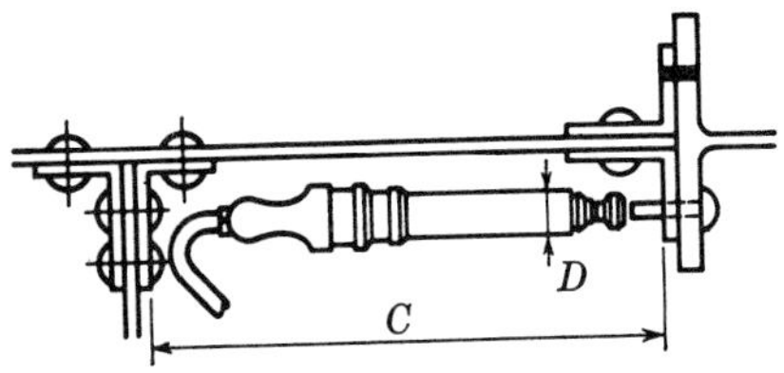

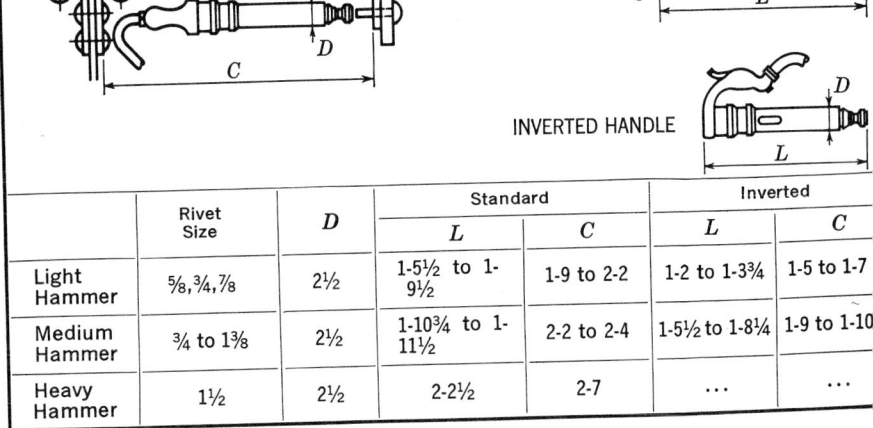

STANDARD OPEN HANDLE

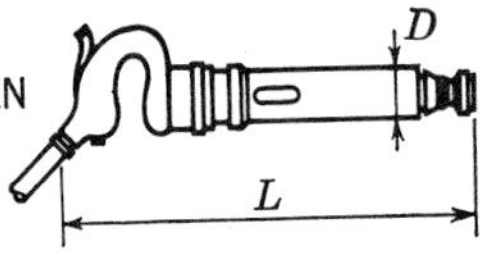

INVERTED HANDLE

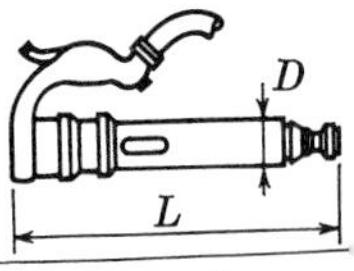

	Rivet Size	D	Standard		Inverted	
			L	C	L	C
Light Hammer	⅝, ¾, ⅞	2½	1-5½ to 1-9½	1-9 to 2-2	1-2 to 1-3¾	1-5 to 1-7
Medium Hammer	¾ to 1⅜	2½	1-10¾ to 1-11½	2-2 to 2-4	1-5½ to 1-8¼	1-9 to 1-10
Heavy Hammer	1½	2½	2-2½	2-7	. . .	. . .

RIVETS AND THREADED FASTENERS

Field erection clearances

RIVET CLEARANCE—W COLUMNS

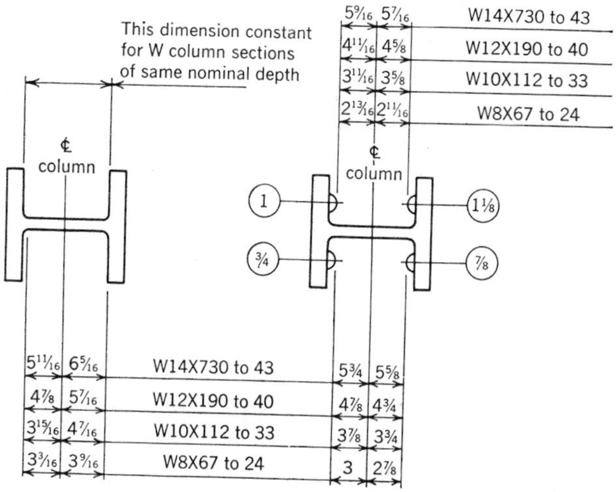

This dimension constant for W column sections of same nominal depth
¢ column
5⁹⁄₁₆ 5⁷⁄₁₆ W14X730 to 43
4¹¹⁄₁₆ 4⅝ W12X190 to 40
3¹¹⁄₁₆ 3⅝ W10X112 to 33
2¹³⁄₁₆ 2¹¹⁄₁₆ W8X67 to 24
1
1⅛
¾
⅞
5¹¹⁄₁₆ 6⁵⁄₁₆ W14X730 to 43 5¾ 5⅝
4⅞ 5⁷⁄₁₆ W12X190 to 40 4⅞ 4¾
3¹⁵⁄₁₆ 4⁷⁄₁₆ W10X112 to 33 3⅞ 3¾
3³⁄₁₆ 3⁹⁄₁₆ W8X67 to 24 3 2⅞

Based on Dimensions of Structural Rivets, page **4 - 116**.

BOLT CLEARANCE—W COLUMNS

Values shown above for clearances over rivet heads are conservative when applied to bolts. See "Specification for Structural Joints using ASTM A325 or A490 Bolts" to compute overall lengths for various grips.

FLANGE CUTS FOR COLUMN WEB CONNECTIONS

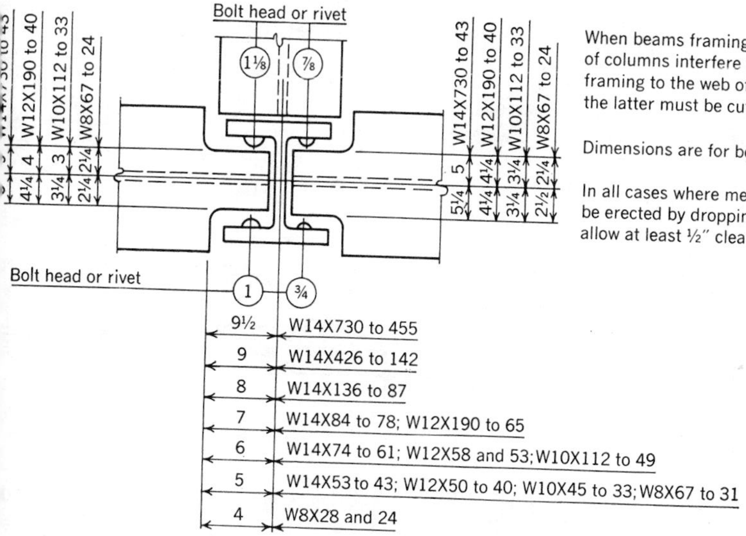

Bolt head or rivet
1⅛
⅞
W12X190 to 40
W10X112 to 33
W8X67 to 24
4 3 2¼
4¼ 3¼ 2¼
W14X730 to 43
W12X190 to 40
W10X112 to 33
W8X67 to 24
5 4¼ 3¼ 2¼
5¼ 4¼ 3¼ 2½
Bolt head or rivet
1
¾
9½ W14X730 to 455
9 W14X426 to 142
8 W14X136 to 87
7 W14X84 to 78; W12X190 to 65
6 W14X74 to 61; W12X58 and 53; W10X112 to 49
5 W14X53 to 43; W12X50 to 40; W10X45 to 33; W8X67 to 31
4 W8X28 and 24

When beams framing to the flanges of columns interfere with beams framing to the web of the column, the latter must be cut as shown.

Dimensions are for bolts and rivets.

In all cases where members must be erected by dropping down, allow at least ½″ clearance.

Based on Dimensions of Structural Rivets, page **4 - 116**, and Bolts, pages **4 - 120**, **4 - 121**.

RIVETS AND THREADED FASTENERS

DIMENSIONS OF STRUCTURAL RIVETS (HIGH BUTTON OR ACORN HEADS)

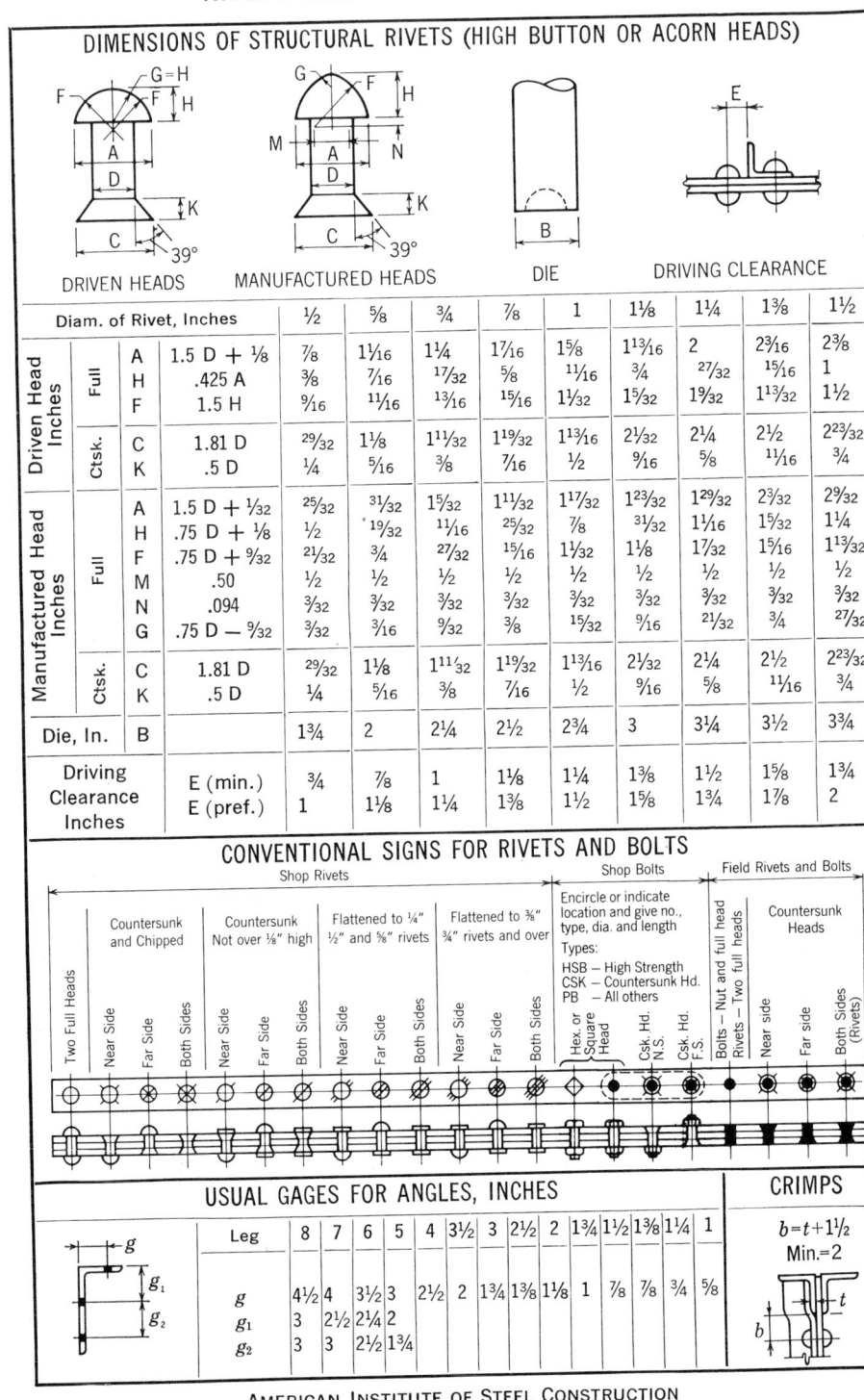

DRIVEN HEADS · MANUFACTURED HEADS · DIE · DRIVING CLEARANCE

			Diam. of Rivet, Inches	½	⅝	¾	⅞	1	1⅛	1¼	1⅜	1½
Driven Head Inches	Full	A	1.5 D + ⅛	⅞	1 1/16	1¼	1 7/16	1⅝	1 13/16	2	2 3/16	2⅜
		H	.425 A	⅜	7/16	17/32	⅝	11/16	¾	27/32	15/16	1
		F	1.5 H	9/16	11/16	13/16	15/16	1 1/32	1 5/32	1 9/32	1 13/32	1½
	Ctsk.	C	1.81 D	29/32	1⅛	1 11/32	1 19/32	1 13/16	2 1/32	2¼	2½	2 23/32
		K	.5 D	¼	5/16	⅜	7/16	½	9/16	⅝	11/16	¾
Manufactured Head Inches	Full	A	1.5 D + 1/32	25/32	31/32	1 5/32	1 11/32	1 17/32	1 23/32	1 29/32	2 3/32	2 9/32
		H	.75 D + ⅛	½	19/32	11/16	25/32	⅞	31/32	1 1/16	1 5/32	1¼
		F	.75 D + 9/32	21/32	¾	27/32	15/16	1 1/32	1⅛	1 7/32	1 5/16	1 13/32
		M	.50	½	½	½	½	½	½	½	½	½
		N	.094	3/32	3/32	3/32	3/32	3/32	3/32	3/32	3/32	3/32
		G	.75 D − 9/32	3/32	3/16	9/32	⅜	15/32	9/16	21/32	¾	27/32
	Ctsk.	C	1.81 D	29/32	1⅛	1 11/32	1 19/32	1 13/16	2 1/32	2¼	2½	2 23/32
		K	.5 D	¼	5/16	⅜	7/16	½	9/16	⅝	11/16	¾
Die, In.		B		1¾	2	2¼	2½	2¾	3	3¼	3½	3¾
Driving Clearance Inches		E (min.)		¾	⅞	1	1⅛	1¼	1⅜	1½	1⅝	1¾
		E (pref.)		1	1⅛	1¼	1⅜	1½	1⅝	1¾	1⅞	2

CONVENTIONAL SIGNS FOR RIVETS AND BOLTS

Shop Rivets · Shop Bolts · Field Rivets and Bolts

Countersunk and Chipped · Countersunk Not over ⅛" high · Flattened to ¼" ½" and ⅝" rivets · Flattened to ⅜" ¾" rivets and over

Encircle or indicate location and give no., type, dia. and length
Types:
HSB – High Strength
CSK – Countersunk Hd.
PB – All others

Countersunk Heads

Two Full Heads · Near Side · Far Side · Both Sides · Near Side · Far Side · Both Sides · Near Side · Far Side · Both Sides · Near Side · Far Side · Both Sides · Hex. or Square Head · Csk. Hd. N.S. · Csk. Hd. F.S. · Bolts – Nut and full head · Rivets – Two full heads · Near side · Far side · Both Sides (Rivets)

USUAL GAGES FOR ANGLES, INCHES

Leg	8	7	6	5	4	3½	3	2½	2	1¾	1½	1⅜	1¼	1
g	4½	4	3½	3	2½	2	1¾	1⅜	1⅛	1	⅞	⅞	¾	⅝
g₁	3	2½	2¼	2										
g₂	3	3	2½	1¾										

CRIMPS

$b = t + 1½$
Min. = 2

AMERICAN INSTITUTE OF STEEL CONSTRUCTION

RIVETS
Lengths of undriven rivets
In inches, for various grips

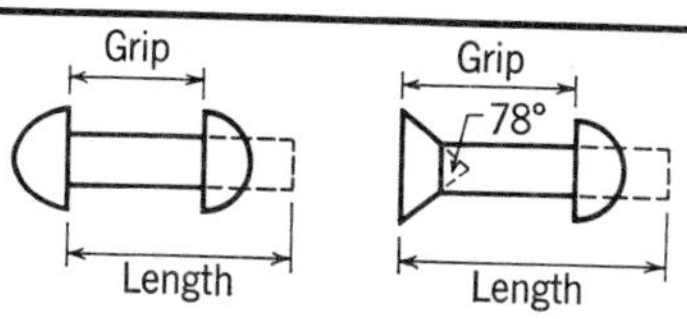

FULL HEAD   COUNTERSUNK HEAD

FULL HEAD

Grip Inches	Diameter of Rivet, Inches						
	½	⅝	¾	⅞	1	1⅛	1¼
½	1⅝	1⅞	1⅞	2	2⅛		
⅝	1¾	2	2	2⅛	2¼		
¾	1⅞	2⅛	2⅛	2¼	2⅜		
⅞	2	2¼	2¼	2⅜	2½		
1	2¼	2⅜	2⅜	2½	2⅝	2¾	2⅞
⅛	2⅜	2½	2½	2⅝	2¾	2⅞	3
¼	2½	2⅝	2⅝	2¾	2⅞	3	3⅛
⅜	2⅝	2¾	2¾	2⅞	3	3⅛	3¼
½	2⅞	3	3	3⅛	3¼	3⅜	3½
⅝	3	3⅛	3⅛	3¼	3⅜	3½	3⅝
¾	3⅛	3¼	3¼	3½	3⅝	3¾	3¾
⅞	3¼	3⅜	3⅜	3⅝	3¾	3⅞	3⅞
2	3½	3½	3⅝	3¾	3⅞	4	4
⅛	3⅝	3⅝	3¾	3⅞	4	4⅛	4⅛
¼	3¾	3⅞	3⅞	4	4⅛	4¼	4¼
⅜	4	4	4	4⅛	4¼	4⅜	4⅜
½	4⅛	4⅛	4⅛	4¼	4⅜	4½	4½
⅝	4¼	4¼	4¼	4⅜	4½	4⅝	4⅝
¾	4⅜	4⅜	4⅜	4½	4⅝	4¾	4¾
⅞	4⅝	4⅝	4⅝	4⅝	4¾	4⅞	5
3	...	4¾	4¾	4⅞	5	5	5⅛
⅛	...	4⅞	4⅞	5	5⅛	5¼	5¼
¼	...	5	5	5⅛	5¼	5⅜	5⅜
⅜	...	5⅛	5⅛	5¼	5⅜	5½	5½
½	...	5⅜	5⅜	5⅜	5½	5⅝	5⅝
⅝	...	5½	5½	5½	5⅝	5¾	5¾
¾	...	5⅝	5⅝	5⅝	5¾	5⅞	5⅞
⅞	...	5¾	5¾	5¾	5⅞	6	6
4	...	...	5⅞	6	6	6⅛	6¼
⅛	...	...	6	6⅛	6⅛	6⅜	6⅜
¼	...	...	6⅛	6¼	6½	6½	6½
⅜	...	...	6⅜	6½	6½	6⅝	6⅝
½	...	...	6½	6⅝	6⅝	6¾	6¾
⅝	...	...	6⅝	6¾	6¾	6¾	6⅞
¾	...	...	6¾	6⅞	6⅞	7	7
⅞	...	...	6⅞	7	7	7⅛	7⅛
5	...	...	...	7⅛	7⅛	7¼	7¼
⅛	...	...	...	7¼	7¼	7⅜	7⅜
¼	...	...	...	7⅜	7⅜	7½	7½
⅜	...	...	...	7⅝	7⅝	7¾	7⅝
½	...	...	...	7¾	7¾	7⅞	7⅞
⅝	...	...	...	7⅞	7⅞	8	8
¾	...	...	...	8	8	8⅛	8⅛
⅞	...	...	...	8⅛	8⅛	8¼	8¼

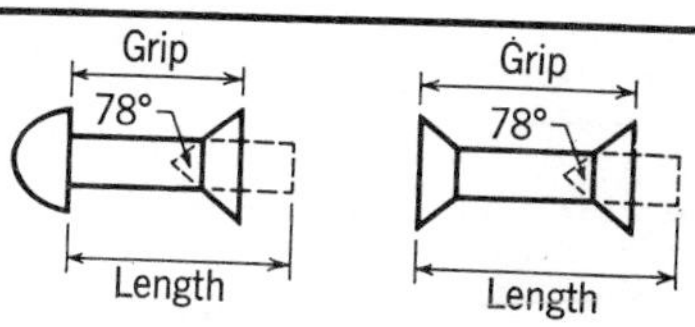

COUNTERSUNK HEAD

Grip Inches	Diameter of Rivet, Inches						
	½	⅝	¾	⅞	1	1⅛	1¼
½	1	1	1⅛	1¼	1¼		
⅝	1⅛	1¼	1¼	1⅜	1⅜		
¾	1⅜	1⅜	1⅜	1½	1½		
⅞	1½	1½	1½	1⅝	1⅝		
1	1⅝	1⅝	1⅝	1¾	1¾	1⅞	1⅞
⅛	1¾	1¾	1⅞	1⅞	1⅞	2	2
¼	2	2	2	2	2	2⅛	2⅛
⅜	2⅛	2⅛	2⅛	2¼	2¼	2⅜	2⅜
½	2¼	2¼	2¼	2⅜	2⅜	2½	2½
⅝	2⅜	2⅜	2⅜	2½	2½	2⅝	2⅝
¾	2⅝	2⅝	2⅝	2⅝	2⅝	2¾	2¾
⅞	2¾	2¾	2¾	2¾	2¾	2⅞	2⅞
2	2⅞	2⅞	2⅞	2⅞	2⅞	3	3
⅛	3⅛	3	3	3	3	3⅛	3⅛
¼	3¼	3⅛	3⅛	3⅛	3¼	3¼	3¼
⅜	3⅜	3⅜	3⅜	3⅜	3⅜	3⅜	3⅜
½	3½	3½	3½	3½	3½	3⅝	3⅝
⅝	3¾	3⅝	3⅝	3⅝	3⅝	3¾	3¾
¾	3⅞	3¾	3¾	3¾	3¾	3⅞	3⅞
⅞	4	3⅞	3⅞	3⅞	3⅞	4	4
3	...	4⅛	4⅛	4⅛	4⅛	4⅛	4⅛
⅛	...	4¼	4¼	4¼	4¼	4¼	4¼
¼	...	4⅜	4⅜	4⅜	4⅜	4⅜	4⅜
⅜	...	4½	4½	4½	4½	4½	4½
½	...	4⅝	4⅝	4⅝	4⅝	4⅝	4⅝
⅝	...	4¾	4¾	4¾	4¾	4⅞	4⅞
¾	...	5	5	5	5	5	5
⅞	...	5⅛	5⅛	5⅛	5⅛	5⅛	5⅛
4	...	...	5¼	5¼	5¼	5¼	5¼
⅛	...	...	5⅜	5⅜	5⅜	5⅜	5⅜
¼	...	...	5½	5½	5½	5½	5½
⅜	...	...	5⅝	5⅝	5⅝	5⅝	5⅝
½	...	...	5¾	5¾	5¾	5¾	5¾
⅝	...	...	6	6	6	6	6
¾	...	...	6⅛	6⅛	6⅛	6⅛	6⅛
⅞	...	...	6¼	6¼	6¼	6¼	6¼
5	...	...	...	6⅜	6⅜	6⅜	6⅜
⅛	...	...	...	6½	6½	6½	6½
¼	...	...	...	6⅝	6⅝	6⅝	6⅝
⅜	...	...	...	6¾	6¾	6¾	6¾
½	...	...	...	6⅞	6⅞	6⅞	6⅞
⅝	...	...	...	7	7	7	7
¾	...	...	...	7¼	7¼	7¼	7¼
⅞	...	...	...	7⅜	7⅜	7⅜	7⅜

Above table may vary from standard practice of individual fabricators and should be checked against such standards by user.

AMERICAN INSTITUTE OF STEEL CONSTRUCTION

RIVETS
Weights

WEIGHT WITH ONE HIGH BUTTON (ACORN) MANUFACTURED HEAD IN POUNDS PER 100

Length Inches	Diameter of Rivet, Inches						
	½	⅝	¾	⅞	1	1⅛	1¼
1¼	11						
⅜	12						
½	12	20	31	45	60	81	104
⅝	13	21	32	47	63	85	108
¾	14	22	33	49	66	88	113
⅞	14	23	35	51	69	92	117
2	15	24	37	53	72	95	122
⅛	16	25	39	55	74	99	126
¼	17	26	40	57	77	102	130
⅜	17	27	42	59	80	106	135
½	18	28	43	62	83	109	139
⅝	19	29	45	64	85	113	143
¾	19	31	46	66	88	116	148
⅞	20	32	48	68	91	120	152
3	21	33	50	70	94	123	156
⅛	21	34	51	72	97	127	161
¼	22	35	53	74	99	131	165
⅜	23	36	54	76	102	134	169
½	23	37	56	79	105	138	174
⅝	24	38	57	81	108	141	178
¾	25	39	59	83	110	145	182
⅞	26	40	60	85	113	148	187
4	26	41	62	87	116	152	191
⅛	27	42	64	89	119	155	195
¼	28	44	65	91	122	159	200
⅜	28	45	67	93	124	162	204
½	29	46	68	96	127	166	208
⅝	30	47	70	98	130	169	213
¾	30	48	71	100	133	173	217
⅞	31	49	73	102	135	176	221

Length Inches	Diameter of Rivet, Inches						
	½	⅝	¾	⅞	1	1⅛	1¼
5	...	50	74	104	138	180	226
⅛	...	51	76	106	141	183	230
¼	...	52	78	108	144	187	234
⅜	...	53	79	110	147	190	239
½	...	54	81	113	149	194	243
⅝	...	55	82	115	152	197	247
¾	...	57	84	117	155	201	252
⅞	...	58	85	119	158	204	256
6	...	...	87	121	161	208	261
⅛	...	...	89	123	163	212	265
¼	...	...	90	125	166	215	269
⅜	...	...	92	127	169	219	274
½	...	...	93	130	172	222	278
⅝	...	...	95	132	174	226	282
¾	...	...	96	134	177	229	287
⅞	...	...	98	136	180	233	291
7	...	...	100	138	183	236	295
⅛	...	...	101	140	186	240	30…
¼	...	...	103	142	188	243	30…
⅜	...	...	104	144	191	247	30…
½	...	...	106	147	194	250	31…
⅝	...	...	107	149	197	254	31…
¾	...	...	109	151	199	257	32…
⅞	...	...	110	153	202	261	32…
8	...	...	...	155	205	264	33…
⅛	...	...	...	157	208	268	33…
¼	...	...	...	159	211	271	33…
⅜	...	...	...	161	213	275	34…
½	...	...	...	164	216	278	34…
⅝	...	...	...	166	219	282	35…
¾	...	...	...	168	222	285	35…
⅞	...	...	...	170	224	289	36…

WEIGHT WITH ONE COUNTERSUNK HEAD IN POUNDS PER 100

For Countersunk Rivets, use weight given above with following deductions.	Diameter of Rivet, Inches						
	½	⅝	¾	⅞	1	1⅛	1¼
Deduction, Lb.	3	4	7	12	18	26	36

WEIGHT OF HIGH BUTTON (ACORN) HEADS AFTER DRIVING

	½	⅝	¾	⅞	1	1⅛	1¼
Diameter of Rivet, Inches							
Weight per 100 Heads, Lb.	4	7	12	18	26	36	48

AMERICAN INSTITUTE OF STEEL CONSTRUCTION

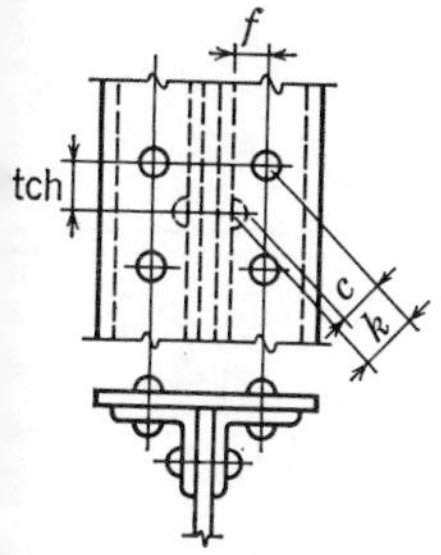

RIVETS
Spacing

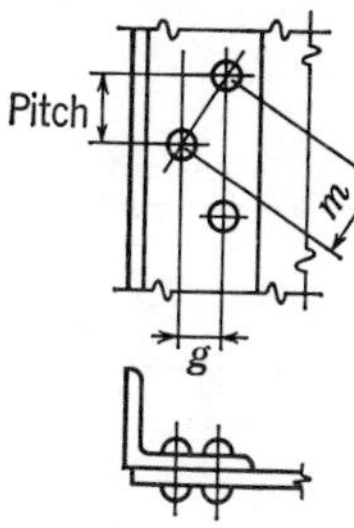

MINIMUM PITCH FOR MACHINE RIVETING

m. f vet	c	k	Distance, f, inches													
			1⅛	1¼	1⅜	1½	1⅝	1¾	1⅞	2	2⅛	2¼	2⅜	2½	2¾	3
⅜	⅞	1³⁄₁₆	¼	0												
½	1	1⅜	¾	½	0											
⅝	1⅛	1⁹⁄₁₆	1⅛	1	¾	⅜	0									
¾	1¼	1¾	...	1¼	1⅛	1	¾	0								
⅞	1⅜	2	...	...	1½	1⅜	1⅛	⅞	⅝	0						
	1½	2³⁄₁₆	...	...	...	1⅝	1½	1⅜	1⅛	⅞	½	0				
⅛	1⅝	2⅜	...	...	...	...	1¾	1⅝	1½	1⅜	1⅛	⅞	0			
¼	1¾	2⅝	...	...	...	...	...	2	1⅞	1¾	1½	1¼	1	⅝	0	
⅜	1⅞	2¹³⁄₁₆	...	...	...	...	...	...	2⅛	2	1⅞	1¾	1½	1¼	½	0
½	2	3	...	...	...	...	...	...	...	2¼	2⅛	2	1⅞	1⅝	1⅛	0

MINIMUM PITCH TO MAINTAIN 3 DIAMETERS C. TO C.

m. f vet	m	Distance, g, Inches														
		1	1¼	1½	1¾	2	2¼	2½	2¾	3	3¼	3½	3¾	4	4¼	4½
⅜	1⅛	½	0													
½	1½	1⅛	⅞	0												
⅝	1⅞	1⅝	1⅜	1⅛	⅝	0										
¾	2¼	2	1⅞	1⅝	1⅜	1	0									
⅞	2⅝	2½	2⅜	2⅛	2	1¾	1⅜	¾	0							
	3	2⅞	2¾	2⅝	2½	2¼	2	1⅝	1⅛	0						
⅛	3⅜	3¼	3⅛	3	2⅞	2¾	2½	2¼	2	1½	⅞	0				
¼	3¾	3⅝	3½	3⅜	3⅜	3¼	3	2¾	2½	2¼	1⅞	1⅜	0			
⅜	4⅛	4	4	3⅞	3¾	3⅝	3½	3¼	3⅛	2⅞	2½	2⅛	1¾	1	0	
½	4½	4⅜	4⅜	4¼	4⅛	4	3⅞	3¾	3½	3⅜	3⅛	2⅞	2½	2	1½	0

COVER PLATE RIVETING

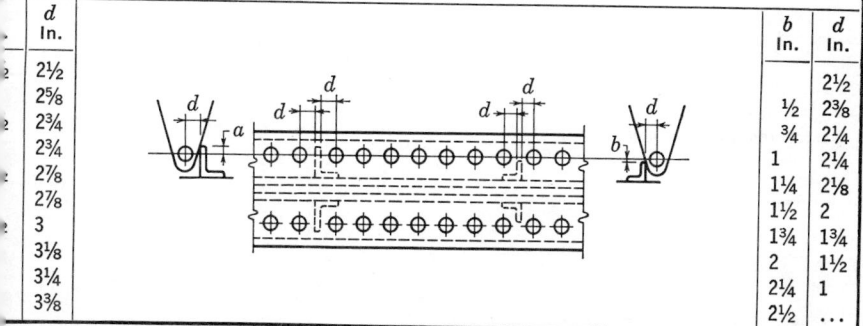

	d In.
	2½
	2⅝
	2¾
	2¾
	2⅞
	2⅞
	3
	3⅛
	3¼
	3⅜

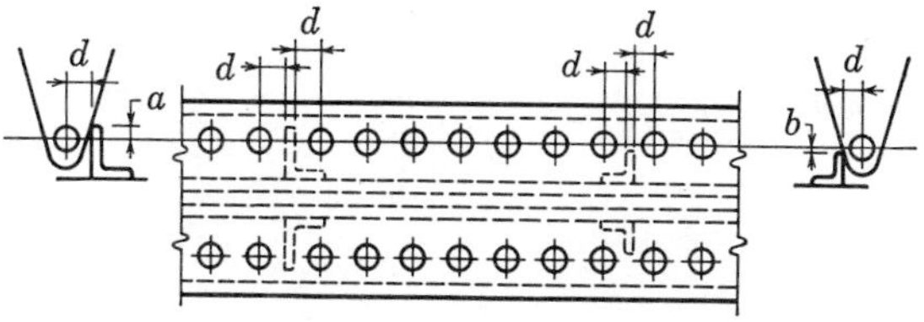

b In.	d In.
	2½
½	2⅜
¾	2¼
1	2¼
1¼	2⅛
1½	2
1¾	1¾
2	1½
2¼	1
2½	...

THREADED FASTENERS
Bolt heads

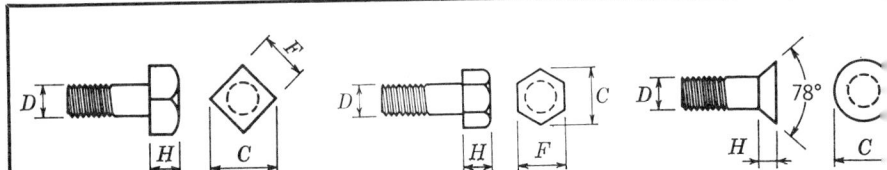

Square Hex Countersunk

Bolt head dimensions, rounded to nearest $\frac{1}{16}$ inch, are in accordance with
ANSI B18.2.1—1965 (Square and Hex) and ANSI 18.5—1959 (Countersunk)

Standard Dimensions for Bolt Heads

Diam. of Bolt D	Square			Hex			Heavy Hex			Countersunk	
	Width F	Width C	Height H	Width F	Width C	Height H	Width F	Width C	Height H	Diam. C	Heig H
In.	In.	In.	In.	In.	In.	In.	In.	In.	In.	In.	In.
$\frac{1}{4}$	$\frac{3}{8}$	$\frac{1}{2}$	$\frac{3}{16}$	$\frac{7}{16}$	$\frac{1}{2}$	$\frac{3}{16}$	...	...	...	$\frac{1}{2}$	$\frac{1}{8}$
$\frac{3}{8}$	$\frac{9}{16}$	$\frac{13}{16}$	$\frac{1}{4}$	$\frac{9}{16}$	$\frac{5}{8}$	$\frac{1}{4}$	...	...	...	$\frac{11}{16}$	$\frac{3}{16}$
$\frac{1}{2}$	$\frac{3}{4}$	$1\frac{1}{16}$	$\frac{3}{8}$	$\frac{3}{4}$	$\frac{7}{8}$	$\frac{3}{8}$	$\frac{7}{8}$	1	$\frac{3}{8}$	$\frac{7}{8}$	$\frac{1}{4}$
$\frac{5}{8}$	$\frac{15}{16}$	$1\frac{5}{16}$	$\frac{7}{16}$	$\frac{15}{16}$	$1\frac{1}{16}$	$\frac{7}{16}$	$1\frac{1}{16}$	$1\frac{1}{4}$	$\frac{7}{16}$	$1\frac{1}{8}$	$\frac{5}{16}$
$\frac{3}{4}$	$1\frac{1}{8}$	$1\frac{9}{16}$	$\frac{1}{2}$	$1\frac{1}{8}$	$1\frac{5}{16}$	$\frac{1}{2}$	$1\frac{1}{4}$	$1\frac{7}{16}$	$\frac{1}{2}$	$1\frac{3}{8}$	$\frac{3}{8}$
$\frac{7}{8}$	$1\frac{5}{16}$	$1\frac{7}{8}$	$\frac{5}{8}$	$1\frac{5}{16}$	$1\frac{1}{2}$	$\frac{5}{8}$	$1\frac{7}{16}$	$1\frac{11}{16}$	$\frac{5}{8}$	$1\frac{9}{16}$	$\frac{7}{16}$
1	$1\frac{1}{2}$	$2\frac{1}{8}$	$\frac{11}{16}$	$1\frac{1}{2}$	$1\frac{3}{4}$	$\frac{11}{16}$	$1\frac{5}{8}$	$1\frac{7}{8}$	$\frac{11}{16}$	$1\frac{13}{16}$	$\frac{1}{2}$
$1\frac{1}{8}$	$1\frac{11}{16}$	$2\frac{3}{8}$	$\frac{3}{4}$	$1\frac{11}{16}$	$1\frac{15}{16}$	$\frac{3}{4}$	$1\frac{13}{16}$	$2\frac{1}{16}$	$\frac{3}{4}$	$2\frac{1}{16}$	$\frac{9}{16}$
$1\frac{1}{4}$	$1\frac{7}{8}$	$2\frac{5}{8}$	$\frac{7}{8}$	$1\frac{7}{8}$	$2\frac{3}{16}$	$\frac{7}{8}$	2	$2\frac{5}{16}$	$\frac{7}{8}$	$2\frac{1}{4}$	$\frac{5}{8}$
$1\frac{3}{8}$	$2\frac{1}{16}$	$2\frac{15}{16}$	$\frac{15}{16}$	$2\frac{1}{16}$	$2\frac{3}{8}$	$\frac{15}{16}$	$2\frac{3}{16}$	$2\frac{1}{2}$	$\frac{15}{16}$	$2\frac{1}{2}$	$\frac{11}{1}$
$1\frac{1}{2}$	$2\frac{1}{4}$	$3\frac{3}{16}$	$1\frac{1}{16}$	$2\frac{1}{4}$	$2\frac{5}{8}$	$1\frac{1}{16}$	$2\frac{3}{8}$	$2\frac{3}{4}$	$1\frac{1}{16}$	$2\frac{11}{16}$	$\frac{3}{4}$
$1\frac{3}{4}$	...	...	...	$2\frac{5}{8}$	3	$1\frac{3}{16}$	$2\frac{3}{4}$	$3\frac{3}{16}$	$1\frac{3}{16}$	...	..
2	...	...	...	3	$3\frac{7}{16}$	$1\frac{3}{8}$	$3\frac{1}{8}$	$3\frac{5}{8}$	$1\frac{3}{8}$	...	..
$2\frac{1}{4}$	...	...	...	$3\frac{3}{8}$	$3\frac{7}{8}$	$1\frac{9}{16}$	$3\frac{1}{2}$	$4\frac{1}{16}$	$1\frac{9}{16}$	...	..
$2\frac{1}{2}$	...	...	...	$3\frac{3}{4}$	$4\frac{5}{16}$	$1\frac{11}{16}$	$3\frac{7}{8}$	$4\frac{1}{2}$	$1\frac{11}{16}$	...	..
$2\frac{3}{4}$	...	...	...	$4\frac{1}{8}$	$4\frac{3}{4}$	$1\frac{7}{8}$	$4\frac{1}{4}$	$4\frac{15}{16}$	$1\frac{7}{8}$	...	..
3	...	...	...	$4\frac{1}{2}$	$5\frac{3}{16}$	$2\frac{1}{16}$	$4\frac{5}{8}$	$5\frac{5}{16}$	$2\frac{1}{16}$	...	..
$3\frac{1}{4}$	...	...	...	$4\frac{7}{8}$	$5\frac{5}{8}$	$2\frac{1}{4}$	...	...	...	...	..
$3\frac{1}{2}$	...	...	...	$5\frac{1}{4}$	$6\frac{1}{16}$	$2\frac{3}{8}$	...	...	...	...	..
$3\frac{3}{4}$	...	...	...	$5\frac{5}{8}$	$6\frac{1}{2}$	$2\frac{9}{16}$	...	...	...	...	..
4	...	...	...	6	$6\frac{15}{16}$	$2\frac{3}{4}$	...	...	...	...	..

For dimensions for high strength bolts, refer to "Specifications for Structural Joints Using ASTM
A325 or A490 Bolts" in Part 5 of this manual.

THREADED FASTENERS

Nuts

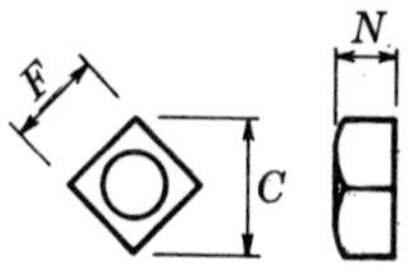

Square

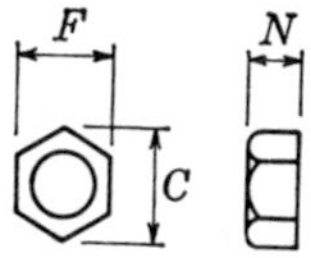

Hex

Nut dimensions, rounded to nearest 1/16 inch, are in accordance with ANSI B18.2.2—1965.

Dimensions for Nuts

Nut Size	Square			Hex			Heavy Square			Heavy Hex		
	Width F	Width C	Height N	Width F	Width C	Height N	Width F	Width C	Height N	Width F	Width C	Height N
In.	In.	In.	In.	In.	In.	In.	In.	In.	In.	In.	In.	In.
1/4	7/16	5/8	1/4	7/16	1/2	1/4	1/2	11/16	1/4	1/2	9/16	1/4
3/8	5/8	7/8	3/8	9/16	5/8	5/16	11/16	1	3/8	11/16	13/16	3/8
1/2	13/16	1 1/8	7/16	3/4	7/8	7/16	7/8	1 1/4	1/2	7/8	1	1/2
5/8	1	1 7/16	9/16	15/16	1 1/16	9/16	1 1/16	1 1/2	5/8	1 1/16	1 1/4	5/8
3/4	1 1/8	1 9/16	11/16	1 1/8	1 5/16	11/16	1 1/4	1 3/4	3/4	1 1/4	1 7/16	3/4
7/8	1 5/16	1 7/8	13/16	1 5/16	1 1/2	3/4	1 7/16	2 1/16	7/8	1 7/16	1 11/16	7/8
1	1 1/2	2 1/8	7/8	1 1/2	1 3/4	7/8	1 5/8	2 5/16	1	1 5/8	1 7/8	1
1 1/8	1 11/16	2 3/8	1	1 11/16	1 15/16	1	1 13/16	2 9/16	1 1/8	1 13/16	2 1/16	1 1/8
1 1/4	1 7/8	2 5/8	1 1/8	1 7/8	2 3/16	1 1/8	2	2 13/16	1 5/16	2	2 5/16	1 1/4
1 3/8	2 1/16	2 15/16	1 1/4	2 1/16	2 3/8	1 3/16	2 3/16	3 1/8	1 7/16	2 3/16	2 1/2	1 3/8
1 1/2	2 1/4	3 3/16	1 3/8	2 1/4	2 5/8	1 5/16	2 3/8	3 3/8	1 9/16	2 3/8	2 3/4	1 1/2
1 3/4	...	...	...	...	...	...	...	...	...	2 3/4	3 3/16	1 3/4
2	...	...	...	...	...	...	...	...	...	3 1/8	3 5/8	2
2 1/4	...	...	...	...	...	...	...	...	...	3 1/2	4 1/16	2 1/4
2 1/2	...	...	...	...	...	...	...	...	...	3 7/8	4 1/2	2 1/2
2 3/4	...	...	...	...	...	...	...	...	...	4 1/4	4 15/16	2 3/4
3	...	...	...	...	...	...	...	...	...	4 5/8	5 5/16	3
3 1/4	...	...	...	...	...	...	...	...	...	5	5 3/4	3 1/4
3 1/2	...	...	...	...	...	...	...	...	...	5 3/8	6 3/16	3 1/2
3 3/4	...	...	...	...	...	...	...	...	...	5 3/4	6 5/8	3 3/4
4	...	...	...	...	...	...	...	...	...	6 1/8	7 1/16	4

For dimensions for high strength bolts, refer to "Specifications for Structural Joints Using ASTM A325 or A490 Bolts" in Part 5 of this manual.

THREADED FASTENERS
Weight of bolts

With square heads and hexagon nuts in pounds per 100

Length Under Head Inches	Diameter of Bolt in Inches								
	¼	⅜	½	⅝	¾	⅞	1	1⅛	1¼
1	2.38	6.11	13.0	24.1	38.9	...	...	...	...
1¼	2.71	6.71	14.0	25.8	41.5	...	...	...	...
1½	3.05	7.47	15.1	27.6	44.0	67.3	95.1	...	...
1¾	3.39	8.23	16.5	29.3	46.5	70.8	99.7	...	...
2	3.73	8.99	17.8	31.4	49.1	74.4	104	143	...
2¼	4.06	9.75	19.1	33.5	52.1	77.9	109	149	...
2½	4.40	10.5	20.5	35.6	55.1	82.0	114	155	206
2¾	4.74	11.3	21.8	37.7	58.2	86.1	119	161	213
3	5.07	12.0	23.2	39.8	61.2	90.2	124	168	221
3¼	5.41	12.8	24.5	41.9	64.2	94.4	129	174	229
3½	5.75	13.5	25.9	44.0	67.2	98.5	135	181	237
3¾	6.09	14.3	27.2	46.1	70.2	103	140	188	246
4	6.42	15.1	28.6	48.2	73.3	107	145	195	254
4¼	6.76	15.8	29.9	50.3	76.3	111	151	202	262
4½	7.10	16.6	31.3	52.3	79.3	115	156	208	271
4¾	7.43	17.3	32.6	54.4	82.3	119	162	215	279
5	7.77	18.1	33.9	56.5	85.3	123	167	222	288
5¼	8.11	18.9	35.3	58.6	88.4	127	172	229	296
5½	8.44	19.6	36.6	60.7	91.4	131	178	236	304
5¾	8.78	20.4	38.0	62.8	94.4	136	183	242	313
6	9.12	21.1	39.3	64.9	97.4	140	188	249	321
6¼	9.37	21.7	40.4	66.7	100	143	193	255	329
6½	9.71	22.5	41.8	68.7	103	147	198	262	337
6¾	10.1	23.3	43.1	70.8	106	151	204	269	345
7	10.4	24.0	44.4	72.9	109	156	209	275	354
7¼	10.7	24.8	45.8	75.0	112	160	214	282	362
7½	11.0	25.5	47.1	77.1	115	164	220	289	371
7¾	11.4	26.3	48.5	79.2	118	168	225	296	379
8	11.7	27.0	49.8	81.3	121	172	231	303	387
8½	...	28.6	52.5	85.5	127	180	241	316	404
9	...	30.1	55.2	89.7	133	189	252	330	421
9½	...	31.6	57.9	93.9	139	197	263	343	438
10	...	33.1	60.6	98.1	145	205	274	357	454
10½	...	34.6	63.3	102	151	213	284	371	471
11	...	36.2	66.0	106	157	221	295	384	488
11½	...	37.7	68.7	110	163	230	306	398	505
12	...	39.2	71.3	115	170	238	316	411	522
12½	...	...	74.0	119	176	246	327	425	538
13	...	...	76.7	123	182	254	338	439	556
13½	...	...	79.4	127	188	263	349	452	572
14	...	...	82.1	131	194	271	359	466	589
14½	...	...	84.8	135	200	279	370	479	605
15	...	...	87.5	140	206	287	381	493	622
15½	...	...	90.2	144	212	296	392	507	639
16	...	...	92.9	148	218	304	402	520	656
Per Inch Additional	1.3	3.0	5.4	8.4	12.1	16.5	21.4	27.2	33.

Note: Bolt is Square Bolt, ANSI B18.2.1—65 and nut is Hex Nut, ANSI B18.2.2—65. This table conforms to weight standards adopted by the Industrial Fasteners Institute.

AMERICAN INSTITUTE OF STEEL CONSTRUCTION

THREADED FASTENERS
Weight of bolts
Special cases in pounds per 100

VARIATIONS IN BOLT AND NUT TYPES

Weights for combinations of bolt heads and nuts, other than square heads and hex nuts, may be determined by making the appropriate additions and deductions tabulated below from the weight per 100 shown on the previous page.

Combination	Add or Subtract	Diameter of Bolt in Inches								
		¼	⅜	½	⅝	¾	⅞	1	1⅛	1¼
Square bolt with square nut	+	0.1	1.0	2.0	3.4	3.5	5.5	8.0	12.2	16.3
Square bolt with heavy square nut	+	0.6	2.1	4.1	7.0	11.6	17.2	23.2	32.1	41.2
Square bolt with heavy hex nut	+	0.4	1.5	2.8	4.6	7.6	10.7	14.2	18.9	24.3
Hex bolt with square nut	+	0.1	0.6	1.1	1.4	0.2	0.5	−0.2	−0.1	−1.7
Hex bolt with hex nut	−	0.0	0.4	0.9	2.0	3.3	5.0	8.2	12.3	18.0
Hex bolt with heavy square nut	+	0.6	1.7	3.2	5.0	8.3	12.2	15.0	19.8	23.2
Hex bolt with heavy hex nut	+	0.4	1.1	1.9	2.6	4.3	5.7	6.0	6.6	6.3
Heavy hex bolt with heavy square nut	+	...	...	4.7	7.3	11.3	16.5	20.7	27.0	33.6
Heavy hex bolt with heavy hex nut	+	...	...	3.4	4.9	7.3	10.0	11.7	13.8	16.7

LARGE DIAMETER BOLTS

Weights of bolts over 1¼ inches in diameter may be calculated from the following data. Standard practice is hex head bolts with heavy hex nut. Square head bolts and square nuts are not standard in sizes over 1½ inches.

Weight of 100 Each	Diameter of Bolt in Inches											
	1⅜	1½	1¾	2	2¼	2½	2¾	3	3¼	3½	3¾	4
Square heads	105	130	...	...	...	...	...	...	...	...	...	...
Hex heads	84	112	178	259	369	508	680	900	1120	1390	1730	2130
Heavy hex heads	95	124	195	280	397	541	720	950	...	...	...	...
Square nuts	94.5	122	...	...	...	...	...	...	...	...	...	...
Heavy square nuts	125	161	...	...	...	...	...	...	...	...	...	...
Heavy hex nuts	102	131	204	299	419	564	738	950	1190	1530	1810	2180
Per inch of threaded shank	35.0	42.5	57.4	75.5	97.4	120	147	178	210	246	284	325
Per inch of unthreaded shank	42.0	50.0	68.2	89.0	113	139	168	200	235	272	313	356

THREADED FASTENERS
Weight of ASTM A325 or A490 high strength bolts
Heavy hex structural bolts with heavy hex nuts in pounds per 100

Length Under Head Inches	Diameter of Bolt in Inches								
	½	⅝	¾	⅞	1	1⅛	1¼	1⅜	1½
1	16.5	29.4	47.0	...	104	...	...	...	...
1¼	17.8	31.1	49.6	74.4	109	148	197	...	...
1½	19.2	33.1	52.2	78.0	114	154	205	261	333
1¾	20.5	35.3	55.3	81.9	...	...	...	...	...
2	21.9	37.4	58.4	86.1	119	160	212	270	344
2¼	23.3	39.8	61.6	90.3	124	167	220	279	35■
2½	24.7	41.7	64.7	94.6	130	174	229	290	36■
2¾	26.1	43.9	67.8	98.8	135	181	237	300	37■
3	27.4	46.1	70.9	103	141	188	246	310	39■
3¼	28.8	48.2	74.0	107	146	195	255	321	40■
3½	30.2	50.4	77.1	111	151	202	263	332	41■
3¾	31.6	52.5	80.2	116	157	209	272	342	42■
4	33.0	54.7	83.3	120	162	216	280	353	44■
4¼	34.3	56.9	86.4	124	168	223	289	363	45■
4½	35.7	59.0	89.5	128	173	230	298	374	46■
4¾	37.1	61.2	92.7	133	179	237	306	384	47■
5	38.5	63.3	95.8	137	184	244	315	395	49■
5¼	39.9	65.5	98.9	141	190	251	324	405	50■
5½	41.2	67.7	102	146	196	258	332	416	51■
5¾	42.6	69.8	105	150	201	265	341	426	52■
6	44.0	71.9	108	154	207	272	349	437	54■
6¼	...	74.1	111	158	212	279	358	447	55■
6½	...	76.3	114	163	218	286	367	458	56■
6¾	...	78.5	118	167	223	293	375	468	5■
7	...	80.6	121	171	229	300	384	479	58■
7¼	...	82.8	124	175	234	307	392	489	6■
7½	...	84.9	127	179	240	314	401	500	6■
7¾	...	87.1	130	183	246	321	410	510	6■
8	...	89.2	133	187	251	328	418	521	6■
8¼	...	...	...	192	257	335	427	531	6■
8½	...	...	...	196	262	342	435	542	6■
8¾	...	...	...	...	...	...	444	552	6■
9	...	...	...	...	...	...	453	563	6■
Per inch additional and	5.5	8.6	12.4	16.9	22.1	28.0	34.4	42.5	49
For each 100 plain round washers add	2.1	3.6	4.8	7.0	9.4	11.3	13.8	16.8	2(
For each 100 beveled square washers add	23.1	22.4	21.0	20.2	19.2	34.0	31.6	...	·

Note: This table conforms to weight standards adopted by the Industrial Fasteners Institute 1965, updated for washer weights.

THREADED FASTENERS

SCREW THREADS
Unified Standard Series—UNC and 4 UN
ANSI B1.1—1960

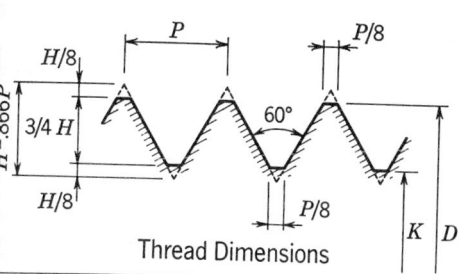

Thread Dimensions

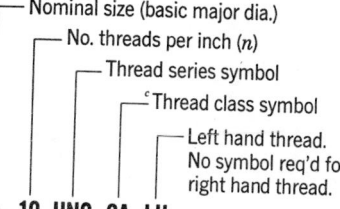

- Nominal size (basic major dia.)
- No. threads per inch (n)
- Thread series symbol
- ^{c}Thread class symbol
- Left hand thread. No symbol req'd for right hand thread.

$$\text{3/4} - 10 \text{ UNC 2A LH}$$

Standard Designations

Diameter		Area			^{b}Th'ds per Inch n	Diameter		Area			^{b}Th'ds per Inch n
Basic Major D	Root K	Gross A_D	Root A_K	^{a}Tensile Stress		Basic Major D	Root K	Gross A_D	Root A_K	^{a}Tensile Stress	
In.	In.	In.²	In.²	In.²		In.	In.	In.²	In.²	In.²	
1/4	.185	.049	.027	.032	20	2¾	2.425	5.940	4.62	4.93	4
3/8	.294	.110	.068	.078	16	3	2.675	7.069	5.62	5.97	4
1/2	.400	.196	.126	.142	13	3¼	2.925	8.296	6.72	7.10	4
5/8	.507	.307	.202	.226	11	3½	3.175	9.621	7.92	8.33	4
3/4	.620	.442	.302	.334	10	3¾	3.425	11.045	9.21	9.66	4
7/8	.731	.601	.419	.462	9	4	3.675	12.566	10.6	11.1	4
	.838	.785	.551	.606	8	4¼	3.925	14.186	12.1	12.6	4
⅛	.939	.994	.693	.763	7	4½	4.175	15.904	13.7	14.2	4
¼	1.064	1.227	.890	.969	7	4¾	4.425	17.721	15.4	16.0	4
⅜	1.158	1.485	1.05	1.16	6	5	4.675	19.635	17.2	17.8	4
½	1.283	1.767	1.29	1.41	6	5¼	4.925	21.648	19.1	19.7	4
¾	1.490	2.405	1.74	1.90	5	5½	5.175	23.758	21.0	21.7	4
	1.711	3.142	2.30	2.50	4½	5¾	5.425	25.967	23.1	23.8	4
¼	1.961	3.976	3.02	3.25	4½	6	5.675	28.274	25.3	26.0	4
½	2.175	4.909	3.72	4.00	4						

^{a} Tensile stress area $= 0.7854 \left(D - \dfrac{.9743}{n} \right)^2$.

^{b} For basic major diameters of ¼ to 4 in. incl., thread series is UNC (coarse); for 4¼ in. diameter and larger, thread series is 4UN.

^{c} 2A denotes Class 2A fit applicable to external threads, 2B denotes corresponding Class 2B fit for internal threads.

MINIMUM LENGTH OF THREAD ON BOLTS
ANSI B18.2.1—1965

Length of Bolt	Diameter of Bolt, D, Inches																
	¼	⅜	½	⅝	¾	⅞	1	1⅛	1¼	1⅜	1½	1¾	2	2¼	2½	2¾	3
To 6 in. Incl.	¾	1	1¼	1½	1¾	2	2¼	2½	2¾	3	3¼	3¾	4¼	4¾	5¼	5¾	6
Over 6 in.	1	1¼	1½	1¾	2	2¼	2½	2¾	3	3¼	3½	4	4½	5	5½	6	6½

Note 1. Thread length for bolts up to 6 in. long is $2D + \frac{1}{4}$. For bolts over 6 in. long, thread length is $2D + \frac{1}{2}$. These proportions may be used to compute thread length for diameters not shown in the table. Bolts which are too short for listed or computed thread lengths are threaded as close to the head as possible.

Note 2. For thread lengths for high strength bolts, refer to "Specifications for Structural Joints Using ASTM A325 or A490 Bolts," in Part 5 of this manual.

AMERICAN INSTITUTE OF STEEL CONSTRUCTION

CLEVISES

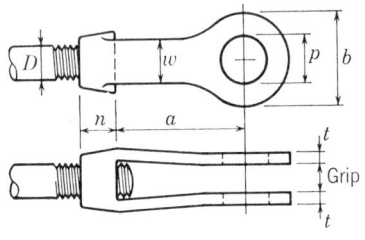

Thread: UNC Class 2B

Grip = thickness
plate + ¼"

Clevis Number	Dimensions, Inches							Weight Pounds	Safe Work Load, Kip
	Max. D	Max. p	b	n	a	w	t		
2	5/8	¾	1 7/16	5/8	3⅞	1 1/16	5/16(+ 1/32 − 0)	1.0	7.0
2½	7/8	1½	2½	1⅛	4	1¼	5/16(+ 1/32 − 0)	2.0	7.5
3	1⅜	1¾	3	1 5/16	5	1½	½(+ 1/32 − 0)	4.0	15
3½	1½	2	3½	1⅝	6	1¾	½(+ 1/32 − 0)	6.0	18
4	1¾	2¼	4	1¾	6	2	½(+ 1/32 − 0)	8.0	21
5	2	2½	5	2¼	7	2½	5/8(+ 1/16 − 0)	16.0	37.5
6	2½	3	6	2¾	8	3	¾(+ 3/32 − 0)	26.0	54
7	3	3¾	7	3	9	3½	7/8(+ 1/8 − 0)	36.0	68.5
8	4	4	8	4	10	4	1½(+ 1/8 − 0)	80.0	135

* Safe working load based on 5:1 safety factor using maximum pin diameter.

CLEVIS NUMBERS FOR VARIOUS RODS AND PINS

Diameter of Tap Inches	Diameter of Pin, Inches														
	5/8	¾	7/8	1	1¼	1½	1¾	2	2¼	2½	2¾	3	3¼	3½	3¾
5/8	2	2	2½	2½	2½	2½									
¾		2½	2½	2½	2½	2½									
7/8			2½	2½	2½	2½									
1				3	3	3	3								
1¼				3	3	3	3	3½							
1⅜				3	3	3	3½	3½	4						
1½				3½	3½	3½	4	4	5						
1¾					4	4	5	5	5	5					
2						5	5	5	5	5	6	6	7	7	
2¼								6	6	6	6	7	7	7	7
2½								6	6	6	7	7	7	8	8
2¾										7	7	7	7	8	8
3										7	8	8	8	8	8
3¼											8	8	8	8	8
3½											8	8	8	8	8
3¾											8	8	8	8	8
4											8	8	8	8	8

Above Table of Clevis Sizes is based on the Net Area of Clevis through Pin Hole being equal to o[r] greater than 125 per cent of Net Area of Rod. Table applies to round rods without upset ends[.] Pins are sufficient for shear but must be investigated for bending. For other combinations o[f] pin and rod or net area ratios, required clevis size can be calculated by reference to the tabu-lated dimensions.

Weights and dimensions of clevises are typical. Products of all suppliers are similar and es-sentially the same.

American Institute of Steel Construction

TURNBUCKLES

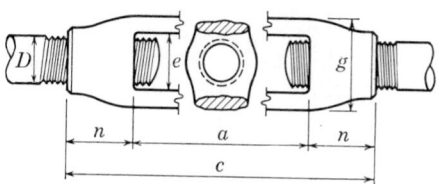

Thread: UNC and 4 UN Class 2B

Diam. D In.	Standard Turnbuckles — Dimensions, Inches					Weight of Turnbuckles, Pounds — Length, a, Inches						Turnbuckle Safe Working Load, Kips*
	a	n	c	e	g	6	9	12	18	24	36	
3/8	6	9/16	7 1/8	9/16	1 1/32	.41						1.2
1/2	6	3/4	7 1/2	11/16	15/16	.75	.80	1.00				2.2
5/8	6	29/32	7 13/16	13/16	1 1/2	1.00	1.38	1.50	2.43			3.5
3/4	6	1 1/16	8 1/8	15/16	1 23/32	1.45	1.63	2.13	3.06	4.25		5.2
7/8	6	1 7/32	8 7/16	1 3/32	1 7/8	1.85		2.83	4.20	5.43		7.2
1	6	1 3/8	8 3/4	1 9/32	2 1/32	2.60		3.20	4.40	6.85	10.0	9.3
1 1/8	6	1 9/16	9 1/8	1 13/32	2 9/32	2.72		4.70	6.10			11.6
1 1/4	6	1 3/4	9 1/2	1 9/16	2 17/32	3.58		4.70	7.13	11.30	13.1	15.2
1 3/8	6	1 15/16	9 7/8	1 11/16	2 3/4	4.50						17.4
1 1/2	6	2 1/8	10 1/4	1 27/32	3 1/32	5.50		8.00	9.13	16.80	19.4	21.0
1 5/8	6	2 1/4	10 1/2	1 31/32	3 3/32	7.50						24.5
1 3/4	6	2 1/2	11	2 1/8	3 3/16	9.50		15.25	16.00	19.50		28.3
1 7/8	6	2 3/4	11 1/2	2 3/8	4	11.50						37.2
2	6	2 3/4	11 1/2	2 3/8	4	11.50		15.25		27.50		37.2
2 1/4	6	3 3/8	12 3/4	2 11/16	4 5/8	18.00		35.25		43.50		48.0
2 1/2	6	3 3/4	13 1/2	3	5	23.25		33.60		42.38		60.0
2 3/4	6	4 1/8	14 1/4	3 1/4	5 5/8	31.50				54.00		75.0
3	6	4 1/2	15	3 5/8	6 1/8	39.50						96.7
3 1/4	6	5 1/4	16 1/2	3 7/8	6 3/4	60.50						122.2
3 1/2	6	5 1/4	16 1/2	3 7/8	6 3/4	60.50						122.2
3 3/4	6	6	18	4 5/8	8 1/2	95.00						167.8
4	6	6	18	4 5/8	8 1/2	95.00						167.8
4 1/4	9	6 3/4	22 1/2	5 1/4	9 3/4		152.0					233.8
4 1/2	9	6 3/4	22 1/2	5 1/4	9 3/4		152.0					233.8
4 3/4	9	6 3/4	22 1/2	5 1/4	9 3/4		152.0					233.8
5	9	7 1/2	24	6	10		200.0					294.7

*Safe working load based on 5:1 safety factor.

Weights and dimensions of turnbuckles are typical. Products of all suppliers are similar and essentially the same.

SLEEVE NUTS

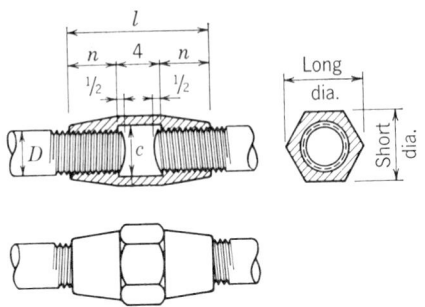

Thread: UNC and 4 UN Class 2B

Diameter of Screw D Inches	Dimensions, Inches					Weight Pounds
	Short Diameter	Long Diameter	Length l	Nut n	Clear c	
3/8	11/16	25/32	4	...	...	.27
7/16	25/32	7/8	4	...	...	.34
1/2	7/8	1	4	...	...	.43
9/16	15/16	1 1/16	5	...	...	.64
5/8	1 1/16	1 7/32	5	...	...	.93
3/4	1 1/4	1 7/16	5	...	...	1.12
7/8	1 7/16	1 5/8	7	1 7/16	1	1.75
1	1 5/8	1 13/16	7	1 7/16	1 1/8	2.46
1 1/8	1 13/16	2 1/16	7 1/2	1 5/8	1 1/4	3.10
1 1/4	2	2 1/4	7 1/2	1 5/8	1 3/8	4.04
1 3/8	2 3/16	2 1/2	8	1 7/8	1 1/2	4.97
1 1/2	2 3/8	2 11/16	8	1 7/8	1 5/8	6.16
1 5/8	2 9/16	2 15/16	8 1/2	2 1/16	1 3/4	7.36
1 3/4	2 3/4	3 1/8	8 1/2	2 1/16	1 7/8	8.87
1 7/8	2 15/16	3 5/16	9	2 5/16	2	10.42
2	3 1/8	3 1/2	9	2 5/16	2 1/8	12.24
2 1/4	3 1/2	3 15/16	9 1/2	2 1/2	2 3/8	16.23
2 1/2	3 7/8	4 3/8	10	2 3/4	2 5/8	21.12
2 3/4	4 1/4	4 13/16	10 1/2	2 15/16	2 7/8	26.71
3	4 5/8	5 1/4	11	3 3/16	3 1/8	33.22
3 1/4	5	5 5/8	11 1/2	3 3/8	3 3/8	40.62
3 1/2	5 3/8	6	12	3 5/8	3 5/8	49.07
3 3/4	5 3/4	6 3/8	12 1/2	3 13/16	3 7/8	58.57
4	6 1/8	6 7/8	13	4 1/16	4 1/8	69.22
4 1/4	6 1/2	7 1/2	13 1/2	4 3/4	4 3/8	75.00
4 1/2	6 7/8	7 15/16	14	5	4 3/4	90.00
4 3/4	7 1/4	8 3/8	14 1/2	5 1/4	5	98.00
5	7 5/8	8 7/8	15	5 1/2	5 1/4	110.0
5 1/4	8	9 1/4	15 1/2	5 3/4	5 1/2	122.0
5 1/2	8 3/8	9 3/4	16	6	5 3/4	142.0
5 3/4	8 3/4	10 1/8	16 1/2	6 1/4	6	157.0
6	9 1/8	10 5/8	17	6 1/2	6 1/4	176.0

Strengths are greater than the corresponding connecting rod when same material is used. Weights and dimensions are typical. Products of all suppliers are similar and essentially the same.

AMERICAN INSTITUTE OF STEEL CONSTRUCTION

RECESSED PIN NUTS AND COTTER PINS

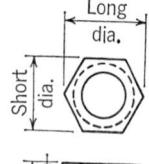

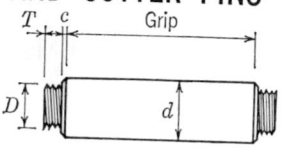

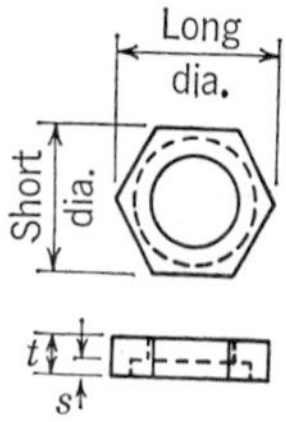

Material: Steel   Thread: 6 UN Class 2A/2B

Diameter of Pin d		PIN			NUT (Suggested Dimensions)					Weight Pounds
		Thread			Thickness t	Diameter		Recess		
		D	T	c		Short Diam.	Long Diam.	Rough Diam.	s	
2	2¼	1½	1	⅛	⅞	3	3⅜	2⅝	¼	1
2½	2¾	2	1⅛	⅛	1	3⅝	4⅛	3⅛	¼	2
3¼	3½	2½	1¼	⅛	1⅛	4⅜	5	3⅞	⅜	3
3¾	4	3	1⅜	¼	1¼	4⅞	5⅝	4⅜	⅜	4
4½	4¾	3½	1½	¼	1⅜	5¾	6⅝	5¼	½	5
5	5¼	4	1⅝	¼	1½	6¼	7¼	5¾	½	6
5¾	6	4½	1¾	¼	1⅝	7	8⅛	6½	⅝	8
6¼	6½	5	1⅞	⅜	1¾	7⅝	8⅞	7	⅝	10
6¾	7	5½	2	⅜	1⅞	8⅛	9⅜	7½	¾	12
7¼	7½	5½	2	⅜	1⅞	8⅝	10	8	¾	14
8	8¼	6	2¼	⅜	2⅛	9⅜	10⅞	8¾	¾	19
8¾	9	6	2¼	⅜	2⅛	10¼	11⅞	9⅝	¾	24
9¼	9½	6	2⅜	⅜	2¼	11¼	13	10⅝	¾	32
9¾	10	6	2⅜	⅜	2¼	11¼	13	10⅝	¾	32

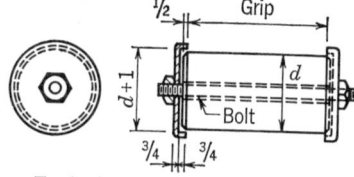

Although nuts may be used on all sizes of pins as shown above, for pins over 10″ in diameter the preferred practice is a detail similar to that shown at the left, in which the pin is held in place by a recessed cap at each end and secured by a bolt passing completely through the caps and pin. Suitable provision must be made for attaching pilots and driving nuts.

Typical Pin Cap Detail for Pins over 10 Inches in Diameter
Dimensions shown are approximate

HORIZONTAL OR VERTICAL PIN   HORIZONTAL PIN

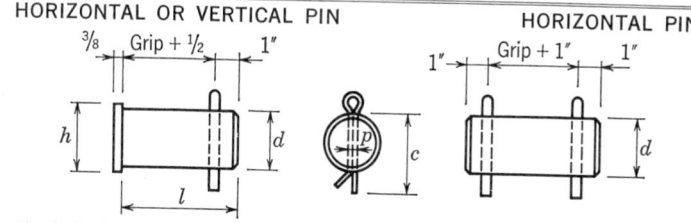

l = Length of pin, in inches.

Pin Diam. d	Pins With Heads		Cotter			Pin Diam. d	Pins With Heads		Cotter		
	Head Diam. h	Weight of One (Lb.)	Length c	Diam. p	Wt. per 100 (Lb.)		Head Diam. h	Weight of One (Lb.)	Length c	Diam. p	Wt. per 100 (Lb.)
¼	1½	.19+ .35l	2	¼	2.64	2¾	3⅛	.82+1.68l	4	⅜	11.4
½	1¾	.26+ .50l	2½	¼	3.10	3	3½	1.02+2.00l	5	⅜	28.5
¾	2	.33+ .68l	2¾	¼	3.50	3¼	3¾	1.17+2.35l	5	½	28.5
	2⅜	.47+ .89l	3	⅜	9.00	3½	4	1.34+2.73l	6	½	33.8
¼	2⅝	.58+1.13l	3¼	⅜	9.40	3¾	4¼	1.51+3.13l	6	½	33.8
½	2⅞	.70+1.39l	3¾	⅜	10.9						

AMERICAN INSTITUTE OF STEEL CONSTRUCTION

BENT PLATES
Minimum radius for cold bending

The following table gives the generally accepted minimum inside radii of bends in terms of thickness, t, for various steels listed. Values are for bend lines transverse to the direction of final rolling. When bend lines are parallel to the direction of final rolling, the values may have to be approximately doubled. When bend lines are longer than 36 inches, all radii may have to be increased if problems in bending are encountered.

Before bending, special attention should be paid to the condition of plate edges transverse to the bend lines. Flame cut edges of hardenable steels should be machined or softened by heat treatment. Nicks should be ground out. Sharp corners should be rounded.

ASTM Designation		Thickness, inches				
		Up to ¼	Over ¼ to ½	Over ½ to 1	Over 1 to 1½	Over 1½ to 2
A36		1½t	1½t	2t	3t	4t
A242		2t	3t	5t	[a]...	[a]...
A440		2½t	3½t	6t	[a]...	[a]...
A441		2t	3t	5t	[a]...	[a]...
A529		2t	2t	...	...	...
A572	Gr. 42	2t	2t	3t	4t	5t
	Gr. 45	2t	2t	3t	4t	...
	Gr. 50	2½t	2½t	4t	[a]...	...
	Gr. 55	3t	3t	5t	[a]...	...
	Gr. 60	3½t	3½t	6t	...	...
	Gr. 65	4t	4t	...	...	...
A588		2t	3t	5t	[a]...	[a]...
A514[b]		2t	2t	2t	3t	3t

[a] It is recommended that steel in this thickness range be bent hot. Hot bending, however, may result in a slight decrease in the as-rolled mechanical properties.
[b] The mechanical properties of ASTM A514 steel results from a quench-and-temper operation. Hot bending may adversely affect these mechanical properties. If necessary to hot-bend, fabricator should discuss procedure with the steel supplier.

WELDED JOINTS
Requirements

The AISC Specification and the *Structural Welding Code* of the American Welding Society exempt from tests and qualification most of the common welded joints applicable to steel structures. When the joints detailed on the following pages are welded in accordance with these standards they are designated as *prequalified* for building construction.

AWS prequalification of a weld joint is based upon experience that sound weld metal with appropriate mechanical properties can be deposited. However, use of prequalified joints does not necessarily assure satisfactory performance in heavy highly restrained connections. For additional information refer to *Design, Fabrication and Erection of Highly Restrained Joints to Minimize Lamellar Tearing*, AISC, 1973.

In general, all fillet welds are deemed prequalified, whether illustrated or not, provided they conform to requirements of the AWS Code and the AISC Specification.

These prequalified joints are limited to those made by the manual shielded metal-arc, submerged arc, gas metal-arc and flux cored arc welding processes. Small deviations from dimensions, angles of grooves, and variation in the depth of groove joints are permissible; consult the AWS Code for allowable variation of dimensions and for workmanship tolerances. Other joint forms and welding procedures may be employed provided they are tested and qualified in accordance with AWS D1.1-72.

Most prequalified joints illustrated are also applicable for bridge construction. (See footnotes to joint illustrations in Section 2 and to prohibited types in Section 9 of D1.1-72.)

The designations such as **B-L1a, B-L2, B-U2, B-P3** which are given on the following pages are those used in the AWS standards. Groove welds are classified using the following convention:

1. *Symbols for Joint Types*
   B—butt joint
   C—corner joint
   T—tee joint
   BC—butt or corner joint
   TC—tee or corner joint
   BTC—butt, tee or corner joint

2. *Symbols for Base Metal Thickness and Penetration*
   L—limited thickness, complete joint penetration
   U—unlimited thickness, complete joint penetration
   P—partial joint penetration

3. *Symbols for Weld Types*
   1—square groove
   2—single-vee groove
   3—double-vee groove
   4—single-bevel groove
   5—double-bevel groove
   6—single-U groove
   7—double-U groove
   8—single-J groove
   9—double-J groove

4. *Symbols for Welding Processes*
   If not manual shielded metal arc:
   S—submerged arc
   G—gas metal arc
   F—flux cored arc

AMERICAN INSTITUTE OF STEEL CONSTRUCTION

WELDED JOINTS
Standard symbols

BASIC WELD SYMBOLS

			GROOVE OR BUTT						
BACK	FILLET	PLUG OR SLOT	SQUARE	V	BEVEL	U	J	FLARE V	FLARE BEVEL
⌒	◺	▭	‖	V	V	Y	Y	V	Ⅱ

SUPPLEMENTARY WELD SYMBOLS

		WELD ALL AROUND	FIELD WELD	CONTOUR		For other basic and supplementary weld symbols, see AWS A2.0-68
				FLUSH	CONVEX	
		○	●	—	⌒	

STANDARD LOCATION OF ELEMENTS OF A WELDING SYMBOL

Finish symbol

Contour symbol

Root opening, depth of filling for plug and slot welds

Size in inches

Reference line

Specification, process or other reference

Tail (may be omitted when reference is not used)

Basic weld symbol or detail reference

Groove angle or included angle of countersink for plug welds

Length of weld in inches

Pitch (c. to c. spacing) of welds in inches

Weld-all-around symbol

Field weld symbol

Arrow connects reference line to arrow side of joint. Use break as at A or B to signify that arrow is pointing to the grooved member in bevel or J-grooved joints.

Note:

    Size, weld symbol, length of weld and spacing must read in that order from left to right along the reference line. Neither orientation of reference line nor location of the arrow alter this rule.

    The perpendicular leg of ◺, V, Y, Ⅱ weld symbols must be at left.

    Arrow and Other Side welds are of the same size unless otherwise shown.

    Symbols apply between abrupt changes in direction of welding unless governed by the "all around" symbol or otherwise dimensioned.

    These symbols do not explicitly provide for the case that frequently occurs in structural work, where duplicate material (such as stiffeners) occurs on the far side of a web or gusset plate. The fabricating industry has adopted this convention; that when the billing of the detail material discloses the identity of far side with near side, the welding shown for the near side shall also be duplicated on the far side.

AMERICAN INSTITUTE OF STEEL CONSTRUCTION

WELDED JOINTS
Complete penetration
Manual Shielded Metal-Arc Welded Joints of LIMITED Thickness

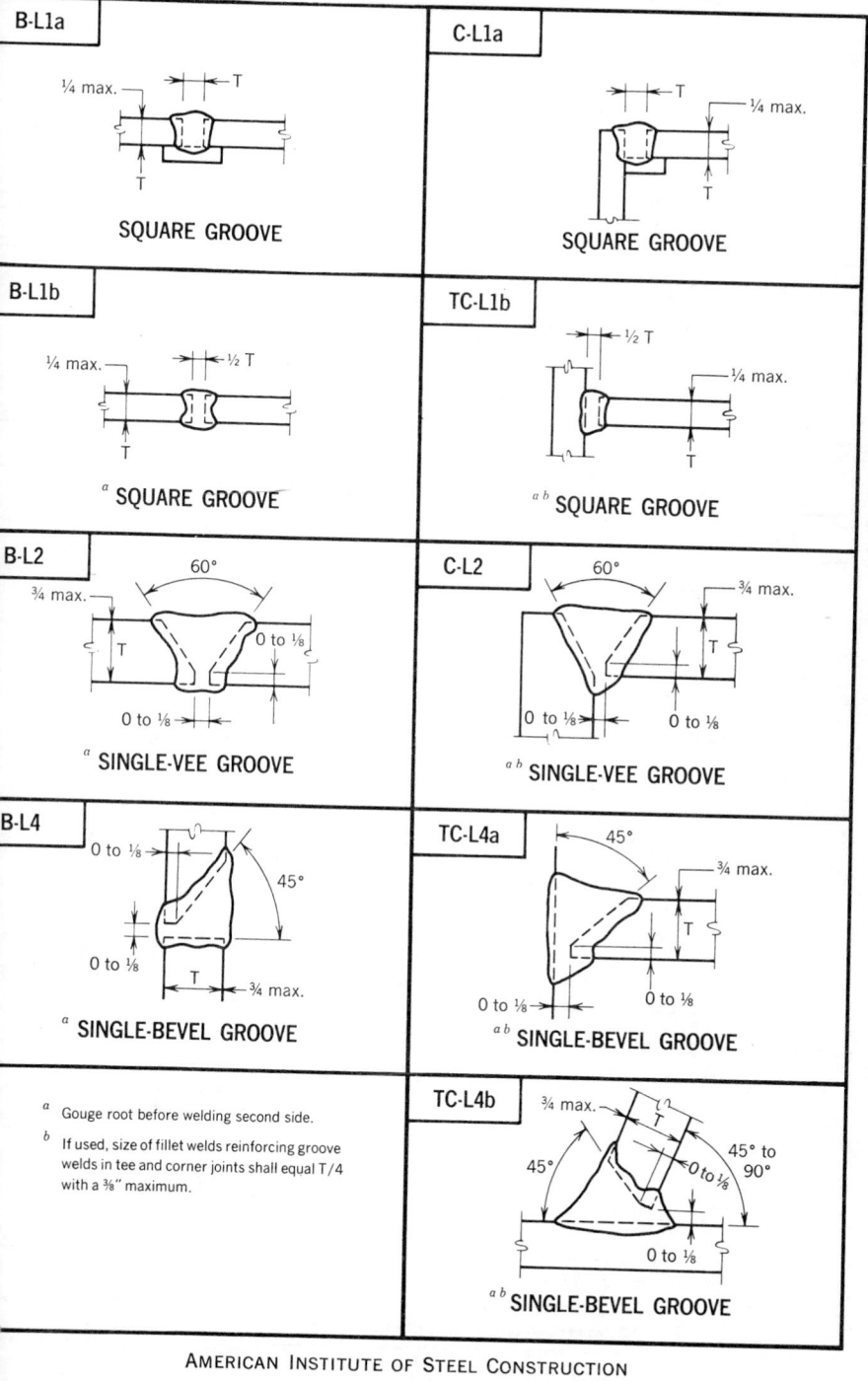

B-L1a

¼ max. — T

T

SQUARE GROOVE

C-L1a

T — ¼ max.

T

SQUARE GROOVE

B-L1b

¼ max. — ½ T

T

[a] SQUARE GROOVE

TC-L1b

½ T

¼ max.

T

[a b] SQUARE GROOVE

B-L2

60°

¾ max.

T — 0 to ⅛

0 to ⅛

[a] SINGLE-VEE GROOVE

C-L2

60°

¾ max.

T

0 to ⅛ — 0 to ⅛

[a b] SINGLE-VEE GROOVE

B-L4

0 to ⅛

45°

0 to ⅛

T — ¾ max.

[a] SINGLE-BEVEL GROOVE

TC-L4a

45°

¾ max.

T

0 to ⅛ — 0 to ⅛

[a b] SINGLE-BEVEL GROOVE

[a] Gouge root before welding second side.

[b] If used, size of fillet welds reinforcing groove welds in tee and corner joints shall equal T/4 with a ⅜″ maximum.

TC-L4b

¾ max. — T

45° to 90°

45° — 0 to ⅛

0 to ⅛

[a b] SINGLE-BEVEL GROOVE

WELDED JOINTS
Complete penetration
Manual Shielded Metal-Arc Welded Joints of UNLIMITED Thickness

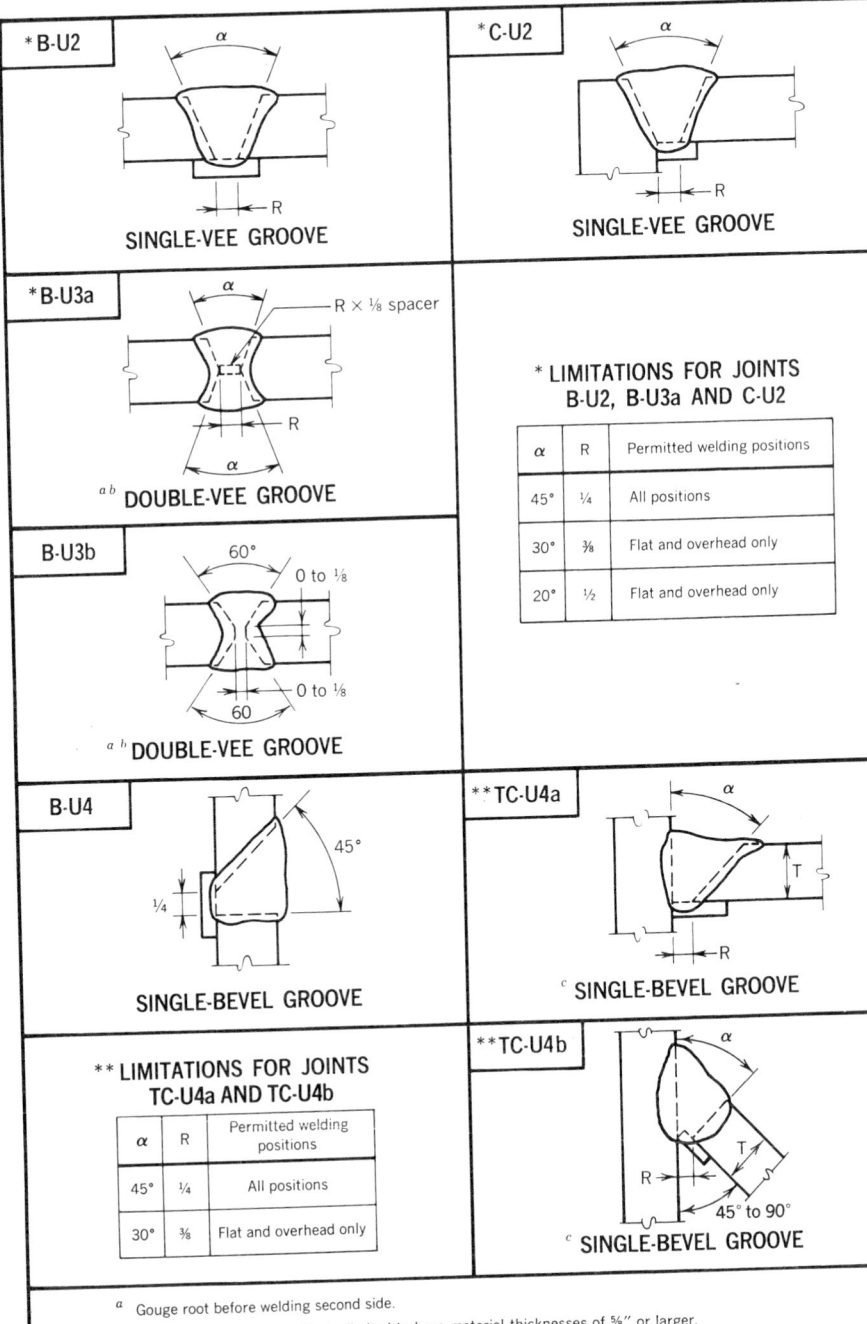

* B-U2

SINGLE-VEE GROOVE

* C-U2

SINGLE-VEE GROOVE

* B-U3a

R × ⅛ spacer

[a][b] DOUBLE-VEE GROOVE

B-U3b

60°

0 to ⅛

0 to ⅛

60

[a][b] DOUBLE-VEE GROOVE

* LIMITATIONS FOR JOINTS
B-U2, B-U3a AND C-U2

α	R	Permitted welding positions
45°	¼	All positions
30°	⅜	Flat and overhead only
20°	½	Flat and overhead only

B-U4

45°

¼

SINGLE-BEVEL GROOVE

** TC-U4a

T

R

[c] SINGLE-BEVEL GROOVE

** LIMITATIONS FOR JOINTS
TC-U4a AND TC-U4b

α	R	Permitted welding positions
45°	¼	All positions
30°	⅜	Flat and overhead only

** TC-U4b

T

R

45° to 90°

[c] SINGLE-BEVEL GROOVE

[a] Gouge root before welding second side.

[b] This joint should preferably be limited to base material thicknesses of ⅝″ or larger.

[c] If used, size of fillet welds reinforcing groove welds in tee and corner joints shall equal T/4 with a ⅜″ maximum.

AMERICAN INSTITUTE OF STEEL CONSTRUCTION

WELDED JOINTS
Complete penetration
Manual Shielded Metal-Arc Welded Joints of UNLIMITED Thickness

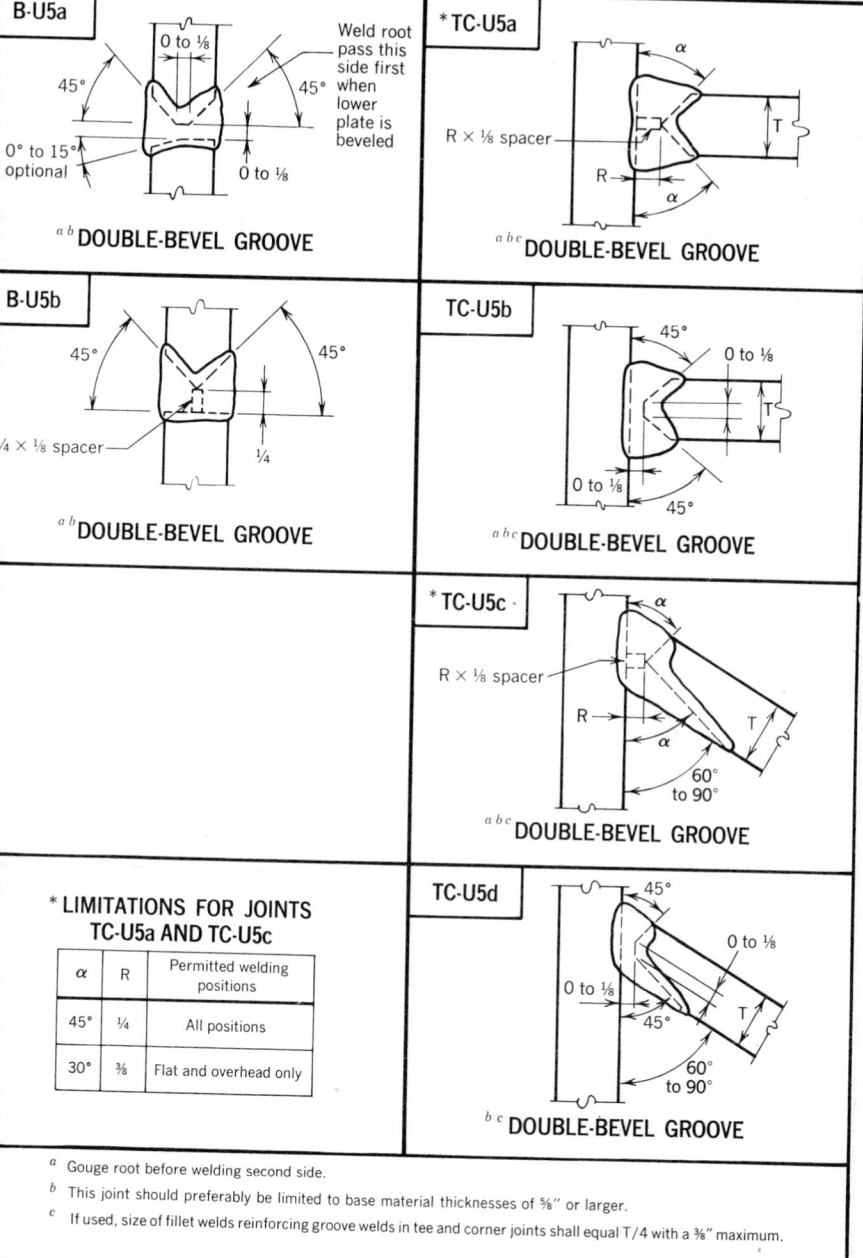

B-U5a

45°

0 to 1/8

0° to 15° optional

0 to 1/8

Weld root pass this side first when lower plate is beveled

$^{a\,b}$ **DOUBLE-BEVEL GROOVE**

*TC-U5a

α

R × 1/8 spacer

R

T

α

$^{a\,b\,c}$ **DOUBLE-BEVEL GROOVE**

B-U5b

45°

45°

1/4 × 1/8 spacer

1/4

$^{a\,b}$ **DOUBLE-BEVEL GROOVE**

TC-U5b

45°

0 to 1/8

T

0 to 1/8

45°

$^{a\,b\,c}$ **DOUBLE-BEVEL GROOVE**

*TC-U5c

α

R × 1/8 spacer

R

T

α

60° to 90°

$^{a\,b\,c}$ **DOUBLE-BEVEL GROOVE**

* LIMITATIONS FOR JOINTS TC-U5a AND TC-U5c

α	R	Permitted welding positions
45°	1/4	All positions
30°	3/8	Flat and overhead only

TC-U5d

45°

0 to 1/8

0 to 1/8

45°

T

60° to 90°

$^{b\,c}$ **DOUBLE-BEVEL GROOVE**

^{a} Gouge root before welding second side.

^{b} This joint should preferably be limited to base material thicknesses of 5/8" or larger.

^{c} If used, size of fillet welds reinforcing groove welds in tee and corner joints shall equal T/4 with a 3/8" maximum.

WELDED JOINTS
Complete penetration
Manual Shielded Metal-Arc Welded Joints of UNLIMITED Thickness

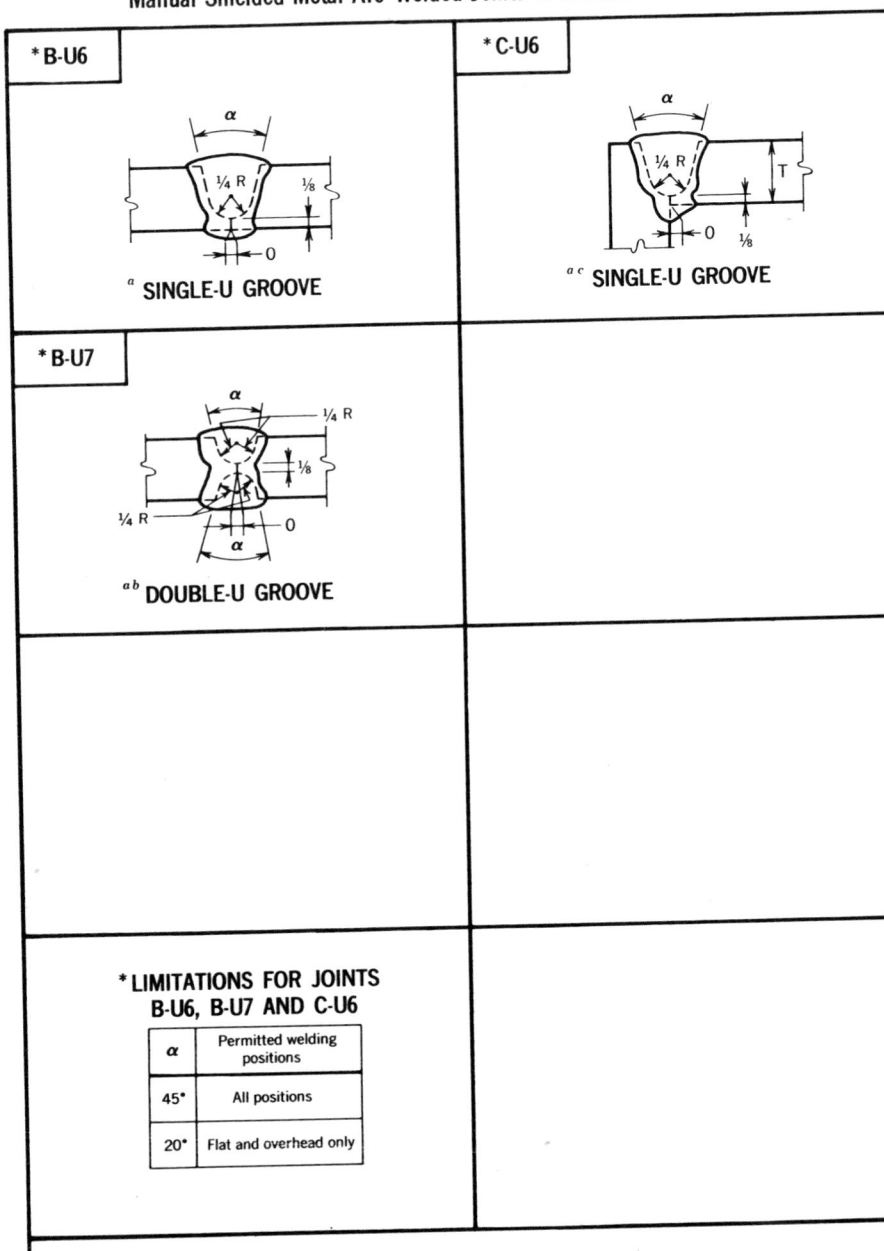

* B-U6

[a] SINGLE-U GROOVE

* C-U6

[a c] SINGLE-U GROOVE

* B-U7

[a b] DOUBLE-U GROOVE

*** LIMITATIONS FOR JOINTS
B-U6, B-U7 AND C-U6**

α	Permitted welding positions
45°	All positions
20°	Flat and overhead only

[a] Gouge root before welding second side.

[b] This joint should preferably be limited to base material thicknesses of ⅜″ or larger.

[c] If used, size of fillet welds reinforcing groove welds in tee and corner joints shall equal T/4 with a ⅜″ maximum.

AMERICAN INSTITUTE OF STEEL CONSTRUCTION

WELDED JOINTS
Complete penetration
Manual Shielded Metal-Arc Welded Joints of UNLIMITED Thickness

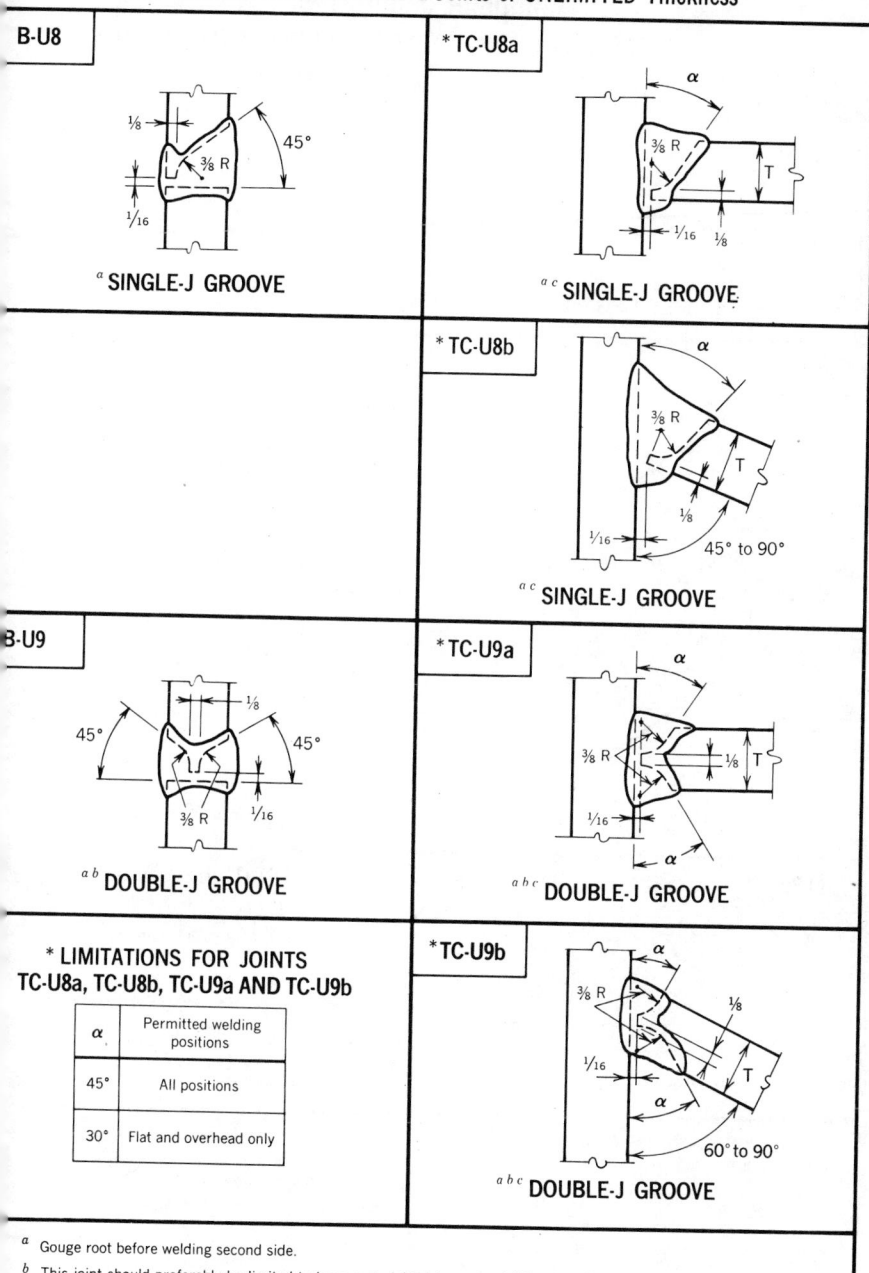

B-U8

^{a} SINGLE-J GROOVE

*TC-U8a

$^{a\,c}$ SINGLE-J GROOVE

*TC-U8b

45° to 90°

$^{a\,c}$ SINGLE-J GROOVE

B-U9

$^{a\,b}$ DOUBLE-J GROOVE

*TC-U9a

$^{a\,b\,c}$ DOUBLE-J GROOVE

* LIMITATIONS FOR JOINTS TC-U8a, TC-U8b, TC-U9a AND TC-U9b

α	Permitted welding positions
45°	All positions
30°	Flat and overhead only

*TC-U9b

60° to 90°

$^{a\,b\,c}$ DOUBLE-J GROOVE

^{a} Gouge root before welding second side.

^{b} This joint should preferably be limited to base material thicknesses of ⅜″ or larger.

^{c} If used, size of fillet welds reinforcing groove welds in tee and corner joints shall equal T/4 with a ⅜″ maximum.

WELDED JOINTS
Complete penetration
Submerged Arc Welded Joints of LIMITED and UNLIMITED Thickness

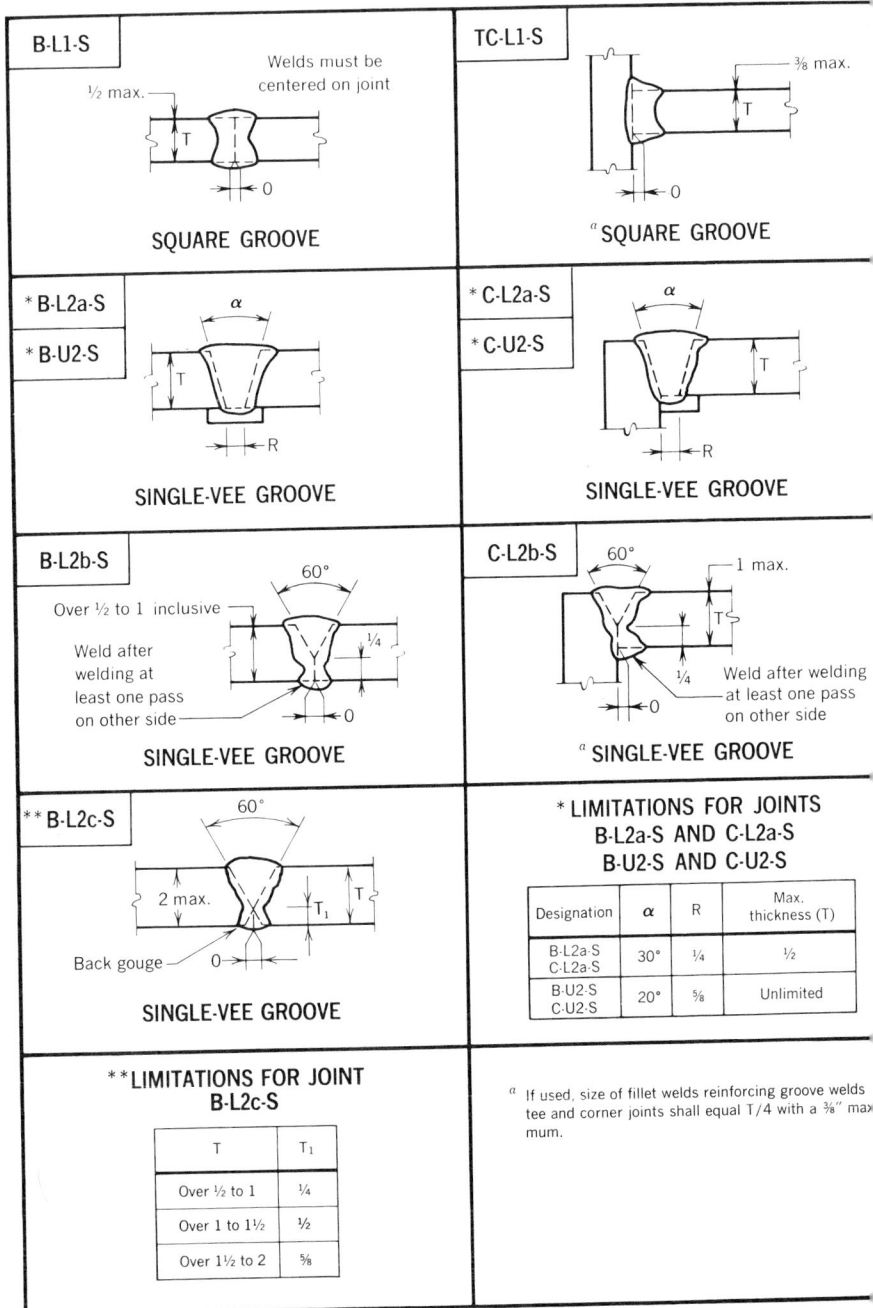

B-L1-S

Welds must be centered on joint

½ max.

T

0

SQUARE GROOVE

TC-L1-S

⅜ max.

T

0

a SQUARE GROOVE

* **B-L2a-S**

* **B-U2-S**

α

T

R

SINGLE-VEE GROOVE

* **C-L2a-S**

* **C-U2-S**

α

T

R

SINGLE-VEE GROOVE

B-L2b-S

60°

Over ½ to 1 inclusive

Weld after welding at least one pass on other side

¼

0

SINGLE-VEE GROOVE

C-L2b-S

60°

1 max.

T

¼

Weld after welding at least one pass on other side

0

a SINGLE-VEE GROOVE

** **B-L2c-S**

60°

2 max.

Back gouge

T_1

T

0

SINGLE-VEE GROOVE

* LIMITATIONS FOR JOINTS
B-L2a-S AND C-L2a-S
B-U2-S AND C-U2-S

Designation	α	R	Max. thickness (T)
B-L2a-S C-L2a-S	30°	¼	½
B-U2-S C-U2-S	20°	⅝	Unlimited

**LIMITATIONS FOR JOINT
B-L2c-S

T	T_1
Over ½ to 1	¼
Over 1 to 1½	½
Over 1½ to 2	⅝

a If used, size of fillet welds reinforcing groove welds tee and corner joints shall equal T/4 with a ⅜" max mum.

WELDED JOINTS
Complete penetration
Submerged Arc Welded Joints of LIMITED and UNLIMITED Thickness

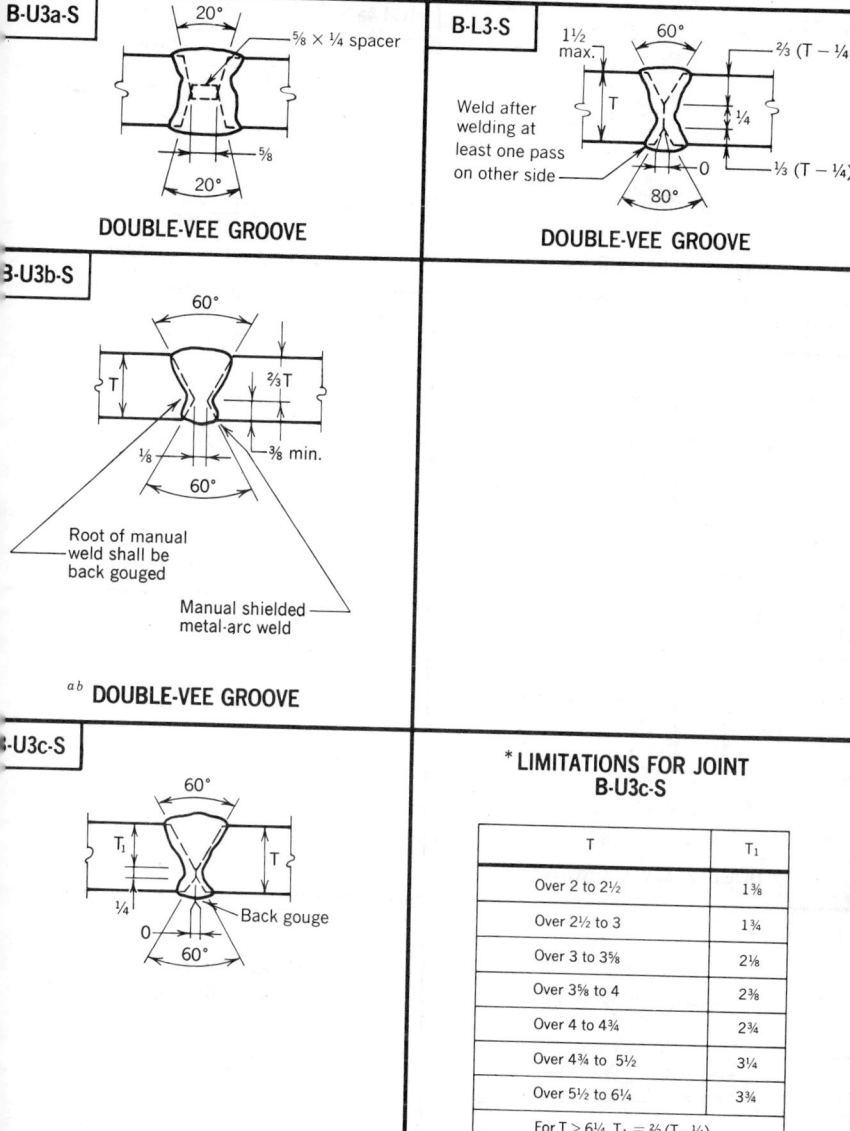

B-U3a-S

20°

⅝ × ¼ spacer

⅝

20°

DOUBLE-VEE GROOVE

B-L3-S

1½ max.

60°

⅔ (T − ¼)

T

¼

Weld after welding at least one pass on other side

0

⅓ (T − ¼)

80°

DOUBLE-VEE GROOVE

3-U3b-S

60°

T

⅔ T

⅛

⅜ min.

60°

Root of manual weld shall be back gouged

Manual shielded metal-arc weld

[a][b] **DOUBLE-VEE GROOVE**

3-U3c-S

60°

T_1

T

¼

Back gouge

0

60°

DOUBLE-VEE GROOVE

* LIMITATIONS FOR JOINT B-U3c-S

T	T_1
Over 2 to 2½	1⅜
Over 2½ to 3	1¾
Over 3 to 3⅝	2⅛
Over 3⅝ to 4	2⅜
Over 4 to 4¾	2¾
Over 4¾ to 5½	3¼
Over 5½ to 6¼	3¾
For T > 6¼, $T_1 = \frac{2}{3}(T-\frac{1}{4})$	

Manual shielded metal-arc weld made first with low hydrogen electrodes.

Single or multiple pass submerged arc weld made in flat position after manual welding is completed on other side.

AMERICAN INSTITUTE OF STEEL CONSTRUCTION

WELDED JOINTS
Complete penetration
Submerged Arc Welded Joints of LIMITED and UNLIMITED Thickness

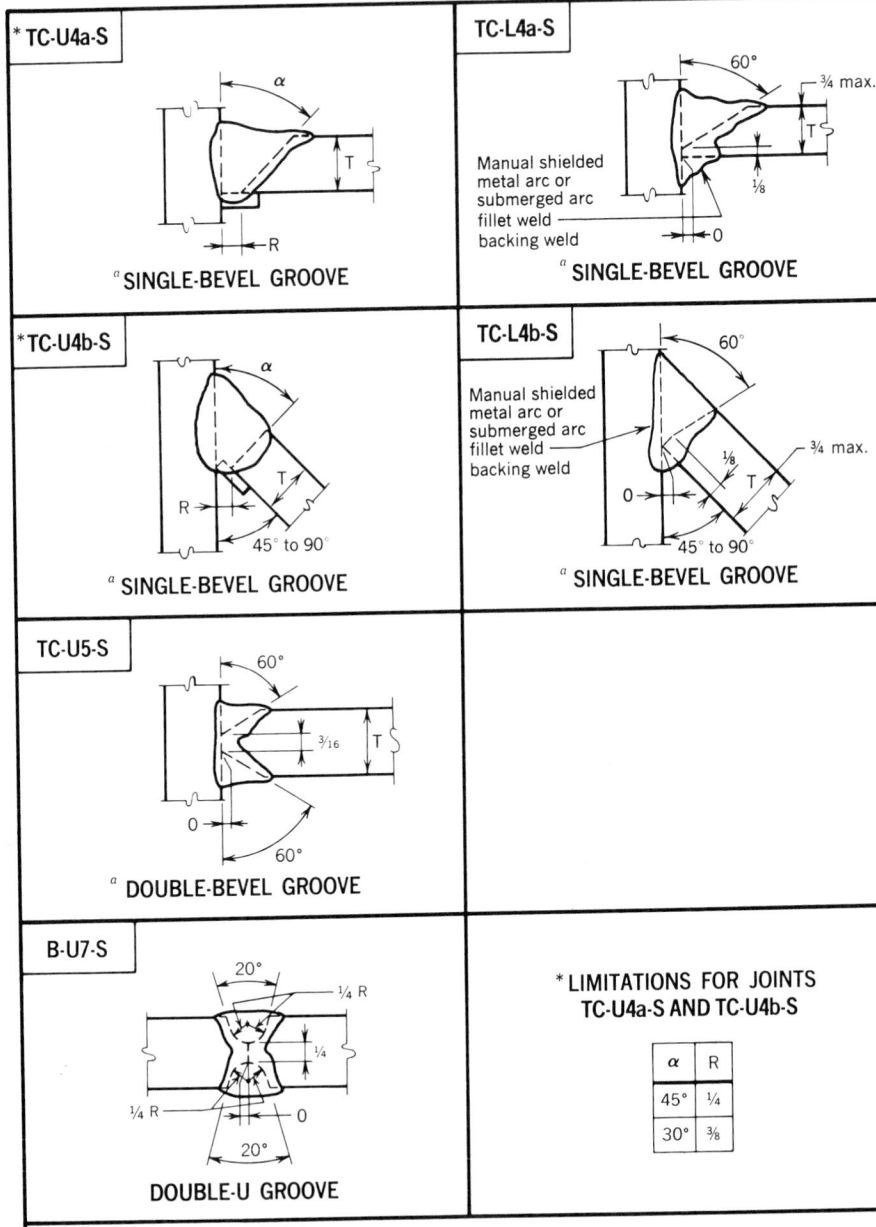

* TC-U4a-S

α

T

R

a SINGLE-BEVEL GROOVE

TC-L4a-S

60°

¾ max.

T

Manual shielded metal arc or submerged arc fillet weld backing weld

⅛

0

a SINGLE-BEVEL GROOVE

*TC-U4b-S

α

R

T

45° to 90°

a SINGLE-BEVEL GROOVE

TC-L4b-S

60°

Manual shielded metal arc or submerged arc fillet weld backing weld

⅛

¾ max.

0

T

45° to 90°

a SINGLE-BEVEL GROOVE

TC-U5-S

60°

³⁄₁₆

T

0

60°

a DOUBLE-BEVEL GROOVE

B-U7-S

20°

¼ R

¼

¼ R

0

20°

DOUBLE-U GROOVE

* LIMITATIONS FOR JOINTS TC-U4a-S AND TC-U4b-S

$α$	R
45°	¼
30°	⅜

a If used, size of fillet welds reinforcing groove welds in tee and corner joints shall equal T/4 with a ⅜" maximum.

AMERICAN INSTITUTE OF STEEL CONSTRUCTION

WELDED JOINTS
Complete penetration
Gas Metal and Flux Cored Arc Welded Joints of LIMITED Thickness

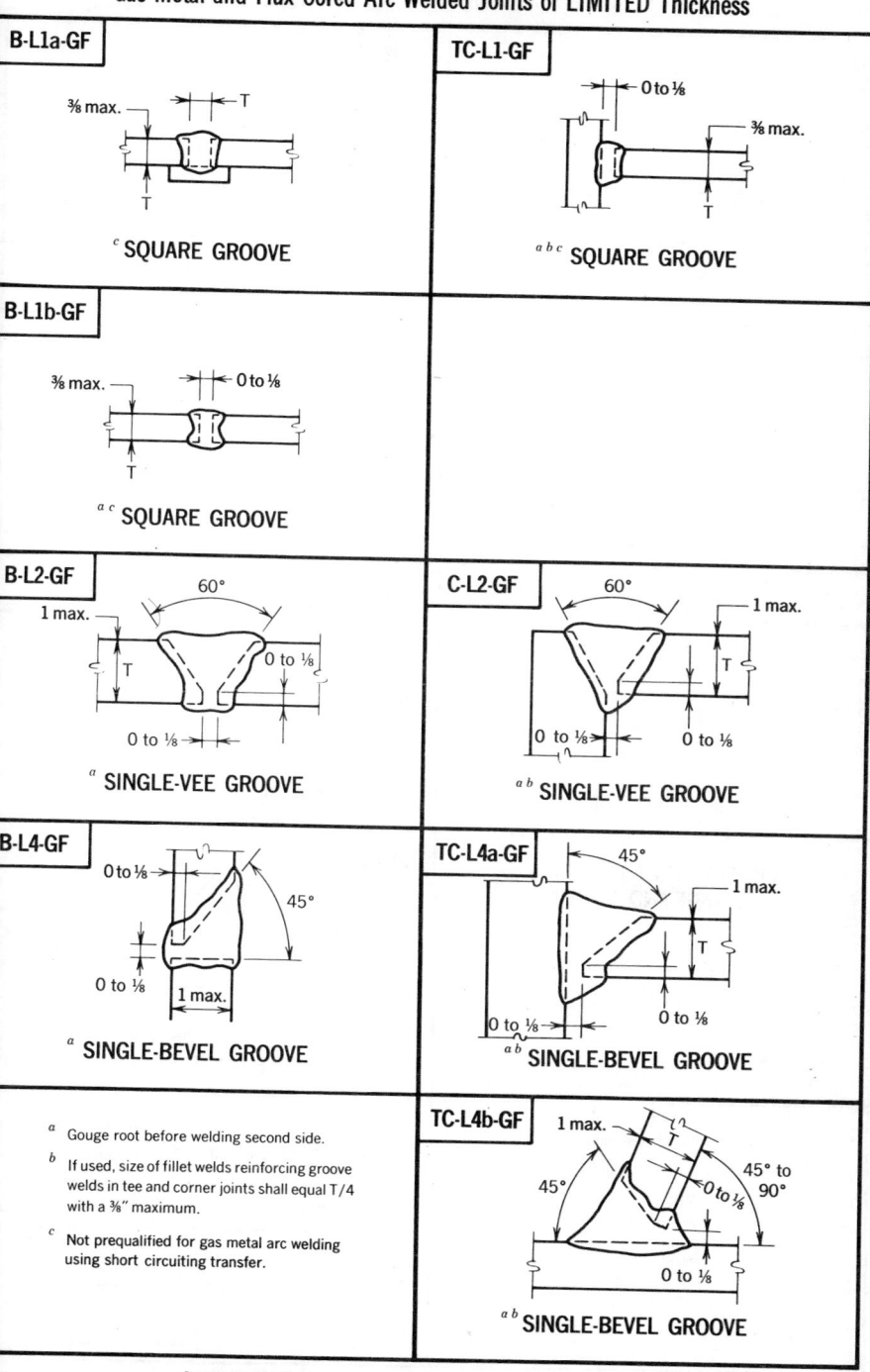

B-L1a-GF

³/₈ max. — T

T

[c] SQUARE GROOVE

TC-L1-GF

0 to ⅛

³/₈ max.

T

[a b c] SQUARE GROOVE

B-L1b-GF

³/₈ max. — 0 to ⅛

T

[a c] SQUARE GROOVE

B-L2-GF

60°

1 max.

T

0 to ⅛

0 to ⅛

[a] SINGLE-VEE GROOVE

C-L2-GF

60°

1 max.

T

0 to ⅛

0 to ⅛

[a b] SINGLE-VEE GROOVE

B-L4-GF

0 to ⅛

45°

0 to ⅛

1 max.

[a] SINGLE-BEVEL GROOVE

TC-L4a-GF

45°

1 max.

T

0 to ⅛

0 to ⅛

[a b] SINGLE-BEVEL GROOVE

[a] Gouge root before welding second side.

[b] If used, size of fillet welds reinforcing groove welds in tee and corner joints shall equal T/4 with a ³/₈" maximum.

[c] Not prequalified for gas metal arc welding using short circuiting transfer.

TC-L4b-GF

1 max. T

45° to 90°

45°

0 to ⅛

0 to ⅛

[a b] SINGLE-BEVEL GROOVE

WELDED JOINTS
Complete penetration
Gas Metal and Flux Cored Arc Welded Joints of UNLIMITED Thickness

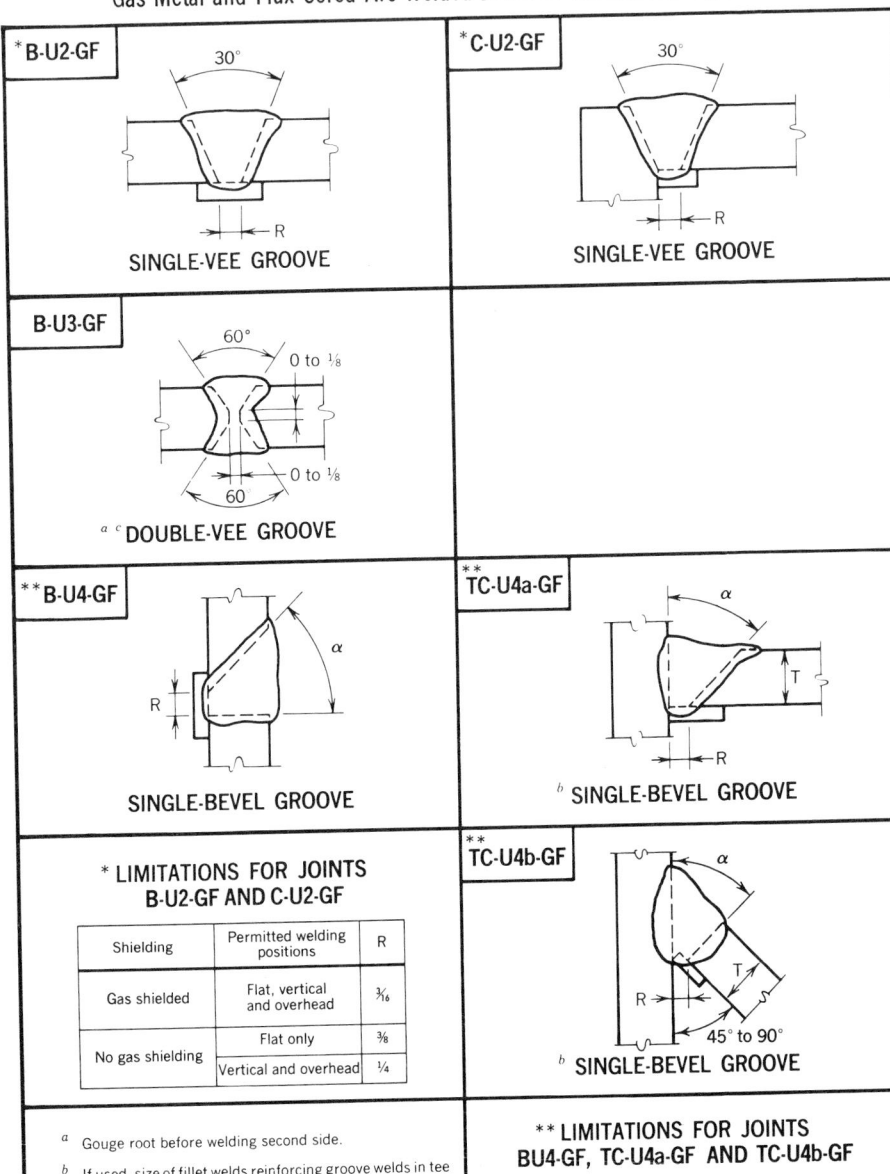

* B-U2-GF

30°

R

SINGLE-VEE GROOVE

* C-U2-GF

30°

R

SINGLE-VEE GROOVE

B-U3-GF

60°

0 to ⅛

0 to ⅛

60

a c DOUBLE-VEE GROOVE

** B-U4-GF

α

R

SINGLE-BEVEL GROOVE

** TC-U4a-GF

α

T

R

b SINGLE-BEVEL GROOVE

*** LIMITATIONS FOR JOINTS
B-U2-GF AND C-U2-GF**

Shielding	Permitted welding positions	R
Gas shielded	Flat, vertical and overhead	³⁄₁₆
No gas shielding	Flat only	⅜
	Vertical and overhead	¼

** TC-U4b-GF

α

T

R

45° to 90°

b SINGLE-BEVEL GROOVE

a Gouge root before welding second side.

b If used, size of fillet welds reinforcing groove welds in tee and corner joints shall equal T/4 with a ⅜″ maximum.

c This joint should preferably be limited to base material thicknesses of ⅝″ or larger.

**** LIMITATIONS FOR JOINTS
BU4-GF, TC-U4a-GF AND TC-U4b-GF**

Shielding	Permitted welding positions	α	R
Gas shielded	All	30°	³⁄₁₆
		45°	¼
No gas shielding	Flat only	30°	⅜
	All	45°	¼

WELDED JOINTS
Complete penetration
Gas Metal and Flux Cored Arc Welded Joints of UNLIMITED Thickness

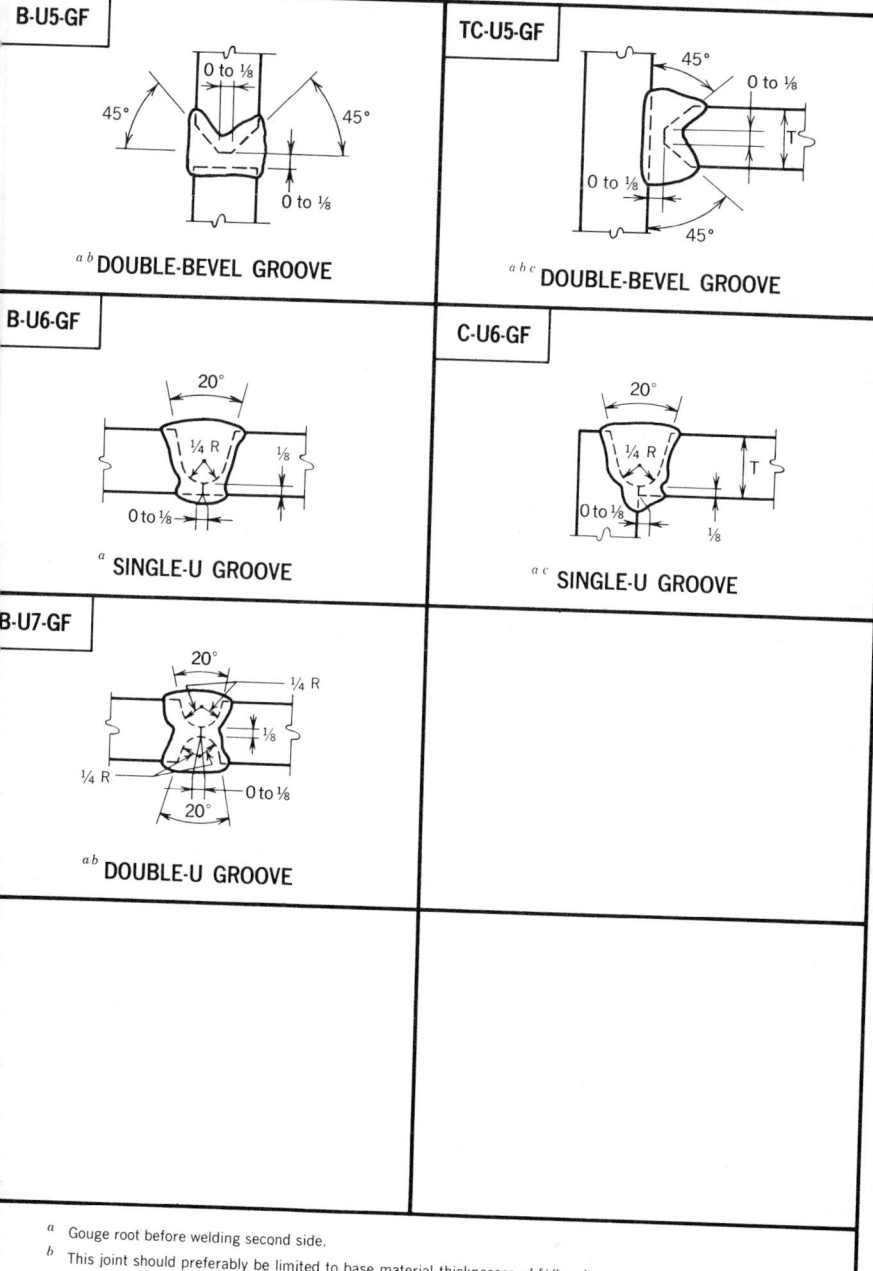

B-U5-GF

0 to ⅛

45°   45°

0 to ⅛

[a][b] DOUBLE-BEVEL GROOVE

TC-U5-GF

45°

0 to ⅛

T

0 to ⅛

45°

[a][b][c] DOUBLE-BEVEL GROOVE

B-U6-GF

20°

¼ R   ⅛

0 to ⅛

[a] SINGLE-U GROOVE

C-U6-GF

20°

¼ R   T

0 to ⅛

⅛

[a][c] SINGLE-U GROOVE

B-U7-GF

20°   ¼ R

⅛

¼ R   0 to ⅛

20°

[a][b] DOUBLE-U GROOVE

[a] Gouge root before welding second side.

[b] This joint should preferably be limited to base material thicknesses of ⅝" or larger.

[c] If used, size of fillet welds reinforcing groove welds in tee and corner joints shall equal T/4 with a ⅜" maximum.

AMERICAN INSTITUTE OF STEEL CONSTRUCTION

WELDED JOINTS
Complete penetration
Gas Metal and Flux Cored Arc Welded Joints of UNLIMITED Thickness

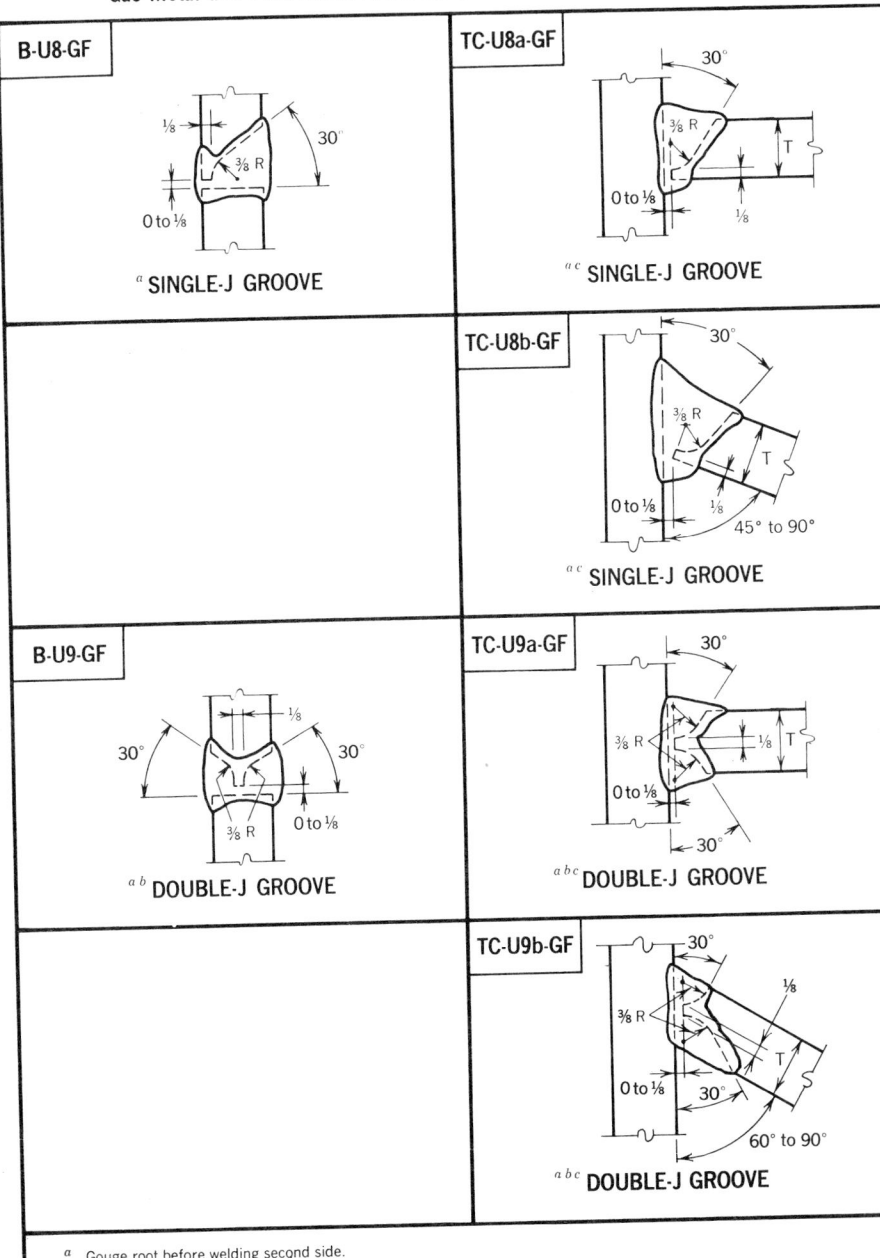

B-U8-GF

[a] SINGLE-J GROOVE

TC-U8a-GF

30°
3/8 R
T
0 to 1/8
1/8

[ac] SINGLE-J GROOVE

TC-U8b-GF

30°
3/8 R
T
0 to 1/8
1/8
45° to 90°

[ac] SINGLE-J GROOVE

B-U9-GF

30°   30°
1/8
3/8 R
0 to 1/8

[ab] DOUBLE-J GROOVE

TC-U9a-GF

30°
3/8 R
1/8   T
0 to 1/8
30°

[abc] DOUBLE-J GROOVE

TC-U9b-GF

30°
1/8
3/8 R
T
0 to 1/8
30°
60° to 90°

[abc] DOUBLE-J GROOVE

[a] Gouge root before welding second side.

[b] This joint should preferably be limited to base material thicknesses of 5/8" or larger.

[c] If used, size of fillet welds reinforcing groove welds in tee and corner joints shall equal T/4 with a 3/8" maximum.

WELDED JOINTS
Partial penetration
Manual Shielded Metal-Arc Welded Joints

B-P1a

$T_e = T$
$T \le 1/8$

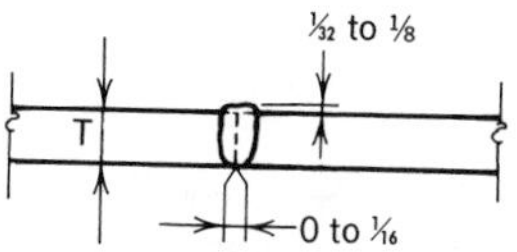
1/32 to 1/8
T
0 to 1/16

[a] **SQUARE GROOVE**

B-P4

$T_e = T$
$T \le 1/2$

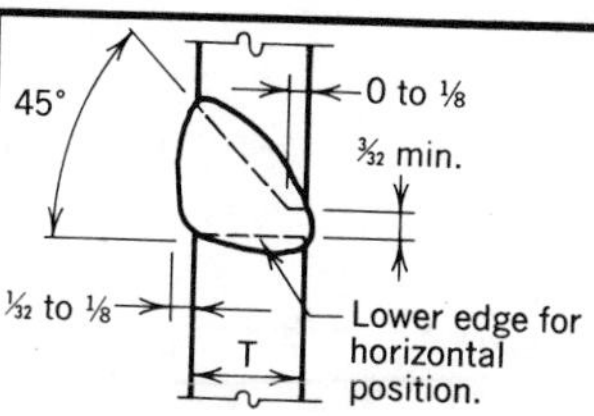
45°
0 to 1/8
3/32 min.
1/32 to 1/8
T
Lower edge for horizontal position.

[a] **SINGLE-BEVEL GROOVE**

B-P1b

Root need not be chipped before welding second side.

$T_e = T$
$T \le 1/4$

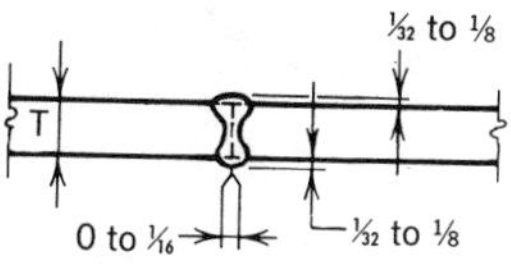
1/32 to 1/8
T
0 to 1/16
1/32 to 1/8

SQUARE GROOVE

B-P1c

$T_e = 3/4\ T$
$T \le 1/4$

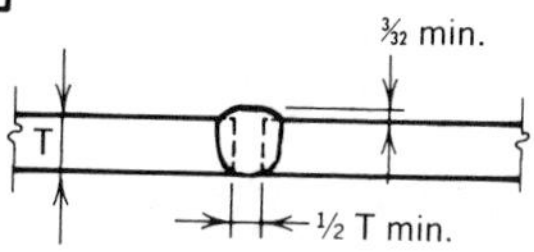
3/32 min.
T
1/2 T min.

[a] **SQUARE GROOVE**

B-P2

$T_e = T$
$T \le 1/2$

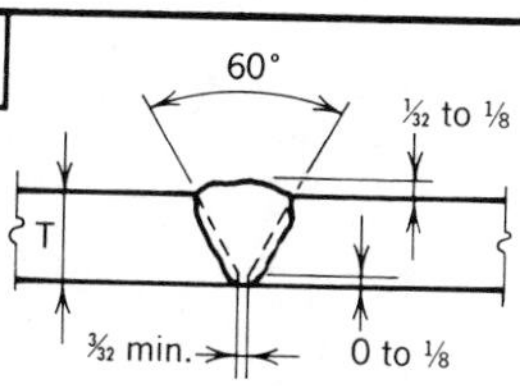
60°
1/32 to 1/8
T
3/32 min.
0 to 1/8

[a] **SINGLE-VEE GROOVE**

[b] **T_e FOR PARTIAL PENETRATION GROOVE WELDS WHEN COMBINED WITH FILLET WELDS**

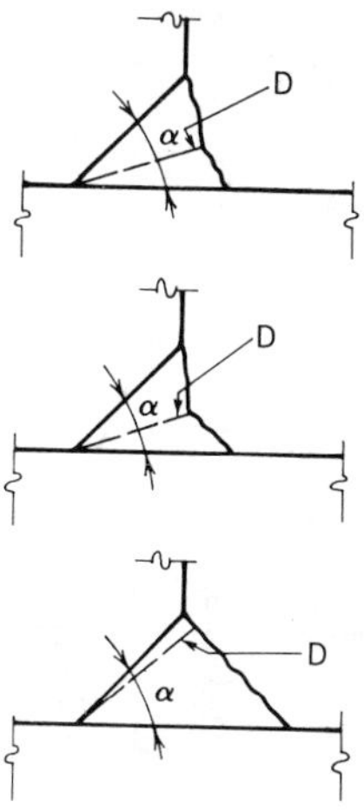
D
α
D
α
D
α

[b] Assume $\alpha = 90°$ for J grooves.
$T_e = D - 1/8$

T_e = Effective Throat.
D = Shortest distance from root to face of diagrammatic weld.
[a] Joints welded from one side.
[b] See BTC-P9.

WELDED JOINTS
Partial penetration
Manual Shielded Metal-Arc Welded Joints

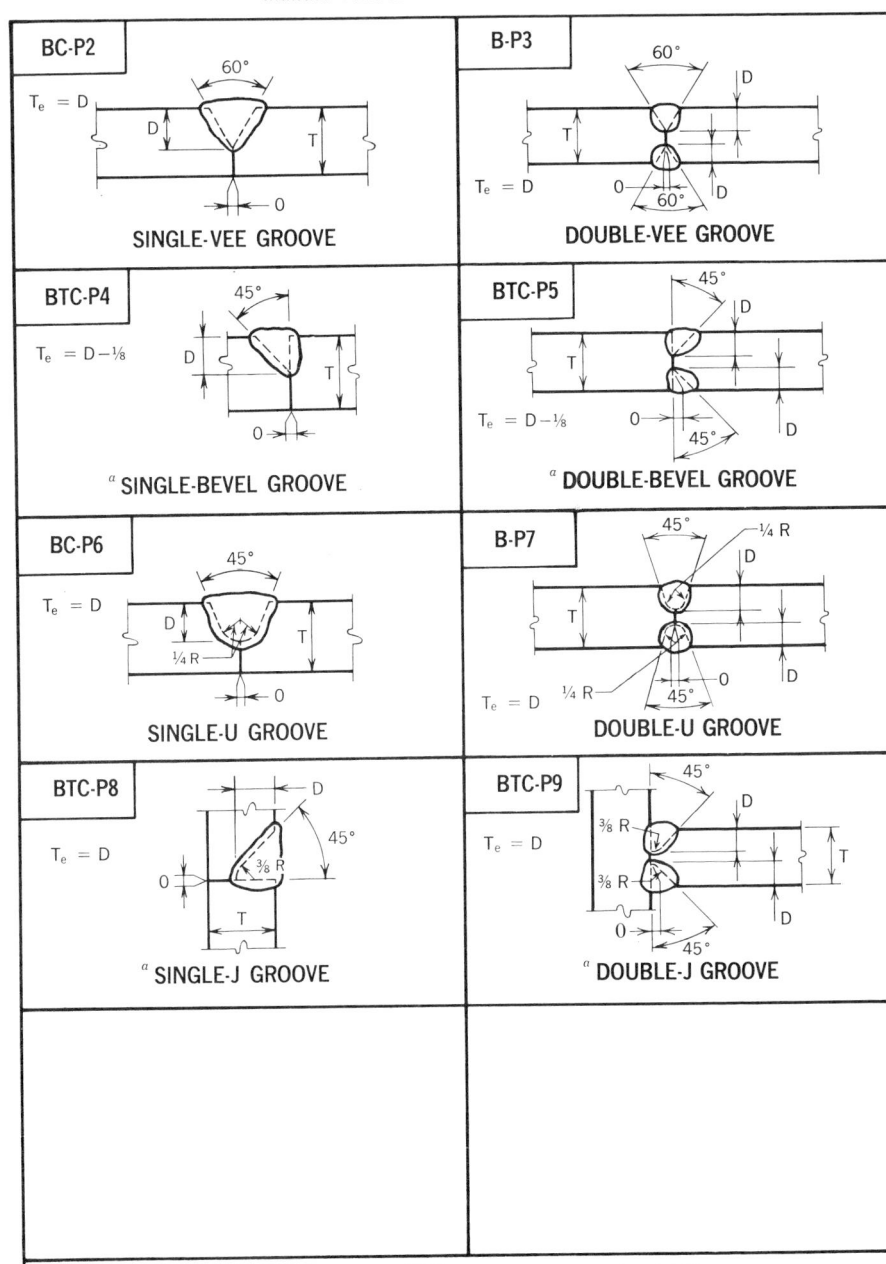

BC-P2		B-P3	
$T_e = D$	60°		60°
	SINGLE-VEE GROOVE	$T_e = D$	DOUBLE-VEE GROOVE
BTC-P4	45°	BTC-P5	45°
$T_e = D - \frac{1}{8}$	*a* SINGLE-BEVEL GROOVE	$T_e = D - \frac{1}{8}$	*a* DOUBLE-BEVEL GROOVE
BC-P6	45°	B-P7	45° ¼ R
$T_e = D$	¼ R		¼ R
	SINGLE-U GROOVE	$T_e = D$	DOUBLE-U GROOVE
BTC-P8	45°	BTC-P9	45°
$T_e = D$	⅜ R	$T_e = D$	⅜ R ⅜ R
	a SINGLE-J GROOVE		*a* DOUBLE-J GROOVE

T_e = Effective Throat each weld. Min. $T_e = \sqrt{T/6}$, See AISC Specification, Sect. 1.14.7.

Minimum root face of joints shall be ⅛ inch.

a When T or C joint is combined with fillet weld see first page of partial penetration welded joints for effective throat.

AMERICAN INSTITUTE OF STEEL CONSTRUCTION

WELDED JOINTS
Partial penetration
Submerged Arc Welded Joints

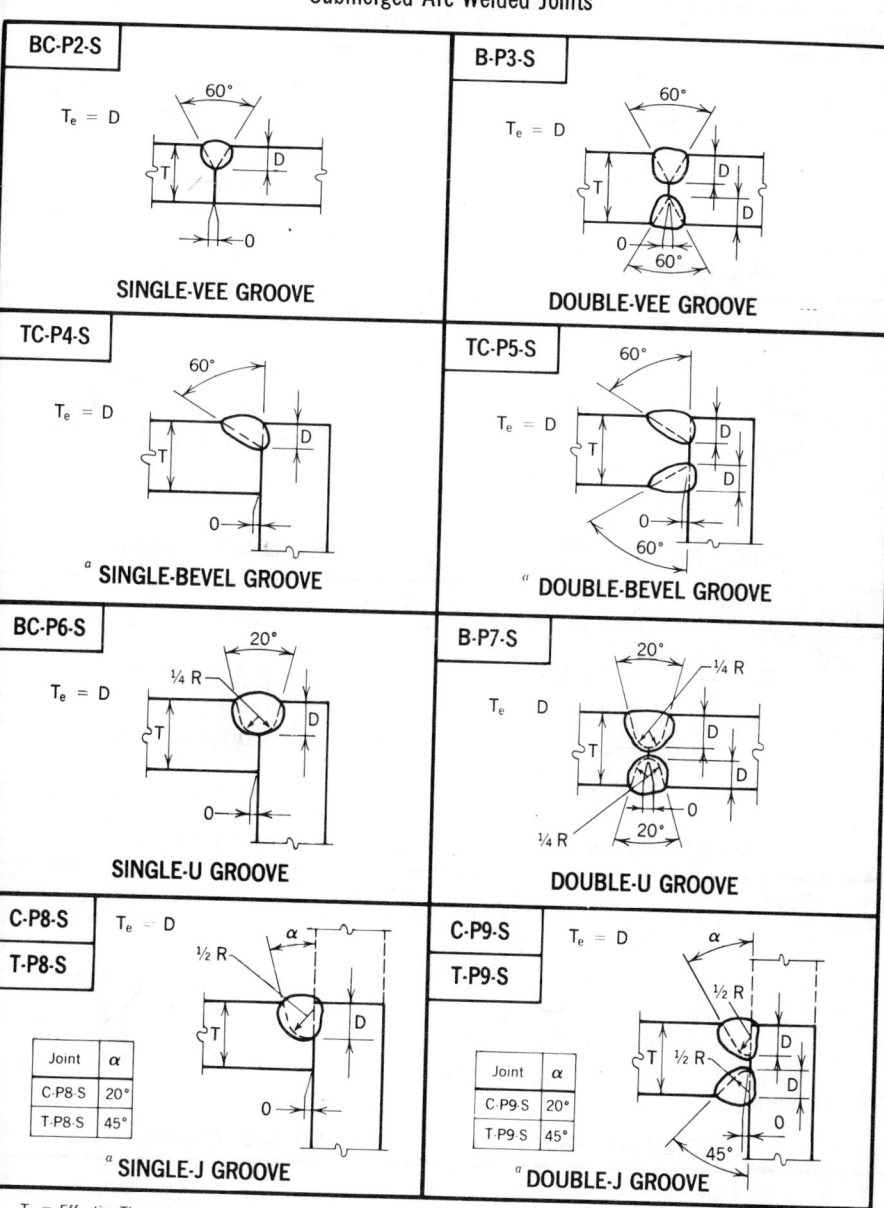

BC-P2-S

$T_e = D$

60°

SINGLE-VEE GROOVE

B-P3-S

$T_e = D$

60°

0 — 60°

DOUBLE-VEE GROOVE

TC-P4-S

$T_e = D$

60°

[a] SINGLE-BEVEL GROOVE

TC-P5-S

$T_e = D$

60°

60°

[a] DOUBLE-BEVEL GROOVE

BC-P6-S

$T_e = D$

20°

¼ R

SINGLE-U GROOVE

B-P7-S

$T_e \quad D$

20° ¼ R

¼ R 20°

DOUBLE-U GROOVE

C-P8-S

T-P8-S

$T_e = D$

½ R

α

Joint	α
C-P8-S	20°
T-P8-S	45°

[a] SINGLE-J GROOVE

C-P9-S

T-P9-S

$T_e = D$

α

½ R

½ R

Joint	α
C-P9-S	20°
T-P9-S	45°

45°

[a] DOUBLE-J GROOVE

T_e = Effective Throat each weld.

Min. $T_e = \sqrt{T/6}$, See AISC Specification, Sect. 1.14.7.

Minimum root face of joints shall be ¼ inch.

[a] When T or C joint is combined with fillet weld see first page of partial penetration welded joints for effective throat.

AMERICAN INSTITUTE OF STEEL CONSTRUCTION

WELDED JOINTS
Partial penetration
Gas Metal and Flux Cored Arc Welded Joints

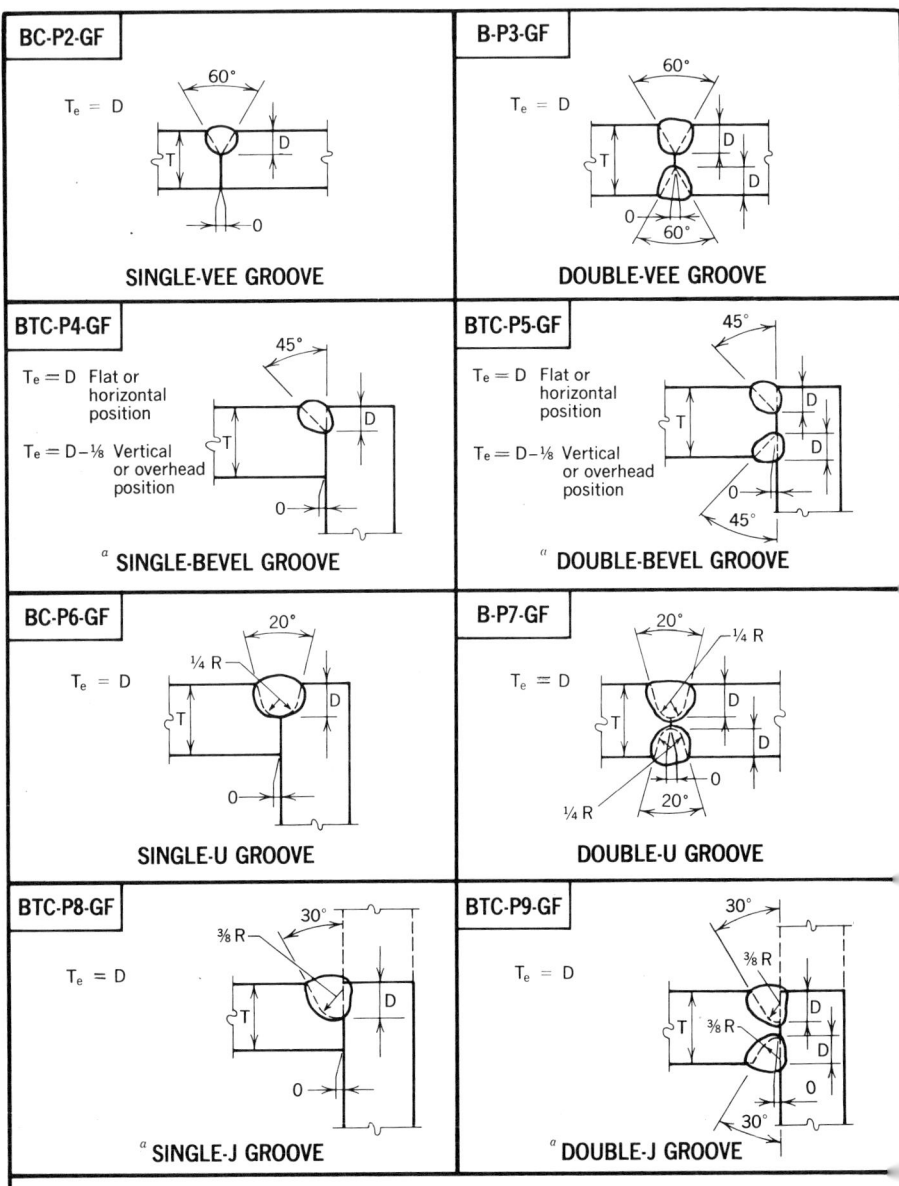

BC-P2-GF

$T_e = D$

60°

D

T

O

SINGLE-VEE GROOVE

B-P3-GF

$T_e = D$

60°

D

D

T

O

60°

DOUBLE-VEE GROOVE

BTC-P4-GF

$T_e = D$ Flat or horizontal position

$T_e = D - \frac{1}{8}$ Vertical or overhead position

45°

D

T

O

a **SINGLE-BEVEL GROOVE**

BTC-P5-GF

$T_e = D$ Flat or horizontal position

$T_e = D - \frac{1}{8}$ Vertical or overhead position

45°

D

T

D

O

45°

a **DOUBLE-BEVEL GROOVE**

BC-P6-GF

$T_e = D$

20°

¼ R

D

T

O

SINGLE-U GROOVE

B-P7-GF

$T_e = D$

20°

¼ R

D

T

D

O

¼ R

20°

DOUBLE-U GROOVE

BTC-P8-GF

$T_e = D$

30°

⅜ R

D

T

O

a **SINGLE-J GROOVE**

BTC-P9-GF

$T_e = D$

30°

⅜ R

D

T   ⅜ R

D

O

30°

a **DOUBLE-J GROOVE**

T_e = Effective Throat each weld.

Min. $T_e = \sqrt{T/6}$. See AISC Specification, Sect. 1.14.7.

Minimum root face of joints shall be ⅛ inch.

a When T or C joint is combined with fillet weld see first page of partial penetration welded joints for effective throat.

AMERICAN INSTITUTE OF STEEL CONSTRUCTION

WELDED JOINTS
Details of fillet welds
For Manual Shielded Metal-Arc, Submerged Arc, Gas Metal and Flux Cored Arc Welded Joints

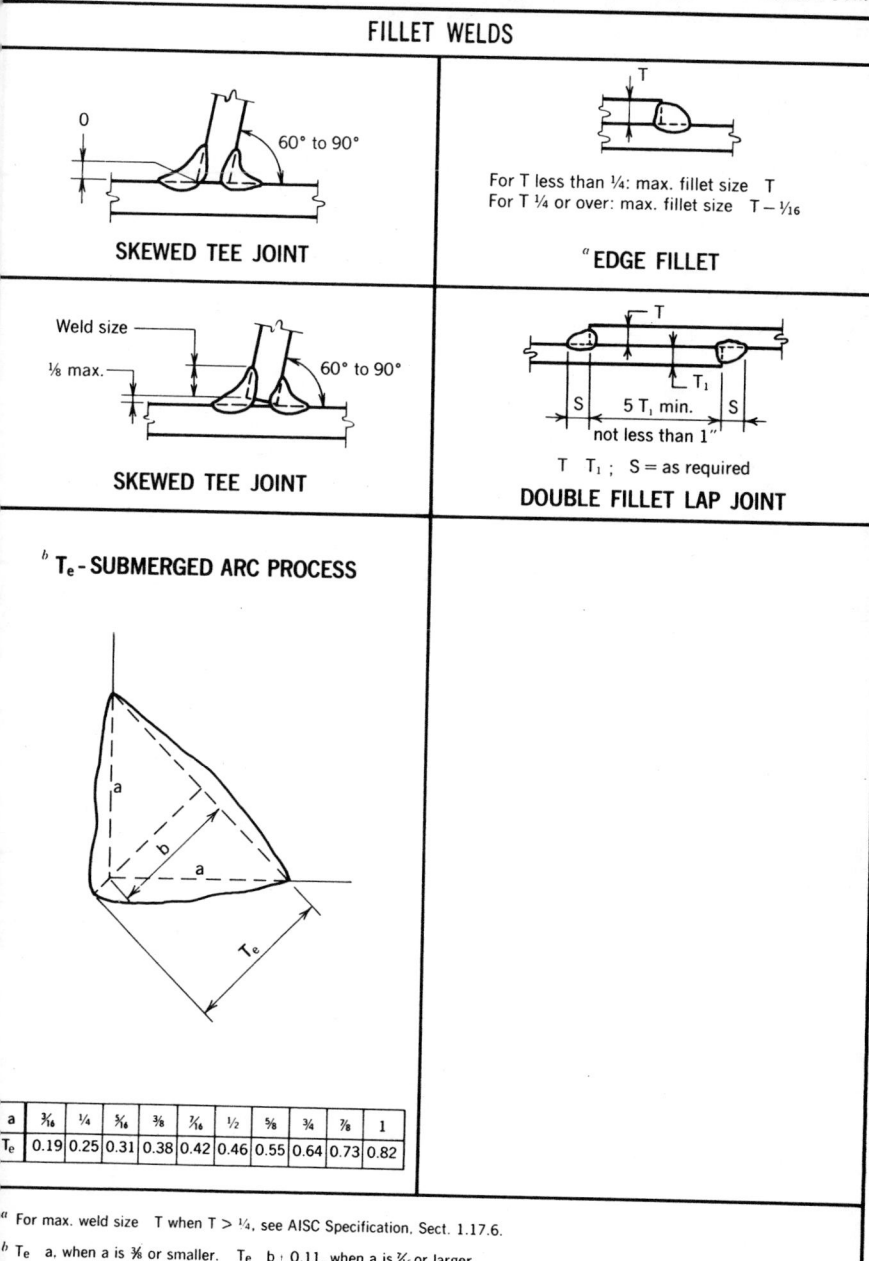

FILLET WELDS

0

60° to 90°

SKEWED TEE JOINT

T

For T less than ¼: max. fillet size   T
For T ¼ or over: max. fillet size   T − 1/16

[a] **EDGE FILLET**

Weld size

⅛ max.

60° to 90°

SKEWED TEE JOINT

T

T₁

S   5 T₁ min.   S

not less than 1"

T   T₁ ;   S = as required

DOUBLE FILLET LAP JOINT

[b] **Tₑ - SUBMERGED ARC PROCESS**

a

b

a

Tₑ

a	3/16	¼	5/16	⅜	7/16	½	⅝	¾	⅞	1
Tₑ	0.19	0.25	0.31	0.38	0.42	0.46	0.55	0.64	0.73	0.82

[a] For max. weld size   T when T > ¼, see AISC Specification, Sect. 1.17.6.

[b] Tₑ   a, when a is ⅜ or smaller.   Tₑ   b + 0.11, when a is 7/16 or larger.
See AISC Specification, Sect. 1.14.7.

Tₑ   Effective throat.

AMERICAN INSTITUTE OF STEEL CONSTRUCTION

PART 5
Specifications and Codes

AMERICAN INSTITUTE OF STEEL CONSTRUCTION

SPECIFICATION FOR THE DESIGN, FABRICATION & ERECTION OF

STRUCTURAL STEEL FOR BUILDINGS

FEBRUARY 12, 1969

AMERICAN INSTITUTE
OF STEEL CONSTRUCTION
101 PARK AVENUE, NEW YORK, N.Y. 10017

Foreword

The AISC Specification for the Design, Fabrication, and Erection o Structural Steel for Buildings is under constant review. As new develop ments warrant, it will from time to time be revised. To this end, the AIS(Advisory Committee on Specifications will consider on a continuing basi possible changes and modifications to update the specification. Whe officially adopted by the Institute, these changes will constitute Supplemen to the Specification. These Supplements will be consecutively numbere and issued with an effective date.

Supplements No. 1 and No. 2 have been adopted and appear on pag 5-118.1 through 5-118.13. The location of changes made by these tw Supplements is indicated along the page margins by encircled numbers thu ① and ②.

American Institute of Steel Construction.

June 1973

Preface

Research completed since the last revision of the AISC *Specification for the Design, Fabrication and Erection of Structural Steel for Buildings* in 1963, together with the publication of new ASTM specifications covering grades of structural steel often affording improved economy, account for the additions and most of the changes in this revision of the AISC Specification.

Among the new provisions attributable to recent research are those covering the use of hybrid flexural members, that is, beams and girders having higher strength steel in the flanges than in the web. Also included are: a more rational set of working stresses for fillet welds that consider the mechanical properties of both weld and base metal and cover a much wider strength range than heretofore; the extension of existing working stress provisions and geometric limitations, expressed in terms of specified minimum yield stress, to steels having a yield stress of 100 ksi; and the extension of plastic design rules to cover braced multi-story structures and steels having a yield stress up to 65 ksi.

As in the past, in order to avoid reference to proprietary steels which may be available from but one source, only steels which can be identified by ASTM specifications are listed. However, steels covered by ASTM specifications but subject to more costly manufacturing and inspection techniques than deemed essential for structures covered by this Specification are not listed, even though they may provide all of the necessary characteristics of less expensive steels which are listed.

Steels covered by the listed ASTM specifications which have been adopted since the 1963 revision of the AISC Specification have been available for some time as proprietary products and considerable experience has already been acquired in their use. Also listed for the first time are several grades of steel having less frequent applications in building construction, which have been covered by ASTM specifications for many years. Their inclusion is for clarification. They have proven entirely satisfactory when used in accordance with the provisions of the AISC Specification.

With the extension of plastic design to steels having a yield stress in excess of the previous 36 ksi limitation, more restrictive width-thickness ratios are imposed on compression elements in Sect. 2.7 than in Sect. 1.5.1.4.1. This is because the required plastic hinge rotations in structures designed according to the provisions of Part 2 may be considerably greater than in designs executed according to the provisions of Sect. 1.5.1.4.1. The term *compact section* will continue to apply to members meeting the geometric limitations of Sect. 1.5.1.4.1 with respect to profile; shapes conforming to the requirements of Sect. 2.7 may be referred to as *plastic design sections*.

In order to simplify design calculations, the forces, stresses, and formulas related to them are now expressed in kips or kips per square inch, instead of pounds or pounds per square inch as in the past.

As used throughout the Specification, the term *structural steel* refers exclusively to those items enumerated in Section 2 of the AISC *Code of Standard Practice for Steel Buildings and Bridges,* and nothing herein contained is intended as a recommended practice for skylights, fire escapes, or other items not specifically enumerated in that Code. For the design of cold-formed steel structural members, whose profiles contain rounded corners and slender flat elements, the provisions of the American Iron and Steel Institute *Specification for the Design of Cold-Formed Steel Structural Members* are recommended.

Many provisions of the Specification, notably in the sections dealing with fabrication and erection practices, have evolved from years of shop and field experience and need no further elaboration. Others are the outgrowth of recent extensive research. A separate *Commentary,* providing the background for such provisions, published by the American Institute of Steel Construction, is available at no cost to users of the Specification.

By the Committee,

Milton E. Eliot, Chairman	Edwin H. Gaylord	William A. Milek, Jr.
William C. Alsmeyer	John A. Gilligan	William H. Munse
Stephenson B. Barnes	John D. Griffiths	Anthony Nassetta
Lynn S. Beedle	Robert L. Haenel	Lowell A. Napper
Walter E. Blessey	Robert S. Henry	Egor P. Popov
Omer W. Blodgett	Theodore R. Higgins	Norman W. Rimmer
John S. Carter	Ira M. Hooper	Victor P. Scott
James Chinn	John W. Hubler	John B. Skilling
Carson F. Diefenderfer	Bruce G. Johnston	Ivan M. Viest
Edward R. Estes, Jr.	John E. Lothers	Glen P. Willard
Richard F. Ferguson	William J. LeMessurier	George Winter
Robert R. Gavin	Carl A. Metz	Charles A. Zwissler

February 12, 1969

Table of Contents

Nomenclature

A_b Nominal body area of a fastener

A_c Actual area of effective concrete flange in composite design

A_{bc} Planar area of web at beam-to-column connection

A_f Area of compression flange

A_s Area of steel beam in composite design

A_{sr} Area of reinforcing steel providing composite action at point of negative moment

A_{st} Cross-sectional area of stiffener or pair of stiffeners

A_w Area of girder web

C Ratio of bolt tensile strength to tensile strength of connected part

C_a Coefficient used in Table 1-A

C_b Bending coefficient dependent upon moment gradient; equal to

$$1.75 + 1.05 \left(\frac{M_1}{M_2}\right) + 0.3 \left(\frac{M_1}{M_2}\right)^2$$

C_c Column slenderness ratio dividing elastic and inelastic buckling; equal to

$$\sqrt{\frac{2\pi^2 E}{F_y}}$$

C_m Coefficient applied to bending term in interaction formula and dependent upon column curvature caused by applied moments

C_p Stiffness factor for primary member in a flat roof

C_s Stiffness factor of secondary member in a flat roof

C_v Ratio of "critical" web stress, according to the linear buckling theory, to the shear yield stress of web material; equal to

$$\frac{\pi^2 E k \sqrt{3}}{12(1 - \nu^2)(h/t)^2 F_y} \quad \text{or} \quad \frac{190}{h/t}\sqrt{\frac{k}{F_y}} \quad \text{(See Sect. 1.10.5.2)}$$

C_1 Ratio of beam yield stress to column yield stress

C_2 Ratio of column yield stress to stiffener yield stress

D Factor depending upon type of transverse stiffeners

E Modulus of elasticity of steel (29,000 kips per square inch)

E_c Modulus of elasticity of concrete

F Load factor in plastic design

F_a Axial stress permitted in the absence of bending moment

F_{as} Axial compressive stress, permitted in the absence of bending moment for bracing and other secondary members

F_b Bending stress permitted in the absence of axial force

F'_b Allowable bending stress in compression flange of plate girders as reduced for hybrid girders or because of large web depth-to-thickness ratio

F'_e Euler stress divided by factor of safety; equal to

$$\frac{12\pi^2 E}{23(Kl_b/r_b)^2}$$

F_p Allowable bearing stress

F_{sr} Stress range
F_t Allowable tensile stress
F_v Allowable shear stress
F_y Specified minimum yield stress of the type of steel being used (kips per square inch). As used in this Specification, "yield stress" denotes either the specified minimum yield point (for those steels that have a yield point) or specified minimum yield strength (for those steels that do not have a yield point).
F_{yr} Yield stress of reinforcing steel providing composite action at point of negative moment
I_d Moment of inertia of steel deck on a flat roof
I_p Moment of inertia of primary member in flat roof framing
I_s Moment of inertia of secondary member in flat roof framing
I_{tr} Moment of inertia of transformed composite section
K Effective length factor
L Span length (feet)
L_p Length of primary member in a flat roof (feet)
L_s Length of secondary member in a flat roof (feet)
M Moment (kip-feet)
M_1 Smaller moment at end of unbraced length of beam-column
M_2 Larger moment at end of unbraced length of beam-column
M_D Moment produced by dead load
M_L Moment produced by live load
M_m Critical moment that can be resisted by a plastically designed member in absence of axial load
M_o Reduced plastic moment
M_p Plastic moment
N Length of bearing of applied load (inches)
N_1 Number of shear connectors equal to V_h/q or V'_h/q, as applicable
N_2 Number of shear connectors required where closer spacing is needed adjacent to point of zero moment
P Applied load (kips)
$P_{cr} = 1.70\, AF_a$
$P_e = 1.92\, AF'_e$
P_y Plastic axial load; equal to profile area times specified minimum yield stress (kips)
Q_a Ratio of effective profile area of an axially loaded member to its total profile area
Q_s Axial stress reduction factor where width-thickness ratio of unstiffened elements exceeds limiting value given in Sect. 1.9.1.2
R Reaction or concentrated transverse load applied to beam or girder (kips)
S Spacing of secondary members in a flat roof (feet)
S_{eff} Effective section modulus corresponding to partial composite action
S_s Section modulus of steel beam used in composite design, referred to the bottom flange
S_{tr} Section modulus of transformed composite cross-section, referred to the bottom flange
T_b Specified pretension of a high strength bolt (kips)
V Statical shear on beam (kips)
V_h Total horizontal shear to be resisted by connectors under full composite action (kips)

V'_h Total horizontal shear to be resisted by connectors in providing partial composite action (kips)

V_u Statical shear produced by "ultimate" load in plastic design (kips)

Y Ratio of yield stress of web steel to yield stress of stiffener steel

a Clear distance between transverse stiffeners

a' Distance required at ends of welded partial length cover plate to develop stress

b Effective width of concrete slab; actual width of stiffened and unstiffened compression elements

b_e Effective width of stiffened compression element

b_f Flange width of rolled beam or plate girder

c Distance from neutral axis to extreme fiber of beam

d Depth of beam or girder. Also diameter of roller or rocker bearing

d_c Column web depth clear of fillets

e Horizontal displacement, in the direction of the span, between top and botton of simply supported beam at its ends

f Axial compression load on member divided by effective area (kips per square inch)

f_a Computed axial stress

f_b Computed bending stress

f'_c Specified compression strength of concrete

f_t Computed tensile stress

f_v Computed shear stress

f_{vs} Shear between girder web and transverse stiffeners (kips per linear inch of single stiffener or pair of stiffeners)

g Transverse spacing between fastener gage lines

h Clear distance between flanges of a beam or girder

k Coefficient relating linear buckling strength of a plate to its dimensions and condition of edge support. Also distance from outer face of flange to web toe of fillet of rolled shape or equivalent distance on welded section

l Actual unbraced length (inches)

l_b Actual unbraced length in plane of bending (inches)

l_{cr} Critical unbraced length adjacent to plastic hinge (inches)

n Modular ratio; equal to E/E_c

q Allowable horizontal shear to be resisted by a shear connector

r Governing radius of gyration

r_b Radius of gyration about axis of concurrent bending

r_y Lesser radius of gyration

s Spacing (pitch) between successive holes in line of stress

t Girder, beam, or column web thickness

t_b Beam flange thickness at rigid beam-to-column connection

t_f Flange thickness

t_t Thickness of thinner part joined by partial penetration groove weld

w Length of channel shear connectors

x Subscript relating symbol to strong axis bending

y Subscript relating symbol to weak axis bending

α Ratio of hybrid girder web yield stress to flange yield stress

β Ratio S_{tr}/S_s or S_{eff}/S_s

ν Poisson's ratio, may be taken as 0.3 for steel

SPECIFICATION FOR THE

Design, Fabrication and Erection
of Structural Steel for Buildings

PART 1

SECTION 1.1 PLANS AND DRAWINGS

1.1.1 Plans

The plans (design drawings) shall show a complete design with sizes, sections, and the relative locations of the various members. Floor levels, column centers, and offsets shall be dimensioned. Plans shall be drawn to a scale large enough to convey the information adequately.

Plans shall indicate the type or types of construction (as defined in Sect. 1.2) to be employed, and they shall be supplemented by such data concerning the assumed loads, shears, moments and axial forces to be resisted by all members and their connections, as may be required for the proper preparation of the shop drawings.

Where joints are to be assembled with high strength bolts and are required to resist shear between the connected parts, the plans shall indicate the type of connections to be provided, namely, friction or bearing.

Camber of trusses, beams and girders, if required, shall be called for on the design drawings.

1.1.2 Shop Drawings

Shop drawings, giving complete information necessary for the fabrication of the component parts of the structure, including the location, type and size of all rivets, bolts and welds, shall be prepared in advance of the actual fabrication. They shall clearly distinguish between shop and field rivets, bolts and welds.

Shop drawings shall be made in conformity with the best modern practice and with due regard to speed and economy in fabrication and erection.

1.1.3 Notations for Welding

Note shall be made on the plans and on the shop drawings of those joints or groups of joints in which it is especially important that the welding sequence and technique of welding be carefully controlled to minimize welding under restraint and to avoid undue distortion.

Weld lengths called for on the plans and on the shop drawings shall be the net effective lengths.

1.1.4 Standard Symbols and Nomenclature

Welding symbols used on plans and shop drawings shall preferably be the American Welding Society symbols. Other adequate welding symbols may be used, provided a complete explanation thereof is shown on the plans or drawings.

Unless otherwise noted, the standard nomenclature contained in the joint AISC-SJI *Standard Specifications for Open Web Steel Joists and Long-span Steel Joists*, latest edition, shall be used in describing steel joists.

SECTION 1.2 TYPES OF CONSTRUCTION

Three basic types of construction and associated design assumptions are permissible under the respective conditions stated hereinafter, and each will govern in a specific manner the size of members and the types and strength of their connections.

Type 1, commonly designated as "rigid-frame" (continuous frame), assumes that beam-to-column connections have sufficient rigidity to hold virtually unchanged the original angles between intersecting members.

Type 2, commonly designated as "simple" framing (unrestrained, free-ended), assumes that, in so far as gravity loading is concerned, the ends of beams and girders are connected for shear only, and are free to rotate under gravity load.

Type 3, commonly designated as "semi-rigid framing" (partially restrained), assumes that the connections of beams and girders possess a dependable and known moment capacity intermediate in degree between the rigidity of Type 1 and the flexibility of Type 2.

The design of all connections shall be consistent with the assumptions as to type of construction called for on the design drawings.

Type 1 construction is unconditionally permitted under this Specification. Two different methods of design are recognized. Within the limitations laid down in Sect. 2.1, members of continuous frames, or continuous portions of frames, may be proportioned, on the basis of their maximum predictable strength, to resist the specified design loads multiplied by the prescribed load factors. Otherwise Type 1 construction shall be designed, within the limitations of Sect. 1.5, to resist the stresses produced by the specified design loads, assuming moment distribution in accordance with the elastic theory.

Type 2 construction is permitted under this Specification, subject to the stipulations of the following paragraph wherever applicable.

In tier buildings designed as Type 2 construction (that is, with beam-to-column connections other than wind connections assumed flexible under gravity loading) the wind moments may be distributed among selected joints of the frame provided that

1. The connections and connected members have capacity to resist the wind moments.

2. The girders are adequate to carry the full gravity load as "simple beams."

3. The connections have adequate inelastic rotation capacity to avoid overstress of the fasteners or welds under combined gravity and wind loading.

Type 3 (semi-rigid) construction will be permitted only upon evidence that the connections to be used are capable of furnishing, as a minimum, a predictable proportion of full end restraint. The proportioning of main members joined by such connections shall be predicated upon no greater degree of end restraint than this minimum.

Types 2 and 3 construction may necessitate some non-elastic but self-limiting deformation of a structural steel part.

SECTION 1.3 LOADS AND FORCES

1.3.1 Dead Load

The dead load to be assumed in design shall consist of the weight of steelwork and all material permanently fastened thereto or supported thereby.

1.3.2 Live Load

The live load, including snow load if any, shall be that stipulated by the Code under which the structure is being designed or that dictated by the conditions involved. Snow load shall be considered as applied either to the entire roof area or to a portion of the roof area, and any probable arrangement of loads resulting in the highest stresses in the supporting member shall be used in the design.

1.3.3 Impact

For structures carrying live loads which induce impact, the assumed live load shall be increased sufficiently to provide for same.

If not otherwise specified, the increase shall be:

For supports of elevators	100 percent
For traveling crane support girders and their connections	25 percent
For supports of light machinery, shaft or motor driven, not less than	20 percent
For supports of reciprocating machinery or power driven units, not less than	50 percent
For hangers supporting floors and balconies	33 percent

1.3.4 Crane Runway Horizontal Forces

The lateral force on crane runways to provide for the effect of moving crane trolleys shall, if not otherwise specified, be 20 percent of the sum of the weights of the lifted load and of the crane trolley (but exclusive of other parts of the crane). The force shall be assumed to be applied at the top of the rail, one-half on each side of the runway, and shall be considered as acting in either direction normal to the runway rail.

The longitudinal force shall, if not otherwise specified, be taken as 10 percent of the maximum wheel loads of the crane applied at the top of rail.

1.3.5 Wind

Proper provision shall be made for stresses caused by wind both during erection and after completion of the building.

1.3.6 Other Forces

Structures in localities subject to earthquakes, hurricanes and other extraordinary conditions shall be designed with due regard for such conditions.

1.3.7 Minimum Loads

In the absence of any applicable building code requirements, the loads referred to in Sect. 1.3.1, 1.3.2, 1.3.5 and 1.3.6 above shall be not less than those recommended in the *American National Standard Building Code Requirements for Minimum Design Loads in Buildings and Other Structures,* ANSI A58.1, latest edition.

SECTION 1.4 MATERIAL

1.4.1 Structural Steel

1.4.1.1 Material conforming to one of the following listing (latest date of issue) is approved for use under this Specification:

> *Structural Steel, ASTM A36*
> *Welded and Seamless Steel Pipe, ASTM A53, Grade B*
> *High-Strength Low-Alloy Structural Steel, ASTM A242*
> *High-Strength Low-Alloy Hot-Rolled Steel Sheet and Strip, ASTM A375*
> *High-Strength Structural Steel, ASTM A440*
> *High-Strength Low-Alloy Structural Manganese Vanadium Steel, ASTM A441*
> *Cold-Formed Welded and Seamless Carbon Steel Structural Tubing in Rounds and Shapes, ASTM A500*
> *Hot-Formed Welded and Seamless Carbon Steel Structural Tubing, ASTM A501*
> *Structural Steel with 42,000 psi Minimum Yield Point, ASTM A529*
> *Hot-Rolled Carbon Steel Sheets and Strip, Structural Quality, ASTM A570, Grades D and E*
> *High-Strength Low-Alloy Columbium-Vanadium Steels of Structural Quality, ASTM A572*
> *High-Strength Low-Alloy Structural Steel with 50,000 psi Minimum Yield Point to 4 in. Thick, ASTM A588*
> *High-Yield Strength Quenched and Tempered Alloy Steel Plate, Suitable for Welding, ASTM A514.* (Quenched and tempered alloy steel structural shapes and seamless mechanical tubing meeting all of the mechanical and chemical requirements of A514 steel, except that the specified maximum tensile strength may be 140,000 psi for structural shapes and 145,000 psi for seamless mechanical tubing, shall be considered as A514 steel.)

Certified mill test reports or certified reports of tests made by the fabricator or a testing laboratory in accordance with ASTM A6 and the governing specification shall constitute sufficient evidence of conformity with one of the above ASTM specifications. Additionally, the fabricator shall, if requested, provide an affidavit stating that the structural steel furnished meets the requirements of the grade specified.

1.4.1.2 Unidentified steel, if free from surface imperfections, may be used for parts of minor importance, or for unimportant details, where the precise physical properties of the steel and its weldability would not affect the strength of the structure.

---

① See Supplement No. 1 to the AISC Specification.
② See Supplement No. 2 to the AISC Specification.

1.4.2 Other Metals

Cast steel shall conform to one of the following specifications, latest edition:

> *Mild-to-Medium-Strength Carbon-Steel Castings for General Application*, ASTM A27, Grade 65-35
>
> *High-Strength Steel Castings for Structural Purposes*, ASTM A148, Grade 80-50

Certified test reports shall constitute sufficient evidence of conformity with the specifications.

Steel forgings shall conform to one of the following specifications, latest edition:

> *Carbon Steel Forgings for General Industrial Use*, ASTM A235, Class C1, F and G. (Class C1 Forgings that are to be welded shall be ordered in accordance with Supplemental Requirements S5 of A235.)
>
> *Alloy Steel Forgings for General Industrial Use*, ASTM A237, Class A

Certified test reports shall constitute sufficient evidence of conformity with the specifications.

1.4.3 Rivets

Rivets shall conform to the provisions of the *Specification for Structural Rivets*, ASTM A502, Grade 1 or Grade 2, latest edition:

Manufacturer's certification shall constitute sufficient evidence of conformity with the specifications.

1.4.4 Bolts

High strength steel bolts shall conform to one of the following specifications, latest edition:

> *High Strength Bolts for Structural Steel Joints, Including Suitable Nuts and Plain Hardened Washers*, ASTM A325
>
> *Quenched and Tempered Steel Bolts and Studs*, ASTM A449
>
> *Quenched and Tempered Alloy Steel Bolts for Structural Steel Joints*, ASTM A490

Other bolts shall conform to the *Specification for Low-Carbon Steel Externally and Internally Threaded Standard Fasteners*, ASTM A307, latest edition, hereinafter designated as A307 bolts.

Manufacturer's certification shall constitute sufficient evidence of conformity with the specifications.

1.4.5 Filler Metal for Welding

Welding electrodes for manual shielded metal-arc welding shall conform to the *Specification for Mild Steel Covered Arc-Welding Electrodes*, AWS A5.1, latest edition, or the *Specification for Low-Alloy Steel Covered Arc-Welding Electrodes*, AWS A5.5, latest edition.

Bare electrodes and granular flux used in the submerged-arc process shall conform to F60 or F70 AWS-flux classifications of the *Specification for Bare Mild Steel Electrodes and Fluxes for Submerged Arc Welding*, AWS A5.17, latest edition, or the provisions of Sect. 1.17.3.

E60S or E70S electrodes used in the gas metal-arc process shall conform to the *Specification for Mild Steel Electrodes for Gas Metal-Arc Welding,* AWS A5.18, latest edition, or the provisions of Sect. 1.17.3; E60T or E70T electrodes used in the flux cored-arc process shall conform to the *Specification for Mild Steel Electrodes for Flux-Cored-Arc Welding,* AWS A5.20, latest edition, or the provisions of Sect. 1.17.3.

Manufacturer's certification shall constitute sufficient evidence of conformity with the specifications.

SECTION 1.5 ALLOWABLE STRESSES*

Except as provided in Sects. 1.6, 1.7, 1.10, 1.11 and in Part 2, all components of the structure shall be so proportioned that the stress, in kip per square inch, shall not exceed the following values, except as they are rounded off in Appendix A.

1.5.1 Structural Steel

1.5.1.1 Tension

On the net section, except at pin holes:

$$F_t = 0.60F_y$$

but not more than 0.5 times the minimum tensile strength of the steel.

On the net section at pin holes in eyebars, pin-connected plates or built up members:

$$F_t = 0.45F_y$$

For tension on threaded parts see Table 1.5.2.1.

1.5.1.2 Shear

On the gross section: $F_v = 0.40F_y$

(The gross section of rolled and fabricated shapes may be taken as the product of the overall depth and the thickness of the web. See Sect. 1.10 for reduction required for thin webs. For discussion of high shear stress within boundaries of rigid connections of members whose webs lie in common plane, see Commentary Sect. 1.5.1.2.)

1.5.1.3 Compression

1.5.1.3.1 On the gross section of axially loaded compression member, when Kl/r, the largest effective slenderness ratio of any unbraced segment as defined in Sect. 1.8, is less than C_c:

$$F_a = \frac{\left[1 - \dfrac{(Kl/r)^2}{2C_c^2}\right]F_y}{\dfrac{5}{3} + \dfrac{3(Kl/r)}{8C_c} - \dfrac{(Kl/r)^3}{8C_c^3}} \qquad (1.5\text{-}$$

where
$$C_c = \sqrt{\frac{2\pi^2 E}{F_y}}$$

---

* See Appendix A for tables of numerical values **for** various grades of steel corresponding to provisions of this Section.

1.5.1.3.2 On the gross section of axially loaded compression members when Kl/r exceeds C_c:

$$F_a = \frac{12\pi^2 E}{23(Kl/r)^2} \tag{1.5-2}$$

1.5.1.3.3 On the gross section of axially loaded bracing and secondary members, when l/r exceeds 120*:

$$F_{as} = \frac{F_a \text{ (by Formula (1.5-1) or (1.5-2))}}{1.6 - \dfrac{l}{200r}} \tag{1.5-3}$$

1.5.1.3.4 On the gross area of plate girder stiffeners:

$$F_a = 0.60F_y$$

1.5.1.3.5 On the web of rolled shapes at the toe of the fillet (crippling, see Sect. 1.10.10):

$$F_a = 0.75F_y$$

1.5.1.4 Bending

1.5.1.4.1 Tension and compression on extreme fibers of compact hot-rolled or built-up members (except hybrid girders and members of A514 steel) symmetrical about, and loaded in, the plane of their minor axis and meeting the requirements of this section:

$$F_b = 0.66F_y$$

In order to qualify under this section a member must meet the following requirements:

a. The flanges shall be continuously connected to the web or webs.
b. The width-thickness ratio of unstiffened projecting elements of the compression flange, as defined in Sect. 1.9.1.1, shall not exceed $52.2/\sqrt{F_y}$.
c. The width-thickness ratio of stiffened elements of the compression flange, as defined in Sect. 1.9.2.1, shall not exceed $190/\sqrt{F_y}$.
d. The depth-thickness ratio of the web or webs shall not exceed the ① value

$$d/t = 412\left(1 - 2.33\frac{f_a}{F_y}\right)\Big/\sqrt{F_y} \tag{1.5-4}$$

except that it need not be less than $257/\sqrt{F_y}$.
e. The compression flange shall be supported laterally at intervals not to exceed $76.0b_f/\sqrt{F_y}$ nor $\dfrac{20,000}{(d/A_f)F_y}$

Except for hybrid girders and members of A514 steel, beams and girders (including members designed on the basis of composite action) which meet the requirements of sub-paragraphs a, b, c, d and e above and are continuous over supports or are rigidly framed to columns by means of rivets,

* For this case, K is taken as unity.

high strength bolts or welds, may be proportioned for $\frac{9}{10}$ of the negative moments produced by gravity loading which are maximum at points of support, provided that, for such members, the maximum positive moment shall be increased by $\frac{1}{10}$ of the average negative moments. This reduction shall not apply to moments produced by loading on cantilevers. If the negative moment is resisted by a column rigidly framed to the beam or girder, the $\frac{1}{10}$ reduction may be used in proportioning the column for the combined axial and bending loading, provided that the stress, f_a, due to any concurrent axial load on the member, does not exceed $0.15F_a$.

1.5.1.4.2 Members (except hybrid girders and members of A514 steel) which meet the requirements of Sect. 1.5.1.4.1, except that $b_f/2t_f$ exceeds $52.2/\sqrt{F_y}$ but is less than $95.0/\sqrt{F_y}$, may be designed on the basis of an allowable bending stress

①

$$F_b = F_y \left[0.733 - 0.0014 \left(\frac{b_f}{2t_f} \right) \sqrt{F_y} \right] \tag{1.5-5}$$

1.5.1.4.3 Tension and compression on extreme fibers of doubly-symmetrical I- and H-shape members meeting the requirements of Sect. 1.5.1.4.1, subparagraphs a and b, and bent about their minor axes (except members of A514 steel); solid round and square bars; and solid rectangular sections bent about their weaker axes:

$$F_b = 0.75F_y$$

① **1.5.1.4.4** Tension and compression on extreme fibers of box-type flexural members whose compression flange or web width-thickness ratio does not meet the requirements of Sect. 1.5.1.4.1 but does conform to the requirements of Sect. 1.9 and whose compression flange is braced laterally at intervals not exceeding $2,500/F_y$ times the transverse distance out-to-out of the webs:

$$F_b = 0.60F_y$$

1.5.1.4.5 Tension on extreme fibers of flexural members not covered in Sect. 1.5.1.4.1, 1.5.1.4.2, 1.5.1.4.3 or 1.5.1.4.4:

$$F_b = 0.60F_y$$

① **1.5.1.4.6a** Compression on extreme fibers of flexural members included under Sect. 1.5.1.4.5, having an axis of symmetry in, and loaded in the plane of their web, and compression on extreme fibers of channels* bent about their major axis: the larger value computed by Formulas (1.5-6a) or (1.5-6b) and (1.5-7) as applicable (unless a higher value can be justified on the basis of a more precise analysis**), but not more than $0.60F_y$.

When $\sqrt{\dfrac{102 \times 10^3 C_b}{F_y}} \leqslant \dfrac{l}{r_T} \leqslant \sqrt{\dfrac{510 \times 10^3 C_b}{F_y}}$

$$F_b = \left[\frac{2}{3} - \frac{F_y(l/r_T)^2}{1,530 \times 10^3 C_b} \right] F_y \tag{1.5-6a}$$

---

* Only Formula (1.5-7) applicable to channels.
** See Commentary Sects. 1.5.1.4.5 and 1.5.1.4.6, last two paragraphs.

When $\quad l/r_T \geqslant \sqrt{\dfrac{510 \times 10^3 C_b}{F_y}}$

$$F_b = \frac{170 \times 10^3 C_b}{(l/r_T)^2} \tag{1.5-6b}$$

Or, when the compression flange is solid and approximately rectangular in cross-section and its area is not less than that of the tension flange

$$F_b = \frac{12 \times 10^3 C_b}{ld/A_f} \tag{1.5-7}$$

In the foregoing,

l = distance between cross-sections braced against twist or lateral displacement of the compression flange

r_T = radius of gyration of a section comprising the compression flange plus one-third of the compression web area, taken about an axis in the plane of the web

A_f = area of the compression flange

C_b = $1.75 + 1.05 (M_1/M_2) + 0.3 (M_1/M_2)^2$, but not more than 2.3*, where M_1 is the smaller and M_2 the larger bending moment at the ends of the unbraced length, taken about the strong axis of the member, and where M_1/M_2, the ratio of end moments, is positive when M_1 and M_2 have the same sign (reverse curvature bending) and negative when they are of opposite signs, (single curvature bending). When the bending moment at any point within an unbraced length is larger than that at both ends of this length, the value of C_b shall be taken as unity. C_b shall also be taken as unity in computing the value of F_{bx} and F_{by} to be used in Formula (1.6-1a). See Sect. 1.10 for further limitation in plate girder flange stress.

For hybrid plate girders, F_y for Formulas (1.5-6a) and (1.5-6b) is the yield stress of the compression flange. Formula (1.5-7) shall not apply to hybrid girders.

1.5.1.4.6b Compression on extreme fibers of flexural members included under Sect. 1.5.1.4.5, but not included in Sect. 1.5.1.4.6a: ①

$$F_b = 0.60 F_y$$

provided that sections bent about their major axis are braced laterally in the region of compression stress at intervals not exceeding $76.0 b_f / \sqrt{F_y}$.

1.5.1.5 Bearing (on contact area)

1.5.1.5.1 Milled surfaces, including bearing stiffeners and pins in reamed, drilled, or bored holes:

$$F_p = 0.90 F_y **$$

---

* C_b can be conservatively taken as unity. For smaller values see Appendix A, Fig. A1, p. 5-104.
** When parts in contact have different yield stresses, F_y shall be the smaller value.

1.5.1.5.2 Expansion rollers and rockers, kips per linear inch:

$$F_p = \left(\frac{F_y - 13}{20}\right) 0.66d$$

where d is the diameter of roller or rocker in inches.

1.5.2 Rivets, Bolts, and Threaded Parts

1.5.2.1 Allowable tension and shear stresses on rivets, bolts and threaded parts (kips per square inch of area of rivets before driving or unthreaded-body area of bolts and threaded parts except as noted) shall be as given in Table 1.5.2.1. High strength bolts required to support applied load by means of direct tension shall be so proportioned that their average tensile stress, computed on the basis of nominal bolt area and independent of any initial tightening force, will not exceed the appropriate stress given in Table 1.5.2.1. The applied load shall be the sum of the external load and any tension resulting from prying action produced by deformation of the connected parts.

TABLE 1.5.2.1

Description of Fastener	Tension (F_t)	Shear (F_v)	
		Friction-Type Connections	Bearing-Type Connections
A502, Grade 1, hot-driven rivets	20.0		15.0
A502, Grade 2, hot-driven rivets	27.0		20.0
A307 bolts	20.0[1]		10.0
Threaded parts[3] of steel meeting the requirements of Sect. 1.4.1	0.60F_y [1]		0.30F_y
A325 and A449 bolts, when threading is *not* excluded from shear planes	40.0[2]	15.0	15.0
A325 and A449 bolts, when threading is excluded from shear planes	40.0[2]	15.0	22.0
A490 bolts, when threading is *not* excluded from shear planes	54.0[2,4]	20.0	22.5
A490 bolts, when threading is excluded from shear planes	54.0[2,4]	20.0	32.0

[1] Applied to tensile stress area equal to $0.7854\left(D - \dfrac{0.9743}{n}\right)^2$ where D is the major thread diameter and n is the number of threads per inch.

[2] Applied to the nominal bolt area.

[3] Since the nominal area of an upset rod is less than the stress area, the former area will govern.

[4] Static loading only.

TABLE 1.5.3

Kind of Stress	Permissible Stress	Required Electrode[4]	"Matching" Base Metal[4]
nsion and Compression parallel axis of any complete penetration ove weld	Same as for base metal[1]		
nsion normal to effective throat complete-penetration groove 'd	Same as allowable tensile stress for base metal[1]		
mpression normal to effective oat of complete or partial-penetion groove weld	Same as allowable compressive stress for base metal[1]		
ear on effective throat of comte-penetration groove weld and tial-penetration groove weld	Same as allowable shear stress for base metal[1]		
ar stress on effective[2] throat of t weld regardless of direction pplication of load; tension nor-[3] to the axis on the effective oat of a partial-penetration ove weld; and shear stress on ctive area of a plug or slot weld. given stresses shall also apply uch welds made with the specielectrode on steel having a d stress greater than that of the atching" base metal. The persible stress, regardless of elec-e classification used, shall not ed that given in the table the weaker "matching" base al being joined.	18.0 ksi	AWS A5.1, E60XX electrodes AWS A5.17, F6X-EXXX flux-electrode combination AWS A5.20, E60T-X electrodes	A500 Grade A A570 Grade D
	21.0 ksi	AWS A5.1 or A5.5, E70XX electrodes AWS A5.17, F7X-EXXX flux-electrode combination AWS A5.18, E70S-X or E70U-1 electrodes AWS A5.20, E70T-X electrodes	A36 A53 Grade B A242 A375 A441 A500 Grade B A501 A529 A570 Grade E A572 Grades 42 to 60 A588
	24.0 ksi	AWS A5.5, E80XX electrodes Grade 80 Submerged Arc, Gas Metal-Arc or Flux Cored Arc Weld Metal	A572 Grade 65
	27.0 ksi	AWS A5.5, E90XX electrodes Grade 90 Submerged Arc, Gas Metal-Arc or Flux Cored Arc Weld Metal	A514 over 2½ in. thick
	30.0 ksi	AWS A5.5, E100XX electrodes Grade 100 Submerged Arc, Gas Metal-Arc or Flux Cored Arc Weld Metal	A514 over 2½ in. thick
	33.0 ksi	AWS A5.5, E110XX electrodes Grade 110 Submerged Arc, Gas Metal-Arc or Flux Cored Arc Weld Metal	A514 2½ in. and less in thickness

he electrode or flux specified in Table 1.17.2 shall be used.

or definition of effective throat of fillet welds and partial penetration groove welds see Sect.

llet welds and partial penetration groove welds joining the component elements of built-up mem-uch as flange-to-web connections, may be designed without regard to the tension or compression in these elements parallel to the axis of the welds.

ly low-hydrogen electrodes shall be used on A242, A441, A514, A572 and A588.

1.5.2.2 Allowable bearing stress on projected area of bolts in bearing-type connections and on rivets:

$$F_p = 1.35F_y$$

where F_y is the yield stress of the connected part. (Bearing stress is not restricted in friction-type connections assembled with A325, A449 or A490 bolts.)

1.5.3 Welds

Except as modified by the provisions of Sect. 1.7, welds shall be proportioned to meet the stress requirements given in Table 1.5.3.

1.5.4 Cast Steel and Steel Forgings

Allowable stresses same as those provided in Sect. 1.5.1, where applicable.

1.5.5 Masonry Bearing

In the absence of Code regulations the following stresses apply:

On sandstone and limestone. . . . . $F_p = 0.40\,\text{ksi}$
On brick in cement mortar . . . . $F_p = 0.25\,\text{ksi}$
On the full area of a concrete support . . . . $F_p = 0.25f'_c$
On one-third of this area . . . . $F_p = 0.375f'_c$

where f'_c is the specified compression strength of the concrete.

1.5.6 Wind and Seismic Stresses

Allowable stresses may be increased one-third above the values provided in Sect. 1.5.1 1.5.2, 1.5.3, 1.5.4 and 1.5.5 when produced by wind or seismic loading, acting alone or in combination with the design dead and live loads, provided the required section computed on this basis is not less than that required for the design dead and live load and impact (if any), computed without the one-third stress increase.

SECTION 1.6 COMBINED STRESSES

1.6.1 Axial Compression and Bending

Members subjected to both axial compression and bending stresses shall be proportioned to satisfy the following requirements:

$$\frac{f_a}{F_a} + \frac{C_{mx}f_{bx}}{\left(1 - \dfrac{f_a}{F'_{ex}}\right)F_{bx}} + \frac{C_{my}f_{by}}{\left(1 - \dfrac{f_a}{F'_{ey}}\right)F_{by}} \leqslant 1.0 \qquad (1.6\text{-}1a)$$

$$\frac{f_a}{0.60F_y} + \frac{f_{bx}}{F_{bx}} + \frac{f_{by}}{F_{by}} \leqslant 1.0 \qquad (1.6\text{-}1b)$$

When $\dfrac{f_a}{F_a} \leqslant 0.15$, Formula (1.6-2) may be used in lieu of Formulas (1.6-1a) and (1.6-1b)

$$\frac{f_a}{F_a} + \frac{f_{bx}}{F_{bx}} + \frac{f_{by}}{F_{by}} \leqslant 1.0 \qquad (1.6\text{-}2)$$

In Formulas (1.6-1a), (1.6-1b), and (1.6-2) the subscripts x and y, combined with subscripts b, m and e, indicate the axis of bending about which a particular stress or design property applies, and

F_a = axial stress that would be permitted if axial force alone existed

F_b = compressive bending stress that would be permitted if bending moment alone existed

$F'_e = \dfrac{12\pi^2 E}{23(Kl_b/r_b)^2}$ (In the expression for F'_e, l_b is the actual unbraced length *in the plane of bending* and r_b is the corresponding radius of gyration. K is the effective length factor *in the plane of bending*. As in the case of F_a, F_b and 0.6 F_y, F'_e may be increased one-third in accordance with Sect. 1.5.6.)

f_a = computed axial stress

f_b = computed compressive bending stress at the point under consideration

C_m = a coefficient whose value shall be taken as follows:

1. For compression members in frames subject to joint translation (sidesway), $C_m = 0.85$.

2. For restrained compression members in frames braced against joint translation and not subject to transverse loading between their supports in the plane of bending,

$$C_m = 0.6 - 0.4\,\frac{M_1}{M_2}, \text{ but not less than 0.4,}$$

   where M_1/M_2 is the ratio of the smaller to larger moments at the ends of that portion of the member unbraced in the plane of bending under consideration. M_1/M_2 is positive when the member is bent in reverse curvature and negative when it is bent in single curvature.

3. For compression members in frames braced against joint translation in the plane of loading and subjected to transverse loading between their supports, the value of C_m may be determined by rational analysis. However, in lieu of such analysis, the following values may be used: (a) for members whose ends are restrained, $C_m = 0.85$; (b) for members whose ends are unrestrained, $C_m = 1.0$.

1.6.2 Axial Tension and Bending

Members subject to both axial tension and bending stresses shall be proportioned at all points along their length to satisfy the requirements of Formula (1.6-1b) where f_b is the computed bending tensile stress. However, the computed bending compressive stress, taken alone, shall not exceed the applicable value according to Sect. 1.5.1.4.

1.6.3 Shear and Tension

Rivets and bolts subject to combined shear and tension shall be so proportioned that the tension stress, in kips per square inch, produced by forces applied to the connected parts, shall not exceed the following:

For A502 Grade 1 rivets . . . . . . $F_t = 28.0 - 1.6f_v \leqslant 20.0$

For A502 Grade 2 rivets . . . . . . $F_t = 38.0 - 1.6f_v \leqslant 27.0$

For A307 bolts (applied to stress area) $F_t = 28.0 - 1.6f_v \leqslant 20.0$

For A325 and A449 bolts in bearing-
    type joints . . . . $F_t = 50.0 - 1.6f_v \leqslant 40.0$

For A490 bolts in bearing-type joints . $F_t = 70.0 - 1.6f_v \leqslant 54.0$

where f_v, the shear stress produced by the same forces, shall not exceed the value for shear given in Sect. 1.5.2.

For bolts used in friction-type joints, the shear stress allowed in Sect. 1.5.2 shall be reduced so that:

For A325 and A449 bolts . . . . . . $F_v \leqslant 15.0(1 - f_t A_b / T_b)$

For A490 bolts . . . . $F_v \leqslant 20.0(1 - f_t A_b / T_b)$

where f_t is the average tensile stress due to a direct load applied to all of the bolts in a connection and T_b is the specified pretension load of the bolt.

SECTION 1.7   MEMBERS AND CONNECTIONS SUBJECT TO REPEATED VARIATION OF STRESS (FATIGUE)

1.7.1   General

Fatigue, as used in this Specification, is defined as the damage that may result in fracture after a sufficient number of fluctuations of stress. Stress range is defined as the magnitude of these fluctuations. In the case of a stress reversal, stress range shall be computed as the numerical sum of maximum repeated tensile and compressive stresses or the sum of maximum shearing stresses of opposite direction at a given point, resulting from differing arrangements of live load.

Few members or connections in conventional buildings need to be designed for fatigue, since most load changes in such structures occur only a small number of times or produce only minor stress fluctuations. The occurrence of full design wind or earthquake loads is too infrequent to warrant consideration in fatigue design. However, crane runways and supporting structures for machinery and equipment are often subject to fatigue loading conditions.

1.7.2   Design for Fatigue

Members and their connections, subject to fatigue loading as defined in Appendix B, shall be proportioned to satisfy the stress range limitations as provided therein.

SECTION 1.8   STABILITY AND SLENDERNESS RATIOS

1.8.1   General

General stability shall be provided for the structure as a whole and for each compression element.

In determining the slenderness ratio of an axially loaded compression member, except as provided in Sect. 1.5.1.3.3, the length shall be taken as its effective length Kl and r as the corresponding radius of gyration.

1.8.2 Sidesway Prevented

In frames where lateral stability is provided by adequate attachment to diagonal bracing, shear walls, an adjacent structure having adequate lateral stability, or to floor slabs or roof decks secured horizontally by walls or bracing systems parallel to the plane of the frame, and in trusses, the effective length factor, K, for the compression members shall be taken as unity, unless analysis shows that a smaller value may be used.

1.8.3 Sidesway Not Prevented

In frames where lateral stability is dependent upon the bending stiffness of rigidly connected beams and columns, the effective length Kl of compression members, shall be determined by a rational method and shall not be less than the actual unbraced length.

1.8.4 Maximum Ratios

The slenderness ratio, Kl/r, of compression members shall not exceed 200.

The slenderness ratio, Kl/r, of tension members, other than rods, preferably should not exceed:

②

For main members 240

For bracing and other secondary members 300

SECTION 1.9 WIDTH-THICKNESS RATIOS

1.9.1 Unstiffened Elements Under Compression

1.9.1.1 Unstiffened (projecting) compression elements are those having one free edge parallel to the direction of compression stress. The width of unstiffened plates shall be taken from the free edge to the first row of fasteners or welds; the width of legs of angles, channel and zee flanges, and stems of tees shall be taken as the full nominal dimension; the width of flanges of I-shape members and tees shall be taken as one-half the full nominal width. The thickness of a sloping flange shall be measured halfway between a free edge and the corresponding face of the web.

1.9.1.2 Unstiffened elements subject to axial compression or compression due to bending shall be considered as fully effective when the ratio of width to thickness is not greater than the following:

Single-angle struts;
   double-angle struts with separators . . . . $76.0/\sqrt{F_y}$

Struts comprising double angles in contact; angles or plates
   projecting from girders, columns or other compression
   members; compression flanges of beams; stiffeners on
   plate girders . . . . $95.0/\sqrt{F_y}$

Stems of tees . . . . $127/\sqrt{F_y}$

When the actual width-to-thickness ratio exceeds these values, the design stress shall be governed by the provisions of Appendix C.

1.9.2 Stiffened Elements Under Compression

1.9.2.1 Stiffened compression elements are those having lateral support along both edges which are parallel to the direction of the compression stress. The width of such elements shall be taken as the distance between nearest lines of fasteners or welds, or between the roots of the flanges in the case of rolled sections.

1.9.2.2 Stiffened elements subject to axial compression, or to uniform compression due to bending as in the case of the flange of a flexural* member, shall be considered as fully effective when the ratio of width to thickness is not greater than the following:

Flanges of square and rectangular sections of uniform thickness . . . . $238/\sqrt{F_y}$

Unsupported width of cover plates perforated with a succession of access holes** . . . . $317/\sqrt{F_y}$

All other uniformly compressed stiffened elements . . . . . $253/\sqrt{F_y}$

Except in the case of perforated cover plates, when the actual width-to-thickness ratio exceeds these values the design shall be governed by the provisions of Appendix C.

SECTION 1.10 PLATE GIRDERS AND ROLLED BEAMS

1.10.1 Proportions

Riveted and welded plate girders, cover-plated beams and rolled or welded beams shall in general be proportioned by the moment of inertia of the gross section. No deduction shall be made for shop or field rivet or bolt holes in either flange, except that in cases where the reduction of the area of either flange by such holes, calculated in accordance with the provisions of Sect. 1.14.3, exceeds 15 percent of the gross flange area, the excess shall be deducted.

Hybrid girders may be proportioned by the moment of inertia of their gross section,† subject to the applicable provisions in Sect. 1.10, provided that they are not required to resist an axial force greater than $0.15F_y$ times the area of the gross section, where F_y is the yield stress of the flange material. To qualify as hybrid girders the flanges at any given section shall have the same cross-sectional area and be made of the same grade of steel.

1.10.2 Web

The clear distance between flanges, in inches, shall not exceed

$$\frac{14,000}{\sqrt{F_y(F_y + 16.5)}}$$

times the web thickness, where F_y is the yield stress of the compression flange, except that it need not be less than $2,000/\sqrt{F_y}$ when transverse stiffeners are provided, spaced not more than $1\frac{1}{2}$ times the girder depth.

---

* Webs of flexural members are covered by the provisions of Sects. 1.10.2 and 1.10.6 and are not subject to the provisions of this section.

** Assumes net area of plate at widest hole as basis for computing compression stress.

† No limit is placed on the web stresses produced by the applied bending moment for which a hybrid girder is designed, except as provided in Sect. 1.7 and Appendix B

1.10.3 Flanges

The thickness of outstanding parts of flanges shall conform to the requirements of Sect. 1.9.1.2.

Flanges of welded plate girders may be varied in thickness or width by splicing a series of plates or by the use of cover plates.

The total cross-sectional area of cover plates of riveted girders shall not exceed 70 percent of the total flange area.

1.10.4 Flange Development

Rivets, high strength bolts or welds connecting flange to web, or cover plate to flange, shall be proportioned to resist the total horizontal shear resulting from the bending forces on the girder. The longitudinal distribution of these rivets, bolts or intermittent welds shall be in proportion to the intensity of the shear. But the longitudinal spacing shall not exceed the maximum permitted, respectively, for compression or tension members in Sect. 1.18.2.3 or 1.18.3.1. Additionally, rivets or welds connecting flange to web shall be proportioned to transmit to the web any loads applied directly to the flange unless provision is made to transmit such loads by direct bearing.

Partial length cover plates shall be extended beyond the theoretical cut-off point and the extended portion shall be attached to the beam or girder by rivets, high strength bolts (friction-type joint), or fillet welds adequate, at the applicable stresses allowed in Sect. 1.5.2 or 1.5.3 or Sect. 1.7, to develop the cover plate's portion of the flexural stresses in the beam or girder at the theoretical cut-off point. In addition, for welded cover plates, the welds connecting the cover plate termination to the beam or girder in the length a', defined below, shall be adequate, at the allowed stresses, to develop the cover plate's portion of the flexural stresses in the beam or girder at the distance a' from the end of the cover plate.* The length a', measured from the end of the cover plate, shall be:

1. A distance equal to the width of the cover plate when there is a continuous weld equal to or larger than $3/4$ of the plate thickness across the end of the plate and continued welds along both edges of the cover plate in the length a'.

2. A distance equal to $1\frac{1}{2}$ times the width of the cover plate when there is a continuous weld smaller than $3/4$ of the plate thickness across the end of the plate and continued welds along both edges of the cover plate in the length a'.

3. A distance equal to 2 times the width of the cover plate when there is no weld across the end of the plate but continuous welds along both edges of the cover plate in the length a'.

1.10.5 Stiffeners

1.10.5.1 Bearing stiffeners shall be placed in pairs at unframed ends on the webs of plate girders and where required** at points of concentrated

---

* This may require the cover plate termination to be placed at a point in the beam or girder that has lower bending stress than the stress at the theoretical cut-off point.

** For provisions governing welded plate girders, see Sect. 1.10.10.

loads. Such stiffeners shall have a close bearing against the flange, or flanges, through which they receive their loads or reactions, and shall extend approximately to the edge of the flange plates or flange angles. They shall be designed as columns subject to the provisions of Sect. 1.5.1, assuming the column section to comprise the pair of stiffeners and a centrally located strip of the web whose width is equal to not more than 25 times its thickness at interior stiffeners or a width equal to not more than 12 times its thickness when the stiffeners are located at the end of the web. The effective length shall be taken as not less than $3/4$ of the length of the stiffeners in computing the ratio l/r. Only that portion of the stiffener outside of the flange angle fillet or the flange-to-web welds shall be considered effective in bearing.

1.10.5.2 Except as hereinafter provided, the largest average web shear, f_v, in kips per square inch, computed for any condition of complete or partial loading, shall not exceed the value given by Formula (1.10-1).

$$F_v = \frac{F_y}{2.89} (C_v) \leqslant 0.4F_y \qquad (1.10\text{-}1)$$

where

$$C_v = \frac{45{,}000k}{F_y(h/t)^2}, \text{ when } C_v \text{ is less than } 0.8$$

$$= \frac{190}{h/t} \sqrt{\frac{k}{F_y}}, \text{ when } C_v \text{ is more than } 0.8$$

$$k = 4.00 + \frac{5.34}{(a/h)^2}, \text{ when } a/h \text{ is less than } 1.0$$

$$= 5.34 + \frac{4.00}{(a/h)^2}, \text{ when } a/h \text{ is more than } 1.0$$

t = thickness of web, in inches
a = clear distance between transverse stiffeners, in inches
h = clear distance between flanges, in inches

Alternatively, for girders other than hybrid girders, if intermediate stiffeners are provided and spaced to satisfy the provisions of Sect. 1.10.5.3 and if $C_v \leqslant 1$, the allowable shear given by Formula (1.10-2) may be used in lieu of the value given by Formula (1.10-1).

$$F_v = \frac{F_y}{2.89} \left[C_v + \frac{1 - C_v}{1.15\sqrt{1 + (a/h)^2}} \right] \leqslant 0.4F_y \qquad (1.10\text{-}2)*$$

②   **1.10.5.3** Intermediate stiffeners are not required when the ratio h/t is less than 260 and the maximum web shear stress f_v is less than that permitted by Formula (1.10-1).

The spacing of intermediate stiffeners, where stiffeners are required, shall be such that the web shear stress will not exceed the value for F_v given by Formulas (1.10-1) or (1.10-2), as applicable, and the ratio a/h shall not exceed $\left(\dfrac{260}{h/t}\right)^2$, nor 3.0.

---

* Formula (1.10-2) recognizes the contribution of tension field action. For values of F_v provided by this formula, see Tables 3-36 through 3-100 in Appendix A

In girders designed on the basis of tension field action, the spacing between stiffeners at end panels and panels containing large holes shall be such that the smaller panel dimension, a or h, shall not exceed $348t/\sqrt{f_v}$.

1.10.5.4 The moment of inertia of a pair of intermediate stiffeners, or a single intermediate stiffener, with reference to an axis in the plane of the web, shall not be less than $(h/50)^4$.

The gross area, in square inches, of intermediate stiffeners spaced as required for Formula (1.10-2) (*total* area, when stiffeners are furnished in pairs) shall be not less than that computed by Formula (1.10-3).

$$A_{st} = \frac{1 - C_v}{2}\left[\frac{a}{h} - \frac{(a/h)^2}{\sqrt{1 + (a/h)^2}}\right] YDht \qquad (1.10\text{-}3)$$

where

C_v, a, h and t are defined in Sect. 1.10.5.2

$Y = \dfrac{\text{yield stress of web steel}}{\text{yield stress of stiffener steel}}$

D = 1.0 for stiffeners furnished in pairs
  = 1.8 for single angle stiffeners
  = 2.4 for single plate stiffeners

When the greatest shear stress f_v in a panel is less than that permitted by Formula (1.10-2) this gross area requirement may be reduced in like proportion.

Intermediate stiffeners required by Formula (1.10-2) shall be connected for a total shear transfer, in kips per linear inch of single stiffener or pair of stiffeners, not less than that computed by the formula

$$f_{vs} = h\sqrt{\left(\frac{F_y}{340}\right)^3} \qquad (1.10\text{-}4)$$

where F_y = yield stress of web steel.

This shear transfer may be reduced in the same proportion that the largest computed shear stress f_v in the adjacent panels is less than that permitted by Formula (1.10-2). However, rivets and welds in intermediate stiffeners which are required to transmit to the web an applied concentrated load or reaction shall be proportioned for not less than the applied load or reaction.

Intermediate stiffeners may be stopped short of the tension flange a distance not to exceed 4 times the web thickness, provided bearing is not needed to transmit a concentrated load or reaction. When single stiffeners are used they shall be attached to the compression flange, if it consists of a rectangular plate, to resist any uplift tendency due to torsion in the plate. When lateral bracing is attached to a stiffener, or a pair of stiffeners, these, in turn, shall be connected to the compression flange to transmit 1 percent of the total flange stress, unless the flange is composed only of angles.

Rivets connecting stiffeners to the girder web shall be spaced not more than 12 inches on center. If intermittent fillet welds are used, the clear distance between welds shall be not more than 16 times the web thickness nor more than 10 inches.

1.10.6 Reduction in Flange Stress

When the web depth-to-thickness ratio exceeds $760/\sqrt{F_b}$, the maximum stress in the compression flange shall not exceed

$$F'_b \leqslant F_b \left[1.0 - 0.0005 \frac{A_w}{A_f} \left(\frac{h}{t} - \frac{760}{\sqrt{F_b}} \right) \right] \qquad (1.10\text{-}5)$$

where

F_b = applicable bending stress given in Sect. 1.5.1
A_w = area of the web
A_f = area of compression flange

The maximum stress in either flange of a hybrid girder shall not exceed the value given by Formula (1.10-5) nor

$$F'_b \leqslant F_b \left[\frac{12 + \left(\dfrac{A_w}{A_f} \right)(3\alpha - \alpha^3)}{12 + 2 \left(\dfrac{A_w}{A_f} \right)} \right] \qquad (1.10\text{-}6)$$

where α = ratio of web yield stress to flange yield stress.

1.10.7 Combined Shear and Tension Stress

Plate girder webs, which depend upon tension field action as provided in Formula (1.10-2) shall be so proportioned that bending tensile stress, due to moment in the plane of the girder web, shall not exceed $0.6F_y$ nor

$$\left(0.825 - 0.375 \frac{f_v}{F_v} \right) F_y \qquad (1.10\text{-}7)$$

where

f_v = computed average web shear stress (total shear divided by web area)
F_v = allowable web shear stress according to Formula (1.10-2)

The allowable shear stress in the webs of girders having A514 flanges and webs shall not exceed the values given by Formula (1.10-1) if the flexural stress in the flange, f_b, exceeds $0.75F_b$.

1.10.8 Splices

② Groove welded splices in plate girders and beams shall be complete penetration groove welds and shall develop the full strength of the smaller spliced section. Other types of splices in cross-sections of plate girders and in beams shall develop the strength required by the stresses, at the point of splice.

1.10.9 Horizontal Forces

The flanges of plate girders supporting cranes or other moving loads shall be proportioned to resist the horizontal forces produced by such loads. (See Sect. 1.3.4.)

1.10.10   Web Crippling

1.10.10.1   Webs of beams and welded plate girders shall be so proportioned that the compressive stress at the web toe of the fillets, resulting from concentrated loads not supported by bearing stiffeners, shall not exceed the value of $0.75F_y$; otherwise, bearing stiffeners shall be provided. The governing formulas shall be:

For interior loads,

$$\frac{R}{t(N + 2k)} \leqslant 0.75F_y \tag{1.10-8}$$

For end-reactions,

$$\frac{R}{t(N + k)} \leqslant 0.75F_y \tag{1.10-9}$$

where

R = concentrated load or reaction, in kips
t = thickness of web, in inches
N = length of bearing in inches (not less than k for end reactions)
k = distance from outer face of flange to web toe of fillet, in inches

1.10.10.2   Webs of plate girders shall also be so proportioned or stiffened that the sum of the compression stresses resulting from concentrated and distributed loads, bearing directly on or through a flange plate, upon the compression edge of the web plate, and not supported directly by bearing stiffeners, shall not exceed

$$\left[5.5 + \frac{4}{(a/h)^2}\right]\frac{10,000}{(h/t)^2} \text{ kips per square inch} \tag{1.10-10}$$

when the flange is restrained against rotation, nor

$$\left[2 + \frac{4}{(a/h)^2}\right]\frac{10,000}{(h/t)^2} \text{ kips per square inch} \tag{1.10-11}$$

when the flange is not so restrained.

These stresses shall be computed as follows:

Concentrated loads and loads distributed over partial length of a panel shall be divided by the product of the web thickness and the girder depth or the length of panel in which the load is placed, whichever is the lesser panel dimension.

Any other distributed loading, in kips per linear inch of length, shall be divided by the web thickness.

1.10.11   Rotational Restraint at Points of Support

Beams, girders and trusses shall be restrained against rotation, about their longitudinal axis, at points of support.

SECTION 1.11 COMPOSITE CONSTRUCTION

1.11.1 Definition

Composite construction shall consist of steel beams or girders supporting a reinforced concrete slab, so inter-connected that the beam and slab act together to resist bending.   When the slab extends on both sides of the beam, the effective width of the concrete flange shall be taken as not more than one-fourth of the span of the beam, and its effective projection beyond the edge of the beam shall not be taken as more than one-half the clear distance to the adjacent beam, nor more than eight times the slab thickness.   When the slab is present on only one side of the beam, the effective width of the concrete flange (projection beyond the beam) shall be taken as not more than one-twelfth of the beam span, nor six times its thickness, nor one-half the clear distance to the adjacent beam.

Beams totally encased 2 inches or more on their sides and soffit in concrete cast integrally with the slab may be assumed to be inter-connected to the concrete by natural bond, without additional anchorage, provided the top of the beam is at least $1\frac{1}{2}$ inches below the top and 2 inches above the bottom of the slab, and provided that the encasement has adequate mesh or other reinforcing steel throughout the whole depth and across the soffit of the beam to prevent spalling of the concrete.   When shear connectors are provided in accordance with Sect. 1.11.4, encasement of the beam to achieve composite action is not required.

1.11.2 Design Assumptions

1.11.2.1   Encased beams shall be proportioned to support unassisted all dead loads applied prior to the hardening of the concrete (unless these loads are supported temporarily on shoring) and, acting in conjunction with the slab, to support all dead and live loads applied after hardening of the concrete, without exceeding a computed bending stress of $0.66F_y$, where F_y is the yield stress of the steel beam.   The bending stress produced by loads after the concrete has hardened shall be computed on the basis of the section properties of the composite section.   Concrete tension stresses shall be neglected.   Alternatively, the steel beam alone may be proportioned to resist unassisted the positive moment produced by all loads, live and dead, using a bending stress equal to $0.76F_y$, in which case temporary shoring is not required.

1.11.2.2   When shear connectors are used in accordance with Sect. 1.11.4 the composite section shall be proportioned to support all of the loads without exceeding the allowable stress prescribed in Sect. 1.5.1.4, even when the steel section is not shored during construction.

Reinforcement parallel to the beam within the effective width of the slab, when anchored in accordance with the provisions of the applicable code, may be included in computing the properties of composite sections subject to negative bending moment, provided shear connectors are furnished in accordance with the requirements of Sect. 1.11.4.   The section properties of the composite section shall be computed in accordance with the elastic theory.   Concrete tension stresses shall be neglected.   The compression area of the concrete on the compression side of the neutral axis shall be treated as an equivalent area of steel by dividing it by the modular ratio *n*.

In cases where it is not feasible or necessary to provide adequate connectors to satisfy the horizontal shear requirements for full composite action, the effective section modulus shall be determined as

$$S_{eff} = S_s + \frac{V'_h}{V_h} (S_{tr} - S_s) \qquad (1.11\text{-}1)$$

where

V_h and V'_h are as defined in Sect. 1.11.4

S_s = section modulus of the steel beam referred to its bottom flange

S_{tr} = section modulus of the transformed composite section referred to its bottom flange

For construction without temporary shoring, the value of the section modulus of the transformed composite section used in stress calculations (referred to the bottom flange of the steel beam) shall not exceed

$$S_{tr} = \left(1.35 + 0.35 \frac{M_L}{M_D}\right) S_s \qquad (1.11\text{-}2)$$

where M_L is the moment caused by loads applied subsequent to the time when the concrete has reached 75 percent of its required strength, M_D is the moment caused by loads applied prior to this time, and S_s is the section modulus of the steel beam (referred to its bottom flange). The steel beam alone, supporting the loads before the concrete has hardened, shall not be stressed to more than the applicable bending stress given in Sect. 1.5.1.

The actual section modulus of the transformed composite section shall be used in calculating the concrete flexural compression stress and, for construction without temporary shores, this stress shall be based upon loading applied after the concrete has reached 75 percent of its required strength. The stress in the concrete shall not exceed $0.45f'_c$.

1.11.3 End Shear

The web and the end connections of the steel beam shall be designed to carry the total dead and live load.

1.11.4 Shear Connectors

Except in the case of encased beams as defined in Sect. 1.11.1, the entire horizontal shear at the junction of the steel beam and the concrete slab shall be assumed to be transferred by shear connectors welded to the top flange of the beam and embedded in the concrete. For full composite action with concrete subject to flexural compression, the total horizontal shear to be resisted between the point of maximum positive moment and points of zero moment shall be taken as the smaller value using Formulas (1.11-3) and (1.11-4).

$$V_h = \frac{0.85f'_c A_c}{2} \qquad (1.11\text{-}3)$$

and

$$V_h = \frac{A_s F_y}{2} \qquad (1.11\text{-}4)$$

where

f'_c = specified compression strength of concrete
A_c = actual area of effective concrete flange defined in Sect. 1.11.1
A_s = area of steel beam

In continuous composite beams where longitudinal reinforcing steel is considered to act compositely with the steel beam in the negative moment regions, the total horizontal shear to be resisted by shear connectors between an interior support and each adjacent point of contraflexure shall be taken as

$$V_h = \frac{A_{sr}F_{yr}}{2} \qquad (1.11\text{-}5$$

where

A_{sr} = total area of longitudinal reinforcing steel at the interior support located within the effective flange width specified in Sect. 1.11.1
F_{yr} = specified minimum yield stress of the longitudinal reinforcing steel

For full composite action, the number of connectors resisting the horizontal shear, V_h, each side of the point of maximum moment, shall not be less than that determined by the relationship V_h/q, where q, the allowable shear load for one connector, is given in Table 1.11.4. Working values for use with concrete having aggregate not conforming to ASTM C33 and for connector types other than those shown in Table 1.11.4 must be established by a suitable test program.

TABLE 1.11.4

Connector	Allowable Horizontal Shear Load (q) (kips) (Applicable only to concrete made with ASTM C33 aggregates)		
	f'_c (kips per square inch)		
	3.0	3.5	4.0
½″ diam. × 2″ hooked or headed stud	5.1	5.5	5.9
⅝″ diam. × 2½″ hooked or headed stud	8.0	8.6	9.2
¾″ diam. × 3″ hooked or headed stud	11.5	12.5	13.3
⅞″ diam. × 3½″ hooked or headed stud	15.6	16.8	18.0
3″ channel, 4.1 lb.	4.3w	4.7w	5.0w
4″ channel, 5.4 lb.	4.6w	5.0w	5.3w
5″ channel, 6.7 lb.	4.9w	5.3w	5.6w

w = length of channel in inches.

For incomplete composite action with concrete subject to flexural compression, the horizontal shear, V'_h, to be used in computing S_{eff} shall be taken as the product of q times the number of connectors furnished between the point of maximum moment and the nearest point of zero moment.

The connectors required each side of the point of maximum moment in an area of positive bending may be uniformly distributed between that point and adjacent points of zero moment, except that N_2, the number of shear connectors required between any concentrated load in that area and the nearest point of zero moment, shall be not less than that determined by Formula (1.11-6).

$$N_2 = \frac{N_1 \left[\dfrac{M\beta}{M_{max}} - 1 \right]}{\beta - 1} \qquad (1.11\text{-}6)$$

where

M = moment (less than the maximum moment) at a concentrated load point

N_1 = number of connectors required between point of maximum moment and point of zero moment, determined by the relationship V_h/q or V'_h/q, as applicable

β = $\dfrac{S_{tr}}{S_s}$ or $\dfrac{S_{eff}}{S_s}$, as applicable

Connectors required in the region of negative bending on a continuous beam may be uniformly distributed between the point of maximum moment and each point of zero moment.

Shear connectors shall have at least 1 inch of concrete cover in all directions. Unless located directly over the web, the diameter of studs shall not be greater than 2.5 times the thickness of the flange to which they are welded.

②

SECTION 1.12   SIMPLE AND CONTINUOUS SPANS

1.12.1   Simple Spans

Beams, girders and trusses shall ordinarily be designed on the basis of simple spans whose effective length is equal to the distance between centers of gravity of the members to which they deliver their end reactions.

1.12.2   End Restraint

When designed on the assumption of full or partial end restraint, due to continuous, semi-continuous or cantilever action, the beams, girders and trusses, as well as the sections of the members to which they connect, shall be designed to carry the shears and moments so introduced, as well as all other forces, without exceeding at any point the unit stresses prescribed in Sect. 1.5.1; except that some non-elastic but self-limiting deformation of a part of the connection may be permitted when this is essential to the avoidance of overstressing of fasteners.

SECTION 1.13   DEFLECTIONS, VIBRATION, AND PONDING

1.13.1   Deflections

Beams and girders supporting floors and roofs shall be proportioned with due regard to the deflection produced by the design loads. Beams and girders supporting plastered ceilings shall be so proportioned that the maximum live load deflection does not exceed $\frac{1}{360}$ of the span.

1.13.2 Vibration

Beams and girders supporting large open floor areas free of partitions or other sources of damping, where transient vibration due to pedestrian traffic might not be acceptable, shall be designed with due regard for vibration.

1.13.3 Ponding

Unless a roof surface is provided with sufficient slope toward points of free drainage or adequate individual drains to prevent the accumulation of rain water, the roof system shall be investigated by rational analysis to assure stability under ponding conditions, except as follows:

The roof system shall be considered stable and no further investigation will be needed if

$$C_p + 0.9C_s \leqslant 0.25 \text{ and } I_d \geqslant 25S^4/10^6$$

where

$$C_p = \frac{32L_sL_p{}^4}{10^7I_p} \text{ and } C_s = \frac{32SL_s{}^4}{10^7I_s}$$

L_p = Column spacing in direction of girder, feet (length of primary members)

L_s = Column spacing perpendicular to direction of girder, feet (length of secondary member)

S = Spacing of secondary members, feet

I_p = Moment of inertia for primary members, inches^4

I_s = Moment of inertia for secondary member, inches^4

I_d = Moment of inertia of the steel deck supported on secondary members, inches^4 per foot

For trusses and steel joists, the moment of inertia, I_s, shall be decreased 15 percent when used in the above formulas. A steel deck shall be considered a secondary member when it is directly supported by the primary members.

Total bending stress due to dead loads, gravity live loads (if any) and ponding shall not exceed $0.80F_y$ for primary and secondary members. Stresses due to wind or seismic forces need not be included in a ponding analysis.

SECTION 1.14 GROSS AND NET SECTIONS

1.14.1 Definitions

The gross section of a member at any point shall be determined by summing the products of the thickness and the gross width of each element as measured normal to the axis of the member. The net section shall be determined by substituting for the gross width the net width computed in accordance with Sects. 1.14.3 to 1.14.6, inclusive.

1.14.2 Application

Unless otherwise specified, tension members shall be designed on the basis of net section. Compression members shall be designed on the basis of gross section. Beams and girders shall be designed in accordance with Sect. 1.10.1.

1.14.3   Net Section

In the case of a chain of holes extending across a part in any diagonal or zigzag line, the net width of the part shall be obtained by deducting from the gross width the sum of the diameters of all the holes in the chain, and adding, for each gage space in the chain, the quantity

$$\frac{s^2}{4g}$$

where

s = longitudinal spacing (pitch, in inches) of any two consecutive holes
g = transverse spacing (gage, in inches) of the same two holes

The critical net section of the part is obtained from that chain which gives the least net width; however, the net section taken through a hole shall in no case be considered as more than 85 percent of the corresponding gross section.

In determining the net section across plug or slot welds, the weld metal shall not be considered as adding to the net area.

1.14.4   Angles

For angles, the gross width shall be the sum of the widths of the legs less the thickness.   The gage for holes in opposite legs shall be the sum of the gages from back of angles less the thickness.

1.14.5   Size of Holes

In computing net area the diameter of a rivet or bolt hole shall be taken as $\frac{1}{8}$-inch greater than the nominal diameter of the rivet or bolt.   (2)

1.14.6   Pin-Connected Members

Eyebars shall be of uniform thickness without reinforcement at the pin holes.*   They shall have "circular" heads in which the periphery of the head beyond the pin hole is concentric with the pin hole.   The radius of transition between the circular head and the body of the eyebar shall be equal to or greater than the diameter of the head.

The width of the body of the eyebar shall not exceed 8 times its thickness, and the thickness shall not be less than $\frac{1}{2}$-inch.   The net section of the head through the pin hole, transverse to the axis of the eyebar, shall not be less than 1.33 nor more than 1.50 times the cross-sectional area of the body of the eyebar.   The diameter of the pin shall not be less than $\frac{7}{8}$ the width of the body of the eyebar.   The diameter of the pin hole shall not be more than $\frac{1}{32}$-inch greater than the diameter of the pin.   For steels having a yield stress greater than 70 ksi, the diameter of the pin hole shall not exceed 5 times the plate thickness.

The minimum net section across the pin hole, transverse to the axis of the member, in pin-connected plates and built-up members shall be determined at the stress allowed for such sections in Sect. 1.5.1.1.   The net section beyond the pin hole, parallel to the axis of the member, shall not be less than $\frac{2}{3}$ of the net section across the pin hole.   The corners beyond the pin hole may be cut

---

* Members having a different thickness at the pin hole location are termed "built-up."

at 45° to the axis of the member provided the net section beyond the pin hole on a plane perpendicular to the cut is not less than that required beyond the pin hole parallel to the axis of the member. The parts of members built up at the pin hole shall be attached to each other by sufficient fasteners to support the stress delivered to them by the pin.

The distance transverse to the axis of a pin-connected plate or any separated element of a built-up member, from the edge of the pin hole to the edge of the member or element, shall not exceed 4 times the thickness at the pin hole. The diameter of the pin hole shall not be less than 1.25 times the smaller of the distances from the edge of the pin hole to the edge of a pin-connected plate or separated element of a built-up member at the pin hole. The diameter of the pin hole shall not be more than $\frac{1}{32}$-inch greater than the diameter of the pin. In the case of pin-connected plates of uniform thickness, for steels having a yield stress greater than 70 ksi, the diameter of the pin hole shall not exceed 5 times the plate thickness.

Thickness limitations on both eyebars and pin-connected plates may be waived whenever external nuts are provided so as to tighten pin plates and filler plates into snug contact. When the plates are thus contained, the allowable stress in bearing shall be no greater than as specified in Sect. 1.5.1.5.1.

1.14.7 Effective Areas of Weld Metal

The effective area of groove and fillet welds shall be considered as the effective length of the weld times the effective throat thickness.

The effective shearing area of plug and slot welds shall be considered as the nominal cross-sectional area of the hole or slot, in the plane of the faying surface.

The effective area of fillet welds in holes and slots shall be computed as above specified for fillet welds, using for effective length, the length of center line of the weld through the center of the plane through the throat. However, in the case of overlapping fillets, the effective area shall not exceed the nominal cross-sectional area of the hole or slot, in the plane of the faying surface.

The effective length of a fillet weld shall be the overall length of full-size fillet including returns.

The effective length of a groove weld shall be the width of the part joined.

The effective throat thickness of a fillet weld shall be the shortest distance from the root to the face of the diagrammatic weld, except that, for fillet welds made by the submerged arc process, the effective throat thickness shall be taken equal to the leg size for $\frac{3}{8}$-inch and smaller fillet welds and equal to the theoretical throat plus 0.11-inch for fillet welds over $\frac{3}{8}$ inch.

The effective throat thickness of a complete penetration groove weld (i.e., a groove weld conforming to the requirements of Sect. 1.23.6) shall be the thickness of the thinner part joined.

The effective throat thickness of single and double partial penetration groove welds shall be the depth of the groove, except that the effective throat thickness of a bevel joint made by manual shielded metal-arc welding shall be $\frac{1}{8}$-inch less than the depth of the groove, and the effective throat thickness of each weld shall be not less than $\sqrt{t_t/6}$, where t_t is the thickness of the thinner part connected by the weld.

SECTION 1.15 CONNECTIONS

1.15.1 Minimum Connections

Connections carrying calculated stresses, except for lacing, sag bars, and girts, shall be designed to support not less than 6 kips.

1.15.2 Eccentric Connections

Axially stressed members meeting at a point shall have their gravity axes intersect at a point if practicable; if not, provision shall be made for bending stresses due to the eccentricity.

1.15.3 Placement of Rivets, Bolts, and Welds

Except as hereinafter provided, groups of rivets, bolts or welds at the ends of any member transmitting axial stress into that member shall have their centers of gravity on the gravity axis of the member unless provision is made for the effect of the resulting eccentricity.   Except in members subject to repeated variation in stress, as defined in Sect. 1.7, disposition of fillet welds to balance the forces about the neutral axis or axes for end connections of single angle, double angle, and similar type members is not required. Eccentricity between the gravity axes of such members and the gage lines or their riveted or bolted end connections may be neglected.

1.15.4 Unrestrained Members

Except as otherwise indicated by the designer, connections of beams, girders or trusses shall be designed as flexible, and may ordinarily be proportioned for the reaction shears only.

Flexible beam connections shall permit the ends of the beam to rotate sufficiently to accommodate its deflection by providing for a horizontal displacement of the top flange determined as follows: ②

$$e = 0.007d, \text{ when the beam is designed for full uniform load and for}$$
$$\text{live load deflection not exceeding } \tfrac{1}{360} \text{ of the span}$$

$$= \frac{f_b L}{3,600}, \text{ when the beam is designed for full uniform load pro-}$$
$$\text{ducing the stress } f_b \text{ at mid-span}$$

where

e = the horizontal displacement of the end of the top flange, in the direction of the span, in inches
f_b = the flexural stress in the beam at mid-span, in kips per square inch
d = the depth of the beam, in inches
L = the span of the beam, in feet

1.15.5 Restrained Members

Fasteners or welds for end connections of beams, girders and trusses not conforming to the requirements of Sect. 1.15.4 shall be designed for the combined effect of end reaction shear and tensile or compressive stresses resulting from moment induced by the rigidity of the connection when the member is fully loaded. *

---

* For a discussion of high column web shear stress opposite rigid beam connections, Commentary Sect. 1.5.1.2.

①   When fully restrained beams are framed to the flange of an I- or H-shape column, stiffeners shall be provided on the column web as follows:

Opposite the compression flange when $t < \dfrac{C_1 A_f}{t_b + 5k}$ (1.15-1)

or when $t \leqslant \dfrac{d_c \sqrt{F_y}}{180}$ (1.15-2)

Opposite the tension flange when $t_f < 0.4 \sqrt{C_1 A_f}$ (1.15-3)

where

    t = thickness of web to be stiffened
    k = distance from outer face of flange to web toe of fillet of member to be stiffened, if a member is a rolled shape
      = flange thickness plus the distance to the farthest toe of the connecting weld, if a member is a welded section
    t_b = thickness of flange delivering concentrated load
    t_f = thickness of flange of member to be stiffened
    A_f = area of flange delivering concentrated load
    d_c = column web depth clear of fillets
    C_1 = ratio of beam flange yield stress to column yield stress
    C_2 = ratio of column yield stress to stiffener yield stress

The area of such stiffeners, A_{st}, shall be such that

$$A_{st} \geqslant [C_1 A_f - t(t_b + 5k)]C_2 \qquad (1.15\text{-}4$$

Their ends shall be welded to the inside face of the flange opposite the concentrated tensile load, so as to transfer the load from the beam flange to the column web. The stiffeners may be fitted against the inside face of the flange opposite the concentrated compression load. When the concentrated load delivered by a beam occurs on one side only, the web stiffener need not exceed one-half the depth of the member, but the welding connecting it to the web shall be sufficient to develop $F_y A_{st}$.

1.15.6 Fillers

    When rivets or bolts carrying computed stress pass through fillers thicker than ¼-inch, except in friction-type connections assembled with high strength bolts, the fillers shall be extended beyond the splice material and the filler extension shall be secured by enough rivets or bolts to distribute the total stress in the member uniformly over the combined section of the member and the filler, or an equivalent number of fasteners shall be included in the connection.

    In welded construction, any filler ¼-inch or more in thickness shall extend beyond the edges of the splice plate and shall be welded to the part on which it is fitted with sufficient weld to transmit the splice plate stress applied at the surface of the filler as an eccentric load. The welds joining the splice plate to the filler shall be sufficient to transmit the splice plate stress and shall be long enough to avoid overstressing the filler along the toe of the weld. Any filler less than ¼-inch thick shall have its edges made flush with the edges of the splice plate and the weld size shall be the sum of the size necessary to carry the splice plate stress plus the thickness of the filler plate.

1.15.7 Connections of Tension and Compression Members in Trusses

The connections at ends of tension or compression members in trusses shall develop the force due to the design load, but not less than 50 percent of the effective strength of the member.

1.15.8 Compression Members with Bearing Joints

Where columns bear on bearing plates, or are finished to bear at splices, there shall be sufficient rivets, bolts, or welds to hold all parts securely in place.

Where other compression members are finished to bear, the splice material and its riveting, bolting or welding shall be arranged to hold all parts in line and shall be proportioned for 50 percent of the computed stress.

All of the foregoing joints shall be proportioned to resist any tension that would be developed by specified lateral forces acting in conjunction with 75 percent of the calculated dead load stress and no live load.

1.15.9 Combination of Welds

If two or more of the general types of weld (groove, fillet, plug, slot) are combined in a single joint, the effective capacity of each shall be separately computed with reference to the axis of the group, in order to determine the allowable capacity of the combination.

1.15.10 Rivets and Bolts in Combination with Welds

In new work, rivets, A307 bolts, or high strength bolts used in bearing-type connections, shall not be considered as sharing the stress in combination with welds. Welds, if used, shall be provided to carry the entire stress in the connection. High strength bolts installed in accordance with the provisions of Sect. 1.16.1 as a friction-type connection prior to welding may be considered as sharing the stress with the welds.

In making welded alterations to structures, existing rivets and properly tightened high strength bolts may be utilized for carrying stresses resulting from existing dead loads, and the welding need be adequate only to carry all additional stress.

1.15.11 High Strength Bolts (in Friction-Type Joints) in Combination with Rivets

In new work and in making alterations, rivets and high strength bolts, installed in accordance with the provisions of Sect. 1.16.1 as friction-type connections, may be considered as sharing the stresses resulting from dead and live loads.

1.15.12 Field Connections

Rivets, high strength bolts or welds shall be used for the following connections:

Column splices in all tier structures 200 feet or more in height.
Column splices in tier structures 100 to 200 feet in height, if the least horizontal dimension is less than 40 percent of the height.
Column splices in tier structures less than 100 feet in height, if the least horizontal dimension is less than 25 percent of the height.

Connections of all beams and girders to columns and of any other beams and girders on which the bracing of columns is dependent, in structures over 125 feet in height.

Roof-truss splices and connections of trusses to columns, column splices, column bracing, knee braces and crane supports, in all structures carrying cranes of over 5-ton capacity.

Connections for supports of running machinery, or of other live loads which produce impact or reversal of stress.

Any other connections stipulated on the design plans.

In all other cases field connections may be made with A307 bolts.

For the purpose of this Section, the height of a tier structure shall be taken as the vertical distance from the curb level to the highest point of the roof beams, in the case of flat roofs, or to the mean height of the gable, in the case of roofs having a rise of more than $2\frac{2}{3}$ in 12. Where the curb level has not been established, or where the structure does not adjoin a street, the mean level of the adjoining land shall be used instead of curb level. Penthouses may be excluded in computing the height of structure.

SECTION 1.16 RIVETS AND BOLTS

1.16.1 High Strength Bolts

Use of high strength bolts shall conform to the provisions of the *Specifications for Structural Joints Using ASTM A325 or A490 Bolts* as approved by the Research Council on Riveted and Bolted Structural Joints. ASTM A449 bolts no greater than $1\frac{1}{2}$ inches in diameter may be used in lieu of ASTM A325 bolts, provided that a hardened washer is installed under the bolt head. However, nuts used with A449 bolts shall meet the requirements of ASTM A325.

1.16.2 Effective Bearing Area

The effective bearing area of rivets and bolts shall be the diameter multiplied by the length in bearing, except that for countersunk rivets and bolts half the depth of the countersink shall be deducted.

1.16.3 Long Grips

Rivets and A307 bolts which carry calculated stress, and the grip of which exceeds 5 diameters, shall have their number increased 1 percent for each additional $\frac{1}{16}$-inch in the grip.

1.16.4 Minimum Pitch

The minimum distance between centers of rivet and bolt holes shall be not less than $2\frac{2}{3}$ times the nominal diameter of the rivet or bolt but preferably not less than 3 diameters.

1.16.5 Minimum Edge Distance

The minimum distance from the center of a rivet or bolt hole to any edge used in design or in preparation of shop drawings, shall be that given in Table 1.16.5.

TABLE 1.16.5

Rivet or Bolt Diameter (Inches)	Minimum Edge Distance for Punched, Reamed or Drilled Holes (Inches)	
	At Sheared Edges	At Rolled Edges of Plates, Shapes or Bars or Gas Cut Edges**
½	⅞	¾
⅝	1⅛	⅞
¾	1¼	1
⅞	1½*	1⅛
1	1¾*	1¼
1⅛	2	1½
1¼	2¼	1⅝
Over 1¼	1¾ × Diameter	1¼ × Diameter

* These may be 1¼-in. at the ends of beam connection angles.
** All edge distances in this column may be reduced ⅛-in. when the hole is at a point where stress does not exceed 25% of the maximum allowed stress in the element.

1.16.6 Minimum Edge Distance in Line of Stress

1.16.6.1 In connections of tension members, where there are not more than two rivets in a line parallel to the direction of stress, the distance from the center of the end rivet to that end of the connected part toward which the stress is directed shall be not less than the area of the rivet divided by the thickness of the connected part for rivets in single shear or twice this distance for rivets in double shear.

1.16.6.2 In bearing-type connections of tension members, where there are not more than two high strength bolts in a line parallel to the direction of stress, the distance from the center of the end bolt to that end of the connected part toward which the stress is directed shall be not less than A_bC/t for single shear or $2A_bC/t$ for double shear, where A_b is the nominal cross-sectional area of the bolt, t is the thickness of the connected part, and C is the ratio of specified minimum tensile strength of the bolt to the specified minimum tensile strength of the connected part.

1.16.6.3 However, the end distance prescribed in Sects. 1.16.6.1 and 1.16.6.2 may be decreased in such proportion as the fastener stress is less than that permitted in Sect. 1.5.2, but it shall not be less than the distance specified in Sect. 1.16.5 and need not exceed 1½ times the transverse spacing of fasteners.

1.16.6.4 When more than two fasteners are provided in the line of stress, the provisions of Sect. 1.16.5 shall govern.

1.16.7 Maximum Edge Distance

The maximum distance from the center of any rivet or bolt to the nearest edge of parts in contact with one another shall be 12 times the thickness of the plate, but shall not exceed 6 inches.

SECTION 1.17 WELDS

1.17.1 Welder, Tacker, and Welding Operator Qualifications

Welds shall be made only by welders, tackers, and welding operators who have been previously qualified by tests as prescribed in the *Code for Welding in Building Construction*, AWS D1.0-69, of the American Welding Society to perform the type of work required.

1.17.2 Qualification of Weld and Joint Details

Weld grooves for complete and partial penetration welds which are accepted without welding procedure qualification under the provisions of AWS D1.0-69, may be used under this specification without welding procedure qualification.

Joint forms, details, welding processes, or welding procedures other than those included in the foregoing may be employed provided they shall have been qualified in accordance with the requirements of AWS D1.0-69.

The electrodes or flux specified in Table 1.17.2 shall be used in making complete penetration groove welds designed on the basis of the allowable stresses for the base metal, as provided in Table 1.5.3. The electrodes and fluxes as listed in Table 1.5.3 may be used in making fillet welds and partial penetration groove welds.

Welding of A440 steel is not recommended.

1.17.3 Submerged-Arc, Gas Metal-Arc, and Flux Cored-Arc Welding of High Strength Steel

Electrodes for use in submerged-arc, gas metal-arc, and flux cored-arc welding listed in Tables 1.5.3 and 1.17.2 by grade designation and not covered in AWS A5.17, A5.18 or A5.20, shall meet the provisions of Sections 412, 417 or 418 of AWS D1.0-69, as applicable.

1.17.4 Electroslag and Electrogas Welding

Weld metal deposited by the electroslag or electrogas welding process shall conform to the requirements of Article 422 of AWS D1.0-69. Weldments of A514 steel, made by either process, shall be quenched and tempered after welding.

1.17.5 Minimum Size of Fillet Welds

In joints connected only by fillet welds, the minimum size of fillet weld to be used shall be as shown in Table 1.17.5. Weld size is determined by the thicker of the two parts joined, except that the weld size need not exceed the thickness of the thinner part joined unless a larger size is required by calculated stress:

TABLE 1.17.5

Material Thickness of Thicker Part Joined (Inches)	Minimum Size of Fillet Weld (Inches)	Material Thickness of Thicker Part Joined (Inches)	Minimum Size of Fillet Weld (Inches)
To ¼ inclusive	⅛	Over 1½ to 2¼	⅜
Over ¼ to ½	³⁄₁₆	Over 2¼ to 6	½
Over ½ to ¾	¼	Over 6	⅝
Over ¾ to 1½	⁵⁄₁₆		

TABLE 1.17.2

Base Metal[3]	Welding Process[1,2]			
	Shielded Metal-Arc	Submerged-Arc	Gas Metal-Arc	Flux Cored-Arc
ASTM A36, A53 Gr. B, A375, A500, A501, A529, and A570 Gr. D and E	AWS A5.1 or A5.5, E60XX or E70XX[3]	AWS A5.17 F6X or F7X-EXXX	AWS A5.18 E70S-X or E70U-1	AWS 5.20 E60T-X or E70T-X (except EXXT-2 and EXX-3)
ASTM A242, A441, A572 Grades 42 thru 60 and A588[4]	AWS A5.1 or A5.5, E70XX[5]	AWS A5.17 F7X-EXXX	AWS A5.18 E70S-X or E70U-1	AWS 5.20 E70T-X (except E70T-2 and E70T-3)
ASTM A572 Grade 65	AWS A5.5 E80XX[5]	Grade F80	Grade E80S	Grade E80T
ASTM A514 over 2½" thick	AWS A5.5 E100XX[5]	Grade F100	Grade E100S	Grade E100T
ASTM A514 2½" thick and under	AWS A5.5 E110XX[5]	Grade F110	Grade E110S	Grade E110T

Use of the same type filler metal having next higher mechanical properties is permitted.

[1] When welds are to be stress relieved the deposited weld metal shall not exceed 0.05 percent vanadium.

[2] See Article 422 of AWS D1.0-69 for electroslag and electrogas weld metal requirements.

[3] On joints involving base metals of different yield strengths, filler metals applicable to the lower yield strength may be used.

[4] For architectural exposed bare unpainted applications, the deposited weld metal shall have similar atmospheric corrosion resistance and coloring characteristics as the base metal used. The steel manufacturer's recommendation shall be followed.

[5] Low hydrogen classifications.

1.17.6 Maximum Effective Size of Fillet Welds

The maximum size of a fillet weld that may be assumed in the design of a connection shall be such that the stresses in the adjacent base material do not exceed the values allowed in Sect. 1.5.1. The maximum size that may be used along edges of connected parts shall be:

1. Along edges of material less than $\frac{1}{4}$-inch thick, the maximum size may be equal to the thickness of the material.
2. Along edges of material $\frac{1}{4}$-inch or more in thickness, the maximum size shall be $\frac{1}{16}$-inch less than the thickness of the material, unless the weld is especially designated on the drawings to be built out to obtain full throat thickness.

1.17.7 Length of Fillet Welds

The minimum effective length of a strength fillet weld shall be not less than 4 times the nominal size, or else the size of the weld shall be considered not to exceed one-fourth of its effective length.

If longitudinal fillet welds are used alone in end connections of flat bar tension members, the length of each fillet weld shall be not less than the perpendicular distance between them. The transverse spacing of longitudinal fillet welds used in end connections shall not exceed 8 inches, unless the design otherwise prevents excessive transverse bending in the connection.

1.17.8 Intermittent Fillet Welds

Intermittent fillet welds may be used to transfer calculated stress across a joint or faying surfaces when the strength required is less than that developed by a continuous fillet weld of the smallest permitted size, and to join components of built-up members. The effective length of any segment of intermittent fillet welding shall be not less than 4 times the weld size with a minimum of $1\frac{1}{2}$ inches.

1.17.9 Lap Joints

The minimum amount of lap on lap joints shall be 5 times the thickness of the thinner part joined and not less than 1 inch. Lap joints joining plates or bars subjected to axial stress shall be fillet welded along the end of both lapped parts except where the deflection of the lapped parts is sufficiently restrained to prevent opening of the joint under maximum loading.

1.17.10 End Returns of Fillet Welds

Side or end fillet welds terminating at ends or sides, respectively, of parts or members shall, wherever practicable, be returned continuously around the corners for a distance not less than twice the nominal size of the weld. This provision shall apply to side and top fillet welds connecting brackets, beam seats and similar connections, on the plane about which bending moments are computed. End returns shall be indicated on the design and detail drawings.

1.17.11 Fillet Welds in Holes and Slots

Fillet welds in holes or slots may be used to transmit shear in lap joints or to prevent the buckling or separation of lapped parts, and to join components of built-up members. Such fillet welds may overlap, subject to the provisions of Sect. 1.14.7. Fillet welds in holes or slots are not to be considered plug or slot welds.

1.17.12   Plug and Slot Welds

Plug or slot welds may be used to transmit shear in a lap joint or to prevent buckling of lapped parts and to join component parts of built-up members.

The diameter of the holes for a plug weld shall be not less than the thickness of the part containing it plus $5/16$-inch, rounded to the next greater odd $1/16$-inch, nor greater than $2\frac{1}{4}$ times the thickness of the weld metal.

The minimum center-to-center spacing of plug welds shall be 4 times the diameter of the hole.

The length of slot for a slot weld shall not exceed 10 times the thickness of the weld. The width of the slot shall be not less than the thickness of the part containing it, plus $5/16$-inch, rounded to the next greater odd $1/16$-inch, nor shall it be greater than $2\frac{1}{4}$ times the thickness of the weld. The ends of the slot shall be semicircular or shall have the corners rounded to a radius not less than the thickness of the part containing it, except those ends which extend to the edge of the part.

The minimum spacing of lines of slot welds in a direction transverse to their length shall be 4 times the width of the slot. The minimum center-to-center spacing in a longitudinal direction on any line shall be 2 times the length of the slot.

The thickness of plug or slot welds in material $5/8$-inch or less in thickness shall be equal to the thickness of the material. In material over $5/8$-inch in thickness, it shall be at least one-half the thickness of the material but not less than $5/8$-inch.

SECTION 1.18   BUILT-UP MEMBERS

1.18.1   Open Box-Type Beams and Grillages

Where two or more rolled beams or channels are used side-by-side to form a flexural member, they shall be connected together at intervals of not more than 5 feet. Through-bolts and separators may be used, provided that in beams having a depth of 12 inches or more, no fewer than 2 bolts shall be used at each separator location. When concentrated loads are carried from one beam to the other, or distributed between the beams, diaphragms having sufficient stiffness to distribute the load shall be riveted, bolted or welded between the beams. Where beams are exposed, they shall be sealed against corrosion of interior surfaces, or spaced sufficiently far apart to permit cleaning and painting.

1.18.2   Compression Members

1.18.2.1   All parts of built-up compression members and the transverse spacing of their lines of fasteners shall meet the requirements of Sects. 1.8 and 1.9.

1.18.2.2   At the ends of built-up compression members bearing on base plates or milled surfaces, all components in contact with one another shall be connected by rivets or bolts spaced longitudinally not more than 4 diameters apart for a distance equal to $1\frac{1}{2}$ times the maximum width of the member, or by continuous welds having a length not less than the maximum width of the member.

1.18.2.3 The longitudinal spacing for intermediate rivets, bolts or intermittent welds in built-up members shall be adequate to provide for the transfer of calculated stress. However, where a component of a built-up compression member consists of an outside plate, the maximum spacing shall not exceed the thickness of the thinner outside plate times $127/\sqrt{F_y}$ when rivets are provided on all gage lines at each section, or when intermittent welds are provided along the edges of the components, but this spacing shall not exceed 12 inches. When rivets or bolts are staggered, the maximum spacing on each gage line shall not exceed the thickness of the thinner outside plate times $190/\sqrt{F_y}$ nor 18 inches. The maximum longitudinal spacing of rivets, bolts or intermittent welds connecting two rolled shapes in contact with one another shall not exceed 24 inches.

1.18.2.4 Compression members composed of two or more rolled shapes separated from one another by intermittent fillers shall be connected to one another at these fillers at intervals such that the slenderness ratio l/r of either shape, between the fasteners, does not exceed the governing slenderness ratio of the built-up member. The least radius of gyration r shall be used in computing the slenderness ratio of each component part.

1.18.2.5 Open sides of compression members built up from plates or shapes shall be provided with lacing having tie plates at each end, and at intermediate points if the lacing is interrupted. Tie plates shall be as near the ends as practicable. In main members carrying calculated stress the end tie plates shall have a length of not less than the distance between the lines of rivets, bolts or welds connecting them to the components of the member. Intermediate tie plates shall have a length not less than one-half of this distance. The thickness of tie plates shall be not less than $\frac{1}{50}$ of the distance between the lines of rivets, bolts or welds connecting them to the segments of the members. In riveted and bolted construction the pitch in tie plates shall be not more than 6 diameters and the tie plates shall be connected to each segment by at least three fasteners. In welded construction, the welding on each line connecting a tie plate shall aggregate not less than one-third the length of the plate.

1.18.2.6 Lacing, including flat bars, angles, channels or other shapes employed as lacing, shall be so spaced that the ratio l/r of the flange included between their connections shall not exceed the governing ratio for the member as a whole. Lacing shall be proportioned to resist a shearing stress normal to the axis of the member equal to 2 percent of the total compressive stress in the member. The ratio l/r for lacing bars arranged in single systems shall not exceed 140. For double lacing this ratio shall not exceed 200. Double lacing bars shall be joined at their intersections. In determining the required section for lacing bars, Formula (1.5-1) or (1.5-2) shall be used, l being taken as the unsupported length of the lacing bar between rivets or welds connecting it to the components of the built-up member for single lacing and 70 percent of that distance for double lacing. The inclination of lacing bars to the axis of the member shall preferably be not less than 60 degrees for single lacing and 45 degrees for double lacing. When the distance between the lines of rivets or welds in the flanges is more than 15 inches, the lacing shall preferably be double or be made of angles.

1.18.2.7 The function of tie plates and lacing may be performed by continuous cover plates perforated with a succession of access holes. The width of such plates at access holes, as defined in Sect. 1.9.2, is assumed available to resist axial stress, provided that: the width-to-thickness ratio conforms to the limitations of Sect. 1.9.2; the ratio of length (in direction of stress) to width of hole shall not exceed 2; the clear distance between holes in the direction of stress shall be not less than the transverse distance between nearest lines of connecting rivets, bolts or welds; and the periphery of the holes at all points shall have a minimum radius of $1\frac{1}{2}$ inches.

1.18.3 Tension Members

1.18.3.1 The longitudinal spacing of rivets, bolts and intermittent fillet welds connecting a plate and a rolled shape in a built-up tension member, or two plate components in contact with one another, shall not exceed 24 times the thickness of the thinner plate nor 12 inches. The longitudinal spacing of rivets, bolts and intermittent welds connecting two or more shapes in contact with one another in a tension member shall not exceed 24 inches. Tension members composed of two or more shapes or plates separated from one another by intermittent fillers shall be connected to one another at these fillers at intervals such that the slenderness ratio of either component between the fasteners does not exceed 240.

1.18.3.2 Either perforated cover plates or tie plates without lacing may be used on the open sides of built-up tension members. Tie plates shall have a length not less than two-thirds the distance between the lines of rivets, bolts or welds connecting them to the components of the member. The thickness of such tie plates shall not be less than $\frac{1}{50}$ of the distance between these lines. The longitudinal spacing of rivets, bolts or intermittent welds at tie plates shall not exceed 6 inches. The spacing of tie plates shall be such that the slenderness ratio of any component in the length between tie plates will not exceed 240.

SECTION 1.19 CAMBER

1.19.1 Trusses and Girders

Trusses of 80 feet or greater span should generally be cambered for approximately the dead load deflection. Crane girders of 75 feet or greater span should generally be cambered for approximately the dead and half live load deflection.

1.19.2 Camber for Other Trades

If any special camber requirements are necessary in order to bring a loaded member into proper relation with the work of other trades, as for the attachment of runs of sash, the requirements shall be set forth on the plans and on the detail drawings.

1.19.3 Erection

Beams and trusses detailed without specified camber shall be fabricated so that after erection any minor camber due to rolling or shop assembly shall be upward. If camber involves the erection of any member under a straining force, this shall be noted on the erection diagram.

SECTION 1.20 EXPANSION

Adequate provision shall be made for expansion and contraction appropriate to the service conditions of the structure.

SECTION 1.21 COLUMN BASES

1.21.1 Loads

Proper provision shall be made to transfer the column loads, and moments if any, to the footings and foundations.

1.21.2 Alignment

Column bases shall be set level and to correct elevation with full bearing on the masonry.

1.21.3 Finishing

Column bases shall be finished in accordance with the following requirements:

1. Rolled steel bearing plates, 2 inches or less in thickness, may be used without planing, provided a satisfactory contact bearing is obtained; rolled steel bearing plates over 2 inches but not over 4 inches in thickness may be straightened by pressing; or, if presses are not available, by planing for all bearing surfaces (except as noted under requirement 3 of this Section), to obtain a satisfactory contact bearing; rolled steel bearing plates over 4 inches in thickness shall be planed for all bearing surfaces (except as noted under requirement 3 of this Section).

2. Column bases other than rolled steel bearing plates shall be planed for all bearing surfaces (except as noted under requirement 3 of this Section).

3. The bottom surfaces of bearing plates and column bases which are grouted to insure full bearing contact on foundations need not be planed.

SECTION 1.22 ANCHOR BOLTS

Anchor bolts shall be designed to provide resistance to all conditions of tension and shear at the bases of columns, including the net tensile components of any bending moments which may result from fixation or partial fixation of columns.

SECTION 1.23 FABRICATION

1.23.1 Straightening Material

① Rolled material, before being laid off or worked, must be straight within the tolerances allowed by ASTM Specification A6. If straightening is necessary, it may be done by mechanical means or by the application of a limited amount of localized heat. The temperature of heated areas, as measured by approved methods, shall not exceed 1100°F for A514 steel nor 1200°F for other steels.

1.23.2 Oxygen Cutting

Oxygen cutting shall preferably be done by machine. Oxygen cut edges which will be subjected to substantial stress or which are to have weld metal deposited on them shall be reasonably free from gouges; occasional notches or gouges not more than $\frac{3}{16}$-inch deep will be permitted. Gouges greater than $\frac{3}{16}$-inch that remain from cutting shall be removed by grinding. All re-entrant corners shall be shaped notch-free to a radius of at least $\frac{1}{2}$-inch.

1.23.3 Planing of Edges

Planing or finishing of sheared or gas cut edges of plates or shapes will not be required unless specifically called for on the drawings or included in a stipulated edge preparation for welding.

1.23.4 Riveted and Bolted Construction—Holes

Holes for rivets or bolts shall be $\frac{1}{16}$-inch larger than the nominal diameter of the rivet or bolt. If the thickness of the material is not greater than the nominal diameter of the rivet or bolt plus $\frac{1}{8}$-inch, the holes may be punched. If the thickness of the material is greater than the nominal diameter of the rivet or bolt plus $\frac{1}{8}$-inch, the holes shall be either drilled from the solid, or sub-punched and reamed. The die for all sub-punched holes, and the drill for all sub-drilled holes, shall be at least $\frac{1}{16}$-inch smaller than the nominal diameter of the rivet or bolt. Holes in A514 steel plates over $\frac{1}{2}$-inch thick shall be drilled.

1.23.5 Riveted and High Strength Bolted Construction—Assembling

All parts of riveted members shall be well pinned or bolted and rigidly held together while riveting. Drifting done during assembling shall not distort the metal or enlarge the holes. Holes that must be enlarged to admit the rivets or bolts shall be reamed. Poor matching of holes shall be cause for rejection.

Rivets shall be driven by power riveters, of either compression or manually-operated type, employing pneumatic, hydraulic or electric power. After driving they shall be tight and their heads shall be in full contact with the surface.

Rivets shall ordinarily be hot-driven, in which case their finished heads shall be of approximately hemispherical shape and shall be of uniform size throughout the work for the same size rivet, full, neatly finished and concentric with the holes. Hot-driven rivets shall be heated uniformly to a temperature not exceeding 1950° F; they shall not be driven after their temperature has fallen below 1000° F.

Rivets may be driven cold if approved measures are taken to prevent distortion of the riveted material. The requirements for hot-driven rivets shall apply except as modified in the *Tentative Specifications for Cold-Driven Rivets* of the Industrial Fasteners Institute.

Surfaces of high strength bolted parts in contact with the bolt head and nut shall not have a slope of more than 1:20 with respect to a plane normal to the bolt axis. Where the surface of a high strength bolted part has a slope of more than 1:20, a beveled washer shall be used to compensate for the lack of parallelism. High strength bolted parts shall fit solidly together when assembled and shall not be separated by gaskets or any other interposed compressible materials. When assembled, all joint surfaces, including those adjacent to the washers, shall be free of scale except tight mill scale. They shall be free of dirt, loose scale, burrs, and other defects that would prevent solid seating of the parts. Contact surfaces within friction-type joints shall be free of oil, paint, lacquer or galvanizing.

All A325, A449, and A490 bolts shall be tightened to a bolt tension not less than that given in Table 1.23.5. Tightening shall be done by the

TABLE 1.23.5

Bolt Size, Inches	Minimum Bolt Tension,[1] Kips	
	A325 and A449 Bolts	A490 Bolts
½	12	15
⅝	19	24
¾	28	35
⅞	39	49
1	51	64
1⅛	56	80
1¼	71	102
1⅜	85	121
1½	103	148
Over 1½		$0.7 \times$ T.S.

[1] Equal to 70 percent of specified minimum tensile strengths of bolts, rounded off to the nearest kip.

turn-of-nut method* or with properly calibrated wrenches. Bolts tightened by means of a calibrated wrench shall be installed with a hardened washer under the nut or bolt head, whichever is the element turned in tightening. Hardened washers are not required when bolts are tightened by the turn-of-nut method, except that hardened washers are required under the nut and bolt head when A490 bolts are used to connect material having a specified yield point less than 40 ksi and a hardened washer is required under the head of A449 bolts used in lieu of A325 bolts.

1.23.6 Welded Construction

Surfaces to be welded shall be free from loose scale, slag, rust, grease, paint and any other foreign material except that mill scale which withstand vigorous wire brushing may remain. Joint surfaces shall be free from fins and tears. Preparation of edges by gas cutting shall, wherever practicable, b done by a mechanically guided torch.

Parts to be fillet welded shall be brought in as close contact as practicabl and in no event shall be separated by more than 3/16-inch. If the separa tion is 1/16-inch or greater, the size of the fillet welds shall be increase by the amount of the separation. The separation between faying sur faces of lap joints and butt joints on a backing structure shall no exceed 1/16-inch. The fit of joints at contact surfaces which are not com pletely sealed by welds, shall be close enough to exclude water after painting

---

* See Commentary, Sect. 1.23.5.

Abutting parts to be butt welded shall be carefully aligned. Misalignments greater than $\frac{1}{8}$-inch shall be corrected and, in making the correction, the parts shall not be drawn into a sharper slope than 2 degrees ($\frac{7}{16}$-inch in 12 inches).

The work shall be positioned for flat welding whenever practicable.

In assembling and joining parts of a structure or of built-up members, the procedure and sequence of welding shall be such as will avoid needless distortion and minimize shrinkage stresses. Where it is impossible to avoid high residual stresses in the closing welds of a rigid assembly, such closing welds shall be made in compression elements.

In the fabrication of cover-plated beams and built-up members, all shop splices in each component part shall be made before such component part is welded to other parts of the member. Long girders or girder sections may be made by shop splicing not more than three subsections, each made in accordance with this paragraph.

All complete penetration groove welds made by manual welding, except when produced with the aid of backing material or welded in the flat position from both sides in square-edge material not more than $\frac{5}{16}$-inch thick with root opening not less than one-half the thickness of the thinner part joined, shall have the root of the initial layer gouged out on the back side before welding is started from that side, and shall be so welded as to secure sound metal and complete fusion throughout the entire cross-section. Oxygen gouging shall not be permitted on ASTM A514 steel; all carbon deposits shall be removed by grinding after arc gouging A514 steel. Groove welds made with use of a backing of the same material as the base metal shall have the weld metal thoroughly fused with the backing material. Backing strips need not be removed. If required, they may be removed by gouging or gas cutting after welding is completed, provided no injury is done to the base metal and weld metal and the weld metal surface is left flush or slightly convex with full throat thickness.

Groove welds shall be terminated at the ends of a joint in a manner that will ensure their soundness. Where possible, this should be done by use of extension bars or run-off plates. Extension bars or run-off plates, if used, shall be removed upon completion of the weld and the ends of the weld made smooth and flush with the abutting parts.   ②

Base metal shall be preheated as required to the temperature called for in Table 1.23.6 prior to welding, except tack welding which is to be remelted and incorporated into continuous submerged-arc welds. When base metal not otherwise required to be preheated is at a temperature below 32° F, it shall be preheated to at least 70° F prior to tack welding or welding. Preheating shall bring the surface of the base metal within 3 inches of the point of welding to the specified preheat temperature, and this temperature shall be maintained as a minimum interpass temperature while welding is in progress. Minimum preheat and interpass temperatures shall be as specified in Table 1.23.6. Heat input for the welding of ASTM A514 steel should not exceed the steel producer's recommendations or suggestions.

Where required, intermediate layers of multiple-layer welds may be peened with light blows from a power hammer, using a round-nose tool. Peening shall be done after the weld has cooled to a temperature warm to the hand. Care shall be exercised to prevent scaling, or flaking of weld and base metal from over-peening.

TABLE 1.23.6
Minimum Preheat and Interpass Temperature, °F[1]

Thickness of Thickest Part at Point of Welding (inches)	Welding Process				
	Shielded Metal-Arc Welding with other than Low Hydrogen Electrodes	Shielded Metal-Arc Welding with Low Hydrogen Electrodes; Submerged Arc Metal-Arc Welding; or Flux Cored Arc Welding		Shielded Metal-Arc Welding with Low Hydrogen Electrodes; Submerged Arc Welding with Carbon or Alloy Steel Wire, Neutral Flux; Gas Metal-Arc Welding; or Flux Cored Arc Welding	Submerged Arc Welding with Carbon Steel Wire, Alloy Flux
	ASTM A36; A53 Grade B; A375; A500; A501; A529; A570 Grades D and E	ASTM A36; A242 Weldable Grade; A375; A441; A529; A570 Grades D & E; A572 Grades 42, 45, and 50; A588	ASTM A572 Grades 55, 60, and 65	ASTM A514	ASTM A514
To ¾, incl.	None[2,3]	None[2]	70	50	50
Over ¾ to 1½, incl.	150	70[4]	150	125	200
Over 1½ to 2½, incl.	225	150[4]	225	175	300
Over 2½	300	225	300	225	400

[1] Welding shall not be done when the ambient temperature is lower than 0° F. When the base metal is below the temperature listed for the welding process being used and the thickness of material being welded, it shall be preheated (except as otherwise provided) in such manner that the surface of the parts on which weld metal is being deposited are at or above the specified minimum temperature for a distance equal to the thickness of the part being welded, but not less than 3 in., both laterally and in advance of the welding. Preheat and interpass temperatures must be sufficient to prevent crack formation. Temperature above the minimum shown may be required for highly restrained welds. For A514 steel the maximum preheat and interpass temperature shall not exceed 400° F for thicknesses up to 1½ in., inclusive, and 450° F for greater thicknesses.

[2] When base metal temperature is below 32° F, preheat base metal to at least 70° F and maintain this minimum temperature during welding.

[3] This provision also applies to A36 steel in thicknesses up to 1 in.

When required by the plans or specifications, welded assemblies shall be stress relieved by heat treating in accordance with the the provisions of Article 310 of AWS D1.0-69.

The technique of welding employed, the appearance and quality of welds made, and the methods used in correcting defective work shall conform to Section 3—Workmanship and Section 4—Technique of the *Code for Welding in Building Construction*, D1.0-69, of the American Welding Society, except that the tolerance for flatness of girder webs given in Article 305 need not apply for statically loaded girders.

1.23.7 Finishing

Compression joints depending upon contact bearing shall have the bearing surfaces prepared to a common plane by milling, sawing or other suitable means.

1.23.8 Tolerances

1.23.8.1 Straightness

Structural members consisting primarily of a single rolled shape shall, unless otherwise specified, be straight within the appropriate tolerances allowed by ASTM Specification A6 or as prescribed in the following paragraph. Built-up structural members fabricated by riveting or welding, unless otherwise specified, shall be straight within the tolerances allowed for wide flange shapes by ASTM Specification A6 or by the requirements of the following paragraph.

Compression members shall not deviate from straightness by more than $\frac{1}{1000}$ of the axial length between points which are to be laterally supported.

Completed members shall be free from twists, bends, and open joints. Sharp kinks or bends shall be cause for rejection of material.

1.23.8.2 Length

A variation of $\frac{1}{32}$-inch is permissible in the overall length of members with both ends finished for contact bearing as in Sect. 1.23.7.

Members without ends finished for contact bearing, which are to be framed to other steel parts of the structure, may have a variation from the detailed length not greater than $\frac{1}{16}$-inch for members 30 feet or less in length, and not greater than $\frac{1}{8}$-inch for members over 30 feet in length.

SECTION 1.24 SHOP PAINTING

1.24.1 General Requirements

Unless otherwise specified, steelwork which will be concealed by interior building finish need not be painted; steelwork to be encased in concrete shall not be painted. Unless specifically exempted, all other steelwork shall be given one coat of shop paint, applied thoroughly and evenly to dry surfaces which have been cleaned, in accordance with the following paragraph, by brush, spray, roller coating, flow coating, or dipping, at the election of the fabricator.

After inspection and approval and before leaving the shop, all steelwork specified to be painted shall be cleaned by hand-wire brushing, or by other methods elected by the fabricator, of loose mill scale, loose rust, weld slag or flux deposit, dirt and other foreign matter. Oil and grease deposits shall be removed by solvent. Steelwork specified to have no shop paint shall, after fabrication, be cleaned of oil or grease by solvent cleaners and be cleaned of dirt and other foreign material by thorough sweeping with a fiber brush. The shop coat of paint is intended to protect the steel for only a short period of exposure, even if it is a primer for subsequent painting to be performed in the field by others.

1.24.2 Inaccessible Surfaces

Surfaces inaccessible after assembly shall be treated in accordance with Sect. 1.24.1 before assembly.

1.24.3 Contact Surfaces

Contact surfaces shall be cleaned in accordance with Sect. 1.24.1 before assembly but shall not be painted.

1.24.4 Finished Surfaces

Machine finished surfaces shall be protected against corrosion by a rust-inhibiting coating that can be easily removed prior to erection or which has characteristics that make removal unnecessary prior to erection.

1.24.5 Surfaces Adjacent to Field Welds

Unless otherwise provided, surfaces within two inches of any field weld location shall be free of materials that would prevent proper welding or produce objectionable fumes while welding is being done.

SECTION 1.25 ERECTION

1.25.1 Bracing

The frame of steel skeleton buildings shall be carried up true and plumb, within the limits defined in Section 7(h) of the AISC *Code of Standard Practice*, and temporary bracing shall be introduced wherever necessary to take care of all loads to which the structure may be subjected, including equipment and the operation of same.   Such bracing shall be left in place as long as may be required for safety.

Wherever piles of material, erection equipment or other loads are carried during erection, proper provision shall be made to take care of stresses resulting from such loads.

1.25.2 Adequacy of Temporary Connections

As erection progresses, the work shall be securely bolted, or welded, to take care of all dead load, wind and erection stresses.

1.25.3 Alignment

No riveting, permanent bolting or welding shall be done until as much of the structure as will be stiffened thereby has been properly aligned.

1.25.4 Field Welding

Any shop paint on surfaces adjacent to joints to be field welded shall be wire brushed to reduce the paint film to a minimum.

1.25.5   Field Painting

Responsibility for touch-up painting and cleaning, as well as for general painting shall be allocated in accordance with accepted local practices and this allocation shall be set forth explicitly in the contract.

SECTION 1.26   QUALITY CONTROL

1.26.1   General

The fabricator shall provide quality control procedures to the extent that he deems necessary to assure that all work is performed in accordance with this Specification.   In addition to the fabricator's quality control procedures, material and workmanship at all times may be subject to inspection by qualified inspectors representing the purchaser.   If such inspection by representatives of the purchaser will be required, it shall be so stated in the information furnished to the bidders.

1.26.2   Cooperation

As far as possible all inspection by representatives of the purchaser shall be made at the fabricator's plant.   The fabricator shall cooperate with the inspector, permitting access for inspection to all places where work is being done.   The purchaser's inspector shall so schedule his work as to provide the minimum interruption to the work of the fabricator.

1.26.3   Rejections

Material or workmanship not in reasonable conformance with the provisions of this Specification may be rejected at any time during the progress of the work.   The fabricator shall receive copies of all reports furnished to the purchaser by the inspection agency.

1.26.4   Inspection of Welding

The inspection of welding shall be performed in accordance with the provisions of Section 6 of the *Code for Welding in Building Construction*, D1.0-69, of the American Welding Society.

When non-destructive testing is required, the process, extent, technique and standards of acceptance shall be clearly defined in information furnished to the bidders.

1.26.5   Identification of High Strength Steel

Steel which is used for main components and which is required to have a yield stress greater than 36 kips per square inch shall, at all times in the fabricator's plant, be marked to identify its ASTM Specification.   Identification of such steel in completed members or assemblies shall be marked by painting the ASTM Specification designation on the piece, over any shop coat of paint, prior to shipment from the fabricator's plant.

PART 2

SECTION 2.1   SCOPE

Subject to the limitations contained herein, simple or continuous beams, one and two-story rigid frames, braced multi-story rigid frames, and similar portions of structures rigidly constructed so as to be continuous over at least one interior support,* may be proportioned on the basis of plastic design, i.e., on the basis of their maximum strength. This strength, as determined by rational analysis, shall not be less than that required to support a factored load equal to 1.7 times the given live load and dead load or 1.3 times these loads acting in conjunction with 1.3 times any specified wind or earthquake forces.

Rigid frames shall satisfy the requirements for Type 1 construction in the plane of the frame as provided in Sect. 1.2.   Type 2 construction is permitted for members between rigid frames.   Connections joining a portion of a structure designed on the basis of plastic behavior with a portion not so designed need be no more rigid than ordinary seat-and-cap angle or standard web connections.

Where plastic design is used as the basis for proportioning continuous beams and structural frames, the provisions relating to allowable working stress, contained in Part 1, are waived.   Except as modified by these rules, however, all other pertinent provisions of Part 1 shall govern.

It is not recommended that crane runways be designed continuous over interior vertical supports on the basis of maximum strength.   However, rigid frame bents supporting crane runways may be considered as coming within the scope of the rules.

SECTION 2.2   STRUCTURAL STEEL

Structural steel shall conform to one of the following specifications, latest edition:

Structural Steel, ASTM A36
High-Strength Low-Alloy Structural Steel, ASTM A242
High-Strength Low-Alloy Structural Manganese Vanadium Steel, ASTM A441
Structural Steel with 42,000 psi Minimum Yield Point, ASTM, A529
High-Strength Low-Alloy Columbium-Vanadium Steels of Structural Quality, ASTM A572
High-Strength Low-Alloy Structural Steel with 50,000 psi Minimum Yield Point to 4 in. Thick, ASTM A588

---

* As used here, "interior support" may be taken to include a rigid frame knee formed by the junction of a column and a sloping or horizontal beam or girder.

SECTION 2.3   VERTICAL BRACING SYSTEM

The vertical bracing system for a plastically designed braced multistory frame shall be adequate, as determined by a rational analysis, to:

1.   Prevent buckling of the structure under factored gravity loads.
2.   Maintain the lateral stability of the structure, including the overturning effects of drift, under factored gravity plus factored horizontal loads.

The vertical bracing system may be considered to function together with in-plane shear-resisting exterior and interior walls, floor slabs, and roof decks, if these walls, slabs, and decks are secured to the structural frames. The columns, girders, beams, and diagonal members, when used as the vertical bracing system, may be considered to comprise a vertical-cantilever, simply-connected truss in the analyses for frame buckling and lateral stability. Axial deformation of all members in the vertical bracing system shall be included in the lateral stability analysis. The axial force in these members, caused by factored gravity plus factored horizontal loads, shall not exceed $0.85P_y$, where P_y is the product of yield stress times area of the member.

Girders and beams included in the vertical bracing system of a braced multi-story frame shall be proportioned for axial force and moment caused by the concurrent factored horizontal and gravity loads, in accordance with Formula (2.4-2), with P_{cr} taken as the maximum axial strength of the beam, based on the actual slenderness ratio between braced points in the plane of bending.

SECTION 2.4   COLUMNS

In the plane of bending of columns which would develop a plastic hinge at ultimate loading, the slenderness ratio l/r shall not exceed C_c, defined in Sect. 1.5.1.3.

The maximum strength of an axially loaded compression member shall be taken as

$$P_{cr} = 1.7AF_a \tag{2.4-1}$$

where A is the gross area of the member and F_a, as defined by Formula (1.5-1), is based upon the applicable slenderness ratio.*

Members subject to combined axial load and bending moment shall be proportioned so as to satisfy the following interaction formulas:

$$\frac{P}{P_{cr}} + \frac{C_m M}{\left(1 - \dfrac{P}{P_e}\right) M_m} \leqslant 1.0 \tag{2.4-2}$$

$$\frac{P}{P_y} + \frac{M}{1.18M_p} \leqslant 1.0; \quad M \leqslant M_p \tag{2.4-3}$$

---

* See Commentary p. 5-162.

in which

M = maximum applied moment
P = applied axial load
P_e = $(23/12)\ AF'_e$, where F'_e is as defined in Sect. 1.6.1
C_m = coefficient defined in Sect. 1.6.1
M_m = maximum moment that can be resisted by the member in the absence of axial load

For columns braced in the weak direction:

$$M_m = M_p$$

For columns unbraced in the weak direction:

$$M_m = \left[1.07 - \frac{(l/r_y)\sqrt{F_y}}{3,160} \right] M_p \leqslant M_p \qquad (2.4\text{-}4)$$

SECTION 2.5   SHEAR

Unless reinforced by diagonal stiffeners or a doubler plate, the webs of columns, beams, and girders, including areas within the boundaries of the connections, shall be so proportioned that

$$V_u \leqslant 0.55 F_y td \qquad (2.5\text{-}1)$$

where V_u is the shear, in kips, that would be produced by the required factored loading, d is the depth of the member, and t is its web thickness.

SECTION 2.6   WEB CRIPPLING

Web stiffeners are required on a member at a point of load application where a plastic hinge would form.

At points on a member where the concentrated load delivered by the flanges of a member framing into it would produce web crippling opposite the compression flange or high tensile stress in the connection of the tension flange, web stiffeners are required in accordance with the provisions of Sect. 1.15.5.

SECTION 2.7   MINIMUM THICKNESS (WIDTH-THICKNESS RATIOS)

The width-thickness ratio for flanges of rolled W shapes and similar built-up single-web shapes that would be subjected to compression involving hinge rotation under ultimate loading shall not exceed the following values:

F_y	$b_f/2t_f$
36	8.5
42	8.0
45	7.4
50	7.0
55	6.6
60	6.3
65	6.0

The thickness of sloping flanges may be taken as their average thickness.

The width-thickness ratio of similarly compressed flange plates in box sections and cover-plates shall not exceed $190/\sqrt{F_y}$. For this purpose the width of a cover-plate shall be taken as the distance between longitudinal lines of connecting rivets, high strength bolts or welds.

The depth-thickness ratio of webs of members subjected to plastic bending shall not exceed the value given by Formula (2.7-1a) or (2.7-1b), as applicable.

$$\frac{d}{t} = \frac{412}{\sqrt{F_y}} \left(1 - 1.4 \frac{P}{P_y} \right) \quad \text{when } \frac{P}{P_y} \leqslant 0.27 \qquad (2.7\text{-}1a)$$

$$\frac{d}{t} = \frac{257}{\sqrt{F_y}} \quad \text{when } \frac{P}{P_y} > 0.27 \qquad (2.7\text{-}1b)$$

SECTION 2.8   CONNECTIONS

All connections, the rigidity of which is essential to the continuity assumed as the basis of the analysis, shall be capable of resisting the moments, shears and axial loads to which they would be subjected by the full factored loading, or any probable partial distribution thereof.

Corner connections (haunches), tapered or curved for architectural reasons, shall be so proportioned that the full plastic bending strength of the section adjacent to the connection can be developed, if required.

Stiffeners shall be used, as required, to preserve the flange continuity of interrupted members at their junction with other members in a continuous frame. Such stiffeners shall be placed in pairs on opposite sides of the web of the member which extends continuously through the joint.

High strength bolts, A307 bolts, rivets, and welds shall be proportioned to resist the forces produced at factored load, using stresses equal to 1.7 times those given in Part 1. In general, groove welds are preferable to fillet welds, but their use is not mandatory.

High strength bolts may be used in joints having painted contact surfaces when these joints are of such size that the slip required to produce bearing would not interfere with the formation, at factored loading, of the plastic hinges assumed in the design.

SECTION 2.9   LATERAL BRACING

Members shall be adequately braced to resist lateral and torsional displacements at the plastic hinge locations associated with the failure mechanism. The laterally unsupported distance, l_{cr}, from such braced hinge locations to similarly braced adjacent points on the member or frame shall not exceed the value determined from Formula (2.9-1a) or (2.9-1b), as applicable.

$$\frac{l_{cr}}{r_y} = \frac{1,375}{F_y} + 25 \quad \text{when} + 1.0 > \frac{M}{M_p} > -0.5 \qquad (2.9\text{-}1a)$$

$$\frac{l_{cr}}{r_y} = \frac{1,375}{F_y} \quad \text{when} - 0.5 \geq \frac{M}{M_p} > -1.0 \qquad (2.9\text{-}1b)$$

where

r_y = the radius of gyration of the member about its weak axis

M = the lesser of the moments at the ends of the unbraced segment

M/M_p = the end moment ratio, is positive when the segment is bent in reverse curvature and negative when bent in single curvature.

The foregoing provisions need not apply in the region of the last hinge to form in the failure mechanism assumed as the basis for proportioning a given member, nor in members oriented with their weak axis normal to the plane of bending. However, in the region of the last hinge to form, and in regions not adjacent to a plastic hinge, the maximum distance between points of lateral support shall be such as to satisfy the requirements of Formulas (1.5-6a), (1.5-6b) or (1.5-7) as well as Formulas (1.6-1a) and (1.6-1b) in Part 1 of this Specification. For this case the value of f_a and f_b shall be computed from the moment and axial force at factored loading, divided by the applicable load factor.

Members built into a masonry wall and having their web perpendicular to this wall can be assumed to be laterally supported with respect to their weak axis of bending.

SECTION 2.10 FABRICATION

The provisions of Part 1 with respect to workmanship shall govern the fabrication of structures, or portions of structures, designed on the basis of maximum strength, subject to the following limitations:

The use of sheared edges shall be avoided in locations subject to plastic hinge rotation at factored loading. If used they shall be finished smooth by grinding, chipping or planing.

In locations subject to plastic hinge rotation at factored loading, holes for rivets or bolts in the tension area shall be sub-punched and reamed or drilled full size.

APPENDIX A

	Yield Stress — F_y (ksi)		
	36.0	42.0	45.0

SECTION 1.5   ALLOWABLE STRESSES

1.5.1.1   Tension

	36.0	42.0	45.0
Tension on the net section, except at pin holes: $F_t = 0.60F_y \leq 0.50F_{TS}$ where F_{TS} = minimum tensile strength	22.0	25.2	27.0
Tension on the net section at pin holes in eyebars, pin-connected plates or built-up members: $F_t = 0.45F_y$	16.2	19.0	20.3

1.5.1.2   Shear

	36.0	42.0	45.0
Shear on the gross section (see Table 3 for reduced values for girder webs): $F_v = 0.40F_y$	14.5	17.0	18.0

1.5.1.3   Compression

	36.0	42.0	45.0
1.5.1.3.1 Compression on the gross section of axially loaded compression members when Kl/r is less than C_c: Formula (1.5-1) $$F_a = \frac{\left[1 - \frac{(Kl/r)^2}{2C_c^2}\right]F_y}{\frac{5}{3} + \frac{3(Kl/r)}{8C_c} - \frac{(Kl/r)^3}{8C_c^3}}$$	Table 1-36	Table 1-42	Table 1-45
1.5.1.3.2 Compression on the gross section of axially loaded compression members when Kl/r exceeds C_c: Formula (1.5-2) $$F_a = \frac{12\pi^2 E}{23(Kl/r)^2}$$	Table 1-36	Table 1-42	Table 1-4
1.5.1.3.3 Compression on the gross section of axially loaded bracing and secondary members when l/r exceeds 120: Formula (1.5-3) $$F_{as} = \frac{F_a \text{ [by Formula (1.5-1) or (1.5-2)]}}{1.6 - \frac{l}{200r}}$$	Table 1-36	Table 1-42	Table 1-4

* Value equal to 0.50 times minimum tensile strength ($= 0.50F_{TS}$)

Yield Stress — F_y (ksi)					
50.0	55.0	60.0	65.0	90.0	100.0
30.0	33.0	36.0	39.0	52.5*	57.5*
22.5	24.8	27.0	29.3	40.5	45.0
20.0	22.0	24.0	26.0	36.0	40.0
'able 1-50	Table 1-55	Table 1-60	Table 1-65	Table 1-90	Table 1-100
able 1-50	Table 1-55	Table 1-60	Table 1-65	Table 1-90	Table 1-100
able 1-50	Table 1-55	Table 1-60	Table 1-65	Table 1-90	Table 1-100

	Yield Stress — F_y (ksi)		
	36.0	42.0	45.0

1.5.1.3 Compression (cont'd)

	36.0	42.0	45.0
1.5.1.3.4 Compression on the gross area of plate girder stiffeners: $$F_a = 0.60F_y$$	22.0	25.2	27.0
1.5.1.3.5 Compression on the web of rolled shapes at the toe of fillet: $$F_a = 0.75F_y$$	27.0	31.5	33.8

1.5.1.4 Bending

	36.0	42.0	45.0
1.5.1.4.1 Tension and compression for compact, adequately braced members symmetrical about, and loaded in, the plane of their minor axis: $$F_b = 0.66F_y$$	24.0	28.0	29.7
when			
a. Flanges are continuously connected to web			
b. $b_f/2t_f \leq 52.2/\sqrt{F_y}$	8.7	8.1	7.8
c. $b/t_f \leq 190/\sqrt{F_y}$	31.7	29.3	28.3
d. Use Formula (1.5-4): $$d/t \leq 412\left(1 - 2.33\frac{f_a}{F_y}\right)\Big/\sqrt{F_y}$$	$68.7 - 4.4f_a$	$63.6 - 3.5f_a$	$61.4 - 3.$
except that d/t need not be less than $257/\sqrt{F_y}$	42.8	39.7	38.3
e. $l \leq 76.0b_f/\sqrt{F_y}$	$12.7b_f$	$11.7b_f$	$11.3b_f$
and			
$$l \leq \frac{20{,}000}{(d/A_f)F_y}$$	$\dfrac{556}{d/A_f}$	$\dfrac{476}{d/A_f}$	$\dfrac{444}{d/A_f}$

Yield Stress — F_y (ksi)					
50.0	55.0	60.0	65.0	90.0	100.0
30.0	33.0	36.0	39.0	54.0	60.0
37.5	41.3	45.0	48.8	67.5	75.0
33.0	36.3	39.6	42.9	—	—
7.4	7.0	6.7	6.5	—	—
26.9	25.6	24.5	23.6	—	—
$3 - 2.7f_a$	$55.6 - 2.4f_a$	$53.2 - 2.1f_a$	$51.1 - 1.8f_a$	—	—
36.3	34.7	33.2	31.9	—	—
$0.7b_f$	$10.2b_f$	$9.8b_f$	$9.4b_f$	—	—
$\dfrac{400}{d/A_f}$	$\dfrac{364}{d/A_f}$	$\dfrac{333}{d/A_f}$	$\dfrac{308}{d/A_f}$	—	—

	Yield Stress — F_y (ksi)		
	36.0	42.0	45.0

1.5.1.4 Bending (cont'd)

1.5.1.4.2
Tension and compression for members which meet the requirements of Sect. 1.5.1.4.1 except subparagraph b:

when

$$\frac{52.2}{\sqrt{F_y}} < \frac{b_f}{2t_f}$$

8.7	8.1	7.8

and

$$\frac{b_f}{2t_f} < \frac{95.0}{\sqrt{F_y}}$$

15.8	14.7	14.2

use Formula (1.5-5):

$$F_b = F_y \left[0.733 - 0.0014 \left(\frac{b_f}{2t_f} \right) \sqrt{F_y} \right]$$

$\dfrac{b_f}{2t_f}$	36.0	42.0	45.0
7.0	—	—	—
8.0	—	—	29.6
9.0	23.7	27.3	29.2
10.0	23.4	27.0	28.8
11.0	23.1	26.6	28.4
12.0	22.8	26.2	27.9
13.0	22.5	25.8	27.5
14.0	22.1	25.5	27.1
15.0	22.0	—	—

Values of F_b

1.5.1.4.3
Tension and compression for: doubly-symmetrical I and H shape members meeting the requirements of Sect. 1.5.1.4.1, except subparagraphs c, d and e, and bent about their minor axis (except members of A514 steel); solid round and square bars; and solid rectangular bars bent about their weaker axis:

$$F_b = 0.75F_y$$

27.0	31.5	33.8

1.5.1.4.4
Tension and compression for box-type flexural members not included in Sect. 1.5.1.4.1, but which meet the requirements of Sect. 1.9:

$$F_b = 0.60F_y$$

22.0	25.2	27.0

when

$$l \leq 2500b/F_y$$

69.4b	59.5b	55.6b

Yield Stress — F_y (ksi)					
50.0	55.0	60.0	65.0	90.0	100.0
7.4	7.0	6.7	6.5	—	—
13.4	12.8	12.3	11.8	—	—
—	—	39.4	42.5	—	—
32.7	35.7	38.8	41.8	—	—
32.2	35.2	38.1	41.0	—	—
31.7	34.6	37.5	40.3	—	—
31.2	34.0	36.8	39.6	—	—
30.7	33.5	36.2	—	—	—
30.2	—	—	—	—	—
—	—	—	—	—	—
—	—	—	—	—	—
37.5	41.3	45.0	48.8	—	—
30.0	33.0	36.0	39.0	54.0	60.0
50.0*b*	45.5*b*	41.7*b*	38.5*b*	27.8*b*	25.0*b*

	Yield Stress — F_y (ksi)		
	36.0	42.0	45.0

1.5.1.4 Bending (cont'd)

1.5.1.4.5
Tension for flexural members not covered in Sect. 1.5.1.4.1, 1.5.1.4.2, 1.5.1.4.3 or 1.5.1.4.4:

	36.0	42.0	45.0
$F_b = 0.60F_y$	22.0	25.2	27.0

1.5.1.4.6a
Compression for flexural members included under Sect. 1.5.1.4.5, having an axis of symmetry in, and loaded in, the plane of their web; compression for channels bent about their major axis: The larger value computed by Formula (1.5-6a) or (1.5-6b) and Formula (1.5-7), but not more than

$$F_b = 0.60F_y \qquad 22.0 \qquad 25.2 \qquad 27.0$$

when

$$l/r_T \leq \sqrt{\frac{102 \times 10^3 \times C_b}{F_y}} \,^* \qquad 53\sqrt{C_b} \qquad 49\sqrt{C_b} \qquad 48\sqrt{C_b}$$

When this limit is exceeded, use Formula (1.5-6a):

$$F_b = \left[\frac{2}{3} - \frac{F_y(l/r_T)^2}{1,530 \times 10^3 \times C_b}\right]F_y \,^* \qquad 24.0 - \frac{(l/r_T)^2}{1181C_b} \qquad 28.0 - \frac{(l/r_T)^2}{867C_b} \qquad 30.0 - \frac{(l/r_T)^2}{78}$$

unless

$$l/r_T \geq \sqrt{\frac{510 \times 10^3 \times C_b}{F_y}} \,^* \qquad 119\sqrt{C_b} \qquad 110\sqrt{C_b} \qquad 106\sqrt{C_b}$$

in which case, use Formula (1.5-6b):

$$F_b = \frac{170 \times 10^3 \times C_b}{(l/r_T)^2} \,^*$$

When the compression flange is solid and approximately rectangular in cross-section and its area is not less than that of the tension flange, use Formula (1.5-7):

$$F_b = \frac{12 \times 10^3 \times C_b}{ld/A_f} \,^*$$

*For values of C_b see Fig. A1, p. 5-104.

Yield Stress — F_y (ksi)					
50.0	55.0	60.0	65.0	90.0	100.0
30.0	33.0	36.0	39.0	54.0	60.0
30.0	33.0	36.0	39.0	54.0	60.0
$45\sqrt{C_b}$	$43\sqrt{C_b}$	$41\sqrt{C_b}$	$40\sqrt{C_b}$	$34\sqrt{C_b}$	$32\sqrt{C_b}$
$3 - \dfrac{(l/r_T)^2}{612C_b}$	$36.7 - \dfrac{(l/r_T)^2}{506C_b}$	$40.0 - \dfrac{(l/r_T)^2}{425C_b}$	$43.3 - \dfrac{(l/r_T)^2}{362C_b}$	$60.0 - \dfrac{(l/r_T)^2}{189C_b}$	$66.7 - \dfrac{(l/r_T)^2}{153C_b}$
$101\sqrt{C_b}$	$96\sqrt{C_b}$	$92\sqrt{C_b}$	$89\sqrt{C_b}$	$75\sqrt{C_b}$	$71\sqrt{C_b}$

	Yield Stress — F_y (ksi)		
	36.0	42.0	45.0

1.5.1.4. Bending (cont'd)

1.5.1.4.6b
Compression for flexural members included under Sect. 1.5.1.4.5, which do not satisfy the requirements of Sect. 1.5.1.4.6a, and which if bent about their major axis are braced so that

	36.0	42.0	45.0
$l \leq (76.0b_f/\sqrt{F_y})$	$12.7b_f$	$11.7b_f$	$11.3b_f$
$F_b = 0.60F_y$	22.0	25.2	27.0

1.5.1.5 Bearing (on contact area)

1.5.1.5.1
Bearing on milled surfaces, including bearing stiffeners and pins in reamed, drilled, or bored holes:

	36.0	42.0	45.0
$F_p = 0.90F_y$	33.0	38.0	40.5

1.5.1.5.2
Bearing on expansion rollers and rockers:

	36.0	42.0	45.0
$F_p = \left(\dfrac{F_y - 13}{20}\right)0.66d$	$0.76d$	$0.96d$	$1.06d$

1.5.2 Rivets, Bolts, and Threaded Parts

1.5.2.2
Bearing on projected area of bolts in bearing-type connections and on rivets:

	36.0	42.0	45.0
$F_p = 1.35F_y$	48.6	56.7	60.8

SECTION 1.9 WIDTH-THICKNESS RATIOS

1.9.1 Unstiffened Elements Under Compression

1.9.1.2
Maximum width-to-thickness ratios for unstiffened elements of:

Single-angle struts; double-angle struts with separators:

	36.0	42.0	45.0
$76.0/\sqrt{F_y}$	12.7	11.7	11.3

Double-angle struts in contact; angles or plates projecting from girders, columns or other compression members, compression flanges of beams; stiffeners on plate girders:

	36.0	42.0	45.0
$95.0/\sqrt{F_y}$	15.8	14.7	14.2
Stems of tees: $127/\sqrt{F_y}$	21.2	19.6	18.9

	Yield Stress — F_y (ksi)				
50.0	55.0	60.0	65.0	90.0	100.0
$10.7b_f$	$10.2b_f$	$9.8b_f$	$9.4b_f$	$8.0b_f$	$7.6b_f$
30.0	33.0	36.0	39.0	54.0	60.0
45.0	49.5	54.0	58.5	81.0	90.0
$1.22d$	$1.39d$	$1.55d$	$1.72d$	$2.54d$	$2.87d$
67.5	74.3	81.0	87.8	121.5	135.0
10.7	10.2	9.8	9.4	8.0	7.6
13.4	12.8	12.3	11.8	10.0	9.5
18.0	17.1	16.4	15.8	13.4	12.7

	Yield Stress — F_y (ksi)		
	36.0	42.0	45.0

1.9.2 Stiffened Elements Under Compression

1.9.2.2
Maximum width-to-thickness ratios for stiffened elements of:

	36.0	42.0	45.0
Flanges of square and rectangular sections of uniform thickness: $\dfrac{238}{\sqrt{F_y}}$	39.7	36.7	35.5
Unsupported width of perforated cover plates: $\dfrac{317}{\sqrt{F_y}}$	52.8	48.9	47.3
All other uniformly compressed elements: $\dfrac{253}{\sqrt{F_y}}$	42.2	39.0	37.7

SECTION 1.10 PLATE GIRDERS AND ROLLED BEAMS

1.10.1 Proportions

	36.0	42.0	45.0
Maximum axial force resisted by hybrid girders: $$P = 0.15F_y A$$ where A = gross sectional area	5.4A	6.3A	6.8A

1.10.2 Web

	36.0	42.0	45.0
Maximum clear distance between flanges: $$\dfrac{14{,}000}{\sqrt{F_y(F_y + 16.5)}}\, t$$	322t	282t	266t
When transverse stiffeners are spaced $1.5 \times d$ or less, the clear distance between flanges need not be less than $$\dfrac{2{,}000}{\sqrt{F_y}}\, t$$ where t = thickness of web F_y = yield stress of compression flange	333t	309t	298t

Yield Stress — F_y (ksi)					
50.0	55.0	60.0	65.0	90.0	100.0
33.7	32.1	30.7	29.5	25.1	23.8
44.8	42.7	40.9	39.3	33.4	31.7
35.8	34.1	32.7	31.4	26.7	25.3
7.5A	8.3A	9.0A	9.8A	13.5A	15.0A
243t	223t	207t	192t	143t	130t
283t	270t	258t	248t	211t	200t

	Yield Stress — F_y (ksi)		
	36.0	42.0	45.0

1.10.5   Stiffeners

1.10.5.2 Largest average web shear, F_v, by Formula (1.10-1) or (1.10-2), as applicable	Table 3-36	Table 3-42	Table 3-45
1.10.5.4 Required gross area of intermediate stiffeners, by Formula (1.10-3)	Table 3-36	Table 3-42	Table 3-45
Intermediate stiffeners required by Formula (1.10-2) shall be connected for a total shear transfer not less than $$f_{vs} = h\sqrt{\left(\frac{F_y}{340}\right)^3}$$ where F_y = yield stress of web steel	0.034h	0.043h	0.048h

1.10.7   Combined Shear and Tension Stress

Bending tensile stress due to moment in the plane of the web shall not exceed $0.6F_y$ nor Formula (1.10-7):

$$F_b = \left(0.825 - 0.375\,\frac{f_v}{F_v}\right)F_y$$

	f_v/F_v			
Values of F_b	0.1	22.0	25.2	27.0
	0.2	22.0	25.2	27.0
	0.3	22.0	25.2	27.0
	0.4	22.0	25.2	27.0
	0.5	22.0	25.2	27.0
	0.6	22.0	25.2	27.0
	0.7	20.3	23.6	25.3
	0.8	18.9	22.1	23.6
	0.9	17.6	20.5	21.9
	1.0	16.2	18.9	20.3

1.10.10   Web Crippling

1.10.10.1 Bearing stiffeners are not required under interior concentrated loads when, by Formula (1.10-8) $$\frac{R}{t(N+2k)} \leq 0.75F_y$$	27.0	31.5	33.8
or under end reactions when, by Formula (1.10-9) $$\frac{R}{t(N+k)} \leq 0.75F_y$$	27.0	31.5	33.8

Yield Stress — F_y (ksi)					
50.0	55.0	60.0	65.0	90.0	100.0
Table 3-50	Table 3-55	Table 3-60	Table 3-65	Table 3-90	Table 3-100
Table 3-50	Table 3-55	Table 3-60	Table 3-65	Table 3-90	Table 3-100
0.056h	0.065h	0.074h	0.084h	0.136h	0.160h
30.0	33.0	36.0	39.0	54.0	60.0
30.0	33.0	36.0	39.0	54.0	60.0
30.0	33.0	36.0	39.0	54.0	60.0
30.0	33.0	36.0	39.0	54.0	60.0
30.0	33.0	36.0	39.0	54.0	60.0
30.0	33.0	36.0	39.0	54.0	60.0
28.1	30.9	33.8	36.6	50.6	56.3
26.3	28.9	31.5	34.1	47.3	52.5
24.4	26.8	29.3	31.7	43.9	48.8
22.5	24.8	27.0	29.3	40.5	45.0
37.5	41.3	45.0	48.8	67.5	75.0
37.5	41.3	45.0	48.8	67.5	75.0

	Yield Stress — F_y (ksi)		
	36.0	42.0	45.0

SECTION 1.11 COMPOSITE CONSTRUCTION

1.11.2 Design Assumptions

	36.0	42.0	45.0
1.11.2.1 Tension and compression for encased composite beams based upon the section properties of the composite section: $$F_b = 0.66F_y$$	24.0	28.0	29.7
Tension and compression for encased composite beams based upon the section properties of the steel beam alone: $$F_b = 0.76F_y$$	27.4	31.9	34.2

SECTION 1.13 DEFLECTIONS, VIBRATION AND PONDING

1.13.3 Ponding

	36.0	42.0	45.0
Total bending stress due to dead loads, gravity live loads (if any) and ponding, for primary and secondary members: $$F_b = 0.80F_y$$	28.8	33.6	36.0

SECTION 1.18 BUILT-UP MEMBERS

1.18.2 Compression Members

	36.0	42.0	45.0
1.18.2.3 Maximum longitudinal spacing for intermediate rivets, bolts or intermittent welds in built-up members having a component consisting of an outside plate shall not exceed 12 in. nor $$\frac{127}{\sqrt{F_y}}t$$ where t = thickness of thinnest outside plate	$21.2t$	$19.6t$	$18.9t$
Maximum longitudinal spacing when rivets or bolts are staggered shall not exceed 18 in. nor $$\frac{190}{\sqrt{F_y}}t$$ where t = thickness of thinnest outside plate	$31.7t$	$29.3t$	$28.3t$

Yield Stress — F_y (ksi)					
50. 0	55.0	60.0	65.0	90.0	100.0
33.0	36.3	39.6	42.9	59.4	66.0
38.0	41.8	45.6	49.4	68.4	76.0
40.0	44.0	48.0	52.0	72.0	80.0
18.0*t*	17.1*t*	16.4*t*	15.8*t*	13.4*t*	12.7*t*
26.9*t*	25.6*t*	24.5*t*	23.6*t*	20.0*t*	19.0*t*

	Yield Stress — F_y (ksi)		
	36.0	42.0	45.0

SECTION 2.3   VERTICAL BRACING SYSTEM

Maximum axial force due to factored gravity plus factored horizontal loads in members comprising the vertical bracing system: $$P = 0.85F_yA$$ where A = gross area of the member	$30.6A$	$35.7A$	$38.3A$

SECTION 2.4   COLUMNS

The ratio of critical moment of a column without axial load and unbraced in the weak direction to the plastic moment of the column section shall not exceed 1 nor Formula (2.4-4): $$\frac{M_m}{M_p} \leq \left[1.07 - \frac{(l/r_y)\sqrt{F_y}}{3,160}\right]$$	$1.07 - \dfrac{(l/r_y)}{527}$	$1.07 - \dfrac{(l/r_y)}{488}$	$1.07 - \dfrac{(l/r_y)}{471}$

SECTION 2.5   SHEAR

Shear in unreinforced webs of columns, beams and girders due to factored loading: Formula (2.5-1) $$V_u = 0.55F_y\,td$$ where t = thickness of web d = depth of member	$19.8td$	$23.1td$	$24.8td$

SECTION 2.7   MINIMUM THICKNESS (WIDTH-THICKNESS RATIOS)

Maximum width-thickness ratios of similarly compressed flange plates in box sections and cover plates: $$\frac{b}{t} \leq \frac{190}{\sqrt{F_y}}$$	31.7	29.3	28.3
Maximum depth-thickness ratios of webs of members subjected to plastic bending without axial load: When $P/P_y \leq 0.27$, use Formula (2.7-1a): $$\frac{d}{t} \leq \frac{412}{\sqrt{F_y}}\left(1 - 1.4\frac{P}{P_y}\right)$$	$68.7 - 96.1\dfrac{P}{P_y}$	$63.6 - 89.0\dfrac{P}{P_y}$	$61.4 - 86.0\dfrac{P}{P_y}$
When $P/P_y > 0.27$, use Formula (2.7-1b): $$\frac{d}{t} \leq \frac{257}{\sqrt{F_y}}$$	42.8	39.6	38.3

		Yield Stress — F_y (ksi)			
50.0	55.0	60.0	65.0	90.0	100.0
42.5A	46.8A	51.0A	55.3A	—	—
$1.07 - \dfrac{(l/r_y)}{447}$	$1.07 - \dfrac{(l/r_y)}{426}$	$1.07 - \dfrac{(l/r_y)}{408}$	$1.07 - \dfrac{(l/r_y)}{392}$	—	—
27.5td	30.3td	33.0td	35.8td	—	—
26.9	25.6	24.5	23.6	—	—
$3 - 81.6\dfrac{P}{P_y}$	$55.6 - 77.8\dfrac{P}{P_y}$	$53.2 - 74.5\dfrac{P}{P_y}$	$51.1 - 71.5\dfrac{P}{P_y}$	—	—
36.3	34.7	33.2	31.9	—	—

	Yield Stress — F_y (ksi)		
	36.0	42.0	45.0

SECTION 2.9   LATERAL BRACING

Maximum critical slenderness ratio, l_{cr}/r_y, from braced hinge locations to similarly braced adjacent points on a beam or frame: When $1.0 > \dfrac{M}{M_p} > -0.5$, use Formula (2.9-1a): $\qquad \dfrac{l_{cr}}{r_y} \le \dfrac{1{,}375}{F_y} + 25$	63.2	57.7	55.6
When $-0.5 > \dfrac{M}{M_p} > -1.0$, use Formula (2.9-1b): $\qquad \dfrac{l_{cr}}{r_y} \le \dfrac{1{,}375}{F_y}$	38.2	32.7	30.6

Yield Stress — F_y (ksi)					
50.0	55.0	60.0	65.0	90.0	100.0
52.5	50.0	47.9	46.2	—	—
27.5	25.0	22.9	21.2	—	—

TABLE 1-36

ALLOWABLE STRESS (KSI)
FOR COMPRESSION MEMBERS OF 36 KSI SPECIFIED YIELD STRESS STEEL

$F_y = 36$ ksi

Main and Secondary Members Kl/r not over 120						Main Members Kl/r 121 to 200				Secondary Members* l/r 121 to 200			
$\frac{Kl}{r}$	F_a (ksi)	$\frac{Kl}{r}$	F_a (ksi)	$\frac{Kl}{r}$	F_a (ksi)	$\frac{Kl}{r}$	F_a (ksi)	$\frac{Kl}{r}$	F_a (ksi)	$\frac{l}{r}$	F_{as} (ksi)	$\frac{l}{r}$	F_{as} (ksi)
1	21.56	41	19.11	81	15.24	121	10.14	161	5.76	121	10.19	161	7.25
2	21.52	42	19.03	82	15.13	122	9.99	162	5.69	122	10.09	162	7.20
3	21.48	43	18.95	83	15.02	123	9.85	163	5.62	123	10.00	163	7.16
4	21.44	44	18.86	84	14.90	124	9.70	164	5.55	124	9.90	164	7.12
5	21.39	45	18.78	85	14.79	125	9.55	165	5.49	125	9.80	165	7.08
6	21.35	46	18.70	86	14.67	126	9.41	166	5.42	126	9.70	166	7.04
7	21.30	47	18.61	87	14.56	127	9.26	167	5.35	127	9.59	167	7.00
8	21.25	48	18.53	88	14.44	128	9.11	168	5.29	128	9.49	168	6.96
9	21.21	49	18.44	89	14.32	129	8.97	169	5.23	129	9.40	169	6.93
10	21.16	50	18.35	90	14.20	130	8.84	170	5.17	130	9.30	170	6.89
11	21.10	51	18.26	91	14.09	131	8.70	171	5.11	131	9.21	171	6.85
12	21.05	52	18.17	92	13.97	132	8.57	172	5.05	132	9.12	172	6.82
13	21.00	53	18.08	93	13.84	133	8.44	173	4.99	133	9.03	173	6.79
14	20.95	54	17.99	94	13.72	134	8.32	174	4.93	134	8.94	174	6.76
15	20.89	55	17.90	95	13.60	135	8.19	175	4.88	135	8.86	175	6.73
16	20.83	56	17.81	96	13.48	136	8.07	176	4.82	136	8.78	176	6.70
17	20.78	57	17.71	97	13.35	137	7.96	177	4.77	137	8.70	177	6.67
18	20.72	58	17.62	98	13.23	138	7.84	178	4.71	138	8.62	178	6.64
19	20.66	59	17.53	99	13.10	139	7.73	179	4.66	139	8.54	179	6.61
20	20.60	60	17.43	100	12.98	140	7.62	180	4.61	140	8.47	180	6.58
21	20.54	61	17.33	101	12.85	141	7.51	181	4.56	141	8.39	181	6.56
22	20.48	62	17.24	102	12.72	142	7.41	182	4.51	142	8.32	182	6.53
23	20.41	63	17.14	103	12.59	143	7.30	183	4.46	143	8.25	183	6.51
24	20.35	64	17.04	104	12.47	144	7.20	184	4.41	144	8.18	184	6.49
25	20.28	65	16.94	105	12.33	145	7.10	185	4.36	145	8.12	185	6.46
26	20.22	66	16.84	106	12.20	146	7.01	186	4.32	146	8.05	186	6.4
27	20.15	67	16.74	107	12.07	147	6.91	187	4.27	147	7.99	187	6.4
28	20.08	68	16.64	108	11.94	148	6.82	188	4.23	148	7.93	188	6.4
29	20.01	69	16.53	109	11.81	149	6.73	189	4.18	149	7.87	189	6.3
30	19.94	70	16.43	110	11.67	150	6.64	190	4.14	150	7.81	190	6.3
31	19.87	71	16.33	111	11.54	151	6.55	191	4.09	151	7.75	191	6.3
32	19.80	72	16.22	112	11.40	152	6.46	192	4.05	152	7.69	192	6.3
33	19.73	73	16.12	113	11.26	153	6.38	193	4.01	153	7.64	193	6.3
34	19.65	74	16.01	114	11.13	154	6.30	194	3.97	154	7.59	194	6.3
35	19.58	75	15.90	115	10.99	155	6.22	195	3.93	155	7.53	195	6.2
36	19.50	76	15.79	116	10.85	156	6.14	196	3.89	156	7.48	196	6.2
37	19.42	77	15.69	117	10.71	157	6.06	197	3.85	157	7.43	197	6.2
38	19.35	78	15.58	118	10.57	158	5.98	198	3.81	158	7.39	198	6.2
39	19.27	79	15.47	119	10.43	159	5.91	199	3.77	159	7.34	199	6.2
40	19.19	80	15.36	120	10.28	160	5.83	200	3.73	160	7.29	200	6.2

* K taken as 1.0 for secondary members.

Note: $C_c = 126.1$

TABLE 1-42

ALLOWABLE STRESS (KSI)
FOR COMPRESSION MEMBERS OF 42 KSI SPECIFIED YIELD STRESS STEEL

Main and Secondary Members Kl/r not over 120						Main Members Kl/r 121 to 200				Secondary Members* l/r 121 to 200			
$\dfrac{Kl}{r}$	F_a (ksi)	$\dfrac{Kl}{r}$	F_a (ksi)	$\dfrac{Kl}{r}$	F_a (ksi)	$\dfrac{Kl}{r}$	F_a (ksi)	$\dfrac{Kl}{r}$	F_a (ksi)	$\dfrac{l}{r}$	F_{as} (ksi)	$\dfrac{l}{r}$	F_{as} (ksi)
1	25.15	41	21.98	81	16.92	121	10.20	161	5.76	121	10.25	161	7.25
2	25.10	42	21.87	82	16.77	122	10.03	162	5.69	122	10.13	162	7.20
3	25.05	43	21.77	83	16.62	123	9.87	163	5.62	123	10.02	163	7.16
4	24.99	44	21.66	84	16.47	124	9.71	164	5.55	124	9.91	164	7.12
5	24.94	45	21.55	85	16.32	125	9.56	165	5.49	125	9.80	165	7.08
6	24.88	46	21.44	86	16.17	126	9.41	166	5.42	126	9.70	166	7.04
7	24.82	47	21.33	87	16.01	127	9.26	167	5.35	127	9.59	167	7.00
8	24.76	48	21.22	88	15.86	128	9.11	168	5.29	128	9.49	168	6.96
9	24.70	49	21.10	89	15.71	129	8.97	169	5.23	129	9.40	169	6.93
10	24.63	50	20.99	90	15.55	130	8.84	170	5.17	130	9.30	170	6.89
11	24.57	51	20.87	91	15.39	131	8.70	171	5.11	131	9.21	171	6.85
12	24.50	52	20.76	92	15.23	132	8.57	172	5.05	132	9.12	172	6.82
13	24.43	53	20.64	93	15.07	133	8.44	173	4.99	133	9.03	173	6.79
14	24.36	54	20.52	94	14.91	134	8.32	174	4.93	134	8.94	174	6.76
15	24.29	55	20.40	95	14.75	135	8.19	175	4.88	135	8.86	175	6.73
16	24.2	56	20.28	96	14.59	136	8.07	176	4.82	136	8.78	176	6.70
17	24.15	57	20.16	97	14.43	137	7.96	177	4.77	137	8.70	177	6.67
18	24.07	58	20.03	98	14.26	138	7.84	178	4.71	138	8.62	178	6.64
19	24.00	59	19.91	99	14.09	139	7.73	179	4.66	139	8.54	179	6.61
20	23.92	60	19.79	100	13.93	140	7.62	180	4.61	140	8.47	180	6.58
21	23.84	61	19.66	101	13.76	141	7.51	181	4.56	141	8.39	181	6.56
22	23.76	62	19.53	102	13.59	142	7.41	182	4.51	142	8.32	182	6.53
23	23.68	63	19.40	103	13.42	143	7.30	183	4.46	143	8.25	183	6.51
24	23.59	64	19.27	104	13.25	144	7.20	184	4.41	144	8.18	184	6.49
25	23.51	65	19.14	105	13.08	145	7.10	185	4.36	145	8.12	185	6.46
26	23.42	66	19.01	106	12.90	146	7.01	186	4.32	146	8.05	186	6.44
27	23.33	67	18.88	107	12.73	147	6.91	187	4.27	147	7.99	187	6.42
28	23.24	68	18.75	108	12.55	148	6.82	188	4.23	148	7.93	188	6.40
29	23.15	69	18.61	109	12.37	149	6.73	189	4.18	149	7.87	189	6.38
30	23.06	70	18.48	110	12.19	150	6.64	190	4.14	150	7.81	190	6.36
31	22.97	71	18.34	111	12.01	151	6.55	191	4.09	151	7.75	191	6.35
32	22.88	72	18.20	112	11.83	152	6.46	192	4.05	152	7.69	192	6.33
33	22.78	73	18.06	113	11.65	153	6.38	193	4.01	153	7.64	193	6.31
34	22.69	74	17.92	114	11.47	154	6.30	194	3.97	154	7.59	194	6.30
35	22.59	75	17.78	115	11.28	155	6.22	195	3.93	155	7.53	195	6.28
36	22.49	76	17.64	116	11.10	156	6.14	196	3.89	156	7.48	196	6.27
37	22.39	77	17.50	117	10.91	157	6.06	197	3.85	157	7.43	197	6.26
38	22.29	78	17.35	118	10.72	158	5.98	198	3.81	158	7.39	198	6.24
39	22.19	79	17.21	119	10.55	159	5.91	199	3.77	159	7.34	199	6.23
40	22.08	80	17.06	120	10.37	160	5.83	200	3.73	160	7.29	200	6.22

$F_y = 42$ ksi

* K taken as 1.0 for secondary members.

Note: $C_c = 116.7$

TABLE 1-45

ALLOWABLE STRESS (KSI)
FOR COMPRESSION MEMBERS OF 45 KSI SPECIFIED YIELD STRESS STEEL

$F_y = 45$ ksi

Main and Secondary Members Kl/r not over 120						Main Members Kl/r 121 to 200				Secondary Members* l/r 121 to 200			
$\frac{Kl}{r}$	F_a (ksi)	$\frac{Kl}{r}$	F_a (ksi)	$\frac{Kl}{r}$	F_a (ksi)	$\frac{Kl}{r}$	F_a (ksi)	$\frac{Kl}{r}$	F_a (ksi)	$\frac{l}{r}$	F_{as} (ksi)	$\frac{l}{r}$	F_{as} (ksi)
1	26.95	41	23.39	81	17.67	121	10.20	161	5.76	121	10.25	161	7.25
2	26.89	42	23.27	82	17.51	122	10.03	162	5.69	122	10.13	162	7.20
3	26.83	43	23.15	83	17.34	123	9.87	163	5.62	123	10.02	163	7.16
4	26.77	44	23.03	84	17.17	124	9.71	164	5.55	124	9.91	164	7.12
5	26.71	45	22.90	85	17.00	125	9.56	165	5.49	125	9.80	165	7.08
6	26.64	46	22.78	86	16.82	126	9.41	166	5.42	126	9.70	166	7.04
7	26.58	47	22.65	87	16.65	127	9.26	167	5.35	127	9.59	167	7.00
8	26.51	48	22.53	88	16.48	128	9.11	168	5.29	128	9.49	168	6.96
9	26.44	49	22.40	89	16.30	129	8.97	169	5.23	129	9.40	169	6.93
10	26.37	50	22.27	90	16.12	130	8.84	170	5.17	130	9.30	170	6.89
11	26.30	51	22.14	91	15.95	131	8.70	171	5.11	131	9.21	171	6.85
12	26.22	52	22.01	92	15.77	132	8.57	172	5.05	132	9.12	172	6.82
13	26.15	53	21.88	93	15.59	133	8.44	173	4.99	133	9.03	173	6.79
14	26.07	54	21.74	94	15.40	134	8.32	174	4.93	134	8.94	174	6.76
15	25.99	55	21.61	95	15.22	135	8.19	175	4.88	135	8.86	175	6.73
16	25.91	56	21.47	96	15.04	136	8.07	176	4.82	136	8.78	176	6.70
17	25.82	57	21.33	97	14.85	137	7.96	177	4.77	137	8.70	177	6.67
18	25.74	58	21.19	98	14.66	138	7.84	178	4.71	138	8.62	178	6.64
19	25.65	59	21.05	99	14.47	139	7.73	179	4.66	139	8.54	179	6.61
20	25.57	60	20.91	100	14.28	140	7.62	180	4.61	140	8.47	180	6.58
21	25.48	61	20.77	101	14.09	141	7.51	181	4.56	141	8.39	181	6.56
22	25.39	62	20.63	102	13.90	142	7.41	182	4.51	142	8.32	182	6.53
23	25.29	63	20.48	103	13.71	143	7.30	183	4.46	143	8.25	183	6.51
24	25.20	64	20.34	104	13.51	144	7.20	184	4.41	144	8.18	184	6.49
25	25.11	65	20.19	105	13.32	145	7.10	185	4.36	145	8.12	185	6.46
26	25.01	66	20.04	106	13.12	146	7.01	186	4.32	146	8.05	186	6.44
27	24.91	67	19.89	107	12.92	147	6.91	187	4.27	147	7.99	187	6.42
28	24.81	68	19.74	108	12.72	148	6.82	188	4.23	148	7.93	188	6.40
29	24.71	69	19.59	109	12.52	149	6.73	189	4.18	149	7.87	189	6.38
30	24.61	70	19.43	110	12.31	150	6.64	190	4.14	150	7.81	190	6.36
31	24.50	71	19.28	111	12.11	151	6.55	191	4.09	151	7.75	191	6.35
32	24.40	72	19.12	112	11.90	152	6.46	192	4.05	152	7.69	192	6.33
33	24.29	73	18.97	113	11.69	153	6.38	193	4.01	153	7.64	193	6.31
34	24.18	74	18.81	114	11.49	154	6.30	194	3.97	154	7.59	194	6.30
35	24.07	75	18.65	115	11.29	155	6.22	195	3.93	155	7.53	195	6.28
36	23.96	76	18.49	116	11.10	156	6.14	196	3.89	156	7.48	196	6.27
37	23.85	77	18.33	117	10.91	157	6.06	197	3.85	157	7.43	197	6.26
38	23.74	78	18.17	118	10.72	158	5.98	198	3.81	158	7.39	198	6.24
39	23.62	79	18.00	119	10.55	159	5.91	199	3.77	159	7.34	199	6.23
40	23.51	80	17.84	120	10.37	160	5.83	200	3.73	160	7.29	200	6.22

* K taken as 1.0 for secondary members.

Note: $C_c = 112.8$

TABLE 1-50

ALLOWABLE STRESS (KSI)
FOR COMPRESSION MEMBERS OF 50 KSI SPECIFIED YIELD STRESS STEEL

$F_y = 50$ ksi

Main and Secondary Members Kl/r not over 120						Main Members Kl/r 121 to 200				Secondary Members* l/r 121 to 200			
$\dfrac{Kl}{r}$	F_a (ksi)	$\dfrac{Kl}{r}$	F_a (ksi)	$\dfrac{Kl}{r}$	F_a (ksi)	$\dfrac{Kl}{r}$	F_a (ksi)	$\dfrac{Kl}{r}$	F_a (ksi)	$\dfrac{l}{r}$	F_{as} (ksi)	$\dfrac{l}{r}$	F_{as} (ksi)
1	29.94	41	25.69	81	18.81	121	10.20	161	5.76	121	10.25	161	7.25
2	29.87	42	25.55	82	18.61	122	10.03	162	5.69	122	10.13	162	7.20
3	29.80	43	25.40	83	18.41	123	9.87	163	5.62	123	10.02	163	7.16
4	29.73	44	25.26	84	18.20	124	9.71	164	5.55	124	9.91	164	7.12
5	29.66	45	25.11	85	17.99	125	9.56	165	5.49	125	9.80	165	7.08
6	29.58	46	24.96	86	17.79	126	9.41	166	5.42	126	9.70	166	7.04
7	29.50	47	24.81	87	17.58	127	9.26	167	5.35	127	9.59	167	7.00
8	29.42	48	24.66	88	17.37	128	9.11	168	5.29	128	9.49	168	6.96
9	29.34	49	24.51	89	17.15	129	8.97	169	5.23	129	9.40	169	6.93
10	29.26	50	24.35	90	16.94	130	8.84	170	5.17	130	9.30	170	6.89
11	29.17	51	24.19	91	16.72	131	8.70	171	5.11	131	9.21	171	6.85
12	29.08	52	24.04	92	16.50	132	8.57	172	5.05	132	9.12	172	6.82
13	28.99	53	23.88	93	16.29	133	8.44	173	4.99	133	9.03	173	6.79
14	28.90	54	23.72	94	16.06	134	8.32	174	4.93	134	8.94	174	6.76
15	28.80	55	23.55	95	15.84	135	8.19	175	4.88	135	8.86	175	6.73
16	28.71	56	23.39	96	15.62	136	8.07	176	4.82	136	8.78	176	6.70
17	28.61	57	23.22	97	15.39	137	7.96	177	4.77	137	8.70	177	6.67
18	28.51	58	23.06	98	15.17	138	7.84	178	4.71	138	8.62	178	6.64
19	28.40	59	22.89	99	14.94	139	7.73	179	4.66	139	8.54	179	6.61
20	28.30	60	22.72	100	14.71	140	7.62	180	4.61	140	8.47	180	6.58
21	28.19	61	22.55	101	14.47	141	7.51	181	4.56	141	8.39	181	6.56
22	28.08	62	22.37	102	14.24	142	7.41	182	4.51	142	8.32	182	6.53
23	27.97	63	22.20	103	14.00	143	7.30	183	4.46	143	8.25	183	6.51
24	27.86	64	22.02	104	13.77	144	7.20	184	4.41	144	8.18	184	6.49
25	27.75	65	21.85	105	13.53	145	7.10	185	4.36	145	8.12	185	6.46
26	27.63	66	21.67	106	13.29	146	7.01	186	4.32	146	8.05	186	6.44
27	27.52	67	21.49	107	13.04	147	6.91	187	4.27	147	7.99	187	6.42
28	27.40	68	21.31	108	12.80	148	6.82	188	4.23	148	7.93	188	6.40
29	27.28	69	21.12	109	12.57	149	6.73	189	4.18	149	7.87	189	6.38
30	27.15	70	20.94	110	12.34	150	6.64	190	4.14	150	7.81	190	6.36
31	27.03	71	20.75	111	12.12	151	6.55	191	4.09	151	7.75	191	6.35
32	26.90	72	20.56	112	11.90	152	6.46	192	4.05	152	7.69	192	6.33
33	26.77	73	20.38	113	11.69	153	6.38	193	4.01	153	7.64	193	6.31
34	26.64	74	20.19	114	11.49	154	6.30	194	3.97	154	7.59	194	6.30
35	26.51	75	19.99	115	11.29	155	6.22	195	3.93	155	7.53	195	6.28
36	26.38	76	19.80	116	11.10	156	6.14	196	3.89	156	7.48	196	6.27
37	26.25	77	19.61	117	10.91	157	6.06	197	3.85	157	7.43	197	6.26
38	26.11	78	19.41	118	10.72	158	5.98	198	3.81	158	7.39	198	6.24
39	25.97	79	19.21	119	10.55	159	5.91	199	3.77	159	7.34	199	6.23
40	25.83	80	19.01	120	10.37	160	5.83	200	3.73	160	7.29	200	6.22

* K taken as 1.0 for secondary members.

Note: $C_c = 107.0$

$F_y = 55$ ksi

TABLE 1-55

ALLOWABLE STRESS (KSI)
FOR COMPRESSION MEMBERS OF 55 KSI SPECIFIED YIELD STRESS STEEL

Main and Secondary Members Kl/r not over 120						Main Members Kl/r 121 to 200				Secondary Members* l/r 121 to 200			
$\frac{Kl}{r}$	F_a (ksi)	$\frac{Kl}{r}$	F_a (ksi)	$\frac{Kl}{r}$	F_a (ksi)	$\frac{Kl}{r}$	F_a (ksi)	$\frac{Kl}{r}$	F_a (ksi)	$\frac{l}{r}$	F_{as} (ksi)	$\frac{l}{r}$	F_{as} (ksi)
1	32.93	41	27.94	81	19.80	121	10.20	161	5.76	121	10.25	161	7.25
2	32.85	42	27.78	82	19.56	122	10.03	162	5.69	122	10.13	162	7.20
3	32.77	43	27.61	83	19.32	123	9.87	163	5.62	123	10.02	163	7.16
4	32.69	44	27.43	84	19.08	124	9.71	164	5.55	124	9.91	164	7.12
5	32.60	45	27.26	85	18.83	125	9.56	165	5.49	125	9.80	165	7.08
6	32.51	46	27.08	86	18.58	126	9.41	166	5.42	126	9.70	166	7.04
7	32.42	47	26.91	87	18.34	127	9.26	167	5.35	127	9.59	167	7.00
8	32.33	48	26.73	88	18.08	128	9.11	168	5.29	128	9.49	168	6.96
9	32.23	49	26.55	89	17.83	129	8.97	169	5.23	129	9.40	169	6.93
10	32.14	50	26.36	90	17.58	130	8.84	170	5.17	130	9.30	170	6.89
11	32.03	51	26.18	91	17.32	131	8.70	171	5.11	131	9.21	171	6.85
12	31.93	52	25.99	92	17.06	132	8.57	172	5.05	132	9.12	172	6.82
13	31.82	53	25.80	93	16.80	133	8.44	173	4.99	133	9.03	173	6.79
14	31.72	54	25.61	94	16.53	134	8.32	174	4.93	134	8.94	174	6.76
15	31.61	55	25.42	95	16.27	135	8.19	175	4.88	135	8.86	175	6.73
16	31.49	56	25.23	96	16.00	136	8.07	176	4.82	136	8.78	176	6.70
17	31.38	57	25.03	97	15.73	137	7.96	177	4.77	137	8.70	177	6.67
18	31.26	58	24.83	98	15.46	138	7.84	178	4.71	138	8.62	178	6.64
19	31.14	59	24.63	99	15.19	139	7.73	179	4.66	139	8.54	179	6.61
20	31.02	60	24.43	100	14.91	140	7.62	180	4.61	140	8.47	180	6.58
21	30.89	61	24.23	101	14.63	141	7.51	181	4.56	141	8.39	181	6.56
22	30.76	62	24.03	102	14.35	142	7.41	182	4.51	142	8.32	182	6.53
23	30.63	63	23.82	103	14.08	143	7.30	183	4.46	143	8.25	183	6.51
24	30.50	64	23.61	104	13.81	144	7.20	184	4.41	144	8.18	184	6.49
25	30.37	65	23.40	105	13.54	145	7.10	185	4.36	145	8.12	185	6.46
26	30.23	66	23.19	106	13.29	146	7.01	186	4.32	146	8.05	186	6.44
27	30.09	67	22.98	107	13.04	147	6.91	187	4.27	147	7.99	187	6.42
28	29.95	68	22.76	108	12.80	148	6.82	188	4.23	148	7.93	188	6.40
29	29.81	69	22.54	109	12.57	149	6.73	189	4.18	149	7.87	189	6.38
30	29.67	70	22.33	110	12.34	150	6.64	190	4.14	150	7.81	190	6.36
31	29.52	71	22.11	111	12.12	151	6.55	191	4.09	151	7.75	191	6.35
32	29.37	72	21.88	112	11.90	152	6.46	192	4.05	152	7.69	192	6.33
33	29.22	73	21.66	113	11.69	153	6.38	193	4.01	153	7.64	193	6.31
34	29.07	74	21.43	114	11.49	154	6.30	194	3.97	154	7.59	194	6.30
35	28.91	75	21.21	115	11.29	155	6.22	195	3.93	155	7.53	195	6.28
36	28.76	76	20.98	116	11.10	156	6.14	196	3.89	156	7.48	196	6.27
37	28.60	77	20.75	117	10.91	157	6.06	197	3.85	157	7.43	197	6.26
38	28.44	78	20.51	118	10.72	158	5.98	198	3.81	158	7.39	198	6.24
39	28.28	79	20.28	119	10.55	159	5.91	199	3.77	159	7.34	199	6.23
40	28.11	80	20.04	120	10.37	160	5.83	200	3.73	160	7.29	200	6.22

* K taken as 1.0 for secondary members.

Note: $C_c = 102.0$

TABLE 1-60

ALLOWABLE STRESS (KSI)
FOR COMPRESSION MEMBERS OF 60 KSI SPECIFIED YIELD STRESS STEEL

Main and Secondary Members Kl/r not over 120						Main Members Kl/r 121 to 200				Secondary Members* l/r 121 to 200			
$\frac{l}{r}$	F_a (ksi)	$\frac{Kl}{r}$	F_a (ksi)	$\frac{Kl}{r}$	F_a (ksi)	$\frac{Kl}{r}$	F_a (ksi)	$\frac{Kl}{r}$	F_a (ksi)	$\frac{l}{r}$	F_{as} (ksi)	$\frac{l}{r}$	F_{as} (ksi)
1	35.92	41	30.15	81	20.65	121	10.20	161	5.76	121	10.25	161	7.25
2	35.83	42	29.95	82	20.37	122	10.03	162	5.69	122	10.13	162	7.20
3	35.74	43	29.75	83	20.09	123	9.87	163	5.62	123	10.02	163	7.16
4	35.64	44	29.55	84	19.80	124	9.71	164	5.55	124	9.91	164	7.12
5	35.54	45	29.35	85	19.51	125	9.56	165	5.49	125	9.80	165	7.08
6	35.44	46	29.15	86	19.22	126	9.41	166	5.42	126	9.70	166	7.04
7	35.34	47	28.94	87	18.93	127	9.26	167	5.35	127	9.59	167	7.00
8	35.23	48	28.73	88	18.63	128	9.11	168	5.29	128	9.49	168	6.96
9	35.12	49	28.52	89	18.34	129	8.97	169	5.23	129	9.40	169	6.93
10	35.01	50	28.31	90	18.04	130	8.84	170	5.17	130	9.30	170	6.89
11	34.89	51	28.09	91	17.73	131	8.70	171	5.11	131	9.21	171	6.85
12	34.77	52	27.87	92	17.43	132	8.57	172	5.05	132	9.12	172	6.82
13	34.65	53	27.66	93	17.12	133	8.44	173	4.99	133	9.03	173	6.79
14	34.52	54	27.43	94	16.81	134	8.32	174	4.93	134	8.94	174	6.76
15	34.40	55	27.21	95	16.50	135	8.19	175	4.88	135	8.86	175	6.73
16	34.27	56	26.98	96	16.19	136	8.07	176	4.82	136	8.78	176	6.70
17	34.13	57	26.76	97	15.87	137	7.96	177	4.77	137	8.70	177	6.67
18	34.00	58	26.53	98	15.55	138	7.84	178	4.71	138	8.62	178	6.64
19	33.86	59	26.29	99	15.24	139	7.73	179	4.66	139	8.54	179	6.61
20	33.71	60	26.06	100	14.93	140	7.62	180	4.61	140	8.47	180	6.58
21	33.57	61	25.82	101	14.64	141	7.51	181	4.56	141	8.39	181	6.56
22	33.42	62	25.58	102	14.35	142	7.41	182	4.51	142	8.32	182	6.53
23	33.27	63	25.34	103	14.08	143	7.30	183	4.46	143	8.25	183	6.51
24	33.12	64	25.10	104	13.81	144	7.20	184	4.41	144	8.18	184	6.49
25	32.96	65	24.86	105	13.54	145	7.10	185	4.36	145	8.12	185	6.46
26	32.81	66	24.61	106	13.29	146	7.01	186	4.32	146	8.05	186	6.44
27	32.65	67	24.36	107	13.04	147	6.91	187	4.27	147	7.99	187	6.42
28	32.48	68	24.11	108	12.80	148	6.82	188	4.23	148	7.93	188	6.40
29	32.32	69	23.86	109	12.57	149	6.73	189	4.18	149	7.87	189	6.38
30	32.15	70	23.60	110	12.34	150	6.64	190	4.14	150	7.81	190	6.36
31	31.98	71	23.34	111	12.12	151	6.55	191	4.09	151	7.75	191	6.35
32	31.81	72	23.08	112	11.90	152	6.46	192	4.05	152	7.69	192	6.33
33	31.63	73	22.82	113	11.69	153	6.38	193	4.01	153	7.64	193	6.31
34	31.45	74	22.56	114	11.49	154	6.30	194	3.97	154	7.59	194	6.30
35	31.28	75	22.29	115	11.29	155	6.22	195	3.93	155	7.53	195	6.28
36	31.09	76	22.02	116	11.10	156	6.14	196	3.89	156	7.48	196	6.27
37	30.91	77	21.75	117	10.91	157	6.06	197	3.85	157	7.43	197	6.26
38	30.72	78	21.48	118	10.72	158	5.98	198	3.81	158	7.39	198	6.24
39	30.53	79	21.21	119	10.55	159	5.91	199	3.77	159	7.34	199	6.23
40	30.34	80	20.93	120	10.37	160	5.83	200	3.73	160	7.29	200	6.22

F_y = 60 ksi

K taken as 1.0 for secondary members.

Note: $C_c = 97.7$

TABLE 1-65

ALLOWABLE STRESS (KSI)

FOR COMPRESSION MEMBERS OF 65 KSI SPECIFIED YIELD STRESS STEEL

$F_y = 65$ ksi

Main and Secondary Members Kl/r not over 120						Main Members Kl/r 121 to 200				Secondary Members l/r 121 to 200			
$\frac{Kl}{r}$	F_a (ksi)	$\frac{Kl}{r}$	F_a (ksi)	$\frac{Kl}{r}$	F_a (ksi)	$\frac{Kl}{r}$	F_a (ksi)	$\frac{Kl}{r}$	F_a (ksi)	$\frac{l}{r}$	F_{as} (ksi)	$\frac{l}{r}$	F_a (ksi)
1	38.90	41	32.30	81	21.36	121	10.20	161	5.76	121	10.25	161	7.2
2	38.81	42	32.08	82	21.03	122	10.03	162	5.69	122	10.13	162	7.2
3	38.70	43	31.85	83	20.70	123	9.87	163	5.62	123	10.02	163	7.1
4	38.59	44	31.62	84	20.37	124	9.71	164	5.55	124	9.91	164	7.1
5	38.48	45	31.39	85	20.04	125	9.56	165	5.49	125	9.80	165	7.0
6	38.37	46	31.35	86	19.70	126	9.41	166	5.42	126	9.70	166	7.0
7	38.25	47	30.92	87	19.36	127	9.26	167	5.35	127	9.59	167	7.0
8	38.13	48	30.68	88	19.02	128	9.11	168	5.29	128	9.49	168	6.9
9	38.00	49	30.43	89	18.67	129	8.97	169	5.23	129	9.40	169	6.9
10	37.87	50	30.19	90	18.32	130	8.84	170	5.17	130	9.30	170	6.8
11	37.74	51	29.94	91	17.97	131	8.70	171	5.11	131	9.21	171	6.8
12	37.61	52	29.69	92	17.62	132	8.57	172	5.05	132	9.12	172	6.8
13	37.47	53	29.44	93	17.26	133	8.44	173	4.99	133	9.03	173	6.
14	37.32	54	29.18	94	16.90	134	8.32	174	4.93	134	8.94	174	6.
15	37.18	55	28.92	95	16.55	135	8.19	175	4.88	135	8.86	175	6.
16	37.03	56	28.66	96	16.20	136	8.07	176	4.82	136	8.78	176	6.
17	36.87	57	28.40	97	15.87	137	7.96	177	4.77	137	8.70	177	6.
18	36.72	58	28.14	98	15.55	138	7.84	178	4.71	138	8.62	178	6.
19	36.56	59	27.87	99	15.24	139	7.73	179	4.66	139	8.54	179	6.
20	36.40	60	27.60	100	14.93	140	7.62	180	4.61	140	8.47	180	6.
21	36.23	61	27.33	101	14.64	141	7.51	181	4.56	141	8.39	181	6.
22	36.06	62	27.05	102	14.35	142	7.41	182	4.51	142	8.32	182	6.
23	35.89	63	26.78	103	14.08	143	7.30	183	4.46	143	8.25	183	6.
24	35.71	64	26.50	104	13.81	144	7.20	184	4.41	144	8.18	184	6.
25	35.54	65	26.21	105	13.54	145	7.10	185	4.36	145	8.12	185	6.
26	35.36	66	25.93	106	13.29	146	7.01	186	4.32	146	8.05	186	6.
27	35.17	67	25.64	107	13.04	147	6.91	187	4.27	147	7.99	187	6.
28	34.99	68	25.35	108	12.80	148	6.82	188	4.23	148	7.93	188	6.
29	34.80	69	25.06	109	12.57	149	6.73	189	4.18	149	7.87	189	6
30	34.60	70	24.76	110	12.34	150	6.64	190	4.14	150	7.81	190	6.
31	34.41	71	24.47	111	12.12	151	6.55	191	4.09	151	7.75	191	6
32	34.21	72	24.17	112	11.90	152	6.46	192	4.05	152	7.69	192	6
33	34.01	73	23.87	113	11.69	153	6.38	193	4.01	153	7.64	193	6
34	33.81	74	23.56	114	11.49	154	6.30	194	3.97	154	7.59	194	6
35	33.60	75	23.25	115	11.29	155	6.22	195	3.93	155	7.53	195	6
36	33.39	76	22.94	116	11.10	156	6.14	196	3.89	156	7.48	196	6
37	33.18	77	22.63	117	10.91	157	6.06	197	3.85	157	7.43	197	6
38	32.96	78	22.32	118	10.72	158	5.98	198	3.81	158	7.39	198	6
39	32.75	79	22.00	119	10.55	159	5.91	199	3.77	159	7.34	199	6
40	32.53	80	21.68	120	10.37	160	5.83	200	3.73	160	7.29	200	6

* K taken as 1.0 for secondary members.

Note: $C_c = 93.8$.

TABLE 1-90

ALLOWABLE STRESS (KSI)
FOR COMPRESSION MEMBERS OF 90 KSI SPECIFIED YIELD STRESS STEEL

$F_y = 90$ ksi

Main and Secondary Members Kl/r not over 120						Main Members Kl/r 121 to 200				Secondary Members* l/r 121 to 200			
$\frac{Kl}{r}$	F_a (ksi)	$\frac{Kl}{r}$	F_a (ksi)	$\frac{Kl}{r}$	F_a (ksi)	$\frac{Kl}{r}$	F_a (ksi)	$\frac{Kl}{r}$	F_a (ksi)	$\frac{l}{r}$	F_{as} (ksi)	$\frac{l}{r}$	F_{as} (ksi)
1	53.84	41	42.39	81	22.76	121	10.20	161	5.76	121	10.25	161	7.25
2	53.68	42	42.00	82	22.21	122	10.03	162	5.69	122	10.13	162	7.20
3	53.51	43	41.59	83	21.68	123	9.87	163	5.62	123	10.02	163	7.16
4	53.33	44	41.19	84	21.16	124	9.71	164	5.55	124	9.91	164	7.16
5	53.15	45	40.78	85	20.67	125	9.56	165	5.49	125	9.80	165	7.08
6	52.95	46	40.36	86	20.19	126	9.41	166	5.42	126	9.70	166	7.04
7	52.75	47	39.94	87	19.73	127	9.26	167	5.35	127	9.59	167	7.00
8	52.55	48	39.51	88	19.28	128	9.11	168	5.29	128	9.49	168	6.96
9	52.33	49	39.08	89	18.85	129	8.97	169	5.23	129	9.40	169	6.93
10	52.11	50	38.65	90	18.44	130	8.84	170	5.17	130	9.30	170	6.89
11	51.89	51	38.21	91	18.03	131	8.70	171	5.11	131	9.21	171	6.85
12	51.65	52	37.77	92	17.64	132	8.57	172	5.05	132	9.12	172	6.82
13	51.41	53	37.32	93	17.27	133	8.44	173	4.99	133	9.03	173	6.79
14	51.17	54	36.86	94	16.90	134	8.32	174	4.93	134	8.94	174	6.76
15	50.92	55	36.41	95	16.55	135	8.19	175	4.88	135	8.86	175	6.73
16	50.66	56	35.94	96	16.20	136	8.07	176	4.82	136	8.78	176	6.70
17	50.39	57	35.47	97	15.87	137	7.96	177	4.77	137	8.70	177	6.67
18	50.12	58	35.00	98	15.55	138	7.84	178	4.71	138	8.62	178	6.64
19	49.85	59	34.52	99	15.24	139	7.73	179	4.66	139	8.54	179	6.61
20	49.56	60	34.04	100	14.93	140	7.62	180	4.61	140	8.47	180	6.58
21	49.28	61	33.56	101	14.64	141	7.51	181	4.56	141	8.39	181	6.56
22	48.98	62	33.06	102	14.35	142	7.41	182	4.51	142	8.32	182	6.53
23	48.68	63	32.57	103	14.08	143	7.30	183	4.46	143	8.25	183	6.51
24	48.38	64	32.07	104	13.81	144	7.20	184	4.41	144	8.18	184	6.49
25	48.07	65	31.56	105	13.54	145	7.10	185	4.36	145	8.12	185	6.46
26	47.75	66	31.05	106	13.29	146	7.01	186	4.32	146	8.05	186	6.44
27	47.43	67	30.53	107	13.04	147	6.91	187	4.27	147	7.99	187	6.42
28	47.10	68	30.01	108	12.80	148	6.82	188	4.23	148	7.93	188	6.40
29	46.77	69	29.48	109	12.57	149	6.73	189	4.18	149	7.87	189	6.38
30	46.43	70	28.95	110	12.34	150	6.64	190	4.14	150	7.81	190	6.36
31	46.09	71	28.41	111	12.12	151	6.55	191	4.09	151	7.75	191	6.35
32	45.74	72	27.87	112	11.90	152	6.46	192	4.05	152	7.69	192	6.33
33	45.39	73	27.32	113	11.69	153	6.38	193	4.01	153	7.64	193	6.31
34	45.03	74	26.77	114	11.49	154	6.30	194	3.97	154	7.59	194	6.30
35	44.67	75	26.21	115	11.29	155	6.22	195	3.93	155	7.53	195	6.28
36	44.30	76	25.65	116	11.10	156	6.14	196	3.89	156	7.48	196	6.27
37	43.93	77	25.08	117	10.91	157	6.06	197	3.85	157	7.43	197	6.26
38	43.55	78	24.50	118	10.72	158	5.98	198	3.81	158	7.39	198	6.24
39	43.17	79	23.92	119	10.55	159	5.91	199	3.77	159	7.34	199	6.23
40	42.78	80	23.33	120	10.37	160	5.83	200	3.73	160	7.29	200	6.22

K taken as 1.0 for secondary members.

Note: $C_c = 79.8$

TABLE 1-100

ALLOWABLE STRESS (KSI)
FOR COMPRESSION MEMBERS OF 100 KSI SPECIFIED YIELD STRESS STEEL

$F_y = 100$ ksi

Main and Secondary Members Kl/r not over 120						Main Members Kl/r 121 to 200				Secondary Members* l/r 121 to 200			
$\frac{Kl}{r}$	F_a (ksi)	$\frac{Kl}{r}$	F_a (ksi)	$\frac{Kl}{r}$	F_a (ksi)	$\frac{Kl}{r}$	F_a (ksi)	$\frac{Kl}{r}$	F_a (ksi)	$\frac{l}{r}$	F_{as} (ksi)	$\frac{l}{r}$	F_{as} (ksi)
1	59.82	41	46.12	81	22.76	121	10.20	161	5.76	121	10.25	161	7.2
2	59.62	42	45.64	82	22.21	122	10.03	162	5.69	122	10.13	162	7.2
3	59.42	43	45.16	83	21.68	123	9.87	163	5.62	123	10.02	163	7.1
4	59.21	44	44.67	84	21.16	124	9.71	164	5.55	124	9.91	164	7.1
5	58.99	45	44.17	85	20.67	125	9.56	165	5.49	125	9.80	165	7.0
6	58.76	46	43.67	86	20.19	126	9.41	166	5.42	126	9.70	166	7.0
7	58.53	47	43.17	87	19.73	127	9.26	167	5.35	127	9.59	167	7.0
8	58.28	48	42.65	88	19.28	128	9.11	168	5.29	128	9.49	168	6.9
9	58.03	49	42.14	89	18.85	129	8.97	169	5.23	129	9.40	169	6.9
10	57.77	50	41.61	90	18.44	130	8.84	170	5.17	130	9.30	170	6.8
11	57.50	51	41.08	91	18.03	131	8.70	171	5.11	131	9.21	171	6.8
12	57.22	52	40.55	92	17.64	132	8.57	172	5.05	132	9.12	172	6.8
13	56.93	53	40.00	93	17.27	133	8.44	173	4.99	133	9.03	173	6.7
14	56.64	54	39.46	94	16.90	134	8.32	174	4.93	134	8.94	174	6.7
15	56.34	55	38.90	95	16.55	135	8.19	175	4.88	135	8.86	175	6.7
16	56.03	56	38.35	96	16.20	136	8.07	176	4.82	136	8.78	176	6.7
17	55.72	57	37.78	97	15.87	137	7.96	177	4.77	137	8.70	177	6.6
18	55.39	58	37.21	98	15.55	138	7.84	178	4.71	138	8.62	178	6.6
19	55.06	59	36.63	99	15.24	139	7.73	179	4.66	139	8.54	179	6.6
20	54.72	60	36.05	100	14.93	140	7.62	180	4.61	140	8.47	180	6.
21	54.38	61	35.46	101	14.64	141	7.51	181	4.56	141	8.39	181	6.
22	54.03	62	34.87	102	14.35	142	7.41	182	4.51	142	8.32	182	6.
23	53.67	63	34.26	103	14.08	143	7.30	183	4.46	143	8.25	183	6.
24	53.30	64	33.66	104	13.81	144	7.20	184	4.41	144	8.18	184	6.
25	52.93	65	33.04	105	13.54	145	7.10	185	4.36	145	8.12	185	6.
26	52.55	66	32.42	106	13.29	146	7.01	186	4.32	146	8.05	186	6.
27	52.17	67	31.80	107	13.04	147	6.91	187	4.27	147	7.99	187	6.
28	51.78	68	31.16	108	12.80	148	6.82	188	4.23	148	7.93	188	6.
29	51.38	69	30.52	109	12.57	149	6.73	189	4.18	149	7.87	189	6.
30	50.97	70	29.88	110	12.34	150	6.64	190	4.14	150	7.81	190	6.
31	50.56	71	29.22	111	12.12	151	6.55	191	4.09	151	7.75	191	6.
32	50.15	72	28.56	112	11.90	152	6.46	192	4.05	152	7.69	192	6.
33	49.72	73	27.90	113	11.69	153	6.38	193	4.01	153	7.64	193	6.
34	49.29	74	27.22	114	11.49	154	6.30	194	3.97	154	7.59	194	6.
35	48.86	75	26.54	115	11.29	155	6.22	195	3.93	155	7.53	195	6.
36	48.42	76	25.85	116	11.10	156	6.14	196	3.89	156	7.48	196	6.
37	47.97	77	25.19	117	10.91	157	6.06	197	3.85	157	7.43	197	6.
38	47.51	78	24.54	118	10.72	158	5.98	198	3.81	158	7.39	198	6.
39	47.05	79	23.93	119	10.55	159	5.91	199	3.77	159	7.34	199	6
40	46.59	80	23.33	120	10.37	160	5.83	200	3.73	160	7.29	200	6

* K taken as 1.0 for secondary members.

Note: $C_c = 75.7$

TABLE 1-A

VALUES OF C_a

For determining F_a from equation $F_a = C_a F_y$, for all grades of steel

$\dfrac{Kl/r}{C_c}$	C_a	$\dfrac{Kl/r}{C_c}$	C_a	$\dfrac{Kl/r}{C_c}$	C_a	$\dfrac{Kl/r}{C_c}$	C_a
.01	.599	.26	.548	.51	.472	.76	.375
.02	.597	.27	.546	.52	.469	.77	.371
.03	.596	.28	.543	.53	.465	.78	.366
.04	.594	.29	.540	.54	.462	.79	.362
.05	.593	.30	.538	.55	.458	.80	.357
.06	.591	.31	.535	.56	.455	.81	.353
.07	.589	.32	.532	.57	.451	.82	.348
.08	.588	.33	.529	.58	.447	.83	.344
.09	.586	.34	.527	.59	.444	.84	.339
.10	.584	.35	.524	.60	.440	.85	.335
.11	.582	.36	.521	.61	.436	.86	.330
.12	.580	.37	.518	.62	.432	.87	.325
.13	.578	.38	.515	.63	.428	.88	.321
.14	.576	.39	.512	.64	.424	.89	.316
.15	.574	.40	.509	.65	.420	.90	.311
.16	.572	.41	.506	.66	.416	.91	.306
.17	.570	.42	.502	.67	.412	.92	.301
.18	.568	.43	.499	.68	.408	.93	.296
.19	.565	.44	.496	.69	.404	.94	.291
.20	.563	.45	.493	.70	.400	.95	.286
.21	.561	.46	.489	.71	.396	.96	.281
.22	.558	.47	.486	.72	.392	.97	.276
.23	.556	.48	.483	.73	.388	.98	.271
.24	.553	.49	.479	.74	.384	.99	.266
.25	.551	.50	.476	.75	.379	1.00	.261

Note: Use $\dfrac{Kl/r}{C_c{}'}$ in lieu of $\dfrac{Kl/r}{C_c}$ values when ratios exceed the limits of Sect. 1.9.

TABLE 1-B

VALUES OF C_c

For use in Formulas (1.5-1), (1.5-2), and (1.5-3),
Sect. 1.5.1.3, and in Table 1-A

F_y (ksi)	C_c	F_y (ksi)	C_c
33	131.7	46	111.6
35	127.9	50	107.0
36	126.1	55	102.0
39	121.2	60	97.7
40	119.6	65	93.8
42	116.7	90	79.8
45	112.8	100	75.7

TABLE 2

VALUES OF F'_e (KSI)

For use in Formula (1.6–1a), Sect. 1.6.1, for all grades of steel

$\frac{Kl_b}{r_b}$	F'_e (ksi)	$\frac{Kl_b}{r_b}$	F'_e (ksi)	$\frac{Kl_b}{r_b}$	F'_e (ksi)	$\frac{Kl_b}{r_b}$	F'_e (ksi)	$\frac{Kl_b}{r_b}$	F'_e (ksi)	$\frac{Kl_b}{r_b}$	F'_e (ksi)
21	338.62	51	57.41	81	22.76	111	12.12	141	7.51	171	5.11
22	308.54	52	55.23	82	22.21	112	11.90	142	7.41	172	5.05
23	282.29	53	53.16	83	21.68	113	11.69	143	7.30	173	4.99
24	259.26	54	51.21	84	21.16	114	11.49	144	7.20	174	4.93
25	238.93	55	49.37	85	20.67	115	11.29	145	7.10	175	4.88
26	220.90	56	47.62	86	20.19	116	11.10	146	7.01	176	4.82
27	204.84	57	45.96	87	19.73	117	10.91	147	6.91	177	4.77
28	190.47	58	44.39	88	19.28	118	10.72	148	6.82	178	4.71
29	177.56	59	42.90	89	18.85	119	10.55	149	6.73	179	4.66
30	165.92	60	41.48	90	18.44	120	10.37	150	6.64	180	4.61
31	155.39	61	40.13	91	18.03	121	10.20	151	6.55	181	4.56
32	145.83	62	38.85	92	17.64	122	10.03	152	6.46	182	4.51
33	137.13	63	37.62	93	17.27	123	9.87	153	6.38	183	4.46
34	129.18	64	36.46	94	16.90	124	9.71	154	6.30	184	4.41
35	121.90	65	35.34	95	16.55	125	9.56	155	6.22	185	4.36
36	115.22	66	34.28	96	16.20	126	9.41	156	6.14	186	4.32
37	109.08	67	33.27	97	15.87	127	9.26	157	6.06	187	4.27
38	103.42	68	32.29	98	15.55	128	9.11	158	5.98	188	4.23
39	98.18	69	31.37	99	15.24	129	8.97	159	5.91	189	4.18
40	93.33	70	30.48	100	14.93	130	8.84	160	5.83	190	4.14
41	88.83	71	29.62	101	14.64	131	8.70	161	5.76	191	4.09
42	84.65	72	28.81	102	14.35	132	8.57	162	5.69	192	4.05
43	80.76	73	28.02	103	14.08	133	8.44	163	5.62	193	4.01
44	77.13	74	27.27	104	13.81	134	8.32	164	5.55	194	3.97
45	73.74	75	26.55	105	13.54	135	8.19	165	5.49	195	3.93
46	70.57	76	25.85	106	13.29	136	8.07	166	5.42	196	3.89
47	67.60	77	25.19	107	13.04	137	7.96	167	5.35	197	3.85
48	64.81	78	24.54	108	12.80	138	7.84	168	5.29	198	3.81
49	62.20	79	23.93	109	12.57	139	7.73	169	5.23	199	3.77
50	59.73	80	23.33	110	12.34	140	7.62	170	5.17	200	3.73

All grades of steel

$$F'_e = \frac{12\pi^2 E}{23(Kl_b/r_b)^2}$$

TABLE 3-36

ALLOWABLE SHEAR STRESSES (F_v) IN PLATE GIRDERS (KSI) FOR 36 KSI SPECIFIED YIELD STRESS STEEL

(*Italic* values indicate gross area, as percent of web area, required for **pairs** of intermediate stiffeners of 36 ksi yield stress steel.) *

	\multicolumn{14}{c}{Aspect ratios a/h: stiffener spacing to web depth}
	0.5	0.6	0.7	0.8	0.9	1.0	1.2	1.4	1.6	1.8	2.0	2.5	3.0	over 3
60										14.5	14.5	14.5	14.5	14.5
70							14.5	14.5	14.5	14.4	14.2	13.8	13.6	13.0
80					14.5	14.5	14.0	13.4	13.0	12.6	12.4	12.2	12.0	11.4
												0.3	*0.4*	
90				14.5	14.3	13.4	12.5	12.2	11.9	11.8	11.6	11.3	11.1	10.1
								0.6	*0.9*	*1.1*	*1.2*	*1.2*	*1.2*	
100			14.5	13.9	12.8	12.3	11.9	11.6	11.3	11.1	10.9	10.3	10.0	8.3
						0.5	*1.4*	*1.8*	*2.0*	*2.1*	*2.2*	*2.3*	*2.1*	
110		14.5	13.8	12.6	12.2	11.9	11.5	11.0	10.5	10.1	9.8	9.2	8.8	6.9
					0.9	*1.8*	*2.5*	*3.1*	*3.5*	*3.6*	*3.6*	*3.4*	*3.1*	
120		14.3	12.7	12.2	11.8	11.5	10.8	10.2	9.8	9.4	9.0	8.4	8.0	5.8
				1.1	*2.1*	*2.8*	*4.1*	*4.7*	*4.9*	*4.9*	*4.7*	*4.3*	*3.8*	
130	14.5	13.2	12.2	11.9	11.5	11.0	10.3	9.7	9.2	8.8	8.4	7.8	7.3	4.9
			0.9	*2.2*	*3.2*	*4.5*	*5.6*	*5.9*	*6.0*	*5.8*	*5.6*	*5.0*	*4.4*	
140	14.2	12.4	12.0	11.6	11.0	10.5	9.8	9.2	8.7	8.3	7.9	7.2	6.8	4.2
		0.3	*1.9*	*3.2*	*4.8*	*5.9*	*6.7*	*6.9*	*6.8*	*6.6*	*6.3*	*5.5*	*4.9*	
150	13.2	12.2	11.8	11.2	10.6	10.1	9.4	8.8	8.3	7.9	7.5	6.8	6.3	3.7
		1.2	*2.8*	*4.7*	*6.1*	*7.0*	*7.6*	*7.7*	*7.5*	*7.2*	*6.8*	*6.0*	*5.2*	
160	12.4	12.0	11.5	10.9	10.3	9.8	9.1	8.5	8.0	7.6	7.2	6.5		3.2
		2.1	*4.1*	*6.0*	*7.2*	*8.0*	*8.4*	*8.3*	*8.1*	*7.7*	*7.3*	*6.3*		
170	12.3	11.8	11.2	10.6	10.1	9.6	8.9	8.3	7.7	7.3	6.9			2.9
	0.9	*2.8*	*5.3*	*7.0*	*8.1*	*8.7*	*9.0*	*8.9*	*8.5*	*8.1*	*7.7*			
180	12.1	11.6	10.9	10.4	9.9	9.4	8.7	8.1	7.5	7.1	6.7			2.6
	1.6	*4.0*	*6.3*	*7.9*	*8.8*	*9.4*	*9.6*	*9.3*	*8.9*	*8.5*	*8.0*			
200	11.9	11.2	10.5	10.0	9.5	9.1	8.3	7.7	7.2					2.1
	2.9	*6.0*	*8.0*	*9.2*	*10.0*	*10.4*	*10.4*	*10.0*	*9.5*					
220	11.5	10.8	10.3	9.7	9.3	8.8	8.1	7.5						1.7
	4.8	*7.5*	*9.2*	*10.2*	*10.8*	*11.1*	*11.0*	*10.6*						
240	11.2	10.6	10.0	9.5	9.1	8.6								1.4
	6.2	*8.6*	*10.1*	*11.0*	*11.5*	*11.7*								
260	11.0	10.4	9.9	9.4	8.9	8.5								1.2
	7.3	*9.5*	*10.8*	*11.6*	*12.0*	*12.1*								
280	10.8	10.2	9.7	9.2										
	8.2	*10.2*	*11.4*	*12.1*										
300	10.7	10.1	9.6											
	9.0	*10.8*	*11.8*											
320	10.5	10.0												
	9.5	*11.2*												

$F_y = 36$ ksi

...rders so proportioned that the computed shear is less than that given in right-hand column ...ot require intermediate stiffeners.

...or single angle stiffeners, multiply by 1.8; for single plate stiffeners, multiply by 2.4.

TABLE 3-42

ALLOWABLE SHEAR STRESSES (F_v) IN PLATE GIRDERS (KSI)
FOR 42 KSI SPECIFIED YIELD STRESS STEEL

(*Italic* values indicate gross area, as percent of web area, required for **pairs** of intermediate stiffeners of 42 ksi yield stress steel.)*

$F_y = 42$ ksi

Slenderness ratios h/t: web depth to web thickness

h/t	Aspect ratios a/h: stiffener spacing to web depth													
	0.5	0.6	0.7	0.8	0.9	1.0	1.2	1.4	1.6	1.8	2.0	2.5	3.0	over
50														17
60								17.0	17.0	17.0	17.0	17.0	17.0	16
70						17.0	17.0	16.5	16.0	15.6	15.3	14.9	14.6	14
80				17.0	17.0	16.3	15.2	14.5	14.2	14.0	13.8	13.5	13.3	12
80 (italic)								*0.1*	*0.5*	*0.7*	*0.8*	*0.9*	*0.9*	
90			17.0	16.6	15.4	14.5	14.1	13.7	13.4	13.1	12.9	12.5	12.1	10
90 (italic)						*0.1*	*1.0*	*1.5*	*1.8*	*1.9*	*1.9*	*1.9*	*1.8*	
100		17.0	16.4	15.0	14.3	14.0	13.5	13.0	12.5	12.1	11.7	11.0	10.5	8
100 (italic)					*0.7*	*1.5*	*2.3*	*2.7*	*3.2*	*3.3*	*3.4*	*3.2*	*2.9*	
110		16.8	15.0	14.2	13.9	13.5	12.7	12.0	11.5	11.0	10.6	9.9	9.4	6
110 (italic)				*1.0*	*2.0*	*2.7*	*3.9*	*4.5*	*4.7*	*4.7*	*4.6*	*4.2*	*3.8*	
120	17.0	15.4	14.3	13.9	13.4	12.8	12.0	11.3	10.7	10.2	9.8	9.1	8.5	
120 (italic)			*0.9*	*2.1*	*3.2*	*4.5*	*5.5*	*5.9*	*5.9*	*5.8*	*5.6*	*5.0*	*4.4*	
130	16.5	14.5	14.0	13.5	12.8	12.3	11.4	10.7	10.1	9.6	9.2	8.4	7.9	4
130 (italic)		*0.3*	*1.9*	*3.3*	*4.9*	*6.0*	*6.7*	*6.9*	*6.8*	*6.6*	*6.3*	*5.6*	*4.9*	
140	15.3	14.2	13.7	13.0	12.4	11.8	10.9	10.2	9.7	9.2	8.7	7.9	7.3	
140 (italic)		*1.3*	*2.9*	*4.9*	*6.3*	*7.2*	*7.7*	*7.8*	*7.6*	*7.3*	*6.9*	*6.0*	*5.3*	
150	14.5	14.0	13.3	12.6	12.0	11.4	10.6	9.9	9.3	8.8	8.3	7.5	6.9	
150 (italic)	*0.2*	*2.2*	*4.3*	*6.2*	*7.4*	*8.1*	*8.5*	*8.5*	*8.2*	*7.8*	*7.4*	*6.4*	*5.6*	
160	14.3	13.8	13.0	12.3	11.7	11.1	10.3	9.6	9.0	8.4	8.0	7.2		
160 (italic)	*1.1*	*3.1*	*5.6*	*7.3*	*8.3*	*8.9*	*9.2*	*9.0*	*8.6*	*8.2*	*7.8*	*6.7*		
170	14.1	13.4	12.7	12.0	11.4	10.9	10.0	9.3	8.7	8.2	7.7			
170 (italic)	*1.8*	*4.4*	*6.7*	*8.1*	*9.0*	*9.6*	*9.7*	*9.5*	*9.0*	*8.6*	*8.1*			
180	14.0	13.1	12.4	11.8	11.2	10.7	9.8	9.1	8.5	8.0	7.5			
180 (italic)	*2.5*	*5.5*	*7.6*	*8.9*	*9.7*	*10.1*	*10.2*	*9.9*	*9.4*	*8.9*	*8.3*			
200	13.5	12.7	12.0	11.4	10.9	10.3	9.5	8.8	8.1					
200 (italic)	*4.4*	*7.2*	*9.0*	*10.0*	*10.7*	*11.0*	*10.9*	*10.5*	*9.9*					
220	13.1	12.4	11.7	11.1	10.6	10.1	9.2	8.5						
220 (italic)	*6.1*	*8.5*	*10.0*	*10.9*	*11.4*	*11.6*	*11.4*	*10.9*						
240	12.8	12.1	11.5	10.9	10.4	9.9								
240 (italic)	*7.3*	*9.5*	*10.8*	*11.6*	*12.0*	*12.1*								
260	12.6	11.9	11.3	10.8	10.3	9.8								
260 (italic)	*8.3*	*10.2*	*11.4*	*12.1*	*12.4*	*12.5*								
280	12.4	11.8	11.2	10.7										
280 (italic)	*9.0*	*10.8*	*11.9*	*12.5*										
300	12.3	11.7	11.1											
300 (italic)	*9.6*	*11.3*	*12.3*											

Girders so proportioned that the computed shear is less than that given in right-hand co[lumn] do not require intermediate stiffeners.

* For areas of other intermediate stiffeners, multiply *italic* values by appropriate f[actor] below:

Stiffener Steel Grade	Pairs of Stiffeners	Single Angle Stiffeners	Single Plate Stiffeners
$F_y = 42$ ksi	1.0	1.8	2.4
$F_y = 36$ ksi	1.2	2.1	2.8

TABLE 3-45

ALLOWABLE SHEAR STRESSES (F_v) IN PLATE GIRDERS (KSI) FOR 45 KSI SPECIFIED YIELD STRESS STEEL

(*Italic* values indicate gross area, as percent of web area, required for **pairs** of intermediate stiffeners of 45 ksi yield stress steel.)*

Aspect ratios a/h: stiffener spacing to web depth

	0.5	0.6	0.7	0.8	0.9	1.0	1.2	1.4	1.6	1.8	2.0	2.5	3.0	over 3
50													18.0	18.0
60								18.0	18.0	18.0	18.0	18.0	17.7	17.0
70					18.0	18.0	18.0	17.1	16.6	16.2	15.9	15.5	15.3	14.6
												0.1	*0.2*	
80				18.0	17.9	16.8	15.7	15.3	15.0	14.7	14.5	14.2	13.9	12.7
								0.5	*0.8*	*1.0*	*1.1*	*1.2*	*1.1*	
90			18.0	17.2	15.9	15.3	14.9	14.5	14.1	13.8	13.5	12.8	12.3	10.3
						0.6	*1.4*	*1.9*	*2.1*	*2.2*	*2.3*	*2.3*	*2.2*	
100		18.0	17.0	15.5	15.1	14.8	14.2	13.6	13.0	12.5	12.1	11.3	10.8	8.3
				0.1	*1.2*	*2.0*	*2.7*	*3.4*	*3.8*	*3.9*	*3.9*	*3.6*	*3.2*	
110		17.4	15.5	15.1	14.7	14.2	13.3	12.6	12.0	11.5	11.0	10.2	9.7	6.9
			0.1	*1.4*	*2.4*	*3.3*	*4.6*	*5.1*	*5.2*	*5.2*	*5.0*	*4.5*	*4.0*	
120	18.0	15.9	15.2	14.7	14.1	13.5	12.6	11.8	11.2	10.7	10.2	9.4	8.8	5.8
			1.3	*2.6*	*3.9*	*5.1*	*6.1*	*6.4*	*6.3*	*6.2*	*5.9*	*5.2*	*4.6*	
130	17.1	15.4	14.9	14.2	13.5	12.9	12.0	11.2	10.6	10.1	9.6	8.8	8.1	4.9
		0.8	*2.4*	*4.0*	*5.6*	*6.6*	*7.2*	*7.3*	*7.2*	*6.9*	*6.6*	*5.8*	*5.1*	
140	15.9	15.1	14.5	13.7	13.0	12.4	11.5	10.8	10.1	9.6	9.1	8.2	7.6	4.2
		1.8	*3.6*	*5.6*	*6.8*	*7.7*	*8.1*	*8.1*	*7.9*	*7.5*	*7.1*	*6.2*	*5.4*	
150	15.4	14.9	14.1	13.3	12.7	12.1	11.2	10.4	9.8	9.2	8.7	7.8	7.2	3.7
	0.7	*2.6*	*5.0*	*6.8*	*7.9*	*8.6*	*8.9*	*8.8*	*8.4*	*8.0*	*7.6*	*6.6*	*5.7*	
160	15.2	14.5	13.7	13.0	12.3	11.8	10.9	10.1	9.4	8.9	8.4	7.5		3.2
	1.5	*3.8*	*6.2*	*7.8*	*8.7*	*9.3*	*9.5*	*9.3*	*8.9*	*8.4*	*7.9*	*6.9*		
170	15.0	14.2	13.4	12.7	12.1	11.5	10.6	9.8	9.2	8.6	8.1			2.9
	2.2	*5.1*	*7.2*	*8.6*	*9.4*	*9.9*	*10.0*	*9.7*	*9.3*	*8.7*	*8.2*			
180	14.8	13.9	13.2	12.5	11.9	11.3	10.4	9.6	9.0	8.4	7.9			2.6
	3.0	*6.1*	*8.1*	*9.3*	*10.0*	*10.4*	*10.4*	*10.1*	*9.6*	*9.0*	*8.5*			
200	14.3	13.5	12.8	12.1	11.5	11.0	10.1	9.3	8.6					2.1
	5.1	*7.7*	*9.4*	*10.4*	*11.0*	*11.2*	*11.1*	*10.6*	*10.1*					
220	13.9	13.2	12.5	11.8	11.3	10.7	9.8	9.0						1.7
	6.6	*8.9*	*10.3*	*11.2*	*11.6*	*11.8*	*11.6*	*11.1*						
240	13.6	12.9	12.3	11.6	11.1	10.5								1.4
	7.7	*9.8*	*11.1*	*11.8*	*12.2*	*12.3*								
260	13.4	12.7	12.1	11.5	10.9	10.4								1.2
	8.6	*10.5*	*11.6*	*12.3*	*12.6*	*12.6*								
280	13.2	12.6	11.9	11.4										
	9.3	*11.1*	*12.1*	*12.6*										
300	13.1	12.4	11.8											
	9.9	*11.5*	*12.5*											

$F_y = 45$ ksi

irders so proportioned that the computed shear is less than that given in right-hand column ot require intermediate stiffeners.

For areas of other intermediate stiffeners, multiply *italic* values by appropriate factor w:

Stiffener Steel Grade	Pairs of Stiffeners	Single Angle Stiffeners	Single Plate Stiffeners
$F_y = 45$ ksi	1.0	1.8	2.4
$F_y = 36$ ksi	1.3	2.3	3.0

TABLE 3-50

ALLOWABLE SHEAR STRESSES (F_v) IN PLATE GIRDERS (KSI)
FOR 50 KSI SPECIFIED YIELD STRESS STEEL

(*Italic* values indicate gross area, as percent of web area, required for **pairs** of intermediate stiffeners of 50 ksi yield stress steel.) *

$F_y = 50$ ksi

Slenderness ratios h/t: web depth to web thickness

h/t	Aspect ratios a/h: stiffener spacing to web depth													
	0.5	0.6	0.7	0.8	0.9	1.0	1.2	1.4	1.6	1.8	2.0	2.5	3.0	over 3
50										20.0	20.0	20.0	20.0	20.
60							20.0	20.0	20.0	19.9	19.5	18.9	18.6	17.
70					20.0	20.0	18.9	18.0	17.4	17.1	16.9	16.6	16.3	15.
										0.2	*0.4*	*0.5*	*0.6*	
80			20.0	20.0	18.9	17.8	17.0	16.6	16.2	15.9	15.7	15.2	14.9	13.
							0.6	*1.1*	*1.4*	*1.6*	*1.6*	*1.6*	*1.5*	
90			19.9	18.1	17.1	16.7	16.2	15.7	15.1	14.6	14.2	13.4	12.8	10.
					0.4	*1.3*	*2.1*	*2.5*	*2.8*	*3.1*	*3.1*	*3.0*	*2.8*	
100		20.0	17.9	17.0	16.5	16.1	15.2	14.4	13.8	13.2	12.8	11.9	11.3	8.
				0.8	*1.9*	*2.6*	*3.7*	*4.4*	*4.6*	*4.6*	*4.5*	*4.1*	*3.7*	
110	20.0	18.3	17.0	16.5	16.0	15.3	14.3	13.4	12.8	12.2	11.7	10.8	10.2	6
			0.9	*2.1*	*3.2*	*4.5*	*5.5*	*5.9*	*5.9*	*5.8*	*5.6*	*5.0*	*4.4*	
120	19.5	17.2	16.6	16.0	15.2	14.5	13.5	12.7	12.0	11.4	10.9	10.0	9.3	5
		0.4	*2.0*	*3.4*	*5.0*	*6.1*	*6.9*	*7.0*	*6.9*	*6.7*	*6.4*	*5.6*	*4.9*	
130	18.0	16.8	16.3	15.4	14.6	14.0	12.9	12.1	11.4	10.8	10.3	9.3	8.6	4
		1.5	*3.1*	*5.1*	*6.5*	*7.4*	*7.9*	*7.9*	*7.7*	*7.4*	*7.0*	*6.1*	*5.3*	
140	17.2	16.6	15.7	14.9	14.2	13.5	12.5	11.6	10.9	10.3	9.8	8.8	8.1	4
	0.5	*2.4*	*4.7*	*6.5*	*7.7*	*8.4*	*8.7*	*8.6*	*8.3*	*7.9*	*7.5*	*6.5*	*5.7*	
150	16.9	16.2	15.3	14.5	13.8	13.1	12.1	11.3	10.5	9.9	9.4	8.4	7.7	3
	1.4	*3.6*	*6.0*	*7.6*	*8.6*	*9.2*	*9.4*	*9.2*	*8.8*	*8.3*	*7.9*	*6.8*	*5.9*	
160	16.7	15.8	14.9	14.2	13.5	12.8	11.8	11.0	10.2	9.6	9.1	8.0		3
	2.1	*4.9*	*7.1*	*8.5*	*9.3*	*9.8*	*9.9*	*9.7*	*9.2*	*8.7*	*8.2*	*7.1*		
170	16.5	15.5	14.6	13.9	13.2	12.6	11.6	10.7	10.0	9.4	8.8			2
	2.9	*6.0*	*8.0*	*9.2*	*10.0*	*10.4*	*10.4*	*10.0*	*9.5*	*9.0*	*8.5*			
180	16.2	15.2	14.4	13.7	13.0	12.4	11.4	10.5	9.8	9.1	8.6			2
	4.1	*6.9*	*8.8*	*9.9*	*10.5*	*10.8*	*10.8*	*10.4*	*9.8*	*9.3*	*8.7*			
200	15.7	14.8	14.0	13.3	12.6	12.0	11.0	10.2	9.4					2
	5.9	*8.4*	*9.9*	*10.8*	*11.3*	*11.6*	*11.4*	*10.9*	*10.3*					
220	15.3	14.4	13.7	13.0	12.4	11.8	10.8	9.9						1
	7.3	*9.5*	*10.8*	*11.6*	*12.0*	*12.1*	*11.8*	*11.2*						
240	15.0	14.2	13.5	12.8	12.2	11.6								1
	8.3	*10.3*	*11.5*	*12.1*	*12.4*	*12.5*								
260	14.8	14.0	13.3	12.7	12.0	11.5								—
	9.2	*10.9*	*12.0*	*12.5*	*12.8*	*12.8*								
280	14.6	13.9	13.2	12.5										
	9.8	*11.4*	*12.4*	*12.9*										

Girders so proportioned that the computed shear is less than that given in right-hand col᷉ do not require intermediate stiffeners.

* For areas of other intermediate stiffeners, multiply *italic* values by appropriate fa᷉ below:

Stiffener Steel Grade	Pairs of Stiffeners	Single Angle Stiffeners	Single Plate Stiffeners
$F_y = 50$ ksi	1.0	1.8	2.4
$F_y = 36$ ksi	1.4	2.5	3.3

TABLE 3-55

ALLOWABLE SHEAR STRESSES (F_v) IN PLATE GIRDERS (KSI) FOR 55 KSI SPECIFIED YIELD STRESS STEEL

(*Italic* values indicate gross area, as percent of web area, required for **pairs** of intermediate stiffeners of 55 ksi yield stress steel.) *

	0.5	0.6	0.7	0.8	0.9	1.0	1.2	1.4	1.6	1.8	2.0	2.5	3.0	over 3
50									22.0	22.0	22.0	22.0	22.0	22.0
60						22.0	22.0	22.0	21.3	20.8	20.5	19.9	19.5	18.8
70				22.0	22.0	21.3	19.8	19.0	18.6	18.4	18.1	17.7	17.4	16.1
								0.1	*0.5*	*0.7*	*0.8*	*0.9*	*0.9*	
80			22.0	21.4	19.8	18.9	18.3	17.8	17.4	17.1	16.8	16.0	15.4	13.0
						0.3	*1.2*	*1.7*	*1.9*	*2.0*	*2.0*	*2.1*	*2.0*	
90		22.0	20.9	19.0	18.5	18.1	17.4	16.6	15.9	15.3	14.8	13.9	13.3	10.3
					1.1	*1.9*	*2.6*	*3.3*	*3.7*	*3.8*	*3.8*	*3.5*	*3.2*	
100		21.2	19.0	18.4	17.9	17.3	16.2	15.3	14.6	14.0	13.4	12.5	11.8	8.3
			0.2	*1.5*	*2.5*	*3.5*	*4.7*	*5.2*	*5.3*	*5.2*	*5.1*	*4.6*	*4.1*	
110	22.0	19.2	18.5	17.9	17.1	16.3	15.2	14.3	13.6	12.9	12.4	11.4	10.6	6.9
			1.5	*2.7*	*4.2*	*5.4*	*6.3*	*6.5*	*6.5*	*6.3*	*6.0*	*5.3*	*4.7*	
120	20.5	18.7	18.1	17.2	16.4	15.6	14.5	13.6	12.8	12.1	11.6	10.5	9.8	5.8
		1.1	*2.6*	*4.5*	*5.9*	*6.9*	*7.5*	*7.6*	*7.4*	*7.1*	*6.8*	*5.9*	*5.2*	
130	19.0	18.3	17.5	16.6	15.8	15.0	13.9	13.0	12.2	11.5	11.0	9.9	9.1	4.9
	0.1	*2.1*	*4.2*	*6.0*	*7.3*	*8.0*	*8.4*	*8.4*	*8.1*	*7.7*	*7.3*	*6.4*	*5.5*	
140	18.7	18.0	17.0	16.1	15.3	14.6	13.5	12.5	11.7	11.1	10.5	9.4	8.6	4.2
	1.1	*3.1*	*5.6*	*7.3*	*8.3*	*8.9*	*9.2*	*9.0*	*8.7*	*8.2*	*7.8*	*6.7*	*5.8*	
150	18.4	17.5	16.5	15.7	14.9	14.2	13.1	12.1	11.3	10.7	10.1	8.9	8.1	3.7
	1.9	*4.6*	*6.8*	*8.3*	*9.2*	*9.7*	*9.8*	*9.5*	*9.1*	*8.6*	*8.1*	*7.0*	*6.1*	
160	18.2	17.1	16.2	15.3	14.6	13.9	12.8	11.8	11.0	10.3	9.8	8.6		3.2
	2.7	*5.8*	*7.8*	*9.1*	*9.9*	*10.3*	*10.3*	*10.0*	*9.5*	*8.9*	*8.4*	*7.2*		
170	17.8	16.8	15.9	15.1	14.3	13.6	12.5	11.6	10.8	10.1	9.5			2.9
	3.9	*6.8*	*8.6*	*9.8*	*10.4*	*10.8*	*10.7*	*10.3*	*9.8*	*9.2*	*8.7*			
180	17.5	16.5	15.6	14.8	14.1	13.4	12.3	11.4	10.6	9.9	9.3			2.6
	5.0	*7.6*	*9.3*	*10.3*	*10.9*	*11.2*	*11.1*	*10.6*	*10.0*	*9.4*	*8.9*			
200	17.0	16.1	15.2	14.5	13.8	13.1	12.0	11.0	10.2					2.1
	6.7	*9.0*	*10.4*	*11.2*	*11.7*	*11.8*	*11.6*	*11.1*	*10.4*					
220	16.6	15.7	14.9	14.2	13.5	12.9	11.8	10.8						1.7
	7.9	*9.9*	*11.2*	*11.9*	*12.2*	*12.3*	*12.0*	*11.4*						
240	16.3	15.5	14.7	14.0	13.3	12.7								
	8.8	*10.7*	*11.8*	*12.4*	*12.7*	*12.7*								
260	16.1	15.3	14.5	13.8	13.2	12.5								
	9.6	*11.2*	*12.2*	*12.8*	*13.0*	*13.0*								

Aspect ratios *a/h*: stiffener spacing to web depth

F_y = 55 ksi

[Gi]rders so proportioned that the computed shear is less than that given in right-hand column [d]ot require intermediate stiffeners.

For areas of other intermediate stiffeners, multiply *italic* values by appropriate factor [belo]w:

Stiffener Steel Grade	Pairs of Stiffeners	Single Angle Stiffeners	Single Plate Stiffeners
$F_y = 55$ ksi	1.0	1.8	2.4
$F_y = 36$ ksi	1.5	2.8	3.7

TABLE 3-60

ALLOWABLE SHEAR STRESSES (F_v) IN PLATE GIRDERS (KSI)
FOR 60 KSI SPECIFIED YIELD STRESS STEEL

(*Italic* values indicate gross area, as percent of web area, required for **pairs** of intermediate stiffeners of 60 ksi yield stress steel.) *

$F_y = 60$ ksi — Slenderness ratios h/t: web depth to web thickness

Aspect ratios a/h: stiffener spacing to web depth

h/t	0.5	0.6	0.7	0.8	0.9	1.0	1.2	1.4	1.6	1.8	2.0	2.5	3.0	ov 3
40														24
50								24.0	24.0	24.0	24.0	24.0	24.0	23
60					24.0	24.0	24.0	23.1	22.3	21.8	21.4	20.8	20.5 *0.1*	19
70				24.0	23.7	22.2	20.7	20.3 *0.6*	19.9 *1.0*	19.5 *1.1*	19.3 *1.2*	18.7 *1.3*	18.4 *1.2*	16
80			24.0	22.4	20.7	20.3 *0.9*	19.6 *1.8*	19.0 *2.2*	18.6 *2.4*	18.0 *2.6*	17.5 *2.7*	16.6 *2.7*	15.9 *2.5*	13
90		24.0	21.8	20.5 *0.6*	19.9 *1.7*	19.4 *2.4*	18.5 *3.5*	17.5 *4.1*	16.7 *4.4*	16.1 *4.4*	15.5 *4.4*	14.5 *4.0*	13.8 *3.6*	10
100	24.0	22.1	20.4 *0.8*	19.8 *2.1*	19.3 *3.1*	18.4 *4.4*	17.2 *5.4*	16.2 *5.8*	15.4 *5.9*	14.7 *5.7*	14.1 *5.5*	13.0 *4.9*	12.2 *4.4*	8
110	23.3	20.6 *0.5*	19.9 *2.1*	19.2 *3.5*	18.2 *5.1*	17.4 *6.2*	16.2 *6.9*	15.2 *7.1*	14.4 *7.0*	13.7 *6.7*	13.1 *6.4*	11.9 *5.6*	11.1 *4.9*	6
120	21.4	20.2 *1.6*	19.4 *3.3*	18.4 *5.4*	17.5 *6.7*	16.7 *7.5*	15.4 *8.0*	14.4 *8.0*	13.6 *7.8*	12.9 *7.4*	12.3 *7.1*	11.1 *6.2*	10.2 *5.4*	5
130	20.5 *0.7*	19.8 *2.6*	18.7 *5.1*	17.7 *6.8*	16.9 *7.9*	16.1 *8.6*	14.9 *8.9*	13.9 *8.8*	13.0 *8.4*	12.3 *8.0*	11.6 *7.6*	10.4 *6.6*	9.6 *5.7*	4
140	20.2 *1.6*	19.3 *4.1*	18.2 *6.4*	17.2 *7.9*	16.4 *8.9*	15.6 *9.4*	14.4 *9.6*	13.4 *9.4*	12.5 *8.9*	11.8 *8.5*	11.2 *8.0*	9.9 *6.9*	9.0 *6.0*	4
150	19.9 *2.4*	18.8 *5.4*	17.8 *7.5*	16.8 *8.8*	16.0 *9.6*	15.3 *10.1*	14.0 *10.1*	13.0 *9.8*	12.1 *9.4*	11.4 *8.8*	10.8 *8.3*	9.5 *7.2*	8.6 *6.2*	3
160	19.6 *3.6*	18.4 *6.5*	17.4 *8.4*	16.5 *9.6*	15.7 *10.3*	15.0 *10.6*	13.7 *10.6*	12.7 *10.2*	11.8 *9.7*	11.1 *9.1*	10.4 *8.6*	9.2 *7.4*		3
170	19.2 *4.7*	18.1 *7.4*	17.1 *9.2*	16.2 *10.2*	15.4 *10.8*	14.7 *11.1*	13.5 *11.0*	12.5 *10.5*	11.6 *10.0*	10.8 *9.4*	10.2 *8.8*			2
180	18.9 *5.7*	17.8 *8.2*	16.8 *9.8*	16.0 *10.7*	15.2 *11.2*	14.5 *11.5*	13.3 *11.3*	12.2 *10.8*	11.4 *10.2*	10.6 *9.6*	9.9 *9.0*			2
200	18.3 *7.2*	17.3 *9.4*	16.5 *10.8*	15.6 *11.5*	14.9 *11.9*	14.2 *12.1*	13.0 *11.8*	11.9 *11.2*	11.0 *10.6*					
220	18.0 *8.4*	17.0 *10.3*	16.2 *11.5*	15.4 *12.1*	14.6 *12.5*	13.9 *12.5*	12.7 *12.2*	11.7 *11.5*						
240	17.7 *9.3*	16.8 *11.0*	15.9 *12.0*	15.2 *12.6*	14.4 *12.8*	13.7 *12.9*								
260	17.4 *9.9*	16.6 *11.5*	15.8 *12.5*	15.0 *13.0*	14.3 *13.1*	13.6 *13.1*								

Girders so proportioned that the computed shear is less than that given in right-hand column do not require intermediate stiffeners.

* For areas of other intermediate stiffeners, multiply *italic* values by appropriate factor below:

Stiffener Steel Grade	Pairs of Stiffeners	Single Angle Stiffeners	Single Plate Stiffeners
$F_y = 60$ ksi	1.0	1.8	2.4
$F_y = 36$ ksi	1.7	3.0	4.0

TABLE 3-65

ALLOWABLE SHEAR STRESSES (F_v) IN PLATE GIRDERS (KSI) FOR 65 KSI SPECIFIED YIELD STRESS STEEL

(*Italic* values indicate gross area, as percent of web area, required for **pairs** of intermediate stiffeners of 65 ksi yield stress steel.) *

	Aspect ratios a/h: stiffener spacing to web depth													
	0.5	0.6	0.7	0.8	0.9	1.0	1.2	1.4	1.6	1.8	2.0	2.5	3.0	over 3
40												26.0	26.0	26.0
50							26.0	26.0	26.0	26.0	26.0	25.9	25.5	24.5
60					26.0	26.0	25.2	24.0	23.2	22.7	22.3	21.9	21.6	20.4
											0.1	*0.4*	*0.4*	
70			26.0	26.0	24.6	23.1	22.1	21.5	21.1	20.7	20.4	19.8	19.4	17.0
							0.6	*1.1*	*1.4*	*1.5*	*1.6*	*1.6*	*1.5*	
80		26.0	25.6	23.3	22.2	21.6	20.9	20.3	19.4	18.7	18.2	17.1	16.4	13.0
					0.6	*1.5*	*2.2*	*2.6*	*3.1*	*3.3*	*3.3*	*3.2*	*2.9*	
90		25.6	22.7	21.9	21.3	20.8	19.4	18.4	17.5	16.8	16.2	15.0	14.2	10.3
				1.2	*2.2*	*2.9*	*4.3*	*4.8*	*5.0*	*5.0*	*4.8*	*4.4*	*3.9*	
100	26.0	23.0	21.9	21.2	20.4	19.4	18.1	17.1	16.2	15.4	14.8	13.6	12.7	8.3
			1.3	*2.6*	*4.0*	*5.2*	*6.1*	*6.4*	*6.3*	*6.2*	*5.9*	*5.2*	*4.6*	
110	24.3	22.1	21.4	20.4	19.4	18.5	17.2	16.1	15.2	14.4	13.7	12.5	11.6	6.9
		1.0	*2.6*	*4.4*	*5.9*	*6.8*	*7.4*	*7.5*	*7.4*	*7.1*	*6.7*	*5.9*	*5.1*	
120	22.4	21.6	20.7	19.6	18.6	17.7	16.4	15.3	14.4	13.6	12.9	11.6	10.7	5.8
	0.2	*2.2*	*4.2*	*6.1*	*7.3*	*8.1*	*8.5*	*8.4*	*8.1*	*7.7*	*7.3*	*6.4*	*5.6*	
130	22.1	21.2	20.0	18.9	18.0	17.1	15.8	14.7	13.8	13.0	12.3	11.0	10.0	4.9
	1.2	*3.3*	*5.8*	*7.4*	*8.4*	*9.0*	*9.3*	*9.1*	*8.7*	*8.3*	*7.8*	*6.8*	*5.9*	
140	21.7	20.6	19.4	18.4	17.5	16.7	15.4	14.3	13.3	12.5	11.8	10.5	9.5	4.2
	2.1	*4.9*	*7.1*	*8.5*	*9.3*	*9.8*	*9.9*	*9.6*	*9.2*	*8.7*	*8.2*	*7.1*	*6.1*	
150	21.4	20.1	19.0	18.0	17.1	16.3	15.0	13.9	12.9	12.1	11.4	10.1	9.1	3.7
	3.0	*6.1*	*8.1*	*9.3*	*10.0*	*10.4*	*10.4*	*10.1*	*9.6*	*9.0*	*8.5*	*7.3*	*6.3*	
160	20.9	19.7	18.6	17.7	16.8	16.0	14.7	13.6	12.6	11.8	11.1	9.7		3.2
	4.3	*7.1*	*8.9*	*10.0*	*10.6*	*10.9*	*10.9*	*10.4*	*9.9*	*9.3*	*8.7*	*7.5*		
170	20.5	19.4	18.3	17.4	16.6	15.8	14.5	13.3	12.4	11.5	10.8			2.9
	5.4	*8.0*	*9.6*	*10.6*	*11.1*	*11.4*	*11.2*	*10.7*	*10.1*	*9.5*	*9.0*			
180	20.2	19.1	18.1	17.2	16.3	15.6	14.3	13.1	12.2	11.3	10.6			2.6
	6.3	*8.7*	*10.2*	*11.1*	*11.5*	*11.7*	*11.5*	*11.0*	*10.4*	*9.7*	*9.1*			
200	19.7	18.6	17.7	16.8	16.0	15.2	13.9	12.8						
	7.8	*9.8*	*11.1*	*11.8*	*12.2*	*12.3*	*12.0*	*11.4*						
220	19.3	18.3	17.4	16.5	15.7	15.0	13.7	12.5						
	8.8	*10.6*	*11.7*	*12.4*	*12.6*	*12.7*	*12.3*	*11.7*						
240	19.0	18.1	17.2	16.3	15.5	14.8								
	9.6	*11.3*	*12.3*	*12.8*	*13.0*	*13.0*								

$F_y = 65$ ksi

rders so proportioned that the computed shear is less than that given in right-hand column ot require intermediate stiffeners.

For areas of other intermediate stiffeners, multiply *italic* values by appropriate factor w:

Stiffener Steel Grade	Pairs of Stiffeners	Single Angle Stiffeners	Single Plate Stiffeners
$F_y = 65$ ksi	1.0	1.8	2.4
$F_y = 36$ ksi	1.8	3.3	4.3

TABLE 3-90

ALLOWABLE SHEAR STRESSES (F_v) IN PLATE GIRDERS (KSI)
FOR 90 KSI SPECIFIED YIELD STRESS STEEL

(*Italic* values indicate gross area, as percent of web area, required for **pairs** of intermediate stiffeners of 90 ksi yield stress steel.) *

$F_y = 90$ ksi

Slenderness ratios h/t: web depth to web thickness

| h/t | Aspect ratios a/h: stiffener spacing to web depth | | | | | | | | | | | | | |
	0.5	0.6	0.7	0.8	0.9	1.0	1.2	1.4	1.6	1.8	2.0	2.5	3.0	over 3
40							36.0	36.0	36.0	36.0	36.0	36.0	36.0	36
50					36.0	36.0	35.5	33.9	32.8	32.0	31.4	30.7	30.3	28
												0.2	*0.3*	
60			36.0	36.0	33.8	31.8	30.5	29.7	29.1	28.5	28.1	27.3	26.7	23
							0.7	*1.2*	*1.5*	*1.6*	*1.7*	*1.6*	*1.5*	
70		36.0	34.4	31.3	30.4	29.6	28.6	27.3	26.2	25.2	24.4	22.9	21.9	17
					1.0	*1.8*	*2.6*	*3.2*	*3.6*	*3.7*	*3.7*	*3.5*	*3.2*	
80	36.0	33.8	30.8	29.9	29.1	27.9	26.1	24.6	23.4	22.4	21.5	19.9	18.8	13
			0.5	*1.8*	*2.8*	*4.0*	*5.1*	*5.5*	*5.6*	*5.5*	*5.3*	*4.8*	*4.2*	
90	34.9	30.9	29.9	28.8	27.3	26.1	24.3	22.8	21.5	20.5	19.6	17.8	16.6	10
		0.5	*2.1*	*3.6*	*5.2*	*6.2*	*6.9*	*7.1*	*7.0*	*6.7*	*6.4*	*5.6*	*4.9*	
100	31.4	30.1	28.9	27.3	26.0	24.7	22.9	21.4	20.1	19.1	18.1	16.4	15.1	8
		1.9	*3.8*	*5.7*	*7.0*	*7.8*	*8.3*	*8.2*	*8.0*	*7.6*	*7.2*	*6.3*	*5.5*	
110	30.6	29.4	27.7	26.2	24.9	23.8	22.0	20.4	19.1	18.0	17.1	15.3	14.0	6
	1.1	*3.2*	*5.7*	*7.4*	*8.4*	*9.0*	*9.2*	*9.1*	*8.7*	*8.2*	*7.8*	*6.7*	*5.9*	
120	30.0	28.4	26.8	25.4	24.2	23.0	21.2	19.7	18.4	17.3	16.3	14.4	13.1	5
	2.2	*5.0*	*7.2*	*8.6*	*9.4*	*9.9*	*9.9*	*9.7*	*9.2*	*8.7*	*8.2*	*7.1*	*6.2*	
130	29.4	27.6	26.1	24.8	23.6	22.5	20.7	19.1	17.8	16.7	15.7	13.8	12.4	4
	3.5	*6.4*	*8.3*	*9.5*	*10.2*	*10.6*	*10.6*	*10.2*	*9.7*	*9.1*	*8.6*	*7.4*	*6.4*	
140	28.7	27.0	25.6	24.3	23.1	22.0	20.2	18.6	17.3	16.2	15.2	13.3	11.9	4
	4.9	*7.6*	*9.3*	*10.3*	*10.9*	*11.2*	*11.0*	*10.6*	*10.0*	*9.4*	*8.8*	*7.6*	*6.6*	
150	28.1	26.5	25.2	23.9	22.7	21.6	19.8	18.3						
	6.0	*8.5*	*10.0*	*10.9*	*11.4*	*11.6*	*11.4*	*10.9*						
160	27.6	26.1	24.8	23.6	22.4	21.3	19.5	18.0						
	7.0	*9.2*	*10.6*	*11.4*	*11.8*	*12.0*	*11.7*	*11.2*						
170	27.3	25.8	24.5	23.3	22.1	21.1	19.3	17.7						
	7.8	*9.8*	*11.1*	*11.8*	*12.2*	*12.3*	*12.0*	*11.4*						
180	26.9	25.5	24.2	23.0	21.9	20.9	19.1	17.5						
	8.4	*10.3*	*11.5*	*12.2*	*12.5*	*12.5*	*12.2*	*11.6*						
200	26.4	25.1	23.9	22.7	21.6	20.5	18.7	17.2						
	9.4	*11.1*	*12.1*	*12.7*	*12.9*	*12.9*	*12.5*	*11.8*						

Girders so proportioned that the computed shear is less than that given in right-hand col do not require intermediate stiffeners.

* For areas of other intermediate stiffeners, multiply *italic* values by appropriate fac below:

Stiffener Steel Grade	Pairs of Stiffeners	Single Angle Stiffeners	Single Plate Stiffeners
$F_y = 90$ ksi	1.0	1.8	2.4
$F_y = 36$ ksi	2.5	4.5	6.0

TABLE 3-100

ALLOWABLE SHEAR STRESSES (F_v) IN PLATE GIRDERS (KSI) FOR 100 KSI SPECIFIED YIELD STRESS STEEL

(*Italic* values indicate gross area, as percent of web area, required for **pairs** of intermediate stiffeners of 100 ksi yield stress steel.)*

	Aspect ratios a/h: stiffener spacing to web depth													
	0.5	0.6	0.7	0.8	0.9	1.0	1.2	1.4	1.6	1.8	2.0	2.5	3.0	over 3
30													40.0	40.0
40							40.0	40.0	40.0	40.0	40.0	40.0	39.5	38.0
50				40.0	40.0	40.0	37.5	35.7	34.6	34.1	33.7	32.9	32.4	30.4
										0.3	*0.5*	*0.6*	*0.7*	
60			40.0	38.5	35.7	34.2	33.1	32.2	31.5	30.8	30.2	28.7	27.7	23.1
						0.5	*1.4*	*1.8*	*2.0*	*2.1*	*2.2*	*2.3*	*2.1*	
70		40.0	36.3	34.1	33.2	32.3	30.7	29.1	27.8	26.7	25.8	24.0	22.8	17.0
				0.7	*1.7*	*2.5*	*3.5*	*4.2*	*4.5*	*4.5*	*4.4*	*4.0*	*3.6*	
80	40.0	35.7	33.8	32.8	31.5	30.0	28.0	26.4	25.0	23.9	22.9	21.0	19.7	13.0
			1.2	*2.5*	*3.8*	*5.0*	*6.0*	*6.3*	*6.3*	*6.1*	*5.9*	*5.2*	*4.6*	
90	36.8	33.9	32.8	31.1	29.6	28.2	26.2	24.5	23.1	21.9	20.9	19.0	17.6	10.3
		1.2	*2.8*	*4.7*	*6.1*	*7.0*	*7.6*	*7.7*	*7.5*	*7.2*	*6.8*	*6.0*	*5.2*	
100	34.3	33.1	31.3	29.7	28.2	26.9	24.9	23.2	21.7	20.5	19.5	17.5	16.0	8.3
	0.6	*2.6*	*4.9*	*6.7*	*7.8*	*8.5*	*8.8*	*8.7*	*8.4*	*8.0*	*7.5*	*6.5*	*5.7*	
110	33.6	32.0	30.2	28.6	27.2	25.9	23.9	22.2	20.7	19.5	18.4	16.4	14.9	6.9
	1.8	*4.4*	*6.7*	*8.1*	*9.0*	*9.6*	*9.7*	*9.5*	*9.0*	*8.6*	*8.1*	*7.0*	*6.0*	
120	33.0	31.0	29.3	27.8	26.4	25.2	23.2	21.4	20.0	18.7	17.6	15.6	14.0	5.8
	2.9	*6.0*	*8.0*	*9.2*	*10.0*	*10.4*	*10.4*	*10.0*	*9.5*	*9.0*	*8.5*	*7.3*	*6.3*	
130	32.1	30.2	28.6	27.1	25.8	24.6	22.6	20.9	19.4	18.1	17.0	14.9	13.4	4.9
	4.5	*7.3*	*9.0*	*10.1*	*10.7*	*11.0*	*10.9*	*10.5*	*9.9*	*9.3*	*8.8*	*7.5*	*6.5*	
140	31.4	29.6	28.1	26.6	25.3	24.1	22.1	20.4						
	5.8	*8.3*	*9.8*	*10.8*	*11.3*	*11.5*	*11.3*	*10.8*						
150	30.8	29.1	27.6	26.2	25.0	23.8	21.8	20.0						
	6.8	*9.1*	*10.5*	*11.3*	*11.7*	*11.9*	*11.6*	*11.1*						
160	30.3	28.7	27.3	25.9	24.6	23.5	21.5	19.7						
	7.7	*9.7*	*11.0*	*11.8*	*12.1*	*12.2*	*11.9*	*11.3*						
170	29.9	28.4	27.0	25.6	24.4	23.2	21.2	19.5						
	8.4	*10.3*	*11.5*	*12.1*	*12.4*	*12.5*	*12.1*	*11.5*						
180	29.6	28.1	26.7	25.4	24.2	23.0	21.0	19.2						
	9.0	*10.8*	*11.8*	*12.4*	*12.7*	*12.7*	*12.3*	*11.7*						
200	29.1	27.7	26.3	25.0	23.8	22.7	20.7	18.9						
	9.9	*11.5*	*12.4*	*12.9*	*13.1*	*13.1*	*12.6*	*12.0*						

$F_y = 100$ ksi

Girders so proportioned that the computed shear is less than that given in right-hand column not require intermediate stiffeners.

For areas of other intermediate stiffeners, multiply *italic* values by appropriate factor ow:

Stiffener Steel Grade	Pairs of Stiffeners	Single Angle Stiffeners	Single Plate Stiffeners
$F_y = 100$ ksi	1.0	1.8	2.4
$F_y = 36$ ksi	2.8	5.0	6.7

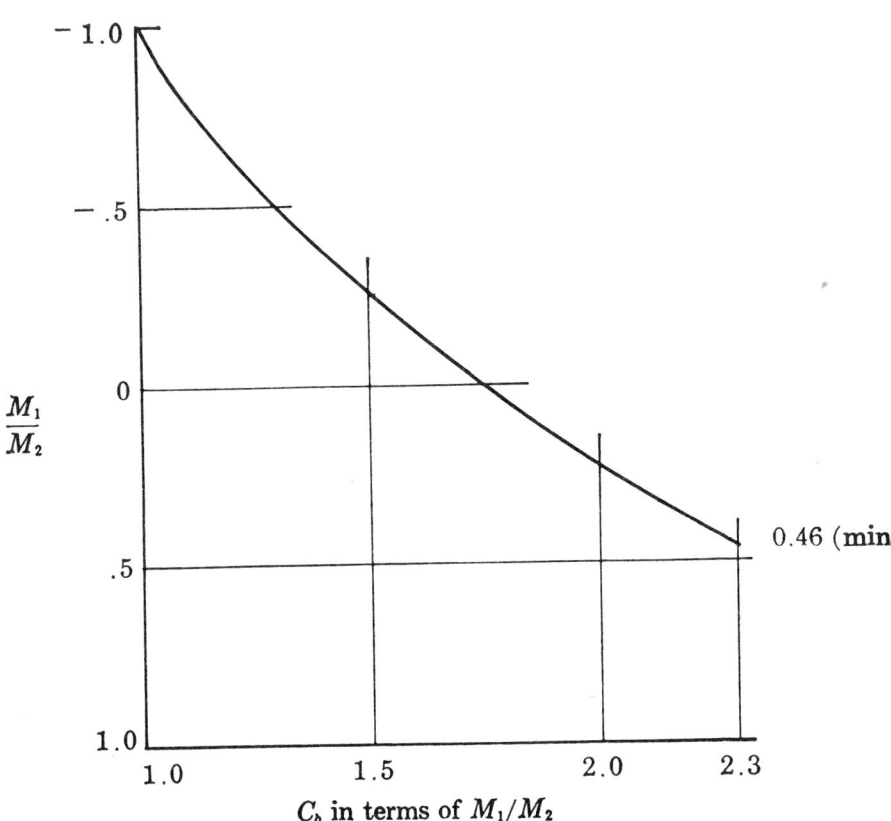

Fig. A1

APPENDIX B
Fatigue

SECTION B1 LOADING CONDITIONS AND TYPE AND LOCATION OF MATERIAL

In the design of members and connections subject to repeated variation of live load stress, consideration shall be given to the number of stress cycles, the expected range of stress, and type and location of member or detail.

Loading conditions shall be classified as shown in Table B1.

TABLE B1

Loading Condition	Number of Loading Cycles	
	From	To
1	20,000[1]	100,000[2]
2	100,000	500,000[3]
3	500,000	2,000,000[4]
4	Over 2,000,000	

[1] Approximately equivalent to two applications every day for 25 years.
[2] Approximately equivalent to ten applications every day for 25 years.
[3] Approximately equivalent to fifty applications every day for 25 years.
[4] Approximately equivalent to two hundred applications every day for 25 years.

The type and location of material shall be categorized as shown in Table B2.

SECTION B2 ALLOWABLE STRESSES

The maximum stress shall not exceed the basic allowable stress provided in Sects. 1.5 and 1.6 of this Specification, and the maximum range of stress shall not exceed that given in Table B3 except that, in the case of stress reversal only, the value F'_{sr} given by Formula (B1) may be used as the stress range for those categories marked with an asterisk in Table B2.

$$F'_{sr} = \left(\frac{f_t + f_c}{f_t + 0.6f_c}\right) F_{sr} \tag{B1}$$

where f_t and f_c are, respectively, calculated tensile and compressive stresses considered as positive quantities, and F_{sr} is the allowable stress range given in Table B3.

TABLE B2

General Condition	Situation	Kind of Stress[1]	Stress Category (See Table B3)	Illustrative Example Nos. (See Fig. B1)[2]
Plain material	Base metal with rolled or cleaned surfaces.	T or Rev.	A	1, 2
Built-up members	Base metal and weld metal in members, without attachments, built up of plates or shapes connected by continuous full penetration groove welds parallel to the direction of applied stress.	Rev. Rev. T or C	B*[3] B B	3 4 3, 4
	Base metal and weld metal in members, without attachments, built up of plates or shapes connected by continuous fillet welds parallel to the direction of applied stress.	T, C or Rev.	B	4, 5, 6
	Calculated flexural stress, f_b, at toe of welds on girder webs or flanges adjacent to welded transverse stiffeners:			
	When $f_v \leqslant F_v/2$	T or Rev.	C	7
	When $f_v > F_v/2$	T or Rev.	D	7
	where F_v = allowable shear stress.			
	Base metal at end of partial length welded cover plates having square or tapered ends, with or without welds across the ends.	T, C or Rev.	E	5

[1] "T" signifies range in tensile stress only: "C" signifies range in compressive stress only; "Rev." signifies a range involving reversal of tensile or compressive stress; "S" signifies range in shear including shear stress reversal.

[2] These examples are provided as guide lines and are not intended to exclude other reasonably similar situations.

[3] Formula (B1) applicable in situations identified by asterisk (*).

[4] Where stress reversal is involved, use of A307 bolts is not recommended.

TABLE B2 *(continued)*

General Condition	Situation	Kind of Stress[1]	Stress Category. (See Table B3)	Illustrative Example Nos. (See Fig. B1)[2]
Mechanically fastened connections	Base metal at net section of high-strength-bolted connections, except bearing-type connections subject to stress reversal and axially loaded joints which induce out-of-plane bending in connected material.	T or Rev.	**A**	8
	Base metal at net section of other mechanically fastened joints.[4]	T or Rev.	**B**	8, 9
Groove welds	Base metal and weld metal at full penetration groove welded splices of parts of similar cross section ground flush, with grinding in the direction of applied stress and with weld soundness established by radiographic or ultrasonic inspection.	T or Rev.	**A**	10
	Base metal and weld metal at full penetration groove welded splices of rolled and welded sections having similar profiles, when welds are ground flush.	T or Rev.	**B**	10, 11
	Base metal and weld metal in or adjacent to full penetration groove welded splices at transitions in width or thickness, with welds ground to provide slopes no steeper than 1 to 2½, with grinding in the direction of applied stress, and with weld soundness established by radiographic or ultrasonic inspection.	T or Rev.	**B**	12, 13

TABLE B2 (*continued*)

General Condition	Situation	Kind of Stress[1]	Stress Category. (See Table B3)	Illustrative Example Nos. (See Fig. B1)[2]
Groove welds (cont'd)	Base metal and weld metal in or adjacent to full penetration groove welded splices, with or without transitions having slopes no greater than 1 to 2½, when reinforcement is not removed and/or weld soundness is not established by radiographic or ultrasonic inspection.	T Rev. T or Rev.	C C* C	10 10 11, 12, 13
	Base metal or weld metal in or adjacent to full penetration groove welds in tee or cruciform joints.	T Rev.	D D*	14 14
	Base metal at details attached by groove welds subject to transverse and/or longitudinal loading.	T, C or Rev.	E	15
	Weld metal of partial penetration transverse groove welds, based on effective throat area of the weld or welds.	T or Rev.	G	16
Fillet welded connections	Base metal at intermittent fillet welds.	T, C or Rev.	E	
	Base metal at junction of axially loaded members with fillet welded end connections. Welds shall be disposed about the axis of the member so as to balance weld stresses.	T, C or Rev.	E	17, 18, 19, 20
	Continuous or intermittent longitudinal or transverse fillet welds (except transverse fillet welds in tee joints) and continuous fillet welds	S	F	5, 17, 18, 19, 21

TABLE B2 *(continued)*

General Condition	Situation	Kind of Stress[1]	Stress Category. (See Table B3)	Illustrative Example Nos. (See Fig. B1)[2]
Fillet welded connections (cont'd)	subject to shear parallel to the weld axis in combination with shear due to flexure.			
	Transverse fillet welds in tee joints.	S	G	20
Miscellaneous details	Base metal adjacent to short (2 in. maximum length in direction of stress) welded attachments.	C T or Rev.	C D	22, 23, 24 22, 23, 24, 25
	Base metal adjacent to longer fillet welded attachments.	T, C or Rev.	E	26
	Base metal at plug or slot welds.	T, C or Rev.	E	27
	Shear stress on nominal area of stud-type shear connectors.	S	G	22
	Shear on plug or slot welds.	S	G	27

TABLE B3

Category (From Table B2)	Allowable Range of Stress, F_{sr} (ksi)			
	Loading Condition 1 F_{sr1}	Loading Condition 2 F_{sr2}	Loading Condition 3 F_{sr3}	Loading Condition 4 F_{sr4}
A[1]	40	32	24	24
B	33	25	17	15
C	28	21	14	12
D	24	17	10	9
E	17	12	7	6
F	17	14	11	9
G	15	12	9	8

[1] For A514 steels in Category A, substitute the following values: $F_{sr1} = 45$, $F_{sr2} = 35$, $F_{sr3} = 25$ and $F_{sr4} = 25$.

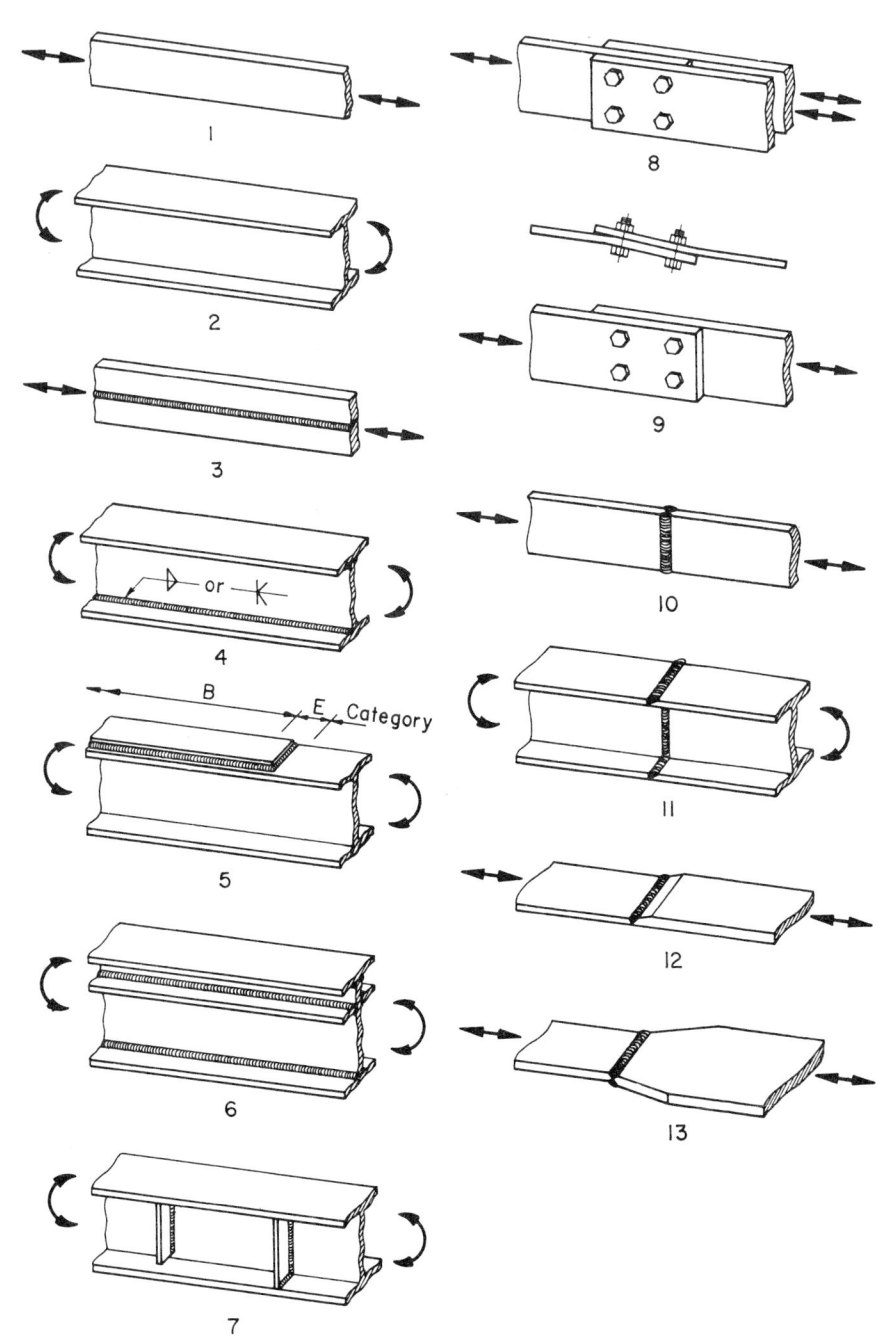

Fig. B1.   Illustrative Examples

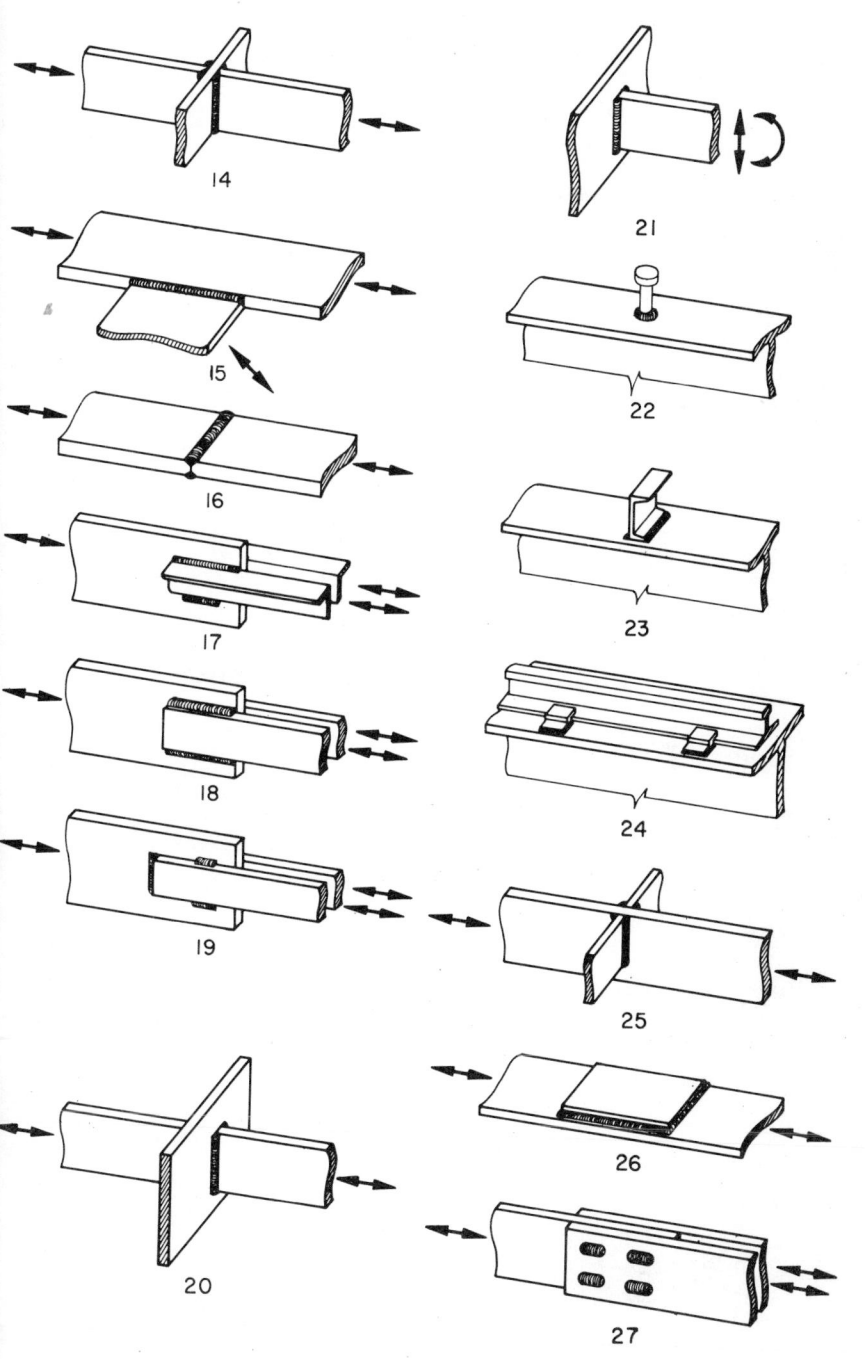

Fig. B1. Illustrative Examples (continued)

APPENDIX C

Slender Compression Elements

SECTION C1   GENERAL

Axially loaded members and flexural members containing elements subject to compression and having a width-thickness ratio in excess of the applicable limit given in Sect. 1.9 shall be proportioned to meet the requirements of this Appendix.

SECTION C2   STRESS REDUCTION FACTOR—UNSTIFFENED COMPRESSION ELEMENTS

Except as hereinafter provided, unstiffened compression elements whose width-thickness ratio exceeds the applicable limit given in Sect. 1.9.1.2 shall be subject to a reduction factor Q_s. The value of Q_s shall be determined by Formulas (C2-1) to (C2-6), as applicable, where b is the width of the unstiffened element as defined in Sect. 1.9.1.1.   When such elements comprise the compression flange of a flexural member the maximum allowable bending stress shall not exceed $0.6F_yQ_s$ nor the applicable value as provided in Sect. 1.5.1.4.6.   The allowable stress of axially loaded compression members shall be modified by the appropriate reduction factor Q_s as provided in Sect. C5.

For single angles:

When $76.0/\sqrt{F_y} < b/t < 155/\sqrt{F_y}$:

$$Q_s = 1.340 - 0.00447(b/t)\sqrt{F_y} \tag{C2-1}$$

When $b/t \geqslant 155/\sqrt{F_y}$:

$$Q_s = 15{,}500/[F_y(b/t)^2] \tag{C2-2}$$

For angles or plates projecting from columns or other compression members, and for compression flanges of girders:

When $95.0/\sqrt{F_y} < (b/t) < 176/\sqrt{F_y}$:

$$Q_s = 1.415 - 0.00437(b/t)\sqrt{F_y} \tag{C2-3}$$

When $b/t \geqslant 176/\sqrt{F_y}$:

$$Q_s = 20{,}000/[F_y(b/t)^2] \tag{C2-4}$$

For stems of tees:

When $127/\sqrt{F_y} < (b/t) < 176/\sqrt{F_y}$:

$$Q_s = 1.908 - 0.00715(b/t)\sqrt{F_y} \tag{C2-5}$$

When $b/t \geqslant 176/\sqrt{F_y}$:

$$Q_s = 20{,}000/[F_y(b/t)^2] \tag{C2-6}$$

However, unstiffened elements of channels and tees whose proportions exceed the limits of Sect. 1.9.1.2 shall conform to the limits given in Table C1.

TABLE C1
Limiting Proportions for Channels and Tees

Shape	Ratio of flange width to profile depth	Ratio of flange thickness to web or stem thickness
Built-up or Rolled Channels	$\leqslant 0.25$	$\leqslant 3.0$
	$\leqslant 0.50$	$\leqslant 2.0$
Built-up Tees	$\geqslant 0.50$	$\geqslant 1.25$
Rolled Tees	$\geqslant 0.50$	$\geqslant 1.10$

SECTION C3 EFFECTIVE WIDTH—STIFFENED COMPRESSION ELEMENTS

When the width-thickness ratio of a uniformly compressed stiffened element (except perforated cover plates) exceeds the applicable limit given in Sect. 1.9.2.2, a reduced effective width, b_e, shall be used in computing the flexural design properties of the section containing the element and the permissible axial stress, except that the ratio b_e/t need not be taken as less than the applicable value permitted in Sect. 1.9.2.2.

For the flanges of square and rectangular sections of uniform thickness:

$$b_e = \frac{253t}{\sqrt{f}} \left(1 - \frac{50.3}{(b/t)\sqrt{f}} \right) \leqslant b \qquad \text{(C3-1)}$$

For other uniformly compressed elements:

$$b_e = \frac{253t}{\sqrt{f}} \left(1 - \frac{44.3}{(b/t)\sqrt{f}} \right) \leqslant b \qquad \text{(C3-2)}$$

where

b = actual width of a stiffened compression element as defined in Sect. 1.9.2.1

t = its thickness

f = compressive stress in the element computed on the basis of its section properties as provided hereinafter. In the case of axial loading and flexure on extreme fibers, $f = 0.6F_yQ_s$, except as otherwise provided for wind and seismic loading

When the allowable stresses are increased due to wind or seismic loading, in accordance with the provisions of Sect. 1.5.6, the effective width shall be determined on the basis of 0.75 times the stress caused by wind or seismic loading acting alone or in combination with the design dead and live loading.

SECTION C4 DESIGN PROPERTIES

Properties of sections shall be determined in accordance with conventional methods, using the full cross-section of the member except as follows:

In computing the moment of inertia and section modulus of flexural members, with respect to the axis of bending under consideration, the effective width of stiffened compression elements parallel to the axis of bending and having a width-thickness ratio in excess of the applicable limit given in Sect. 1.9.2.2, rather than the actual width, shall be used and the axis of bending shall be located accordingly, except that, for sections otherwise symmetrical, the properties may conservatively and more easily be computed using a corresponding effective area on the tension side of the neutral axis as well. That portion of the area which is neglected in arriving at the effective area shall be located at and symmetrically about the center line of the stiffened element to which it applies.

The stress f_a due to axial loading and the radius of gyration r shall be computed on the basis of actual cross-sectional area. However, the allowable axial stress F_a, as provided in Sect. C5, shall be subject to the form factor

$$Q_a = \frac{\text{effective area}}{\text{actual area}}$$

where the effective area is equal to the actual area less $\Sigma(b - b_e)t$.

SECTION C5   AXIALLY LOADED COMPRESSION MEMBERS

The allowable stress for axially loaded compression members containing unstiffened or stiffened elements shall not exceed:

$$F_a = \frac{Q_s Q_a \left[1 - \frac{(Kl/r)^2}{2C'_c{}^2} \right] F_y}{\frac{5}{3} + \frac{3(Kl/r)}{8C'_c} - \frac{(Kl/r)^3}{8C'_c{}^3}} \tag{C5-1}$$

where

$$C'_c = \sqrt{\frac{2\pi^2 E}{Q_s Q_a F_y}}$$

when the largest effective slenderness ratio of any unbraced segment of the member is less than C'_c, nor the value given by Formula (1.5-2) or (1.5-3) when Kl/r exceeds C'_c or l/r exceeds 120, as applicable.

SECTION C6   COMBINED AXIAL AND FLEXURAL STRESS

In applying the provisions of Sect. 1.6 to members subject to combined axial and flexural stress and containing stiffened elements whose width-thickness ratio exceeds the applicable limit given in Sect. 1.9, the stresses F_a, f_{bx} and f_{by} shall be calculated on the basis of the section properties as provided in Sects. C4 and C5, as applicable. The allowable bending stress, F_b, for members containing unstiffened elements whose width-thickness ratio exceeds the applicable limit given in Sect. 1.9 shall be the smaller value, $0.6F_y Q_s$ or that provided in Sect. 1.5.1.4.6.

SUPPLEMENT NO. 1

TO THE SPECIFICATION FOR THE DESIGN, FABRICATION & ERECTION OF STRUCTURAL STEEL FOR BUILDINGS

(ADOPTED FEBRUARY 12, 1969)

Effective November 1, 1970

AMERICAN INSTITUTE
OF STEEL CONSTRUCTION
101 PARK AVENUE, NEW YORK, N.Y. 10017

Supplement No. 1

TO THE SPECIFICATION FOR THE DESIGN, FABRICATION AND ERECTION OF STRUCTURAL STEEL FOR BUILDINGS (*Adopted February 12, 1969*)

Effective November 1, 1970

SECTION 1.4   MATERIAL

1.4.1   Structural Steel

1.4.1.1   After the words "ASTM A514", delete the following:

"(Quenched and tempered alloy steel structural shapes and seamless mechanical tubing meeting all of the mechanical and chemical requirements of A514 steel, except that the specified maximum tensile strength may be 140,000 psi for structural shapes and 145,000 psi for seamless mechanical tubing, shall be considered as A514 steel.)"

Add to the list of approved materials:

"*Hot-Formed Welded and Seamless High-Strength Low-Alloy Structural Tubing*, ASTM A618"

Add a new Section as follows:

"1.4.6   Stud Shear Connectors

Steel stud shear connectors shall conform to the requirements of Articles 429 and 430, *Code for Welding in Building Construction*, AWS D1.0-69, of the American Welding Society.

Manufacturer's certification shall constitute sufficient evidence of conformity with specifications."

SECTION 1.5   ALLOWABLE STRESSES

1.5.1   Structural Steel

1.5.1.3   Compression

1.5.1.3.1   Immediately following the words "compression members", add: "whose cross-sections meet the provisions of Sect. 1.9"

1.5.1.4 Bending

1.5.1.4.1 Delete subparagraph d in its entirety and substitute the following:

"d. The depth-thickness ratio of the web or webs shall not exceed the value given by Formulas (1.5-4a) or (1.5-4b) as applicable.

$$\frac{d}{t} = \frac{412}{\sqrt{F_y}} \left(1 - 2.33 \frac{f_a}{F_y}\right) \quad \text{when } \frac{f_a}{F_y} \leqslant 0.16 \qquad (1.5\text{-}4a)$$

$$\frac{d}{t} = \frac{257}{\sqrt{F_y}} \qquad\qquad \text{when } \frac{f_a}{F_y} > 0.16 \qquad (1.5\text{-}4b)"$$

1.5.1.4.2 Immediately following the words "of Sect. 1.5.1.4.1" add a comma, and immediately following the words "except that $b_f/2t_f$," delete the comma.

Change formula number "(1.5-5)" to "(1.5-5a)".

1.5.1.4.3 Add a second paragraph as follows:

"Doubly-symmetrical I- and H-shape members bent about their minor axis (except hybrid girders and members of A514 steel) meeting the requirements of Sect. 1.5.1.4.1, subparagraph a, except where $b_f/2t_f$ exceeds $52.2/\sqrt{F_y}$ but is less than $95.0/\sqrt{F_y}$, may be designed on the basis of an allowable bending stress

$$F_b = F_y \left[0.933 - 0.0035 \left(\frac{b_f}{2t_f}\right) \sqrt{F_y}\right] \qquad (1.5\text{-}5b)"$$

1.5.1.4.6a Immediately following the words "under Sect. 1.5.1.4.5," add: "and meeting the requirements of Sect. 1.9.1.2,".

1.5.1.4.6b Immediately following the words "under Sect. 1.5.1.4.5," add: "and meeting the requirements of Sect. 1.9.1.2,".

SECTION 1.10 PLATE GIRDERS AND ROLLED BEAMS

1.10.5 Stiffeners

1.10.5.3 In the third paragraph, immediately following the words "holes shall be such that", delete: "the smaller panel dimension, a or h, shall not exceed $348t/\sqrt{f_v}$," and substitute the words "f_v does not exceed the value given by Formula (1.10-1)".

SECTION 1.11   COMPOSITE CONSTRUCTION

1.11.2   Design Assumptions

1.11.2.2   At the beginning of the fourth paragraph, delete the words "For construction without temporary shoring, the value of the section modulus of the transformed composite section used in stress calculations (referred to the bottom flange of the steel beam) shall not exceed", and substitute the following:

"For construction without temporary shoring, the bottom flange steel stress may be computed from the total load moment and the actual transformed section modulus S_{tr}, except that the numerical value of S_{tr} so used shall not exceed that of Formula (1.11-2).   This stress shall not exceed the appropriate value of Sect. 1.5.1."

SECTION 1.15   CONNECTIONS

1.15.5   Restrained Members

In the first line of the second paragraph delete the words "fully restrained".

SECTION 1.23   FABRICATION

1.23.1   Straightening Material

Delete this subhead and the entire text of the paragraph beginning with the words "Rolled material", and substitute a new subheading and paragraph reading as follows:

"1.23.1   Cambering, Curving, and Straightening

The local application of heat or mechanical means may be used to introduce or correct camber, curvature, and straightness.   The temperature of heated areas, as measured by approved methods, shall not exceed 1100°F for A514 steel nor 1200°F for other steels."

1.23.6   Welded Construction

In Table 1.23.6, for thickness "To $\frac{3}{4}$, incl.", in the second column under the heading "Welding Process", change "None[2]" to "None[2,3]".

SUPPLEMENT NO. 2

TO THE
SPECIFICATION
FOR THE
DESIGN,
FABRICATION
& ERECTION
OF
STRUCTURAL
STEEL FOR
BUILDINGS

(ADOPTED FEBRUARY 12, 1969)

Effective December 8, 1971

AMERICAN INSTITUTE
OF STEEL CONSTRUCTION
101 PARK AVENUE, NEW YORK, N.Y. 10017

Supplement No. 2

TO THE SPECIFICATION FOR THE DESIGN, FABRICATION AND ERECTION OF STRUCTURAL STEEL FOR BUILDINGS (*Adopted February 12, 1969*)

Effective December 8, 1971

SECTION 1.4 MATERIAL

1.4.1 Structural Steel

1.4.1.1 Delete "*High-Strength Low Alloy Hot Rolled Steel Sheet and Strip, ASTM A375*".

Add the following to the list of approved materials:

"*Steel Sheet and Strip, Hot-Rolled and Cold-Rolled, High-Strength, Low-Alloy, with Improved Corrosion Resistance, ASTM A606*"
"*Steel Sheet and Strip, Hot-Rolled and Cold-Rolled, High-Strength, Low-Alloy, Columbium and/or Vanadium, ASTM A607*"

SECTION 1.8 STABILITY AND SLENDERNESS RATIOS

1.8.4 Maximum Ratios

In the second sentence, referring to tension members, delete the term "*K*" from the expression "*Kl/r*".

SECTION 1.9 WIDTH-THICKNESS RATIOS

1.9.2 Stiffened Elements Under Compression

1.9.2.2 In the fifth line, add the word "box" between the words "rectangular" and "sections".

SECTION 1.10 PLATE GIRDERS AND ROLLED BEAMS

1.10.2 Web

Delete the paragraph in its entirety and substitute the following:

"The ratio of the clear distance between flanges to the web thickness shall not exceed

$$\frac{14,000}{\sqrt{F_y(F_y + 16.5)}}$$

except that when transverse stiffeners are provided, spaced not more than 1½ times the girder depth, the limiting ratio may be $2,000/\sqrt{F_y}$, where F_y is the yield stress of the compression flange."

1.10.5 Stiffeners

1.10.5.3 In the first line, immediately ahead of "Intermediate stiffeners", add the phrase "Subject to the limitations of Sect. 1.10.2,"

Delete the third paragraph in its entirety and substitute the following:

"In girders designed on the basis of tension field action, the spacing between stiffeners at end panels, at panels containing large holes and panels adjacent thereto shall be such that f_v does not exceed the value given by Formula (1.10-1)."

1.10.8 Splices

In the first sentence, delete the words "be complete penetration groove welds and shall"

SECTION 1.11   COMPOSITE CONSTRUCTION

1.11.2 Design Assumptions

1.11.2.2 Delete the last sentence of the second paragraph and substitute the following:

"For stress computations the compression area of lightweight or normal weight concrete shall be treated as an equivalent area of steel by dividing it by the modular ratio, n, for normal weight concrete of the strength specified when determining the section properties. For deflection calculations, the transformed section properties shall be based on the appropriate modular ratio, n, for the strength and weight concrete specified."

1.11.4 Shear Connectors

In the third paragraph, fourth line, immediately following the words "is given in Table 1.11.4", add the following:

"for concrete made with ASTM C33 aggregates. For concrete made with rotary kiln produced aggregates, conforming to ASTM C330 with concrete unit weight not less than 90 pcf, the allowable shear load for one connector is obtained by multiplying the values from Table 1.11.4 by the coefficient from Table 1.11.4A."

Immediately following the footnote to Table 1.11.4, add Table 1.11.4A as follows:

TABLE 1.11.4A

Air dry unit weight, pcf	90	95	100	105	110	115	120
Coefficient	0.73	0.76	0.78	0.81	0.83	0.86	0.88

In the fourth paragraph, referring to incomplete composite action, add a second sentence as follows:

"The value of V'_h shall not be less than half the smaller value using Formulas (1.11-3) and (1.11-4)."

In the final (seventh) paragraph, add the following two sentences:

"Stud shear connectors shall be at least 4 diameters in length and not greater than $7/8$-in. diameter. The minimum center-to-center spacing shall not be less than 3 diameters."

SECTION 1.14   GROSS AND NET SECTION

1.14.5   Size of Holes

Delete the section in its entirety and substitute the following:

"In computing net area the diameter of a rivet or bolt hole shall be taken as $1/16$-inch greater than the nominal dimension of the hole normal to the direction of applied stress."

SECTION 1.15   CONNECTIONS

1.15.4   Unrestrained Members

Delete the second paragraph in its entirety and substitute the following:

"Flexible beam connections shall accommodate end rotations of unrestrained (simple) beams. To accomplish this, inelastic action in the connection is permitted."

SECTION 1.16   RIVETS AND BOLTS

1.16.5   Minimum Edge Distance

In the heading of the right hand portion of Table 1.16.5, after "Minimum Edge Distance", add a triple asterisk. Below the footnotes to the Table, add a third footnote as follows:

"*** When oversized or slotted holes are used, edge distances shall be increased so as to maintain the clear distance from edge of hole to free edge provided by distances tabulated."

SECTION 1.18   BUILT-UP MEMBERS

1.18.2   Compression Members

1.18.2.6   Delete that portion of the sixth sentence which reads: "In determining the required section for lacing bars, Formulas (1.5-1) or (1.5-2) shall be used," and substitute the following:

"Lacing bars in compression may be treated as secondary members with"

SECTION 1.23   FABRICATION

1.23.5   Riveted and High Strength Bolted Construction—Assembling

Delete the fourth paragraph, referring to cold driven rivets, in its entirety.

In the fifth paragraph, delete the final word, "galvanizing", and replace with the following:

"other coatings except as listed below:

(1)   Hot-dip galvanizing, if contact surfaces are scored by wire brushing or blasting after galvanizing and prior to assembly.

(2)   Inorganic zinc rich paints as defined in those sections of the Steel Structures Painting Council Systems, SSPC PS 12.00 covering zinc rich paints with inorganic vehicles.

(3)   Metallized zinc or aluminum applied in accordance with AWS C2.2 Recommended Practice for Metallizing with Aluminum and Zinc for Protection of Iron and Steel, except that subsequent sealing treatments, described in Section IV therein, shall not be used."

1.23.6   Welded Construction

In the eighth paragraph, delete the third sentence, which reads: "Extension bars or run-off plates, if used, shall be removed upon completion of the weld and the ends of the weld made smooth and flush with the abutting parts." and substitute the following:

"Extension bars or run-off plates need not be removed upon completion of the weld unless so specified in bid documents."

APPENDIX C

SECTION C2   STRESS REDUCTION FACTOR—UNSTIFFENED COMPRESSION ELEMENTS

In the first sentence, between "hereinafter provided," and "unstiffened compression", add the words "stress on".

In the sentence following Formula (C2-2), immediately ahead of the words "compression flanges of girders:" add the words "projecting elements of".

In Table C1, change the heading of the second column to read: "Ratio of full flange width to profile depth".

SECTION C3 EFFECTIVE WIDTH—STIFFENED COMPRESSION ELEMENTS

Delete the definition for f and substitute the following:

"f = computed compressive stress in the stiffened elements based on the design properties as specified in Sect. C4. If unstiffened elements are included in the total cross-section, f for the stiffened element must be such that the maximum compressive stress in the unstiffened element does not exceed F_aQ_s or F_bQ_s as applicable."

COMMENTARY

ON THE

SPECIFICATION FOR THE DESIGN, FABRICATION & ERECTION

OF

STRUCTURAL STEEL FOR BUILDINGS

FEBRUARY 12, 1969

AMERICAN INSTITUTE
OF STEEL CONSTRUCTION
101 PARK AVENUE, NEW YORK, N.Y. 10017

Commentary

ON THE SPECIFICATION FOR THE DESIGN, FABRICATION AND ERECTION OF STRUCTURAL STEEL FOR BUILDINGS

INTRODUCTION

In the belief that the designer can make more efficient use of the Specification if he knows the basis for its various provisions, this Commentary has been prepared.

Many provisions, notably in the sections dealing with fabrication and erection practices, have evolved from years of shop and field experience and need no further elaboration. Attention is directed primarily to less widely understood measures and particularly to modifications appearing for the first time. Many of these are the outgrowth of extensive research which has been carried out in recent years.

Part 1 of the Specification includes all of the provisions necessary for a working-stress design covering all three types of construction. Part 2 covers provisions applicable to plastic design.

SECTION 1.2   TYPES OF CONSTRUCTION

In order that adequate instructions can be issued to the shop and erection forces, the basic assumptions underlying the design must be thoroughly understood by all concerned. As in the earlier AISC Specification, these assumptions are classified under three separate but generally recognized types of construction.

For better clarity, the provisions covering tier buildings of Type 2 construction designed for wind loading have been reworded in the current Specification, but without change in intent. Justification for these provisions has been discussed by Sourochnikoff,* Disque** and others.

SECTION 1.3   LOADS AND FORCES

The Specification does not presume to establish the loading requirements for which structures should be designed. In most cases these are adequately covered in the applicable local building codes. Where such is not the case, the generally recognized standards of the American National Standards Institute are recommended as the basis for design.

---

* *Sourochnikoff, B.* Wind Stresses in Semi-Rigid Connections of Steel Framework, *1950 ASCE Transactions.*

** *Disque, R. O.* Wind Connections with Simple Framing, *AISC Engineering Journal, Vol. 1, No. 3.*

SECTION 1.4 MATERIAL

The 1961 edition of the Specification provided for the use of structural steel having a specified minimum yield point up to, but not exceeding, 50 kips per square inch. The grades of structural steel now approved for use under the Specification, covered by ASTM standards adopted since that time, extend the yield stress to 100 kips per square inch.

A number of other ASTM specifications are also now listed, covering types of material having infrequent application but suitable for use under the Specification.

Some of these ASTM standards specify a minimum yield point, while others specify a minimum yield strength. The term "yield stress" is used in the Specification as a generic term to denote either the yield point or the yield strength. However, the specified terms "yield point" and "yield stress" are used where they are uniquely applicable.

In keeping with the inclusion of steels of several strength grades, a number of corresponding specifications for cast steel forgings and other appurtenant materials such as rivets, bolts, and welding electrodes are also included.

When requested to do so, the fabricator must make affidavit that all steel specified to a yield stress in excess of 36 kips per square inch has been provided in accordance with the plans and Specification.

SECTION 1.5 ALLOWABLE STRESSES

1.5.1. Structural Steel

Because of the introduction of steels having various specified minimum yield stresses, it is convenient to express permissible working stresses in terms of yield stress, F_y.

Where provisions are given in terms of F_y together with numerical values, it should be noted that, throughout the Specification, all stresses including the applicable value of F_y are expressed in kips per square inch.

For ready reference, numerical values are presented in Appendix A for several of the yield stress levels represented in Sect. 1.4.1.

1.5.1.1 Tension

The 5/3 factor of safety with respect to yield stress used in determining the basic working stress for the newer and stronger steels is the same as that provided since the Specification was first adopted.

However, a further precaution has been added, applicable only at the net section of axially loaded members. Here a factor of safety of 2 with respect to specified minimum tensile strength must also be provided. This latter provision, of course, would apply only to steel having a yield stress-to-tensile strength ratio 5/6 or greater.

The working stress at the net section at pin holes is based upon research* and experience with eye-bars.

---

* *Johnston, B. G.* Pin-Connected Plate Links, *1939 ASCE Transactions.*

1.5.1.2 Shear

While the shear yield stress of structural steel has been variously estimated as between one-half and five-eighths of the tension and compression yield stress and is frequently taken as $F_y/\sqrt{3}$, it will be noted that the permissible working value is given as two-thirds the recommended basic allowable tensile stress, substantially as it has been since the first edition of the AISC Specification, published in 1923. This apparent reduction in factor of safety is justified by the minor consequences of shear yielding, as compared with those associated with tension and compression yielding, and by the effect of strain hardening.

The webs of rolled shapes are all of such thickness that shear is seldom the criterion for design. However, the web shear stresses are generally high within the boundaries of the rigid connection of two or more members whose webs lie in a common plane. Such webs should be reinforced when the web thickness is less than

$$\frac{32M}{A_{bc}F_y}$$

where M is the algebraic sum of clockwise and counter-clockwise moments (in kip-feet) applied on opposite sides of the connection boundary and A_{bc} is the planar area of the connection web, expressed in square inches. This expression is based upon the assumption that the moment M is resisted by a couple having an arm equal to $0.95d_b$, where d_b is the depth of the member introducing the moment. Designating as d_c the depth of the member entering the joint more or less at right angles to it, and noting that A_{bc} is approximately equal to $d_b \times d_c$, the minimum thickness of the web not requiring reinforcement can be computed from the equation

$$\text{allowable shear stress} = 0.40F_y = \frac{12M}{0.95A_{bc}t_{\min}}$$

1.5.1.3 Compression

1.5.1.3.1 Formulas (1.5-1) and (1.5-2) are founded upon the basic column strength estimate suggested by the Column Research Council.* This estimate assumes that the upper limit of elastic buckling failure is defined by an average column stress equal to one-half of yield stress. The slenderness ratio C_c, corresponding to this limit, can be expressed in terms of the yield stress of a given grade of structural steel as

$$C_c = \sqrt{\frac{2\pi^2 E}{F_y}}$$

A variable factor of safety has been applied to the column strength estimate to obtain allowable working stresses. For very short columns this factor has been taken as equal to, or only slightly greater than, that required for members axially loaded in tension, and can be justified by the insensitivity of such members to accidental eccentricities. For longer columns, approaching the Euler slenderness range, the factor is increased 15 percent, to approximately the value provided in the AISC Specification since it was first published 46 years ago.

---

* Column Research Council Guide to Design Criteria for Metal Compression Members, *Second Edition, Eqs. (2.11) and (2.12)*.

In order to provide a smooth transition between these limits, the factor of safety has been arbitrarily defined by the algebraic equivalent of a quarter sine curve whose abscissas are the ratio of given Kl/r values to the limiting value C_c, and whose ordinates vary from $5/3$ when Kl/r equals 0 to $23/12$ when Kl/r equals C_c. Substituting $12\pi^2E/23$ for the previous rounded-off value, 149,000,000, in Formula (1.5-2) affords an exact convergence with Formula (1.5-1).

Tables giving the permissible stress for columns and other compression members for a number of the approved structural steels are included in Appendix A of the Specification for the convenience of the designer.

1.5.1.3.2 Formula (1.5-2), covering columns slender enough to fail by elastic buckling, is based upon a constant factor of safety of $23/12$ with respect to the elastic (Euler) column strength.

1.5.1.3.3 By dividing the values obtained from Formulas (1.5-1) and (1.5-2) by the factor $\left(1.6 - \dfrac{l}{200r}\right)$ when l/r exceeds 120, to obtain Formula (1.5-3), substantially the same allowable stresses are still recommended for bracing and secondary members as those formerly given by the Rankine-Gordon formula which, until 1961, had been included in the AISC Specification since its first adoption.

The more liberal working stress for this type of member was justified in part by the relative unimportance of such members and in part by the greater effectiveness of end restraint likely to be present at their ends.

Since Formula (1.5-3) does take advantage of end restraint, the full unbraced length of the member (rather than a reduced effective length, assuming $K < 1.0$) should always be used, and the formula should be restricted to members which are more or less fixed against rotation and translation at braced points.

1.5.1.4 Bending

1.5.1.4.1 When flexural members are proportioned in accordance with the provisions of Sects. 1.9.1.2 and 1.9.2.2 and are adequately braced to prevent the lateral displacement of the compression flange, they provide bending resistance equal at least to the product of their section modulus and yield stress, even when the width-thickness ratio of compressed elements of their profile is such that local buckling may be imminent.

Research in plastic design has demonstrated that local buckling will not occur in homogeneous sections meeting the requirements of subparagraphs a to e, inclusive, of Sect. 1.5.1.4.1 before the full plastic moment is reached. Practically all rolled W shapes of A36 steel and a large proportion of these shapes having a yield stress of 50 ksi meet these provisions and are termed "compact" sections. It is obvious that the possibility of overload failure in bending of such rolled shapes must involve a higher level of stress (computed on the basis of M/S) than members having more slender compression elements. Since the shape factor of rolled W shapes is generally in excess of 1.12, the allowable bending stress for such members has been raised 10 percent from $0.60F_y$ to $0.66F_y$.

The further provision, permitting the arbitrary redistribution of 10 percent of the moment at points of support, due to gravity loading, gives partial recognition to the philosophy of plastic design. Subject to the restrictions provided in Sect. 1.5.1.4.1, continuous framing consisting of compact members may safely be proportioned on the basis of the working stress provisions of Part 1 of the Specification when the moments, before redistribution, are determined on the basis of an elastic analysis. Fig. C 1.5.1 illustrates the application of this provision by comparing calculated moment diagrams with the diagrams as altered by this provision.

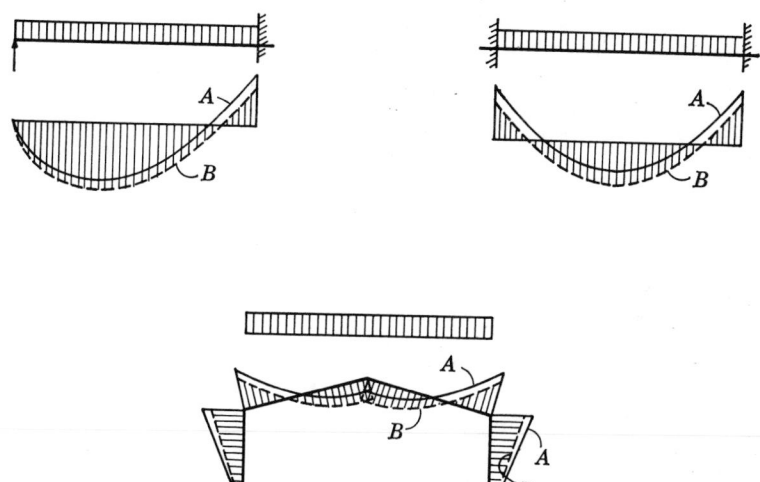

A = Actual moment diagram
B = Modified diagram corresponding to 10 percent moment reduction allowance at interior supports

Fig. C 1.5.1

In order to assure maximum advantage of moment redistribution, designs should be executed in accordance with the rules for plastic design given in Part 2. However, for many cases commonly encountered, the provisions of Sect. 1.5.1.4.1 afford approximately the same overall economy.

1.5.1.4.2 Formula (1.5-5) avoids an abrupt transition between an allowable bending stress of $0.66F_y$ when the half-flange width-to-thickness ratio of laterally supported compression flanges exceeds $52.2/\sqrt{F_y}$, and $0.60F_y$ when this ratio is no more than $95.0/\sqrt{F_y}$. The assured hinge rotation capacity in this range is too small to permit redistribution of computed moment.

1.5.1.4.3 The 25 percent increase in allowable bending stress for compact sections and solid rectangular bars bent about their weak axis, as well as for square and rectangular bars, is based upon the favorable shape factor present when these sections are bent about their weakest axis, and the fact that, in this position, they are not subject to lateral-torsional buckling. While the plastic bending strength of these shapes, bent in this direction, is considerably more than 25 percent in excess of their elastic bending strength, full advantage is not taken of this fact in order to provide elastic behavior at service loading.

1.5.1.4.4. Box-type members are torsionally very stiff.* The critical flexural stress due to lateral-torsional buckling, for the compression flange of a box-type beam loaded in the plane of its minor axis so as to bend about its major axis, can be obtained using Formula (1.5-1) with an equivalent slenderness ratio, by the expression

$$\left(\frac{l}{r}\right)_{equiv} = \sqrt{\frac{5.1lS_x}{\sqrt{JI_y}}}$$

where l is the distance between points of lateral support and S_x, I_y and J are, respectively, the major axis section modulus, minor axis moment of inertia and the torsional constant of the beam cross-section. It can be shown that, when $d < 10b$ and $l/b < 2,500/F_y$, the allowable compression flange stress indicated by the above equation will approximate $0.60F_y$. Beyond this limit deflection rather than stress is likely to be the design criterion.

1.5.1.4.5 and **1.5.1.4.6** The allowable bending stress for all other flexural members is given as $0.60F_y$, provided the compression flange is braced laterally at relatively close intervals ($l/b_f \leqslant 76.0/\sqrt{F_y}$).

Members bent about their major axis and having an axis of symmetry in the plane of loading may be adequately braced laterally at greater intervals if the maximum bending stress is reduced sufficiently to prevent premature buckling of the compression flange. Mathematical expressions affording an exact estimate of the buckling strength of such members, which take into account their torsional rigidity about their longitudinal axis (St. Venant torsion) as well as the bending stiffness of their compression flange between points of lateral support (warping torsion), are too complex for general design office use. Furthermore, their accuracy is dependent upon the validity of assumptions regarding restraint at points of lateral support and conditions of loading which, at best, can be no more than engineering judgments.

The combination of Formulas (1.5-6a) or (1.5-6b) and (1.5-7) provides a reasonable design criterion in more convenient form.

As in Formula (4) of the 1963 edition of the Specification, Formulas (1.5-6a) and (1.5-6b) are based on the assumption that only the bending stiffness of the compression flange will prevent the lateral displacement of that element between bracing points. The new Formulas (1.5-6a) and (1.5-6b) differ from the earlier Formula (4) in two ways:

1. Whereas the earlier provisions required no stress reduction when l/r was less than 40 (regardless of yield stress value) and then a reduction to the value obtained from the parabolic expression, the new formulas, by increasing F_b at $l = 0$ from $0.60F_y$ to $2F_y/3$, provides a continuous stress relationship with the unbraced length when F_b is reduced from the maximum permissible value of $0.60F_y$.

2. Whereas the earlier single Formula (4) applied even in the range of elastic buckling stress (on the assumption that Formula (5) would govern), the replacement of Formula (4) is liberalized in this range by the addition of an Euler-type expression, since this assumption is not always correct.

---

* Column Research Council Guide to Design Criteria for Metal Compression Members, *Second Edition*, Sect. 4.2.

Formula (1.5-7) is a convenient approximation which assumes the presence of both lateral bending resistance and St. Venant torsional resistance. Due to the difference between flange and web yield strength of a hybrid girder, it is desirable to base the lateral buckling resistance solely on warping torsion of the flange. Hence, use of Formula (1.5-7) is not permitted for such members. Its agreement with more exact expressions for the buckling strength of intermittently braced flexural members* is closest for homogeneous sections having substantial resistance to St. Venant torsion, identifiable in the case of doubly-symmetrical sections by a relatively low d/A_f ratio.

For some sections having a compression flange area distinctly smaller than the tension flange area, Formula (1.5-7) may be unconservative; hence, its use is limited to sections whose compression flange area is at least as great as the tension flange. In plate girders, which usually have a much higher d/A_f ratio than rolled W shapes, Formula (1.5-7) may err grossly on the conservative side. For such members the larger stress permitted by Formula (1.5-6a) and, at times by Formula (1.5-6b), affords the better estimate of buckling strength. While these latter formulas underestimate this strength somewhat because they ignore the St. Venant torsional rigidity of the profile, this rigidity for such sections is relatively small and the margin of overconservatism, therefore, is likewise small.

It should be noted that Formula (1.5-7), like the more precise, complex expressions it replaces, is written for the case of elastic buckling. A transition is not provided for this formula in the inelastic stress range because, when actual conditions of load application and variation in bending moment are considered, any unconservative error without it must be small.

Singly-symmetrical, built-up, I-shape members, such as some crane girders, often have an increased compression flange area in order to resist bending due to lateral loading action in conjunction with the vertical loads. Such members usually can be proportioned for the full permissible bending stress when that stress is produced by the combined vertical and horizontal loading. Where the failure mode of a singly-symmetrical I-shape member having a larger compression than tension flange would be by lateral buckling, the permissible bending stress can be obtained by using Formula (1.5-6a) or (1.5-7).

Through the introduction of the modifier** C_b, some liberalization in stress is permissible when there is moment gradient over the unbraced length except where, in the case of combined bending and axial compression, this adjustment is provided by the factor C_m in Formula (1.6-1a).

Formulas (1.5-6a) and (1.5-6b) may be refined to include both St. Venant and warping torsion by substituting a derived value for r_T. This equivalent radius of gyration, r_{equiv}, can be obtained by equating the appropriate expression giving the critical elastic bending stress for the compression flange of a beam† with that of an axially loaded column.‡

---

* Column Research Council Guide to Design Criteria for Metal Compression Members, *Second Edition, Eq. 4.8.*
** Ibid., *Eq. 4.13.*
† Ibid., *Eqs. (4.9c), (4.30), (4.31) or (4.32).*
‡ Ibid., *Eq. (2.2).*

For the case of a doubly-symmetrical I-shape beam,

$$r^2_{equiv} = \frac{I_y}{2S_x} \sqrt{d^2 + \frac{0.156 l^2 J}{I_y}}$$

where I_y is the minor axis moment of inertia of the member, S_x is its major axis section modulus, and

$$J = \frac{2b_f t_f^3}{3} + \frac{dt^3}{3}$$

1.5.1.5 Bearing

1.5.1.5.1 As used throughout the Specification the terms "milled surface," "milled" or "milling" are intended to include surfaces which have been accurately sawed or finished to a true plane by any suitable means. The recommended bearing stress on pins is not the same as for rivets. The lower value, nine-tenths of the yield stress of the part containing the pin hole, provides a safeguard against instability of the plate beyond the hole, * which is considerably larger than a rivet hole.

1.5.2 Rivets, Bolts, and Threaded Parts

1.5.2.1 Tension

As in earlier editions, permissible stresses for rivets are given in terms applicable to the nominal cross-sectional area of the rivet before driving. For greater convenience in the proportioning of high strength bolted connections, permissible stresses for the bolts are given in terms applicable to their nominal body area, i.e., the area of the unthreaded shank. However, for A307 bolts (which are available in sizes up to 4 in. in diameter) and threaded parts other than high strength bolts, the allowable tensile stress is applicable to a stress area equal to $0.7854 [D - (0.9743/n)]^2$. This area (intermediate between gross area and area at the root of the thread) when multiplied by the mechanical properties of the unthreaded material, has been found to more closely predict the tensile strength of larger diameter threaded parts, such as might be used for anchor bolts or upset rods.

In recognition of the protection against notch effect in the threading, assured by the required initial tightening of high strength bolts, the Research Council on Riveted and Bolted Structural Joints has recommended a relatively higher working stress in tension for high strength bolts.

Any additional fastener tension resulting from prying action due to distortion of the connection details should be added to the stress calculated directly from the applied tension in proportioning fasteners for an applied tensile force, using the specified working stresses. Depending upon the relative stiffness of the fasteners and the connection material, this prying action may be negligible or it may be a substantial part of the total tension in the fasteners.**

---

* *Johnston, B. G.* Pin-Connected Plate Links, *1939 ASCE Transactions.*
** *Munse, W. H.* Research on Bolted Connections, *1956 ASCE Transactions,* p. 1265.

1.5.2.1 Shear

Connections which transmit load by means of shear in their fasteners are categorized as "friction-type" or "bearing-type". The former depend upon sufficiently high clamping force to prevent slip of the connected parts. The latter depend upon contact of the fasteners against the sides of their holes to transfer the load from one connected part to another.

The amount of clamping force developed by shrinkage of a rivet after cooling and by A307 bolts is unpredictable and generally insufficient to prevent complete slippage at the permissible working stress. Hence riveted connections and connections made with A307 bolts for shear are treated as bearing-type. The high clamping force produced by properly tightened high strength bolts is sufficient to prevent slip of the connected parts when an equal number of these bolts are substituted for the rivets of equal size that would be required to transmit a given load — A325 bolts for A502 Grade 1 rivets and A490 bolts for A502 Grade 2 rivets.

The efficiency of threaded fasteners in resisting shear in bearing-type connections is reduced when the threading extends into the shear plane between the connected parts. In the case of high strength bolts, two allowable shear stress values are given: one where threading is excluded from the shear plane and one where it is not. Since it is not customary to control this feature in the case of A307 bolts, it is assumed that threading may extend into the shear plane and the allowable shear value, applicable to the gross area, is reduced accordingly.

1.5.2.2 Bearing

Bearing values are provided, not as a protection to the fastener, because it needs no such protection, but as an index of the efficiency of net sections computed in accordance with Sect. 1.14.3. The same index is valid for joints assembled with rivets or with bolts, regardless of fastener shear strength or the presence or absence of threads in the bearing area. Tests of riveted joints* have shown that the tensile strength of the connected part is not impaired when the bearing pressure on the computed contact area of the fastener is as much as $2\frac{1}{4}$ times the tensile stress permitted on the net area of the part. In this investigation the contact (bearing) area was computed, according to the usual convention, as the product of nominal fastener diameter and thickness of the connected part. No difference was observed between single-shear bearing and enclosed bearing. Based on these findings, the recommended working stress is the same for single-shear and double-shear bearing, and approximately equal to $2\frac{1}{4}$ times the tensile working stress recommended for determining required net area.

.5.3 Welds

As in the past, the allowable working stresses for statically loaded full-penetration welds are the same as those permitted for the base metal, provided the mechanical properties of the electrodes used are such as to match or exceed those of the weakest grade of base metal being joined.

---

* *Jones, Jonathan* Effect of Bearing Ratio on Static Strength of Riveted Joints, *1958 ASCE Transactions*.

In earlier editions of the AISC Specification, working stresses were not given for fillet welds made with electrodes stronger than the E70 classification. The stresses that were given were known to be overly conservative for their recommended use with E60 and E70 classifications. Based upon recent tests,* the allowable stress on fillet welds, deposited on "matching" base metal or steel having mechanical properties higher than those specified for such base metal, is now given in terms of the specified tensile strength of the weld metal.

As in the past, the same working value is given to a transverse as to a longitudinal weld, even though the force that the former can resist is substantially greater than that of the latter. In the case of tension on the throat of partial penetration groove welds normal to their axis (more nearly analagous to that of transverse than longitudinal fillets), the working stress is conservatively taken the same as for fillet welds.

When partial penetration groove welds are so disposed that they are stressed primarily in compression, bearing, or in tension parallel to the longitudinal axis of the groove, they may be proportioned to resist such stress at the same unit value permitted in the base metal.

1.5.4. Cast Steel

In keeping with the inclusion of high strength low-alloy steels, the Specification recognizes high strength steel castings. Allowable stresses are expressed in terms of the specified minimum yield stress for castings.

SECTION 1.6 COMBINED STRESSES

1.6.1 Axial Compression and Bending

The application of moment along the unbraced length of axially loaded members, with its attendant axial displacement in the plane of bending, generates a secondary moment equal to the product of resulting eccentricity and the applied axial load, which is not reflected in the computed stress f_b. To provide for this added moment in the design of members subject to combined axial and bending stress, Formula (1.6-1a) requires that f_b be amplified by the factor

$$\frac{1}{\left(1 - \dfrac{f_a}{F'_e}\right)}$$

Depending upon the shape of the applied moment diagram (and, hence, the critical location and magnitude of the induced eccentricity), this factor may overestimate the extent of the secondary moment. To take care of this condition the amplification factor is modified, as required, by a reduction factor C_m.

When bending occurs about both the x- and y-axes, the bending stress calculated about each axis is adjusted by the value of C_m and F'_e corresponding to the distribution of moment and the slenderness ratio in its plane of bending, and is then taken as a fraction of the stress permitted for bending about that axis, with due regard to the unbraced length of compression flange where this is a factor.

---

* *Higgins, T. R. and Preece, F. R.* Proposed Working Stresses for Fillet Welds in Building Construction, *Welding Journal Research Supplement*, Oct., 1968.

When the computed axial stress is no greater than 15 percent of the permissible axial stress, the influence of

$$\frac{C_m}{\left(1 - \dfrac{f_a}{F'_e}\right)}$$

is generally small and may be neglected, as provided in Formula (1.6-2). However, its use in Formula (1.6-1a) is not intended to permit a value of f_b greater than F_b when the value of C_m and f_a are both small.

Depending upon the slenderness ratio of the given unbraced length of a member in the plane of bending, the combined stress computed at one or both ends of this length may exceed the combined stress at all intermediate points where lateral displacement is created by the applied moments. The limiting value of the combined stress in this case is established by Formula (1.6-1b).

The classification of members subject to combined axial compression and bending stresses is dependent upon two conditions: the stability against sidesway of the frame of which they are an integral part, and the presence or absence of transverse loading between points of support in the plane of bending. Three categories and the appropriate provisions of Sect. 1.6.1 are listed in Table C 1.6.1.1.

TABLE C 1.6.1.1

Category	Loading conditions $(f_a > 0.15F_a)$	f_b	C_m	Remarks
A	Computed moments maximum at end; joint translation not prevented	$\dfrac{M_2}{S}$	0.85	$M_1 < M_2$; $\dfrac{M_1}{M_2}$ negative as shown. Check both Formulas (1.6-1a) & (1.6-1b)
B	Computed moments maximum at end; no transverse loading; joint translation prevented	$\dfrac{M_2}{S}$	$\left(0.6 \pm 0.4 \dfrac{M_1}{M_2}\right)$ but not less than 0.4	Check both Formulas (1.6-1a) & (1.6-1b)
C	Transverse loading; joint translation prevented	$\dfrac{M_2}{S}$ Using Formula (1.6-1b) ——— $\dfrac{M_3}{S}$ Using Formula (1.6-1a)	$1 + \psi \dfrac{f_a}{F'_e}$	Check both Formulas (1.6-1a) & (1.6-1b)

Note that f_b is defined as the computed bending stress *at the point under consideration.* In the absence of transverse loading between points of support, f_b is computed from the larger of the moments at these points of support. When intermediate transverse loading is present, the larger moment at one of the two supported points is used to compute f_b for use in Formula (1.6-1b). The maximum moment between points of support, however, is used to compute the bending stress for use in Formula (1.6-1a).

Category A covers columns in frames subject to sidesway, i.e., frames which depend upon the bending stiffness of their several members for overall lateral stability. For determining the value of F_a and F'_e, the effective length of such members, as discussed hereinafter under Sect. 1.8, is never less than the actual length, unbraced in the plane of bending, and may be greater than this length. The actual length is used in computing moments. For this case the value of C_m can be taken as

$$C_m = 1 - 0.18 f_a/F'_e.$$

However, under the combination of compression stress and bending stress most affected by the amplification factor, a value of 0.15 can be substituted for $0.18 f_a/F'_e$. Hence, a constant value of 0.85 is recommended for C_m here.

Category B applies to columns not subject to transverse loading in frames where sidesway is prevented. For determining the value of F_a and F'_e, the effective length of such members is never greater than the actual unbraced length and may be somewhat less. The actual length is used in computing moments.

For this category, the greatest eccentricity, and hence the greatest amplification, occurs when M_1 and $-M_2$* are numerically equal and cause single curvature. It is least when they are numerically equal and of a direction to cause reverse curvature.

To evaluate properly the relationship between end moment and amplified moment, the concept of an equivalent moment, M_e, to be used in lieu of the numerically smaller end moment, has been suggested. M_e can be defined as the value of equal end moments of opposite signs which would cause failure at the same concurrent axial load as would the given unequal end moments. Then M_e/M_2 can be written** in terms of $\pm M_1/M_2$ as

$$\frac{M_e}{M_2} = C_m = \sqrt{0.3 \left(\frac{M_1}{M_2}\right)^2 - 0.4 \left(\pm \frac{M_1}{M_2}\right) + 0.3}$$

It has been noted† that the simpler formulation

$$C_m = 0.6 - 0.4 \left(\pm \frac{M_1}{M_2}\right) \geq 0.4$$

affords a good approximation to this expression. When M_1/M_2 is greater

---

* The sign convention for moments here and in Sect. 1.6 is that generally used in frame analysis. It should not be confused with the beam sign convention used in many textbooks. Moments are considered positive when acting clockwise about a fixed point, negative when acting counter-clockwise.

** Column Research Council Guide to Design Criteria for Metal Compression Members, *p. 163.* (*Discussion in the Guide uses beam sign convention.*)

† *Austin, W. J.* Strength and Design of Metal Beam-Columns, *ASCE Journal of the Structural Division, April, 1961.*

than 0.5 the combined axial and bending stress is usually limited by general yielding rather than by stability, in which case Formula (1.6-1b) would govern. Therefore, a tentatively selected column section should be tested by both Formulas (1.6-1a) and (1.6-1b).

Category C is exemplified by the compression chord of a truss, subject to transverse loading between panel points. For this case the value for C_m can be computed using the expression

$$C_m = 1 + \psi \, \frac{f_a}{F'_e}$$

where

$$\psi = \frac{\pi^2 \delta_0 EI}{M_0 L^2} - 1$$

δ_0 = maximum deflection due to transverse loading

M_0 = maximum moment between supports due to transverse loading

Values for ψ for several conditions of loading and end restraint are given in Table C 1.6.1.2.

TABLE C 1.6.1.2

Case	ψ	C_m
	0	1.0
	-0.3	$1 - 0.3\dfrac{f_a}{F'_e}$
	-0.4	$1 - 0.4\dfrac{f_a}{F'_e}$
	-0.2	$1 - 0.2\dfrac{f_a}{F'_e}$
	-0.4	$1 - 0.4\dfrac{f_a}{F'_e}$
	-0.6	$1 - 0.6\dfrac{f_a}{F'_e}$

Note that F_a is governed by the maximum slenderness ratio, regardless of the plane of bending. F'_e, on the other hand, is always governed by the slenderness ratio in the plane of bending. Thus, when flexure is about the strong axis only, two different values of slenderness ratio may be required in solving a given problem.

1.6.2 Axial Tension and Bending

Contrary to the behavior in compression members, axial tension tends to *reduce* the bending stress between points of lateral support because the secondary moment, which is the product of the deflection and the axial tension, is opposite in sense to the applied moment, instead of being of the same sense and additive, as in columns.

1.6.3 Shear and Tension

Tests have shown* that the strength of rivets subject to combined tension and shear resulting from externally applied forces (in addition to existing internal shrinkage stresses) can be closely defined by either (1) an ellipse, or (2) three straight lines, as shown in Fig. C 1.6.3.1.

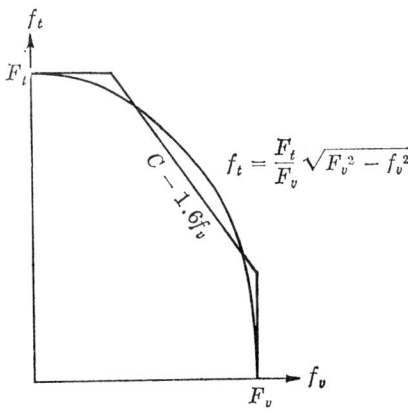

$$f_t = \frac{F_t}{F_v}\sqrt{F_v^2 - f_v^2}$$

Fig. C 1.6.3.1

In most cases the latter representation is the more simple of application, since it requires no modification of the stress recommended for either shear or tension when these stresses act in conjunction, respectively, with relatively large concurrent tension or shear stresses. Therefore, it is the only one given in Sect. 1.6.3, since the inclusion of more than one method is hardly warranted. However, solutions based upon use of the ellipse are equally valid and should be allowed. Any differences in the number of fasteners required by the two prescriptions would be small.

Similar interaction formulas have been derived for the other approved types of fasteners from ellipses constructed with major and minor axis half-lengths equal, respectively, to the tension and shear stress given in Sect. 1.5.2.

---

* *Higgins, T. R. and Munse, W. H.* How much Combined Stress Can A Rivet Take? *Engineering News-Record, Dec. 4, 1962.*

SECTION 1.7 MEMBERS AND CONNECTIONS SUBJECT TO REPEATED VARIATION OF STRESS (FATIGUE)

Because most members in building frames need not be designed for fatigue, the provisions covering such designs have been placed in Appendix B.

Where fatigue is a design consideration, its severity is most significantly affected by the number of load applications and the magnitude of the stress range. It is aggravated by the presence of stress raisers to a varying degree, depending on the particular detail. Consequently, when fatigue is of concern, all the applicable provisions of Appendix B must be satisfied.

Members or connections subject to less than 20,000 cycles of loading will not involve a fatigue condition except in the case of repeated loading involving large ranges of stress. For such conditions the admissible range of stress can conservatively be taken as 1½ times the applicable value given in Table B3 for Loading Condition 1.

Except where indicated by "C" under "Kind of Stress" in Table B2, fluctuation in stress which does not involve tensile stress is not considered a fatigue situation.

When fabrication details involving more than one category occur at the same location in a member, the stress range at that location must be limited to that of the most restrictive category. By loading notch-producing fabrication details in regions subject to a small range of stress, the need for a member larger than required by static loading will often be eliminated.

The use of a constant stress *range*, which can be read directly from a table for a particular category and loading condition, greatly simplifies designs involving fatigue when compared with designs based on maximum or minimum allowable stress obtained from fatigue strength formulas on the basis of a stress *ratio*.

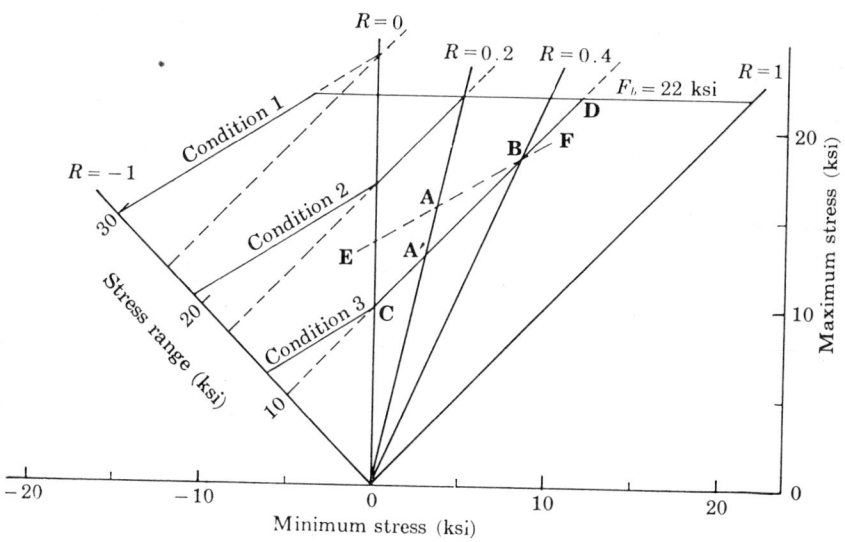

Fig. C1.7.1

The reason for this shift in design criteria is apparent when the provisions of Appendix B are presented in the form of the familiar modified Goodman diagram often used as a design aid in lieu of such formulas. In Fig. C 1.7.1 the provisions of a category "D*" detail of A36 Steel are plotted diagramatically in this form. With maximum stress and stress ratio as the governing parameters, note that points **A** and **B** define substantially different critical maximum stress, with only slightly different stress ratios. However, with the line **CD** drawn parallel to the 45° boundary line representing static loading (min = max; $R = 1$) the permissible range in stress for points **A'** and **B** (or any point between **C** and **D**) is the same. Only minor change in stress range would result had the slope of line **CD** been varied somewhat from 1 on 1, as often indicated in earlier evaluations of fatigue test results and as indicated by the line **EF**.

The allowable range of stress for Loading Condition 3, regardless of maximum stress value, can be read on the maximum stress scale and is represented by the distance **OC**.

This is the value F_{sr3} given in Table B3. It might also be read from a scale plotted on the $R = -1$ boundary line, so laid off that

$$\text{stress range scale : max stress scale} = 1 : \sqrt{2}$$

In developing the stress range values given in Table B3, published fatigue data and data obtained in continuing research were reviewed. In adopting a constant stress range basis for designs involving fatigue (in the interest of a simpler design procedure), it was realized that a number of known characteristics of fatigue strength data would not be taken into consideration. For example, except for A514 steel in category "A", the provisions do not recognize any increase in fatigue strength for the higher strength steels, as compared with that of A36 steel. For a particular category, this increased strength varies for the different steels depending upon the number of cycles of repeated loading.

As a consequence, the provisions may not provide a uniform factor of safety for the different strength steels. However, deviations from a uniform factor of safety are on the conservative side. Comparison of the fatigue provisions of this Specification with available test data indicate that the safety factors inherent in the recommended fatigue provisions are commensurate with static stress provisions.

In a few instances, identified by asterisks in Table B2, the extent of this conservatism warranted the liberalization provided by Formula (B1), which was derived from the expression for maximum permissible fatigue stress:

$$F_r = \frac{f_{ro}}{1 - mR}$$

where

R = Stress ratio, having a negative value with reversal of stress
f_{ro} = Maximum permissible stress when $R = 0$
m = Slope of a fatigue strength line as presented in a modified Goodman diagram ($m \sim 0.6$)

Substituting f_t for F_r, F_{sr} for f_{ro}, 0.6 for m, and $- (f_c/f_t)$ for R, and noting that $F'_{sr} = f_t + f_c$,

$$F'_{sr} = \frac{f_t + f_c}{f_t + 0.6f_c} F_{sr} \tag{B1}$$

Since Fig. C 1.7.1 was drawn for category "D*", where Formula (B1) applies when a reversal of stress is involved, the fatigue strength lines (shown solid) represent the liberalization in stress range provided by Formula (B1) as compared with the dashed lines which would govern for category "D".

While greater fatigue strength than indicated by the provisions of Appendix B is attainable using special treatment, and is often provided in the case of manufactured products, the application of such treatment to as-fabricated structural steel is seldom economical. An exception is the grinding flush of full penetration groove welded splices which must be located where the alternate to the higher stress range permitted would be a substantial increase in required member size.

SECTION 1.8   STABILITY AND SLENDERNESS RATIOS

Considerable attention has been given in the technical literature to the subject of "effective" column length (as contrasted with actual unbraced length) as a factor in estimating column strength. The topic is reviewed at some length in Sect. 2.8 of the *Guide to Design Criteria for Metal Compression Members*.

Two conditions, opposite in their effect upon column strength under axial loading, must be considered. If enough axial load is applied to the columns in a frame dependent entirely upon its own bending stiffness for stability against sidesway, i.e., uninhibited lateral movement, as shown in

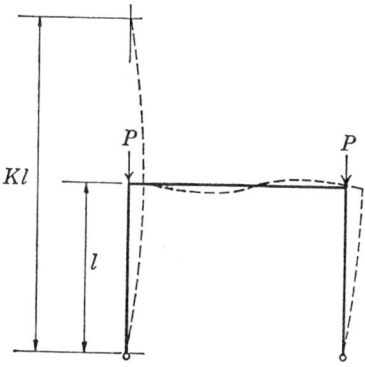

Fig. C 1.8.1

Fig. C 1.8.1, the "effective" length of these columns will exceed their actual length. On the other hand, if the same frame were braced in such a way that lateral movement of the tops of the columns with respect to their bases (translation or sidesway) were prevented, the effective length would be less than the actual length, due to the restraint (resistance to joint rotation) provided by the horizontal member. The ratio K, effective column length to actual unbraced length, may be greater or less than 1.0.

The theoretical K-values for six idealized conditions in which joint rotation and translation are either fully realized or non-existent are tabulated in Table C 1.8.1. Also shown are suggested design values recommended by the Column Research Council for use when these conditions are approximated in actual design. In general, these suggested values are slightly higher than their theoretical equivalents, since joint fixity is seldom fully realized.

TABLE C 1.8.1

	(a)	(b)	(c)	(d)	(e)	(f)
Buckled shape of column is shown by dashed line						
Theoretical K value	0.5	0.7	1.0	1.0	2.0	2.0
Recommended design value when ideal conditions are approximated	0.65	0.80	1.2	1.0	2.10	2.0
End condition code		Rotation fixed and translation fixed				
		Rotation free and translation fixed				
		Rotation fixed and translation free				
		Rotation free and translation free				

If the column base in case (f) of Table C 1.8.1 were truly pinned, K would actually exceed 2.0 for a frame such as that pictured in Fig. C 1.8.1, because the flexibility of the horizontal member would prevent realization of full fixity at the top of the column. On the other hand, it has been shown* that the restraining influence of foundations, even where these footings are designed only for vertical load, can be very substantial in the case of flat-ended column base details with ordinary anchorage. For this condition, a design K-value of 1.5 would generally be conservative in case (f).

While ordinarily the existence of masonry walls provides enough lateral support for tier building frames to prevent sidesway, the increasing use of light curtain wall construction and wide column spacing, for high-rise structures not provided with a positive system of diagonal bracing, can create a situation where only the bending stiffness of the frame itself provides this support.

In this case the effective length factor, K, for an unbraced length of column, l, is dependent upon the amount of bending stiffness provided by the other in-plane members entering the joint at each end of the unbraced

---

* *Galambos, T. V.* Influence of Partial Base Fixity on Frame Stability, *ASCE Journal of the Structural Division*, May, 1960.

segment. If the combined stiffness provided by the beams is sufficiently small, relative to that of the unbraced column segments, *Kl* could exceed two or more story heights.*

Several rational methods are available by means of which the effective length of the columns in a laterally unbraced frame can be estimated with sufficient accuracy. These range from simple interpolation between the idealized cases shown in Table C 1.8.1 to very complex analytical procedures.

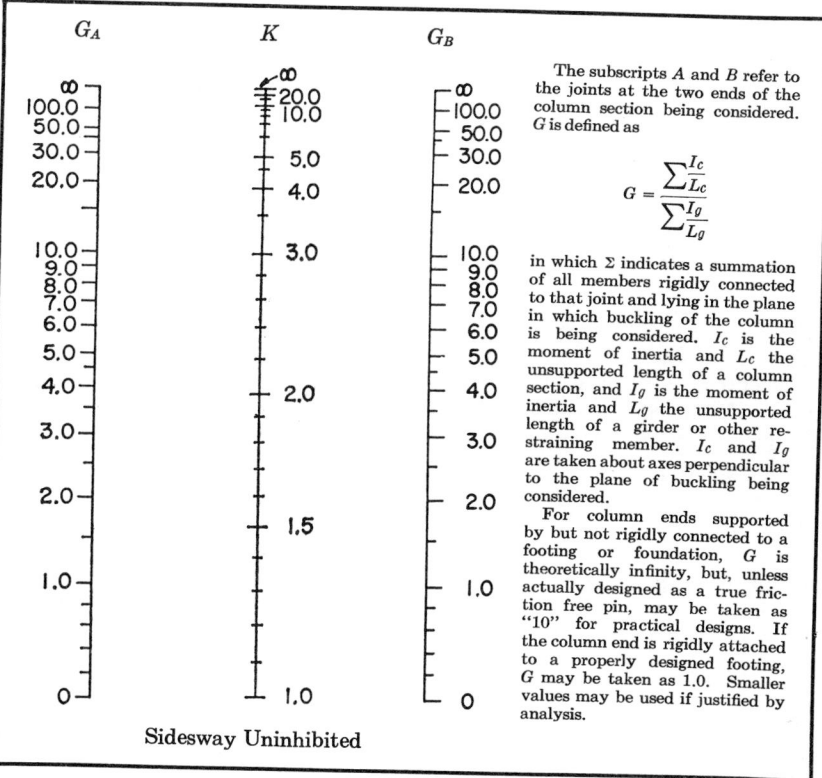

The subscripts *A* and *B* refer to the joints at the two ends of the column section being considered. *G* is defined as

$$G = \frac{\sum \dfrac{I_c}{L_c}}{\sum \dfrac{I_g}{L_g}}$$

in which Σ indicates a summation of all members rigidly connected to that joint and lying in the plane in which buckling of the column is being considered. I_c is the moment of inertia and L_c the unsupported length of a column section, and I_g is the moment of inertia and L_g the unsupported length of a girder or other re-straining member. I_c and I_g are taken about axes perpendicular to the plane of buckling being considered.

For column ends supported by but not rigidly connected to a footing or foundation, *G* is theoretically infinity, but, unless actually designed as a true friction free pin, may be taken as "10" for practical designs. If the column end is rigidly attached to a properly designed footing, *G* may be taken as 1.0. Smaller values may be used if justified by analysis.

Sidesway Uninhibited

Alignment Chart for Effective Length of Columns in Continuous Frames

Fig. C 1.8.2

Once a trial selection of framing members has been made, the use of the alignment chart in Fig. C 1.8.2 affords a fairly rapid method for determining suitable *K*-values.

If roof decks or floor slabs, anchored to shear walls or vertical plane bracing systems, are counted upon to provide lateral support for individual columns in a building frame, due consideration must be given to their stiff-ness when functioning as a horizontal diaphragm.**

---

* *Bleich, F.* Buckling Strength of Metal Structures, *pp. 260–265.*
** *Winter, G.* Lateral Bracing of Columns and Beams, *ASCE Journal of the Structural Division, March, 1958.*

While translation of the joints in the plane of a truss is inhibited and, due to end restraint, the effective length of compression members might therefore be assumed as less than the distance between panel points, it is usual practice to take K as equal to 1.0, since, if all members of the truss reached their ultimate load capacity simultaneously the restraints at the ends of the compression members would disappear or, at least, be greatly reduced.

The slenderness limitations recommended for tension members are not essential to the structural integrity of such members; they merely afford a degree of stiffness such that undesirable lateral movement ("slapping" or vibration) will be avoided. These limitations are not mandatory.

SECTION 1.9 WIDTH-THICKNESS RATIOS

When the width-thickness ratio of the compressed elements in a member does not exceed the applicable limit specified in Sects. 1.9.1.2 or 1.9.2.2, no reduction in allowable stress is necessary in order to prevent local buckling. The design of members containing compression elements having a width-thickness ratio somewhat in excess of these limits is generally conservative if the area provided by the excessive width is ignored, as has been permitted in earlier editions of the Specification.

This expediency, in the case of unstiffened elements, raises a question as to eccentricity between actual and admissible cross-sectional area axes, makes no provision for computing an "effective" section modulus, and may even result in unconservative design. For the infrequent situation where width-thickness ratios substantially in excess of the limits given in Sect. 1.9 are involved, the provisions of Appendix C afford a better design procedure.

Formulas (C2-1) to (C2-6) are based upon the expression* for critical buckling stress for a plate having one or both edges parallel to an in-plane compressive force supported against lateral deflection, with or without torsional restraint along these edges. For this case

$$\sigma_c = k \left[\frac{\pi^2 E \sqrt{\eta}}{12(1 - \nu^2)(b/t)^2} \right] \tag{C1}$$

where η is the ratio of the tangent modulus to the elastic modulus, E_t/E, and ν is Poisson's ratio. The idealized value $k = 0.425$, assumes nothing more than knife-edge lateral support, applied along one edge of the unstiffened element, at the mid-plane of the element providing it. Some increase in this value is warranted because of the torsional restraint provided by the supporting element and because of the difference between b as defined in Sect. 1.9.1.2, and the theoretical width b.

In the interest of simplification, when $\sqrt{\eta} < 1.0$ a linear formula is substituted for the theoretical expression. Its agreement with the latter may be judged by the comparison shown in Fig. C 1.9.1.

Formula (C2-5) assumes a decrease in the torsional restraint characteristic of tees cut from rolled shapes, which might be expected of tees of quite different proportions formed by welding two plates together.

---

* Column Research Council Guide to Design Criteria for Metal Compression Members, *Sect. 3.3.*

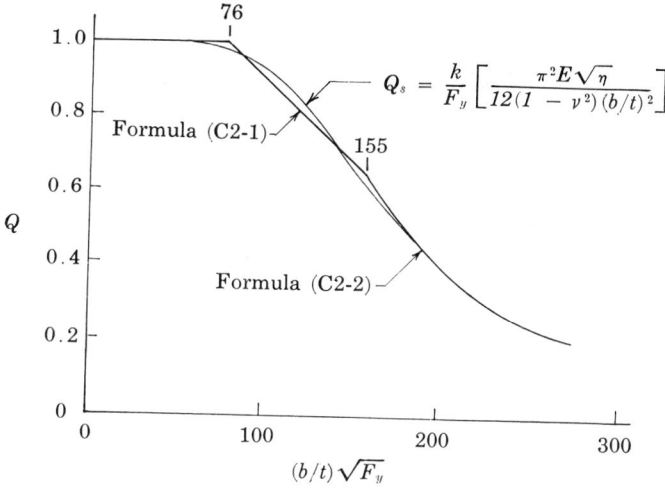

Fig. C1.9.1

It has been shown* that singly-symmetrical members whose cross-section consists of elements having large width-thickness ratios may fail by twisting under a smaller axial load than that associated with general column failure. Such is not generally the case with hot-rolled shapes. To guard against this type of failure, particularly when relatively thin-walled members are fabricated from plates, Table C1 places an upper limit on the proportions permissible for channels and tees.

With both edges parallel to the applied load supported against local buckling, stiffened compression elements can support a load producing an average stress, σ_c, greater than that given in the above expression for critical plate buckling stress. This is true even when k is taken as 4.0, applicable to the case where both edges are simply supported, or a value between 4.0 and 6.97, applicable when some torsional restraint is also provided along these edges.

A better estimate of the compressive strength of stiffened elements, based upon an "effective width" concept, was first proposed by von Karman.** This was later modified by Winter† to provide a transition between very slender elements and stockier elements shown by tests to be fully effective.

As modified, the ratio of effective width to actual width increases as the level of compressive stress applied to a stiffened element in a member is decreased, and takes the form

$$\frac{b_e}{t} = 1.9\sqrt{\frac{E}{f}}\left[1 - \frac{C}{(b/t)}\sqrt{\frac{E}{f}}\right]$$

---

* *Chajes, A. and Winter, G.* Torsional Flexural Buckling of Thin-Walled Members, *ASCE Journal of the Structural Division, August, 1965.*

** *v. Karman, T., Sechler, E. E. and Donnell, L. H.* The Strength of Thin Plates in Compression, *1932 ASME Transactions, Vol. 54, APM-54-5, p. 53.*

† *Winter, G.* Strength of Steel Compression Flanges, *1947 ASCE Transactions.*

where f is the level of uniformly distributed stress to which the element would be subjected based upon the design of the member, and C is an arbitrary constant based on engineering judgment supported by observed test results.

Obviously, holding the effective width of a stiffened element to no greater value than given by the limits provided in Sect. 1.9.2.2 is unnecessarily conservative when the maximum uniformly distributed design stress is substantially less than $0.6F_y$, or when b/t is considerably in excess of the limit given in Sect. 1.9.2.2.

For the case of square and rectangular box sections, the sides of which, in their buckled condition, afford negligible torsional restraint for one another along their corner edges, the value of C reflected in Formula (C3-1) is higher than for the other case, thereby providing a slightly more conservative evaluation of effective width. For cases where appreciable torsional restraint is provided, as for example the web of an I-shape column, the value of C implicit in Formula (C3-2) is decreased slightly. As in earlier editions of the AISC Specification, for such cases no reduction from actual width is required when the width-thickness ratio does not exceed $253/\sqrt{F_y}$ and, for greater widths, the effective width may be taken as equal to $253t/\sqrt{F_y}$. If the actual width-thickness is substantially greater than $253/\sqrt{F_y}$, however, a larger effective width can be obtained using Formula (C3-2) rather than the earlier provisions.

In computing the section modulus of a member subject to bending, the area of stiffened elements parallel to the axis of bending and subject to compressive stress must be based upon their effective rather than actual width. In computing the effective area of a member subject to axial loading, the effective rather than actual area of all stiffened elements must be used. However, the radius of gyration of the *actual* cross-section together with the form factor Q_a may be used in determining the allowable axial stress. If the cross-section contains an unstiffened element, this allowable stress must be modified by the reduction factor Q_s.

SECTION 1.10 PLATE GIRDERS AND ROLLED BEAMS

1.10.1 Proportions

As in earlier editions, it is provided* that flexural members be proportioned to resist bending on the basis of the moment of inertia of their gross cross-section, with the stipulation that holes in the flanges having an area in excess of 15 percent of the gross flange area must be deducted. This provision is now extended to include the design of hybrid flexural members whose flanges are fabricated from a stronger grade of steel than that in their web. As in the case of flexural members having the same grade of steel throughout their cross-section, their bending strength is defined by the product of the section modulus of the gross cross-section multiplied by the allowable bending stress. On this basis the stress in the web, at its junction with the flanges, may even exceed the yield stress of the web material but under strains controlled by the elastic state of stress in the stronger

---

* *Lilly, S. B. and Carpenter, S. T.* Effective Moment of Inertia of a Riveted Plate Girder, *1940 ASCE Transactions.*

flanges. Numerous tests, summarized in a recent report,* have shown that, with only minor adjustment in the basic allowable bending stress as provided in Formula (1.10-5), the bending strength of a hybrid member is predictable within the same degree of accuracy as that of a homogeneous one.

1.10.2   Web

The limiting web depth-thickness ratio, included in the 1961 edition of the AISC Specification to prevent vertical buckling of the compression flange into the web before attainment of yield stress in the flange due to flexure, may now be increased when transverse stiffeners are provided, spaced not more than $1\frac{1}{2}$ times the girder depth on centers.

The earlier provision, which was based on an analysis** that placed no limitation on the spacing of transverse stiffeners, correlated reasonably well with tests performed on girders made of A7 steel having a specified yield stress of 33 ksi. The more liberal provision ($h/t \leqslant 2000/\sqrt{F_y}$) is based upon more recent tests† on both homogeneous and hybrid girders with flanges having a specified yield stress of 100 ksi and a web of similar or weaker steel.

1.10.4   Flange Development

If a partial length cover plate is to function as an integral part of a beam or girder at the theoretical cut-off point beyond which it is not needed, it must be developed in an extension beyond this point by enough rivets, high strength bolts, or welding to support its portion of the flexural stresses (i.e., the stresses which the plate would have received had it been extended the full length of the member). The cover plate force to be developed by the fasteners in the extension is equal to

$$\frac{MQ}{I}$$

where

M = Moment at beginning of extension

Q = Statical moment of cover plate area about neutral axis of cover-plated section

I = Moment of inertia of cover-plated section

When the nature of the loading is such as to produce repeated variations of stress, the fasteners must be proportioned in accordance with the provisions of Sect. 1.7.

In the case of welded cover plates it is further provided that the amount of stress that may be carried by a partial length cover plate, at a distance a' in from its actual end, may not exceed the capacity of the terminal welds

---

* Design of Hybrid Steel Beams, Report of Subcommittee 1 of the Joint ASCE-AASHO Committee on Flexural Members, *ASCE Journal of the Structural Division, June, 1968.*

** *Basler, K. and Thürlimann, B.* Strength of Plate Girders in Bending, *ASCE Journal of the Structural Division, August, 1961.*

† Design of Hybrid Steel Beams, Report of Subcommittee 1 of the Joint ASCE-AASHO Committee on Flexural Members, *p. 1412, ASCE Journal of the Structural Division, June, 1968.*

deposited along its edges and optionally across its end within this distance a'. If the moment, computed by equating MQ/I to the capacity of the welds in this distance, is less than the value at the theoretical cut-off point, either the size of the welds must be increased or the end of the cover plate must be extended to a point such that the moment on the member at the distance a' from the end of the cover plate is equal to that which the terminal welds will support.

1.10.5 Stiffeners

To provide better clarity, the provisions of Sect. 1.10.5 have been re-arranged in the current edition of the Specification, but without substantive change of the provisions in Sect. 1.10.5 of the 1963 adoption.

Provisions governing the design of plate girders prior to the 1961 revision were based upon the assumption that the limit of structural usefulness of a girder web is attained when the level of stress in the web reaches the so-called "buckling" stage. Unlike columns, however, which actually are on the verge of collapse as their buckling stage is approached, the panels of a plate girder web, bounded on all sides by the girder flanges or transverse stiffeners, are capable of carrying loads far in excess of their "web buckling" load. Upon reaching the theoretical buckling limit, very slight lateral displacements will have developed in the web. Nevertheless, they are of no structural significance because other means are still present to assist in resisting further loading.

When transverse stiffeners are properly spaced and strong enough to act as compression struts, membrane stresses, due to shear forces greater than those associated with the theoretical buckling load, form diagonal tension fields. The resulting combination in effect provides a Pratt truss which, without producing yield stress in the steel, furnishes the capacity to resist applied shear forces unaccounted for by the linear buckling theory.

Analytical methods based upon this action have been developed[*] and corroborated in an extensive program of tests.[**] These methods form the basis for Formula (1.10-2). Use of tension field action is not counted upon when

$$\frac{0.6F_y}{\sqrt{3}} \leqslant F_v \leqslant 0.4F_y$$

or where

$$a/h > 3.0$$

Pending further investigation, it is not recommended for hybrid girders.

When the computed average shear stress in the web is less than that permitted by Formula (1.10-1), intermediate stiffeners are not required provided the depth of girders is limited to not more than 260 times the web thickness. Such girders do not depend upon tension field action.

---

[*] *Basler, K.* Strength of Plate Girders in Shear, *ASCE Journal of the Structural Division*, October, 1961.

[**] *Basler, K., Yen, B. T., Mueller, J. A. and Thürlimann, B.* Web Buckling Tests on Welded Plate Girders, *Welding Research Council Bulletin No. 64.*

In order to facilitate handling during fabrication and erection, when intermediate stiffeners are required, the panel aspect ratio a/h is arbitrarily limited to not more than

$$\left(\frac{260}{h/t} \right)^2$$

with a maximum spacing of 3 times the girder depth.

When required, their maximum permissible longitudinal spacing is dependent upon three parameters: a/h, h/t and f_v. For the convenience of the designer, their relationship with one another is presented in Tables 3-36 through 3-100 of Appendix A for several specified yield stresses covered by the Specification. Given the shear diagram produced by the design loads and a desired depth of girder, it is only necessary to select a web thickness (with due regard for limitations placed on h/t ratios) such that the web shear stress will be equal to or less than the maximum permitted value. With the resulting value for h/t and the computed shear stress, the required aspect ratio a/h can be taken directly from the table. Comparison of the web and stiffener material required with two or three trial web thicknesses will quickly indicate the most economical combination.

The corresponding gross area of intermediate stiffeners, given as a percent of the web area, is shown in italics in the column headed by the required aspect ratio and the line nearest to the selected h/t ratio. Stiffeners which will provide this area usually will be little, if any, larger than those generally called for. No stiffener areas are shown when the a/h and h/t ratios are small enough to permit a shear stress larger than $0.35F_y$, which is covered by Formula (1.10-1). For such cases tension field action is not counted upon.

At the ends of the girder, the spacing between adjacent stiffeners is limited to $11,000t/\sqrt{f_v}$, to provide an "anchor" for the tension fields developed in interior panels. The stiffeners bounding panels containing large holes likewise are required to be spaced close enough together so that the shear in these panels can be supported without tension field action.

To provide adequate lateral support for the web, all stiffeners are required to have a moment of inertia at least equal to $(h/50)^4$. In many cases, however, this provision will be overshadowed by the new gross area requirement. The amount of stiffener area necessary to develop the tension field, which is dependent upon the ratios a/h and h/t, is given by Formula (1.10-3). Larger gross areas are required for one-sided stiffeners than for pairs of stiffeners, because of the eccentric nature of their loading.

The amount of shear to be transferred between web and stiffeners is not affected by the eccentricity of loading, and generally is so small that it can be taken care of by the minimum amount of welding or riveting that might be desired. The specified formula

$$f_{vs} = h \sqrt{\left(\frac{F_y}{340} \right)^3}$$

affords a conservative estimate of required shear transfer under any condition of stress permitted by Formula (1.10-2). The shear transfer between web and stiffener due to tension field action and that due to a concentrated load or reaction in line with the stiffener are not additive. The stiffener need only be connected for the larger of the two shears.

1.10.6 Reduction in Flange Stress

In regions of maximum bending moment, a portion of a thin web may deflect enough laterally on the compression side of the neutral axis that it does not provide the full bending resistance assumed in proportioning the girder on the basis of its moment of inertia. The compression stress which the web would have resisted is, therefore, shifted to the compression flange. But the relative bending strength of this flange being so much greater than that of the laterally displaced portion of the web, the resulting increase in flange stress is at most only a few percent. By reducing the allowable design stress in the compression flange from F_b to F'_b, as provided in Formula (1.10-5), sufficient bending capacity is provided in the flange to compensate for any loss of bending strength in the web due to its lateral displacement.

To compensate for the slight loss of bending resistance when portions of the web of a hybrid flexural member are strained beyond their yield stress limit, Formula (1.10-6)* provides for a reduced allowable flange bending stress applicable to both flanges. The extent of the reduction is dependent upon the ratio of web area to a flange area and the ratio of web yield stress to flange yield stress.

In order to avoid a more complicated formula, the area and grade of steel in both flanges are required to be the same. Since any reductions in bending strength due to buckling of the web on the compression side of the neutral axis is considerably less in the case of a hybrid girder than for a homogeneous member having the same cross-section, it is not required that Formula (1.10-5) apply when the stress permitted by Formula (1.10-6) is less than that given for the former.

1.10.7 Combined Shear and Tension Stress

Unless a flexural member is designed on the basis of tension field action, no stress reduction is required due to the interaction of concurrent bending and shear stress.

It has been shown** that plate girder webs subject to tension field action can be proportioned on the basis of:

1. Maximum permissible bending stress when the concurrent shear is not greater than 0.6 the full permissible value, or

2. Full permissible shear stress when the bending stress is not more than $\frac{3}{4}$ of the maximum allowable.

Beyond these limits a linear interaction formula is provided in the Specification by Formula (1.10-7).

However, because the webs of homogeneous girders of A514 steel loaded to their full capacity in bending develop more waviness than less heavily stressed girder webs of weaker grades of steel, use of tension field action is limited in the case of A514 steel webs to regions where the concurrent bending stress is no more than $0.75F_b$.

---

* Design of Hybrid Steel Beams, Report of Subcommittee 1 of the Joint ASCE-AASHO Committee on Flexural Members, *ASCE Journal of the Structural Division*, June, 1968.

** *Basler, K.* Strength of Plate Girders Under Combined Bending and Shear, *ASCE Journal of the Structural Division*, October, 1961.

1.10.10   Web Crippling

1.10.10.1   Webs of beams and girders not protected by bearing stiffeners could fail by crippling at points of high stress concentration resulting from the application of concentrated loads or reactions.   To guard against this, the stress at the toe of the flange fillet, assumed to be distributed longitudinally a distance no greater than the length of the bearing, plus 1 or 2 times the k-distance of the flange, depending upon the location of the load, is limited by Formula (1.10-8) or (1.10-9) to $0.75F_y$.

1.10.10.2   As a safeguard against instability of relatively thin plate girder webs, a further limitation has been placed on the amount of load which can be applied directly to the girder flange between stiffeners.   Concentrated loads light enough to meet the provisions of Sect. 1.10.10.1 and loading applied longitudinally over partial panel length are treated as if distributed by means of shear over the full panel length within which they occur (or the depth of girder if this is less than the panel length).   Taken together with such other distributed loading as may be applied directly to the flange, the total load divided by the web thickness should not exceed the stress permitted by Formula (1.10-10) or (1.10-11).   If the flange is prevented from rotation about its longitudinal axis by its contact with a rigid slab, Formula (1.10-10) will govern; otherwise, the more conservative Formula (1.10.11) is applicable.

These formulas are derived* from a consideration of the elastic buckling strength of the web plate subject to edge loading.   The loading is resisted in part by column action and in part by a plate intermittently stiffened in the direction of applied loading.

The formulas are likely to be over-conservative in the case of riveted girders, since they ignore any bending capacity the flange angles may have in spanning between adjacent stiffeners to support the loads.

1.10.11   Rotational Restraint at Points of Support

Slender beams and girders resting on top of columns and stayed laterally only in the plane of their top flanges may become unstable due to the flexibility of the column.   Unless lateral support is provided for the bottom flange, either by bracing or continuity at the beam-to-column connection, lateral displacement at the top of the column, accompanied by rotation of the beam about its longitudinal axis, may lead to collapse of the framing.

SECTION 1.11   COMPOSITE CONSTRUCTION

1.11.1   Definition

When the dimensions of a concrete slab supported on steel beams are such that the slab can effectively serve as the flange of a composite T-beam, and the concrete and steel are adequately tied together so as to act as a unit, the beam can be proportioned on the assumption of composite action.

Two cases are recognized: fully encased steel beams which depend upon natural bond for interaction with the concrete and those with mechanical anchorage to the slab (shear connectors), which do not have to be encased.

---

* *Basler, K.*   New Provisions for Plate Girder Design, *Appendix C, 1961 Proceedings AISC National Engineering Conference.*

1.11.2 Design Assumptions

Unless temporary shores are used, beams encased in concrete and interconnected only by means of natural bond must be proportioned to support all of the dead load, unassisted by the concrete, plus the superimposed live load in composite action, without exceeding the allowable bending stress for steel provided in Sect. 1.5.1.

Because the completely encased steel section is restrained from both local and lateral buckling, an allowable stress of $0.66F_y$ rather than $0.60F_y$ can be applied here. The alternate provision, permitting a stress of $0.76F_y$, to be used in designs where a fully encased beam is proportioned to resist all loads unassisted, reflects a common engineering practice where it is desired to eliminate the calculation of composite section properties.

In keeping with the *Tentative Recommendations for the Design and Construction of Composite Beams and Girders for Buildings**, when shear connectors are used to obtain composite action, this action may be assumed, within certain limits, in proportioning the beam for the moments created by both live and dead loads, even for unshored construction. This liberalization is based upon an ultimate strength concept, although the proportioning of the member is based upon the elastic section modulus of the transformed cross-section.

In order that the maximum bending stress in the steel beam, under service loading, will be well below the level of initial yielding, regardless of the ratio of live-load moment to dead-load moment, the section modulus of the composite cross-section, in tension at the bottom of the beam, for unshored construction, is limited to $(1.35 + 0.35\,M_L/M_D)$ times the section modulus of the bare beam.**

On the other hand, the requirement that flexural stress in the concrete slab, due to actual composite action, be computed on the basis of actual transformed section modulus and limited to the generally accepted working stress limit, is necessary in order to avoid excessively conservative slab-to-beam proportions.

Research at Lehigh University† has shown that, for a given beam and concrete slab, the increase in bending strength intermediate between no composite action and full composite action is directly proportional to the shear resistance developed between the steel and concrete, i.e., the number of shear connectors provided between these limits. At times it may not be feasible, nor even necessary, to provide full composite action. Therefore the Specification recognizes two conditions: full and incomplete composite action.

For the case where the total shear (V'_h) developed between steel and concrete each side of the point of maximum moment is less than V_h, Formula (1.11-1) can be used to derive an effective section modulus, S_{eff}, having a value less than the section modulus for fully effective composite action, S_{tr}, but more than that of the steel beam alone.

---

* Progress Report of the Joint ASCE-ACI Committee on Composite Construction, *ASCE Journal of the Structural Division*, December, 1960.

** Ibid., Eq. (3).

† *Slutter, R. G. and Driscoll, G. C.* Flexural Strength of Steel-Concrete Composite Beams, *p. 91, ASCE Journal of the Structural Division, April, 1965.*

1.11.4 Shear Connectors

Based upon tests at Lehigh University,* and a re-examination of previously published test data reported by a number of investigators, more liberal working values are recommended for various types and sizes of shear connectors than in use prior to 1961.

Composite beams in which the longitudinal spacing of shear connectors has been varied according to the intensity of statical shear, and duplicate beams where the required number of connectors were uniformly spaced, have exhibited the same ultimate strength, and the same amount of deflection at normal working loads. Only a slight deformation in the concrete and the more heavily stressed shear connectors is needed to redistribute the horizontal shear to other less heavily stressed connectors. The important consideration is that the total number of connectors, either side of the point of maximum moment, be sufficient to develop the composite action counted upon at that point. The provisions of the Specification are based upon this concept of composite action.

The required shear connectors can generally be spaced uniformly between the points of maximum and zero moment.* However, certain loading patterns can produce a condition where closer spacing is required over a part of this distance.

Consider, for example, the case of a uniformly loaded simple beam also required to support two equal concentrated loads, symmetrically disposed about midspan, of such magnitude that the moment at the concentrated loads is only slightly less than the maximum moment at midspan. The number of shear connectors (N_2) required between each end of the beam and the adjacent concentrated load would be only slightly less than the number (N_1) required between each end and midspan.

Formula (1.11-6) is provided as a check to determine whether the number of connectors, N_1, required to develop M_{max} would, if uniformly distributed, provide N_2 connectors between one of the concentrated loads and the nearest point of zero moment. It is based upon the requirement that

$$S_{eff} : S_{tr} = M : M_{max}$$

where

$$0 < M < M_{max}$$

S_{eff} = section modulus corresponding to the minimum amount of incomplete composite action required at the section subject to the moment M

$$V'_h : V_h = N_2 : N_1$$

In computing the section modulus at points of maximum negative bending, reinforcement parallel to the steel beam and lying within the effective width of slab may be included, provided such reinforcement is properly anchored beyond the region of negative moment. However, enough shear connectors are required to transfer, from the slab to the steel beam, one-half of the ultimate tensile strength of the reinforcement.

---

* *Slutter, R. G. and Driscoll, G. C.* Flexural Strength of Steel-Concrete Composite Beams, *p. 91, ASCE Journal of the Structural Division, April 1965.*

The working values for various types of shear connectors are based upon a factor of safety of approximately 2.50 against their demonstrated ultimate strength.

Working values for use with concrete having aggregate not conforming to ASTM C33 and for connector types other than those shown in Table 1.11.4 must be established by a suitable testing program.

The values of q in Table 1.11.4 must not be confused with shear connection values suitable for use when the required number is measured by the parameter VQ/I, where V is the total shear at any given cross-section. Such a misuse could result in providing less than half the number required by Formula (1.11-3), (1.11-4) or (1.11-5).

Stud welds not located directly over the web of a beam tend to tear out of a thin flange before attaining their full shear-resisting capacity. To guard against this contingency, the size of a stud not located over the beam web is limited to $2\frac{1}{2}$ times the flange thickness.

SECTION 1.13 DEFLECTIONS, VIBRATION AND PONDING

1.13.1 Deflections

Although deformation, rather than stress, is sometimes the criterion of satisfactory design, there is no single scale by which the limit of tolerable deflection can be defined. Where limitations on flexibility are desirable, they are often dictated by the nature of collateral building components, such as plastered walls and ceilings, rather than by considerations of human comfort and safety. The admissible amount of movement varies with the type of component.

Obviously, the most satisfactory solution must rest upon the sound judgment of qualified engineers. As a guide, but only a guide, the following rules are suggested:

The depth of fully stressed beams and girders in floors should, if practicable, be not less than $F_y/800$ times the span. If members of less depth are used, the unit stress in bending should be decreased in the same ratio as the depth is decreased from that recommended above.

The depth of fully stressed roof purlins should, if practicable, be not less than $F_y/1,000$ times the span, except in the case of flat roofs.

1.13.2 Vibration

Where human comfort is the criterion for limiting motion, as in the case of perceptible vibrations, the limit of tolerable amplitude is dependent on the one hand, upon the frequency of the vibration and, on the other, the damping effect provided by components of the construction. When such vibrations are caused by running machinery, they should be isolated by effective damping devices or by the use of independent foundations.

The depth of a steel beam supporting large open floor areas free of partitions or other sources of damping should not be less than $\frac{1}{20}$ of the span in order to minimize perceptible transient vibration due to pedestrian traffic.

1.13.3 Ponding

As used in the Specification, ponding refers to the retention of water due solely to the deflection of flat roof framing. The amount of this water is dependent upon the flexibility of the framing. Lacking sufficient framing stiffness, its accumulated weight can result in collapse of the roof.

Representing the deflected shape of the primary and critical secondary member as a half-sine wave, the weight and distribution of the ponded water can be estimated and, from this, the contribution that the deflection each of these members make to the total ponding deflection can be expressed* as

$$\Delta_w = \frac{\alpha_p \Delta_o \left[1 + \dfrac{\pi}{4} \alpha_s + \dfrac{\pi}{4} \rho(1 + \alpha_s) \right]}{1 - \dfrac{\pi}{4} \alpha_p \alpha_s}$$

for the primary member, and

$$\delta_w = \frac{\alpha_s \delta_o \left[1 + \dfrac{\pi^3}{32} \alpha_p + \dfrac{\pi^2}{8\rho} (1 + \alpha_p) + 0.185 \alpha_s \alpha_p \right]}{1 - \dfrac{\pi}{4} \alpha_p \alpha_s}$$

for the secondary member. In these expressions Δ_o and δ_o are, respectively, the primary and secondary beam deflections due to loading present at the initiation of ponding, $\alpha_p = C_p/(1 - C_p)$, $\alpha_s = C_s/(1 - C_s)$, and $\rho = \delta_o/\Delta_o = C_s/C_p$

Using the above expressions for Δ_w and δ_w, the ratios Δ_w/Δ_o and δ_w/δ_o can be computed for any given combination of primary and secondary beam framing using, respectively, the computed value of parameters C_p and C_s defined in the Specification.

Even on the basis of unlimited elastic behavior, it is seen that the ponding deflections would become infinitely large unless

$$\left(\frac{C_p}{1 - C_p} \right)\left(\frac{C_s}{1 - C_s} \right) < \frac{4}{\pi}$$

Since elastic behavior is not unlimited, the effective bending strength available in each member to resist the stress caused by ponding action is restricted to the difference between the yield stress of the member and the stress, f_o, produced by the total load supported by it before consideration of ponding is included.

Noting that elastic deflection is directly proportional to stress, and providing a factor of safety of 1.25 with respect to stress due to ponding, the admissible amount of ponding deflection in either the primary or critical (midspan) secondary member, in terms of the applicable ratio Δ_w/Δ_o or δ_w/δ_o, can be represented as $(0.8F_y - f_o)/f_o$. Substituting this expression for Δ_w/Δ_o and δ_w/δ_o and combining with the foregoing expressions for Δ_w and δ_w, the relationship between critical values for C_p and C_s and the available elastic bending strength to resist ponding is obtained. The curves presented in Figs. C1.13.3.1 and C1.13.3.2 are based upon this relationship. They constitute a design aid for use when a more exact determination of required flat roof framing stiffness is needed than given by the Specification provision that $C_p + 0.9C_s \leqslant 0.25$.

---

* *Marino, F. J.* Ponding of Two-Way Roof Systems, *AISC Engineering Journal, July, 1966.*

Given any combination of primary and secondary framing, the stress index is computed as

$$U_p = \left(\frac{0.8F_y - f_o}{f_o}\right)_p \text{, for the primary member}$$

$$U_s = \left(\frac{0.8F_y - f_o}{f_o}\right)_s \text{, for the secondary member}$$

where f_o, in each case, is the computed bending stress in the member due to the supported loading, neglecting ponding effect. Depending upon geographic location, this loading should include such amount of snow as might also be present, although ponding failures have occurred more frequently

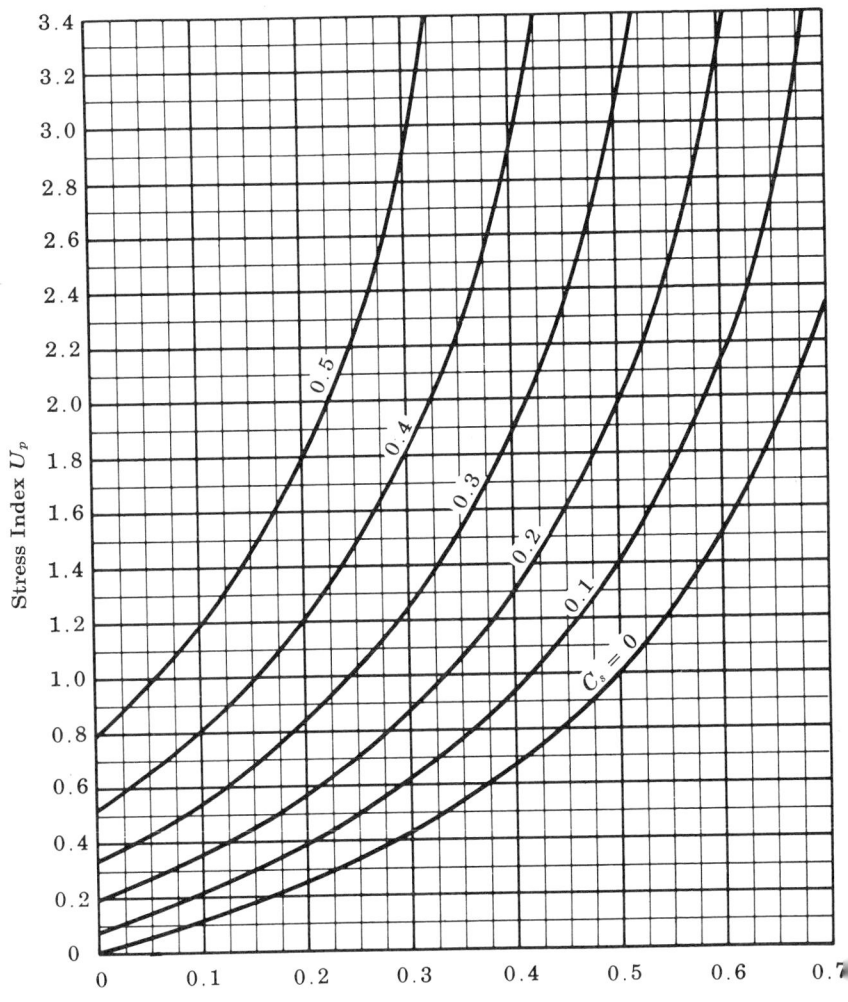

Fig. C 1.13.3.1

during torrential summer rains, when the rate of precipitation exceeded the rate of drainage run-off and the resulting hydraulic gradient over large roof areas caused substantial accumulation of water some distance from the eaves.

Given the size, spacing and span of a tentatively selected combination of primary and secondary beams, for example, one may enter Fig. C1.13.3.1 at the level of the computed stress index, U_p, determined for the primary beam; move horizontally to the computed C_s-value of the secondary beams; and, thence, downward to the abscissa scale. The combined stiffness of the primary and secondary framing is sufficient to prevent ponding if the flexibility constant read from this latter scale is more than the value of C_p computed for the given primary member; if not, a stiffer primary or secondary beam, or combination of both, is required.

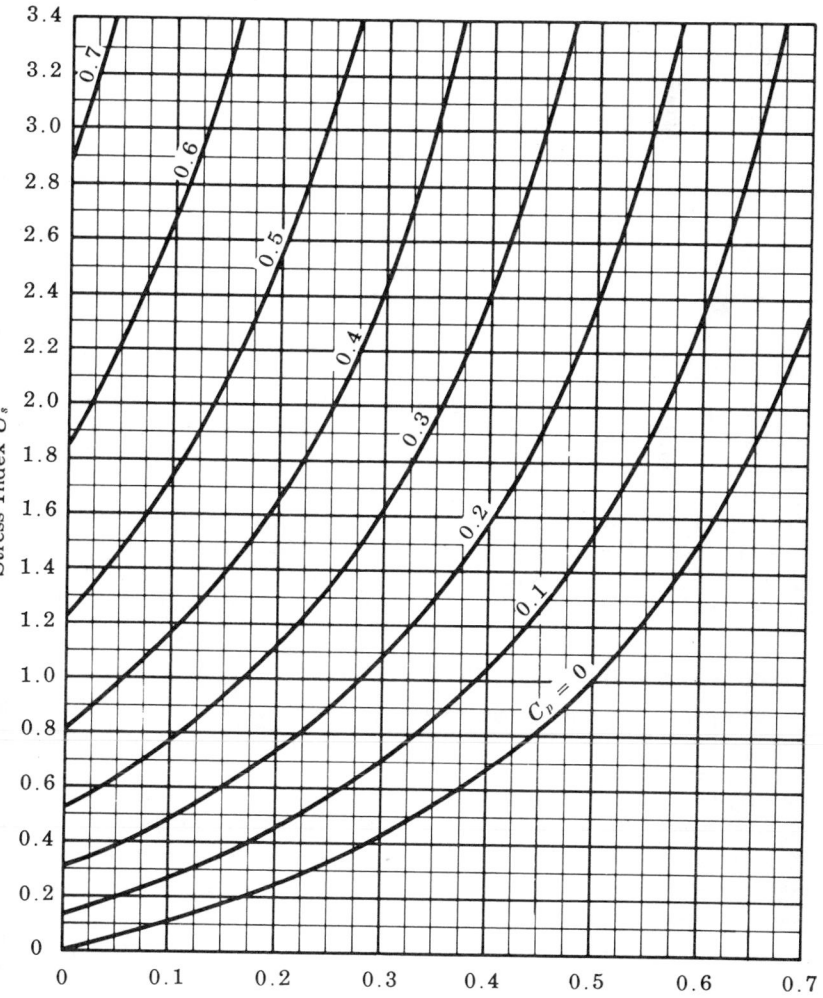

Fig. C1.13.3.2

If the roof framing consists of a series of equally-spaced wall-bearing beams, they would be considered as secondary members, supported on an infinitely stiff primary member. For this case, one would enter Fig. C1.13.3.2. The limiting value of C_s would be determined by the intercept of a horizontal line representing the U_s-value and the curve for $C_p = 0$.

The ponding deflection contributed by a metal deck is usually such a small part of the total ponding deflection of a roof panel, that it is sufficient merely to limit its moment of inertia (per foot of width normal to its span) to 0.000025 times the fourth power of its span length, as provided in the Specification. However, the stability against ponding of a roof consisting of a metal roof deck of relatively slender depth-span ratio, spanning between beams supported directly on columns, may need to be checked. This can be done using Fig. C1.13.3.1 or C1.13.3.2 with the following computed values:

U_p, the stress index for the supporting beam
U_s, the stress index for the roof deck
C_p, the flexibility constant for the supporting beams
C_s, the flexibility constant for one foot width of the roof deck $(S = 1.0)$

Since the shear rigidity of their web system is less than that of a solid plate, the moment of inertia of steel joists and trusses should be taken as somewhat *less* than that of their chords.

SECTION 1.14   GROSS AND NET SECTIONS

1.14.3   Net Section

Tests* have indicated that, as the ratio of net to gross section approaches unity, the ultimate tensile strength of a member may be less than the product of the net section multiplied by the tensile strength of the steel determined by standard coupon tests. A precise evaluation of this relationship would depend upon such parameters as hole spacing normal to the applied tension force versus thickness of section, and the ductility of the steel. Pending further investigation, the Specification places the upper limit of the fully effective net section at 85 percent of the gross section.

1.14.6   Pin-Connected Members

Forged eyebars have been replaced by pin-connected plates or eyebars flame-cut from plates. Provisions for the proportioning of eyebars contained in the Specification are based upon standards evolved from long experience with forged eyebars. Through extensive destructive testing they have been found to provide balanced designs when these members are flame-cut instead of forged. The somewhat more conservative rules for pin-connected members of non-uniform cross-section and those not having enlarged "circular" heads is likewise based on the results of experimental research.**

---

* *Schutz, F. W. and Newmark, N. M.* The Efficiency of Riveted Structural Joints, *Structural Research Series No. 30, University of Illinois.*

Fisher, J. W. Behavior of Fasteners and Plates With Holes, *ASCE Journal of the Structural Division, December, 1965.*

** *Johnston, B. G.* Pin Connected Plate Links, *1939 ASCE Transactions.*

Somewhat stockier proportions are provided for eyebars and pin-connected members fabricated from steel having a yield stress greater than 70 ksi, in order to eliminate any possibility of their "dishing" under the higher working stress for which they may be designed.

1.14.7   Effective Areas of Weld Metal

In recognition of the deeper penetration obtained by the submerged arc process, fillet welds made by this process may be proportioned on the basis of an effective throat thickness somewhat greater than the perpendicular distance from the root to the diagrammatic weld face. For fillet welds of such size as to require more than a single pass, the recognized increase in throat thickness is held constant.

Provision for the use of partial penetration groove welds, which first appeared in the 1961 AISC Specification, has been extended to cover their use on both sides of a joint, in keeping with similar provisions now included in the AWS Building Code.

SECTION 1.15   CONNECTIONS

1.15.3   Placement of Rivets, Bolts and Welds

Slight eccentricities between the gravity axis of single- and double-angle members and the center of gravity of their connecting rivets or bolts have long been ignored as having negligible effect upon the strength of such members. Tests* have shown that similar practice is warranted in the case of welded members in statically loaded structures.

1.15.5   Restrained Members

Whether or not transverse stiffeners are required on the web of a member opposite the flanges of members rigidly connected to its flanges, as in Fig. C1.15.5.1, depends upon the proportions of these members. Formulas

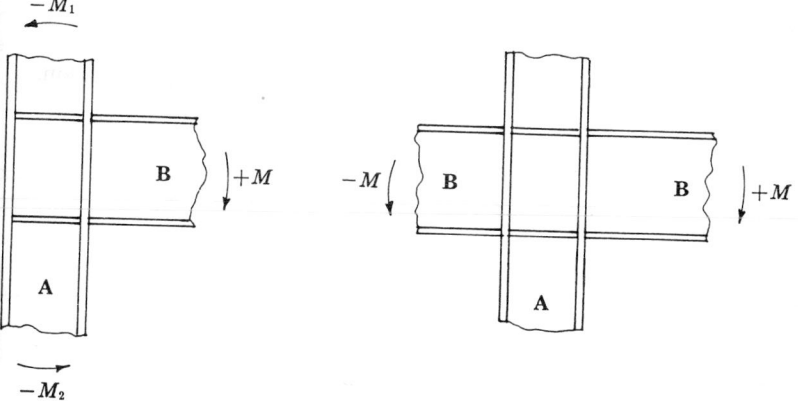

Fig. C 1.15.5.1

Gibson, G. T. and Wake, B. T. An Investigation of Welded Connections for angle Tension Members, *The Welding Journal, January 1942, American Welding* society.

(1.15-1) and (1.15-3) are based on tests* supporting the concept that, in the absence of transverse stiffeners, the web and flange thickness of member A should be such that these elements will not yield inelastically under concentrated forces delivered by member B and equal to the area of the rigidly connected flange times its yield stress.

Formula (1.15-4), giving the required area of stiffeners when stiffeners are needed, is based upon the same concept.

Formula (1.15-2) limits the slenderness ratio of an unstiffened web of the supporting member, in order to avoid possibility of its buckling.

Since these provisions are based upon the maximum force that can be delivered by the supported member flanges, they obviously would be conservative in the case of less rigidly connected members.

1.15.6 Fillers

The practice of securing fillers by means of additional fasteners, so that they are in effect an integral part of a shear-connected component, is not required where a connection is designed as a friction-type joint using high strength bolts. In such connections the resistance to slip between filler and either connected part is comparable to that which would exist between these parts if no fill were required.

1.15.10 Rivets and Bolts in Combination with Welds

The sharing of stress between rivets and A307 bolts in a single group of fasteners is not recommended in new work. High strength bolts used in bearing-type connections should not be required to share shear stress with welds. High strength bolts used in friction-type connections, however, because of the rigidity of the connection, may be proportioned to function in conjunction with welds in resisting the transfer of stress across faying surfaces, provided the welds are made after the bolts have been tightened.

In making alterations to existing structures it is assumed that whatever slip is likely to occur in riveted joints or high strength bolted, bearing-type joints will have already taken place. Hence, in such cases the use of welding to resist all contemplated stresses in addition to those produced by existing dead load, present at the time of making the alteration, is permitted.

SECTION 1.16 RIVETS AND BOLTS

1.16.1 High Strength Bolts

Earlier reference to A354 Grade BC bolts has been deleted since the Specification of the Research Council on Riveted and Bolted Structural Joints has been revised to include A490 bolts, which are better suited and more readily available. At the same time, provision for the use of A449 bolts, in lieu of A325 bolts, has been added. These bolts differ from A325 bolts only as to the size of head and conform to the high strength bolt originally called for in the Council's Specification when the use of hardened washers under head and nut was mandatory.

Graham, J. D., Sherbourne, A. N., Knabbaz, R. N. and Jensen, C. D. Welded Interior Beam-to-Column Connections, *American Institute of Steel Construction.*

1.16.3   Long Grips

Provisions requiring a decrease in calculated stress for rivets having long grips (by arbitrarily increasing the required number an amount in proportion to the grip length) are not required for high strength bolts. Tests* have demonstrated that the ultimate shearing strength of high strength bolts having a grip of 8 or 9 diameters is no less than that of similar bolts with much shorter grips.

1.16.4   Minimum Pitch

The recommendations for minimum pitch in the spacing of rivets and bolts is dictated solely by the need for driving or wrenching clearance during the installation of these fasteners.

1.16.6   Minimum Edge Distance in Line of Stress

The requirements of this section have been revised to provide greater flexibility in their application to various combinations of fastener hardness and yield stress in the connected parts. The earlier provisions, covering the use of A502 Grade 1 rivets in mild carbon steel, have been retained as the basic concept.

SECTION 1.17   WELDS

1.17.2   Qualification of Weld and Joint Details

As in earlier editions, the Specification accepts without further procedure qualification numerous weld and joint details executed in accordance with the provisions of the *AWS Code for Welding in Building Construction*, D1.0-69. Other welding procedures may be used, provided they are qualified to the satisfaction of the designer and the building code authority and are executed in accordance with the provisions of AWS D1.0-69.

SECTION 1.18   BUILT-UP MEMBERS

Requirements dealing with the detailing of built-up members, which cannot be stated in terms of calculated stress, are based upon judgment, tempered by experience.

The longitudinal spacing of fasteners connecting components of built-up compression members must be so limited that buckling of segments between adjacent fasteners would not occur at less load than that required to develop the ultimate strength of the member as a whole. However, maximum fastener spacing less than that necessary to prevent local buckling may be needed to insure a close fit-up over the entire faying surface of components designed to be in contact with one another.

Provisions based on this latter consideration, like those giving maximum spacing of stitch fasteners for separated components of built-up tension mem-

---

* *Bendigo, R. A., Hansen, R. M. and Rumpf, J. L.* Long Bolted Joints, *ASCE Journal of the Structural Division, December, 1963.*

bers, are of little structural significance. Hence, some latitude is warranted in relating them to the given dimensions of a particular member.

The provisions governing the proportioning of perforated cover plates are based upon extensive experimental research.*

SECTION 1.19 CAMBER

The cambering of flexural members, to eliminate the appearance of sagging or to match the elevation of adjacent building components when the member is loaded, is accomplished in various ways. In the case of trusses and girders the desired curvature can be built in during assembly of the component parts. Within limits, rolled beams can be cold-cambered at the producing mill.

The local application of heat has come into common use as a means of straightening or cambering beams and girders. The method depends upon an ultimate shortening of the heat-affected zones. A number of such zones, on the side of the member that would be subject to compression during cold-cambering or "gagging", are heated enough to be "upset" by the restraint provided by surrounding unheated areas. Shortening takes place upon cooling.

While the final curvature of camber produced by any of these methods can be controlled to a remarkable degree, it must be realized that some tolerance, to cover workmanship error and permanent change due to handling, is inevitable.

SECTION 1.20 EXPANSION

As in the case of deflections, the satisfactory control of expansion cannot be reduced to a few simple rules, but must depend largely upon the good judgment of qualified engineers.

The problem is more serious in buildings having masonry wall enclosures than where the walls consist of prefabricated units. Complete divorcement of the framing, at widely spaced expansion joints, is generally more satisfactory than more frequently located devices dependent upon the sliding of parts in bearing, and usually less expensive than rocker or roller expansion bearings.

SECTION 1.23 FABRICATION

1.23.1 Straightening Material

The use of heat for straightening or cambering members is permitted for A514 steel, as it is for other steels. However, the maximum temperature permitted for such straightening is 1100°F for A514 steel, as contrasted with 1200°F for other steels.

1.23.5 Riveted and High Strength Bolted Construction Assembling

Even when used in bearing-type shear connections, high strength bolts are required to be tightened to their proof load in the case of A325 and A449 bolts, and to 0.7 of their tensile strength in the case of A490 bolts

---

* *Stang, A. H. and Jaffe, B. S.* Perforated Cover Plates for Steel Columns *Research Paper RP1861, National Bureau of Standards.*

This may be done either by the turn-of-nut method* or by a calibrated wrench. Since fewer fasteners and stiffer connected parts are involved than is generally the case with A307 bolts, the greater clamping force is recommended in order to ensure solid seating of the connected parts.

1.23.6 Welded Construction

Inclusion of a number of grades of steel in the Specification has created the need for a greater control of preheat and interpass temperature in welding. The rules given reflect present practices as indicated by the standards of the American Welding Society.

SECTION 1.24 SHOP PAINTING

The shop painting of structural steel not to be encased in concrete is not mandatory. Steelwork to be covered up by the building finish will be shop painted only if required by the plans and job specification. The surface condition of steel framing disclosed by the demolition of long-standing buildings has been found to be unchanged from the time of its erection, except at isolated spots where leakage may have occurred. Where such leakage is not eliminated the presence or absence of a shop coat is of minor influence. **

The Specification does not define the type of paint to be used when a shop coat is required. Conditions of exposure and individual preferences with regard to finish paint are factors which have a bearing on the selection of the proper primer. Hence, a single formulation would not suffice.†

SECTION 1.26 QUALITY CONTROL

Starting at the producing mill, and continuing in the fabricator's plant, steel required to have a yield stress in excess of 36 kips per square inch must at all times be so marked as to identify the ASTM specification and grade to which it conforms.

---

* *See* Specification for Structural Joints Using ASTM A325 Or A490 Bolts Research Council on Riveted and Bolted Structural Joints.

** Bigos, J., Smith, G. W., Ball, E. F. and Foehl, P. J. Shop Paint and Painting Practice, *1954 Proceedings* AISC *National Engineering Conference.*

† *For a comprehensive treatment of the subject, see* Systems and Specifications, Steel Structures Painting Manual, Volume 2, *published by the Steel Structures Painting Council, Pittsburgh, Pa.*

SECTION 2.1 SCOPE

When provisions for plastic design were first introduced into the AISC Specification in 1961, their use was limited to one- and two-story rigid frames. However, as noted in the *Commentary* at that time, they were not ruled out in the case of beam design for multi-story buildings if resistance to lateral forces applied to the building was provided by means other than the bending stiffness of these beams.

The bending strength of a compact flexural member is greater than its strength at initial yielding, in an amount measured by the shape factor *f* of its profile; a non-compact member (meeting the provisions of Sect. 1.9, but not those of Sect. 2.7), usually has little reserve strength beyond the elastic limit, because of buckling. Hence, for such members it may be said that the effective shape factor is 1.0.

The superior bending strength of compact sections is recognized in Part 1 of the Specification by increasing the allowable bending stress to $0.66F_y$. By the same token, the logical load factor for plastically designed beams is given by the equation $F = \dfrac{F_y}{0.66F_y} \cdot (f)$. For such shapes listed in the AISC *Steel Construction Manual*, the variation of (f) is from 1.10 to 1.23 with a mode of 1.12. Then the corresponding load factor must vary from 1.67 to 1.86 with a mode of 1.70.

Such a load factor is consistent and in better balance with that inherent in the allowable working stresses for tension members and deep plate girders. While a load factor of 1.7, comparable to the basic 5/3 factor of safety inherent in working stress design, was specified for beams, the recommended load factor for frames as a whole was 1.85, pending further investigation of columns and frame stability problems.

Research which has been completed since 1961* has provided a better understanding of the ultimate strength of heavily loaded columns subjected to concurrent bending moments. Based upon this information, the load factor of frames has been made the same as that provided for members subject only to bending. Consistent with this change, the load factor to be used in designing for gravity loading combined with wind or seismic loading has been reduced from 1.4 to 1.3.

Based on continuing research at Lehigh University on multi-story framing,** application of the Specification provisions has been extended to include the complete design of planar frames in high-rise buildings, provided they are braced to take care of any lateral loading. Systematic procedures for application of plastic design in proportioning the members of such frames have been developed† and are available in the current literature.

---

* *Van Kuren, R. C. and Galambos, T. V.* Beam Column Experiments, *ASCE Journal of the Structural Division, April, 1964.*

** *Driscoll, G. C. et al.* Plastic Design of Multi-Story Frames—Lecture Notes *Fritz Engineering Laboratory Report No. 273.20, Lehigh University, August, 1965.*

Driscoll, G. C. Lehigh Conference on Plastic Design of Multi-Story Frames— A Summary, *AISC Engineering Journal, April, 1966.*

† Plastic Design of Braced Multi-Story Steel Frames, *American Iron and Steel Institute, 1968.*

Lu, Le-Wu Design of Braced Multi-Story Frames by the Plastic Method *AISC Engineering Journal, January, 1967.*

SECTION 2.2 STRUCTURAL STEEL

The 1961 AISC Specification limited the use of plastic design to steels having a specified minimum yield point no higher than 36 ksi. Most of the experimental verification of provisions for plastic design contained in the Specification at that time had used steel of about this strength.

By 1965 the applicability of such provisions, with only minor modifications, to high-strength low-alloy steel furnished to a specified yield point of 50 ksi, had been established.* With the advent of ASTM Specification A572 in 1966, further investigation was undertaken which indicated their applicability for all grades covered by that standard.**

On the basis of these investigations, the list of steels covered by ASTM standard specifications has been increased accordingly.

SECTION 2.3 VERTICAL BRACING SYSTEM

While resistance to wind and seismic loading can be provided in moderate height buildings by means of concrete or masonry shear walls, which also provide for overall frame stability at factored gravity loading, taller building frames must provide this resistance acting alone. This can be achieved in one of two ways: either by a system of bracing or by a moment-resisting frame.

In moment resisting frames, designed in accordance with the provisions of Part 1 of the Specification, the necessary resistance to lateral loading is provided by the bending strength of the beams and columns rigidly connected to one another. Distribution of bending moments is based upon an assumption of completely elastic frame behavior; column strength is based upon an effective unbraced length generally greater than the actual unbraced length.

Neither of these assumptions apply in the analysis of unbraced, plastically designed high-rise frames, although appropriate analytical procedures have been proposed.† Pending further study, design of such framing more than two stories in height, in accordance with the provisions of Part 2 of the Specification, is restricted to fully-braced systems. The role and requirements of such systems‡ are defined by the provisions of Sect. 2.3.

The limitation on axial force of $0.85P_y$ is inserted as a simple means of compensating for three possible effects:¶

a) Loss of stiffness due to residual stress
b) Effect of secondary moments from the vertical bracing system
c) Lateral torsional buckling effect

---

* *Adams, P. F., Lay, M. G. and Galambos, T. V.* Experiments on High Strength Steel Members, *Welding Research Council Bulletin No. 110.*
** Plastic Design in Steel, *ASCE Manual of Engineering Practice No. 41, Second Edition, Section 5.1.*

† *Driscoll, G. C. et al.* Plastic Design of Multi-Story Frames—Lecture Notes, Chapter 14, *Fritz Engineering Laboratory Report No. 273.20, Lehigh University, August, 1965.*

‡ *Lu, Le-Wu* Design of Braced Multi-Story Frames by the Plastic Method, *AISC Engineering Journal, January, 1967.*

¶ Plastic Design in Steel, *ASCE Manual of Engineering Practice No. 41, Second Edition, Chapter 10.*

SECTION 2.4 COLUMNS

Based on research completed since the previous edition of the Specification, provisions for design of beam-columns have been extensively revised.

Formulas (2.4-2) and (2.4-3)* will be recognized as similar in type to Formulas (1.6-1a) and (1.6-lb) in Part 1, except that they are written in terms of factored loads and moments, instead of allowable stresses at service loading. As in the case of Formulas (1.6-1a) and (1.6-1b), P_{cr} is computed on the basis of the larger slenderness ratio for any given unbraced length.**

A column is considered to be fully braced if the slenderness ratio l/r_y between the braced points is less than or equal to that specified in Sect. 2.9. For limiting values of l/r_y applicable to various yield stress steels and end moment ratios, see Sect. 2.9 in Appendix A.

When the unbraced length ratio of a member bent about its strong axis exceeds the limit specified in Sect. 2.9, the rotation capacity of the member may be impaired, due to the combined influence of lateral and torsional deformation, to such an extent that plastic hinge action within the member cannot be counted upon. However, if the computed value of M is small enough so that the limitations of Formulas (2.4-2) and (2.4-3) are met, the member will be strong enough to function at a joint where the required hinge action is provided in another member entering the joint. An assumed reduction in moment-resisting capacity is provided by using the value M_m, computed from Formula (2.4-4), in Formula (2.4-2).

Formula (2.4-4) was developed empirically on the basis of test observations and provides an estimate of the critical lateral buckling moment, in the absence of axial load, for the case where $M_1/M_2 = -1.0$. For other values of M_1/M_2, adjustment is provided by using the appropriate C_m value as defined in Sect. 1.6.1.

Formula (2.4-4) is to be used only in connection with Formula (2.4-2).

Space frames containing plastically designed planar rigid frames are assumed to be supported against sidesway normal to these frames. Depending upon other conditions of restraint, the basis for determination of proper values for P_{cr} and P_e and M_m, for a plastically designed column oriented to resist bending about its strong axis, is outlined in Table C 2.4.1. In each case l is the distance between points of lateral support corresponding to r_x or r_y, as

TABLE C 2.4.1

	Braced Planar Frames	One- and Two-Story Unbraced Planar Frames
P_{cr}	Use larger ratio, $\dfrac{l}{r_y}$ or $\dfrac{l}{r_x}$	[1]Use larger ratio, $\dfrac{l}{r_y}$ or $\dfrac{Kl}{r_x}$
P_e	Use l/r_x	[1]Use Kl/r_x
M_m	Use l/r_y	Use l/r_y

[1] Webs of columns assumed to be in plane of frame.

---

* *Driscoll, G. C. et al.* Plastic Design of Multi-Story Frames—Lecture Notes, *Eq. (4.6) and Eq. (4.7), Fritz Engineering Laboratory Report No. 273.20, Lehigh University,* August, 1965.

** *Ibid.*, p. 4.24.

† *Ibid.*, p. 4.26

applicable. When K is indicated, its value is governed by the provisions of Sect. 1.8.3 of the Specification. Elsewhere, $Kl/r = l/r$.

SECTION 2.5 SHEAR

Using the von Mises criterion, the average stress at which an unreinforced web would be fully yielded in pure shear can be expressed as $F_y/\sqrt{3}$. It has been observed* that the plastic bending strength of an I-shape beam is not appreciably reduced until shear yielding occurs over the full effective depth, which may be taken as the distance between the centroids of its flanges (approx. 0.95 times its actual depth). Thus

$$V_u = \frac{0.95F_y}{\sqrt{3}} dt = 0.55F_y\, dt$$

Shear stresses are generally high within the boundaries of a rigid connection of two or more members whose webs lie in a common plane. Assuming the moment $+M$, in Fig. C 2.5.1, expressed in kip-feet, to be resisted by a couple of forces at the centroid of the beam flanges, the shear, in kips, produced in beam-to-column connection web *abcd* can be computed as

$$V = \frac{+12M}{0.95d_b}$$

when $V = V_u = 0.55F_y\, d_c\, t$

$$\text{Req'd } t = \frac{12M}{0.95d_b \times 0.55F_y\, d_c} = \frac{23M}{A_{bc}\, F_y}$$

where A_{bc} is the planar area *abcd* and F_y is expressed in kips per square inch.

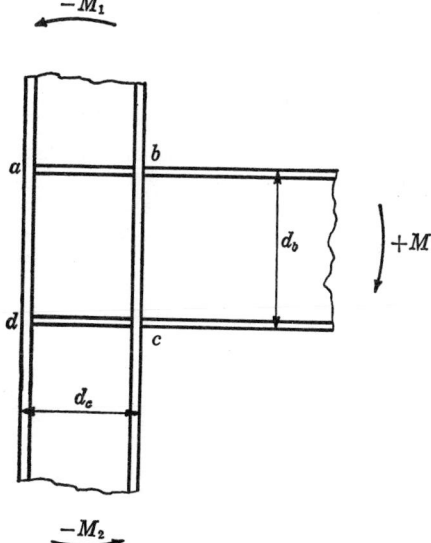

Fig. C 2.5.1

---

* Plastic Design in Steel, *ASCE Manual of Engineering Practice No. 41, Second Edition, Section 6.1.*

If the thickness of the web panel is less than that given by this formula, the deficiency may be compensated by a pair of diagonal stiffeners or by a reinforcing plate in contact with the web panel and welded around its boundary to the column flanges and horizontal stiffeners.

SECTION 2.6   WEB CRIPPLING

Usually stiffeners are needed, as at *ab* and *dc* in Fig. C 2.5.1, in line with the flanges of a beam rigidly connected to the flange of a second member so located that their webs lie in the same plane, in order to prevent crippling of the web of the latter opposite the compression flange of the former. A stiffener may also be required opposite the tension flange, in order to protect the weld joining the two flanges; otherwise the stress in the weld might be too great in the region of the beam web, due to lack of bending stiffness in the flange to which the beam is connected. Since their design is based upon equating the plastic resisting capacity of the supporting member to the plastic moment delivered by the supported member, Formulas (1.15-1), (1.15-2), (1.15-3) and (1.15-4) are equally applicable to allowable stress design and plastic design.

When stiffeners are required, as an alternative to the usual pair of horizontal plates, vertical plates parallel to but separated from the web as shown in Fig. C 2.6.1 may prove advantageous.

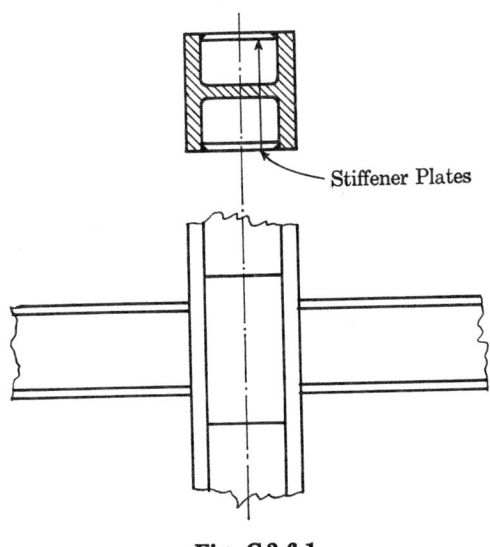

Stiffener Plates

Fig. C 2.6.1

SECTION 2.7   MINIMUM THICKNESS (WIDTH-THICKNESS RATIOS)

In extending the provisions for plastic design to steels having a yield point higher than 36 ksi, considerable research* has been required in order to

---

* Plastic Design in Steel, *ASCE Manual of Engineering Practice No. 41, Second Edition, Section 6.2.*

define limiting flange and web width-thickness ratios below which ample plastic hinge rotations could be relied upon without reduction in the M_p-value due to local buckling.

These studies have shown that the limiting width-thickness ratio is not exactly proportional to $1/\sqrt{F_y}$, although the discrepancy using such a relationship, within the range of yield stress presently permitted by the Specification, is not large. Expressions including other pertinent factors are complex and involve use of mechanical properties that have not been clearly defined. Tabular values for limiting flange width-thickness ratios are given in the Specification for the approved grades of steel.

No change in basic philosophy is involved in extending the earlier expression for limiting web depth-thickness ratio to stronger steels. Formulas (2.7-1a) and (2.7-1b) are derived, with minor adjustments for better correlation with observed test results, by multiplying Formula (25) of the 1963 Specification by the factor $\sqrt{36/F_y}$, in order to cover the accepted range in yield point stress. Formula (2.7-1a) is identical to Formula (1.5-4) in Part 1, except that it is written in terms of factored loads instead of allowable stresses at service loading.

SECTION 2.8 CONNECTIONS

Connections located outside of regions where hinges would have formed at ultimate load can be treated in the same manner that similar connections in frames designed in accordance with the provisions of Part 1 would be treated. Since the moments and forces to be resisted will be those corresponding to the factored loading, the permissible stresses to be used in proportioning parts of the connections can be taken as 1.7 times those given in Sects. 1.5 and 1.6 of the Specification.

The same procedure is valid in proportioning connections located in the region of a plastic hinge. Connections required to resist moments and forces due to wind and earthquake loads combined with gravity loading factored to 1.3, and proportioned on the basis of limiting stresses equal to 1.7 times those given in Sects. 1.5 and 1.6, provide a balance between frame strength and connection strength, provided they are adequate to resist gravity loading alone, factored to 1.7.

The width-thickness ratio and unbraced length of all parts of the connection that would be subject to compression stresses in the region of a hinge must meet the requirements given in Part 2, and sheared edges and punched holes must not be used in portions of the connection subject to tension.

When a haunched connection is proportioned elastically for the moments that would exist within its length, the continuous frame can be analyzed as a mechanism having a hinge at the small end of the haunch, rather than at the intersection point between connected members,* with some attendant economy.

Tests** have shown that splices assembled with high strength bolts are capable of developing the M_p-value of the gross cross-section of the connected

---

* Plastic Design in Steel, *ASCE Manual of Engineering Practice No. 41, Second Edition, Chapter 8.*

** *Douty, R. T. and McGuire, W.* High Strength Bolted Moment Connections, *ASCE Journal of the Structural Division, April, 1965.*

part. It has also been demonstrated* that beam-to-column connections involving use of welded or mechanically fastened fittings, instead of full penetration groove welds matching the full member cross-section, not only are capable of developing the M_p-value of the member, but that the resulting hinge rotation can be reversed several times without failure.

SECTION 2.9 LATERAL BRACING

Portions of members that would be required to rotate inelastically as a plastic hinge, in reducing a continuous frame to a mechanism at ultimate load, need more bracing than similar parts of a continuous frame designed in accordance with the elastic theory.   Not only must they reach yield point at a load factor of 1.7, they must also strain inelastically to provide the necessary hinge rotation.   This is not true at the last hinge to form, since the factored load is assumed to have been reached when this hinge starts to rotate.   When bending takes place about the strong axis, any I-shape member tends to buckle out of the plane of bending.   It is for this reason that lateral bracing is needed.   The same tendency exists with highly stressed members in elastically designed frames, and in portions of plastically designed frames outside of the hinge areas, but here the problem is less severe since hinge rotation is not involved.

For the limited range of steels recognized as suitable for plastic design in earlier editions of the Specification, l_{cr}, the allowable unbraced length of compression flanges subject to plastic bending, was given as

$$\left(60 \; - \; 40\,\frac{M}{M_p}\right) r_y > l_{cr} \geqslant 35 r_y$$

where M/M_p, the ratio of end moments, was considered positive only when the unbraced length was bent in *single* curvature.

Based on research seeking to extend the application of plastic design to stronger steels, it was noted** that this expression could be unduly conservative in the region where $-0.5 < M/M_p < 0.$† The new provision reflects this and also includes a more conservative approach in the region where $0 < M/M_p < +1.0.$†

Both Formulas (2.9-1a) and (2.9-1b) are empirical expressions which closely approximate the suggested revisions.‡

---

* *Popov, E. P. and Pinkney, R. B.* Behavior of Steel Building Connections Subjected to Inelastic Strain Reversals, *Bulletin Nos. 13 and 14, American Iron and Steel Institute, November, 1968.*

** *Lay, M. G. and Galambos, T. V.* Inelastic Beams Under Moment Gradient, *ASCE Journal of the Structural Division, February, 1967, p. 390.*

† In keeping with similar usage of the parameter M/M_p in Sect. 1.6 of the Specification, the sign convention adopted in Formulas (2.9-1a) and (2.9-1b) and used here is that generally found to be more convenient in frame analysis, namely that clockwise moments about a fixed point are positive and counterclockwise moments are negative.

‡ Plastic Design in Steel, *ASCE Manual of Engineering Practice No. 41, Second Edition, Section 6.3.*

Code of Standard Practice

for Steel Buildings and Bridges

Adopted Effective **October 1, 1972**

American Institute of Steel Construction

AMERICAN INSTITUTE OF STEEL CONSTRUCTION

101 Park Avenue, New York N. Y. 10017

FOREWORD

This edition of the Code of Standard
Practice for Steel Buildings and Bridges,
supersedes all previous editions,
effective October 1, 1972.

Changes over the previous July 1, 1970
edition occur in Sections 2, 3(b), 4(d), 6(a), 6(b),
6(d), 6(e), and 7(h).   In addition, a Commentary on
Section 7(h) is included for the first time.

Code of Standard Practice for Steel Buildings and Bridges

Adopted Effective October 1, 1972
American Institute of Steel Construction

Since steel was first used for structural purposes, and concurrently with the development of the structural steel industry, fabricators, erectors, owners, architects, engineers and contractors have developed certain practices relating to the design, fabrication and erection of structural steel which have become standard. While these standards are generally known, it is the purpose of the American Institute of Steel Construction in publishing these standards to make them available for ready reference by all those concerned with the use of structural steel in construction.

The standards herein described have been compiled as the result of studies made by engineers and other members of the staff of the American Institute of Steel Construction and are set forth in reasonable detail in the following resumé.

SECTION 1 GENERAL

(a) Standard Specifications

In the absence of other instructions, the provisions of the following standard specifications, as revised to date, govern the design, fabrication and erection of structural steel:

For buildings and similar structures:

Specification for the Design, Fabrication and Erection of Structural Steel for Buildings of the American Institute of Steel Construction;

For bridges:

Standard Specifications for Highway Bridges of American Association of State Highway Officials;

Specifications for Steel Railway Bridges of American Railway Engineering Association;

Structural Welding Code of American Welding Society.

(b) Plans and Specifications for Bidding

In order to insure adequate and complete bids, plans and specifications accompanying the invitation to bid show:

1. A complete structural steel design including any detached items, such as loose lintels, clearly showing the work to be performed and giving

sizes, sections and the relative location of all members, floor levels, column centers and offsets, bridge bearing centers and elevations, camber of members, with sufficient dimensions to convey accurately the quantity and nature of the structural steel, and

2. Wind bracing, moment connections and other special details, in sufficient detail regarding arrangement of parts, fasteners and welds so that they may be readily understood and supplied.

Plans are made to a scale not less than $\frac{1}{8}$ inch to the foot and the more complex information is furnished to adequate scale.

When the owner* provides the design, plans and specifications the fabricator and erector are not responsible for the suitability, adequacy or legality of the design; nor is the fabricator responsible for the practicability or safety of erection if the structure is erected by others. If the owner desires the fabricator or erector to prepare the design, plans and specifications or to assume any responsibility for the suitability, adequacy or legality of the design, he clearly states his requirements either in the invitation to bid or on such plans and specifications which accompany it.

(c) Patented Devices

Fabricators assume that all necessary patent rights have been obtained and that they (the fabricators) will be fully protected in the use of patented designs, devices or parts shown on the plans which the owner supplies.

SECTION 2 DEFINITION OF STRUCTURAL STEEL

The term "structural steel" comprehends only the following categories of parts:

> Anchors for structural steel;
> Bases of steel or iron;
> Beams, purlins, girts;
> Bearing plates for structural steel;
> Bearing shoes for bridges;
> Bracing;
> Brackets;
> Bridge pins;
> Bridge railings of steel;
> Columns;
> Counterweight boxes for bridges;
> Crane rails and stops;
> Door frames constituting part of the steel framing;
> Expansion joints connected to the steel frame;
> Floor plates (checkered or smooth) connected to the steel frame;
> Girders of steel;
> Grillage beams and girders of steel;
> Hangers of structural steel, if attached to the structural steel framing and shown on the framing plans;

---

* This term is used to designate not only the owner of the proposed structure but also the architect, engineer, general contractor, public authority or other designated representatives of the owner.

Lintels shown on the framing plans or otherwise enumerated or scheduled;

Marquees (structural steel frame only);

Monorail beams of standard structural shapes when attached to structural frame;

Separators, angles, tees, clips and other detail fittings essential to the structural steel frame;

Suspended ceiling supports of structural shapes 3 inches or greater in depth;

Shop rivets, permanent shop bolts, bolts required to assemble parts for shipment and shop welds;

Struts;

Tie, hanger and sag rods forming part of the structural steel frame; and

Trusses.

Field Connection Material

When the fabricator erects the structural steel, the fabricator supplies all materials required for temporary and for permanent connection of the component parts of the structural steel.

When the erection of the structural steel is performed by someone other than the fabricator, the fabricator furnishes:

1. Rivets of suitable size and in sufficient quantity for all field connections of steel to steel which are designated as riveted field connections, plus 10 per cent thereof to cover waste;

2. Bolts of suitable size and sufficient quantity for all field connections of steel to steel which are specified to be permanently bolted. Unless high strength bolts or other special types of bolts and washers are specified, common bolts are furnished. To allow for waste, an extra 2 per cent of bolts are furnished.

Unless specified in the invitation to bid or the specifications which accompany it, welding electrodes, shims, thin bearing plates used in lieu of shims to provide an exact level grade ready to receive steel columns or girders with bases fabricated as an integral part of the member, fitting-up bolts and drift pins required for field connections are not furnished by the fabricator, when the erection is performed by others.

The term "structural steel" does not include steel, iron or other items which are required for the assembly or erection of materials supplied by trades other than structural steel fabricators or erectors, even though such materials are shown on the plans as fastened to the structural steel.

SECTION 3   CALCULATION OF WEIGHTS

On contracts stipulating a price per pound for fabricated structural steel delivered or erected, pay quantities shall be determined by calculating the gross weight of materials shown on shop drawings. It is desirable to calculate such weights utilizing a simple procedure which will produce weights that are consistent throughout the industry and easy for the owner to verify. While this procedure does not produce actual weights, it is used by fabricators and erectors in bidding on a price per pound basis because it obviates the necessity for meticulous and involved calculations or additional shop work that entails substantial expense.

The standard procedure for calculating weights of fabricated structural steel for pay purposes is:

(a) The weight of steel is assumed to be 490 pounds per cubic foot. The weight of cast materials shall be in accordance with manufacturers' published data for the specific products.

(b) The weights of shapes, plates, bars, and steel pipe and structural tubing are calculated on the basis of detailed shop drawings showing actual quantities and dimensions of material furnished as follows:

    1. The weight of all structural shapes, steel pipe, and structural tubing is calculated using the nominal weight per foot and the detailed overall length.

    2. The weight of plates and bars is calculated using the detailed overall rectangular dimensions.

    3. When parts can be economically cut in multiples from material of larger dimensions, the weight is calculated on the basis of the theoretical rectangular dimensions of the material from which the parts are cut.

    4. When parts are cut from structural shapes leaving a non-standard section not useable on the same contract, the weight is calculated on the basis of the nominal unit weight of the section from which the parts are cut.

    5. No deductions are to be made for material removed by cuts, copes, clips, blocks, milling, drilling, punching, boring, planing, or weld joint preparation.

(c) The calculated weights of castings are determined from the detail drawings of the pieces. An allowance of 10% is added for fillets and over-run. Scale weights of rough castings may be used if available.

(d) The weight of shop rivets is calculated using the quantities shown on detailed shop drawings and the unit weights shown in the following table:

Diameter of Rivet	Calculated Weight per 100 Rivets
½ inch	20 pounds
⅝ inch	30 pounds
¾ inch	50 pounds
⅞ inch	100 pounds
1 inch	150 pounds
1⅛ inch	250 pounds
1¼ inch	325 pounds

(e) The weight of field rivets, shop and field bolts, nuts and washers is calculated using the quantities shown on rivet or bolt lists and the weights shown in tables in the AISC Manual. Weights of items not included in the tables are to be taken at their actual weight.

(f) The weight of shop or field weld metal and protective coatings is not to be included in the calculated weight for pay purposes.

SECTION 4 DRAWINGS AND SPECIFICATIONS

(a) To enable the fabricator and erector to proceed properly and expeditiously with the work, the owner furnishes as soon as possible a survey of the construction site or the lot lines and necessary sets of complete structural steel design drawings and specifications consistent with the original bidding plans and specifications. These show:

1. The design of the bridge or the structural steel framework establishing the location of all structural steel items, including detached items, and the location and size of all openings, holes, etc.; also,

2. All materials to be furnished by the fabricator, including all information necessary to determine sizes and quantities of structural steel items.

This information is used by the fabricator for ordering the required material and for the preparation and completion of shop drawings and erection diagrams. Drawings other than structural steel design drawings may be used to define detail configuration, as a supplement to the structural steel design drawings, provided the requirement for the item or items is noted on the structural steel design drawings.

(b) In case of discrepancies between drawings and specifications for buildings, the specifications govern. In the case of discrepancies between drawings and specifications for bridges, the drawings govern. In case of discrepancies between scale dimensions on the drawings and figures written on them, the figures govern.

(c) When shop drawings are made by the fabricator, prints thereof are submitted to the owner for his examination and approval. In order for the fabricator to commence shop work, the owner must return one set of prints to the fabricator (customarily within five days) with a notation of the owner's outright approval or approval subject to corrections as noted. It is usual practice for the fabricator to make the corrections and to furnish one set of corrected prints to the owner.

(d) Approval by the owner of shop drawings prepared by the fabricator indicates that the fabricator has correctly interpreted the contract requirements, and that any connections designed by the fabricator are of adequate capacity for the design requirements. Approval does not relieve the fabricator of the responsibility for accuracy of detail dimensions on shop drawings nor the general fit up of parts to be assembled in the field.

(e) When the shop drawings are furnished by the owner, he must deliver them to the fabricator in time to permit the fabrication to proceed in an orderly manner in accordance with the prescribed time schedule. The owner prepares these shop drawings, insofar as practicable in accordance with the shop and drafting room standards of the fabricator.

The owner is responsible for the completeness and accuracy of shop drawings so furnished.

SECTION 5 STOCK MATERIALS

(a) Many fabricators maintain stocks of steel products for use in their fabricating operations. Such materials as are taken from stock by the fabricator for use for structural purposes must be of a quality at least equal to that required by the specifications of the American Society for Testing and Materials applicable to the classifications covering the intended use. Mill test reports are accepted in the trade as sufficient record of the quality of materials carried in stock by the fabricator.

The fabricator checks and retains the mill test reports covering the materials he purchases for stock, but, because it is obviously impracticable to do so, he does not maintain records such as would identify individual pieces of stock material against individual mill test reports. Such records are not required if the fabricator purchases for stock under established specifications as to grade and quality and the purchases can be checked against mill test reports.

(b) It is common practice for the fabricator to use steel materials from his stock in his fabricating operations whenever he desires to do so, instead of ordering items from the mill for the specific use. Stock materials purchased under no particular specifications or under specifications less rigid than those mentioned above, or stock materials which have not been subject to mill or other recognized test reports, are not used without the express approval of the owner and then only under rigid inspection, except that such material may be used for small unimportant details where the quality of the material could not affect the strength of the structure.

SECTION 6 INSPECTION AND DELIVERY

(a) Test of Materials

Mill tests are performed to demonstrate material conformance to contract requirements. Unless special requirements are included in the invitation to bid, mill testing is limited to those tests required by the applicable ASTM material specifications. Mill test reports are furnished by the fabricator only if requested by the owner in either the invitation to bid or otherwise made in writing prior to the time the fabricator places his material orders with the mill.

The fabricator customarily makes no tests of steel material. The owner must rely on mill tests required by contract and on such additional tests as he orders the fabricator to have made at the owner's expense. If tests other than mill tests are desired, the owner so specifies in the invitation to bid and should arrange for such testing through the fabricator.

(b) Inspection

If the owner wishes an inspection of the steel by someone other than the fabricator's own inspectors, he reserves the right to do so in his invitation to bid or the accompanying specifications. Arrangements may be made with the fabricator for inspection of materials at the fabricating shop by the owner's inspectors. When non-destructive testing of welding is required, the process, extent, technique and standards of acceptance shall be clearly defined in information furnished to the bidders.

When the owner specifies shop inspection by a third party or by his own representatives, the owner has the obligation to see that such inspection is performed to the fullest extent possible in the fabricator's shop. The inspection will be performed in a manner to minimize disruptions in operations and to permit the repair of all nonconforming work while the material is in the fabricating shop.

(c) Shop Painting

Prior to painting, the fabricator cleans the steel of loose rust, loose mill scale, dirt, and other foreign material by means of hand wire brushing or by other methods elected by the fabricator. Unless specified, the fabricator need not sandblast, flame clean, or pickle the material prior to painting.

The shop coat of paint, unless otherwise specified, is a prime coat, intended to protect the steel for only a short period of exposure in ordinary atmospheric conditions, and must be considered an impermanent and provisional coating. Fabricators do not assume responsibility for deterioration of such a prime coat of paint that may result from extended exposure to ordinary atmospheric conditions, or from exposure to corrosive conditions more severe than ordinary atmospheric conditions.

(d) Delivery of Materials

The fabricator will deliver the fabricated structural steel to the job site in such sequence as will permit the most efficient and economical performance of his own work. If the owner wishes to prescribe or control the sequence of delivery of materials, he reserves such right and defines the requirements in his invitation to bid or the specifications which accompany it.

The quantities of material shown by the shipping statement are customarily accepted by the owner, fabricator and erector as correct. Accordingly, if any shortage is claimed, the owner should immediately notify the carrier and the fabricator in order that the claim may be investigated.

If materials arrive at destination in damaged condition, it is the responsibility of the receiving party to notify the fabricator and carrier prior to unloading the material.

(e) Marking and Shipping of Materials

Erection marks are painted on the structural steel members.

Rivets and bolts are commonly shipped in separate containers according to length and diameter and loose nuts and washers are shipped in separate containers according to sizes. Pins and other small parts, and packages of rivets, bolts, nuts and washers are usually shipped in boxes, crates, kegs or barrels. A list and description of the material will usually appear on the outside of each closed container.

Anchor bolts, washers, and other anchorage or grillage materials to be built into the masonry should be shipped so that they will be on hand when needed. To make this possible, the owner should give the fabricator sufficient time to fabricate and ship such materials before they are needed.

SECTION 7 ERECTION

(a) Method of Erection

If the owner wishes to control the method and sequence of erection, he so specifies in the invitation to bid or the specifications that accompany it. Otherwise the fabricator will proceed according to the most economical method and sequence available to him consistent with the plans and specifications and such information as may be furnished to him prior to the execution of the contract.

(b) Foundations, Piers and Abutments

The invitation to bid, or the specifications which accompany it, should specify the time when all foundations, piers, and abutments will be ready, free from obstruction, and accessible to the erector. Unless the owner specifies to the contrary in inviting bids, the fabricator will bid on the basis that erection will start at a designated time without interference or delay caused by the owner or by others. The accurate location, strength, and suitability of all foundations, piers, and abutments is the sole responsibility of the owner.

(c) Building Lines and Bench Marks

The owner must accurately locate building lines and bench marks at the site of the structure and furnish the fabricator a plan containing all such information.

(d) Anchor Bolts

All anchor or foundation bolts and other connections between the structural steel and the work of other trades are located and set by the owner. In order to avoid unnecessary expense, the owner must assume responsibility for the accurate and complete performance of such work in time so as not to delay or interfere with the erection of the structural steel.

(e) Supporting Bases, Weldments, Castings and Bearing Plates

All steel grillages, rolled steel bearing plates, castings, weldments or other bearing devices which are too heavy to be set without a derrick or crane are set and wedged or shimmed by the steel erector, to grade or level lines which are determined and fixed by the owner who in turn grouts all such parts in place. All other loose bearing plates are set to grade and are grouted by the owner. Before grouting, the owner checks the grades and levels of the parts to be grouted, and is responsible for the accuracy of the same. For steel columns or girders with bases fabricated as an integral part of the member, the foundation is finished to exact grade level and ready to receive the steel work.

(f) Loose Lintels

Unless otherwise specified in the invitation to bid or the specifications which accompany it, the owner sets, without assistance from the erector of the structural steel, such loose lintels, shelf angles, and other pieces not attached to the structural steel as are required by the plans and specifications.

(g) Working Space

The owner provides adequate access roads into and through the site for the safe delivery of derricks, cranes and other necessary equipment as well as the material to be erected. The owner affords the erector properly graded, convenient and adequate space at the site for the operation of his derricks, cranes and other necessary equipment and removes all overhead obstructions such as power lines, telephone lines, etc. in order to provide a safe working area for erection of the steelwork. When the structure does not occupy the full available site, the owner provides adequate storage space to enable the fabricator and erector to operate at maximum practicable speed

(h) Tolerances

Some variation is to be expected in the finished overall dimensions of structural steel frames. Such variations are deemed to be within the limits of good practice when they do not exceed the cumulative effect of the following:

Rolling tolerances for cross-sectional dimensions, camber and sweep permitted under ASTM Specification A6, General Requirements for Delivery of Rolled Plates, Shapes, Sheet Piling and Bars for Structural Use.

Fabricating tolerances for finished parts permitted in the current AISC Specification for the Design, Fabrication and Erection of Structural Steel for Buildings unless otherwise specified in the bid documents or reference specifications.

Erection tolerances of member working points and working lines as provided in this section.

(1) Member working points and working lines are defined as follows:

(a) For members, other than horizontal members, the member work point is the actual center of the member at each end of the shipping piece. For horizontal members, the working point is the actual centerline of the top flange or top surface at each end. Other working points may be established for ease of reference providing they are consistent with this definition.

(b) The member working line is a straight line connecting the member working points.

(2) Erection Tolerances of Member Working Points and Working Lines are as follows:

(a) Individual column shipping pieces shall be considered plumb if the slope of the working line does not exceed 1:500 provided that:

The member working points of column shipping pieces adjacent to elevator shafts are displaced no more than 1 inch from the established column line in the first 20 stories; above this level, the displacement may be increased $\frac{1}{32}$ inch for each additional story up to a maximum of 2 inches.

The member working points of exterior column shipping pieces are displaced from the established column line no more than 1 inch toward nor 2 inches away from the building line in the first 20 stories; above the 20th story, the displacement may be increased $\frac{1}{16}$ inch for each additional story, but may not exceed a total displacement of 2 inches toward nor 3 inches away from the building line.

The member working points of exterior column shipping pieces at any splice level for multi-tier buildings and at the tops of columns for single tier buildings shall fall within a horizontal envelope parallel to the building line not exceeding $1\frac{1}{2}$ inches wide for buildings up to 300 feet in length. The width of the envelope may be increased by $\frac{1}{2}$ inch for each additional 100 feet in length, but shall not exceed 3 inches.

The displacement of the center line of exterior columns parallel to the plane of the wall, from the established column lines shall be no more than 2 inches in any direction at any point in the first 20 stories plus $\frac{1}{16}$ inch per floor above 20 stories, to a maximum of 3 inches.

(b) The horizontal alignment of members connecting to columns shall be considered acceptable if any error in alignment is caused solely by the variation in column alignment within permissible limits.

(c) The elevation of members connecting to columns shall be considered acceptable if the distance from the member working point to the upper milled splice line at the column is not more than plus $3/16$ inch or minus $5/16$ inch of the distance specified on the drawings.

(d) Tolerances of members not covered above shall be considered plumb, level, and aligned if the displacement of the individual member does not exceed 1:500 from a straight line struck between its support points.

(e) The alignment of lintels, wall supports, curb angles, mullions, and similar supporting members for the use of other trades requiring limits closer than the foregoing tolerances cannot be assured unless the Owner's plans call for adjustable connections of these members to the supporting structural frame, as follows:

When adjustable connections are specified, the Owner's plans shall provide for the total adjustment required to meet the proper alignment of these supports for other trades.

When adjustable connections are specified, such supports are considered to be properly located in their vertical position when their location is within $3/8$ inch of the location established from the upper milled splice line of the nearest column to the support location as specified on the drawings.

When adjustable connections are specified, such supports are considered to be properly located in their horizontal position when their location is within $3/8$ inch of the location established for the facia at any particular floor line.

(3) In the design of steel structures, the Owner shall be responsible for providing clearances and adjustments of materials furnished by other trades to accommodate all of the foregoing tolerances of the structural steel frame.

(4) The Owner shall determine promptly, prior to placing or applying any other materials, that the location of the structural steel is acceptable for plumbness, level, and alignment within these tolerances. The erector shall be given timely notice of acceptance, or a listing of specific items to be corrected in order to obtain acceptance by the Owner. Such notice shall be rendered immediately upon completion of any part of the work and prior to the start of other trade work that may be supported, attached, or applied to the structural steelwork.

(i) Temporary Bracing

Unless adequate bracing is included as a part of the permanent framing, the erector during erection installs temporary guys and bracing where needed to secure the framing against loads such as wind and seismic forces comparable in intensity to that for which the structure was designed, acting upon exposed framing, as well as loads due to erection equipment and erection operations, but not including loads resulting from the performance of work by or the acts of others, nor such unpredictable loads as those due to tornado, explosion or collisions.

If additional temporary guys are required to resist wind and seismic forces acting upon components of the finished structure installed by others during the course of the erection of the steel framing, arrangement for their installation by the erector are made by the owner.

The responsibility of the fabricator and erector in this connection ceases when the structural steel is once located, plumbed, leveled and aligned within the tolerances permitted and guyed and braced to the satisfaction of the owner.

The temporary guys, braces, falsework and cribbing are not the property of the owner and may be removed immediately upon completion of the steel erection unless other arrangements are made. The owner removes, and returns them in good condition if they are left in place under such arrangements.

(j) Correction of Errors

Corrections of minor misfits by the moderate use of drift pins, and a moderate amount of reaming, chipping or cutting are considered a part of erection. Any errors which prevent the proper assembly of parts by these measures, or which require correction or adjustment, must be immediately reported to the fabricator and erector to enable whoever is responsible either to correct the error or to approve the most efficient and economic method of correction to be used by others.

(k) Field Assembling

The size of assembled pieces of structural steel may be limited by the permissible weight and clearance dimensions of transportation. Unless otherwise directed by the owner, the fabricator will provide for such field connections as will, in his opinion, require the least amount of field work.

(l) Cuts and Alterations

Neither the fabricator nor the erector will cut, drill or otherwise alter the work of other trades, or his own work to accommodate other trades, unless such work is clearly specified in the bidding information. Whenever such work is specified, complete information as to size, location and number of alterations must be received prior to preparation of shop detail drawings covering the pieces requiring such work.

(m) Temporary Floors for Buildings

It is customary for the owner to provide planking and to cover such floors as may be required by municipal or state laws, excepting the floor upon which the erecting derricks are located; the steel erector will cover this floor for his working purposes, moving his planking as the work progresses. If other arrangements are desired, the owner's invitation to bid and specifications should so specify.

(n) Field Painting

The erector does not paint field bolt heads and nuts, field rivet heads, field welds, or touch up abrasions in the shop coat, or perform any other field painting unless specified in the owner's specifications accompanying the invitation to bid.

(o) Final Cleaning Up

Upon completion of erection and before final acceptance, the erector removes all falsework, rubbish and temporary buildings furnished by him.

Commentary

SECTION 7 ERECTION

(h) Tolerances

Over the years, the American Institute of Steel Construction has constantly monitored its design specifications and *Code of Standard Practice* in order that these documents reflect current building construction methods. This Commentary describes the background for these recent changes which basically reflect the application of tolerances of long-standing use applied to the erection of structural steel. Mill, fabrication and erection tolerances combined actually result in the final accuracy of the structural steel frame.

Mill dimensional tolerances are completely outlined as part of ASTM Specification A6. Figure 1 of this Commentary shows tolerances for the cross sections of rolled members. Fabrication tolerances and practices are established in the AISC *Specification for the Design, Fabrication and Erection of Structural Steel*, AWS *Structural Welding Code*, and other state and federal specifications relating to construction. The AISC has also published *Quality Criteria and Inspection Standards*, which covers recommended dimensional tolerances for fabrication. All of these documents have been reviewed and considered in establishing these erection tolerances for the actual structural steel building frame.

The AISC *Code of Standard Practice*, dated October, 1924, under paragraph 7(f), Plumbing Up, defined tolerances for steel erection as follows:

"In the setting or erecting of structural steelwork, the individual pieces shall be considered plumb or level where the error does not exceed 1 to 500.

"For exterior columns and columns adjacent to elevator shafts of multiple story buildings, the error from plumb shall not exceed 1 to 1,000 for the total height of the column."

The above criteria remained unchanged from 1924 through 1958. With the changes that took place in the types and use of materials in building construction after World War II, and the increasing demand by Architects and Owners for more specific tolerances, the AISC adopted new standards for erection tolerances in Section 7(h) of the March 15, 1959 revision of the *Code of Standard Practice*.

Experience has proved that the tolerances published in 1959 can be economically attained. It has become evident since then that there is a need to bring together the elements making up these tolerances and to more fully define the working points and lines governing the measurements of the actual steel location. These elements, working points, lines and the application of these tolerances are defined in Section 7(h)1 of this revision of the Code. This Commentary also provides illustrations for defining and applying the allowable Code tolerances (see Figs. 1, 2, and 3).

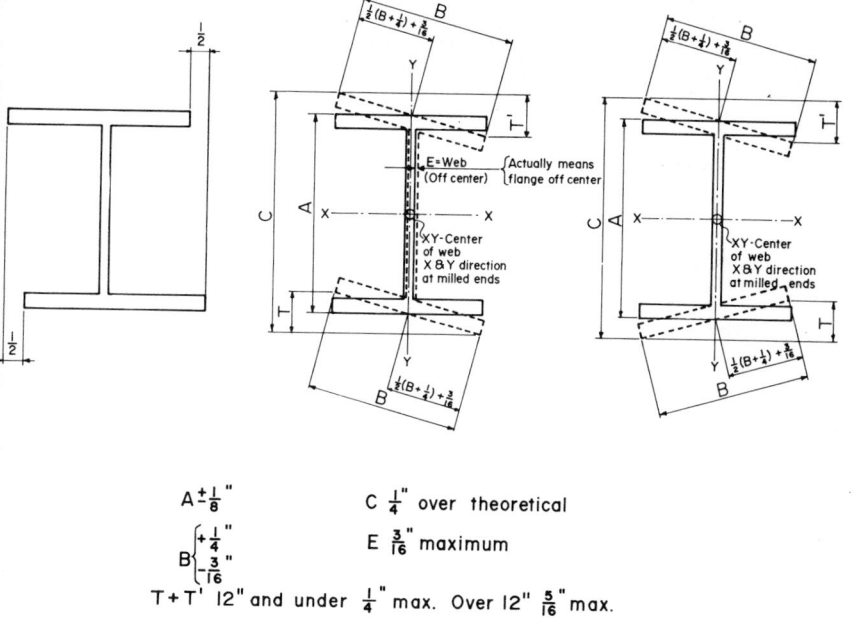

$A \pm \frac{1}{8}"$ $C \frac{1}{4}"$ over theoretical

$B \begin{cases} +\frac{1}{4}" \\ -\frac{3}{16}" \end{cases}$ $E \frac{3}{16}"$ maximum

$T + T'$ 12" and under $\frac{1}{4}"$ max. Over 12" $\frac{5}{16}"$ max.

Fig. 1.   Mill tolerances for rolled shapes

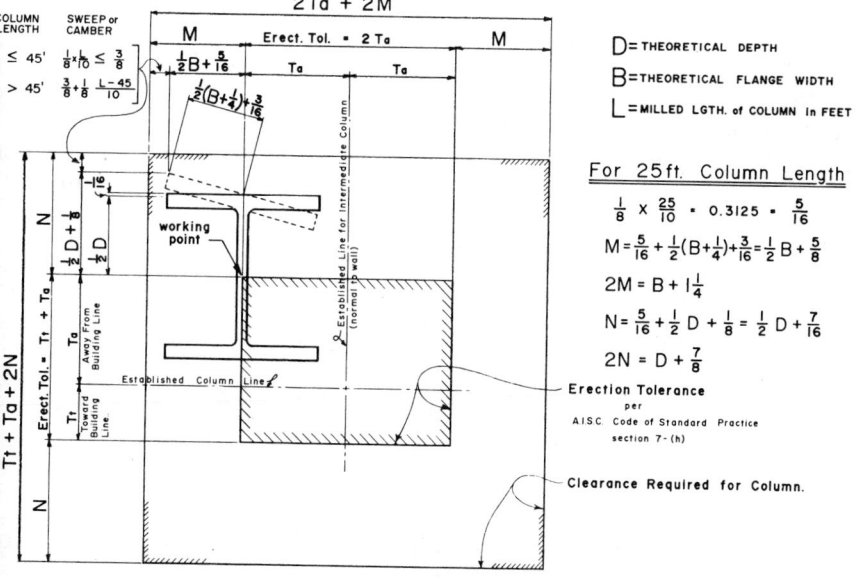

D = THEORETICAL DEPTH

B = THEORETICAL FLANGE WIDTH

L = MILLED LGTH. of COLUMN In FEET

For 25ft. Column Length

$\frac{1}{8} \times \frac{25}{10} = 0.3125 = \frac{5}{16}$

$M = \frac{5}{16} + \frac{1}{2}(B + \frac{1}{4}) + \frac{3}{16} = \frac{1}{2}B + \frac{5}{8}$

$2M = B + 1\frac{1}{4}$

$N = \frac{5}{16} + \frac{1}{2}D + \frac{1}{8} = \frac{1}{2}D + \frac{7}{16}$

$2N = D + \frac{7}{8}$

Erection Tolerance
per
A.I.S.C. Code of Standard Practice
section 7-(h)

Clearance Required for Column.

Fig. 2.   Calculation of clearances required for columns

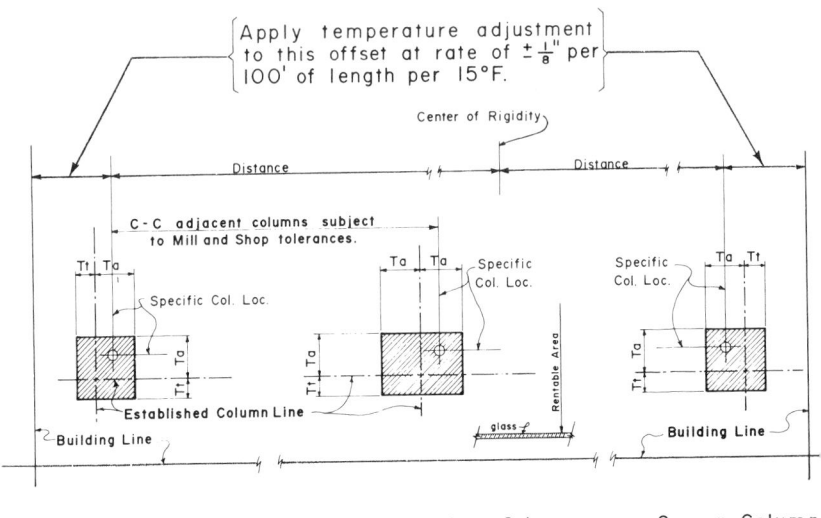

Fig. 3. Plan location of columns

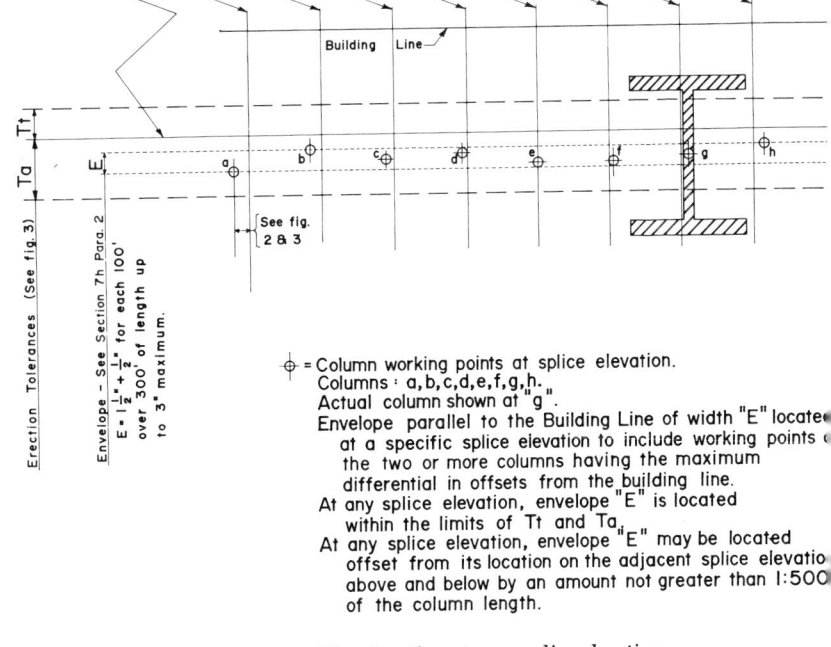

Fig. 4. Plan location at any splice elevation

The wide range of building facades available today, the trend away from built-in-place construction, toward building by assembling prefabricated components, have made the magnitude of the tolerances allowable in a structural steel building frame increasingly important to Owners, Architects, and Engineers. It has led to inclusion in job specifications of unrealistically small tolerances. Such job tolerances are not economically feasible and do not measureably increase a structures functional value.

This revised Code incorporates the tolerances previously found to be practical and presents them in a more precise and clear manner. Actual application methods have been considered and the Code defines the application of the tolerance limitations to the actual structure.

In this revision of the Code, a limitation of 1½ inches in up to 300 feet length has been placed on the differential offsets to be expected between exterior columns at any one particular splice elevation, as shown in Fig. 4 (see Section 7(h)2a). This limitation requires all columns at a particular splice elevation to be located within a narrow horizontal envelope parallel to the building line. In plan the envelope is located to enclose the column working point nearest the building line and the column working point farthest from the building line. The horizontal location of this envelope on successive floors is not necessarily directly over its location on the floor below, but may be shifted as necessary at each splice elevation within the limitation of the 1:500 allowable tolerance in plumbness of the controlling columns.

The limitation described above and shown in Fig. 4 makes it possible, provided small adjustments are made in the plane of the facade above the 20th floor, to limit to 3 inches the provision required for adjustment of the facade connections to the structural frame. A maximum deviation of the facade from a truly vertical plane of ⅟₁₆ inch per story above the 20th floor up to a maximum displacement +1 inch would insure that the 3 inch adjustment would accommodate the maximum relative displacement between any column and the facade.

Adjustable connections providing +2 inches to −3 inches (5 inches total) will be necessary in cases where the Architect or Owner insists on attempting to construct the facade to a vertical plane.

Often there is a differential shortening of the internal vs. the external columns during construction due to unequal dead load unit stresses (see Fig.). The amount of such shortenings is indeterminate, since it varies from day to day as the construction progresses and does not reach its designed limit until the building is completed. If the finished floor is to be level under full dead load, it follows that when constructed under partial dead load it must be finished on a slope. The above, plus mill camber and deflections, all become very important when there is little cover over the steel, when there are electrical fittings mounted on the steel flooring whose tops are supposed to be flush with the finished floor, or when there is little clearance around ductwork.

Observations in the field have shown that where a precast concrete facade is erected to a greater height on one side of a multistory building than on the other, the steel framing will be pulled out of alignment.

Steel structures are usually aligned using surveying instruments referenced to marks on adjacent buildings or on the ground. Since a long uncased steel frame will expand or contract ⅛ inch per 100 feet for each change of 15°F in temperature, and since this can be assumed to act about

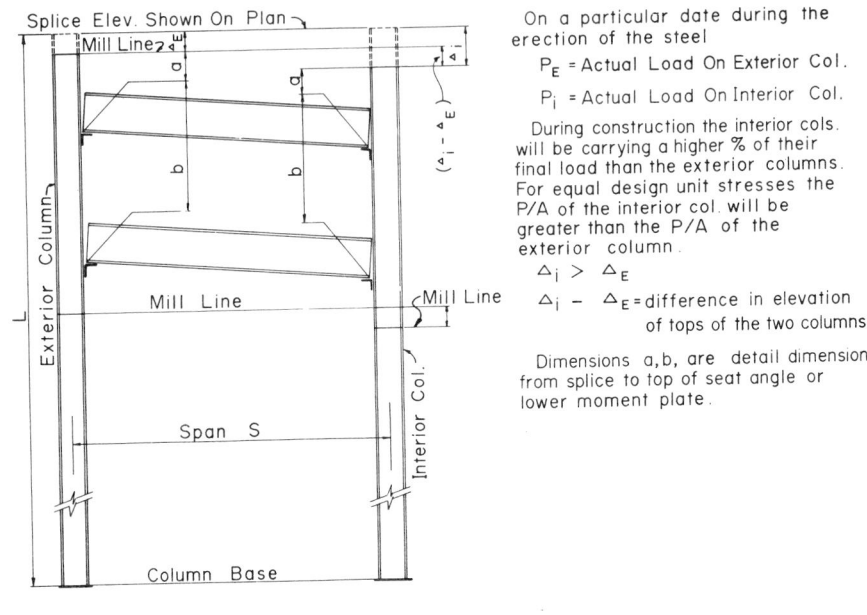

On a particular date during the erection of the steel

P_E = Actual Load On Exterior Col.

P_i = Actual Load On Interior Col.

During construction the interior cols. will be carrying a higher % of their final load than the exterior columns. For equal design unit stresses the P/A of the interior col. will be greater than the P/A of the exterior column.

$$\Delta_i > \Delta_E$$

$\Delta_i - \Delta_E$ = difference in elevation of tops of the two columns.

Dimensions a,b, are detail dimensions from splice to top of seat angle or lower moment plate.

Fig. 5. Effect of differential column shortening

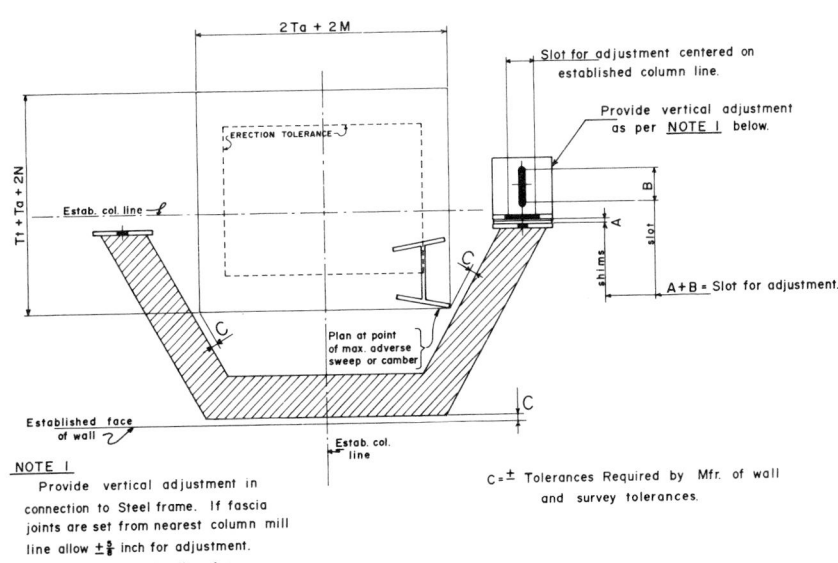

NOTE I
Provide vertical adjustment in connection to Steel frame. If fascia joints are set from nearest column mill line allow $\pm\frac{3}{8}$ inch for adjustment. Owners Plans must allow for progressive shortening of steel columns.

Fig. 6. Effect of erection and mill tolerances on design of fascia and its connections

the center of rigidity, the end columns will be plumb only when the steel is at normal temperature. It is, therefore, necessary to correct field measurements of offsets to the structure from established base lines for the expansion or contraction of the steel frame. For example, a building 200 feet long that is plumbed up at 0°F should have the end columns leaning in ½ inch in order for them to be plumb at say 60°F.

The alignment of lintels, spandrels, wall supports or similar members used to connect other building construction units to the steel frame have to have adjustment of the magnitude to allow for the cumulative effects of mill, fabrication, and erection tolerances on the actual erected structural steel frame (see Fig. 6). The precision of setting has not been changed.

SPECIFICATION FOR

Architecturally Exposed
Structural Steel

Adopted by the American Institute of Steel Construction, August, 1960

AMERICAN INSTITUTE OF STEEL CONSTRUCTION

101 Park Avenue, New York, N. Y. 10017

FOREWORD

TO THE SPECIFICATION FOR ARCHITECTURALLY EXPOSED STRUCTURAL STEEL

The rapidly increasing use of exposed structural steel as a medium of architectural expression in recent years has given rise to a demand for closer dimensional tolerances and smoother finished surfaces than required for ordinary structural steel framing. This specification establishes standards for these requirements which reconcile finished appearance with construction costs.

In order to avoid misunderstandings and to hold costs to a minimum, it is recommended that only those steel surfaces and connections which will remain exposed and subject to normal view by pedestrians or occupants in the completed structure be included under this specification.

SPECIFICATION FOR

Architecturally Exposed Structural Steel

Adopted by the American Institute of Steel Construction, Inc., August 25, 1960

SECTION 1   SCOPE

(a)   This specification shall only apply to members specifically designated on the design drawings as "architecturally exposed structural steel" which shall be fabricated, handled and erected as directed in this specification, and except as noted below, in conformity with the American Institute of Steel Construction Specification for the Design, Fabrication and Erection of Structural Steel for Buildings.   Because these members so designated are subject to close inspection by the public, the fabrication tolerances in this specification shall govern when such tolerances are in conflict with those of the AISC Specification.

SECTION 2   MATERIAL

(a)   Material shall be the same as specified for Structural Steel by the AISC Specification.

(b)   Permissible tolerances for out-of-square or out-of-parallel, depth, width and symmetry of rolled shapes shall conform to ASTM Specification A6.   Overall profile dimensions of built-up members shall be adequate to provide for the accumulated permissible overrun of the component parts.

(c)   The as-fabricated straightness tolerances of members shall not exceed one-half of the standard camber and sweep tolerances in ASTM A6.

SECTION 3   FABRICATION

(a)   Fabrication shall be performed with special care and necessary straightening to maintain the condition of the material as described above.

(b)   Shop details shall show clearly the required fabrication tolerances. Erection plans and/or anchor bolt plans shall show the required tolerances for setting embedded items.

(c)   All copes, mitres and butt cuts in surfaces exposed to view shall be made with uniform gaps of ⅛" if shown by the architect to be open joints, or in uniform contact if shown without gap.

(d)   Where the fit-up of adjacent members is such that permissible tolerances specified in Sections 2b and 2c may result in an unsightly joint, the architect shall specify on the design plans the tolerances required.   These tolerances shall be maintained by special attention in detailing the joint, or if necessary by refined fabrication techniques.

SECTION 4 WELDING

(a) Fillet Welds

Faces of welds exposed to view shall have as-welded surfaces that are reasonably smooth and uniform. No finishing or grinding shall be required except where clearances or fit of other items may so necessitate, or as specifically required by design drawings.

(b) Butt and Plug Welds

Faces of butt and plug welds exposed to view shall have as-welded surfaces that are reasonably smooth and uniform and shall not project more than $\frac{1}{16}''$ above the surfaces joined. No finishing or grinding shall be required except where clearances or fit of other items may so necessitate, or as specifically required by design drawings.

SECTION 5 PAINTING

(a) After inspection and approval and before leaving the shop, all steelwork shall be cleaned by hand wire brushing, or by other means, elected by the fabricator, of loose mill scale, loose rust, accessible weld slag or flux deposit, dirt and other foreign matter. Oil and grease deposits shall be removed by solvent.

(b) After cleaning all steelwork shall be given one coat of shop paint applied thoroughly and evenly to dry surfaces, by brush, spray, roller coating, flow coating, or dipping, at the election of the fabricator.

(c) Surfaces within two inches of any field weld location shall be free of materials that would prevent proper welding or produce objectionable fumes while welding is being done. If shop painted, surfaces to be welded shall be wire brushed in the field before welding to reduce the paint film to a minimum.

SECTION 6 ERECTION

(a) The erector shall use special care in unloading, handling, and erecting the steel to avoid bending, twisting, or otherwise distorting the steel members. The erector shall handle the material in such a way as to minimize the damage to shop coat of paint.

(b) The erector shall plan and execute the erection in such a way that the close fit and neat appearance of the joints and the structure as a whole will not be impaired.

(c) If temporary braces or erection clips are employed, care shall be taken to avoid any unsightliness upon removal. Tack welds shall be ground smooth and holes shall be filled with weld metal or body solder and smoothed by grinding or filing.

SECTION 7 INSPECTION

(a) The architect shall inspect the steel at the point of fabrication prior to shipment.

SPECIFICATION FOR

Structural Joints Using ASTM A325 or A490 Bolts

Approved by the Research Council on Riveted and Bolted Structural Joints

of the Engineering Foundation, April 18, 1972

Endorsed by American Institute of Steel Construction

Endorsed by Industrial Fasteners Institute

AMERICAN INSTITUTE OF STEEL CONSTRUCTION

101 Park Avenue, New York, N. Y. 10017

SPECIFICATION FOR

Structural Joints Using ASTM A325 or A490 Bolts

Approved by Research Council on Riveted and Bolted Structural Joints of the
Engineering Foundation, April 18, 1972
Endorsed by American Institute of Steel Construction, Inc.
Endorsed by Industrial Fasteners Institute

1 Scope

(a) This specification covers the design and assembly of structural joints using ASTM A325 high-strength carbon steel bolts, ASTM A490 high-strength alloy steel bolts, or equivalent fasteners, tightened to a specified tension.

(b) Construction shall conform to an applicable existing code or specification for structures of wrought iron, carbon structural steel or high-strength steel, except as otherwise provided herein.

(c) Joints required to resist shear between their connected parts are designated as either *friction-type* or *bearing-type* connections. Shear connections subjected to stress reversal, severe stress fluctuation, or where slippage would be undesirable, shall be *friction-type*.

(d) The attached Commentary provides guidance in the application of the specification.

2 Bolts, Nuts and Washers

(a) Except as provided in paragraph (d) of this section, bolts, nuts and circular washers if required, shall conform to requirements of the current edition of the specifications of the American Society for Testing and Materials for High-Strength Bolts for Structural Steel Joints, Including Suitable Nuts and Plain Hardened Washers, ASTM A325, or for Quenched and Tempered Alloy Steel Bolts for Structural Steel Joints, ASTM A490. The designer shall specify the grade of bolts to be used.

(b) Except as provided in paragraph (d) of this section, bolt dimensions shall conform to the current requirements of the American National Standards Institute for heavy hex structural bolts, ANSI Standard B18.2.1.

(c) Except as provided in paragraph (d) of this section, nut dimensions shall conform to current requirements of the American National Standards Institute for heavy hex nuts, ANSI Standard B18.2.2.

(d) Other fasteners which meet the materials, manufacturing, and chemical composition requirements of ASTM specification A325 or A490 and which meet the mechanical property requirements of the same specification in full-size tests and which have body diameter and bearing areas under the head and nut, or their equiva-

Table 1 Washer Dimensions[a]

Bolt Size D	Circular Washers				Square or Rectangular Beveled Washers for American Standard Beams and Channels		
	Nominal Outside Diameter	Nominal Diameter of Hole	Thickness		Minimum Side Dimension	Mean Thickness	Slope or Taper in Thickness
			Min.	Max.			
1/2	1 1/16	17/32	0.097	0.177	1 3/4	5/16	1:6
5/8	1 5/16	21/32	0.122	0.177	1 3/4	5/16	1:6
3/4	1 15/32	13/16	0.122	0.177	1 3/4	5/16	1:6
7/8	1 3/4	15/16	0.136	0.177	1 3/4	5/16	1:6
1	2	1 1/16	0.136	0.177	1 3/4	5/16	1:6
1 1/8	2 1/4	1 1/4	0.136	0.177	2 1/4	5/16	1:6
1 1/4	2 1/2	1 3/8	0.136	0.177	2 1/4	5/16	1:6
1 3/8	2 3/4	1 1/2	0.136	0.177	2 1/4	5/16	1:6
1 1/2	3	1 5/8	0.136	0.177	2 1/4	5/16	1:6
1 3/4	3 3/8	1 7/8	0.178[b]	0.28[b]	—	—	—
2	3 3/4	2 1/8	0.178[b]	0.28[b]	—	—	—
Over 2 to 4 incl.	2D − 1/2	D + 1/8	0.24[c]	0.34[c]	—	—	—

[a] Dimensions in inches. (Tolerances as noted in Table 1-A.)
[b] 3/16 in. nominal.
[c] 1/4 in. nominal.

lent, not less than those provided by a bolt and nut of the same nominal dimensions prescribed by paragraphs 2(b) and 2(c), may be used. Such alternate fasteners may differ in other dimensions from those of the specified bolts and nuts. Their installation procedure may differ from those specified in paragraphs 5(c) and 5(d) and their inspection may differ from that specified in Section 6. When a different installation procedure or inspection is used, it shall be detailed in a supplemental specification applying to the alternate fastener and this specification must be approved by the engineer responsible for the design of the structure.

(e) Circular washers and square or rectangular beveled washers shall conform to the dimensions in Table 1 within tolerances given in Table 1-A. Washers shall have no raised markings on their bearing surfaces.

   Where necessary, washers may be clipped on one side to a point not closer than 1/8 of the bolt diameter from the center of the washer.

Table 1-A Washer Dimension Tolerances (inches)

Dimension	Washer Size	
	To 1 1/2 in. Nominal Bolt Size, incl.	Over 1 1/2 in. Nominal Bolt Size
Nominal diameter of hole	−0; +1/32	−0; +1/16
Nominal outside dimensions	−1/32; +1/4	−1/32; +1/4
Flatness; max. deviation from straight edge placed on "cut" side shall not exceed	0.01	0.015
Burr shall not project above immediately adjacent washer surface more than	0.01	0.015

Table 2 Allowable Working Stresses for Fasteners[a]

Specification Paragraph	Loading Conditions	ASTM A325 Bolts		ASTM A490 Bolts	
		Bridges	Buildings	Bridges	Buildings
4(b)	Applied tension, psi	36,000	40,000	48,000[b]	54,000[b]
4(c)	Shear, psi				
	1. Friction-type connection	13,500	15,000	18,000	20,000
	2. Bearing-type connection, shear plane through threads	13,500	15,000	20,000	22,500
	3. Bearing-type connection, threads excluded	20,000	22,000	29,000	32,000
4(d)	Bearing, psi[c]	$1.22\,F_y$	$1.35\,F_y$	$1.22\,F_y$	$1.35\,F_y$

[a] The tabulated stresses, except for bearing stress, apply to bolts used in any grade of steel.
[b] Static loading only.
[c] F_y = Specified minimum yield point of the lowest strength connected part.

3 Bolted Parts

(a) The slope of surfaces of bolted parts in contact with the bolt head and nut shall not exceed 1 : 20 with respect to a plane normal to the bolt axis. Bolted parts shall fit solidly together when assembled and shall not be separated by gaskets or any other interposed compressible material. Holes may be punched, subpunched and reamed, or drilled, as required by the applicable code or specification and, except as hereinafter provided, shall be a nominal diameter not more than 1/16-in. in excess of the nominal bolt diameter.

Where shown in the design drawings and at other locations approved by the designer, oversize, short-slotted, and long-slotted holes* may be used with high strength bolts 5/8-in. in diameter and larger proportioned to meet the allowable working stresses given in Table 2 except as hereinafter restricted:

1. *Oversize holes* are 3/16-in. larger than bolts 7/8-in. and less in diameter, 1/4-in. larger than bolts 1-in. in diameter, and 5/16-in. larger than bolts 1 1/8-in. and greater in diameter. They may be used in any or all plies of *friction-type* connections. Hardened washers shall be installed over exposed oversize holes.

2. *Short slotted holes* are 1/16-in. wider than the bolt diameter and have a length which does not exceed the oversize diameter provisions of paragraph 3(a)1 by more than 1/16-in. They may be used in any or all plies of *friction-type* or *bearing-type* connections. The slots may be used without regard to direction of loading in *friction-type* connections but shall be normal to the direction of the load in *bearing-type* connections. Hardened washers shall be installed over exposed short slotted holes.

3. *Long slotted holes* are 1/16-in. wider than the bolt diameter and have a length more than allowed in sub-paragraph 2 but not more than 2 1/2 times the bolt diameter.

In *friction-type* connections, they may be used without regard to direction of loading if one-third more bolts are provided than needed to satisfy the allowable working stress given in Table 2.

* See Table 7 in Commentary.

In *bearing-type* connections, the long diameter of the slot shall be normal to the direction of loading. No increase in the number of bolts over those necessary for the allowable stress given in Table 2 is required.

Long slotted holes may be used in only one of the connected parts of either a friction-type or bearing-type connection at an individual faying surface.

Structural plate washers or a continuous bar not less than $5/16$-in. in thickness are required to cover long slots that are in the outer plies of joints. These washers or bars shall have a size sufficient to completely cover the slot after installation.

(b) When assembled, all joint surfaces, including those adjacent to the bolt heads, nuts or washers, shall be free of scale, except tight mill scale, and shall also be free of burrs, dirt and other foreign material that would prevent solid seating of the parts.

(c) Contact surfaces within *friction-type* joints shall be free of oil, paint, lacquer or other coatings, except as listed below:

1. Hot-dip galvanizing, if contact surfaces are scored by wire brushing or blasting after galvanizing and prior to assembly.

2. Inorganic zinc rich paints as defined in those sections of the Steel Structures Painting Council Systems, SSPC PS 12.00, covering zinc rich paints with inorganic vehicles.

3. Metallized zinc or aluminum applied in accordance with AWS C2.2 Recommended Practice for Metallizing with Aluminum and Zinc for Protection of Iron and Steel, except that subsequent sealing treatments, described in Section IV therein, shall not be used.

4 Allowable Working Stresses

(a) *Design Stresses.* The allowable working stresses for A325 and A490 bolts specified in the following paragraphs are given, respectively, for bridges and buildings in Table 2. As used in paragraphs (b) and (c), nominal bolt area is defined as the area corresponding to the nominal diameter of the bolt.

(b) *Applied Tension.* Bolts required to support applied load by means of direct tension shall be so proportioned that their average tensile stress, computed on the basis of nominal bolt area and independent of any initial tightening force, will not exceed the appropriate stress given in Table 2. The applied load shall be the sum of the external load and any tension resulting from prying action produced by deformation of the connected parts.

(c) *Shear*

1. Bolts in *friction-type* connections assembled in accordance with the requirements of paragraph 3(c) shall be proportioned on the basis of the appropriate stress given in Table 2. These shear stresses may be used to proportion high-strength bolts used in combination with rivets or welds designed in accordance with the provisions of the applicable code or specification. In *friction-type* connections there need be no consideration of bearing, and fillers need not be "developed." However, eccentricity of forces at short thick fillers must be considered.

2. Bolts in *bearing-type* connections having thread in a plane of contact surfaces of the connected parts shall be proportioned on the basis of the appropriate stress given in Table 2.

3. Bolts in *bearing-type* connections, where bolt threads are excluded from the shear planes of the contact surfaces between the connected parts, shall be proportioned on the basis of the appropriate stress given in Table 2.

(d) *Bearing.* In *bearing-type* connections the computed bearing pressure, assumed to be distributed over an area equal to the nominal bolt diameter times the thickness of the connected part, shall not exceed the appropriate stress given in Table 2.

In *bearing-type* connections having no more than two bolts in a line parallel to the direction of stress, the distance between the center of the nearest bolt and that end of the connected member towards which the pressure from the bolt is directed shall be not less than AC/t for single shear or $2AC/t$ for double shear, where A is the nominal cross-sectional area of the fastener, t is the thickness of the connected part and C is the ratio of specified minimum tensile strength of the fastener to the specified minimum tensile strength of the connected part. This end distance may be proportionately less where the shear stress per bolt is less than that permitted in this section, but not less than $1\frac{1}{2}$ times the bolt diameter. It need not exceed $1\frac{1}{2}$ times the transverse spacing of the fasteners.

(e) *Increase in Working Stress.* Increase in working stress allowed in the applicable code or specification may be applied to the stresses given in this section (see Commentary for *Shear; Friction-Type Connections*).

5   Installation

(a) *Fastener Tension.* Each fastener shall be tightened to provide, when all fasteners in the joint are tight, at least the minimum tension shown in Table 3 for the size and grade of fastener used.

Threaded bolts shall be tightened by methods described in subparagraphs (c), (d), or (e) of this section. If required because of bolt entering and wrench operation clearances, tightening by

Table 3   Fastener Tension

Bolt Size, in Inches	Minimum Fastener Tension[a] in Thousands of Pounds (kips)	
	A325 Bolts	A490 Bolts
$\frac{1}{2}$	12	15
$\frac{5}{8}$	19	24
$\frac{3}{4}$	28	35
$\frac{7}{8}$	39	49
1	51	64
$1\frac{1}{8}$	56	80
$1\frac{1}{4}$	71	102
$1\frac{3}{8}$	85	121
$1\frac{1}{2}$	103	148

[a] Equal to 70 percent of specified minimum tensile strengths of bolts, rounded off to the nearest kip.

either procedure described in subparagraphs (c) or (d) may be done by turning the bolt while the nut is prevented from rotating.

Impact wrenches, if used, shall be of adequate capacity and sufficiently supplied with air to perform the required tightening of each bolt in approximately ten seconds.

(b) *Washers.* A325 fasteners meeting the provisions of Section 2 may be installed without hardened washers when tightening is by the turn-of-nut method except as noted in Section 3. A490 bolts installed by the turn-of-nut method and A325 or A490 bolts tightened by the calibrated wrench method (i.e., by torque control) shall have a hardened washer under the element (nut or bolt head) turned in tightening and as provided in Section 3, if applicable. Two hardened washers shall be used with all A490 bolts used to connect material having a specified minimum yield point less than 40 ksi.

Where an outer face of the bolted parts has a slope greater than 1:20 with respect to a plane normal to the bolt axis, a beveled washer shall be used to compensate for the lack of parallelism.

(c) *Turn-of-Nut Tightening.* When the turn-of-nut method is used to provide the bolt tension specified in paragraph 5(a), there shall first be enough bolts brought to a "snug tight" condition to insure that the parts of the joint are brought into good contact with each other. Snug tight is defined as the tightness attained by a few impacts of an impact wrench or the full effort of a man using an ordinary spud wrench. Following this initial operation, bolts shall be placed in any remaining holes in the connection and brought to snug tightness. All bolts in the joint shall then be tightened additionally by the applicable amount of nut rotation specified in Table 4, with tightening progressing systematically from the most rigid part of the joint to its free edges. During this operation there shall be no rotation of the part not turned by the wrench.

(d) *Calibrated Wrench Tightening.* When calibrated wrenches are used, they should be set to provide a tension at least 5% in excess of the minimum bolt tension specified in 5(a). The wrenches shall be calibrated at least once each working day for each bolt diameter being installed. Wrenches shall be recalibrated when significant changes are made in the equipment or when a significant difference is noted in the surface condition of the bolts, nuts or washers. Calibration shall be accomplished by tightening, in a device capable

Table 4 Nut Rotation[a] from Snug Tight Condition

Disposition of Outer Faces of Bolted Parts		
Both faces normal to bolt axis, or one face normal to axis and other face sloped not more than 1:20 (bevel washer not used)		Both faces sloped not more than 1:20 from normal to bolt axis (bevel washers not used)
Bolt length[b] not exceeding 8 diameters or 8 inches	Bolt length[b] exceeding 8 diameters or 8 inches	For all length of bolts
½ turn	⅔ turn	¾ turn

[a] Nut rotation is rotation relative to bolt regardless of the element (nut or bolt) being turned. Tolerance on rotation: 30° (one-twelfth full turn) over or under.
For coarse thread heavy hex structural bolts of all sizes and length and heavy hex semi-finished nuts.
[b] Bolt length is measured from underside of head to extreme end of point.

of indicating actual bolt tension, three typical bolts of each diameter from the bolts being installed.

When adjusting the wrenches to provide the required tension, it shall be verified during actual installation in the assembled steelwork that the calibration selected does not produce a nut or bolt head rotation from snug tight greater than that permitted in Table 4. If manual torque wrenches are used, nuts shall be in tightening motion when torque is measured.

When using calibrated wrenches to install several bolts in a single joint, the wrench shall be returned to "touch up" bolts previously tightened, which may have been loosened by the tightening of subsequent bolts, until all are tightened to the prescribed amount.

(e) *Tightening by Use of a Direct Tension Indicator.* Tightening by this means is permitted provided it can be demonstrated by an accurate direct measurement procedure that the bolt has been tightened in accordance with Table 3.

6 Inspection

(a) The Inspector shall determine that the requirements of Sections 2, 3 and 5 of this specification are met in the work. When the calibrated wrench method of tightening is used, the Inspector shall have full opportunity to witness the calibration tests prescribed in paragraph 5(d).

(b) The Inspector shall observe the installation of bolts to determine that the selected procedure is properly used and shall determine that all bolts are tightened. Bolts installed by the turn-of-nut method may reach tensions above the value given in Table 3 but this shall not be cause for rejection.

(c) When there is need for more inspection of bolt tension in the turn-of-nut and calibrated wrench methods than that provided in paragraph 6(b), the following arbitration inspection shall be used unless a more extensive or different procedure is specified in the inquiry and order for the work:

1. The Inspector shall use an *inspecting wrench* which may be either a torque wrench or a power wrench that can be adjusted in accordance with the requirements of paragraph 5(d).

2. Three bolts of the same grade, size* and condition as those under inspection shall be placed individually in a calibration device capable of indicating bolt tension. The surface under the part to be turned in tightening each bolt shall be like that under the corresponding part in the structure; i.e., there shall be a washer under the part turned if washers are so used in the structure or, if no washer is used, the material abutting the part turned shall be of the same specification as that in the structure.

3. When the *inspecting wrench* is a torque wrench, each bolt specified in paragraph 6(c)2 shall be tightened in the calibration device by any convenient means to an initial condition equal to approximately 15% of the required fastener tension and then to

---

* Length may be any length representative of bolts used in the structure.

the minimum tension specified for its size in paragraph 5(a). Tightening beyond the initial condition must not produce greater nut rotation than that permitted in Table 4. The *inspecting wrench* then shall be applied to the tightened bolt and the torque necessary to turn the nut or head 5 degrees (approximately 1 inch at 12 inch radius) in the tightening direction shall be determined. The average torque measured in the tests of three bolts shall be taken as the *job inspecting torque* to be used in the manner specified in paragraph 6(c)5.

4. When the *inspecting wrench* is a power wrench it shall be adjusted so that it will tighten each bolt specified in paragraph 6(c)2 to a tension at least 5% but not more than 10% greater than the minimum tension specified for its size in paragraph 5(a). However, this power wrench setting must not produce greater nut rotation from the snug condition than that permitted in Table 4. This setting of wrench shall be taken as the *job inspecting torque* to be used in the manner specified in paragraph 6(c)5.

5. Bolts represented by the sample prescribed in paragraph 6(c)2 which have been tightened in the structure shall be inspected by applying, in the tightening direction, the *inspecting wrench* and its *job inspecting torque* to 10% of the bolts, but not less than two bolts, selected at random in each connection. If no nut or bolt head is turned by this application of the *job inspecting torque*, the connection shall be accepted as properly tightened. If any nut or bolt head is turned by the application of the *job inspecting torque*, this torque shall be applied to all bolts in the connection, and all bolts whose nut or head is turned by the *job inspecting torque* shall be tightened and re-inspected, or alternatively, the fabricator or erector, at his option may re-tighten all of the bolts in the connection and then re-submit the connection for the specified inspection.

COMMENTARY

C1 Scope

When first approved by the Research Council on Riveted and Bolted Structural Joints of the Engineering Foundation, January, 1951, the Specification for Assembly of Structural Joints Using High-Strength Bolts merely permitted the substitution of a like number of A325 high-strength bolts for hot-driven ASTM A141* steel rivets of the same nominal diameter. It was required that all contact surfaces be free of paint. As revised in 1954, the omission was required to apply only to "joints subjected to stress reversal impact or vibration, or to cases where stress redistribution due to joint slippage would be undesirable." This relaxation of the earlier provision recognized the fact that, in a great many cases, movement of the connected parts that brings the bolts into bearing against the sides of their holes is in no way detrimental. When the nature of the loading—whether

---

* Presently identified as A502, Grade 1.

static or cyclic—is such that fatigue-type failure or reversal of movement will not occur, the high clamping force in the bolts provides a rigid assembly in the "slipped" position, and the shear strength of the high-strength bolts, when threads are excluded from contact surface shear planes, is substantially greater than that of hot-driven rivets required to function under similar circumstances. Since allowable stresses as well as the requirements for treatment of contact surfaces appropriate to these service conditions are different, the present specification recognizes two kinds of shear connections, designated as *friction-type* and *bearing-type*, respectively.

Just how much stronger the high-strength bolts are in resisting actual shearing forces and what effect the higher stresses in the bolts have upon the strength of the connected parts have been the subjects of extensive study in the bolt sizes generally used in construction sponsored by the Research Council since 1954. The results of these studies, together with improvements in installation practices which are the outgrowth of extensive experience in the use of high-strength bolts, formed the background for the 1960 edition. The 1962 revision reflected the results of additional research which had shown that washers may be omitted from A325 bolt assemblies. This revision incorporates the results of research conducted since that time, especially on A490 bolts.

The increasing use of high-strength steels has created the need for bolts substantially stronger than A325, in order to resist, with well-proportioned joints, the much greater forces that they support. To meet this need, a new ASTM standard, A490, has been developed.

When provisions for the use of these bolts were included in the Specification in 1964 it was required that they be tightened to their specified proof load, as was required for the installation of A325 bolts. However, the ratio of proof load to specified minimum tensile strength is approximately 0.7 for A325 bolts, whereas it is 0.8 for A490 bolts. Calibration studies have shown that high strength bolts have ultimate load capacities in torqued tension which vary from about 80% to 90% of the direct tensile strength.[1] Hence, if minimum strength bolts were supplied and they experienced the maximum reduction due to torquing, there is a possibility that these bolts could not be tightened to proof load by any method of installation. Also, statistical studies have shown that, tightening to the 0.8 ratio under calibrated wrench control may result in some "twist-off" bolt failures during installation or in some cases a slight amount of under-tightening.[2] Therefore the required installed tension for A490 bolts has been reduced to 70 percent of the specified minimum tensile strength. For consistency, but with only minor change, the initial tension required for A325 bolts has also been set at 0.7 of their specified minimum tensile strength and at the same time the values in Table 3 have been rounded off to the nearest kip.

Because greater clamping force is used with A490 bolts it is required that hardened washers, conforming to the requirements of ASTM Specifica-

---

[1] "Calibration of Alloy Steel Bolts," by Christopher, R. J., Kulak, G. L., and Fisher, J. W., *Journal of the Structural Division*, ASCE, Vol. 92, No. ST2, Proc. Paper 4768, April, 1966, pp. 19–40.

[2] "Specification of Minimum Preloads for Structural Bolts," by Gill, P. J., Memorandum 30, G. K. N. Group Research Laboratory, England, 1966 (Unpublished Report).

tion A325, be installed under both the nut and bolt head when A490 bolts are used in steels having a yield point less than 40 ksi and under the turned element when they are used in higher-strength steels.

The ASTM specification A325 now provides for three types of high strength structural bolts.

Type 1. Bolts of medium carbon steel, supplied in sizes ½-in. to 1½-in., inclusive.

Type 2. Bolts of low carbon martensite steel, supplied in sizes ½-in. to 1-in., inclusive.

Type 3. Bolts having atmospheric corrosion resistance and weathering characteristics comparable to that of A588 and A242 steels, supplied in sizes ½-in. to 1½-in., inclusive.

When the type of bolt is not specified, Type 1 bolts shall be supplied. However, since the mechanical properties of all three types of bolts are comparable, the manufacturer may supply Type 2 or Type 3 bolts if agreed upon by the purchaser.

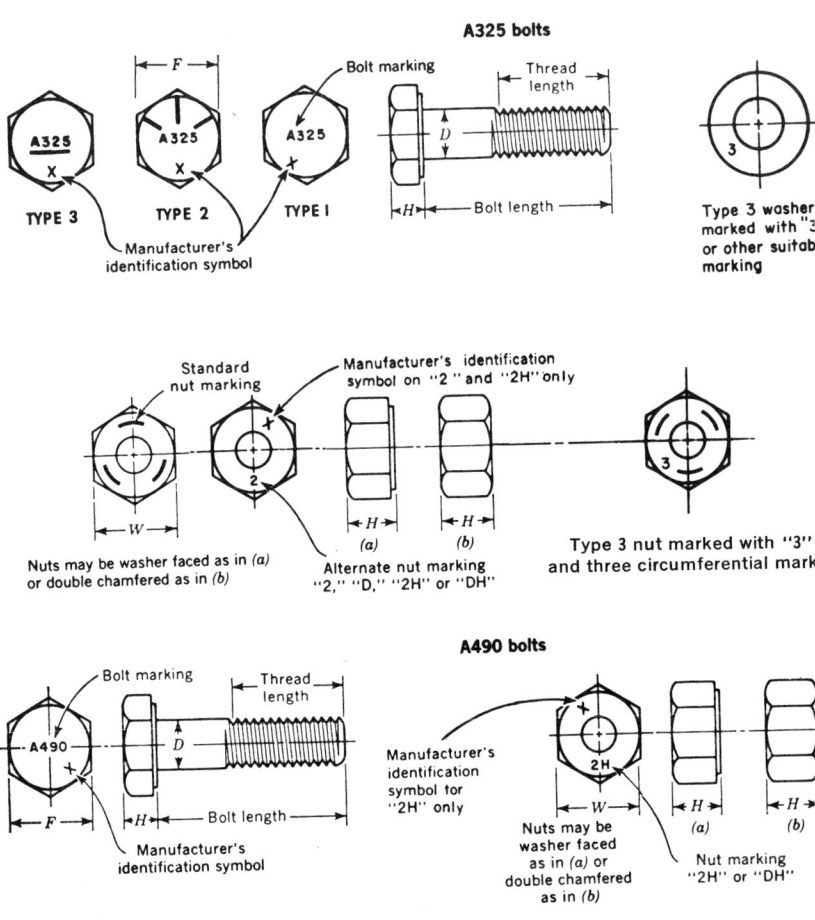

Fig. 1

Recent research[3] has demonstrated that galvanized A325 bolts may be used for friction-type connections, providing the contact surfaces are properly prepared (see Section 3c). However, it may be necessary to provide a lubricant to insure adequate rotational capacity during torquing and to provide the required minimum clamping force in the bolts. Research has demonstrated that hot-dip galvanized A490 bolts should not be used.[4] Other types of A490 bolt finishes have not been studied.

C2 Bolts, Nuts and Washers

In this edition of the specification a single style of fastener, available in two strength grades (A325 and A490) is described as a principal style, but conditions for acceptance of other types of fasteners are provided.

Heavy hex structural bolts manufactured to ASTM Specification A325, Types 1, 2 and 3, the dimensions for which are shown in Table 5 and Figure 1, are identified on the top of the head by the legend "A325", and the manufacturer's symbol. In addition, Type 1 bolts, at the option of the manufacturer, may be marked with three radial lines 120 degrees apart. Type 2 bolts shall be marked with three radial lines 60 degrees apart. Type 3 bolts shall have the A325 underlined and the manufacturer may add other distinguishing marks indicating that the bolt is of a weathering type. Bolts manufactured to ASTM Specification A490 are marked with the legend "A490" and the manufacturer's symbol. Heavy hex nuts for A325 bolts are identified on at least one face by the manufacturer's mark and the number "2" or "2H"; by three equally spaced circumferential lines; or by the legend "D" or "DH". Heavy hex nuts for A325 Type 3 bolts shall be

Table 5

Nominal bolt size, *D*	Bolt Dimensions, in Inches — Heavy Hex Structural Bolts			Nut Dimensions, in Inches — Heavy Hex Nuts	
	Width across flats *F*	Height, *H*	Thread length	Width across flats *W*	Height, *H*
½	⅞	5/16	1	⅞	31/64
⅝	1 1/16	25/64	1¼	1 1/16	39/64
¾	1¼	15/32	1⅜	1¼	47/64
⅞	1 7/16	35/64	1½	1 7/16	55/64
1	1⅝	39/64	1¾	1⅝	63/64
1⅛	1 13/16	11/16	2	1 13/16	1 7/64
1¼	2	25/32	2	2	1 7/32
1⅜	2 3/16	27/32	2¼	2 3/16	1 11/32
1½	2⅜	15/16	2¼	2⅜	1 15/32

marked on one face with three circumferential marks and the numeral 3, in addition to any other distinguishing marks the manufacturer may elect to use. Heavy hex nuts for use on A490 bolts are identified with the legend "2H" and the manufacturer's mark; or by the legend "DH". Washers for

[3] "High Strength Bolting of Galvanized Structural Connections," University of Illinois Engineering Experiment Station Bulletin . . . . .

[4] "Studies of Hydrogen Stress Cracking and Stress-Corrosion Cracking of High-Strength Bolts," Boyd, W. K., *Journal of the Structural Division*, ASCE.

A325 Type 3 bolts shall be marked on one face near the outer edge with the numeral 3, or other distinguishing marks indicating that the washer is of a weathering type. The marking on bearing surfaces of nuts and washers shall be depressed.

Heavy hex structural bolts have shorter thread lengths than other standard bolts. By making the body length of the bolt the control dimension it has been possible to exclude the thread from all shear planes, except in the case of thin outside parts adjacent to the nut. Depending on the amount of bolt length added to adjust for incremental stock lengths, the full thread may extend into the grip as much as $3/8$-inch for $1/2$-inch, $5/8$-inch, $3/4$-inch, $7/8$-inch, $1 1/4$-inch and $1 1/2$-inch diameter bolts and as much as $1/2$-inch for 1-inch, $1 1/8$-inch, and $1 3/8$-inch diameter bolts. Inclusion of some of the thread run-out into the plane of shear is permissible. At the other extreme, care should be taken to provide sufficient thread for nut tightening to keep the nut from jamming into the thread run-out. When the thickness of an outside part adjacent to the nut is less than these values, it may be necessary to call for the next increment of bolt length together with a sufficient number of flat circular washers to insure full seating of the nut. Then the higher working value in shear permitted in bearing-type joints can still be the basis for determining the number of bolts in the connection.

In order to determine the required bolt length, the value shown in Table 6 should be added to the grip (that is, the total thickness of all connected material, exclusive of washers).

Table 6

Bolt Size, in Inches	To Determine Required Bolt Length Add to Grip, in Inches
$1/2$	$11/16$
$5/8$	$7/8$
$3/4$	1
$7/8$	$1 1/8$
1	$1 1/4$
$1 1/8$	$1 1/2$
$1 1/4$	$1 5/8$
$1 3/8$	$1 3/4$
$1 1/2$	$1 7/8$

The preceding values are generalized, with due allowance for manufacturing tolerances, to provide for full thread engagement of a heavy hex nut, when installed. For each hardened flat washer that is used, add $5/32$-inch, and for each beveled washer add $5/16$-inch. The length determined by the use of Table 6 should be adjusted to the next longer $1/4$-inch.

The circular washer dimensions shown in Table 1 are somewhat reduced from those tabulated in 1962 and earlier editions. They have been developed on the principle that the primary function of the washer is to provide a non-galling surface under the part turned in tightening. As discussed more fully under Section C5 of this Commentary, tests have shown that washers play only a minor role in distributing the pressure due to bolt tension, except where oversize or short slotted holes are used. Hence, no consideration is given to this function and the minimum thickness for commonly used washers has been reduced by one or two gages. The maximum thickness is now alike for all washers up to and including the 1½-inch size, so that these washers can be produced from a single stock of material.

In order to span and fully cover long slotted holes, structural washers or bars are required.

C3 Bolted Parts

Joints which must transmit the forces in adjacent parts by means of shear are divided into two categories in the current specification; *friction-type* and *bearing-type*. High initial bolt tension provides worthwhile advantages, therefore the same initial tensioning is recommended for *bearing-type* connections as for the *friction-type*. Among these benefits are overall joint rigidity, a better stress pattern and security against nut loosening.

Since its first publication the Specification has permitted the use of bolt holes $\frac{1}{16}$-in. larger than the bolts installed in them. More recently research[5] has shown that, where greater latitude is needed in meeting dimensional tolerances during erection, somewhat larger holes can be permitted for bolts $\frac{5}{8}$-in. diameter and larger without adversely affecting the performance of shear connections assembled with high strength bolts. Provisions based upon these findings are now included in the Specification. Since an increase in hole size generally reduces the net area of a connected part, their use is subject to approval by the designer.

Table 7   Oversize and Slotted Holes

Bolt Dia. (in.)	Maximum Hole Size (in.)		
	Oversize Holes	Short Slotted Holes	Long Slotted Holes
⅝	¹³⁄₁₆	¹¹⁄₁₆ x ⅞	¹¹⁄₁₆ x 1⁹⁄₁₆
¾	¹⁵⁄₁₆	¹³⁄₁₆ x 1	¹³⁄₁₆ x 1⅞
⅞	1¹⁄₁₆	¹⁵⁄₁₆ x 1⅛	¹⁵⁄₁₆ x 2³⁄₁₆
1	1¼	1¹⁄₁₆ x 1⁵⁄₁₆	1¹⁄₁₆ x 2½
1⅛	1⁷⁄₁₆	1³⁄₁₆ x 1½	1³⁄₁₆ x 2¹³⁄₁₆
1¼	1⁹⁄₁₆	1⁵⁄₁₆ x 1⅝	1⁵⁄₁₆ x 3⅛
1⅜	1¹¹⁄₁₆	1⁷⁄₁₆ x 1¾	1⁷⁄₁₆ x 3⁷⁄₁₆
1½	1¹³⁄₁₆	1⁹⁄₁₆ x 1⅞	1⁹⁄₁₆ x 3¾

Extensive research conducted over the years has shown that various surface treatments can provide the frictional resistance required in *friction-type* connections. The specifications for several of these treatments are listed in Section 3 of this Specification.

In order to provide adequate frictional resistance in *friction-type* galvanized connections, the contact surfaces within the joints must be wire brushed or blasted prior to assembly. The wire brushing treatment should be a light application of manual or power brushing that marks or scores the surface, but removes relatively little of the zinc coating. The blasting

---

[5] "Bolted Joints With Oversize or Slotted Holes," by Ronald N. Allen and John W. Fisher, *ASCE Journal*, Vol. 94, ST9, September, 1968.

treatment should be a light "brush-off" treatment which will produce a dull gray appearance. However, neither treatment should be severe enough to produce any break or discontinuity in the zinc surface.

C4 Allowable Working Stresses

While the provisions contained in the Council specification to a limited extent affect general design considerations, it is not the intent to present a complete design specification. Only those features influenced by the properties of high-strength bolts, as distinct from other types of fasteners, are included. Working stresses applicable to bridges and to buildings (two values differing by about 10%) reflect the historic difference in basic stress between the AREA and AASHO Specifications governing bridge design and the AISC Specification governing the design of buildings and similar structures. Except as modified by the provisions of the Council's specification, it is assumed that all of the applicable provisions of the standard specifications under which the structure is designed will be observed.

Tension

The working stresses recommended are intended to apply to the calculated bolt load plus any tension resulting from prying action produced by deformation of the connected parts. When subjected in tension to the recommended working value (approximately equal to two-thirds of the initial tightening force), high-strength bolts will experience little if any actual change in stress. Since the tensile strength of the A490 bolt is approximately one-third greater than the corresponding average value for the A325 bolt, this ratio has been used to set the allowable tensile stress for the A490 bolt.

Tests[6] on properly tightened A325 bolts have demonstrated that their fatigue strength is not adversely affected by repeated applied tension of this amount.

Similar studies on A490 bolts are under way. Pending completion of these studies the allowable working stress in tension for A490 bolts, given in Section 4(a), is intended for static loading only and no recommendation covering cyclic applied loading in tension is made.

Shear: Friction-Type Connections

No change has been made in the recommended working value for A325 bolts used in *friction-type* joints. They are, as heretofore, given the "shear" value recommended in the applicable design specification for hot-driven ASTM A502, Grade 1 steel rivets of the same nominal diameter. The one-third increase in required tightening tension mentioned under *Tension* is the justification for the one-third increase in working stress for A490 bolts used in *friction-type* connections. Resistance to slip is dependent upon the amount of bolt clamping force and the nature of the contact surfaces in a given connection, and is independent of the working stress for which the connected parts are proportioned.

---

[6] "Research on Bolted Connections," by William H. Munse, *Transactions*, ASCE Vol. 121, 1956, pp. 1255–1266.

Connections having contact surfaces of unrusted mill scale offer the least resistance to slip of any unpainted joints; rusted surfaces which have been well cleaned may provide up to two times as much resistance. The recommended "shear" value using A325 bolts to connect parts having a specified yield point of about 33 ksi, based on numerous tests[7,8,9,10] correlates with a slip coefficient of 0.35. Similar observations have been made in tests of joints of higher-strength steels.[11] While lower coefficients have been observed in some laboratory tests of joints having contact surfaces of tight unrusted mill scale, or surfaces made smooth by grinding, a slip factor of 0.35 is more representative of values likely to be encountered in actual construction.

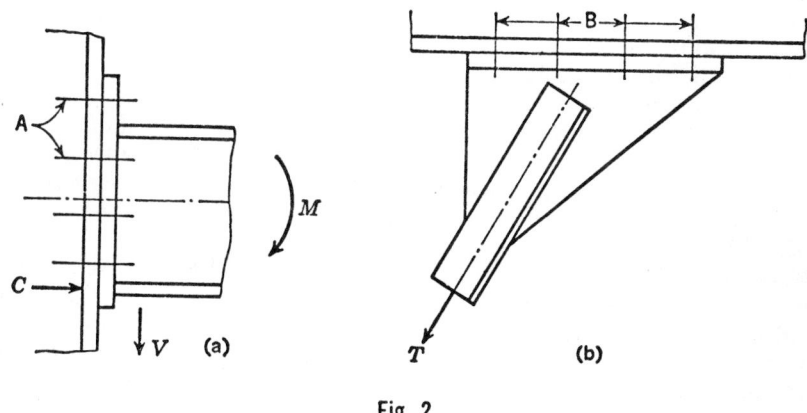

Fig. 2

Applying this value to the recommended minimum bolt tension, the factor of safety against slip can be computed as

$$N = \frac{(0.35)\ (\text{minimum bolt tension})}{(\text{allowable shear stress})\ (\text{nominal bolt area})} \tag{1}$$

For ⅞-inch and 1-inch A325 bolts, N equals 1.68 for bridges designed in accordance with the AASHO and AREA Specifications, and 1.52 for structures designed in accordance with the AISC Specification. These factors of

[7] "High-Strength Bolts in Structural Joints: A Symposium: Slip of Joints under Static Loads," by R. A. Hechtman, D. R. Young, A. G. Chin, and E. R. Savikko, *Transactions*, ASCE, Vol. 120, 1955, pp. 1335–1352.

[8] "Effects of Fabrication Techniques," by Desi D. Vasarhelyi, Said Y. Beano, Ronald B. Madison, Zung-An Lu, and Umseh C. Vasishth, *Transactions*, ASCE, Vol. 126, Part II, 1961, pp. 764–796.

[9] "Static Tension Tests of Compact Bolted Joints," by Robert T. Foreman and John L. Rumpf, *Transactions*, ASCE, Vol. 126, Part II, 1961, pp. 228–254.

[10] "Long Bolted Joints," by R. A. Bendigo, R. H. Hansen, and J. L. Rumpf, *ASCE Journal*, Vol. 89, ST6, December, 1963.

[11] "Static Tension Tests of A440 Steel Joints Connected with A325 Bolts," by J. W. Fisher, P. O. Ramseier, and L. S. Beedle, Publications, IABSE, Vol. 23, 1963.

safety against slip compare with design factors of safety against yield of the connected parts of 1.83 and 1.67, respectively. For other sizes of A325 bolts, the values of N are within 10% of those for $\frac{7}{8}$-inch and 1-inch bolts. For A490 bolts, the N values are approximately the same as for A325 bolts.

Under repeated loading the factor of safety against slip indicates the margin against the condition where a reduced fatigue strength may develop. Under static load conditions it may represent the margin against a one-time displacement movement, as under lateral shock or maximum wind loading, which is seldom likely to be reversed. A factor of safety against slip, lower than that implicit in the design stress used in proportioning the connected parts, is acceptable except where there must not be movement under such overloads as may occur within the allowable design stress factor of safety.

When the allowable "shear" value is increased one-third for wind, the value of N in the above equation approaches unity. If the satisfactory performance of the structure depends upon joints which must not move, the designer should so proportion these joints as to satisfy himself that the margin against slip is adequate.

Connections of the type shown in Figure 2(a), in which some of the bolts (A) lose a part of their clamping force due to applied tension, suffer no overall loss of frictional shear resistance. The bolt tension produced by the moment is coupled with a compensating compressive force (C) on the other side of the axis of bending. In a connection of the type shown in Figure 2(b), however, all of the fasteners (B) receive applied tension which reduces the initial compression at the contact surface. If bolts are used, and slip under load cannot be tolerated, the working value of the bolts in shear should be reduced in proportion to the ratio of residual tension to initial tension.

Because bolts in *friction-type* connections do not depend upon bearing against the sides of their holes, those provisions of the general design specifications intended to guard against high bearing stresses, and bending of the bolt due to bearing, are waived.

Shear: Bearing-Type Connections

In connections where the bolts may bear against the holes in the connected parts, the allowable stress of bolts is dependent upon the presence or absence of bolt threading at the plane of contact surfaces where shearing occurs. If the unthreaded shank of an A325 bolt is available to resist this shear at all planes where it occurs, tests[9,10] have shown that a shear stress equal to 20 ksi for bridges and 22 ksi for buildings (based on nominal fastener area) affords at least as large a factor of safety against high strength bolt shear failure as that provided in the standard design specification for rivets. On the other hand, it was found that failure occurs at 15% less load when threading is present at one of the two shear planes of an enclosed part, and at 30% less load when threads are present in both shear planes. This latter failure load could be expected also for single-shear joints with threads in the shear plane. Similar observations have been made from tests using ordinary bolts. They merely reflect the ratio of area at the root of thread to the nominal bolt area. The allowable shear stresses for A325 bolts with threads in a shear plane (13.5 ksi for bridges and 15 ksi for buildings as shown in Table 2) are developed by applying the above 30% reduction to the stresses allowed in unthreaded shanks.

The shear stresses allowed for A490 bolts in *bearing-type* connections have been similarly determined from tests[12, 13, 14] to give them at least as much factor of safety against failure as is provided for A502 rivets.

For both the A325 and A490 bolts, it may be noted that no special allowance is made for the condition where a bolt in double shear has unthreaded shank in one shear plane and threaded section in the other. This does not deny designers the advantage of such an analysis. It recognizes, however, that any use of the advantage requires knowledge of bolt placement that is not ordinarily available to designer or detailer, and that the fully conservative procedure is to use the lower allowable shear stress for all shear planes when the joint detail allows bolt thread in any shear plane of the joint.

Bearing

Tests[15, 16, 17] have shown that bearing pressure on rivets in double or single shear, computed on the basis of an area equal to the product of the part thickness and nominal rivet diameter, had no significant effect on the strength of the connected parts of A7 steel when this pressure was not more than 2.25 times the tensile stress applied to the net area of these parts. It would appear that the ratio of fastener spacing normal to the line of force, to fastener diameter, rather than unit pressure *per se*, is the critical factor, and that computed bearing stress is simply a convenient index of effective net section. In consequence, no increase in allowable bearing value seems warranted when high-strength bolts are substituted for rivets.

When there are not more than two bolts in the line of stress and the pressure from the bolt is directed toward the end of a connected part, an increase in end distance, above that required for rivets under similar circumstances, is recommended. To insure that the end fastener will not tear out of the connected part before the full tensile strength of the net section is attained, it has long been required that the end distance of a connected part having substantially the same mechanical properties as the connecting rivets be not less than the nominal area of the rivet divided by the part thickness and multiplied by the number of shears applied to the part. This rule is retained for use with high-strength bolts, but the end distance is increased in proportion to the ratio of bolt tensile strength to the tensile strength of the part. Above a length equal to $1\frac{1}{2}$ times the transverse bolt spacing, failure by rupture along the net plate section, at full fastener efficiency, is assured.

[12] "High-Strength Bolts Subjected to Combined Tension and Shear," by E. Chesson, Jr., N. L. Faustino, and W. H. Munse, *ASCE Journal*, Vol. 91, ST5, October, 1965.

[13] "Shear Strength of High Strength Bolts," by James J. Wallaert and John W. Fisher, *ASCE Journal*, Vol. 91, ST3, June, 1965.

[14] "A440 Steel Joints Connected by A490 Bolts," by Gordon H. Sterling and John W. Fisher, *ASCE Journal*, Vol. 92, ST3, June, 1966.

[15] "Bearing Ratio Effect on Static Strength of Riveted Joints," by Jonathan Jones, *Transactions*, ASCE, Vol. 123, 1958, pp. 964–972.

[16] "The Effect of Bearing Pressure on the Static Strength of Riveted Connections," Bulletin No. 454, Univ. of Illinois, Engrg. Experiment Sta., Urbana, Ill., July 1959.

[17] "Effect of Bearing Pressures on Fatigue Strength of Riveted Connections," by E. Chesson, Jr., J. F. Parola, and W. H. Munse, Univ. of Illinois, Engrg. Experiment Sta. Bulletin No. 481, 1965.

C5   Installation

Tests[18] have shown that a hardened washer is not needed to prevent minor bolt relaxation resulting from the high stress concentration under the bolt head or nut in connections assembled with A325 bolts. Such relaxations were less than 5% of the initial tension; took place within hours of bolt tightening, after which further loss of tension was negligible; and were substantially the same with and without the use of washers. Tests[18] have also shown that any galling which may take place where nuts for A325 bolts are tightened directly against the connected parts is not detrimental to the static or fatigue strength of the joint. However, to minimize irregularity in the torque-tension ratio where bolts are tightened by the calibrated wrench method, a washer is still required under the nut or bolt head which is turned in tightening. Otherwise, the use of flat circular washers is no longer required with A325 bolts installed in nominal diameter holes. They are required with A490 bolts in steel parts having a specified minimum yield point less than 40 ksi, to reduce galling and brinnelling of these parts. In high-strength steel they are only required to prevent galling of the rotated part. For repair work on existing structures, especially where bolts are used to replace rivets, the use of hardened washers under the bolt head and nut may be required to minimize the effect of surface irregularities adjacent to, and enlargement of, the holes.

Where oversize or short slotted holes are used, standard hardened washers are required to provide adequate bearing area. These washers are to be placed on the exposed face of the oversized or short slotted hole.

Where long slotted holes are used, experimental evidence has shown that a plate washer or continuous bar of at least $\frac{5}{16}$-in. thickness is necessary to provide adequate bearing. This washer or bar shall be of structural grade material but need not be hardened. However, if hardened washers are required to satisfy Specification provisions, the hardened washer shall be placed over the outer surface of the plate washer or bar.

Bolts properly installed and inspected by torquing can sustain additional direct tension loads in excess of the initial tension without any apparent reduction in their ultimate strength. Because of this reserve strength it is apparent that if the fastener does not fail while being installed, it should not fail thereafter, provided the loads to which it is subjected do not exceed those for which it has been designed.

Without preference, the Council endorses both the calibrated wrench and the turn-of-nut methods for bolt tightening.

Earlier editions of the Council's specifications have listed torque values described as the approximate equivalent of the minimum bolt tension specified for various size bolts. It was explained that these values were no more than observed experimental averages, and that the value to be used, both in installing bolts and in inspection procedures, should be that **determined by the actual condition of the application.** This point cannot be emphasized too much. The present specification requires that both torque and impact wrenches be calibrated, by means of a device capable of measuring the actual tension produced by a given wrench effort applied to a representative sample, when the tightening of bolts is controlled on the basis of calibrated wrench operation.

---

[18] "Studies of The Behavior of High-Strength Bolts and Bolted Joints," by E Chesson, Jr., and W. H. Munse, Univ. of Illinois Engrg. Experiment Sta. Bulletin No. 469, 1964.

Hydraulic calibrating devices capable of indicating bolt tension undergo a slight deformation under large bolt heads. Hence the nut rotation corresponding to a given tension reading may be somewhat larger than it would be if the same bolt were tightened against a solid steel abutment. Stated differently, the reading of the calibrating device tends to under-estimate the tension which a given rotation of the turned element would induce in a bolt in an actual joint. This should be borne in mind when using such devices to establish a tension-rotation relationship.

Instead of suggesting one full turn of the nut from a finger-tight position,[19] when tightening is controlled by the turn-of-nut prescription, a somewhat smaller rotation, from a *snug-tight* condition, is now specified in Table 4.[1,20,21,22] On an average, the bolt tension provided by either prescription is approximately the same. However, measuring the nut rotation from a snug-tight condition, which necessitates first drawing the several parts of the connection tightly together, has been found to produce more uniform bolt tension.

Tests[22] have shown that A490 bolts longer than eight diameters or 8 inches require a somewhat greater nut rotation in order to achieve the bolt tension shown in Table 3. Although the need does not exist with A325 bolts, the ⅔ turn provision has been applied to the A325 bolts as well, in the interest of uniformity in field practice.

The percentage of bolts in a given connection which must be made snug-tight in order to compact the joint will depend upon the stiffness of the several connected parts and their initial straightness. In extreme cases it may be necessary to snug-up bolts in all of the holes not used for pinning, in order to seat the parts.

After the parts are suitably drawn together, bolts are installed in any remaining open holes, tightened to a snug-tight condition, and all nuts are then rotated by the prescribed amount, after which bolts are installed in the holes originally pinned, and tightened using the same procedure.

Tightening of the bolts in a joint should commence at the most rigidly fixed or stiffest point, and progress toward the free edges, both in the initial snugging up and in the final tightening. During tightening, the bolt head or the nut should be held by a hand wrench to prevent turning.

6 Inspection

Bolts, nuts and washers are normally received with a light residual coating of oil which should not be removed. This coating is not detrimental even to friction-type connections and need not be removed.

Bolts tightened by the turn-of-nut method may have the outer face of the nut match-marked with the protruding bolt point before final tightening, thus affording the inspector visual means of noting the actual nut rotation. Such marks can be made by the wrench operator with a crayon or dab of paint, after the bolts have been brought up snug tight.

[19] "Tightening High-Strength Bolts," by F. P. Drew, Proc. Sep. No. 786, ASCE, Vol. 81, August, 1955.

[20] "Installation and Tightening of High-Strength Bolts," by E. F. Ball and J. J. Higgins, *Transactions*, ASCE, Vol. 126, 1961, pp. 797–820.

[21] "Calibration of A325 Bolts," by J. L. Rumpf and J. W. Fisher, *ASCE Journal Structural Division*, Vol. 89, No. ST6, Proc. Paper 3731, December, 1963, pp. 15–234.

[22] "Calibration Tests of A490 High-Strength Bolts," by G. H. Sterling, E. W. J. Troup, E. Chesson, and J. W. Fisher, *ASCE Journal*, Vol. 19, ST5, Oct. 1965.

The sides of bolt heads and nuts tightened with an impact wrench will appear slightly peened and thus indicate that the wrench has been applied to the fastener.

If a torque wrench is used to inspect bolts, the procedure to be followed is described in detail in Section 6(c) of the Specification. Because of the variability of the torque-tension relationship, a range of tension from $+5\%$ to $+10\%$ was utilized to adjust the inspecting power wrench to the minimum job inspecting torque.

Where no washers are used, torque readings will be relatively high and may vary considerably. For this case the use of a torque multiplier device may be necessary.

SUMMARY OF SCOPE
AND PRINCIPAL TENSILE PROPERTIES

ASTM Specifications

For steels permitted by Sect. 1.4.1.1 of the AISC Specification, including a partial summary of ASTM Specification A6. For additional and supplementary information refer to the applicable ASTM specification.

AMERICAN INSTITUTE OF STEEL CONSTRUCTION

101 Park Avenue, New York, N. Y. 10017

PARTIAL SUMMARY

ASTM Specification A6

General Requirements for Delivery of Rolled Steel Plates,
Shapes, Sheet Piling, and Bars for Structural Use

SCOPE	REMARKS

A6-72

Covers a group of common requirements which, unless otherwise specified in the purchase order or in an individual specification, shall apply to rolled steel plates, shapes, sheet piling, and bars under each of the following specifications issued by the American Society for Testing and Materials:

ASTM Designation	Title of Specification
	Carbon Steel
A36.........	Structural Steel
A529.........	Structural Steel with 42,000 psi Minimum Yield Point (½-in. Maximum Thickness)
	High-Strength and High-Strength Low-Alloy Steel
A242.........	High-Strength Low-Alloy Structural Steel
A440.........	High-Strength Structural Steel
A441.........	High-Strength Low-Alloy Structural Manganese Vanadium Steel
A572.........	High-Strength Low-Alloy Columbium-Vanadium Steels of Structural Quality
A588.........	High-Strength Low-Alloy Structural Steel with 50,000 psi Minimum Yield Point to 4 in.
	Alloy Steel
A514.........	High-Yield Strength, Quenched and Tempered Alloy Steel Plate Suitable for Welding

REMARKS

Certain tables of permissible variations contained in ASTM A6 are published in Part 1 of the 7th Edition Manual under the contents heading "Standard Mill Practice."

Structural shape size groupings used for tensile property classification are listed in Table A of ASTM A6. (See equivalent Table 2 in Part 1 of this Manual, Page 1 - 7.)

Definitions:

Structural-Size Shapes — Rolled flanged sections having at least one dimension of the cross section 3 in. or greater.

Plates — Flat hot-rolled steel classified as follows:

When Ordered to Thickness:
    Over 8 in. in width and 0.230 in. or over in thickness.
    Over 48 in. in width and 0.180 in. or over in thickness.

When Ordered to Weight per Square Foot:
    Over 8 in. in width and 9.62 lb/ft², or heavier,
    Over 48 in. in width and 7.53 lb/ft², or heavier.
    Slabs, sheet bars and skelp, though frequently falling in the foregoing size ranges, are not classed as plates.

Bars — Rounds, squares and hexagons, of all sizes; flats $\frac{13}{64}$ in. (0.2031 in.) and over in specified thickness, not over 6 in. in width; flats 0.230 in. and over in specified thickness, over 6 to 8 in., incl., in specified width.

Bar Size Shapes — Rolled flanged sections having a maximum dimension of the cross section less than 3 in.

SUMMARY OF SCOPE AND PRINCIPAL TENSILE PROPERTIES

ASTM Specifications

For steels permitted by Sect. 1.4.1.1 of the AISC Specification.
For additional and supplementary information
refer to the applicable ASTM Specification

ASTM Designation	SCOPE	PRODUCT	GROUP	Tens. str. ksi	F_y ksi (min)
A36-70a	Covers carbon steel shapes, plates, and bars of structural quality for use in riveted, bolted, or welded construction of bridges and buildings, and for general structural purposes. When the steel is used in welded construction, welding procedure shall be suitable for the steel and the intended service. Supplemental requirements are provided where improved notch toughness is important. These shall apply only when specified by the purchaser in the order.	Shapes[a,d]	All	58–80	36
		Plates[b,c]	All to 8 in. thick incl.	58–80	36
		Bars	All to 4 in. thick incl.	58–80	36
A53-72a	Covers seamless and welded black and hot-dipped galvanized steel pipe in nominal sizes ⅛ in. to 26 in., incl. (See specification for wall thickness.) **Type E** — Electric-resistance welded **Type S** — Seamless Pipe is suitable for welding.	Pipe	Grade B	60 min.	3
A242-70a	Covers high-strength low-alloy structural steel shapes, plates and bars for welded, riveted or bolted construction intended primarily for use as structural members where savings in weight or added durability are important. These steels have enhanced atmospheric corrosion resistance of at least two times that of carbon structural steels with copper (Note 1). Welding technique is of fundamental importance, and it is presupposed that welding procedure will be in accordance with approved methods. This specification is limited to material up to 4 in. inclusive, in thickness.	Shapes	*Groups 1 and 2	70 min.	5
			*Group 3	67 min.	4
			*Groups 4 and 5	63 min.	4
		Plates and bars	To ¾-in. thick incl.	70 min.	5
			Over ¾ to 1½ in., incl.	67 min.	
			Over 1½ to 4 in., incl.	63 min.	4

A36-70a notes:
[a] For wide flange shapes over 426 lb/ft. tensile strength minimum of 58.0 ksi only applies.
[b] Yield point 32.0 ksi for plates over 8 in. in thickness.
[c] Unless otherwise specified, tensile tests shall not be required for plates over 1½ in. in thickness used as bearing plates in structures other than bridges.
[d] Shapes less than 1 sq in. in cross-section and bars, other than flats, less than ½ in. in thickness or diameter need not be subjected to tension tests.

Note 1—Two times carbon structural steel with copper is equivalent to four times carbon structural steel without copper (copper 0.02 max.).

* For grouping of shapes, see page 1 - 7.

ASTM Designation	SCOPE	PRODUCT	GROUP	Tens. str. ksi	F_y ksi (min.)
A440-70a	Covers high-strength steel shapes, plates, and bars of structural quality intended primarily for use in the construction of riveted or bolted bridges and buildings and for other special structural purposes, where saving in weight is important. The atmospheric corrosion resistance of this steel is approximately twice that of structural carbon steel. This specification is limited to material up to 4 in. inclusive in thickness.	Shapes	*Groups 1 and 2	70 min.	50
			*Group 3	67 min.	46
			*Groups 4 and 5	63 min.	42
		Plates and bars	To ¾ in. thick, incl.	70 min.	50
			Over ¾ to 1½ in., incl.	67 min.	46
			Over 1½ to 4 in., incl.	63 min.	42
A441-70a	Covers high-strength low alloy structural steel shapes, plates, and bars for welded, riveted, or bolted construction but intended primarily for use in welded bridges and buildings where saving in weight or added durability are important. The atmospheric corrosion resistance of this steel is approximately twice that of structural carbon steel. This specification is limited to material up to 8 in. inclusive in thickness.	Shapes	*Groups 1 and 2	70 min.	50[b]
			*Group 3	67 min.	46[b]
			*Groups 4 and 5	63 min.	42[b]
		Plates and bars	To ¾ in. thick, incl.	70 min.	50[b]
			Over ¾ to 1½ in., incl.	67 min.	46[b]
			Over 1½ to 4 in., incl.	63 min.	42[b]
			Over 4 to 8 in., incl.	60 min.	40[b]

[b] When the material is normalized, the minimum yield point and minimum tensile strength required shall be reduced 5.0 ksi.
* For grouping of shapes, see page 1 - 7.

ASTM Designation	SCOPE	PRODUCT	GROUP	Tens. str. ksi	F_y ksi (min.)
A500-72 Covers cold-formed welded and seamless carbon steel round, square, rectangular, or special shape structural tubing for welded, riveted, or bolted construction of bridges and buildings, and for general structural purposes. This tubing is produced in welded sizes with a maximum periphery of 48 in. and a maximum wall of 0.500 in., and in seamless with a maximum periphery of 32 in. and a maximum wall of 0.500 in.		Round Tubing	Grade A	45 min.	33
			Grade B	58 min.	42
		Shaped Tubing	Grade A	45 min.	39
			Grade B	58 min.	46
A501-71a Covers hot-formed welded and seamless carbon steel square, round, rectangular, or special shape structural tubing for welded, riveted, or bolted construction of bridges and buildings, and for general structural purposes. Square and rectangular tubing is furnished in sizes 1 to 10 in. across flat sides with wall thicknesses 0.095 to 1.000 in., depending on size; round tubing is furnished in nominal diameters ½ to 24 in., incl., with nominal (average) wall thicknesses 0.109 to 1.000 in., depending on size. Pipe having other dimensions may be furnished provided such pipe complies with all other requirements of this specification.		Tubing	All	58	36
A514-70 Covers quenched and tempered alloy steel plates of structural quality in thicknesses 4 in. and under intended primarily for use in welded bridges and other structures. (All types are not available in a maximum thickness of 4 in. See specification for thicknesses available in each grade.) Welding technique is of fundamental importance and must not adversely affect the properties of the plate, especially in the heat affected zone. It is presupposed that welding procedures will be suitable for the materials being welded.		Plates	To ¾-in., incl.	115 to 135	100[a]
			Over ¾ to 2½ in., incl.	115 to 135	100[a]
			Over 2½ to 4 in., incl.	105 to 135	90[a]

[a] Measured at 0.2 per cent offset or 0.5 per cent extension under load as described in Section 13. Methods and Definitions for Mechanical Testing of Steel Products (ASTM Designation: A370).

ASTM Designation	SCOPE	PRODUCT	GROUP	Tens. str. ksi	F_y ksi (min.)
A529-72	Covers carbon steel plates and bars ½-in. and under in thickness or diameter and Group 1 shapes shown in Table A of ASTM Specification A6, General Requirements for Delivery of Rolled Steel Plates, Shapes, Sheet Piling, and Bars for Structural Use, of structural quality for use in buildings and similar riveted, bolted, or welded construction. When used in welded construction, welding procedures shall be suitable for the steel and the intended service.	Shapes[a]	*Group 1	60 to 85	42
		Plates and bars[a]	To ½ in. thick incl.	60 to 85	42
		\[a\] Shapes less than 1 sq. in. in cross section and bars other than flats, less than ½-in. in thickness or diameter need not be subjected to tension tests. * For grouping of shapes, see page 1 - 7.			
A570-72	Covers hot-rolled carbon steel sheets and strip of structural quality in cut lengths or coils. This material is intended for structural purposes where mechanical test values are required.	Sheets and strip	Grade D	55 min.	40
			Grade E	58 min.	42
A572-72	Covers six grades of high-strength low-alloy structural steel shapes, plates, sheet piling, and bars. Grades 42, 45, and 50 are intended for riveted, bolted, or welded construction of bridges, buildings, and other structures. Grades 55, 60, and 65 are intended for riveted or bolted construction of bridges, and for riveted, bolted, or welded construction in other applications. When the steel is used in welded construction, welding procedure shall be suitable for the steel and the intended service. For welded bridge construction notch toughness is an important requirement. For this or other applications where notch-toughness requirements are indicated, they shall be negotiated between the purchaser and the producer.	Shapes	Grade 42 up to 426 lb/ft incl.	60 min.	42
			Grade 45 up to 426 lb/ft incl.	60 min.	45
			Grade 50 up to 426 lb/ft incl.	65 min.	50
			Grade 55 up to 426 lb/ft incl.	70 min.	55
			*Grade 60, Groups 1 and 2	75 min.	60
			*Grade 65, Group 1	80 min.	65
		Plates and bars	Grade 42 to 6 in., incl.	60 min.	42
			Grade 45 to 2 in., incl.	60 min.	45
			Grade 50 to 1½ in., incl.	65 min.	50
			Grade 55 to 1½ in., incl.	70 min.	55
			Grade 60 to 1 in., incl.	75 min.	60
			Grade 65 to ½ in., incl.	80 min.	65
		* For grouping of shapes, see page 1 - 7.			

ASTM Designation	SCOPE	PRODUCT	GROUP	Tens. str. ksi	F_y ksi (min
A588-71 Covers high-strength low-alloy structural steel shapes, plates, and bars for welded, riveted, or bolted construction but intended primarily for use in welded bridges and buildings where saving in weight or added durability are important. The atmospheric corrosion resistance of this steel is approximately two times that of carbon structural steel with copper (Note 1). Welding technique is of fundamental importance, and it is presupposed that welding procedure will be suitable for the steel and the intended service. This specification is limited to material up to 8 in. incl. in thickness. Note 1 — Two times carbon structural steel with copper is equivalent to four times carbon structural steel without copper (Cu 0.02 max).		Shapes	*Groups 1, 2, 3, and 4	70 min.	50
			*Group 5	67 min.	46
		Plates and bars	To 4 in., incl.	70 min.	50
			Over 4 to 5 in., incl.	67 min.	46
			Over 5 to 8 in., incl.	63 min.	42
			* For grouping of shapes, see page 1–7.		
A606-71 Covers high-strength, low-alloy, hot- and cold-rolled sheet and strip in cut lengths or coils, intended for use in structural and miscellaneous purposes, where savings in weight or added durability are important. These steels have enhanced atmospheric corrosion resistance. Type 2 has corrosion resistance at least two times that of plain carbon steel. The degree of corrosion resistance is based on data acceptable to the consumer. Note: Type 2 hot-rolled material is intended to replace ASTM Specification A375, for High Strength Low-Alloy Hot-Rolled Steel Sheets and Strip.		Sheet and Strip	Hot Rolled—As-Rolled Cut lengths	70 min.	50
			aHot Rolled—As-Rolled Coils	65 min.	45
			Hot Rolled—Annealed or Normalized	65 min.	45
			a Coiled sheet and strip shall be produced and released to the same strength level as cut length product. Due to the producer's inability to test within the body of the coil, the strength levels are shown as being reduced by 5.0 ksi to reflect the possibility of the inclusion of some lower strength material.		
A607-70 Covers high-strength, low-alloy columbium and/or vanadium hot-rolled and cold-rolled steel sheet and strip in either cut lengths or coils, intended for use in structural and miscellaneous purposes, where greater strength and savings in weight is important. This material is available in six strength levels as provided for in Table 2. Atmospheric corrosion resistance of these steels (without copper specified) is equivalent to plain carbon steel. With copper specified, the atmospheric corrosion resistance is twice that of plain carbon steel.		aSheet and Strip	Grade 45	60 min.	45
			Grade 50	65 min.	5
			Grade 55	70 min.	5
			Grade 60	75 min.	6
			Grade 65	80 min.	6
			Grade 70	85 min.	7
			a All product specified to be furnished in coils w be produced to the same strength level mill pra tices as cut length product. Because testir within the body of the coil cannot be performed the producer, recognition must be given to the fa that some portions of coils could fall below th specified minimums.		

ASTM Designation	SCOPE	PRODUCT	GROUP	Tens. str. ksi	F_y ksi (min.)
A618-71 Covers three grades of hot-formed welded and seamless high-strength low-alloy square, rectangular, round, or special shape structural tubing for welded, riveted, or bolted construction of bridges and buildings and for general structural purposes. When the steel is used in welded construction, the welding procedure shall be suitable for the steel and the intended service. When enhanced corrosion resistance is desired for Grades I and III, copper limits may be specified.		Struct.	Grade I	70 min.	50
		Tubing	Grade II	70 min.	50
			Grade III	65 min.	50

EXCERPTS FROM THE
AMERICAN NATIONAL STANDARD BUILDING CODE
REQUIREMENTS FOR

Minimum Design Loads

in Buildings and Other Structures

ANSI A58.1—1972

Sponsor: National Bureau of Standards

AMERICAN INSTITUTE OF STEEL CONSTRUCTION

101 Park Avenue, New York, N. Y. 10017

EXCERPTS FROM THE AMERICAN NATIONAL STANDARD BUILDING CODE REQUIREMENTS FOR

Minimum Design Loads in Buildings and Other Structures

ANSI A58.1—1972

Sponsor: National Bureau of Standards

2.3 PROVISION FOR PARTITIONS

In office buildings or other buildings where partitions might be subject to erection or rearrangement, provision for partition weight shall be made, whether or not partitions are shown on the plans, unless the specified live load exceeds 80 pounds per square foot.

3.1 UNIFORMLY DISTRIBUTED LOADS

3.1.1 Required Live Loads

The live loads to be assumed in the design of buildings and other structures shall be the greatest loads that probably will be produced by the intended use or occupancy, but in no case less than the minimum uniformly distributed unit loads required by Table 1.

Table 1. Minimum Uniformly Distributed Live Loads

Occupancy or Use	Live Load, lb. per sq. ft.
Apartments (see Residential)	
Armories and drill rooms	150
Assembly halls and other places of assembly:	
Fixed seats	60
Movable seats	100
Platforms (assembly)	100
Balcony (exterior)	100
On one and two family residences only and not exceeding 100 sq ft	60
Bowling alleys, poolrooms, and similar recreational areas	75
Corridors:	
First floor	100
Other floors, same as occupancy served except as indicated	
Dance halls	100
Dining rooms and restaurants	100
Dwellings (see Residential)	
Fire escapes	100
On multi- or single-family residential buildings only	40
Garages (passenger cars only)	50
For trucks and buses use AASHO lane loads (see Table 2 for concentrated load requirements)	
Grandstands (see Reviewing stands)	
Gymnasiums, main floors and balconies	100
Hospitals:	
Operating rooms, laboratories	60
Private rooms	40
Wards	40

Table 1. Minimum Uniformly Distributed Live Loads (continued)

Occupancy or Use	Live Load, lb. per sq. ft.
Corridors, above first floor	80
Hotels (see Residential)	
Libraries:	
Reading rooms	60
Stack rooms (books & shelving at 65 pcf) but not less than	150
Manufacturing	
Light	125
Heavy	250
Marquees	75
Office buildings:	
Offices	50
Lobbies	100
Corridors, above first floor	80
File and computer rooms require heavier loads based upon anticipated occupancy	
Penal institutions:	
Cell blocks	40
Corridors	100
Residential:	
Multifamily houses:	
Private apartments	40
Public rooms	100
Corridors	80
Dwellings:	
First floor	40
Second floor and habitable attics	30
Uninhabitable attics	20
Hotels:	
Guest rooms	40
Public rooms	100
Corridors serving public rooms	100
Corridors	80
Reviewing stands and bleachers*	100
Schools:	
Classrooms	40
Corridors	80
Sidewalks, vehicular driveways, and yards, subject to trucking	250
Skating rinks	100
Stairs, fire escapes, and exitways	100
Storage warehouse, light	125
Storage warehouse, heavy	250
Stores:	
Retail:	
First-floor, rooms	100
Upper floors	75
Wholesale	125
Theaters:	
Aisles, corridors, and lobbies	100
Orchestra floors	60
Balconies	60
Stage floors	150
Yards and terraces, pedestrians	100

* For detailed recommendations, see American National Standard for Tents, Grandstands, and Air-Supported Structures Used for Places of Assembly, Z20.3-1967 (NFPA No. 102-1967), or the latest revision thereof approved by the American National Standards Institute.

3.1.2 Loads Not Specified

For occupancies or uses not listed in 3.1.1 or 3.2, the live load shall be determined in a manner satisfactory to the building official.

For additional information on live loads, see Appendix, Tables A3 and A4 of ANSI A58.1-1972.

3.1.3 THRUSTS ON HANDRAILINGS

Stairway and balcony railings, both exterior and interior, shall be designed to resist a vertical and a horizontal thrust of 50 pounds per linear foot applied at the top of the railing.

3.2 CONCENTRATED LOADS

Floors shall be designed to support safely the uniformly distributed live loads prescribed in section 3.1 or the concentrated load in pounds given in Table 2, whichever produces the greater stresses. Unless otherwise specified, the indicated concentration shall be assumed to occupy an area of $2\frac{1}{2}$ feet square and shall be so located as to produce the maximum stress conditions in the structural members.

Table 2. Concentrated loads

Location	Load, pounds
Elevator machine room grating (on area of 4 sq. in.)	300
Finish light floor plate construction (on area of 1 sq. in.)	200
Garages	*
Office floors	2000
Scuttles, skylight ribs, and accessible ceilings	200
Sidewalks	8000
Stair treads (on area of 4 sq. in. at center of tread)	300

* Floors in garages or portions of buildings used for storage of motor vehicles shall be designed for the uniformly distributed live loads of Table 1 or the following concentrated loads: (1) for passenger cars accommodating not more than nine passengers, 2000 pounds acting on an area of 20 sq in; (2) mechanical parking structures without slab or deck, passenger cars only, 1500 pounds per wheel; (3) for trucks or buses, maximum axle load on an area of 20 sq in.

3.3 PARTIAL LOADING

The full intensity of the appropriately reduced live load applied only to a portion of the length of a structure or member shall be considered if it produces a more unfavorable effect than the same intensity applied over the full length of the structure or member.

3.4 IMPACT LOADS

The live loads specified in 3.1.1 shall be assumed to include adequate allowance for ordinary impact conditions. Provision shall be made in the structural design for uses and loads which involve unusual vibration and impact forces.

3.5 REDUCTION IN LIVE LOADS

3.5.1 Live Loads 100 Pounds per Square Foot or Less

For live loads of 100 pounds or less per square foot, the design live load on any member supporting 150 square feet or more may be reduced at the rate of 0.08 per cent per square foot of area supported by the member, except that no reduction shall be made for areas to be occupied as places of public assembly, for garages, or for roofs. The reduction shall exceed neither R as determined by the following formula, nor 60 percent.

$$R = 23 \left(1 + \frac{D}{L} \right)$$

in which

R = reduction in per cent

D = dead load per square foot of area supported by the member

L = design live load per square foot of area supported by the member

3.5.2 Live Loads Exceeding 100 Pounds per Square Foot

For live loads exceeding 100 pounds per square foot, no reduction shall be made, except that the design live loads on columns may be reduced 20 per cent.

3.8 MINIMUM ROOF LOADS

3.8.1 Flat, Pitched, or Curved Roofs

Ordinary roofs, either flat, pitched, or curved, shall be designed for the live loads as specified in Table 3 or the snow load as specified in 7.2 of ANSI A58.1-1972, whichever produces the greater stresses.

3.8.2 Special Purpose Roofs

When used for incidental promenade purposes, roofs shall be designed for a minimum live load of 60 pounds per square foot; and 100 pounds per square foot when designed for roof-garden or assembly uses. Roofs to be used for other special purposes shall be designed for appropriate loads as directed or approved by the building official.

Table 3
Minimum Roof Live Loads*

Roof Slope	Tributary Loaded Area in Square Feet for any Structural Member		
	0 to 200	201 to 600	Over 600
Flat or rise less than 4 inches per foot Arch or dome with rise less than $\frac{1}{8}$ of span	20	16	12
Rise 4 inches per foot to less than 12 inches per foot Arch or dome with rise $\frac{1}{8}$ of span to less than $\frac{3}{8}$ of span	16	14	12
Rise 12 inches per foot and greater Arch or dome with rise $\frac{3}{8}$ of span or greater	12	12	12

* In pound-force per square foot of horizontal projection.

Recommended Live Loads For Storage Warehouses

United States Department of Commerce, National Bureau of Standards

AMERICAN INSTITUTE OF STEEL CONSTRUCTION

101 Park Avenue, New York, N. Y. 10017

Recommended Live Loads

For Storage Warehouses

United States Department of Commerce, National Bureau of Standards

Material	Weight per Cubic Foot of Space Lb.	Height of Pile Feet	Weight per Square Foot of Floor Lb.	Recommended Live Load Lb. per Sq. Foot
BUILDING MATERIALS				
Asbestos...........................	50	6	300	
Bricks, Building.....................	45	6	270	
Bricks, Fire Clay....................	75	6	450	
Cement, Natural.....................	59	5	354	300
Cement, Portland....................	72 to 105	6	432 to 630	to
Gypsum............................	50	6	300	400
Lime and Plaster....................	53	5	265	
Tiles...............................	50	6	300	
Woods, bulk........................	45	6	270	
DRUGS, PAINTS, OIL, ETC.				
Alum, Pearl, in barrels..............	33	6	198	
Bleaching Powder, in hogsheads......	31	3½	102	
Blue Vitriol, in barrels..............	45	5	226	
Glycerine, in cases..................	52	6	312	
Linseed Oil, in barrels..............	36	6	216	
Linseed Oil, in iron drums...........	45	4	180	
Logwood Extract, in boxes...........	70	5	350	
Rosin, in barrels....................	48	6	288	200
Shellac, Gum.......................	38	6	228	to
Soaps..............................	50	6	300	300
Soda Ash, in hogsheads.............	62	2¾	167	
Soda, Caustic, in iron drums........	88	3⅜	294	
Soda, Silicate, in barrels...........	53	6	318	
Sulphuric Acid......................	60	1⅝	100	
Toilet Articles......................	35	6	210	
Varnishes..........................	55	6	330	
White Lead Paste, in cans..........	174	3½	610	
White Lead, dry.....................	86	4¾	408	
Red Lead and Litharge, dry.........	132	3¾	495	
DRY GOODS, COTTON, WOOL, ETC.				
Burlap, in bales....................	43	6	258	
Carpets and Rugs...................	30	6	180	
Coir Yarn, in bales.................	33	8	264	
Cotton, in bales, American..........	30	8	240	
Cotton, in bales, Foreign...........	40	8	320	
Cotton Bleached Goods, in cases.....	28	8	224	
Cotton Flannel, in cases............	12	8	96	
Cotton Sheeting, in cases...........	23	8	184	
Cotton Yarn, in cases...............	25	8	200	
Excelsior, compressed..............	19	8	152	200
Hemp, Italian, compressed..........	22	8	176	to
Hemp, Manila, compressed.........	30	8	240	250
Jute, compressed...................	41	8	328	
Linen Damask, in cases.............	50	5	250	
Linen Goods, in cases..............	30	8	240	
Linen Towels, in cases.............	40	6	240	
Silk and Silk Goods.................	45	8	360	
Sisal, compressed..................	21	8	168	
Tow, compressed...................	29	8	232	
Wool, in bales, compressed.........	48			
Wool, in bales, not compressed......	13	8	104	
Wool, Worsteds, in cases...........	27	8	216	

Weight p.s.f. and Recommended Live Load p.s.f. are based on height of pile shown.

Material	Weight per Cubic Foot of Space Lb.	Height of Pile Feet	Weight per Square Foot of Floor Lb.	Recommended Live Load Lb. per Sq. Ft.
GROCERIES, WINES, LIQUORS, ETC.				
Beans, in bags	40	8	320	
Beverages	40	8	320	
Canned Goods, in cases	58	6	348	
Cereals	45	8	360	
Cocoa	35	8	280	
Coffee, Roasted, in bags	33	8	264	
Coffee, Green, in bags	39	8	312	
Dates, in cases	55	6	330	
Figs, in cases	74	5	370	
Flour, in barrels	40	5	200	250
Fruits, Fresh	35	8	280	to
Meat and Meat Products	45	6	270	300
Milk, Condensed	50	6	300	
Molasses, in barrels	48	5	240	
Rice, in bags	58	6	348	
Sal Soda, in barrels	46	5	230	
Salt, in bags	70	5	350	
Soap Powder, in cases	38	8	304	
Starch, in barrels	25	6	150	
Sugar, in barrels	43	5	215	
Sugar, in cases	51	6	306	
Tea, in chests	25	8	200	
Wines and Liquors, in barrels	38	6	228	
HARDWARE, ETC.				
Automobile Parts	40	8	320	
Chain	100	6	600	
Cutlery	45	8	360	
Door Checks	45	6	270	
Electrical Goods and Machinery	40	8	320	
Hinges	64	6	384	
Locks, in cases, packed	31	6	186	
Machinery, Light	20	8	160	
Plumbing, Fixtures	30	8	240	
Plumbing, Supplies	55	6	330	300
Sash Fasteners	48	6	288	to
Screws	101	6	606	400
Shafting Steel	125			
Sheet Tin, in boxes	278	2	556	
Tools, Small, Metal	75	6	450	
Wire Cables on reels			425	
Wire, Insulated Copper, in coils	63	5	315	
Wire, Galvanized Iron, in coils	74	4½	333	
Wire, Magnet, on spools	75	6	450	
MISCELLANEOUS				
Automobile Tires	30	6	180	
Automobiles, uncrated	8		64	
Books (solidly packed)	65	6	390	
Furniture	20			
Glass and Chinaware, in crates	40	8	320	
Hides and Leather, in bales	20	8	160	
Leather and Leather Goods	40	8	320	
Paper, Newspaper, and Strawboards	35	6	210	
Paper, Writing and Calendared	60	6	360	
Rope, in coils	32	6	192	
Rubber, Crude	50	8	400	
Tobacco, bales	35	8	280	

Weight p.s.f. and Recommended Live Load p.s.f. are based on height of pile shown

STANDARD SPECIFICATIONS AND LOAD TABLES FOR

Open Web Steel Joists

J-Series and H-Series

Adopted by Steel Joist Institute and
American Institute of Steel Construction, November 1, 1972

AMERICAN INSTITUTE OF STEEL CONSTRUCTION

101 Park Avenue, New York, N. Y. 10017

STANDARD SPECIFICATIONS FOR

Open Web Steel Joists

J-Series and H-Series

Adopted by Steel Joist Institute and
American Institute of Steel Construction, Inc., November 1, 1972

SECTION 1   SCOPE

These specifications cover the design, manufacture and use of Open Web Steel Joists, J- and H-Series.

SECTION 2   DEFINITION

The term "Open Web Steel Joists J- and H-Series", as used herein, refers to open web parallel chord load-carrying members suitable for the direct support of floors and roof decks in buildings, utilizing hot-rolled or cold-formed steel, including cold-formed steel whose yield strength* has been attained by cold working.   They are designed in accordance with these specifications to develop the resisting moments and maximum end reactions shown in the Standard Load Tables for Open Web Steel Joists, J- or H-Series, attached hereto.

The design of J-Series joists shall be based on a yield strength of 36,000 psi and steel used for J-Series joists shall have a minimum yield strength of 36,000 psi in the hot-rolled condition prior to forming or fabrication.

The design of chord sections for H-Series joists shall be based on a yield strength of 50,000 psi.   The design of web sections for H-Series joists shall be based on a yield strength of either 36,000 psi or 50,000 psi.   Steel used for H-Series joist chord or web sections shall have a minimum yield strength, determined in accordance with one of the procedures specified in Section 3.2, which is equal to the yield strength assumed in the design.

SECTION 3   MATERIALS

3.1   Steel

The steel used in the manufacture of chord and web sections shall conform to one of the following ASTM Specifications of latest adoption:

(a)   *Structural Steel*, ASTM A36
(b)   *High-Strength Low-Alloy Structural Steel*, ASTM A242
(c)   *High-Strength Low-Alloy Structural Manganese Vanadium Steel*, ASTM A441
(d)   *Hot-Rolled Carbon Steel Sheets and Strip, Structural Quality*, ASTM A570

---

* The term "yield strength" as used herein shall designate the yield level of a material as determined by the applicable method outlined in paragraph 13—"Yield Strength," or paragraph 12—"Yield Point", of ASTM Standard A370, "Mechanical Testing of Steel Products," or as specified in Section 3.2 of this Specification.

    (e)   *High-Strength Low-Alloy Columbium-Vanadium Steels of Structural Quality, ASTM A572 Grades 42, 45 and 50*

    (f)   *High-Strength Low-Alloy Structural Steel with 50,000 psi Minimum Yield Point to 4 in. Thick, ASTM A588*

    (g)   *Hot-Rolled or Cold-Rolled Sheet, High-Strength Low-Alloy, with Improved Corrosion Resistance, ASTM A606*

    (h)   *Steel, Cold-Rolled Sheet, Carbon Structural, ASTM A611, Type 2*

or shall be of suitable quality ordered or produced to other than the listed specifications, provided that such material in the state used for final assembly and fabrication is weldable and is proved by tests performed by the producer or fabricator to have the properties specified in Section 3.2.

3.2 Mechanical Properties

The yield strength used as a basis for the design stresses prescribed in Section 4 shall be either 36,000 psi or 50,000 psi. Evidence that the steel furnished meets or exceeds the design yield strength shall be provided in the form of witnessed or certified test reports.

For material used without consideration of increase in yield strength resulting from cold forming, the specimens shall be taken from as-rolled material. In the case of material the mechanical properties of which conform to the requirements of one of the listed specifications, test specimens and procedure shall conform to those of such specifications and to ASTM A370. In the case of material the mechanical properties of which do not conform to the requirements of one of the listed specifications, the test specimens and procedure shall conform to the applicable requirements of ASTM A370 and the specimens shall exhibit a yield strength equal to or exceeding the design yield strength and an elongation of not less than (a) 20 percent in 2 inches for sheet and strip or (b) 18 percent in 8 inches for plates, shapes and bars with adjustments for thickness for plates, shapes and bars as prescribed in ASTM A36, A242 and A441 for plates, shapes and bars; and ASTM A570, A606 and A611 for sheet and strip.

If as-formed strength is utilized the test reports shall show the results of tests performed on full section specimens in accordance with the provisions of Sections 3.1.1 and 6.3 of the AISI *Specifications for the Design of Cold-Formed Steel Structural Members* and shall indicate compliance with these provisions and with the following additional requirements:

    (a)   The yield strength measured in the tests shall equal or exceed the design yield strength.

    (b)   Where tension tests are made for acceptance and control purposes the tensile strength shall be at least 6 percent greater than the test yield strength of the section.

    (c)   Where compression tests are used for acceptance and control purposes the specimen shall withstand a gross shortening of 2 percent of its original length without cracking. The length of specimen shall not be greater than 20 times its least radius of gyration.

    (d)   If any test specimen fails to pass the requirements of subparagraphs (a), (b) or (c) above, as applicable, two retests shall be made of specimens from the same lot. Failure of one of the retest specimens to meet such requirements shall be the cause for rejection of the lot represented by the specimens.

3.3 Paint

The standard shop paint shall conform to one of the following:
  (a) Steel Structures Painting Council *Specification 15-68T, Type I* (*red oxide*).
  (b) Steel Structures Painting Council *Specification 15-68T, Type II* (*asphalt coating*).
  (c) *Federal Specification TT-P-636* (*red oxide*).
  (d) Or, shall be a shop paint which meets the minimum performance requirements of one of the above listed specifications.

SECTION 4   DESIGN AND MANUFACTURE

4.1 Method

Joists shall be designed in accordance with these specifications as simply supported uniformly loaded trusses supporting a floor or roof deck so constructed as to brace the top chord of the joists against lateral buckling. Where any applicable design feature is not specifically covered herein, the design shall be in accordance with the following specifications of latest adoption:

  (a) American Institute of Steel Construction *Specification for the Design, Fabrication and Erection of Structural Steel for Buildings*, where the material used consists of plates, shapes or bars.
  (b) American Iron and Steel Institute *Specification for the Design of Cold-Formed Steel Structural Members*, for members which are formed from sheet or strip material.

4.2 Unit Stresses

Joists shall have their components so proportioned that the unit stresses in pounds per square inch shall not exceed the following, where F_y is the yield strength defined in Sect. 3.2.

(a) Tension:

Chord and web members having a minimum yield strength of 50,000 psi
. . . . 30,000
Chord and web members having a minimum yield strength of 36,000 psi
. . . . 22,000

(b) Compression:

For members with l/r less than C_c:

$$\frac{\left[1 - \dfrac{(l/r)^2}{2C_c^2}\right] F_y Q}{\dfrac{5}{3} + \dfrac{3}{8}\left(\dfrac{l/r}{C_c}\right) - \dfrac{1}{8}\left(\dfrac{l/r}{C_c}\right)^3} \quad \text{where} \quad C_c = \sqrt{\frac{2\pi^2 E}{QF_y}} \quad \text{and}$$

where Q is a form factor equal to unity except when the width-thickness ratio of one or more elements of the profile exceeds the limits specified in the AISC Specification, Sect. 1.9 for hot rolled sections and in the AISI Specifications, Sect. 3, for cold formed sections.

For members with l/r greater than C_c:

$$\frac{12\pi^2 E}{23(l/r)^2}$$

In the above formulas l is taken as the distance between panel points for the chord members and the unbraced length clear of attachments for web members, and r is the corresponding least radius of gyration of the member or any component thereof. E is equal to 29,000,000 psi.

(c) **Bending:**

For chords and for web members other than solid rounds having yield strength of

$$50,000 \text{ psi} \dots 30,000 \text{ psi}$$
$$36,000 \text{ psi} \dots 22,000 \text{ psi}$$

For web members of solid round cross-section having yield strength of

$$50,000 \text{ psi} \dots 45,000 \text{ psi}$$
$$36,000 \text{ psi} \dots 32,500 \text{ psi}$$

For bearing plates having yield strength of

$$50,000 \text{ psi} \dots 37,500 \text{ psi}$$
$$36,000 \text{ psi} \dots 27,000 \text{ psi}$$

4.3 Maximum Slenderness Ratios

The slenderness ratio l/r, where l is as used in Section 4.2(b) and r is the corresponding least radius of gyration shall not exceed the following:

$$\text{Top chord interior panels} \dots 90$$
$$\text{Top chord end panels} \dots 120$$
$$\text{Compression members other than top chord} \dots 200$$
$$\text{Tension members} \dots 240$$

4.4 Members

(a) **Chords**

The bottom chord shall be designed as an axially loaded tension member.

The top chord shall be designed for only axial compressive stress when the panel length, l, does not exceed 24 inches. When the panel length exceeds 24 inches, the top chord shall be designed as a continuous member subject to combined axial and bending stresses and shall be so proportioned that when fully loaded the quantity

$$\frac{f_a}{0.6\ F_y} + \frac{f_b}{F_b}$$

does not exceed unity at the panel point and the quantity

$$\frac{f_a}{F_a} + \frac{C_m f_b}{\left(1 - \dfrac{f_a}{F'_e}\right) F_b}$$

does not exceed unity at mid-panel; in which

$C_m = 1 - 0.3 f_a/F'_e$ for end panels
$C_m = 1 - 0.4 f_a/F'_e$ for interior panels
f_a = Computed axial unit compressive stress
f_b = Computed bending unit compressive stress at the point under consideration

F_a = Permissible axial unit compressive stress based on l/r as defined in Section 4.2(b)

F_b = Permissible bending unit stress

F_y = Specified minimum yield strength

$$F'_e = \frac{12\pi^2 E}{23(l/r_x)^2}$$ where l is the panel length as defined in Section 4.2(b) and r_x is the radius of gyration about the axis of bending

The top chord shall be considered as stayed laterally by the floor slab or roof deck when attachments are in accordance with the requirements of Section 5.8(e) of these specifications.

Lateral stability during erection shall be provided by bridging and the chord properties shall be such that $F_a \geq 12,500$ psi where

$$F_a = \frac{14.15 \times 10^6 C_1 C_2}{hS^2 A_t} \sqrt{(I_t + I_b)(J_t + J_b)S^2 + 25.6 I_t I_b h^2}$$

S = Spacing of bridging (in.)

h = Effective joist depth (in.)

A_t = Area of top chord (in.)

I_t = Moment of inertia of top chord about the vertical axis (in.)

I_b = Moment of inertia of bottom chord about vertical axis (in.)

J_t, J_b = Torsion constant of top and bottom chord respectively (in.)

The torsion constant of angles or hat-shaped sections is determined from the formula*

$$J = \frac{At^2}{3}$$

where A is the cross-sectional area of the member being considered and t is its thickness.

The coefficient $C_1 = 0.85$ for two-piece chord joists and $C_1 = 1.0$ for one-piece chord joists. The coefficient C_2 is given in the following table:

Number of Rows of Bridging	C_2
1	4.00
2	3.00
3	4.00
4	3.33
5	4.00

(b) Web

The vertical shears to be used in the design of the web members shall be determined from full uniform loading but such vertical shear shall be not less than 50 percent of the maximum end reaction. Due consideration shall be given to the effect of eccentricity. The effect of combined axial compression and bending may be investigated using the provisions of Section 4.4(a) letting $C_m = 0.4$ when bending due to eccentricity produces reversed curvature.

---

* It should be noted that this equation applies only for open-section chords angles, hat-shapes).

(c) Bearings

The bearing area shall be proportioned so that unit bearing pressure in pounds per square inch does not exceed the following values:

On masonry laid in cement mortar. . . . . 250 psi

On structural concrete. . . . . 750 psi

(d) Fillers or Ties

Fillers or ties are required in interior top chord panels which exceed 24 inches in length and in compression web members of joists more than 28 inches deep. Fillers or ties are not required in top chord end panels; nor are they required in interior panel lengths of 24 inches or less.

(e) Extended Ends

Extended ends shall be designed as cantilever beams with their reactions carried back at least to the first interior panel point of the joist.

4.5 Connections

(a) Method

Joint connections and splices shall be made by attaching the members to one another by arc or resistance welding or other approved methods.

(b) Strength

Joint connections shall be capable of withstanding the forces due to an ultimate load equal to at least two times the design load shown in the applicable Standard Load Table.

(c) Splices

Splices may occur at any point in chord or web members. Butt welded splices shall have a net weld throat area equal to the cross-sectional area of the member spliced and shall develop a minimum tensile strength of 57,000 psi on the full cross-sectional area of the member.

(d) Eccentricity

Members connected at a joint shall have their centroidal axes meet at a point if practical. Otherwise, due consideration shall be given to the effect of eccentricity. In no case shall eccentricity of any web member at a joint exceed $\frac{3}{4}$ of the over-all dimension, measured in the plane of the web, of the largest member connected. Such eccentricity shall be the perpendicular distance from a point at the centroid of the joint located on the centroidal axis of the chord to the centroidal axis of the web member.

Ends of joists shall be proportioned to resist bending produced by eccentricity at the support.

4.6 Design Verification Tests

(a) Chord and Web Members

Each manufacturer shall, at the time of design review by the Steel Joist Institute or the American Institute of Steel Construction, verify by test that his design, in accordance with Sections 4.1 through 4.5 of this specification, will provide a minimum factor of safety of 1.65 on the theoretical de sign capacity of critical members. Such tests shall be evaluated considering the actual yield strength of the members of the test joists.

Material tests for determining mechanical properties of component members may be conducted on full sections.

(b) Joints and Connections

Each manufacturer shall verify by shear tests on representative joints of typical joists that connections will meet the provisions of Section 4.5(b). Chord and web members may be reinforced for such tests.

4.7 Camber

Camber is optional with the manufacturer but when provided, recommended approximate camber is as follows:

Top Chord Length	Approximate Camber
20 feet	$\frac{1}{4}$ inches
30 feet	$\frac{3}{8}$ inches
40 feet	$\frac{5}{8}$ inches
50 feet	1 inch
60 feet	$1\frac{1}{2}$ inches

In no case will joists be manufactured with negative camber.

4.8 Shop Paint

Joists and accessories shall receive one shop coat of paint as specified in Section 3.3.

SECTION 5   APPLICATION

5.1 Usage

These specifications shall apply to any type of structure where floors and roofs are to be supported directly by steel joists installed as hereinafter specified. Where joists are used other than on simple spans under uniformly distributed loading as prescribed in Section 4.1, they shall be investigated and modified if necessary to limit the unit stresses to those listed in Section 4.2.

5.2 Span

The clear span of a joist shall not exceed 24 times its depth except that for floors the clear span of an H-Series joist shall not exceed 20 times its depth.

5.3 End Supports

The ends of steel joists shall extend a distance of not less than 4 inches over masonry or poured concrete supports. The ends of joists shall extend not less than $2\frac{1}{2}$ inches over steel supports. Where it is deemed necessary to butt opposite joists over a narrow steel support with bearing less than noted above, special end designs must be specified, and such ends shall have positive attachment to the support, either by bolting or welding.

5.4 Bridging

Bridging is required and shall consist of one of the following types:

(a) Horizontal

Horizontal bridging shall consist of two continuous horizontal steel members, one attached to the top chord and the other attached to the bottom chord. Attachment to the joists shall be made by welding or mechanical means and shall be capable of resisting a horizontal force of not less than 700 pounds.

The ratio of unbraced length to least radius of gyration (l/r) of the bridging member shall not exceed 300, where l is the distance in inches between attachments and r is the least radius of gyration of the bridging member. If the bridging member is a round bar, the diameter shall be at least $\frac{1}{2}$ inch.

(b) Diagonal

Diagonal bridging shall consist of cross-bracing with l/r ratio of not more than 200, where l is the distance in inches between connections and r is the least radius of gyration of the bracing member. Where cross-bracing members are connected at their point of intersection, the l distance shall be taken as the distance in inches between connections at the point of intersection of the bracing members and the connections to the chord of the joists. Connections to chords of steel joists shall be made by positive mechanical means or by welding.

(c) Quantity

In no case shall the number of rows of bridging be less than shown in the following table. Spaces between rows shall be approximately uniform.

Chord Size*	1 Row	2 Rows	3 Rows	4 Rows	5 Rows**
#3	Up to 13′	13′ to 17′	17′ to 28′		
#4	Up to 16′	16′ to 21′	21′ to 32′		
#5	Up to 16′	16′ to 21′	21′ to 33′	33′ to 38′	38′ to 40′
#6	Up to 18′	18′ to 22′	22′ to 36′	36′ to 40′	40′ to 48′
#7	Up to 20′	20′ to 25′	25′ to 41′	41′ to 46′	46′ to 48′
#8	Up to 21′	21′ to 27′	27′ to 43′	43′ to 50′	50′ to 60′
#9	Up to 23′	23′ to 30′	30′ to 46′	46′ to 53′	53′ to 60′
#10	Up to 24′	24′ to 30′	30′ to 47′	47′ to 53′	53′ to 60′
#11	Up to 24′	24′ to 31′	31′ to 48′	48′ to 55′	55′ to 60′

NUMBER OF ROWS OF BRIDGING
(Distances are clear span dimensions)

* Last digit(s) of joist designation shown in load table.

** Where five rows of bridging are required and spans are 50 feet or more, the middle row shall be diagonal bridging.

5.5 Installation of Bridging

All bridging and bridging anchors shall be completely installed before construction loads are placed on the joists.

Bridging shall support the top chords against lateral movement during the construction period and shall hold the steel joists in the approximate position as shown on the plans.

The ends of all bridging lines terminating at walls or beams shall be anchored thereto at top and bottom chords.

5.6   End Anchorage

(a)   Masonry Supports

Joists resting on masonry supports shall be bedded in mortar and anchored thereto with an anchor equivalent to a $\frac{3}{8}$ inch round steel bar not less than 8 inches long.   Every third joist in floors and every joist in roofs shall be anchored.   In roofs where parapet walls are not present, two $\frac{1}{2}$ inch anchor bolts or other equal means shall be used in lieu of the steel bar.

(b)   Steel Supports

Ends of joists resting on steel supports shall be connected thereto with the equivalent of two $\frac{1}{8}$ inch fillet welds 1 inch long or a $\frac{1}{2}$ inch bolt.   In steel framing, where columns are not framed in at least two directions with structural steel members, joists at column lines shall be field bolted at the columns to add lateral stability.

(c)   Uplift

Where uplift forces are a design consideration, roof joists shall be anchored to resist such forces.

5.7   Joist Spacing

Joists shall be spaced so that the loading on each joist does not exceed the allowable load for the particular joist design.

5.8   Floors and Roof Decks

(a)   Material

Floors and roof decks may consist of cast-in-place or precast concrete or gypsum, formed steel, wood, or other suitable material capable of supporting the required load at the specified joist spacing.

(b)   Thickness

Cast-in-place slabs shall not be less than 2 inches thick.

(c)   Centering

Centering for cast-in-place slabs may be ribbed metal lath, corrugated steel sheets, paper-backed welded wire fabric, removable centering or any other suitable material capable of supporting the slab at the designated joist spacing.   Centering shall not cause lateral displacement or damage to the top chord of joists during installation or removal of the centering or placing of the concrete.

(d)   Bearing

Slabs or decks shall bear uniformly along the top chords of the joists.

(e)   Attachments

Each attachment for slab or deck to top chords of joists shall be capable of resisting a lateral force of not less than 300 pounds.   The spacing shall not exceed 36 inches along the top chord.

(f) Wood Nailers

Where wood nailers are used, such nailers in conjunction with deck or slab shall be attached to the top chords of the joists in conformance with Section 5.8(e).

5.9 Deflection

The deflection due to the design live load shall not exceed the following:

Floors: 1/360 of span

Roofs: 1/360 of span where a plaster ceiling is attached or suspended

1/240 of span for all other cases

5.10 Ponding

Unless a roof surface is provided with sufficient slope toward points of free drainage or adequate individual drains to prevent the accumulation of rain water, the roof system shall be investigated to assure stability under ponding conditions in accordance with Sec. 1.13.3 of the AISC Specification.*

5.11 Inspection

Joists shall be inspected by the manufacturer before shipment to insure compliance of materials and workmanship with the requirements of these specifications. If the purchaser wishes an inspection of the steel joists by someone other than the manufacturer's own inspectors, he may reserve the right to do so in his "Invitation to Bid" or the accompanying "Job Specifications." Arrangements shall be made with the manufacturer for such inspection of the joists at the manufacturing shop by the purchaser's inspectors at purchaser's expense.

SECTION 6 HANDLING AND ERECTION

Care shall be exercised at all times to avoid damage through careless handling during unloading, storing and erecting.

As soon as joists are erected, all bridging shall be completely installed and the joists permanently fastened into place before the application of any loads except the weight of the erectors.

Where five rows of bridging are required in spans of 50 feet or over, each joist shall be adequately braced laterally before the next joist is erected and before any loads are applied. Hoisting cables shall not be released until support has been provided by the center row of diagonal bridging and the bridging line has been anchored to prevent lateral movement, and where joists are bottom bearing, their ends have been restrained laterally.

During the construction period the contractor shall provide means for adequate distribution of concentrated loads so that the carrying capacity of any joist is not exceeded.

Field welding shall not damage the joists. The total length of weld at any one point on cold-formed members whose yield strength has been attained by cold working and whose as-formed strength is used in the design shall not exceed 50 percent of the over-all developed width of the cold formed section.

---

* For further reference, refer to Steel Joist Institute Technical Digest No. 3 "Structural Design of Steel Joist Roofs to Resist Ponding Loads."

Standard Load Table
for Open Web Steel Joists, J-Series
Based on allowable stress of 22,000 psi

Adopted by Steel Joist Institute and
American Institute of Steel Construction, Inc., November 1, 1972

The **boldface** figures in the following table give the TOTAL safe uniformly-distributed load-carrying capacities, in pounds per linear foot, of J-Series Open Web Steel Joists. The weight of DEAD loads, including the joists, must in all cases be deducted to determine the LIVE load-carrying capacities of the joists. The load table may be used for parallel chord joists installed to a maximum slope of ½ inch per foot.

The light face figures in this load table are the LIVE loads per linear foot of joist which will produce an approximate deflection of 1/360 of the span. LIVE loads which will produce a deflection of 1/240 of the span may be obtained by multiplying the figures in light face by 1.5. **In no case shall the total load capacity of the joist be exceeded.*****

Loads above heavy stepped lines are governed by shear.

Footnotes—See tables and text above

* Indicates Nominal Depth of Steel Joists only.

** Approximate Weights per Linear Foot of Steel Joists only. Accessories and nailer strip not included.

*** Section 5.9 of the Standard Specifications for Open Web Steel Joists, J-Series and H-Series limits the design LIVE load deflection as follows: Floors, ⅓₆₀ of span. Roofs, ⅓₆₀ of span where a plaster ceiling is attached or suspended; ½₄₀ of span for all other cases.

See manufacturers' catalogs for detailed information on specific joist types.

Tests on steel joists designed in accordance with the Standard Specifications have demonstrated that the Standard Load Tables are applicable for concentrated top chord loadings (such as are developed in bulb-tee roof construction) when the sum of the equal concentrated top chord loadings does not exceed the allowable uniform loading for the joist type and span and the loads are placed at spacings not exceeding 33″ along the top chord.

Table copyright. Reproduced by courtesy of Steel Joist Institute.

STANDARD LOAD TABLE OPEN WEB STEEL JOISTS, J-SERIES

Allowable total safe loads in pounds per linear foot based on allowable stress of 22,000 psi

Joist Designation		8J3	10J3	10J4	12J3	12J4	12J5	12J6
*Depth in Inches		8	10	10	12	12	12	12
Resisting Moment in Inch Kips		70	89	111	108	135	161	196
Maximum End Reaction in Pounds		2000	2200	2400	2300	2500	2700	3000
**Approximate Weight in Pounds per Foot		4.8	4.8	6.0	5.1	6.0	7.0	8.1
Span in Feet	8	500						
	9	444						
	10	400	440	480				
	11	364 400 436						
	11	345						
	12	324	367	400	383	417	450	500
	12	266						
	13	276	338	369	354	385	415	462
	13	209	337					
	14	238	303	343	329	357	386	429
	14	167	270	334				
	15	207	264	320	307	333	360	400
	15	136	219	271				
	16	182	232	289	281	313	338	375
	16	112	181	223	264			
	17		205	256	249	294	318	353
	17		151	186	220	287		
	18		183	228	222	278	300	333
	18		127	157	185	242	284	
	19		164	205	199	249	284	316
	19		108	133	157	206	241	286
	20		148	185	180	225	268	300
	20		92	114	135	177	207	246
	21				163	204	243	286
	21				117	152	179	212
	22				149	186	222	270
	22				101	133	155	185
	23				136	170	203	247
	23				89	116	136	162
	24				125	156	186	227
	24				78	102	120	142

STANDARD LOAD TABLE OPEN WEB STEEL JOISTS, J-SERIES

Allowable total safe loads in pounds per linear foot based on allowable stress of 22,000 psi

Joist Designation	14J3	14J4	14J5	14J6	14J7	16J4	16J5	16J6	16J7	16J8
*Depth in Inches	14	14	14	14	14	16	16	16	16	16
Resisting Moment in Inch Kips	127	159	190	230	276	173	216	258	310	359
Maximum End Reaction in Pounds	2400	2800	3100	3400	3700	3000	3300	3600	4000	4300
**Approximate Weight in Pounds per Foot	5.2	6.4	7.3	8.4	9.7	6.6	7.6	8.5	10.1	11.3

Span in Feet	14J3	14J4	14J5	14J6	14J7	16J4	16J5	16J6	16J7	16J8
14	343	400	443	486	529					
15	320	373	413	453	493					
16	300	350	388	425	463	375	413	450	500	538
17	282	329	365	400	435	353	388	424	471	506
18	261 257	311	344	378	411	333	367	400	444	478
19	235 218	294 285	326	358	389	316	347	379	421	453
20	212 187	265 245	310 287	340	370	288	330	360	400	430
21	192 162	240 212	287 248	324 295	352 348	262 260	314	343	381	410
22	175 141	219 184	262 215	309 257	336 302	238 226	298 278	327	364	391
23	160 123	200 161	239 189	290 225	322 265	218 198	272 243	313 287	348 346	374
24	147 108	184 142	220 166	266 198	308 233	200 174	250 214	299 253	333 304	358 350
25	135 96	170 125	203 147	245 175	294 206	185 154	230 190	275 224	320 269	344 310
26	125 85	157 111	187 131	227 156	272 183	171 137	213 169	254 199	306 239	331 275
27	116 76	145 99	174 117	210 139	252 164	158 122	198 151	236 177	283 214	319 246
28	108 68	135 89	162 104	196 125	235 147	147 110	184 135	219 159	264 192	305 220
29						137 99	171 121	205 143	246 172	285 198
30						128 89	160 110	191 129	230 156	266 179
31						120 81	150 99	179 117	215 141	249 162
32						113 74	141 90	168 107	202 128	234 148

STANDARD LOAD TABLE OPEN WEB STEEL JOISTS, J-SERIES

Allowable total safe loads in pounds per linear foot based on allowable stress of 22,000 psi

Joist Designation	18J5	18J6	18J7	18J8	18J9	18J10	18J11
*Depth in Inches	18	18	18	18	18	18	18
Resisting Moment in Inch Kips	243	293	352	406	462	517	597
Maximum End Reaction in Pounds	3500	3900	4200	4500	4900	5300	5900
**Approximate Weight in Pounds per Foot	7.9	9.0	10.2	11.3	12.4	13.8	15.6
Span in Feet							
18	389	433	467	500	544	589	
19	368	411	442	474	516	558	621
20	350	390	420	450	490	530	590
21	333	371	400	429	467	505	562
22	318	355	382	409	445	482	536
23	304	339	365	391	426	461	513
24	281 / 274	325 / 324	350	375	408	442	492
25	259 / 243	312 / 286	336	360	392	424	472
26	240 / 216	289 / 255	323 / 305	346	377	408	454
27	222 / 193	268 / 227	311 / 272	333 / 312	363 / 340	393 / 383	437 / 435
28	207 / 173	249 / 204	299 / 244	321 / 280	350 / 305	379 / 344	421 / 390
29	193 / 155	232 / 184	279 / 220	310 / 252	338 / 274	366 / 309	407 / 351
30	180 / 140	217 / 166	261 / 199	300 / 227	327 / 248	353 / 280	393 / 317
31	169 / 127	203 / 150	244 / 180	282 / 206	316 / 224	342 / 253	381 / 287
32	158 / 116	191 / 137	229 / 164	264 / 187	301 / 204	331 / 230	369 / 261
33	149 / 106	179 / 125	215 / 149	249 / 171	283 / 186	316 / 210	358 / 238
34	140 / 96	169 / 114	203 / 136	234 / 156	266 / 170	298 / 192	344 / 218
35	132 / 88	159 / 104	192 / 125	221 / 143	251 / 156	281 / 176	325 / 200
36	125 / 81	151 / 96	181 / 115	209 / 132	238 / 143	266 / 162	307 / 183

STANDARD LOAD TABLE OPEN WEB STEEL JOISTS, J-SERIES

Allowable total safe loads in pounds per linear foot based on allowable stress of 22,000 psi

Joist Designation	20J5	20J6	20J7	20J8	20J9	20J10	20J11
*Depth in Inches	20	20	20	20	20	20	20
Resisting Moment in Inch Kips	265	316	382	455	517	579	669
Maximum End Reaction in Pounds	3800	4100	4300	4600	5000	5400	6000
**Approximate Weight in Pounds per Foot	8.1	9.2	10.6	11.9	12.8	14.4	16.1
20	380	410	430	460	500	540	600
21	362	390	410	438	476	514	571
22	345	373	391	418	455	491	545
23	330	357	374	400	435	470	522
24	307	342	358	383	417	450	500
25	283	328	344	368	400	432	480
26	261	312 / 300	331	354	385	415	462
27	242 / 235	289 / 268	319	341	370	400	444
28	225 / 211	269 / 240	307 / 292	329	357	386	429
29	210 / 190	250 / 216	297 / 263	317	345 / 343	372	414
30	196 / 171	234 / 195	283 / 238	307 / 286	333 / 310	360 / 350	400 / 397
31	184 / 155	219 / 177	265 / 215	297 / 259	323 / 281	348 / 317	387 / 360
32	173 / 141	206 / 161	249 / 196	288 / 236	313 / 255	338 / 288	375 / 327
33	162 / 129	193 / 147	234 / 178	279 / 215	303 / 233	327 / 263	364 / 298
34	153 / 118	182 / 134	220 / 163	262 / 196	294 / 213	318 / 240	353 / 273
35	144 / 108	172 / 123	208 / 150	248 / 180	281 / 195	309 / 220	343 / 250
36	136 / 99	163 / 113	197 / 137	234 / 166	266 / 179	298 / 203	333 / 230
37	129 / 91	154 / 104	186 / 127	222 / 152	252 / 165	282 / 187	324 / 212
38	122 / 84	146 / 96	176 / 117	210 / 141	239 / 153	267 / 172	309 / 195
39	116 / 78	139 / 89	167 / 108	199 / 130	227 / 141	254 / 159	293 / 181
40	110 / 72	132 / 82	159 / 100	190 / 121	215 / 131	241 / 148	279 / 168

STANDARD LOAD TABLE OPEN WEB STEEL JOISTS, J-SERIES

Allowable total safe loads in pounds per linear foot based on allowable stress of 22,000 psi

Joist Designation	22J6	22J7	22J8	22J9	22J10	22J11
*Depth in Inches	22	22	22	22	22	22
Resisting Moment in Inch Kips	335	420	493	572	640	741
Maximum End Reaction in Pounds	4200	4500	4800	5300	5700	6200
**Approximate Weight in Pounds per Foot	9.6	10.5	11.9	13.1	14.4	16.4
Span in Feet						
22	382	409	436	482	518	564
23	365	391	417	461	496	539
24	350	375	400	442	475	517
25	336	360	384	424	456	496
26	323	346	369	408	438	477
27	306	333	356	393	422	459
28	285 / 281	321	343	379	407	443
29	266 / 253	310 / 307	331	366	393	428
30	248 / 228	300 / 277	320	353	380	413
31	232 / 207	290 / 251	310	342	368	400
32	218 / 188	273 / 228	300 / 282	331 / 314	356 / 352	388
33	205 / 172	257 / 208	291 / 257	321 / 286	345 / 321	376 / 366
34	193 / 157	242 / 190	283 / 235	312 / 261	335 / 294	365 / 335
35	182 / 144	229 / 175	268 / 216	303 / 240	326 / 269	354 / 307
36	172 / 132	216 / 160	254 / 198	294 / 220	317 / 247	344 / 282
37	163 / 122	205 / 148	240 / 183	279 / 203	308 / 228	335 / 260
38	155 / 112	194 / 136	228 / 169	264 / 187	295 / 210	326 / 240
39	147 / 104	184 / 126	216 / 156	251 / 173	281 / 195	318 / 222
40	140 / 96	175 / 117	205 / 145	238 / 161	267 / 180	309 / 205
41	133 / 89	167 / 109	196 / 134	227 / 149	254 / 167	294 / 191
42	127 / 83	159 / 101	186 / 125	216 / 139	242 / 156	280 / 177
43	121 / 78	151 / 94	178 / 116	206 / 129	231 / 145	267 / 165
44	115 / 72	145 / 88	170 / 109	197 / 121	220 / 136	255 / 154

STANDARD LOAD TABLE OPEN WEB STEEL JOISTS, J-SERIES

Allowable total safe loads in pounds per linear foot based on allowable stress of 22,000 psi

Joist Desgnation	24J6	24J7	24J8	24J9	24J10	24J11
*Depth in Inches	24	24	24	24	24	14
Resisting Moment in Inch Kips	367	460	540	627	701	813
Maximum End Reaction in Pounds	4400	4700	5000	5600	5900	6400
**Approximate Weight in Pounds per Foot	9.9	11.1	12.4	13.3	14.8	16.7
24	367	392	417	467	492	533
25	352	376	400	448	472	512
26	338	362	385	431	454	492
27	326	348	370	415	437	474
28	312	336	357	400	421	457
29	291	324	345	386	407	441
30	272	313	333	373	393	427
31	255	303	323	361	381	413
	248	299				
32	239 / 225	294 / 272	313	350	369	400
33	225 / 205	282 / 248	303	339	358	388
34	212 / 188	265 / 227	294 / 283	329 / 314	347	376
35	200 / 172	250 / 208	286 / 259	320 / 288	337 / 323	366
36	189 / 158	237 / 191	278 / 238	311 / 264	328 / 297	356 / 339
37	179 / 146	224 / 176	263 / 219	303 / 243	319 / 274	346 / 312
38	169 / 135	212 / 162	249 / 202	289 / 225	311 / 253	337 / 288
39	161 / 124	202 / 150	237 / 187	275 / 208	303 / 234	328 / 266
40	153 / 115	192 / 139	225 / 174	261 / 193	292 / 217	320 / 247
41	146 / 107	182 / 129	214 / 161	249 / 179	278 / 201	312 / 229
42	139 / 100	174 / 120	204 / 150	237 / 166	265 / 187	305 / 213
43	132 / 93	166 / 112	195 / 140	226 / 155	253 / 174	293 / 199
44	126 / 87	158 / 105	186 / 130	216 / 145	241 / 163	280 / 186
45	121 / 81	151 / 98	178 / 122	206 / 135	231 / 152	268 / 173
46	116 / 76	145 / 92	170 / 114	198 / 127	221 / 142	256 / 162
47	111 / 71	139 / 86	163 / 107	189 / 119	212 / 133	245 / 152
48	106 / 67	133 / 81	156 / 100	181 / 111	203 / 125	235 / 143

Span in Feet

STANDARD LOAD TABLE OPEN WEB STEEL JOISTS, J-SERIES

Allowable total safe loads in pounds per linear foot based on allowable stress of 22,000 psi

Joist Designation	26J8	26J9	26J10	26J11	28J8	28J9	28J10	28J11
*Depth in Inches	26	26	26	26	28	28	28	28
Resisting Moment in Inch Kips	574	682	763	885	621	737	824	957
Maximum End Reaction in Pounds	5400	5900	6300	6800	5700	6200	6600	7100
**Approximate Weight in Pounds per Foot	12.2	14.1	15.4	17.1	13.0	14.3	15.9	17.9

Span in Feet

Span	26J8	26J9	26J10	26J11	28J8	28J9	28J10	28J11
26	415	454	485	523				
27	400	437	467	504				
28	386	421	450	486	407	443	471	507
29	372	407	434	469	393	428	455	490
30	360	393	420	453	380	413	440	473
31	348	381	406	439	368	400	426	458
32	338	369	394	425	356	388	413	444
33	327	358	382	412	345	376	400	430
34	318 / 317	347	371	400	335	365	388	418
35	309 / 290	337	360	389	326	354	377	406
36	295 / 267	328 / 312	350	378	317 / 311	344	367	394
37	280 / 246	319 / 288	341 / 324	368	302 / 287	335	357	384
38	265 / 227	311 / 266	332 / 299	358 / 341	287 / 265	326 / 310	347	374
39	252 / 210	299 / 246	323 / 276	349 / 316	272 / 245	318 / 287	338 / 322	364
40	239 / 194	284 / 228	315 / 256	340 / 292	259 / 227	307 / 266	330 / 299	355 / 342
41	228 / 181	270 / 211	303 / 238	332 / 272	246 / 211	292 / 247	322 / 278	346 / 318
42	217 / 168	258 / 197	288 / 221	324 / 253	235 / 196	279 / 229	311 / 258	338 / 295
43	207 / 156	246 / 183	275 / 206	316 / 235	224 / 183	266 / 214	297 / 241	330 / 275
44	198 / 146	235 / 171	263 / 193	305 / 220	214 / 171	254 / 200	284 / 225	323 / 257
45	189 / 137	225 / 160	251 / 180	291 / 205	204 / 159	243 / 187	271 / 210	315 / 240
46	181 / 128	215 / 150	240 / 168	279 / 192	196 / 149	232 / 175	260 / 197	302 / 225
47	173 / 120	206 / 140	230 / 158	267 / 180	187 / 140	222 / 164	249 / 184	289 / 211
48	166 / 112	197 / 132	221 / 148	256 / 169	180 / 131	213 / 154	238 / 173	277 / 198
49	159 / 106	189 / 124	212 / 139	246 / 159	172 / 124	205 / 144	229 / 163	266 / 186
50	153 / 100	182 / 119	203 / 131	236 / 150	166 / 116	197 / 136	220 / 153	255 / 175
51	147 / 94	175 / 110	196 / 124	227 / 141	159 / 110	189 / 128	211 / 144	245 / 165
52	142 / 88	168 / 104	188 / 117	218 / 133	153 / 103	182 / 121	203 / 136	236 / 156
53					147 / 98	175 / 114	196 / 128	227 / 147
54					142 / 92	168 / 108	188 / 121	219 / 139
55					137 / 87	162 / 102	182 / 115	211 / 132
56					132 / 83	157 / 97	175 / 109	203 / 125

STANDARD LOAD TABLE OPEN WEB STEEL JOISTS, J-SERIES

Allowable total safe loads in pounds per linear foot based on allowable stress of 22,000 psi

Joint Designation	30J8	30J9	30J10	30J11		
*Depth in Inches	30	30	30	30		
Resisting Moment in Inch Kips	667	793	885	1029		
Maximum End Reaction in Pounds	5900	6400	6800	7400		
**Approximate Weight in Pounds per Foot	13.8	14.9	16.6	18.3		
30	393	427	453	493		
31	381	413	439	477		
32	369	400	425	463		
33	358	388	412	448		
34	347	376	400	435		
35	337	366	389	423		
36	328	356	378	411		
37	319	346	368	400		
38	308 / 305	337	358	389		
39	292 / 282	328	349	379		
40	278 / 262	320 / 306	340	370		
41	265 / 243	312 / 285	332 / 320	361		
42	252 / 226	300 / 265	324 / 298	352 / 341		
43	240 / 211	286 / 247	316 / 278	344 / 318		
44	230 / 196	273 / 230	305 / 259	336 / 297		
45	220 / 184	261 / 215	291 / 242	329 / 278		
46	210 / 172	250 / 202	279 / 227	322 / 260		
47	201 / 161	239 / 189	267 / 213	311 / 244		
48	193 / 151	229 / 177	256 / 200	298 / 229		
49	185 / 142	220 / 167	246 / 188	286 / 215		
50	178 / 134	211 / 157	236 / 177	274 / 202		
51	171 / 126	203 / 148	227 / 166	264 / 191		
52	164 / 119	196 / 139	218 / 157	254 / 180		
53	158 / 112	188 / 132	210 / 148	244 / 170		
54	152 / 106	181 / 125	202 / 140	235 / 161		
55	147 / 101	175 / 118	195 / 133	227 / 152		
56	142 / 95	169 / 112	188 / 126	219 / 144		
57	137 / 90	163 / 106	182 / 119	211 / 137		
58	132 / 86	157 / 101	175 / 113	204 / 130		
59	128 / 81	152 / 95	169 / 108	197 / 123		
60	124 / 77	147 / 91	164 / 102	191 / 117		

Span in Feet

Standard Load Table
for Open Web Steel Joists, H-Series
Based on allowable stress of 30,000 psi

Adopted by Steel Joist Institute and
American Institute of Steel Construction, Inc., November 1, 1972

The **bold face** figures in the following table give the TOTAL safe uniformly distributed load-carrying capacities in pounds per linear foot, of H-Series High Strength Steel Joists. The weight of DEAD loads, including the joists, must in all cases be deducted to determine the LIVE load-carrying capacities of the joists. The load table may be used for parallel chord joists installed to a maximum slope of $\frac{1}{2}$ inch per foot.

The light face figures in this load table are the LIVE loads per linear foot of joist which will produce an approximate deflection of 1/360 of the span. LIVE loads which will produce a deflection of 1/240 of the span may be obtained by multiplying the figures in light face by 1.5. **In no case shall the total load capacity of the joist be exceeded.*****

Loads above heavy stepped lines are governed by shear.

Loads below dashed lines are to be used for roof construction only.

Footnotes—See tables and text above

* Indicates Nominal Depth of Steel Joists only.

** Approximate Weights per Linear Foot of Steel Joists only. Accessories and nailer strip not included.

*** Section 5.9 of the Standard Specifications for Open Web Steel Joists, J-Series and H-Series limits the design LIVE load deflection as follows: Floors, $\frac{1}{360}$ of span. Roofs, $\frac{1}{360}$ of span where a plaster ceiling is attached or suspended; $\frac{1}{240}$ of span for all other cases.

See manufacturers' catalogs for detailed information on specific joist types.

Tests on steel joists designed in accordance with the Standard Specifications have demonstrated that the Standard Load Tables are applicable for concentrated top chord loadings (such as are developed in bulb-tee roof construction) when the sum of the equal concentrated top chord loadings does not exceed the allowable uniform loading for the joist type and span and the loads are placed at spacings not exceeding 33″ along the top chord.

STANDARD LOAD TABLE OPEN WEB STEEL JOISTS, H-SERIES

Allowable total safe loads in pounds per linear foot based on allowable stress of 30,000 psi

Joist Designation	8H3	10H3	10H4	12H3	12H4	12H5	12H6
*Depth in Inches	8	10	10	12	12	12	12
Resisting Moment in Inch Kips	91	116	148	140	180	222	260
Maximum End Reaction in Pounds	2400	2500	2800	2800	3200	3600	3900
**Approximate Weight in Pounds per Foot	5.0	5.0	6.1	5.2	6.2	7.1	8.2
Span in Feet 8	600						
9	533						
10	480 / 460	500	560				
11	436 / 345	455	509				
12	400 / 266	417	467	467	533	600	650
13	359 / 209	385 / 337	431 / 417	431	492	554	600
14	310 / 167	357 / 270	400 / 334	400 / 393	457	514	557
15	270 / 136	333 / 219	373 / 271	373 / 320	427 / 418	480	520
16	237 / 112	302 / 181	350 / 223	350 / 264	400 / 345	450 / 404	488 / 480
17		268 / 151	329 / 186	323 / 220	376 / 287	424 / 337	459 / 400
18		239 / 127	305 / 157	288 / 185	356 / 242	400 / 284	433 / 337
19		214 / 108	273 / 133	259 / 157	332 / 206	379 / 241	411 / 286
20		193 / 92	247 / 114	233 / 135	300 / 177	360 / 207	390 / 246
21				212 / 117	272 / 152	336 / 179	371 / 212
22				193 / 101	248 / 133	306 / 155	355 / 185
23				176 / 89	227 / 116	280 / 136	328 / 162
24				162 / 78	208 / 102	257 / 120	301 / 142

STANDARD LOAD TABLE OPEN WEB STEEL JOISTS, H-SERIES

Allowable total safe loads in pounds per linear foot based on allowable stress of 30,000 psi

Joist Designation	14H3	14H4	14H5	14H6	14H7	16H4	16H5	16H6	16H7	16H8
*Depth in Inches	14	14	14	14	14	16	16	16	16	16
Resisting Moment in Inch Kips	165	212	259	307	369	221	289	344	413	478
Maximum End Reaction in Pounds	3200	3500	3800	4200	4600	3800	4300	4600	4900	5200
**Approximate Weight in Pounds per Foot	5.5	6.5	7.4	8.6	10.0	6.6	7.8	8.6	10.3	11.4
Span in Feet										
14	457	500	543	600	657					
15	427	467	507	560	613					
16	400 / 366	438	475	525	575	475	538	575	613	650
17	376 / 305	412 / 398	447	494	541	447	506	541	576	612
18	340 / 257	389 / 336	422 / 393	467	511	422 / 413	478	511	544	578
19	305 / 218	368 / 285	400 / 334	442 / 399	484 / 470	400 / 351	453 / 432	484	516	547
20	275 / 187	350 / 245	380 / 287	420 / 342	460 / 403	368 / 301	430 / 370	460 / 437	490	520
21	249 / 162	320 / 212	362 / 248	400 / 295	438 / 348	334 / 260	410 / 320	438 / 377	467 / 454	495
22	227 / 141	292 / 184	345 / 215	382 / 257	418 / 302	304 / 226	391 / 278	418 / 328	445 / 395	473 / 454
23	208 / 123	267 / 161	326 / 189	365 / 225	400 / 265	279 / 198	364 / 243	400 / 287	426 / 346	452 / 398
24	191 / 108	245 / 142	300 / 166	350 / 198	383 / 233	256 / 174	334 / 214	383 / 253	408 / 304	433 / 350
25	176 / 96	226 / 125	276 / 149	327 / 175	368 / 206	236 / 154	308 / 190	367 / 224	392 / 269	416 / 310
26	163 / 85	209 / 111	255 / 131	303 / 156	354 / 183	218 / 137	285 / 169	339 / 199	377 / 239	400 / 275
27	151 / 76	194 / 99	237 / 117	281 / 139	337 / 164	202 / 122	264 / 151	315 / 177	363 / 214	385 / 246
28	140 / 68	180 / 89	220 / 104	261 / 125	314 / 147	188 / 110	246 / 135	293 / 159	350 / 192	371 / 220
29						175 / 99	229 / 121	273 / 143	327 / 172	359 / 198
30						164 / 89	214 / 110	255 / 129	306 / 156	347 / 179
31						153 / 81	200 / 99	239 / 117	287 / 141	332 / 162
32						144 / 74	188 / 90	224 / 107	269 / 128	311 / 148

STANDARD LOAD TABLE OPEN WEB STEEL JOISTS, H-SERIES

Allowable total safe loads in pounds per linear foot based on allowable stress of 30,000 psi

Joist Designation	18H5	18H6	18H7	18H8	18H9	18H10	18H11
*Depth in Inches	18	18	18	18	18	18	8
Resisting Moment in Inch Kips	325	383	466	540	627	705	814
Maximum End Reaction in Pounds	4500	4800	5200	5400	5900	6600	7600
**Approximate Weight in Pounds per Foot	8.0	9.2	10.4	11.6	12.6	14.0	15.8
18	500	533	578	600			
19	474	505	547	568	621		
20	450	480	520	540	590		
21	429 409	457	495	514	562	629	
22	409 356	436 420	473	491	536	600	
23	391 312	417 368	452 441	470	513	574	
24	375 274	400 324	433 388	450 444	492 484	550 546	633 619
25	347 243	384 286	416 343	432 393	472 428	528 483	608 548
26	321 216	369 255	400 305	415 349	454 380	508 429	585 487
27	297 193	350 227	385 272	400 312	437 340	489 383	563 435
28	276 173	326 204	371 244	386 280	421 305	471 344	543 390
29	258 155	304 184	359 220	372 274	407 274	455 309	524 351
30	241 140	284 166	345 199	360 227	393 248	440 280	507 317
31	225 127	266 150	323 180	348 206	381 224	426 253	490 287
32	212 116	249 137	303 164	338 187	369 204	413 230	475 261
33	199 106	234 125	285 149	327 171	358 186	400 210	461 238
34	187 96	221 114	269 136	311 156	347 170	388 192	447 218
35	177 88	208 104	254 125	294 143	337 156	377 176	434 200
36	167 81	197 96	240 115	278 132	323 143	363 162	419 183

Span in Feet

STANDARD LOAD TABLE OPEN WEB STEEL JOISTS, H-SERIES

Allowable total safe loads in pounds per linear foot based on allowable stress of 30,000 psi

Joist Designation	20H5	20H6	20H7	20H8	20H9	20H10	20H11
*Depth in Inches	20	20	20	20	20	20	20
Resisting Moment in Inch Kips	365	406	499	602	701	789	912
Maximum End Reaction in Pounds	4800	5100	5400	5600	6400	7000	7900
**Approximate Weight in Pounds per Foot	8.4	9.6	10.7	12.2	13.2	14.6	16.4
20	480	510	540	560	640		
21	457	486	514	533	610		
22	436	464	491	509	582	636	
23	417 380	443	470	487	557	609	
24	400 335	425 382	450	467	533	583	
25	384 296	408 338	432 411	448	512	560	632
26	360 263	392 300	415 365	431	492 476	538	608
27	334 235	371 268	400 326	415 392	474 425	519 480	585 545
28	310 211	345 240	386 292	400 352	457 381	500 431	564 488
29	289 190	322 216	372 263	386 317	441 343	483 388	545 440
30	270 171	301 195	360 238	373 286	427 310	467 350	527 397
31	253 155	282 177	346 215	361 259	413 281	452 317	510 360
32	238 141	264 161	325 196	350 236	400 255	438 288	494 327
33	223 129	249 147	305 178	339 215	388 233	424 263	479 298
34	210 118	234 134	288 163	329 196	376 213	412 240	465 273
35	199 108	221 123	272 150	320 180	366 195	400 220	451 250
36	188 99	209 113	257 137	310 166	356 179	389 203	439 230
37	178 91	198 104	243 127	293 152	341 165	378 187	427 212
38	169 84	187 96	230 117	278 141	324 153	364 172	416 195
39	160 78	178 89	219 108	264 130	307 141	346 159	400 181
40	152 72	169 82	208 100	251 121	292 131	329 148	380 168

Span in Feet

STANDARD LOAD TABLE OPEN WEB STEEL JOISTS, H-SERIES

Allowable total safe loads in pounds per linear foot based on allowable stress of 30,000 psi

Joist Designation	22H6	22H7	22H8	22H9	22H10	22H11
*Depth in Inches	22	22	22	22	22	22
Resisting Moment in Inch Kips	422	526	653	776	873	1009
Maximum End Reaction in Pounds	5400	5600	5800	6700	7200	8100
**Approximate Weight in Pounds per Foot	9.7	10.7	12.0	13.8	15.2	16.9
Span in Feet						
22	491	509	527	609		
23	470	487	504	583	626	
24	450 446	467	483	558	600	
25	432 395	448	464	536	576	648
26	415 351	431 426	446	515	554	623
27	386 313	415 380	430	496	533	600
28	359 281	400 341	414	479 468	514	579
29	335 253	386 307	400 379	462 421	497 473	559 539
30	313 228	373 277	387 343	447 381	480 428	540 487
31	293 207	361 251	374 311	432 345	465 387	523 441
32	275 188	342 228	363 282	419 314	450 352	506 401
33	258 172	322 208	352 257	406 286	436 321	491 366
34	243 157	303 190	341 235	394 261	424 294	476 335
35	230 144	286 175	331 216	383 240	411 269	463 307
36	217 132	271 160	322 198	372 220	400 247	450 282
37	206 122	256 148	314 183	362 203	389 228	438 260
38	195 112	243 136	301 169	353 187	379 210	426 240
39	185 104	231 126	286 156	340 173	369 195	415 222
40	176 96	219 117	272 145	323 161	360 180	405 205
41	167 89	209 109	259 134	308 149	346 167	395 191
42	159 83	199 101	247 125	293 139	330 156	381 177
43	152 78	190 94	235 116	280 129	315 145	364 165
44	145 72	181 88	225 109	267 121	301 136	347 154

STANDARD LOAD TABLE OPEN WEB STEEL JOISTS, H-SERIES

Allowable total safe loads in pounds per linear foot based on allowable stress of 30,000 psi

Joist Designation	24H6	24H7	24H8	24H9	24H10	24H11
*Depth in Inches	24	24	24	24	24	24
Resisting Moment in Inch Kips	462	576	716	851	957	1106
Maximum End Reaction in Pounds	5600	5800	6000	7000	7500	8200
**Approximate Weight in Pounds per Foot	10.3	11.5	12.7	14.0	15.5	17.5
24	467	483	500	583	625	
25	448	464	480	560	600	
26	431	446	462	538	577	631
27	415 / 375	430	444	519	556	607
28	393 / 336	414 / 406	429	500	536	586
29	366 / 303	400 / 365	414	483	517	566
30	342 / 273	387 / 330	400	467 / 457	500	547
31	320 / 248	374 / 299	387 / 373	452 / 414	484 / 465	529
32	301 / 225	363 / 272	375 / 339	438 / 376	469 / 423	513 / 482
33	283 / 205	352 / 248	364 / 309	424 / 343	455 / 386	497 / 440
34	266 / 188	332 / 227	353 / 283	412 / 314	441 / 353	482 / 402
35	251 / 172	313 / 208	343 / 259	400 / 288	429 / 323	469 / 369
36	238 / 158	296 / 191	333 / 238	389 / 264	417 / 297	456 / 339
37	225 / 146	280 / 176	324 / 219	378 / 243	405 / 274	443 / 312
38	213 / 135	266 / 162	316 / 202	368 / 225	395 / 253	432 / 288
39	202 / 124	252 / 150	308 / 187	359 / 208	385 / 234	421 / 266
40	193 / 115	240 / 139	298 / 174	350 / 193	375 / 217	410 / 247
41	183 / 107	228 / 129	284 / 161	337 / 179	366 / 201	400 / 229
42	175 / 100	218 / 120	271 / 150	322 / 166	357 / 187	390 / 213
43	167 / 93	208 / 112	258 / 140	307 / 155	345 / 174	381 / 199
44	159 / 87	198 / 105	247 / 130	293 / 145	330 / 163	373 / 186
45	152 / 81	190 / 98	236 / 122	280 / 135	315 / 152	364 / 173
46	146 / 76	181 / 92	226 / 114	268 / 127	302 / 142	348 / 162
47	139 / 71	174 / 86	216 / 107	257 / 119	289 / 133	334 / 152
48	134 / 67	167 / 81	207 / 100	246 / 111	277 / 125	320 / 143

Span in Feet

STANDARD LOAD TABLE OPEN WEB STEEL JOISTS, H-SERIES

Allowable total safe loads in pounds per linear foot based on allowable stress of 30,000 psi

Joist Designation	26H8	26H9	26H10	26H11	28H8	28H9	28H10	28H11
*Depth in Inches	26	26	26	26	28	28	28	28
Resisting Moment in Inch Kips	784	925	1040	1203	846	1000	1124	1300
Maximum End Reaction in Pounds	6700	7200	7600	8300	6700	7200	7700	8400
**Approximate Weight in Pounds per Foot	12.8	14.8	16.2	17.9	13.5	15.2	16.8	18.3
Span in Feet								
26	515	554	585	638				
27	496	533	563	615				
28	479	514	543	593	479	514	550	600
29	462	497	524	572	462	497	531	579
30	447	480	507	553	447	480	513	560
31	432 / 418	465	490	535	432	465	497	542
32	419 / 380	450 / 445	475	519	419	450	481	525
33	406 / 346	436 / 405	461 / 456	503	406 / 404	436	467	509
34	394 / 317	424 / 371	447 / 417	488 / 476	394 / 370	424	453	494
35	383 / 290	411 / 340	434 / 383	474 / 437	383 / 339	411 / 396	440	480
36	372 / 267	400 / 312	422 / 352	461 / 401	372 / 311	400 / 364	428 / 410	467
37	362 / 246	389 / 288	411 / 324	449 / 370	362 / 287	389 / 336	416 / 378	454 / 432
38	353 / 227	379 / 266	400 / 299	437 / 341	353 / 265	379 / 310	405 / 349	442 / 399
39	344 / 210	369 / 246	390 / 276	426 / 316	344 / 245	369 / 287	395 / 322	431 / 369
40	327 / 194	360 / 228	380 / 256	415 / 292	335 / 227	360 / 266	385 / 299	420 / 342
41	311 / 181	351 / 211	371 / 238	405 / 272	327 / 211	351 / 247	376 / 278	410 / 318
42	296 / 168	343 / 197	362 / 221	395 / 253	319 / 196	343 / 229	367 / 258	400 / 295
43	283 / 156	334 / 183	353 / 206	386 / 235	305 / 183	335 / 214	358 / 241	391 / 27
44	270 / 146	319 / 171	345 / 193	377 / 220	291 / 171	327 / 200	350 / 225	38 / 25
45	258 / 137	305 / 160	338 / 180	369 / 205	279 / 159	320 / 187	342 / 210	37 / 24
46	247 / 128	291 / 150	328 / 168	361 / 192	267 / 149	313 / 175	335 / 197	36 / 22
47	237 / 120	279 / 140	314 / 158	353 / 180	255 / 140	302 / 164	328 / 184	35 / 21
48	227 / 112	268 / 132	301 / 148	346 / 169	245 / 131	289 / 154	321 / 173	35 / 19
49	218 / 106	257 / 124	289 / 139	334 / 159	235 / 124	278 / 144	312 / 163	34 / 18
50	209 / 100	247 / 117	277 / 131	321 / 150	226 / 116	267 / 136	300 / 153	33 / 17
51	201 / 94	237 / 110	267 / 124	308 / 141	217 / 110	256 / 128	288 / 144	32 / 16
52	193 / 88	228 / 104	256 / 117	297 / 133	209 / 103	247 / 121	277 / 136	32 / 15
53					201 / 98	237 / 114	267 / 128	30 / 14
54					193 / 92	229 / 108	257 / 121	29 / 13
55					186 / 87	220 / 102	248 / 115	28 / 1
56					180 / 83	213 / 97	239 / 109	27 / 1

STANDARD LOAD TABLE OPEN WEB STEEL JOISTS, H-SERIES

Allowable total safe loads in pounds per linear foot based on allowable stress of 30,000 psi

Joist Designation	30H8	30H9	30H10	30H11		
•Depth in Inches	30	30	30	30		
Resisting Moment in Inch Kips	909	1075	1207	1397		
Maximum End Reaction in Pounds	6800	7500	8100	8700		
**Approximate Weight in Pounds per Foot	14.2	15.4	17.3	18.8		
30	453	500	540	580		
31	439	484	523	561		
32	425	469	506	544		
33	412	455	491	527		
34	400	441	476	512		
35	389	429	463	497		
36	378 / 359	417	450	483		
37	368 / 330	405 / 387	438 / 436	470		
38	358 / 305	395 / 357	426 / 402	458		
39	349 / 282	385 / 331	415 / 372	446 / 426		
40	340 / 262	375 / 306	405 / 345	435 / 395		
41	332 / 243	366 / 285	395 / 320	424 / 367		
42	324 / 226	357 / 265	386 / 298	414 / 341		
43	316 / 211	349 / 247	377 / 278	405 / 318		
44	309 / 196	341 / 230	368 / 259	395 / 297		
45	299 / 184	333 / 215	360 / 242	387 / 278		
46	286 / 172	326 / 202	352 / 227	378 / 260		
47	274 / 161	319 / 189	345 / 213	370 / 244		
48	263 / 151	311 / 177	338 / 200	363 / 229		
49	252 / 142	298 / 167	331 / 188	355 / 215		
50	242 / 134	287 / 157	322 / 177	348 / 202		
51	233 / 126	276 / 148	309 / 166	341 / 191		
52	224 / 119	265 / 139	298 / 157	335 / 180		
53	216 / 112	255 / 132	286 / 148	328 / 170		
54	208 / 106	246 / 125	276 / 140	319 / 161		
55	200 / 101	237 / 118	266 / 133	308 / 152		
56	193 / 95	229 / 112	257 / 126	297 / 144		
57	187 / 90	221 / 106	248 / 119	287 / 137		
58	180 / 86	213 / 101	239 / 113	277 / 130		
59	174 / 81	206 / 95	231 / 108	268 / 123		
60	168 / 77	199 / 91	224 / 102	259 / 117		

STANDARD SPECIFICATIONS AND LOAD TABLES FOR

Longspan Steel Joists

LJ-Series and LH-Series

Deep Longspan Steel Joists

DLJ-Series and DLH-Series

Adopted by Steel Joist Institute and
American Institute of Steel Construction, November 1, 1972

AMERICAN INSTITUTE OF STEEL CONSTRUCTION

101 Park Avenue, New York, N. Y. 10017

STANDARD SPECIFICATIONS FOR

Longspan Steel Joists
LJ-Series and LH-Series

Deep Longspan Steel Joists
DLJ-Series and DLH-Series

Adopted by Steel Joist Institute and
American Institute of Steel Construction, Inc., November 1, 1972

SECTION 100   SCOPE

These specifications cover the design, manufacture and use of Longspan Steel Joists, LJ- and LH-Series, and Deep Longspan Steel Joists, DLJ- and DLH-Series.

SECTION 101   DEFINITION

The term "Longspan Steel Joists LJ- and LH-Series, and Deep Longspan Steel Joists, DLJ- and DLH-Series", as used herein, refers to open web load-carrying members utilizing hot-rolled or cold-formed steel, including cold-formed steel whose yield strength* has been attained by cold working. LJ- and LH-Series are suitable for the direct support of floors and roof decks in buildings and DLJ- and DLH-Series are suitable for the direct support of roof decks in buildings.

The design of LJ- and DLJ-Series joists shall be based on a yield strength of 36,000 psi and steel used for LJ- and DLJ-Series joists shall have a minimum yield strength of 36,000 psi in the hot-rolled condition prior to forming or fabrication.   LJ- and DLJ-Series joists shall be designed in accordance with these specifications to support the loads given in the attached Standard Load Tables for LJ- and DLJ-Series joists.

The design of LH- and DLH-Series joist chord or web sections shall be based on a yield strength of at least 36,000 psi but not greater than 50,000 psi.   Steel used for LH- and DLH-Series joist chord or web sections shall have a minimum yield strength determined in accordance with one of the procedures specified in Section 102.2, which is equal to the yield strength assumed in the design.   LH- and DLH-Series joists shall be designed in accordance with these specifications to support the loads given in the attached Standard Load Tables for LH- and DLH-Series joists.

SECTION 102   MATERIALS

102.1   Steel

The steel used in the manufacture of chord and web sections shall conform to one of the following ASTM Specifications of latest adoption:

---

* The term "yield strength" as used herein shall designate the yield level of a material as determined by the applicable method outlined in paragraph 13—"Yield Strength", or paragraph 12—"Yield Point", of ASTM Standard A370, "Mechanical Testing of Steel Products", or as specified in Section 102.2 of this Specification.

(a) *Structural Steel*, ASTM A36.
(b) *High-Strength Low-Alloy Structural Steel*, ASTM A242.
(c) *Flat Rolled Carbon Steel Sheets of Structural Quality*, ASTM A245.
(d) *Hot-Rolled Carbon Steel Strip of Structural Quality*, ASTM A303.
(e) *High-Strength Low-Alloy Structural Manganese Vanadium Steel*, ASTM A441.
(f) *Hot-Rolled Carbon Steel Sheets and Strip, Structural Quality*, ASTM A570.
(g) *High-Strength Low-Alloy Columbium-Vanadium Steels of Structural Quality*, ASTM A572 Grades 42, 45, and 50.
(h) *High-Strength Low-Alloy Structural Steel with 50,000 psi Minimum Yield Point to 4 in. Thick*, ASTM A588.
(i) *Hot-Rolled or Cold-Rolled Sheet, High-Strength Low-Alloy, with Improved Corrosion Resistance*, ASTM A606.

or shall be of suitable quality ordered or produced to other than the listed specifications, provided that such material in the state used for final assembly and fabrication is weldable and is proved by tests performed by the producer or fabricator to have the properties specified in Section 102.2.

102.2   Mechanical Properties

The yield strength used as a basis for the design stresses prescribed in Section 103 shall be at least 36,000 psi but shall not be greater than 50,000 psi.   Evidence that the steel furnished meets or exceeds the design yield strength shall be provided in the form of witnessed or certified test reports.

For material used without consideration of increase in yield strength resulting from cold forming, the specimens shall be taken from as-rolled material.   In the case of material the mechanical properties of which conform to the requirements of one of the listed specifications, test specimens and procedure shall conform to those of such specifications and to ASTM A370.

In the case of material the mechanical properties of which do not conform to the requirements of one of the listed specifications, the test specimens and procedure shall conform to the applicable requirements of ASTM A370 and the specimens shall exhibit a yield strength equal to or exceeding the design yield strength and an elongation of not less than (a) 20 percent in 2 inches for sheet and strip or (b) 18 percent in 8 inches for plates, shapes and bars with adjustments for thickness for plates, shapes and bars as prescribed in ASTM A36, A242 and A441.   The number of tests shall be the same as prescribed in ASTM A36, A242 and A441 for plates, shapes and bars; and ASTM A245 and A303 for sheet and strip.

If as-formed strength is utilized, the test reports shall show the results of tests performed on full section specimens in accordance with the provisions of Sections 3.1.1 and 6.3 of the AISI *Specification for the Design of Cold-Formed Steel Structural Members*, and shall indicate compliance with these provisions and with the following additional requirements:

1.   The yield strength measured in the tests shall equal or exceed the design yield strength.
2.   Where tension tests are made for acceptance and control purposes the tensile strength shall be at least 6 percent greater than the yield strength of the section.
3.   Where compression tests are used for acceptance and control purposes the specimen shall withstand a gross shortening of 2 percent of

its original length without cracking. The length of specimen shall not be greater than 20 times its least radius of gyration.

4. If any test specimen fails to pass the requirements of subparagraphs 1, 2 or 3 above, as applicable, two retests shall be made of specimens from the same lot. Failure of one of the retest specimens to meet such requirements shall be cause for rejection of the lot represented by the specimens.

102.3 Welding Electrodes

The following electrodes shall be used for arc welding:

(a) For connected members both having a specified minimum yield strength greater than 36,000 psi:

> AWS A5.1 or A5.5, E70XX
> AWS A5.17, F7X-EXXX flux-electrode combination
> AWS A5.18, E70S-X or E70U-1
> AWS A5.20, E70T-X

(b) For connected members both having a specified minimum yield strength of 36,000 psi, or one having a specified minimum yield strength of 36,000 psi and the other having a specified minimum yield strength greater than 36,000 psi:

> AWS A5.1, E60XX
> AWS A5.17, F6X-EXXX flux-electrode combination
> AWS A5.20, E60T-X
> or any of those listed in Section 102.3(a)

Other welding methods, providing equivalent strength as demonstrated by tests, may be used.

102.4 Paint

The standard shop paint shall conform to one of the following:

(a) Steel Structures Painting Council *Specification 15-68T, Type I (red oxide)*.

(b) Steel Structures Painting Council *Specification 15-68T, Type II (asphalt coating)*.

(c) *Federal Specification TT-P-636 (red oxide)*.

(d) Or, shall be a shop paint which meets the minimum performance requirements of one of the above listed specifications.

SECTION 103 DESIGN AND MANUFACTURE

103.1 Method

Joists shall be designed in accordance with these specifications as simply supported uniformly loaded trusses supporting a floor or roof deck so constructed as to brace the top chord of the joists against lateral buckling. Where any applicable design feature is not specifically covered herein, the design shall be in accordance with the following specifications of latest adoption:

(a) American Institute of Steel Construction *Specification for the Design, Fabrication and Erection of Structural Steel for Buildings*, where the material used consists of plates, shapes or bars.

(b) American Iron and Steel Institute *Specification for the Design of Cold-Formed Steel Structural Members*, for members which are cold-formed from sheet or strip material.

103.2 Unit Stresses

Joists shall have their components so proportioned that the unit stresses in pounds per square inch shall not exceed the following where F_y is the yield strength defined in Section 102.2:

(a) **Tension:** All members . . . . $0.6F_y$

(b) **Compression:**

For members with l/r less than C_c:

$$\frac{\left[1 - \dfrac{(l/r)^2}{2C_c{}^2}\right]F_y Q}{\dfrac{5}{3} + \dfrac{3(l/r)}{8C_c} - \dfrac{(l/r)^3}{8C_c{}^3}} \quad \text{where} \quad C_c = \sqrt{\frac{2\pi^2 E}{QF_y}} \quad \text{and}$$

where Q is a form factor equal to unity except when the width-thickness ratio of one or more elements of the profile exceeds the limits specified in the AISC Specification, Section 1.9, for hot rolled sections and in the AISI Specification, Section 3., for cold-formed sections.

For members with l/r greater than C_c:

$$\frac{12\pi^2 E}{23(l/r)^2}$$

In the above formulas l is the length center-to-center of panel points, and r is the corresponding least radius of gyration of the member or any components thereof, both in inches and E is equal to 29,000,000 psi. However, the slenderness ratio l/r of web members may be taken as $3l/4r_x$ where the value exceeds l/r_y, where r_x is the radius of gyration in the plane of the joist and r_y is normal to it.

(c) **Bending**

For chords, and for web members other than solid rounds . . . $0.6F_y$
For web members of solid round cross-section . . . . $0.9F_y$
For bearing plates . . . . $0.75F_y$

(d) **Weld Stresses**

Shear at throat of fillet welds:
Made with E70 series electrodes or F7X-EXXX flux-
electrode combinations . . . . 21,000 psi
Made with E60 series electrodes or F6X-EXXX flux-
electrode combinations . . . . 18,000 psi
Tension or compression on groove or butt welds shall be the same as those specified for the connected material.

103.3 Maximum Slenderness Ratios

The slenderness ratio l/r, where l is the length center-to-center of panel points and r is the corresponding least radius of gyration, shall not exceed the following:

Top chord interior panels 90
Top chord end panels 120
Compression members other than top chord 200
Tension members 240

103.4 Members

(a) Chords

The bottom chord shall be designed as an axially loaded tension member.

The top chord shall be designed as a continuous member subject to combined axial and bending stresses and shall be so proportioned that when fully loaded the quantity

$$f_a + f_b$$

does not exceed $0.6F_y$ at the panel point and the quantity

$$\frac{f_a}{F_a} + \frac{C_m f_b}{\left(1 - \dfrac{f_a}{F'_e}\right) F_b}$$

does not exceed unity at mid-panel; in which

C_m = $1 - 0.3f_a/F'_e$ for end panels
C_m = $1 - 0.4f_a/F'_e$ for interior panels
f_a = Computed axial unit compressive stress
f_b = Computed bending unit compressive stress at the point under consideration
F_a = Permissible axial unit compressive stress based on l/r for the panel length center-to-center of panel points
F_b = Permissible bending unit stress; $0.6F_y$
$F'_e = \dfrac{12\pi^2 E}{23(l/r_x)^2}$ where full panel length, center-to-center of panel points, shall be used for l
r_x = Radius of gyration about the axis of bending

The radius of gyration of the top chord about its vertical axis shall be not less than $l/170$ where l is the spacing in inches between lines of bridging as specified in Section 104.5(b).

The top chord shall be considered as stayed laterally by the floor or roof deck provided the requirements of Section 104.9(e) of these specifications are met.

(b) Web

The vertical shears to be used in the design of the web members shall be determined from full uniform loading but such vertical shear shall be not less than 25 percent of the end reaction.

(c) Depth

Joists may have either parallel chords or a top chord slope of $\frac{1}{8}$ inch per foot. The depth, for the purpose of design, in all cases shall be the depth at mid-span.

(d) Bearings

The bearing area shall be proportioned so that the unit bearing pressure in pounds per square inch does not exceed the following values:

On masonry laid in cement mortar	250 psi
On structural concrete	750 psi

(e) **Fillers or Ties**

Chord and web members in compression, composed of two components, shall have fillers, ties, or welds spaced so that the ratio l/r for each component shall not exceed the l/r ratio of the whole member. Chord and web members in tension, composed of two components, shall have fillers, ties or welds spaced so that the l/r ratio of each component shall not exceed 240. The least r shall be used in computing the ratio l/r of a component.

Fillers or ties are required in top chord interior panels which exceed 24 inches in length and in compression web members of joists more than 28 inches deep. Fillers or ties are not required in top chord end panels; nor are they required in interior panel lengths of 24 inches or less.

(f) **Extended Ends**

Extended ends shall be designed as cantilever beams with their reactions carried back at least to the first interior panel point of the joist.

103.5 **Connections**

(a) **Method**

Joint connections and splices shall be made by attaching the members to one another by arc or resistance welding, bolting, or other approved method.

(b) **Strength**

Joint connections shall develop the design stress but not less than 50 percent of the allowable strength of the member.

(c) **Shop Splices**

Shop splices may occur at any point in chord or web members. Splices shall develop the design stress but not less than 50 percent of the allowable strength of the member, except that butt weld splices shall develop the full allowable tensile strength of the member.

(d) **Field Splices**

Field splices shall be designed by the manufacturer and may be either bolted or welded. Splices shall develop the design stress but not less than 50 percent of the allowable strength of the member.

(e) **Eccentricity**

Members connected at a joint shall have their center of gravity lines meet at a point, if practical. Eccentricity on either side of the neutral axis of chord members may be neglected when it does not exceed the distance between the neutral axis and the back of the chord. Otherwise, provision shall be made for the stresses due to eccentricity. Ends of joists shall be proportioned to resist bending produced by eccentricity at the support.

In those cases where a single angle compression member is attached to the outside of the stem of a tee or double angle chord, due consideration shall be given to eccentricity.

103.6   Camber

Joists shall have approximate cambers in accordance with the following:

Top Chord Length	Approximate Camber	Top Chord Length	Approximate Camber
20'-0"	¼"	90'-0"	3½"
30'-0"	⅜"	100'-0"	4¼"
40'-0"	⅝"	110'-0"	5"
50'-0"	1"	120'-0"	6"
60'-0"	1½"	130'-0"	7"
70'-0"	2"	140'-0"	8"
80'-0"	2¾"	144'-0"	8½"

103.7   Shop Painting

Joists and accessories shall receive one shop coat of protective paint as specified in Section 102.4.

SECTION 104   APPLICATION

104.1   Usage

These specifications shall apply to any type of structure where floors and roof decks are to be supported directly by steel joists installed as hereinafter specified.   Where joists are used other than on simple spans under uniformly distributed loading, as prescribed in Section 103.1, they shall be investigated and modified if necessary to limit the unit stresses to those listed in Section 103.2.

104.2   Span

The clear span of joists in roof construction shall not exceed 24 times their nominal depth.   In floor construction, the spans shall not be greater than 20 times the nominal depth of the joist.

104.3   Depth

The nominal depth of sloping chord joists shall be the depth at midspan.   The standard slope of the top chord shall be ⅛ inch per foot.

104.4   End Supports

(a)   **Steel**

Due consideration of the end reactions shall be taken in the design of the supporting steel.

The ends of joists shall extend a distance of not less than 4 inches over steel supports except where opposite joists butt over a narrow steel support and positive attachment to the support is made by welding or bolting. In such cases a shorter end bearing length may be used when proper design provisions are made.

(b) Masonry and Concrete

The following minimum bearing lengths, parallel to the length of joists, shall be provided for bearing on masonry and concrete.

Joist Type	Minimum Bearing Lengths	
	On Masonry	On Concrete
LH 02 thru LH 11 LJ 02 thru LJ 14 DLH 10, DLH 11, and DLH 12 DLJ 12, DLJ 13, and DLJ 14	6 inches	6 inches
LH 12, LH 13, and LH 14 LJ 15, LJ 16, and LJ 17 DLH 13, and DLH 14 DLJ 15 and DLJ 16	8 inches	6 inches
LH 15, LH 16, and LH 17 LJ 18 and LJ 19 DLH 15 and DLH 16 DLJ 17 and DLJ 18	10 inches	8 inches
DLH 17, DLH 18 and DLH 19 DLJ 19 and DLJ 20	12 inches	9 inches

104.5 Bridging

(a) Type

Bridging shall consist of cross-bracing with l/r ratio of not more than 200, where l is the distance in inches between connections and r is the least radius of gyration of the bracing member. Where cross-bracing members are connected at their point of intersection, the distance l shall be taken as the distance in inches between connections at the point of intersection of the bracing members and the connections to the chord of the joists. Connections shall be made by bolting or welding.

(b) Spacing

The maximum spacing of lines of bridging for the different chord sizes shall not exceed the values tabulated below:

LJ- and LH-Chord Size*	Maximum Spacing of Lines of Bridging
02 to 09, incl.	11′–0″
10 to 14, incl.	16′–0″
15 to 19, incl.	21′–0″

DLJ- and DLH-Chord Size*	Maximum Spacing of Lines of Bridging
10	14′–0″
11 to 14, incl.	16′–0″
15 to 17, incl.	21′–0″
18 to 20, incl.	26′–0″

* Last two digits of joist designation shown in load table.

104.6   Installation of Bridging

All bridging and bridging anchors shall be completely installed before construction loads are placed on the joists.

Bridging shall support the top and bottom chords against lateral movement during the construction period and shall hold the steel joists in the approximate position as shown on the plans.

The ends of all bridging lines terminating at walls or beams shall be anchored thereto at top and bottom chords.

104.7   End Anchorage

(a)   Masonry Supports

Joists resting on masonry or concrete shall be attached thereto with an anchor equivalent to a $\frac{3}{4}$ inch round steel bar not less than 12 inches long. In roofs where masonry parapet walls are less than 2 feet high, two $\frac{3}{4}$ inch anchor bolts or other equal means shall be used in lieu of the steel bar.

(b)   Steel Supports

Ends of joists resting on steel supports shall be connected thereto with the equivalent of two $\frac{1}{4}$ inch fillet welds 2 inches long, or with two $\frac{3}{4}$ inch bolts.

In steel frames, where columns are not framed in at least two directions with structural steel members, joists at column lines shall be field bolted at the columns to provide lateral stability during construction.

(c)   Uplift

Where uplift forces are a design consideration, roof joists shall be anchored to resist such forces.

104.8   Joist Spacing

Joists shall be spaced so that the loading on each joist does not exceed the allowable load given for the particular designation and span in the Load Table.

104.9   Floors and Roof Decks

(a)   Material

Floors and roof decks may consist of cast-in-place or precast concrete or gypsum, formed steel, wood, or other suitable material capable of supporting the required load at the specified joist spacing.

(b)   Thickness

Cast-in-place slabs shall not be less than 2 inches thick.

(c)   Centering

Centering for structural slabs may be ribbed metal lath, corrugated steel sheets, paperback welded wire fabric, removable centering, or any other suitable material capable of supporting the slab at the designated joist spacing. Centering shall not cause lateral displacement or damage to the top chord of joists during installation or removal of the centering or placing of the concrete.

(d)   Bearing

Slabs or decks shall bear uniformly along the top chords of the joists.

(e) Attachments

Attachments of slab or deck to top chords of joists, where required, shall be capable of staying the top chords laterally. The spacing of such attachments along the top chords of joists shall not exceed 36 inches.

(f) Wood Nailers

Where wood nailers are used, such nailers in conjunction with the deck or slab shall be firmly attached to the top chords of the joists in conformance with Section 104.9(e).

104.10 Deflection

The deflection due to the design live load shall not exceed the following:

Floors: 1/360 of span
Roofs: 1/360 of span where a plaster ceiling is attached or suspended
1/240 of span for all other cases

104.11 Ponding

Unless a roof surface is provided with sufficient slope toward points of free drainage or adequate individual drains to prevent the accumulation of rain water, the roof system shall be investigated to assure stability under ponding conditions in accordance with Section 1.13.3 of the AISC Specification.*

104.12 Inspection

Joists shall be inspected by the manufacturer before shipment to insure compliance of materials and workmanship with the requirements of these specifications. If the purchaser wishes an inspection of the steel joists by someone other than the manufacturer's own inspectors, he may reserve the right to do so in his "Invitation to Bid" or the accompanying "Job Specifications." Arrangements shall be made with the manufacturer for such inspection of the joists at the manufacturing shop by the purchaser's inspectors at purchaser's expense.

SECTION 105 HANDLING AND ERECTION

Particular attention should be paid to the erection of Longspan and Deep Longspan Steel Joists.

Care shall be exercised at all times to avoid damage through careless handling during unloading, storing and erecting. Dropping of joists shall not be permitted.

Each joist shall be adequately braced laterally before the next joist is erected and before any loads are applied. If lateral support is provided by bridging, the bridging lines as defined below must be anchored to prevent lateral movement.

Hoisting cables shall not be released until one line of bolted bridging nearest mid-span for spans up to 60 feet, and two lines of bolted bridging

---

* For further reference, refer to Steel Joist Institute Technical Digest No. 3 "Structural Design of Steel Joist Roofs to Resist Ponding Loads."

nearest the third points of the span for spans up to 100 feet, and all bridging lines for spans over 100 feet, are installed, and, where joists are bottom bearing, their ends have been restrained laterally.   For ease of alignment, anchorage of joist ends in accordance with Section 104.7 should follow the installation of bridging.   During the construction period, the contractor shall provide means for the adequate distribution of concentrated loads so that the carrying capacity of any joist is not exceeded.

Field welding shall not damage the joists.   The total length of weld at any one cross-section on cold-formed members whose yield strength has been attained by cold working and whose as-formed strength is used in the design shall not exceed 50 percent of the overall developed width of the cold-formed section.

Standard Load Table
for Longspan Steel Joists, LJ-Series
Based on a maximum allowable tensile stress of 22,000 psi

**Adopted by Steel Joist Institute and
American Institute of Steel Construction, Inc., July 1, 1970**

The **bold face** figures in the following table give the TOTAL safe uniformly-distributed load-carrying capacities, in pounds per linear foot, of LJ-Series joists. The weight of DEAD loads, including the joists, must in all cases be deducted to determine the LIVE load-carrying capacities of the joists. The approximate DEAD load of the joists may be determined from the weights per linear foot shown in the tables.*

The light face figures in this load table are the LIVE loads per linear foot of joist which will produce an approximate deflection of $\frac{1}{360}$ of the span. LIVE loads which will produce a deflection of $\frac{1}{240}$ of the span may be obtained by multiplying the light face figures by 1.5. **In no case shall the total load capacity of the joist be exceeded.****

This load table applies to joists with either parallel chords or standard pitched top chords. When top chords are pitched, the carrying capacities are determined by the nominal depth of the joists at center of the span.

Standard top chord pitch is ⅛ inch per foot. If pitch exceeds this standard, the load table does not apply. The load table may be used for parallel chord joists installed to a maximum slope of ½ inch per foot.

When holes are required in top or bottom chords, the carrying capacities must be reduced in proportion to reduction of chord areas.

The top chords are considered as being stayed laterally by floor slab or roof deck.

Loads to the right of the heavy vertical lines are to be used for roof construction only.

---

* Approximate weights per linear foot of joists include accessories.

** Section 104.10 of the "Standard Specifications" limits the design LIVE load deflection as follows: Floors, $\frac{1}{360}$ of span. Roofs, $\frac{1}{360}$ of span where a plaster ceiling is attached or suspended; $\frac{1}{240}$ of span for all other cases.

STANDARD LOAD TABLE FOR LONGSPAN STEEL JOISTS, LJ-SERIES
Pounds per Linear Foot Based on Allowable Stress of 22,000 psi

Joist Designation	Approx. Wt. Lbs. per Lin. Ft.	Nominal Depth in Inches	Safe Load* in Lbs. Between	21-24	25	26	27	28	29	30	31	32	33	34	35	36
LJ02	13	18	8,800	343	324 / 323	306 / 289	290 / 260	275 / 235	260 / 212	244 / 193	230 / 176	217 / 160	206 / 147	195 / 135	185 / 124	
LJ03	14	18	9,800	382	362 / 346	342 / 310	321 / 279	300 / 251	280 / 227	263 / 207	247 / 188	233 / 172	219 / 157	207 / 144	196 / 133	
LJ04	16	18	11,500	449 / 430	423 / 384	394 / 344	367 / 309	343 / 279	321 / 252	301 / 229	283 / 209	266 / 190	251 / 174	237 / 160	224 / 147	
LJ05	17	18	12,800	502	475 / 454	450 / 406	426 / 365	398 / 330	372 / 298	349 / 271	328 / 247	309 / 225	291 / 206	275 / 189	260 / 174	
LJ06	19	18	15,200	593 / 554	549 / 494	510 / 442	475 / 397	444 / 358	415 / 324	389 / 295	366 / 268	344 / 245	325 / 224	307 / 206	290 / 190	
LJ07	20	18	15,800	616	593 / 560	572 / 502	532 / 451	497 / 407	465 / 368	436 / 334	410 / 304	386 / 278	364 / 255	344 / 234	325 / 215	
LJ08	22	18	17,000	664	639 / 620	616 / 555	595 / 499	575 / 450	538 / 408	505 / 370	474 / 337	447 / 308	421 / 282	398 / 259	376 / 238	
LJ09	24	18	17,600	685	660	636 / 601	614 / 540	593 / 488	574 / 441	556 / 401	523 / 365	492 / 333	464 / 305	438 / 280	415 / 258	
LJ10	27	18	18,900	739	711	685 / 676	662 / 608	639 / 548	618 / 496	599 / 451	581 / 410	547 / 375	516 / 343	488 / 315	461 / 290	
LJ11	29	18	20,000	780	751	724	698 / 671	675 / 605	653 / 548	632 / 498	613 / 453	595 / 414	578 / 379	546 / 348	516 / 320	
LJ12	32	18	20,700	807	776	748	722	698 / 656	675 / 594	654 / 539	634 / 491	615 / 449	597 / 411	580 / 377	565 / 347	

Joist Designation	Approx. Wt. Lbs. per Lin. Ft.	Nominal Depth in Inches	Safe Load* in Lbs. Between	22-24	25	26	27	28	29	30	31	32	33	34	35	36	37	38	39	40
LJ03	14	20	9,900	388	369	351	334	318 / 314	304 / 284	290 / 258	276 / 235	260 / 215	245 / 196	232 / 180	219 / 166	208 / 153	197 / 141	187 / 131	178 / 122	
LJ04	16	20	11,900	464	439	416	395 / 387	375 / 349	356 / 316	337 / 287	317 / 262	298 / 239	281 / 219	266 / 201	251 / 185	238 / 170	226 / 158	215 / 146	204 / 135	
LJ05	17	20	13,000	510	485	461	439	419 / 412	399 / 373	381 / 339	364 / 309	346 / 282	326 / 258	308 / 237	291 / 218	276 / 201	262 / 186	249 / 172	237 / 160	
LJ06	19	20	15,400	602	579	559 / 555	530 / 499	498 / 450	466 / 407	437 / 370	410 / 337	386 / 308	364 / 282	344 / 259	326 / 238	308 / 220	293 / 203	278 / 188	265 / 174	
LJ07	20	20	16,500	643	619	597	576 / 565	557 / 510	521 / 462	489 / 419	459 / 382	432 / 349	408 / 319	385 / 293	365 / 270	345 / 249	328 / 230	311 / 213	296 / 198	
LJ08	22	20	17,900	699	673	648	626	605 / 566	585 / 513	567 / 466	533 / 424	502 / 387	473 / 355	447 / 326	423 / 300	401 / 276	380 / 255	361 / 237	344 / 220	
LJ09	24	20	18,600	726	699	674	650	628 / 615	608 / 557	588 / 506	570 / 461	554 / 421	522 / 386	493 / 354	467 / 326	442 / 300	420 / 278	399 / 257	379 / 239	
LJ10	27	20	20,100	783	753	726	701	677	655 / 625	634 / 568	615 / 517	597 / 472	580 / 433	548 / 397	519 / 365	491 / 337	466 / 312	443 / 289	421 / 268	
LJ11	29	20	20,700	807	776	748	722	698	675	654 / 627	634 / 571	615 / 522	597 / 478	580 / 439	565 / 404	550 / 373	522 / 344	496 / 319	472 / 296	
LJ12	32	20	22,100	861	829	799	771	745	721	698 / 680	677 / 620	656 / 566	637 / 518	620 / 476	603 / 438	587 / 404	572 / 374	543 / 346	517 / 321	
LJ13	36	20	23,100	901	867	836	807	779	754	730	708	687 / 648	667 / 593	648 / 545	631 / 501	614 / 462	598 / 427	583 / 396	569 / 367	

extrapolate for safe uniform load between spans shown, divide the Safe Load in Pounds by Net Span in Feet plus .67 feet. (The added .67 feet (eight inches) is necessary to obtain the proper span for which the load tables were developed.)

STANDARD LOAD TABLE FOR LONGSPAN STEEL JOISTS, LJ-SERIES

Pounds per Linear Foot Based on Allowable Stress of 22,000 psi

Joist Desig-nation	Approx. Wt. Lbs. per Lin. Ft.	Nominal Depth in Inches	Safe Load* in Lbs. Between 28–32	33	34	35	36	37	38	39	40	41	42	43	44	45	46	47	48
24LJ04	16	24	11,000	329	315	302 296	290 273	279 251	268 232	258 215	248 200	236 186	225 173	215 161	206 151	197 141	188 132	181 124	173 116
24LJ05	17	24	12,100	361	347	334	322 320	310 295	297 273	284 253	271 235	259 218	248 203	237 189	227 177	218 166	209 155	201 145	194 137
24LJ06	19	24	14,900	443	424 417	407 382	390 352	375 325	356 300	339 278	322 258	307 240	293 223	279 208	267 194	255 182	244 170	234 160	225 150
24LJ07	20	24	16,400	488	468	449 432	431 398	414 367	398 339	379 314	360 291	343 271	327 252	312 235	298 220	285 206	273 193	262 181	251 170
24LJ08	22	24	19,300	574	549 525	525 482	503 444	482 409	460 378	438 351	418 325	399 302	380 282	363 263	347 245	332 230	318 215	305 202	292 190
24LJ09	24	24	20,500	609	592 574	575 527	560 485	537 447	513 414	487 383	464 355	442 330	421 308	402 287	384 268	368 251	352 235	337 221	324 207
24LJ10	27	24	21,700	646	627	610 590	593 543	577 500	563 463	540 428	514 398	490 370	467 344	446 321	426 300	408 281	391 263	374 247	359 232
24LJ11	29	24	22,800	680	660	641	624 600	607 554	592 512	577 474	563 440	542 409	521 381	499 355	477 332	457 310	437 291	419 273	402 256
24LJ12	32	24	24,400	727	706	686	667 652	650 601	633 556	617 515	602 478	587 444	574 413	548 386	524 360	501 337	480 316	460 296	441 278
24LJ13	36	24	25,200	748	727	706	687	669	651 635	635 589	619 546	604 508	590 473	577 441	564 412	552 386	528 361	506 339	486 318
24LJ14	38	24	26,200	780	757	736	716	697	679 666	662 617	646 572	630 532	615 495	601 462	588 432	575 404	563 378	539 355	517 334

Joist Desig-nation	Approx. Wt. Lbs. per Lin. Ft.	Nominal Depth in Inches	Safe Load* in Lbs. Between 33–40	41	42	43	44	45	46	47	48	49	50	51	52	53	54	55	56
28LJ06	19	28	14,000	338 332	327 310	316 289	304 270	292 252	280 237	269 222	259 208	249 196	240 185	232 174	223 164	215 155	208 147	201 139	194 132
28LJ07	20	28	15,500	372	360 349	348 326	337 304	326 285	316 267	304 250	292 235	281 221	271 208	261 196	252 185	243 175	234 166	226 157	218 149
28LJ08	22	28	18,200	439 420	423 391	405 365	388 341	372 319	357 299	343 280	330 263	317 248	305 233	294 220	284 208	274 196	264 186	255 176	246 16
28LJ09	24	28	20,400	491 461	473 429	456 400	441 374	424 350	407 328	391 308	376 289	362 272	348 256	336 241	324 228	312 215	302 204	291 193	28 18
28LJ10	27	28	22,200	535 514	516 479	498 447	481 417	465 390	449 366	434 343	418 322	402 303	387 286	373 269	359 254	347 240	335 227	323 215	31 20
28LJ11	29	28	23,800	571 569	558 530	539 495	521 462	504 432	487 405	471 380	456 357	439 336	423 316	408 298	393 282	379 266	366 252	353 238	34
28LJ12	32	28	25,600	615	601 576	587 538	574 502	562 470	550 440	531 413	513 388	496 365	478 344	460 324	443 306	427 289	413 274	398 259	38 24
28LJ13	36	28	27,300	656	641	626 614	612 574	599 537	586 503	574 472	562 444	551 417	529 393	509 371	490 350	472 331	455 313	438 296	42 28
28LJ14	38	28	28,600	687	670	655 646	640 604	626 565	613 530	600 497	588 467	576 439	565 414	544 390	523 368	504 348	486 329	468 312	45 29
28LJ15	41	28	29,500	708	691	675	660	646 639	632 599	619 562	606 528	594 497	582 468	571 441	560 416	550 394	530 372	511 353	49 33

*To extrapolate for safe uniform load between spans shown, divide the Safe Load in Pounds by Net Span in Feet plus .67 feet. (The added .67 feet (eight inches) is necessary to obtain the proper span for which the load tables were developed.)

STANDARD LOAD TABLE FOR LONGSPAN STEEL JOISTS, LJ-SERIES

Pounds per Linear Foot Based on Allowable Stress of 22,000 psi

Joist desig-nation	Approx. Wt. Lbs. per Lin. Ft.	Nominal Depth in Inches	Safe Load* in Lbs. Between	Clear Opening or Net Span in Feet																
			38–48	49	50	51	52	53	54	55	56	57	58	59	60	61	62	63	64
32LJ07	20	32	14,800	298 / 293	288 / 276	278 / 260	269 / 245	259 / 232	251 / 219	242 / 208	235 / 197	227 / 187	220 / 177	213 / 169	206 / 160	200 / 153	194 / 145	189 / 139	183 / 132
32LJ08	22	32	16,900	342 / 329	330 / 310	318 / 292	307 / 276	296 / 260	286 / 246	277 / 233	267 / 221	259 / 210	250 / 199	243 / 189	235 / 180	228 / 171	221 / 163	214 / 156	208 / 149
32LJ09	24	32	19,500	394 / 362	380 / 341	366 / 321	353 / 303	341 / 287	330 / 271	319 / 257	308 / 243	298 / 231	289 / 219	280 / 208	271 / 198	263 / 189	255 / 180	247 / 171	240 / 164
32LJ10	27	32	21,300	429 / 403	416 / 379	404 / 358	392 / 338	379 / 319	366 / 302	353 / 286	342 / 271	331 / 257	320 / 244	310 / 232	300 / 221	291 / 210	282 / 200	274 / 191	266 / 182
32LJ11	28	32	23,000	464 / 421	451 / 397	435 / 374	418 / 353	403 / 334	388 / 316	374 / 299	361 / 284	349 / 269	337 / 256	326 / 243	315 / 231	305 / 220	295 / 210	286 / 200	277 / 191
32LJ12	30	32	25,900	523 / 457	502 / 431	483 / 406	465 / 383	447 / 362	431 / 343	416 / 325	401 / 308	387 / 292	374 / 277	362 / 264	350 / 251	339 / 239	328 / 227	318 / 217	308 / 207
32LJ13	36	32	29,700	599 / 555	587 / 522	575 / 493	565 / 465	544 / 440	525 / 416	506 / 394	488 / 373	471 / 354	455 / 336	440 / 320	426 / 304	412 / 290	399 / 276	387 / 263	375 / 251
32LJ14	38	32	30,600	617 / 586	605 / 552	593 / 520	582 / 491	571 / 464	561 / 439	541 / 416	522 / 394	504 / 374	487 / 355	471 / 338	456 / 321	441 / 306	427 / 291	414 / 278	401 / 265
32LJ15	41	32	31,700	638	625 / 622	613 / 587	602 / 554	590 / 524	580 / 495	569 / 469	559 / 445	550 / 422	532 / 401	514 / 381	497 / 362	481 / 345	466 / 329	451 / 313	437 / 299
32LJ16	48	32	34,500	696	682	669	656 / 649	644 / 613	632 / 580	621 / 549	610 / 521	599 / 494	589 / 469	579 / 446	570 / 424	560 / 404	552 / 385	535 / 367	518 / 350

Joist desig-nation	Approx. Wt. Lbs. per Lin. Ft.	Nominal Depth in Inches	Safe Load* in Lbs. Between	42–56	57	58	59	60	61	62	63	64	65	66	67	68	69	70	71	72
36LJ08	22	36	15,700	273 / 269	265 / 255	256 / 243	249 / 231	241 / 220	234 / 209	227 / 200	221 / 190	214 / 182	208 / 174	203 / 166	197 / 159	192 / 152	187 / 146	182 / 140	177 / 134
36LJ09	23	36	18,300	318 / 281	308 / 267	298 / 253	288 / 241	279 / 230	270 / 219	262 / 209	254 / 200	246 / 190	239 / 182	232 / 174	225 / 166	219 / 159	212 / 152	206 / 146	201 / 140
36LJ10	26	36	20,200	352 / 311	341 / 295	330 / 281	320 / 267	311 / 254	302 / 242	293 / 231	284 / 220	275 / 210	267 / 201	259 / 192	252 / 184	245 / 176	238 / 169	231 / 162	225 / 155
36LJ11	28	36	22,200	385 / 345	373 / 327	361 / 311	350 / 296	340 / 282	330 / 269	320 / 256	311 / 244	302 / 233	294 / 223	286 / 213	278 / 204	270 / 195	263 / 187	256 / 179	249 / 172
36LJ12	30	36	25,300	439 / 375	424 / 356	410 / 338	397 / 322	384 / 307	372 / 292	360 / 279	349 / 266	339 / 254	329 / 243	319 / 232	310 / 222	301 / 212	292 / 204	284 / 195	276 / 187
36LJ13	36	36	30,200	524 / 454	510 / 432	497 / 410	482 / 390	467 / 372	452 / 354	438 / 338	425 / 322	412 / 308	400 / 294	388 / 281	377 / 269	366 / 258	356 / 247	346 / 237	336 / 227
36LJ14	38	36	32,400	562 / 481	553 / 457	535 / 434	517 / 413	501 / 393	485 / 375	470 / 357	455 / 341	441 / 326	428 / 311	416 / 298	404 / 285	392 / 273	381 / 261	371 / 250	360 / 240
36LJ15	41	36	34,200	593 / 542	583 / 515	573 / 489	564 / 465	546 / 443	528 / 422	512 / 403	496 / 384	481 / 367	467 / 351	453 / 335	440 / 321	427 / 307	415 / 294	404 / 282	393 / 271
36LJ16	48	36	36,800	639 / 635	628 / 603	617 / 573	607 / 545	597 / 519	588 / 495	579 / 472	570 / 450	561 / 430	553 / 411	537 / 393	521 / 376	507 / 360	492 / 345	479 / 330	466 / 317
36LJ17	54	36	39,400	683	671	660 / 650	649 / 619	639 / 589	628 / 561	619 / 535	609 / 511	600 / 488	591 / 466	582 / 446	574 / 427	565 / 408	557 / 391	550 / 375	535 / 360

To extrapolate for safe uniform load between spans shown, divide the Safe Load in Pounds by Net Span in Feet plus .67 feet. (The added .67 feet (eight inches) is necessary to obtain the proper span for which the load tables were developed.)

STANDARD LOAD TABLE FOR LONGSPAN STEEL JOISTS, LJ-SERIES

Pounds per Linear Foot Based on Allowable Stress of 22,000 psi

Values shown as top load / bottom load for each span.

Joist Desig-nation	Approx Wt. Lbs. per Lin. Ft.	Nomi-nal Depth in Inches	Safe Load in Lbs. Between 47–64	65	66	67	68	69	70	71	72	73	74	75	76	77	78	79	80
40LJ09	23	40	17,200	262/237	255/227	248/217	241/207	235/198	229/190	223/182	217/175	212/168	207/161	202/155	197/149	192/143	188/138	183/133	179/128
40LJ10	26	40	19,000	290/263	282/251	274/240	267/230	260/220	253/211	246/202	240/194	234/186	228/179	223/172	217/165	212/159	207/153	202/147	198/141
40LJ11	28	40	20,700	316/291	308/278	299/266	291/255	284/244	276/233	269/224	262/215	256/206	249/198	243/190	237/183	232/176	226/169	221/163	216/157
40LJ12	30	40	24,300	371/317	361/303	351/290	341/277	332/265	323/254	315/244	307/234	299/224	291/216	284/207	277/199	270/191	264/184	257/177	251/171
40LJ13	36	40	28,900	441/384	429/367	417/351	406/336	395/321	385/308	375/295	365/283	356/272	347/261	338/251	330/241	322/232	314/223	307/215	300/207
40LJ14	38	40	32,400	494/407	479/389	465/372	452/356	439/341	426/327	415/313	403/300	392/288	382/277	372/266	362/256	353/246	344/237	335/228	327/220
40LJ15	41	40	35,300	538/458	522/438	507/419	492/401	478/384	464/368	452/352	439/338	427/324	416/312	405/299	394/288	384/277	375/266	365/256	356/247
40LJ16	48	40	38,900	592/537	584/513	575/491	567/470	558/450	551/431	535/413	521/396	507/380	493/365	480/351	468/337	456/324	444/312	433/300	422/289
40LJ17	54	40	41,700	636/610	626/583	617/557	608/533	599/511	591/489	582/469	574/450	566/432	559/415	552/399	537/383	524/368	510/355	498/341	485/329
40LJ18	60	40	45,000	685/656	675/627	665/600	655/575	646/551	636/528	628/506	619/486	611/467	602/448	594/431	587/415	579/399	572/384	565/370	558

Joist Desig-nation	Approx Wt. Lbs. per Lin. Ft.	Nomi-nal Depth in Inches	Safe Load in Lbs. Between 52–72	73	74	75	76	77	78	79	80	81	82	83	84	85	86	87	88
44LJ10	26	44	17,800	242/227	236/218	230/209	225/201	219/194	214/186	209/179	205/173	200/166	196/161	191/155	187/149	183/144	179/139	175/134	172/130
44LJ11	27	44	19,300	263/237	257/227	251/218	245/210	239/202	234/194	228/187	223/180	218/174	213/167	208/161	204/156	199/150	195/145	191/140	187/136
44LJ12	30	44	23,100	314/274	306/263	299/253	292/243	285/234	278/225	271/217	265/209	259/201	253/194	248/187	242/180	237/174	232/168	229/163	222/157
44LJ13	35	44	27,000	367/313	357/301	348/289	339/278	330/267	322/257	314/248	306/239	299/230	291/222	285/214	278/206	271/199	265/192	259/186	253/180
44LJ14	38	44	31,200	424/353	413/339	403/325	393/313	384/301	375/290	366/279	357/269	349/259	341/249	334/241	326/232	319/224	312/216	305/209	299/202
44LJ15	41	44	34,800	473/396	460/381	448/366	436/352	425/338	414/325	404/313	394/302	384/291	375/280	366/270	358/261	349/252	341/243	333/235	326/227
44LJ16	48	44	41,200	560/465	545/446	531/429	517/412	504/396	491/381	479/367	467/354	456/341	445/329	434/317	424/306	414/295	405/285	395/275	387/265
44LJ17	54	44	44,200	600/528	592/507	584/487	576/469	569/451	562/434	548/418	536/402	523/388	511/374	499/360	487/348	476/336	465/324	454/313	444/303
44LJ18	60	44	47,400	644/595	636/571	627/549	619/528	611/508	603/488	596/470	588/453	581/437	574/421	567/406	561/392	548/378	535/365	523/353	511/341
44LJ19	68	44	51,300	696/674	687/647	678/622	669/598	661/575	652/553	644/533	636/513	628/494	621/477	613/460	606/444	599/428	592/414	585/399	577/385

* To extrapolate for safe uniform load between spans shown, divide the Safe Load in Pounds by Net Span in Feet plus .67 feet. (The added .67 feet (eight inches) is necessary to obtain the proper span for which the load tables were developed.)

STANDARD LOAD TABLE FOR LONGSPAN STEEL JOISTS, LJ-SERIES

Pounds per Linear Foot Based on Allowable Stress of 22,000 psi

Joist Desig-nation	Approx. Wt. Lbs. per Lin. Ft.	Nomi-nal Depth in Inches	Safe Load* in Lbs. Between 56–80	Clear Opening or Net Span in Feet																
				81	82	83	84	85	86	87	88	89	90	91	92	93	94	95	96
48LJ11	27	48	18,000	221 208	216 201	212 194	207 187	203 180	199 174	195 168	191 163	187 157	183 152	179 147	176 142	172 138	169 133	166 129	162 125
48LJ12	30	48	21,900	269 241	263 233	257 224	251 217	246 209	241 202	236 195	231 188	226 182	221 176	217 171	213 165	208 160	204 155	200 150	196 145
48LJ13	35	48	26,000	319 276	312 266	305 257	298 248	292 239	286 231	280 223	274 215	268 208	263 201	257 195	252 189	247 183	242 177	237 171	233 166
48LJ14	36	48	29,200	358 299	350 288	341 278	333 268	326 259	318 250	311 242	304 234	297 226	291 218	284 211	278 205	272 198	267 192	261 186	256 180
48LJ15	41	48	34,300	421 349	411 336	401 325	392 313	383 302	374 292	365 282	357 273	349 264	342 255	334 247	327 239	320 231	313 224	307 217	300 210
48LJ16	48	48	39,800	488 409	477 394	466 380	456 367	446 354	437 342	427 331	418 320	409 309	401 299	393 289	385 280	377 271	370 262	362 254	355 246
48LJ17	54	48	44,700	548 465	536 449	524 433	513 418	502 403	491 389	480 376	470 363	460 351	451 340	442 329	433 318	424 308	416 299	407 289	399 280
48LJ18	60	48	49,700	609 525	601 506	594 488	587 471	580 454	573 439	567 424	561 410	548 396	536 383	524 371	513 359	502 348	492 337	481 326	472 316
48LJ19	68	48	52,700	645 594	637 573	630 552	622 533	615 515	608 497	601 480	594 464	588 449	581 434	575 420	569 406	562 394	557 381	545 369	534 358

* To extrapolate for safe uniform load between spans shown, divide the Safe Load in Pounds by Net Span in Feet plus .67 feet. (The added .67 feet (eight inches) is necessary to obtain the proper span for which the load tables were developed.)

Standard Load Table
for Longspan Steel Joists, LH-Series
Based on a maximum allowable tensile stress of 30,000 psi

**Adopted by Steel Joist Institute
and American Institute of Steel Construction, Inc., July 1, 1970**

The **bold face** figures in the following table give the TOTAL safe uniformly-distributed load-carrying capacities, in pounds per linear foot, of LH-Series joists. The weight of DEAD loads, including the joists, must in all cases be deducted to determine the LIVE load-carrying capacities of the joists. The approximate DEAD load of the joists may be determined from the weights per linear foot shown in the tables.*

The light face figures in this load table are the LIVE loads per linear foot of joist which will produce an approximate deflection of $\frac{1}{360}$ of the span. LIVE loads which will produce a deflection of $\frac{1}{240}$ of the span may be obtained by multiplying the light face figures by 1.5. (Note: The tabulated loads corresponding to these deflection limitations have been computed on the basis of 30,000 psi allowable stress provisions. For joists designed to a lower working stress these loads may be increased in the ratio of 30,000 psi to the design stress used, in order to meet the same deflection limitations.) **In no case shall the total load capacity of the joist be exceeded.****

This load table applies to joists with either parallel chords or standard pitched top chords. When top chords are pitched, the carrying capacities are determined by the nominal depth of the joists at center of the span.

Standard top chord pitch is $\frac{1}{8}$ inch per foot. If pitch exceeds this standard, the load table does not apply. The load table may be used for parallel chord joists installed to a maximum slope of $\frac{1}{2}$ inch per foot.

When holes are required in top or bottom chords, the carrying capacities must be reduced in proportion to reduction of chord areas.

The top chords are considered as being stayed laterally by floor slab or roof deck.

Loads to the right of the heavy vertical lines are to be used for roof construction only.

---

* Approximate weights per linear foot of joists include accessories.

** Section 104.10 of the "Standard Specifications" limits the design LIVE load deflection as follows: Floors, $\frac{1}{360}$ of span. Roofs, $\frac{1}{360}$ of span where a plaster ceiling is attached or suspended; $\frac{1}{240}$ of span for all other cases.

STANDARD LOAD TABLE FOR LONGSPAN STEEL JOISTS, LH-SERIES

Pounds per Linear Foot Based on Allowable Stress of 30,000 psi

Joist Desig-nation	Approx. Wt. Lbs. per Lin. Ft.	Nomi-nal Depth in Inches	Safe Load* in Lbs. Between 21–24	Clear Opening or Net Span in Feet											
				25	26	27	28	29	30	31	32	33	34	35	36
18LH02	13	18	12,000	**468** 363	**442** 323	**418** 289	**391** 260	**367** 235	**345** 212	**324** 193	**306** 176	**289** 160	**273** 147	**259** 135	**245** 124
18LH03	14	18	13,300	**521** 388	**493** 346	**467** 310	**438** 279	**409** 251	**382** 227	**359** 207	**337** 188	**317** 172	**299** 157	**283** 144	**267** 133
18LH04	16	18	15,500	**604** 435	**571** 388	**535** 347	**500** 312	**469** 281	**440** 255	**413** 231	**388** 211	**365** 192	**344** 176	**325** 162	**308** 149
18LH05	17	18	17,500	**684** 509	**648** 454	**614** 406	**581** 365	**543** 330	**508** 298	**476** 271	**448** 247	**421** 225	**397** 206	**375** 189	**355** 174
18LH06	19	18	20,700	**809** 554	**749** 494	**696** 442	**648** 397	**605** 358	**566** 324	**531** 295	**499** 268	**470** 245	**443** 224	**418** 206	**396** 190
18LH07	21	18	21,500	**840** 628	**809** 560	**780** 502	**726** 451	**678** 407	**635** 368	**595** 334	**559** 304	**526** 278	**496** 255	**469** 234	**444** 215
18LH08	22	18	22,400	**876** 696	**843** 620	**812** 555	**784** 499	**758** 450	**717** 408	**680** 370	**641** 337	**604** 308	**571** 282	**540** 259	**512** 238
18LH09	24	18	24,000	**936** 753	**901** 671	**868** 601	**838** 540	**810** 488	**783** 441	**759** 401	**713** 365	**671** 333	**633** 305	**598** 280	**566** 258

Joist Desig-nation	Approx. Wt. Lbs. per Lin. Ft.	Nomi-nal Depth in Inches	Safe Load* in Lbs. Between 22–24	Clear Opening or Net Span in Feet															
				25	26	27	28	29	30	31	32	33	34	35	36	37	38	39	40
20LH02	13	20	11,300	**442**	**437** 404	**431** 362	**410** 325	**388** 293	**365** 265	**344** 241	**325** 220	**307** 200	**291** 184	**275** 169	**262** 155	**249** 143	**237** 132	**225** 122	**215** 114
20LH03	14	20	12,000	**469**	**463** 432	**458** 387	**434** 348	**414** 314	**395** 284	**372** 258	**352** 235	**333** 215	**316** 196	**299** 180	**283** 166	**269** 153	**255** 141	**243** 131	122
20LH04	16	20	14,700	**574** 545	**566** 486	**558** 435	**528** 391	**496** 353	**467** 319	**440** 290	**416** 264	**393** 241	**372** 221	**353** 203	**335** 187	**318** 172	**303** 159	**289** 147	**275** 137
20LH05	17	20	15,800	**616**	**609** 568	**602** 508	**595** 457	**571** 412	**544** 373	**513** 339	**484** 309	**458** 282	**434** 258	**411** 237	**390** 218	**371** 201	**353** 186	**336** 172	**321** 160
20LH06	19	20	21,100	**822** 695	**791** 620	**763** 555	**723** 499	**679** 450	**635** 407	**596** 370	**560** 337	**527** 308	**497** 282	**469** 259	**444** 238	**421** 220	**399** 203	**379** 188	**361** 174
20LH07	21	20	22,500	**878** 788	**845** 702	**814** 629	**786** 565	**760** 510	**711** 462	**667** 419	**627** 382	**590** 349	**556** 319	**526** 293	**497** 270	**471** 249	**447** 230	**425** 213	**404** 198
20LH08	22	20	23,200	**908** 875	**873** 780	**842** 698	**813** 628	**785** 566	**760** 513	**722** 466	**687** 424	**654** 387	**621** 355	**588** 326	**558** 300	**530** 276	**503** 255	**479** 237	**457** 220
20LH09	24	20	25,400	**990** 951	**953** 848	**918** 759	**886** 682	**856** 615	**828** 557	**802** 506	**778** 461	**755** 421	**712** 386	**673** 354	**636** 326	**603** 300	**572** 278	**544** 257	**517** 239
20LH10	27	20	27,400	**1,068** 1,067	**1,028** 951	**991** 851	**956** 765	**924** 690	**894** 625	**865** 568	**839** 517	**814** 472	**791** 433	**748** 397	**707** 365	**670** 337	**636** 312	**604** 289	**575** 268

* To extrapolate for safe uniform load between spans shown, divide the Safe Load in Pounds by Net Span in Feet plus .67 feet. (The added .67 feet (eight inches) is necessary to obtain the proper span for which the load tables were developed.)

STANDARD LOAD TABLE FOR LONGSPAN STEEL JOISTS, LH-SERIES

Pounds per Linear Foot Based on Allowable Stress of 30,000 psi

Joist Desig-nation	Approx. Wt. Lbs. per Lin. Ft.	Nomi-nal Depth in Inches	Safe Load* in Lbs. Between 28–32	Clear Opening or Net Span in Feet															
				33	34	35	36	37	38	39	40	41	42	43	44	45	46	47	48
24LH03	14	24	11,500	342	339	336	323	307	293	279	267	255	244	234	224	215	207	199	191
				314	288	264	243	224	207	192	178	166	154	144	134	126	118	110	104
24LH04	16	24	14,100	419	398	379	360	343	327	312	298	285	273	262	251	241	231	222	214
				355	325	298	275	253	234	217	201	187	174	162	152	142	133	125	117
24LH05	17	24	15,100	449	446	440	419	399	380	363	347	331	317	304	291	280	269	258	248
				414	379	348	320	295	273	253	235	218	203	189	177	166	155	145	137
24LH06	19	24	20,300	604	579	555	530	504	480	457	437	417	399	381	364	348	334	320	307
				455	417	382	352	325	300	278	258	240	223	208	194	182	170	160	150
24LH07	21	24	22,300	665	638	613	588	565	541	516	491	468	446	426	407	389	373	357	343
				514	471	432	398	367	339	314	291	271	252	235	220	206	193	181	170
24LH08	22	24	23,800	707	677	649	622	597	572	545	520	497	475	455	435	417	400	384	369
				574	525	482	444	409	378	351	325	302	282	263	245	230	215	202	190
24LH09	24	24	28,000	832	808	785	764	731	696	663	632	602	574	548	524	501	480	460	441
				627	574	527	485	447	414	383	355	330	308	287	268	251	235	221	207
24LH10	27	24	29,600	882	856	832	809	788	768	737	702	668	637	608	582	556	533	511	490
				701	642	590	543	500	463	428	398	370	344	321	300	281	263	247	232
24LH11	29	24	31,200	927	900	875	851	829	807	787	768	734	701	671	642	616	590	567	544
				776	710	652	600	554	512	474	440	409	381	355	332	310	291	273	256
			33–40	41	42	43	44	45	46	47	48	49	50	51	52	53	54	55	56
28LH05	16	28	14,000	337	323	310	297	286	275	265	255	245	237	228	220	213	206	199	193
				277	258	240	224	210	197	185	173	163	154	145	137	129	122	116	110
28LH06	19	28	18,600	448	429	412	395	379	364	350	337	324	313	301	291	281	271	262	253
				332	310	289	270	252	237	222	208	196	185	174	164	155	147	139	132
28LH07	21	28	21,000	505	484	464	445	427	410	394	379	365	352	339	327	316	305	295	285
				375	349	326	304	285	267	250	235	221	208	196	185	175	166	157	149
28LH08	21	28	22,500	540	517	496	475	456	438	420	403	387	371	357	344	331	319	308	297
				385	359	335	313	293	274	257	242	227	214	202	191	180	170	161	153
28LH09	24	28	27,700	667	639	612	586	563	540	519	499	481	463	446	430	415	401	387	374
				461	429	400	374	350	328	308	289	272	256	241	228	215	204	193	183
28LH10	27	28	30,300	729	704	679	651	625	600	576	554	533	513	495	477	460	444	429	415
				514	479	447	417	390	366	343	322	303	286	269	254	240	227	215	204
28LH11	29	28	32,500	780	762	736	711	682	655	629	605	582	561	540	521	502	485	468	453
				569	530	495	462	432	405	380	357	336	316	298	282	266	252	238	226
28LH12	33	28	35,700	857	837	818	800	782	766	737	709	682	656	632	609	587	566	546	527
				645	600	560	523	490	459	430	404	380	358	338	319	301	285	270	256
28LH13	36	28	37,200	895	874	854	835	816	799	782	766	751	722	694	668	643	620	598	577
				707	659	614	574	537	503	472	444	417	393	371	350	331	313	296	281

* To extrapolate for safe uniform load between spans shown, divide the Safe Load in Pounds by Net Span in Feet plus .67 feet. (The added .67 feet (eight inches) is necessary to obtain the proper span for which the load tables were developed.)

STANDARD LOAD TABLE FOR LONGSPAN STEEL JOISTS, LH-SERIES

Pounds per Linear Foot Based on Allowable Stress of 30,000 psi

Joist Desig- nation	Approx. Wt. Lbs. per Lin. Ft.	Nomi- nal Depth in Inches	Safe Load* in Lbs. Between 38–48	49	50	51	52	53	54	55	56	57	58	59	60	61	62	63	64
									Clear Opening or Net Span in Feet										
32LH06	18	32	16,700	338/244	326/229	315/216	304/204	294/193	284/182	275/173	266/164	257/155	249/148	242/140	234/133	227/127	220/121	214/115	208/110
32LH07	20	32	18,800	379/274	366/258	353/243	341/230	329/217	318/205	308/194	298/184	288/175	279/166	271/158	262/150	254/143	247/136	240/130	233/124
32LH08	21	32	20,400	411/301	397/284	383/268	369/253	357/239	345/226	333/214	322/203	312/192	302/183	293/174	284/165	275/157	267/150	259/143	252/136
32LH09	24	32	25,600	516/362	498/341	480/321	463/303	447/287	432/271	418/257	404/243	391/231	379/219	367/208	356/198	345/189	335/180	325/171	315/164
32LH10	26	32	28,300	571/380	550/358	531/337	512/318	495/301	478/285	462/269	445/255	430/242	416/230	402/219	389/208	376/198	364/189	353/180	342/172
32LH11	28	32	31,000	625/421	602/397	580/374	560/353	541/334	522/316	505/299	488/284	473/269	458/256	443/243	429/231	416/220	403/210	390/200	378/191
32LH12	33	32	36,400	734/505	712/476	688/449	664/424	641/401	619/379	598/359	578/340	559/323	541/307	524/291	508/277	492/264	477/251	463/240	449/229
32LH13	36	32	40,600	817/555	801/522	785/493	771/465	742/440	715/416	690/394	666/373	643/354	621/336	600/320	581/304	562/290	544/276	527/263	511/251
32LH14	37	32	41,800	843/586	826/552	810/520	795/491	780/464	766/439	738/416	713/394	688/374	665/355	643/338	622/321	602/306	583/291	564/278	547/265
32LH15	41	32	43,200	870/661	853/622	837/587	821/554	805/524	791/495	776/469	763/445	750/422	725/401	701/381	678/362	656/345	635/329	616/313	597/299

Joist Desig- nation	Approx. Wt. Lbs. per Lin. Ft.	Nomi- nal Depth in Inches	Safe Load* in Lbs. Between 42–56	57	58	59	60	61	62	63	64	65	66	67	68	69	70	71	72
36LH07	20	36	16,800	292/224	283/212	274/202	266/192	258/183	251/174	244/166	237/159	230/151	224/145	218/138	212/132	207/127	201/121	196/116	191/112
36LH08	20	36	18,500	321/230	311/218	302/208	293/197	284/188	276/179	268/171	260/163	253/156	246/149	239/142	233/136	227/130	221/125	215/120	209/115
36LH09	23	36	23,700	411/281	398/267	386/253	374/241	363/230	352/219	342/209	333/199	323/190	314/182	306/174	297/166	289/159	282/152	275/146	267/140
36LH10	26	36	26,100	454/311	440/295	426/281	413/267	401/254	389/242	378/231	367/220	357/210	347/201	338/192	328/184	320/176	311/169	303/162	295/155
36LH11	28	36	28,500	495/345	480/327	465/311	451/296	438/282	425/269	412/256	401/244	389/233	378/223	368/213	358/204	348/195	339/187	330/179	322/172
36LH12	32	36	34,100	593/389	575/370	557/352	540/334	523/318	508/303	493/289	478/276	464/264	450/252	437/241	424/230	412/221	400/211	389/203	378/194
36LH13	36	36	40,100	697/454	675/432	654/410	634/390	615/372	596/354	579/338	562/322	546/308	531/294	516/281	502/269	488/258	475/247	463/237	451/227
36LH14	37	36	44,200	768/481	755/457	729/434	706/413	683/393	661/375	641/357	621/341	602/326	584/311	567/298	551/285	535/273	520/261	505/250	492/240
36LH15	41	36	46,600	809/542	795/515	781/489	769/465	744/443	721/422	698/403	677/384	656/367	637/351	618/335	600/321	583/307	567/294	551/282	536/271

* To extrapolate for safe uniform load between spans shown, divide the Safe Load in Pounds by Net Span in Feet plus .67 feet. (The added .67 feet (eight inches) is necessary to obtain the proper span for which the load tables were developed.)

STANDARD LOAD TABLE FOR LONGSPAN STEEL JOISTS, LH-SERIES

Pounds per Linear Foot Based on Allowable Stress of 30,000 psi

Joist Desig- nation	Approx. Wt. Lbs. per Lin. Ft.	Nomi- nal Depth in Inches	Safe Load* in Lbs. Between 47–64	Clear Opening or Net Span in Feet															
				65	66	67	68	69	70	71	72	73	74	75	76	77	78	79	80
40LH08	20	40	16,600	254 / 194	247 / 185	241 / 177	234 / 170	228 / 162	222 / 156	217 / 149	211 / 143	206 / 137	201 / 132	196 / 127	192 / 122	187 / 117	183 / 113	178 / 108	174 / 104
40LH09	23	40	21,800	332 / 237	323 / 227	315 / 217	306 / 207	298 / 198	291 / 190	283 / 182	276 / 175	269 / 168	263 / 161	256 / 155	250 / 149	244 / 143	239 / 138	233 / 133	228 / 128
40LH10	25	40	24,000	367 / 248	357 / 237	347 / 226	338 / 217	329 / 207	321 / 199	313 / 191	305 / 183	297 / 175	290 / 168	283 / 162	276 / 156	269 / 150	262 / 144	255 / 139	249 / 133
40LH11	27	40	26,200	399 / 274	388 / 262	378 / 250	368 / 240	358 / 229	349 / 220	340 / 211	332 / 202	323 / 194	315 / 186	308 / 179	300 / 172	293 / 165	286 / 159	279 / 153	273 / 148
40LH12	32	40	31,900	486 / 329	472 / 315	459 / 301	447 / 288	435 / 276	424 / 264	413 / 253	402 / 243	392 / 233	382 / 224	373 / 215	364 / 207	355 / 199	346 / 191	338 / 184	330 / 177
40LH13	36	40	37,600	573 / 384	557 / 367	542 / 351	528 / 336	514 / 321	500 / 308	487 / 295	475 / 283	463 / 272	451 / 261	440 / 251	429 / 241	419 / 232	409 / 223	399 / 215	390 / 207
40LH14	37	40	43,000	656 / 407	638 / 389	620 / 372	603 / 356	587 / 341	571 / 327	556 / 313	542 / 300	528 / 288	515 / 277	502 / 266	490 / 256	478 / 246	466 / 237	455 / 228	444 / 220
40LH15	41	40	48,100	734 / 458	712 / 438	691 / 419	671 / 401	652 / 384	633 / 368	616 / 352	599 / 338	583 / 324	567 / 312	552 / 299	538 / 288	524 / 277	511 / 266	498 / 256	486 / 247
40LH16	47	40	53,000	808 / 537	796 / 513	784 / 491	772 / 470	761 / 450	751 / 431	730 / 413	710 / 396	691 / 380	673 / 365	655 / 351	638 / 337	622 / 324	606 / 312	591 / 300	576 / 289

Joist Desig- nation	Approx. Wt. Lbs. per Lin. Ft.	Nomi- nal Depth in Inches	Safe Load* in Lbs. Between 52–72	Clear Opening or Net Span in Feet															
				73	74	75	76	77	78	79	80	81	82	83	84	85	86	87	88
44LH09	22	44	20,000	272 / 186	265 / 179	259 / 172	253 / 165	247 / 159	242 / 153	236 / 147	231 / 142	226 / 137	221 / 132	216 / 127	211 / 123	207 / 118	202 / 114	198 / 110	194 / 107
44LH10	25	44	22,100	300 / 214	293 / 205	286 / 197	279 / 190	272 / 183	266 / 176	260 / 169	254 / 163	249 / 157	243 / 151	238 / 146	233 / 141	228 / 136	223 / 131	218 / 127	214 / 122
44LH11	27	44	23,900	325 / 237	317 / 227	310 / 218	302 / 210	295 / 202	289 / 194	282 / 187	276 / 180	269 / 174	264 / 167	258 / 161	252 / 156	247 / 150	242 / 145	236 / 140	232 / 136
44LH12	31	44	29,600	402 / 267	393 / 256	383 / 246	374 / 237	365 / 228	356 / 219	347 / 211	339 / 203	331 / 196	323 / 189	315 / 182	308 / 176	300 / 170	293 / 164	287 / 158	280 / 153
44LH13	35	44	35,100	477 / 313	466 / 301	454 / 289	444 / 278	433 / 267	423 / 257	413 / 248	404 / 239	395 / 230	386 / 222	377 / 214	369 / 206	361 / 199	353 / 192	346 / 186	338 / 180
44LH14	36	44	40,400	549 / 340	534 / 326	520 / 313	506 / 301	493 / 290	481 / 279	469 / 269	457 / 259	446 / 249	436 / 240	425 / 232	415 / 224	406 / 216	396 / 208	387 / 201	379 / 195
44LH15	41	44	47,000	639 / 396	623 / 381	608 / 366	593 / 352	579 / 338	565 / 325	551 / 313	537 / 302	524 / 291	512 / 280	500 / 270	488 / 261	476 / 252	466 / 243	455 / 235	445 / 227
44LH16	47	44	54,200	737 / 465	719 / 446	701 / 429	684 / 412	668 / 396	652 / 381	637 / 367	622 / 354	608 / 341	594 / 329	580 / 317	568 / 306	555 / 295	543 / 285	531 / 275	520 / 266
44LH17	54	44	58,200	790 / 528	780 / 507	769 / 487	759 / 469	750 / 451	732 / 434	715 / 417	699 / 402	683 / 388	667 / 374	652 / 360	638 / 348	624 / 336	610 / 324	597 / 313	584 / 303

* To extrapolate for safe uniform load between spans shown, divide the Safe Load in Pounds by Net Span in Feet plus .67 feet. (The added .67 feet (eight inches) is necessary to obtain the proper span for which the load tables were developed.)

STANDARD LOAD TABLE FOR LONGSPAN STEEL JOISTS, LH-SERIES

Pounds per Linear Foot Based on Allowable Stress of 30,000 psi

Joist Desig-nation	Approx. Wt. Lbs. per Lin. Ft	Nomi-nal Depth in Inches	Safe Load* in Lbs. Between 56–80	Clear Opening or Net Span in Feet																
				81	82	83	84	85	86	87	88	89	90	91	92	93	94	95	96
48LH10	25	48	20,000	246 188	241 181	236 175	231 169	226 163	221 157	217 152	212 147	208 142	204 137	200 133	196 129	192 124	188 121	185 117	181 113
48LH11	27	48	21,700	266 208	260 201	255 194	249 187	244 180	239 174	234 168	229 163	225 157	220 152	216 147	212 142	208 138	204 133	200 129	196 125
48LH12	31	48	27,400	336 235	329 226	322 218	315 211	308 203	301 196	295 190	289 183	283 177	277 171	272 166	266 161	261 155	256 151	251 146	246 141
48LH13	35	48	32,800	402 276	393 266	384 257	376 248	368 239	360 231	353 223	345 215	338 208	332 201	325 195	318 189	312 183	306 177	300 171	294 166
48LH14	36	48	38,700	475 299	464 288	454 278	444 268	434 259	425 250	416 242	407 234	399 226	390 218	383 211	375 205	367 198	360 192	353 186	346 180
48LH15	41	48	44,500	545 349	533 336	521 325	510 313	499 302	488 292	478 282	468 273	458 264	448 255	439 247	430 239	422 231	413 224	405 217	397 210
48LH16	47	48	51,300	629 409	615 394	601 380	588 367	576 354	563 342	551 331	540 320	528 309	518 299	507 289	497 280	487 271	477 262	468 254	459 246
48LH17	54	48	57,600	706 465	690 449	675 433	660 418	646 403	632 389	619 376	606 363	593 351	581 340	569 329	558 318	547 308	536 299	525 289	515 280

* To extrapolate for safe uniform load between spans shown, divide the Safe Load in Pounds by Net Span in Feet plus .67 feet. (The added .67 feet (eight inches) is necessary to obtain the proper span for which the load tables were developed.)

Standard Load Table
for Deep Longspan Steel Joists, DLJ-Series
Based on a maximum allowable tensile stress of 22,000 psi

Adopted by Steel Joist Institute and
American Institute of Steel Construction, Inc., February 1, 1970

The following table was developed using 22,000 psi allowable tensile stress.

The **bold face** figures give the TOTAL safe uniformly distributed load-carrying capacities, in pounds per linear foot of span. All loads shown are **for roof construction only.** The weight of DEAD loads, including weight of joists, must in all cases be deducted to determine the LIVE load-carrying capacities of the joists. The approximate weights per linear foot of joists include accessories.

The light face figures are the LIVE loads per linear foot of joists which will produce an approximate deflection of $\frac{1}{360}$ of the span. LIVE loads which will produce an approximate deflection of $\frac{1}{240}$ of the span may be obtained by multiplying the light face figures by 1.5.

For roofs, LIVE load deflection is limited to $\frac{1}{360}$ of the span where a plaster ceiling is attached or suspended, and $\frac{1}{240}$ of the span for all other cases. **In no case shall the TOTAL load capacity of the joists be exceeded.** *

The load table applies to joists with either parallel chords or standard pitched chords. When top chords are pitched, the carrying capacities are determined by the nominal depth of the joist at the center of the span.

Standard top chord pitch is $\frac{1}{8}$ inch per foot. If pitch exceeds this standard, the load table does not apply. The load table may be used for parallel chord joists installed to a maximum slope of $\frac{1}{2}$ inch per foot.

When holes are required in the top or bottom chords, the carrying capacities must be reduced in proportion to reduction of chord areas.

The top chords are considered as being stayed laterally by the roof deck.

---

* Section 104.10 of the "Standard Specifications" limits the design LIVE load deflection as follows: Roofs: $\frac{1}{360}$ of span where a plaster ceiling is attached or suspended; $\frac{1}{240}$ of span for all other cases.

STANDARD LOAD TABLE FOR DEEP LONGSPAN STEEL JOISTS, DLJ-SERIES

Pounds per Linear Foot Based on Allowable Stress of 22,000 psi

Joist Designation	Approx. Wt. Lbs. per Lin. Ft.	Nominal Depth in Inches	*Safe Load in Lbs. Between	Clear Opening or Net Span in Feet															
			61–88	89	90	91	92	93	94	95	96	97	98	99	100	101	102	103	104
52DLJ12	31	52	25,700	287	281	275	269	264	258	253	248	243	238	234	229	225	220	216	21|
				228	221	214	207	200	194	188	182	176	171	166	161	156	152	147	14	
52DLJ13	36	52	30,400	340	332	325	319	312	306	300	294	288	282	277	271	266	261	256	25|
				270	262	253	245	237	230	223	216	209	203	197	191	185	180	175	17	
52DLJ14	40	52	33,800	378	370	362	355	347	340	333	326	319	313	306	300	294	289	283	27|
				291	281	272	263	255	247	239	232	225	218	212	205	199	194	188	18	
52DLJ15	44	52	37,300	417	408	399	391	382	374	366	359	352	344	338	331	324	318	312	30|
				328	317	307	297	287	278	270	261	253	246	238	231	225	218	212	20	
52DLJ16	51	52	45,100	503	492	482	471	462	452	443	434	426	417	409	401	393	386	379	37|
				393	380	368	356	345	334	324	314	304	295	286	278	270	262	254	24	
52DLJ17	57	52	50,900	568	556	544	533	522	511	501	490	481	471	462	453	444	436	428	42|
				450	435	421	408	395	382	370	359	348	338	328	318	309	300	291	28	
52DLJ18	64	52	59,000	659	645	631	618	605	592	580	569	557	546	535	525	515	505	496	48|
				501	485	469	454	440	426	413	400	388	376	365	354	344	334	324	31	

Joist Designation	Approx. Wt.	Nominal Depth	Safe Load	66–96	97	98	99	100	101	102	103	104	105	106	107	108	109	110	111	11|
56DLJ13	35	56	28,800	295	289	284	278	273	267	262	257	252	248	243	238	234	230	226	22	
				235	228	221	215	208	202	196	191	185	180	175	170	166	161	157	15	
56DLJ14	40	56	33,100	339	332	326	319	313	307	302	296	291	285	280	275	270	266	261	25	
				263	255	247	240	233	226	220	213	207	201	196	191	185	180	176	17	
56DLJ15	44	56	37,100	380	372	365	358	351	344	337	331	324	318	313	307	301	296	290	28	
				296	287	278	270	262	255	247	240	233	227	221	215	209	203	198	19	
56DLJ16	51	56	43,900	450	441	433	425	416	409	401	394	386	379	372	366	359	353	347	34	
				355	344	334	324	315	306	297	288	280	272	265	258	251	244	237	23	
56DLJ17	57	56	49,600	508	499	489	480	470	462	453	445	436	428	421	413	406	399	392	3	
				406	394	382	371	360	350	340	330	321	312	303	295	287	279	272	26	
56DLJ18	64	56	57,900	593	582	570	559	549	538	528	518	509	499	490	481	473	465	456	4	
				453	439	426	414	402	390	379	368	358	348	338	329	320	311	303	2	
56DLJ19	72	56	65,400	670	657	644	632	620	608	597	585	575	564	554	544	534	525	516	5	
				505	490	475	461	448	435	422	410	399	388	377	367	357	347	338	3	

Joist Designation	Approx. Wt.	Nominal Depth	Safe Load	70–104	105	106	107	108	109	110	111	112	113	114	115	116	117	118	119	1|
60DLJ14	40	60	32,300	306	300	295	290	285	280	275	270	265	261	257	252	248	244	240	2	
				239	233	226	220	214	208	203	197	192	187	182	178	173	169	165	1	
60DLJ15	44	60	36,800	349	342	336	330	324	318	312	307	301	296	291	286	281	276	272	2	
				269	262	255	248	241	235	228	222	216	211	205	200	195	190	185	1	
60DLJ16	51	60	42,900	406	399	392	385	378	371	365	359	353	347	341	335	330	324	319	3	
				324	315	306	297	289	282	274	267	260	253	247	240	234	228	223	2	
60DLJ17	57	60	48,500	459	450	442	434	427	419	412	405	398	391	385	378	372	366	360	3	
				370	360	350	340	331	322	314	305	297	290	282	275	268	261	255	2	
60DLJ18	64	60	56,900	539	529	519	510	501	492	483	475	467	459	451	444	436	429	422	4	
				413	402	390	380	370	360	350	341	332	323	315	307	299	292	284	2	
60DLJ19	72	60	64,300	609	597	587	576	566	556	546	537	528	519	510	501	493	485	477	3	
				461	448	436	424	412	401	390	380	370	361	351	342	334	325	317	3	

* To extrapolate for safe uniform load between spans shown, divide the Safe Load in Pounds by Net Span in Feet plus .67 feet. (The added .67 feet (eight inches) is necessary to obtain the proper span for which the load tables were developed.)

STANDARD LOAD TABLE FOR DEEP LONGSPAN STEEL JOISTS, DLJ-SERIES

Pounds per Linear Foot Based on Allowable Stress of 22,000 psi

Joist Designation	Approx. Wt. Lbs. per Lin. Ft.	Nominal Depth in Inches	*Safe Load in Lbs. Between	Clear Opening or Net Span in Feet															
			75–112	113	114	115	116	117	118	119	120	121	122	123	124	125	126	127	128
64DLJ14	39	64	30,600	270 / 210	265 / 204	260 / 199	256 / 194	252 / 189	247 / 184	243 / 180	239 / 175	235 / 171	231 / 167	228 / 163	224 / 159	221 / 155	217 / 151	214 / 148	210 / 144
64DLJ15	44	64	36,200	319 / 247	314 / 241	309 / 235	304 / 229	299 / 223	294 / 217	289 / 212	284 / 207	280 / 202	275 / 197	271 / 192	267 / 187	263 / 183	259 / 179	255 / 174	251 / 170
64DLJ16	49	64	39,500	348 / 276	342 / 268	336 / 262	330 / 255	324 / 248	319 / 242	314 / 236	308 / 230	303 / 225	298 / 219	294 / 214	289 / 209	284 / 204	280 / 199	275 / 194	271 / 190
64DLJ17	55	64	45,400	400 / 314	393 / 306	386 / 298	380 / 290	373 / 283	367 / 276	361 / 269	355 / 262	349 / 256	343 / 250	338 / 244	332 / 238	327 / 232	322 / 227	317 / 222	312 / 216
64DLJ18	64	64	55,900	492 / 380	483 / 370	475 / 360	467 / 351	460 / 342	452 / 334	445 / 325	438 / 317	431 / 309	424 / 302	417 / 295	411 / 288	404 / 281	398 / 274	392 / 268	386 / 262
64DLJ19	72	64	63,100	556 / 424	546 / 414	537 / 402	528 / 392	519 / 382	511 / 372	503 / 363	495 / 354	487 / 345	479 / 337	471 / 329	464 / 321	457 / 313	450 / 306	443 / 299	436 / 292
64DLJ20	83	64	74,500	656 / 492	645 / 479	634 / 467	623 / 455	612 / 443	602 / 432	592 / 421	582 / 411	573 / 401	563 / 391	554 / 382	545 / 373	537 / 364	528 / 355	520 / 347	512 / 339

Joist Designation	Approx. Wt. Lbs. per Lin. Ft.	Nominal Depth in Inches	*Safe Load in Lbs. Between	Clear Opening or Net Span in Feet															
			80–120	121	122	123	124	125	126	127	128	129	130	131	132	133	134	135	136
68DLJ15	44	68	35,400	291 / 229	287 / 223	282 / 218	278 / 212	273 / 207	269 / 203	265 / 198	261 / 193	257 / 189	254 / 184	250 / 180	246 / 176	243 / 172	239 / 168	236 / 165	232 / 161
68DLJ16	49	68	39,200	323 / 255	318 / 249	313 / 243	308 / 237	303 / 231	298 / 226	293 / 220	289 / 215	284 / 210	280 / 206	276 / 201	272 / 196	268 / 192	264 / 188	260 / 184	256 / 180
68DLJ17	55	68	45,200	372 / 290	366 / 283	360 / 276	354 / 270	348 / 263	343 / 257	338 / 251	332 / 245	327 / 240	322 / 234	317 / 229	313 / 224	308 / 219	303 / 214	299 / 209	295 / 205
68DLJ18	62	68	52,100	429 / 328	422 / 320	415 / 313	408 / 305	402 / 298	395 / 291	389 / 284	383 / 277	377 / 271	372 / 265	366 / 259	360 / 253	355 / 247	350 / 242	345 / 237	340 / 231
68DLJ19	72	68	62,000	510 / 392	502 / 383	494 / 373	486 / 364	479 / 356	472 / 347	464 / 339	457 / 331	451 / 324	444 / 316	437 / 309	431 / 302	425 / 296	418 / 289	412 / 283	407 / 276
68DLJ20	83	68	74,200	610 / 455	600 / 444	591 / 433	581 / 423	572 / 413	563 / 403	554 / 394	546 / 385	537 / 376	529 / 367	521 / 359	513 / 351	506 / 343	498 / 336	491 / 328	484 / 321

Joist Designation	Approx. Wt. Lbs. per Lin. Ft.	Nominal Depth in Inches	*Safe Load in Lbs. Between	Clear Opening or Net Span in Feet															
			84–128	129	130	131	132	133	134	135	136	137	138	139	140	141	142	143	144
72DLJ16	49	72	39,100	302 / 237	297 / 231	293 / 226	288 / 221	284 / 216	280 / 211	275 / 207	271 / 202	268 / 198	264 / 193	260 / 189	256 / 185	253 / 181	249 / 178	246 / 174	242 / 170
72DLJ17	55	72	44,900	347 / 270	342 / 264	337 / 258	332 / 252	327 / 246	322 / 241	317 / 236	312 / 230	308 / 225	304 / 221	299 / 216	295 / 211	291 / 207	287 / 202	283 / 198	279 / 194
72DLJ18	62	72	51,800	400 / 305	394 / 298	388 / 291	383 / 285	377 / 279	371 / 272	366 / 266	360 / 261	355 / 255	350 / 249	345 / 244	340 / 239	335 / 234	331 / 229	326 / 224	322 / 220
72DLJ19	72	72	60,900	470 / 365	463 / 356	457 / 348	450 / 340	443 / 333	437 / 326	431 / 318	425 / 311	419 / 305	413 / 298	407 / 292	401 / 286	396 / 280	390 / 274	385 / 268	380 / 262
72DLJ20	83	72	73,900	570 / 424	562 / 414	553 / 405	545 / 396	537 / 387	529 / 378	521 / 370	513 / 362	506 / 354	499 / 346	492 / 339	485 / 332	478 / 325	471 / 318	465 / 311	458 / 305

* To extrapolate for safe uniform load between spans shown, divide the Safe Load in Pounds by Net Span in Feet plus .67 feet. (The added .67 feet (eight inches) is necessary to obtain the proper span for which the load tables were developed.)

Standard Load Table
for Deep Longspan Steel Joists, DLH-Series
Based on a maximum allowable tensile stress of 30,000 psi

Adopted by Steel Joist Institute and
American Institute of Steel Construction, Inc., February 1, 1970

The following table was developed using 30,000 psi allowable tensile stress. Steels with allowable tensile stresses from 20,000 psi to 30,000 psi may be used to meet this load table.

The **bold face** figures give the TOTAL safe uniformly distributed load-carrying capacities, in pounds per linear foot of span. All loads shown are for roof construction only. The weight of DEAD loads, including weight of joists, must in all cases be deducted to determine the LIVE load-carrying capacities of the joists. The approximate weights per linear foot of joists include accessories.

The light face figures are the LIVE loads per linear foot of joists which will produce an approximate deflection of $\frac{1}{360}$ of the span. LIVE loads which will produce an approximate deflection of $\frac{1}{240}$ of the span may be obtained by multiplying the light face figures by 1.5. (NOTE: The tabulated loads corresponding to these deflection limitations have been computed on the basis of 30,000 psi allowable stress provisions. For joists designed to a lower working stress, these loads may be increased in the ratio of 30,000 psi to the design stress used in order to meet the same deflection limitations.)

For roofs, LIVE load deflection is limited to $\frac{1}{360}$ of the span where a plaster ceiling is attached or suspended, and $\frac{1}{240}$ of the span for all other cases. **In no case shall the TOTAL capacity of the joists be exceeded.** *

The load table applies to joists with either parallel chords or standard pitched chords. When top chords are pitched, the carrying capacities are determined by the nominal depth of the joist at the center of the span.

Standard top chord pitch is $\frac{1}{8}$ inch per foot. If pitch exceeds this standard, the load table does not apply. The load table may be used for parallel chord joists installed to a maximum slope of $\frac{1}{2}$ inch per foot.

When holes are required in top or bottom chords, the carrying capacities must be reduced in proportion to reduction of chord areas.

The top chords are considered as being stayed laterally by the roof deck.

---

* Section 104.10 of the "Standard Specifications" limits the design LIVE load deflection as follows: Roofs: $\frac{1}{360}$ of span where a plaster ceiling is attached or suspended; $\frac{1}{240}$ of span for all other cases.

STANDARD LOAD TABLE FOR DEEP LONGSPAN STEEL JOISTS, DLH-SERIES

Pounds per Linear Foot Based on Allowable Stress of 30,000 psi

Joist Designation	Approx. Wt. Lbs. per Lin. Ft.	Nominal Depth in Inches	*Safe Load in Lbs. Between	Clear Opening or Net Span in Feet															
			61–88	89	90	91	92	93	94	95	96	97	98	99	100	101	102	103	104
52DLH10	27	52	26,700	298 180	291 174	285 168	279 163	273 158	267 153	261 148	256 144	251 139	246 135	241 131	236 127	231 123	227 120	223 116	218 113
52DLH11	29	52	29,300	327 197	320 191	313 184	306 178	299 173	293 167	287 162	281 157	275 152	270 148	264 143	259 139	254 135	249 131	244 127	240 124
52DLH12	31	52	32,700	365 215	357 208	349 202	342 195	334 189	327 183	320 177	314 172	307 167	301 162	295 157	289 152	284 148	278 143	273 139	268 135
52DLH13	36	52	39,700	443 260	433 252	424 244	414 236	406 228	397 221	389 214	381 208	373 201	366 195	358 190	351 184	344 179	338 173	331 168	32? 16?
52DLH14	40	52	45,400	507 291	497 281	486 272	476 263	466 255	457 247	447 239	438 232	430 225	421 218	413 212	405 205	397 199	390 194	382 188	37? 18?
52DLH15	45	52	51,000	569 328	557 317	545 307	533 297	522 287	511 278	500 270	490 261	480 253	470 246	461 238	451 231	443 225	434 218	426 212	41? 20?
52DLH16	50	52	55,000	614 365	601 353	588 342	575 331	563 320	551 310	540 301	528 291	518 282	507 274	497 266	487 258	478 250	468 243	459 236	45? 22?
52DLH17	55	52	63,300	706 416	691 402	676 389	661 376	647 365	634 353	620 342	608 332	595 321	583 312	572 302	560 294	549 285	539 277	528 269	51? 26?
			66–96	97	98	99	100	101	102	103	104	105	106	107	108	109	110	111	11?
56DLH11	29	56	28,100	288 178	283 172	277 167	272 162	267 157	262 153	257 148	253 144	248 140	244 136	239 132	235 129	231 125	227 122	223 119	21? 1??
56DLH12	31	56	32,300	331 194	324 188	318 183	312 177	306 172	300 167	295 162	289 158	284 153	278 149	273 145	268 141	263 137	259 133	254 130	24? 12?
56DLH13	36	56	39,100	401 235	394 228	386 221	379 215	372 208	365 202	358 196	351 191	344 185	338 180	331 175	325 170	319 166	314 161	308 157	30? 1??
56DLH14	40	56	44,200	453 263	444 255	435 247	427 240	419 233	411 226	403 220	396 213	388 207	381 201	375 196	368 191	361 185	355 180	349 176	34? 17?
56DLH15	45	56	50,500	518 296	508 287	498 278	488 270	478 262	469 255	460 247	451 240	443 233	434 227	426 221	419 215	411 209	403 203	396 198	38? 19?
56DLH16	50	56	54,500	559 330	548 320	537 310	526 301	516 292	506 284	496 276	487 268	478 260	469 253	460 246	452 239	444 233	436 226	428 220	4?? 2??
56DLH17	55	56	62,800	643 375	630 364	618 353	605 343	594 333	582 323	571 314	560 305	549 296	539 288	529 280	520 272	510 265	501 258	492 251	4?? 2??
			70–104	105	106	107	108	109	110	111	112	113	114	115	116	117	118	119	1?
60DLH12	31	60	31,100	295 177	289 172	284 167	279 163	274 158	270 154	265 150	261 146	256 142	252 138	248 135	244 131	240 128	236 125	232 122	2?? 1??
60DLH13	36	60	37,800	358 214	351 208	345 202	339 197	333 191	327 186	322 181	316 176	311 172	306 167	301 163	296 159	291 155	286 151	282 147	2?? 1??
60DLH14	39	60	42,000	398 228	391 222	383 216	376 210	370 204	363 199	356 193	350 188	344 183	338 179	332 174	327 170	321 165	316 161	310 157	3?? 1??
60DLH15	45	60	49,300	467 269	458 262	450 255	442 248	434 241	427 235	419 228	412 222	405 216	398 211	392 205	385 200	379 195	373 190	367 185	3?? ???
60DLH16	50	60	54,200	513 300	504 292	494 284	485 276	476 269	468 261	460 254	451 248	444 241	436 235	428 229	421 223	414 217	407 212	400 207	3?? 2??
60DLH17	55	60	62,300	590 342	579 332	569 323	558 314	548 306	538 298	529 290	519 282	510 275	501 268	493 261	485 254	476 248	468 241	460 235	4?? 2??
60DLH18	62	60	71,900	681 386	668 376	656 365	644 355	632 345	621 336	610 327	599 319	589 310	578 302	568 294	559 287	549 280	540 273	531 266	5?? 2??

* To extrapolate for safe uniform load between spans shown, divide the Safe Load in Pounds by Net Span in Feet plus .67 feet. (The added .67 feet (eight inches) is necessary to obtain the proper span for which the load tables were developed.)

STANDARD LOAD TABLE FOR DEEP LONGSPAN STEEL JOISTS, DLH-SERIES

Pounds per Linear Foot Based on Allowable Stress of 30,000 psi

Joist Designation	Approx. Wt. Lbs. per Lin. Ft.	Nominal Depth in Inches	*Safe Load in Lbs. Between	Clear Opening or Net Span in Feet																
			75–112	113	114	115	116	117	118	119	120	121	122	123	124	125	126	127	128
64DLH12	31	64	30,000	264 162	259 158	255 154	251 150	247 146	243 143	239 139	235 136	231 132	228 129	224 126	221 123	218 120	214 117	211 115	208 112
64DLH13	36	64	36,400	321 196	315 191	310 186	305 181	300 177	295 172	291 168	286 164	281 160	277 156	273 152	269 149	264 145	260 142	257 138	253 135
64DLH14	39	64	41,700	367 210	360 204	354 199	349 194	343 189	337 184	332 180	326 175	321 171	316 167	311 163	306 159	301 155	296 151	292 148	287 144
64DLH15	45	64	47,800	421 247	414 241	407 235	400 229	394 223	387 217	381 212	375 207	369 202	363 197	358 192	352 187	347 183	341 179	336 174	331 170
64DLH16	50	64	53,800	474 276	466 268	458 262	450 255	443 248	435 242	428 236	421 230	414 225	407 219	401 214	394 209	388 204	382 199	376 194	370 190
64DLH17	55	64	62,000	546 314	536 306	527 298	518 290	509 283	501 276	492 269	484 262	476 256	468 250	461 244	454 238	446 232	439 227	432 222	426 216
64DLH18	62	64	71,600	630 355	619 346	608 337	598 328	587 320	578 312	568 304	559 297	549 289	540 282	532 275	523 269	515 263	507 256	499 250	491 245

			80–120	121	122	123	124	125	126	127	128	129	130	131	132	133	134	135	136
68DLH13	36	68	35,000	288 181	284 177	279 173	275 168	271 164	267 161	263 157	259 153	255 150	252 146	248 143	244 140	241 137	237 134	234 131	231 128
68DLH14	39	68	40,300	332 194	327 189	322 185	317 180	312 176	308 172	303 168	299 164	294 160	290 156	286 153	281 149	277 146	273 143	269 140	266 137
68DLH15	43	68	45,200	372 217	365 212	360 207	354 202	348 197	343 192	337 188	332 184	327 179	322 175	317 171	312 167	308 164	303 160	299 156	294 153
68DLH16	50	68	53,600	441 255	433 249	427 243	420 237	413 231	407 226	400 220	394 215	388 210	382 206	376 201	371 196	365 192	360 188	354 184	349 180
68DLH17	55	68	60,400	497 290	489 283	481 276	474 270	467 263	460 257	453 251	446 245	439 240	433 234	427 229	420 224	414 219	408 214	403 209	397 205
68DLH18	62	68	69,900	575 328	566 320	557 313	549 305	540 298	532 291	524 284	516 277	508 271	501 265	493 259	486 253	479 247	472 243	465 237	459 231
68DLH19	70	68	80,500	662 372	651 363	641 354	631 346	621 337	611 330	601 322	592 314	583 307	574 300	565 293	557 287	548 280	540 274	532 268	525 262

			84–128	129	130	131	132	133	134	135	136	137	138	139	140	141	142	143	144
72DLH14	39	72	39,200	303 180	298 176	294 172	290 168	285 164	281 161	277 157	274 154	270 151	266 147	262 144	259 141	255 138	252 135	248 132	245 130
72DLH15	43	72	44,900	347 202	342 197	336 193	331 188	326 184	322 180	317 176	312 172	308 169	303 165	299 161	295 158	291 155	286 151	282 148	279 145
72DLH16	50	72	51,900	401 237	395 231	390 226	384 221	378 216	373 211	368 207	363 202	358 198	353 193	348 189	343 185	338 181	334 178	329 174	325 170
72DLH17	55	72	58,400	451 270	445 264	438 258	432 252	426 246	420 241	414 236	408 230	402 225	397 221	391 216	386 211	381 207	376 202	371 198	366 194
72DLH18	62	72	68,400	528 305	520 298	512 291	505 285	497 279	490 272	483 266	479 261	470 255	463 249	457 244	450 239	444 234	438 229	432 224	426 220
72DLH19	70	72	80,200	619 346	609 338	600 330	591 323	582 316	573 309	565 302	557 295	549 289	541 283	533 277	526 271	518 265	511 260	504 254	497 249

* To extrapolate for safe uniform load between spans shown, divide the Safe Load in Pounds by Net Span in Feet plus .67 feet. (The added .67 feet (eight inches) is necessary to obtain the proper span for which the load tables were developed.)

Notes

A Guide to the Shop Painting of Structural Steel

Jointly developed and published by
Steel Structures Painting Council and
American Institute of Steel Construction
June 14, 1972

AMERICAN INSTITUTE OF STEEL CONSTRUCTION
101 Park Avenue, New York, N. Y. 10017

FOREWORD

This guide to the shop painting of structural steel was jointly prepared by the American Institute of Steel Construction and the Steel Structures Painting Council. Its purpose is to provide a checklist of some of the factors which the fabricators should consider in the painting of structural steel for use on buildings, bridges, and similar structures to be exposed in normal atmospheric environment. It also provides, however, a delineation from the fabricator's point of view of some of the factors to be considered by the designer, contractor, paint supplier, owner, and others jointly involved with the fabricator in providing a complete and effective paint system. It emphasizes the fabricator's concern for obtaining a quality coating system appropriate to the end use. In this function, the fabricator assumes his full share of the responsibility for cleaning the surface and applying the specified primer in accordance with the design specification.

While every precaution is taken to insure that all information furnished is as accurate as possible, the Institute or the Council cannot assume responsibility or incur any obligation resulting from the use of any material, paint, or method specified in this guide.

TABLE OF CONTENTS

A Guide to the Shop Painting of Structural Steel

1. SCOPE

This Guide outlines some of the elements involved in surface preparation and priming in the steel fabricating shop, which is an important stage in protective painting of structural steel. Emphasis is placed upon shop painting of building or bridge structural steel which after a limited time is subsequently to be touched-up, field painted, and finish coated in the field, and exposed in a normal atmospheric environment.

Also included is a discussion of the designer's choice of surface preparation and paint system which precedes shop painting, and the contractor's field painting which follows it, using coatings manufactured to meet specified requirements.

2. DISCUSSION

2.1 References

This Guide is designed to be used in conjunction with applicable specifications, and the *Quality Criteria and Inspection Standards* commentaries of the American Institute of Steel Construction. For the technical aspects of surface preparation, paint application, paint thickness, material requirements, and paint systems, it refers to specifications of the *Steel Structures Painting Manual, Volume 2, "Systems & Specifications."* The latter emphasizes the importance of the development of a total paint system. Among the primary considerations for this design decision on the part of the owner, architect, or engineer are: an analysis of the end use of the members; a realistic estimate of the time and severity of exposure of each coat of paint; an economic evaluation of the initial cost, as compared to future maintenance costs; and a practical determination of the division between shop and field work and responsibilities to achieve the overall aim.

2.2 Elements

The elements to be specified in a total paint system are surface preparation, pretreatment (if any), type and condition of paint application (including temperature and humidity), paint thickness, primer, curing time, field coat(s), and finish coat. It is apparent that the type of primer and the cleaning and priming operations carried out in the fabricating shop are important to the paint system and should be fully and clearly specified by the owner or his agents.

2.3 Responsibility

The fabricator should be properly in control of and responsible for carrying out a clearly specified surface preparation, and for satisfactory application of the specified shop primer to specified thickness. Perhaps the first responsibility of the fabricator is the encouragement of good overall specifications and practices, such as those jointly developed by the American Institute of Steel Construction (AISC) and the Steel Structures Painting Council (SSPC) and cited herein. Responsibility thereafter for each successive step resides with the people most in control of that step, including the owner, the designer, the specifier, the fabricator, and the paint manufacturer.

3. RECOMMENDATIONS

3.1 Paint Systems

There is no one "best" paint system that is the most effective and economical for all circumstances. Nor is the latest or the most sophisticated method or material necessarily the appropriate one.

Recommendations for choice of a total paint system are presented in such documents as Volume 2 of the *Steel Structures Painting Manual*, and are briefly summarized in Appendix A, which discusses typical paint systems in zone defense painting. As a fundamental design decision, the choice of the paint system (including choice of surface preparation) is the prerogative and responsibility of the owner, architect, or engineer. Although the specifier must consider such factors as cost, appearance, design (see Appendix E), available facilities, site conditions, and available specifications, he should base his choice of paint system primarily upon proper protection of the steel, considering environment and exposure during the application period, the finished product location, and function of the finished product.

Environmental zones cannot be shown on a map because severity of exposure can change sharply over short distances and even on the same structure. Some typical recommendations for zone defense are listed below, based upon those presented in Appendix A and in Volume 2 of the *Steel Structures Painting Manual*.

3.1.1 (Zone Zero) Unpainted Steel

Unless otherwise specified, steel which is not to be painted should merely be cleaned of heavy deposits of oil or grease. If architectural considerations require cleaning or power wire brushing or grinding of an uncoated member, the amount and extent of such power wire brushing or grinding shall be specifically stated in the bid documents. This category usually includes structural steel that would be enclosed in the masonry in the interior of buildings, where temperature does not fall below the dew point, where humidity does not exceed 70%, and where corrosive chemical conditions do not exist.

3.1.2 (Zone 1-A) Interiors Normally Dry (or Temporary Protection for Short Exposures)

Such surfaces can often be satisfactorily protected by a single coat of properly selected shop paint that will perform adequately over cleaning per *SSPC-PS 7.01**.

3.1.3 (Zone 1-B) Normally Dry Exterior

Typically an oil-alkyd base system over hand-cleaned steel (such as *SSPC-PS 1.01*, see Appendix D) can be used in this zone. It encompasses the locations of most bridges

---

* *SSPC-PS 7.01-64T*: "*The surface shall be cleaned of heavy deposits of oil or grease by solvent. Loose mill scale, loose rust, accessible welding slag and dirt or oil shall be removed by wire brushing or other equivalent methods to be elected by the fabricator.*"

in the U. S. where conventional oil base paints have in the past given a paint life of six years or more. Other alternate primers used in typical paint systems are listed in Appendix C.

3.1.4 (Zones 2-A, 2-B, 3, and 4) Other Exposures Typical recommendations for steel surfaces which are frequently wet by fresh or salt water, exposed in chemical plants, galvanized, etc., or subject to corrosive or industrial atmospheric conditions are given in Appendix A. More detailed discussions are available from such sources as the *Steel Structures Painting Manual, Volume 2.*

3.2 Surface Preparation

Since written surface preparation specifications are sometimes subject to misunderstanding or misinterpretation, the *Pictorial Surface Preparation Standards, SSPC-Vis 1,* as outlined in Sects. 3.2.2 through 3.2.4 and in Appendix B, are to be used as the criterion for surface preparation specifications. These photographs should be used to implement the specifications rather than to replace them, however, since some important aspects of surface preparation (such as removal of grease and dust) are not visual.

Since the degree of surface preparation cannot be readily verified after painting, timely inspection (in accordance with fabricator's shop schedule) of the prepared surface, resulting in acceptance by the owner, architect, or engineer, should be performed prior to application of the shop coat. In the event that, after proper notification, the owner's representative is not present to view the surface preparation, the fabricator in-house quality control group will determine acceptance levels which conform to the specifications.

Inspection and safety (Sects. 4 and 5) are important aspects of the surface preparation specifications.

3.2.1 General In the event no cleaning method has been specified, but a shop coat of paint is required, it is understood that *SSPC-SP 2, Hand Tool Cleaning,* may be used. When no paint is to be applied, (see AISC Specification Sect. 1.24.1) minimum surface preparation shall be *SSPC-SP 1, Solvent Cleaning.* Accessible welding slag, and dirt or soil are to be removed by wire brushing or other equivalent method to be elected by the fabricator (described in *SSPC-PS 7.01*).

3.2.2 Hand Tool Cleaning When a bid document calls for removal of all loose mill scale, loose rust, oil, grease, foreign matter, etc., or a similar general requirement of surface preparation, it is to be interpreted as specifying *SSPC-SP 2, Hand Tool Cleaning,* as visibly depicted in the *Pictorial Surface Preparation Standards for Painting Steel Structures, SSPC-Vis 1-67T* and referred to in Table 1.

Table 1

SSPC-SP 2, Hand Tool Cleaning		
Cleaning Required	Pre-Cleaning Conditions	Pictorial Standard
	A or B	B St 2
SP-2	C	C St 2
	D	D St 2

3.2.3 Power Tool Cleaning When power tool cleaning is stipulated, it is to be interpreted as specifying *SSPC-SP 3, Power Tool Cleaning,* as visibly depicted in the *Pictorial Surface Preparation Standards for Painting Steel Structures, SSPC-Vis 1-67T,* and referred to in Table 2.

Table 2

	SSPC-SP 3, Power Tool Cleaning	
Cleaning Required	Pre-Cleaning Condition	Pictorial Standard
SP-3	A or B	B St 3
	C	C St 3
	D	D St 3

3.2.4 Blast Cleaning The *Pictorial Surface Preparation Standards for Painting Steel Structures, SSPC-Vis 1-67T,* as visibly depicted in the photographs contained therein and referred to in Table 3, should be the acceptance criteria for the degree of preparation for *SSPC-SP 7, Brush-Off Blast Cleaning; SSPC-SP 6, Commercial Blast Cleaning; SSPC-SP 10, Near-White Blast Cleaning;* and *SSPC-SP 5, White Metal Blast Cleaning.*

Table 3

	Blast Cleaning	
Blast Condition Required	Pre-Blast Condition	Pictorial Standard
SP-7	B	B Sa 1
	C	C Sa 1
	D	D Sa 1
SP-6	A or B	B Sa 2
	C	C Sa 2
	D	D Sa 2
SP-10	A	A Sa $2\frac{1}{2}$
	B	B Sa $2\frac{1}{2}$
	C	C Sa $2\frac{1}{2}$
	D	D Sa $2\frac{1}{2}$
SP-5	A	A Sa 3
	B	B Sa 3
	C	C Sa 3
	D	D Sa 3

The degree of surface cleaning of the steel structure is determined by visual comparison with the color reference standards. Since slightly different shades and hues will result from differences in steel and abrasives, the visual standards should be viewed accordingly.

Both the photographs and the surface preparation specifications must be used. Both are important, since visual standards do not necessarily illustrate other necessary factors such as surface profile, tightness of mill scale, removal of grease and dust, permissible cleaning procedures, and equipment used.

Blast cleaning specifications are sometimes misinterpreted. For example, the rate-of-cleaning comments in the appendix of the SSPC specifications for brush-blast and commercial blast cleaning are retained for informational purposes only. They have no relation to the production rate of cleaning and have no bearing on the acceptance criteria for blast cleaning, which are based upon end conditions and not upon a cleaning rate.

Similarly, the definition clause (Sect. 2.2) of the Commercial Blast Cleaning specification is sometimes mistakenly interpreted to require cleaning to white metal, ignoring the clause "except for slight shadows, streaks or discolorations caused by rust stain, mill scale oxides, or slight, tight residues of paint or coating that may remain."

3.2.5 Profile   Each SSPC surface preparation specification lists ranges of surface preparation profile (roughness) which have resulted from the use of various size blast-cleaning abrasives. The specifications also point out, however, that this maximum profile will vary with the angle and velocity of the particle, the shape of piece, the hardness of the surface, the amount of recycling of the working mixture (of shot and grit), and with the thoroughness of blast cleaning.

Although several methods of measurement of surface profile depth (examples: Sects. 3.9 and A.4 of SSPC-SP 6, 1971 printing) are suitable for laboratory or test conditions, they are not at present considered suitably reliable, practical, and reproducible under practical shop conditions.

Present data indicate, however, that the customary variations in profile depth encountered in good shop cleaning practice are not sufficient to affect adversely the performance of conventional paint systems with proper film thickness. Unless and until suitable shop methods for measuring profile have been developed and adopted, and the relationship between profile and paint performance have been further documented, it is not recommended that specific or narrow profile limitations be included among the quality control criteria for surface preparation.

3.3   Applying Shop Paint

3.3.1 Non-Corrosive Service   Steel which is to be exposed in non-corrosive environments is to be painted in a workmanlike manner by brush, spray, roller coating, flow coating, or dipping.

3.3.2 Atmospheric or Corrosive Service   Steel which will be exposed to moisture, water, salt, or other corrosive conditions should, unless otherwise specified, be painted according to the provisions of *SSPC-PA 1, Shop, Field and Maintenance Painting*. Elements that are of special relevance in shop priming are summarized below.

3.3.2.1 Contact Surfaces   Contact surfaces which are ordinarily left unpainted include those in direct bonded contact with concrete or fireproofing, contact surfaces of members joined by high-strength bolts in friction-type joints, and shop contact surfaces.

3.3.2.2 Welds   Shop welds and all areas within 2 inches of welds should be cleaned of all slag as required in Sect. 3.6.1 of *SSPC-SP 1, Solvent Cleaning*. Structural steel is normally left unpainted within 2 inches of edges to be field welded, unless the specified paint is not harmful to the operator, the welding operation, or the finished welds.

3.3.2.3 Application Method Unless otherwise specified, the shop paint may be applied by brush, air spray, airless spray, or hot spray, or a combination of these methods. Roller coat application may be used on flat or slightly curved surfaces or over blast-cleaned or pickled surfaces or over primed or striped portions of surfaces. Dipping or flow coating may be used.

3.3.2.4 Shop Conditions Provision should be made in the paint area, enclosed or open, for conditions which are conducive to keeping the prepared surface free of moisture, frost, and dust and maintaining the steel and paint above the recommended application temperature during application and drying (usually 40°F for conventional paints, 55°F for epoxies and other chemically cured coatings, or 35°F for vinyls).

3.3.2.5 Paint Storage In accordance with Sect. 3.3 or SSPC-PA 1, paint and thinner should be stored with proper attention to ventilation, sparks, flames, sunshine, excessive heat, freezing evaporation, skinning, aging, and identification. Drums of heavily pigmented paints should be inverted about every two weeks.

3.3.2.6 Mixing and Thinning Provisions should be made for proper agitation, removal of skins, ventilation, straining, blending, addition of catalyst (if required), and application without use of unauthorized amounts or types of thinner.

3.4 Paint Thickness

Dry thickness is ordinarily specified, since it represents the depth of film remaining on the surface. In shop painting, however, wet film thickness gages should be used during application. They have the important advantage of providing an immediate indication of thickness at a time when inadequacies can be corrected, usually without the need of an additional coat. When properly used, both wet and dry measurements are a function of the thickness of paint over the highest surface peaks.

To determine conformance to a dry paint thickness specification by means of magnetic gages, make five (5) separate spot measurements spaced evenly over each section of the structure 100 square feet in area, or of other area as may be specified. The average of the five spot measurements for each such section shall not be less than the specified thickness. No single spot measurement in any section shall be less than 80% of the specified thickness. Since unusually low or high readings may occasionally occur, single gage readings which can not be repeated consistently must be discarded and not used in the determination of a spot measurement. (For more information see Sects. 2.2 and 3.0 of *SSPC-PA 2-72P*.)

Since paint thickness is usually specified (or implied) as a minimum, greater thickness is permitted if it does not cause mud cracking or other defects of appearance or function.

3.4.1 Wet film thickness measurements made in the shop should be correlated with average actual dry film thickness measured on several areas or calculated from the volume of percent solids of the paint.

When either the roller gage or the prong gage are used, readings must be taken within a very few seconds after application to minimize the effect of solvent evaporation. (With paint such as vinyls, which use highly volatile solvents, considerable thinner also evaporates during spray application.) The approximate dry film thickness can then be calculated simply by multiplying the wet thickness by the volume percent solids/100 (taking into consideration any thinning of the paint for application).

3.4.2 Most dry film thickness gages use magnetic principles and indicate at best only the distance in mils from the top of the paint surface to the magnetic steel surface. Other films under the paint (such as rust, mill scale, existing paint, or a rough surface profile) also increase the gage readings. Most such gage measurements must therefore be corrected by (1) measuring a known shim of similar thickness on the same substrate (Elcometer; G. E., Type B, etc.) or (2) subtracting a "blank" reading of the same substrate without paint (pull-off magnetic gages such as Mikrotest or Inspector).

Based on these principles, procedures for the use of thickness gages are given in *SSPC-PA2-72P "Method for Measurement of Dry Paint Thickness with Magnetic Gages."*

3.4.3 A minimum dry paint film thickness of 1.5 to 2.0 mils is often specified for the shop primer. If the required paint film thickness is not achieved, additional paint should be applied until the required thickness is obtained. (With certain inorganic zinc-rich primers, additional coats cannot be applied to correct the deficient thickness.) Excess paint film thickness should be permitted if it is not objectionable from an appearance or functional standpoint.

3.4.4 When film thickness is not specified, a thickness of at least one mil shall be required for the shop coat.

3.5 Touch-Up

3.5.1 Abrasions caused by handling after painting are to be expected. Touch-up of these blemished areas shall be the responsibility of the contractor performing the field touch-up or field painting.

3.5.2 The shop coat is intended to protect for a limited period. If a longer exposure is contemplated, then additional shop coats or early field coating should be specified. The structural steel fabricator or fabricator-erector shall be responsible for preparation of the surface and application of the paint according to specifications clearly set forth in the bid documents. The performance of the paint system during construction and in the completed structure is a design consideration and is outside the scope or responsibility of the fabricator or fabricator-erector.

3.5.3 The first field coat of paint should be applied within a reasonable period after the shop coat(s), and in any event before the weathering (and required touch-up of the shop coat) becomes excessive. (This is usually within 3 to 7 months for a single shop coat in normal atmospheric environments, and a shorter period in moist or corrosive environments.) With epoxy paints the interval between coats (usually about 24 hours at 70°F, or longer at lower temperatures) should be specified by the paint manufacturer.

3.5.4   Damaged shop-coated areas should be cleaned of damaged paint, re-prepared, and then repainted with the same number and kind of paint as the undamaged areas.

3.6   Field Storage

Shop-painted steel which is stored in the field pending erection should be kept free of the ground and so positioned as to minimize water-holding pockets, dust, mud, and other contamination of the paint film. Repairs of damage to painted surfaces due to improper field storage are outside the scope of responsibility of the fabricator.

4.   INSPECTION

4.1   Since the degree of surface preparation cannot be readily verified after painting, timely inspection (in accordance with the shop fabricating schedule) of the prepared surface, resulting in acceptance by the owner, architect, or engineer, should be performed prior to application of the shop coat of paint. In the event, after proper notification, the owner's representative is not present to view the surface preparation, the fabricator in-house quality control group will determine acceptance levels which conform to the specifications.

4.2   Any deficiencies in surface preparation, paint thickness, or other specification requirements should be called to the attention of the fabricator or contractor by the inspector or owner's representative at the time of completion of the particular operation and within reasonable time for correction.

4.3   Ordinarily, all work and materials used in shop and field painting are subject to inspection by the owner or his representative. All parts of the work shall be accessible to the inspector. The contractor should correct such work or replace such material as is found defective under the bid contract specification or document. If the contractor does not agree with the inspector, the arbitration or settlement procedure established in the contract, if any, should be followed. If no arbitration or settlement procedure is established, the procedure specified by the American Arbitration Association should be used.

5.   SAFETY PRECAUTIONS

5.1   In the handling and application of paints, certain processes, equipment, materials, and chemical agents are used. When performing any of the operations discussed herein, the applicable standard as it relates to safety, health, or pollution must be followed.

APPENDIX A

TYPICAL ZONE* DEFENSE PAINTING

	ENVIRONMENT	PREFERRED SYSTEM	ALTERNATIVES
ZONE ZERO	Dry interior where structural steel is imbedded in concrete, encased in masonry, or protected by membrane or contact type fireproofing. (See Sect. 3.1.1 of this Guide.)	Leave unpainted.	(1) See Zone 1-A if structural steel is not in a dry interior. (2) See Zone 1-B if structural steel is exposed to weather.
ZONE 1-A	Interior, normally dry (or temporary protection). Very mild. (Oil base paints would last 10 years or more.)	One coat of fast-drying shop paint (example: SSPC-Paint 13) over nominally hand-cleaned steel. Finish coat optional. (See SSPC-PS 7.01.)	(1) Other one-coat primers (example: TT-P-636. (2) Joists (SSPC-Paint 15) (3) Rust proofing (SSPC-PS 8.01), or (4) More durable systems as per Zone 1-B, or (5) Approved proprietary paint.
ZONE 1-B	Exteriors normally dry. (Includes most areas where oil base paints now last six years or more and where bare steel corrosion rate is moderate.)	Apply 2 coats (first coat in shop) oil base primer (example: SSPC-Paint 14) over wire-brushed steel. 1–2 finish coats of long oil alkyd (SSPC-Paint 101 aluminum or SSPC-Paint 104 white, gray or green) 4.0 mils or more thickness. (See SSPC-PS 1.01 or 1.03.)	(1) Blast clean (SSPC-SP 6) and use same paints or shorter oil alkyds. (2) Alternate primer (SSPC-Paint 2; TT-P-57, Type I; or TT-P-615, Type V), or (3) Alternate intermediate (TT-P-86, Type II or non-leafing aluminum), or (4) Same systems as Zone 2-A or 2-B, or (5) Proven proprietary system.
ZONE 2-A	Frequently wet by fresh water. Involves condensation, splash, spray, or frequent immersion. (Oil base paints now last five years or less.)	Near-white blast clean surface; 4 coats (4.5 mils) of vinyl system (example: SSPC-Paints 8 or 9). (See SSPC-PS 4.04 or 4.02.)	(1) Pickle (SSPC-SP 8) instead of blast clean. (2) Alternate vinyls are VR 3 or approved proprietaries. (3) Epoxy system (SSPC-PS 13.00), coal tar epoxy (SSPC-PS 11.01), chlorinated rubber system, or approved proprietary system.
ZONE 2-B	Frequently wet by salt water. Involves condensation, splash, spray, or frequent immersion. (Oil base paints now last three years or less.)	Near-white blast clean surface; apply zinc-rich primer (example: SSPC-PS 12.00 or MIL-P-23236 or California Highway Spec. 66-G-55) followed by approved wash primer and finish coat (example: SSPC-PT 3 plus SSPC Vinyl Paint 8 or 9; 3+ mils.) Assure satisfactory adhesion of finish coats.	(1) Use finish coat with same vehicle as zinc-rich primer (inorganic, epoxy, chlorinated rubber, vinyl, etc.) (2) Use vinyl paint system with wash coat and inhibitive primer (example: SSPC-PS 4.01 or 4.03). (3) Use as alternate finish coats or by themselves: coal tar epoxy (SSPC-PS 11.01), epoxy (SSPC-PS 13.00), or approved chlorinated rubber system, or other proven proprietary system.
ZONE 3	Chemical exposures. (Acidic, alkaline, oxidizing, solvents, etc.)	Same as for Zone 2-B, but with chemically resistant finish coat system specially chosen to protect primer and base metal against specific chemical agent. (Zinc-rich unsatisfactory for acid or alkaline conditions unless top-coated.) Assure satisfactory adhesion of finish coats.	Use as finish coats for zinc-rich primer, or by themselves: (1) Coal tar epoxy (SSPC-PS 11.01) (at least 16 mils). (2) Straight vinyls for acid and alkali. See SSPC-PS 4.01 (5.5 mils) or PS 4.03 (4 mils). (3) Epoxies for alkalies, salts, aliphatics, acid splash; not for strong solvents (SSPC-PS 13). (4) Neoprenes and other proven proprietary systems to resist specific conditions.
ZONE 4	Special conditions. For painting galvanized steel, mildew, temporary protection, rustproofing, painting welds, abrasion resistance, etc., see *Steel Structures Painting Manual, Volume 2*, Tables I, II and III.		

* These are intended as specific exposure zones of the portion of the structure under consideration, rather than geographic localities. Severity of exposure can change sharply over very short distances due to such factors as wind, spray, condensation, fumes, and use of de-icing chemicals.

APPENDIX B

ABSTRACT OF SURFACE PREPARATION SPECIFICATIONS*

SPECIFICATION & SUBJECT	PHOTO SSPC-Vis 1	PURPOSE
SSPC-SP 1 Solvent Cleaning	—	Removal of oil, grease, dirt, soil, salts, and contaminants by cleaning with solvent, vapor, alkali, emulsion or steam.
SSPC-SP 2 Hand Tool Cleaning	B St 2 C St 2 D St 2	Removal of loose rust, loose mill scale, and loose paint to degree specified, by hand chipping, scraping, sanding and wire brushing.
SSPC-SP 3 Power Tool Cleaning	B St 3 C St 3 D St 3	Removal of loose rust, loose mill scale, and loose paint to degree specified, by power tool chipping, descaling, sanding, wire brushing and grinding.
SSPC-SP 4 Flame Cleaning of New Steel	—	Dehydrating and removal of rust, loose mill scale, and some tight mill scale by use of flame, followed by wire brushing.
SSPC-SP 5 White Metal Blast Cleaning	A Sa 3 B Sa 3 C Sa 3 D Sa 3	Removal of all visible rust, mill scale, paint and foreign matter by blast cleaning by wheel or nozzle (dry or wet) using sand, grit or shot. (For very corrosive atmosphere where high cost of cleaning is warranted.)
SSPC-SP 10 Near-White Blast Cleaning	A Sa 2½ B Sa 2½ C Sa 2½ D Sa 2½	Blast cleaning nearly to White Metal cleanliness, until at least 95% of each element of surface area is free of all visible residues. (For high humidity, chemical atmosphere, marine or other corrosive environments.)
SSPC-SP 6 Commercial Blast Cleaning	B Sa 2 C Sa 2 D Sa 2	Blast cleaning until at least two-thirds of each element of surface area is free of all visible residues. (For rather severe conditions of exposure.)
SSPC-SP 7 Brush-Off Blast Cleaning	B Sa 1 C Sa 1 D Sa 1	Blast cleaning of all except tightly adhering residues of mill scale, rust and coatings, exposing numerous evenly distributed flecks of underlying metal.
SSPC-SP 8 Pickling	—	Complete removal of rust and mill scale by acid pickling, duplex pickling or electrolytic pickling. May passify surface.
SSPC-SP 9 Weathering Followed by Blast Cleaning	—	Weathering to remove all or part of mill scale followed by blast cleaning to one of the above standards as required.

* Steel Structures Painting Manual, Volume 2, 1969 Printing, Steel Structures Painting Council, Pittsburgh, Pa. 15213.

APPENDIX C: SOME SHOP PRIMERS FOR STRUCTURAL STEEL
(Thickness 1.5–2.0 mils unless otherwise specified.)

Use	Code	Min. Surface Preparation	Description**	Used in Paint System Number**
Non-Corrosive Uses	SSPC-Paint 13	Nominal Cleaning* or Hand Cleaning or Power Tool Cleaning	Red or brown one-coat shop paint	For non-corrosive exposures up to 6 months before enclosure. Quick drying.	SSPC-PS 7.01
	TT-P-636		Synthetic primer	Zinc chromate and iron oxide alkyd for short term protection or under topcoat.	SSPC-PS 7.01
	TT-P-31		Paint, iron oxide red and brown	Slow drying iron oxide-linseed oil-zinc oxide-varnish primer. Good build.	SSPC-PS 7.01
	SSPC-Paint 15		For steel joists, Steel Joist and Type II, asphalt Shop Paint (fast drying), Type I, red oxide alkyd		SSPC-PS 14.01
Normal Atmospheric Exposures (See SSPC Manual, Vol. 2 for further details)	SSPC-Paint 14	Hand Cleaning* or Power Tool Cleaning* or as per SSPC-SP 2 or 3	Red lead-iron oxide linseed oil primer	75% red lead /25% iron oxide in linseed oil. Good surface wetting and rust inhibition. Slow drying.	SSPC-PS 1.01, 1.02 (Also state highway specs)
	SSPC-Paint 2		Red lead-iron oxide, raw linseed oil and alkyd primer	2–2.5 parts oil/1 part alkyd. 75% Red lead /25% iron oxide. Good weathering. Clean steel well.	SSPC-PS 1.05 (Also state highway specs, Mich., etc.)
	TT-P-86, Type I		Red lead linseed oil paint	Straight red lead raw/bodied linseed oil paint with good wetting. Slow dry. Same as AASHO-M72-70, Type II.	SSPC-PS 1.06 and various state highway specs.
	TT-P-57, Type I		Paint, zinc yellow-iron oxide-alkyd-linseed oil	1/1 raw linseed oil/oil alkyd pigmented with yellow iron oxide and zinc chromate. Slow to semi-quick drying.	SSPC-PS 1.00 (Guide)
	TT-P-641, Type I		Zinc dust-zinc oxide linseed oil paint	Effective for both structural steel and galvanized steel.	SSPC-PS 1.04
	TT-P-615, Type V		Oil alkyd with basic lead silico chromate	2.25/1 linseed oil/alkyd with basic lead silico chromate pigmentation. Exc. performance record.	Numerous state highway specs.
Pretreatment (for salt water)	SSPC-PT 3 or MIL-P-15328	Blast Clean SSPC-SP 6 or 10	Basic zinc chromate vinyl butyral wash-coat	Pretreatment for use under vinyl primers. Also aids adhesion of other coatings.	SSPC-PS 4.01, 4.03, 4.05
Fresh Water or Chemical	SSPC-Paint 9	Blast Clean SSPC-SP 10	White or gray or tinted vinyl	Over bare steel or over wash primer. For severe exposures.	SSPC-PS 4.04, 4.01, 4.03
Marine and Severe Exp.	MIL-P-23236 Type I, Class 3	Blast Clean SSPC-SP 10	Zinc-rich primer (performance specification) developed for fuel and ballast tanks but widely used elsewhere.		SSPC-PS 12.00 (Guide)
Water Immersion Chemical	SSPC-Paint 16	Blast Clean SSPC-SP 10	Coal tar epoxy polyamide	Heavy-bodied. 16 mils in 2 coats. Catalyzed.	SSPC-PS 11.01

* Although suitable for hand-cleaned or wire-brushed steel in normal exposures, these primers perform more consistently when used over blast-cleaned steel.

** Or use proven proprietary primers for steel surfaces as part of a paint system for specific end use. It is recommended that paint used for all coats used on a particular job be obtained from the same supplier.

APPENDIX D
TYPICAL PAINT SYSTEM

Steel Structures Painting Council Specifications SSPC-PS 1.01-64T
(July 31, 1964)

Oil Base Paint System 1.01 With Linseed Oil Primer and Alkyd Topcoat

(For Weather-Exposed Wire-Brushed Steel)

1. SCOPE

1.1 This specification outlines a complete oil base paint system for steel bridges and other structural steel surfaces that will be wire brushed, painted and exposed to the weather in moderately corrosive atmospheres. It consists of hand tool or power tool cleaning, one coat of red lead—iron oxide linseed oil primer, one intermediate coat of medium oil alkyd, and one finish coat of alkyd linseed oil aluminum paint. The alternate finish coat offers a choice of white, grays, tans, or greens.

2. DESCRIPTION

2.1 This paint system is effective and economical where unusual factors, such as condensation, chemical fumes, brine drippings and other extremely corrosive conditions are not present.

The oil base primer is slow in drying, but the intermediate paint and topcoat dry more rapidly.

3. REQUIREMENTS

The surfaces of the steel shall be cleaned and painted as follows:

3.1 Surface Preparation The surface shall be cleaned as specified in either SSPC-SP 2-63, "Hand Tool Cleaning" or SSPC-SP 3-63, "Power Tool Cleaning" as elected by the contractor.

3.2 Pretreatment Pretreatment of the steel shall not be required.

3.3 Paint Application All paint shall be applied in accordance with SSPC-PA 1-64, "Shop, Field and Maintenance Painting."

3.4 Number of Coats A minimum of three coats of paint shall be applied.

3.5 Primer After cleaning, the steel shall be primed with one coat of paint conforming with specification SSPC-Paint 14-64T, "Red Lead-Iron Oxide Linseed Oil Primer."

3.6 Touch-Up Painting Touch-up field painting shall be performed in accordance with specification SSPC-PA 1-64, "Shop, Field and Maintenance Painting" and in particular with Section 3.5.3 thereof entitled "Field Painting."

3.7 Intermediate Coat The intermediate paint coat shall conform with Federal Specification TT-P-86c, "Paint, Red Lead Base, Ready-Mixed," Type II, Red Lead, Mixed Pigment-Alkyd Varnish Linseed Oil

Paint; or AASHO Designation M72-57, Type II, "Red Lead, Ready-Mixed Paint."

3.8.1 Finish Coat The finish coat of paint shall conform with specification SSPC-Paint 101-64T, "Aluminum Alkyd Paint," Type I. Leafing.

3.8.2 Alternate Finish Coat If specified in the contract, a finish coat complying with specification SSPC-Paint 104-64, "White or Tinted Alkyd Paint." Type I, II, III or IV shall be substituted for the standard finish coat. The type and shade shall be agreed upon in advance.

3.9 Paint Film Thickness The dry film thickness of the paint at any point shall not be less than the following: for the primer 1.7 mils (0.0017 inches); for the second coat 1.3 mils; for the finish coat 1.0 mils; for the three-coat paint system 4.0 mils. If the required paint film thickness is not achieved, additional coats shall be applied until the required thickness is obtained.

Summary of Paint System 1.01

Sec.	Item	Specification
3.1	Surf. Prep	SSPC-SP 2-63 (or better)
3.2	Pretreat	None Required
3.3	Paint Appl	SSPC-PA 1-64
3.4	No. Coats	Three minimum
3.5	Primer	SSPC-Paint 14-64T
3.6	Touch-up	SSPC-PA 1-64, Sec. 3.5.3
3.7	2nd Coat	TT-P-86c, Type II
3.8.1	Finish Coat	SSPC-Paint 101-64T, Type I
3.8.2	(Alt. Fin. Ct)	(SSPC-Paint 104-64)
3.9	Dry Film	First Coat 1.7 mils, etc.
	Thickness	Total System 4.0 mils.

4. INSPECTION

4.1 All work and materials supplied under this specification shall be subject to inspection by the owner or his representative. The contractor shall correct such work or replace such material as is found defective under this specification. If the contractor does not agree with the inspector the arbitration or settlement procedure established in the contract, if any, shall be followed. If no arbitration or settlement procedure is established, the procedure specified by the American Arbitration Association shall be used.

4.2 Samples of ingredients or paints used under this paint system should be supplied upon request along with the supplier's name and identification for the materials.

4.3 Unless otherwise specified, the method of sampling and testing should be in accordance with Federal Test Method Standard No. 141, or applicable methods of the American Society for Testing and Materials.

4.4 The contract covering work or purchase should establish the responsibility for testing and for any required affidavit certifying full compliance with the specification.

5. NOTES ON REQUIREMENTS

5.1 Surface Preparation   Under the terms of the surface preparation specifications, oil, grease or salts must first be removed by the method outlined in SSPC-SP 1-63, "Solvent Cleaning." With the mutual agreement of both owner and contractor, any of the SSPC surface preparation specifications requiring more complete cleaning or scale removal may be substituted for the surface cleaning specified. (SSPC Surface Preparation Specifications No. 5, 6, 7, 8 or 10.)

5.2 Paint Application   SSPC-PA 1-64.   "Shop, Field and Maintenance Painting" specified method of application (brush, spray, airless, hot spray and sometimes roller), storage, mixing, temperature, humidity, contact surfaces, tinting of intermediates, treatment of weld areas etc.   If any exceptions or further limitations to these requirements are desired, they should be stipulated.

5.3 Intermediate Coat   When specifically stipulated in the contract, the intermediate coat may instead be the same as the prime coat (tinted for contrast) or the same as the finish coat (tinted or non-leafing for contrast).

5.4 Finish Coat   If the alternate finish coat, SSPC-Paint 104-64, "White or Tinted Alkyd Paint", is specified, the type and shade should be agreed upon between the parties concerned, using a suitable method of color designation such as Federal Color Standard No. 595, or other stable color chips, or spectrophotometric requirements such as those in MIL-Std. 794, "Military Standard Colors" or other specified method.   The paint may be tinted to shades ranging from white (Type I):   to light or medium gray or tan (Type II);   to light green or gray-green (Type III);   to dark green or forest green (Type IV).

5.5 General Notes   All of the requirements and safety precautions of the specifications included by reference are considered a part of this specification and should be fully complied with.

In case of a conflict between a specific provision herein and any requirement of a specification included by reference, the former should govern.

This specification applies to maintenance painting, its specific instructions are included regarding the degree and amount of solvent cleaning, spot cleaning, spot priming, priming and finish painting. (See SSPC Paint Application Guide.)

The latest applicable issue, revision, or amendment of the specifications listed herein in effect on the date of invitation for bids should be used.

All safety requirements shall be considered to supplement any local **or** state safety codes applying to any particular project.

APPENDIX E
DESIGN FOR CORROSION PROTECTION

Appearance and protection from corrosion are two of the principal reasons for painting low carbon structural steel. For corrosion to occur, both oxygen and water must be present in abundance. It has been estimated that mild structural steel begins to corrode at an average rate of 5 mils lost of surface metal per year. After the first year, however, this rate drops to about $\frac{1}{2}$ mil per year in typical normal industrial weather exposures in the United States. (In marine atmospheres, the initial corrosion rate is lower, but does not drop off as rapidly.) Corrosion in rural atmospheres is considerably lower. Much higher corrosion rates can, of course, occur in the vicinity of chemical plants, etc., in the presence of electrolytes, corrosive chemicals, sulphur gases, sea spray, etc., especially under conditions of high humidity and fluctuating temperatures.

At relative humidities below 70%, however, significant corrosion does not occur (at normal temperatures).

Mill scale is a layer of oxides several thousandths of an inch thick, which is present on hot rolled structural steel as it leaves the mill. Initially, this mill scale is tightly adhered to the surface and even provides a measure of protection. It has been found in many studies that this intact mill scale can be successfully painted and provide protection in normal atmospheric environments where moisture is low. In corrosive environments, however (see Zones 1-A, 2, 3, etc.) the mill scale, which eventually becomes broken and penetrated, can cause electrolytic corrosion of the metal under the paint at the interface between metal and mill scale, particularly in the presence of electrolytes such as salt or sulphur dioxide. Due to the great variability of the surface condition of commercial structural steel (varying from rust grades A to B to C to D in SSPC-Vis 1), the painting of steel without removal of this mill scale (by blast cleaning or pickling) is always a calculated risk, especially in corrosive environments. Mill scale removal is, therefore, recommended, not only in corrosive environments (Zones 1-A, 2, 3, etc.), but also in normal atmospheric exposures if appearance is a particularly important factor.

Proper design can do much to prevent localized corrosion and, therefore, make the work of coatings much more effective. This is particularly true of structural members or flat surfaces (Figure E-1) which trap water without proper provision for drainage. It is also important to avoid crevices (Figure E-2), which make the job of original painting and maintenance painting difficult or impossible. Sufficient access for maintenance should also be allowed (Figure E-3). It is also highly desirable to avoid sharp edges (Figure E-4) by using, for example, standard rolled members whenever possible. Otherwise, provision must be made for grinding off sharp edges or striping with an additional coat of paint.

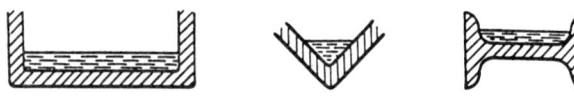

*Fig. E-1. Water trapped by structural members
(courtesy British Iron & Steel Research Association)*

Fig. E-2. Types of crevices (courtesy BISRA)

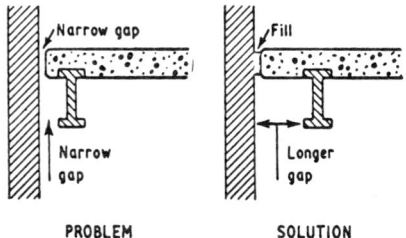

PROBLEM   **SOLUTION**

Fig. E-3. Insufficient access for maintenance (courtesy BISRA)

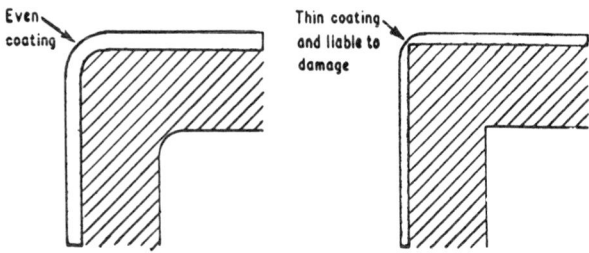

Fig. E-4. Effect of surface contours (courtesy BISRA)

PART 6
Miscellaneous Data and Mathematical Tables

WIRE AND SHEET METAL GAGES
In decimals of an inch

Name of Gage	*United States Standard Gage		The United States Steel Wire Gage	American or Brown & Sharpe Wire Gage	New Birmingham Standard Sheet & Hoop Gage	British Imperial or English Legal Standard Wire Gage	Birmingham or Stubs Iron Wire Gage	Name of Gage
Principal Use	Uncoated Steel Sheets and Light Plates		Steel Wire except Music Wire	Non-Ferrous Sheets and Wire	Iron and Steel Sheets and Hoops	Wire	Strips, Bands, Hoops and Wire	Principal Use
Gage No.	Weight Oz. per Sq. Ft.	Approx. Thickness Inches	Thickness, Inches					Gage No.
7/0's			.4900		.6666	.500		7/0's
6/0's			.4615	.5800	.625	.464		6/0's
5/0's			.4305	.5165	.5883	.432	.500	5/0's
4/0's			.3938	.4600	.5416	.400	.454	4/0's
3/0's			.3625	.4096	.500	.372	.425	3/0's
2/0's			.3310	.3648	.4452	.348	.380	2/0's
1/0			.3065	.3249	.3964	.324	.340	1/0
1			.2830	.2893	.3532	.300	.300	1
2			.2625	.2576	.3147	.276	.284	2
3	160	.2391	.2437	.2294	.2804	.252	.259	3
4	150	.2242	.2253	.2043	.250	.232	.238	4
5	140	.2092	.2070	.1819	.2225	.212	.220	5
6	130	.1943	.1920	.1620	.1981	.192	.203	6
7	120	.1793	.1770	.1443	.1764	.176	.180	7
8	110	.1644	.1620	.1285	.1570	.160	.165	8
9	100	.1495	.1483	.1144	.1398	.144	.148	9
10	90	.1345	.1350	.1019	.1250	.128	.134	10
11	80	.1196	.1205	.0907	.1113	.116	.120	11
12	70	.1046	.1055	.0808	.0991	.104	.109	12
13	60	.0897	.0915	.0720	.0882	.092	.095	13
14	50	.0747	.0800	.0641	.0785	.080	.083	14
15	45	.0673	.0720	.0571	.0699	.072	.072	15
16	40	.0598	.0625	.0508	.0625	.064	.065	16
17	36	.0538	.0540	.0453	.0556	.056	.058	17
18	32	.0478	.0475	.0403	.0495	.048	.049	18
19	28	.0418	.0410	.0359	.0440	.040	.042	19
20	24	.0359	.0348	.0320	.0392	.036	.035	20
21	22	.0329	.0317	.0285	.0349	.032	.032	21
22	20	.0299	.0286	.0253	.0313	.028	.028	22
23	18	.0269	.0258	.0226	.0278	.024	.025	23
24	16	.0239	.0230	.0201	.0248	.022	.022	24
25	14	.0209	.0204	.0179	.0220	.020	.020	25
26	12	.0179	.0181	.0159	.0196	.018	.018	26
27	11	.0164	.0173	.0142	.0175	.0164	.016	27
28	10	.0149	.0162	.0126	.0156	.0148	.014	28
29	9	.0135	.0150	.0113	.0139	.0136	.013	29
30	8	.0120	.0140	.0100	.0123	.0124	.012	30
31	7	.0105	.0132	.0089	.0110	.0116	.010	31
32	6.5	.0097	.0128	.0080	.0098	.0108	.009	32
33	6	.0090	.0118	.0071	.0087	.0100	.008	33
34	5.5	.0082	.0104	.0063	.0077	.0092	.007	34
35	5	.0075	.0095	.0056	.0069	.0084	.005	35
36	4.5	.0067	.0090	.0050	.0061	.0076	.004	36
37	4.25	.0064	.0085	.0045	.0054	.0068		37
38	4	.0060	.0080	.0040	.0048	.0060		38
39			.0075	.0035	.0043	.0052		39
40			.0070	.0031	.0039	.0048		40

* U. S. Standard Gage is officially a weight gage, in oz. per sq. ft. as tabulated. The Approx. Thickness shown is the "Manufacturers' Standard" of the American Iron and Steel Institute, based on steel as weighing 501.81 lb. per cu. ft. (489.6 true weight plus 2.5 per cent for average over-run in area and thickness). The AISI standard nomenclature for flat rolled carbon steel is as follows:

Thickness (Inches)	Width (Inches)					
	To 3½ incl.	Over 3½ To 6	Over 6 To 8	Over 8 To 12	Over 12 To 48	Over 48
.2300 & thicker	Bar	Bar	Bar	Plate	Plate	Plate
.2299 to 0.2031	Bar	Bar	Strip	Strip	Sheet	Plate
.2030 to 0.1800	Strip	Strip	Strip	Strip	Sheet	Plate
.1799 to 0.0449	Strip	Strip	Strip	Strip	Sheet	Sheet
.0448 to 0.0344	Strip	Strip				
.0343 to 0.0255	Strip	Strip	Hot rolled sheet and strip not generally produced in these widths and thicknesses			
.0254 & thinner						

AMERICAN INSTITUTE OF STEEL CONSTRUCTION

CORRUGATED STEEL CONSTRUCTION
Corrugated sheet data

Corrugated steel continues to be an economical and practical construction product as well as a covering for buildings. Its structural usefulness has been extended by increased knowledge of its section properties, and its attractiveness has been enhanced by the development of colored coatings. In addition to its extensive use as roofing and siding, corrugated sheets in trapezoidal-type patterns of higher strength steel are used as permanent structural supporting members for insulating-type concrete roofs as well as permanent forms for structural concrete floor or roof slabs. Properly designed, such forms also become composite forms for poured concrete slabs.

Roofing and siding sheets are procurable in a number of standard styles and many specially designed patterns as shown below. The base sheet is produced with or without copper or other alloying additions. Finishes available include black, painted, galvanized, galvanized and painted, aluminized, laminates, ceramic coated, and asbestos protected. Consult manufacturers' catalogs for various patterns and available widths, lengths, gages, and finishes.

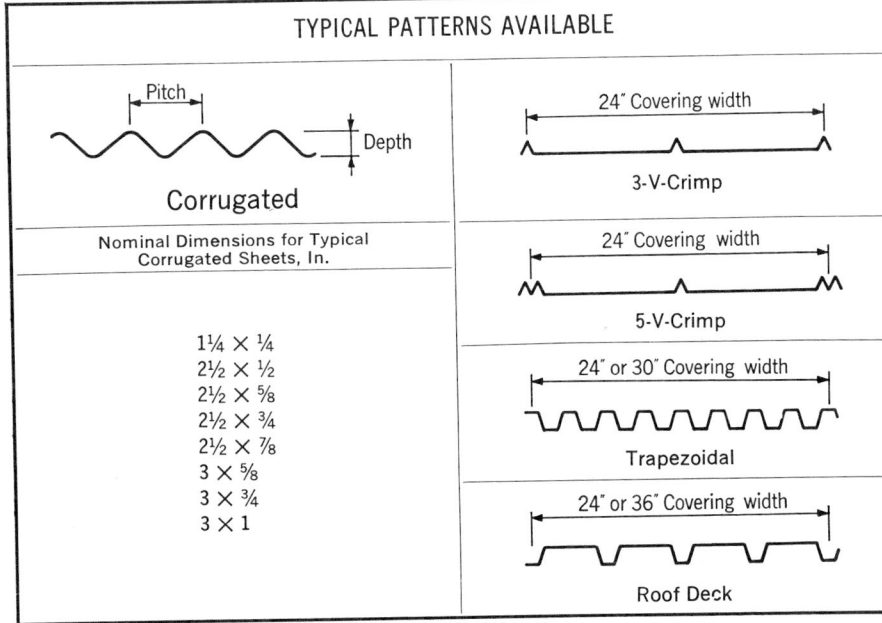

TYPICAL PATTERNS AVAILABLE

Corrugated — Pitch, Depth

Nominal Dimensions for Typical Corrugated Sheets, In.

1¼ × ¼
2½ × ½
2½ × ⅝
2½ × ¾
2½ × ⅞
3 × ⅝
3 × ¾
3 × 1

3-V-Crimp — 24″ Covering width

5-V-Crimp — 24″ Covering width

Trapezoidal — 24″ or 30″ Covering width

Roof Deck — 24″ or 36″ Covering width

The most commonly used corrugated sheet style in the United States is the standard 2½ × ½-in., made in various standard sheet gages. Actually, standard 2½-in. corrugated sheets have nine corrugations exclusive of side lap, and a cover width of 24 in.; therefore, the corrugation pitch measures approximately 2.66 in.

AMERICAN INSTITUTE OF STEEL CONSTRUCTION

Roofing and siding data for the 2½ × ½-in. corrugated sheets are given below.

CORRUGATED SHEET DATA

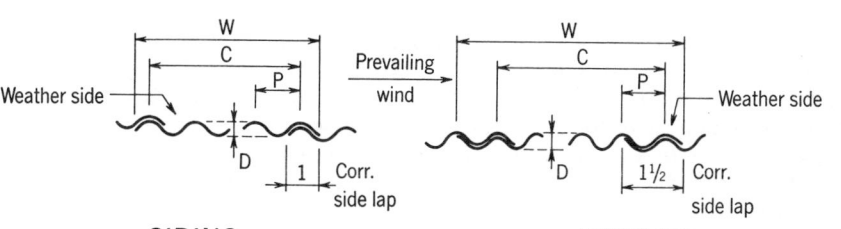

SIDING   ROOFING

Standard 2½ × ½ in.

Dimensions	Siding	Roofing
Pitch P, in.	*2½	*2½
Depth D, in.	½	½
Width W, in.	26	27½
Cover C, in.	24	24
Side Laps, in.	2	3½
No. of Corrugations in Cover	9	9

* Actual Pitch 2⅔ in.

PROPERTIES OF 2½ x ½-IN. CORRUGATED STEEL SHEETS

			Uncoated						Galvanized		
			Properties Per Ft. of Corrugated Width						**Properties Per Ft. of Corrugated Width		
U.S. Mfr's Gage	Equiv. Thickness In.	*Weight Lb./Sq. Ft.	A In.²	I In.⁴	S In.³	Galv. Sheet Gage	Equiv. Thickness In.	*Weight Lb./Sq. Ft.	A In.²	I In.⁴	S In.³
12	.1046	4.77	1.356	.0410	.136	12	.1084	4.94	1.379	.0417	.138
14	.0747	3.41	0.968	.0288	.100	14	.0785	3.58	0.991	.0295	.102
16	.0598	2.73	0.775	.0229	.0818	16	.0635	2.90	0.797	.0236	.0839
18	.0478	2.18	0.620	.0182	.0665	18	.0516	2.35	0.643	.0189	.0688
20	.0359	1.64	0.465	.0136	.0509	20	.0396	1.81	0.487	.0143	.0532
22	.0299	1.36	0.388	.0113	.0428	22	.0336	1.53	0.410	.0120	.0451
24	.0239	1.09	0.310	.00906	.0346	24	.0276	1.26	0.332	.00971	.0369
26	.0179	0.82	0.232	.00678	.0262	26	.0217	0.99	0.255	.00746	.0287
28	.0149	0.68	0.193	.00564	.0219	28	.0187	0.85	0.216	.00632	.0245
29	.0135	0.60	0.175	.00511	.0199	29	.0172	0.78	0.197	.00575	.0223

* Weight for roofing style (27½ in. wide) and no allowance for side or end laps.

** Steel thicknesses upon which sectional properties were based were obtained by subtracting 0.0020 in. from galvanized sheet thicknesses listed. This thickness allowance applies particularly to the 1.25 oz. coating class (commercial).

(Source: "Sectional Properties of Corrugated Steel Sheets", 1964 Edition, AISI.)

CORRUGATED STEEL CONSTRUCTION
Design data

Allowable working stresses for corrugated sheets may be taken as $F_b = 0.6\ F_y$. Laps at sides and ends of sheets are ordinarily ignored in strength calculations. The allowable loads may be increased by 25% for sheets continuous over four or more equally spaced supports and by 33% for sheets subjected to a combination of loads including wind loading, providing that the section thus determined is not smaller than would be required by the loads excluding wind. For concentrated loads, assume a 2-foot width of sheet is effective in supporting loads. It is recommended that deflection of corrugated sheets be limited to $\frac{1}{90}$ of the span.

For further design information refer to (1) manufacturers' catalogs, (2) *Specification for the Design of Cold-Formed Steel Structural Members*, 1968 Edition, AISI, (3) *Sectional Properties of Corrugated Steel Sheets*, 1964, AISI.

DESIGN CHART FOR GALVANIZED 2½ x ½ CORRUGATED STEEL SHEETS

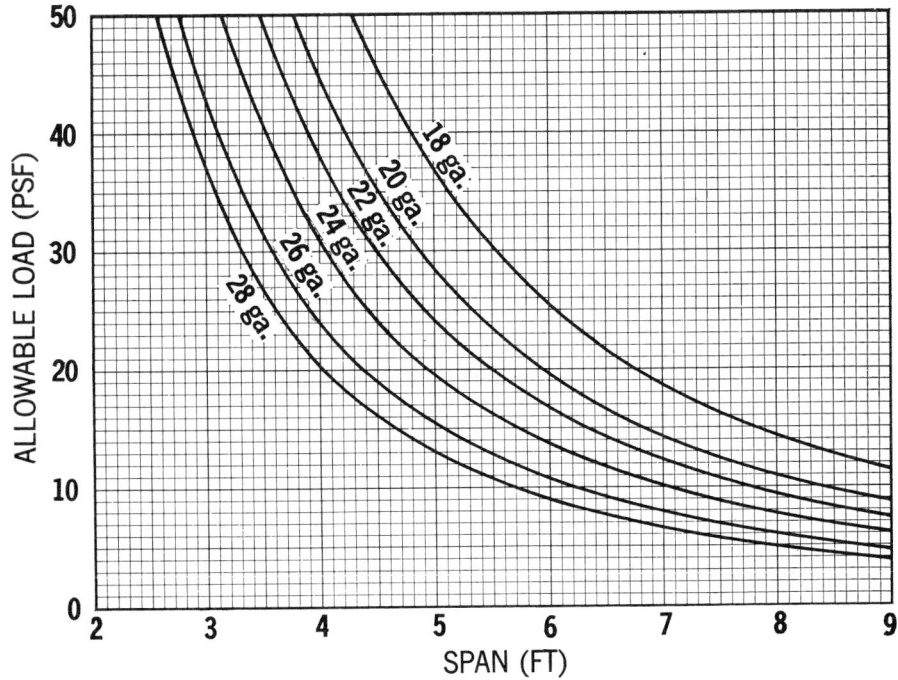

Simple Span Allowable Load Chart ASTM A446 Grade A, $F_y = 33$ ksi and $F_b = 20$ ksi

CORRUGATED STEEL CONSTRUCTION
Estimating data

ROOFING PATTERN

Side laps: 1½ corrugations; fasteners spaced 12 in. max.
End laps (min.): 6 in. end lap: min. roof pitch 3 in 12; laps at purlins; fasteners approximately every third corrugation at each purlin.

SIDING PATTERN

Side laps: 1 corrugation; fasteners spaced 18 in. max.
End laps (min.): 4 in. laps at girts; fasteners approximately every third corrugation at each girt.

AREAS AND WEIGHTS OF SHEETS IN PLACE

Square feet per square:

The number of square feet of corrugated sheets required to cover one square (100 square feet) for any length and lap condition is given by the formula:

$$N = \frac{100 \ WL}{WL - (SL + EC)}$$

where

N = number of square feet of corrugated sheet
W = width of the corrugated sheet (inches)
L = length of the corrugated sheet (inches)
S = width of side lap (inches)
E = length of end lap (inches)
C = covering, width of sheet (inches)

Sheets per square:

The formula adapted to give the number of sheets of any length and lap condition required to cover one square (100 square feet), is as follows:

$$\text{Number of sheets} = \frac{14400}{WL - (SL + EC)}$$

Weight per square:

The weight of corrugated sheets in pounds per square (100 square feet) in place, including side and end laps, is equal to the weight, with no allowance for side and end laps, multiplied by:

$$\frac{100 \ WL}{WL - (SL + EC)}$$

CORRUGATED STEEL CONSTRUCTION

Appurtenant materials

In addition to flat flashing for general closing and sealing purposes, corrugated flashings for end and side walls as well as corrugated and plain ridge rolls are available. Architectural and structural details such as eave, gable and expansion joint closures are also available.

SEALERS AND INSULATION

Where exceptional resistance to weather or sound is required, mastic sealers and insulating materials such as fiberglass can be applied between corrugated sheets. Formed rubber seals may be used as end closures between corrugated sheets and flat flashing.

TRANSLUCENT PANELS

For lighting, in addition to the usual windows and skylights, structural grade translucent corrugated panels are available in various colors and surfaces.

Note: See manufacturers' catalogs for descriptive and engineering data for these and other materials related to corrugated sheet metal construction.

Fasteners

SELF TAPPING SHEET METAL SCREWS (POINTED)

No. 14 hex head of hardened or stainless steel, cadmium plated. Assembly usually used to join sheet metal to sheet metal and includes cupped, galvanized or stainless steel washers with bonded neoprene washers.

SELF TAPPING CAP SCREWS

No. 14 hex head of hardened or stainless steel, cadmium plated. Assembly usually used to connect sheet metal to structural members, and includes cupped, galvanized or stainless steel washers with bonded neoprene washers.

BOLTS

⅜ in. diameter, round head stove bolts, galvanized or cadmium plated, for miscellaneous applications.

CLOSING RIVETS

3⁄16 in. diameter, galvanized or black driven cold. Used to connect side or end laps.

OTHER FASTENING DEVICES

These include arc welding studs, drive screws and nails, special fasteners for attaching insulation and screws with neoprene sleeves for translucent panels.

Note: For available sizes, method of installation of the above and other fasteners not described, see manufacturers' catalogs.

Notes

EFFECT OF HEAT ON STRUCTURAL STEEL

Short-time elevated temperature tensile tests on the steels permitted by the AISC Specification indicate that steels having similar metallurgical characteristics have similar ratios of elevated — and room — temperature yield and tensile strengths. Steels, such as the carbon steels in plates and shapes, exhibit pronounced strain aging in the temperature range 300° F and 700° F, such that at about 500° F the tensile strength is approximately 10 percent higher than at room temperature. Other steels such as the high-strength low-alloy and heat-treated constructional alloy steels exhibit less pronounced strain aging. At temperatures above 700° F, the yield and tensile strengths of all the steels decrease with increasing temperature. At 1000° F, the yield strength of the carbon steels are approximately 70 percent, while the high-strength low-alloy and heat-treated constructional alloy steels are approximately 60 percent, of their respective room temperature values.

FIRE-RESISTANT CONSTRUCTION

ASTM Specification E119, *Standard Methods of Fire Tests of Building Construction and Materials*, outlines the procedures of fire testing. (It requires, as one criterion of rating, that the average temperature of structural steel must not rise above 1000° F for columns and beams tested without load and 1200° F for beams tested with load. Maximum temperature at any one point shall not exceed 1200° F and 1400° F, respectively.)

Steel buildings whose condition of exterior exposure and whose combustible contents under fire hazards will not produce a steel temperature greater than the foregoing criteria may therefore be considered fire-resistive without the provision of insulating protection for the steel.

A fire exposure of severity and duration sufficient to raise the temperature of the steel much above the fire test criteria temperature will seriously impair its ability to sustain loads at the unit stresses or plasticity load factors permitted by the AISC Specification. In such cases, the members upon which the stability of the structure depends should be insulated by fire-resistive materials or constructions capable of holding the average temperature of the steel to not more than that specified for the fire test standard.

Under the E119 specification, each tested assembly is subjected to a standard fire of controlled extent and severity. The fire resistance rating is expressed as the time, in hours, that the assembly is able to withstand the fire exposure before the first critical point in its behavior is reached. These tests indicate the period of time during which structural members, such as columns and beams, are capable of maintaining their strength and rigidity when subjected to the standard fire. They also establish the period of time during which floors, roofs, walls, or partitions will prevent fire spread by protecting against the passage of flame, hot gases, and excessive heat.

Tables of fire resistance ratings for various insulating materials and constructions applied to structural columns, beams, girders and trusses, as well as floor and roof systems, are published in the AISC booklet *Fire-Resistant Construction in Modern Steel-Framed Buildings* and the AISI booklet *Fire Protection Through Modern Building Codes*. Ratings may also be found in publications of the Underwriters' Laboratories, Inc., the National Bureau of Standards, U. S. Department of Commerce, and in many building codes.

To judge the effect of a fire on structural steel, it is necessary to consider what happens in such an exposure. Peculiarities of this exposure are: (1) temperature attained by the steel can only be estimated, (2) time of exposure at any given temperature is unknown, (3) heating is uneven, (4) cooling rates vary and can only be estimated, and (5) the steel is usually under load, and is sometimes restrained from normal expansion.

Carbon and high-strength low-alloy steels that show no evidence of gross damage from exposure to high temperatures, or from sudden cooling from high temperatures, can usually be straightened as necessary and be reused without reduction of working stress. Quenched and tempered alloy steel exposed to temperatures over 1200° F should again be heat treated prior to reuse.

Steel that has been exposed to very high temperatures can be identified by very heavy scale, pitting, and surface erosion, which may result in a loss of cross section and sometimes internal damage. Normally these conditions will be accompanied by such severe deformation that the cost and difficulty of straightening such members, as compared to replacement, dictates that they be discarded.

Steel members that have suffered rapid cooling will usually be so severely distorted that straightening for reuse will seldom be considered practicable.

In some cases, there may be some deformation in members whose normal thermal expansion is inhibited or prevented by the nature of the construction. Such members may usually be straightened and reused.

Connections require special attention to make sure that the stresses induced by a fire, and by subsequent cooling after the fire, have not sheared or loosened bolts or rivets, or cracked welds.

COEFFICIENT OF EXPANSION

The average coefficient of expansion for structural steel between room temperature and 100° F is 0.0000065 for each degree. For temperatures of 100° F to 1200° F the coefficient is given by the approximate formula:

$$\epsilon = (6.1 + 0.0019t) \times 10^{-6}$$

in which ϵ is the coefficient of expansion for each degree Fahrenheit and t is the temperature in degrees Fahrenheit.

The modulus of elasticity of structural steel is approximately 29,000 ksi at room temperature. It decreases linearly to about 25,000 ksi at 900° F, and then begins to drop at an increasing rate at higher temperatures.

EFFECT OF HEAT DUE TO WELDING

Application of heat by welding produces residual stresses, which are generally accompanied by distortion of various amounts. Both the stresses and distortions are minimized by controlled welding procedures and fabrication methods. In normal structural practice, it has not been found necessary or desirable to use heat treatment (stress-relieving) as a means of reducing residual stresses. Procedures normally followed include: (1) proper positioning of the components of joints before welding, (2) selection of welding sequences determined by experience, (3) deposition of a minimum volume of weld metal with a minimum number of passes for the design condition, and (4) preheating as determined by experience (usually above the specified minimums).

AMERICAN INSTITUTE OF STEEL CONSTRUCTION

USE OF HEAT TO STRAIGHTEN, CAMBER, OR CURVE MEMBERS

With modern fabrication techniques, a controlled application of heat can be effectively used to either straighten or to intentionally curve structural members. By this process, the member is rapidly heated in selected areas; the heated areas tend to expand but are restrained by adjacent cooler areas. This action causes a permanent plastic deformation or "upset" of the heated areas and, thus, a change of shape is developed in the cooled member.

"Heat straightening" is used in both normal shop fabrication operations and in the field to remove relatively severe accidental bends in members. Conversely, "heat cambering" and "heat curving" of either rolled beams or welded girders are examples of the use of heat to affect a desired curvature.

As with many other fabrication operations, the use of heat to straighten or curve will cause residual stresses in the member as a result of plastic deformations. These stresses are similar to those that develop in rolled structural shapes as they cool from the rolling temperature; in this case, the stresses arise because all parts of the shape do not cool at the same rate. In like manner, welded girders develop residual stresses from the localized heat of welding.

In general, the residual stresses from heating operations do not affect the ultimate strength of practical members. Any reduction in column strength due to residual stresses is incorporated in the present design provisions.

The mechanical properties of steels are largely unaffected by heating operations, provided that the maximum temperature does not exceed 1100° F for quenched and tempered alloy steels, and 1200° F for other steels. The temperature should be carefully checked by temperature-indicating crayons or other suitable means during the heating process.

COEFFICIENTS OF EXPANSION

The coefficient of linear expansion (ϵ) is the change in length, per unit of length, for a change of one degree of temperature. The coefficient of surface expansion is approximately two times the linear coefficient, and the coefficient of volume expansion, for solids, is approximately three times the linear coefficient.

A bar, free to move, will increase in length with an increase in temperature and will decrease in length with a decrease in temperature. The change in length will be ϵtl, where ϵ is the coefficient of linear expansion, t the change in temperature, and the length. If the ends of a bar are fixed, a change in temperature (t) will cause a change in the unit stress of $E\epsilon t$, and in the total stress of $AE\epsilon t$, where A is the cross sectional area of the bar and E the modulus of elasticity.

The following table gives the coefficient of linear expansion for 100°, or 100 times the value indicated above.

Example: A piece of medium steel is exactly 40 feet long at 60° F. Find the length at 90° F. assuming the ends free to move.

$$\text{Change of length} = \epsilon tl = \frac{.00065 \times 30 \times 40}{100} = .0078 \text{ ft.}$$

The length at 90° F. is 40.0078 feet.

Example: A piece of medium steel is exactly 40 feet long and the ends are fixed. If the temperature increases 30° F., what is the resulting change in the unit stress?

$$\text{Change in unit stress} = E\epsilon t = \frac{29,000,000 \times .00065 \times 30}{100} = 5655 \text{ lbs. per sq. in.}$$

COEFFICIENTS OF EXPANSION FOR 100 DEGREES = 100ϵ

Materials	Centi-grade	Fahren-heit	Materials	Centi-grade	Fahren-heit
METALS AND ALLOYS			**STONE AND MASONRY**		
Aluminum, wrought	.00231	.00128	Ashlar masonry	.00063	.00035
Brass	.00188	.00104	Brick masonry	.00061	.00034
Bronze	.00181	.00101	Cement, portland	.00126	.00070
Copper	.00168	.00093	Concrete	.00099	.00055
Iron, cast, gray	.00106	.00059	Granite	.00080	.00044
Iron, wrought	.00120	.00067	Limestone	.00076	.00042
Iron, wire	.00124	.00069	Marble	.00081	.00045
Lead	.00286	.00159	Plaster	.00166	.00092
Magnesium, various alloys	.0029	.0016	Rubble masonry	.00063	.00035
Nickel	.00126	.00070	Sandstone	.00097	.00054
Steel, mild	.00117	.00065	Slate	.00080	.00044
Steel, stainless, 18-8	.00178	.00099			
Zinc, rolled	.00311	.00173			
TIMBER			**TIMBER**		
Fir ⎫	.00037	.00021	Fir ⎫	.0058	.0032
Maple ⎬ parallel to fiber	.00064	.00036	Maple ⎬ perpendicular to	.0048	.0027
Oak ⎪	.00049	.00027	Oak ⎪ fiber	.0054	.0030
Pine ⎭	.00054	.00030	Pine ⎭	.0034	.0019

EXPANSION OF WATER
Maximum Density = 1

C°	Volume	C°	Volume	C°	Volume	C°	Volume	C°	Volume	C°	Volume
0	1.000126	10	1.000257	30	1.004234	50	1.011877	70	1.022384	90	1.035829
4	1.000000	20	1.001732	40	1.007627	60	1.016954	80	1.029003	100	1.043116

WEIGHTS AND SPECIFIC GRAVITIES

Substance	Weight Lb. per Cu. Ft.	Specific Gravity	Substance	Weight Lb. per Cu. Ft.	Specific Gravity
METALS, ALLOYS, ORES			**TIMBER, U. S. SEASONED**		
Aluminum, cast, hammered	165	2.55-2.75	Moisture Content by Weight:		
Brass, cast, rolled	534	8.4-8.7	Seasoned timber 15 to 20%		
Bronze, 7.9 to 14% Sn	509	7.4-8.9	Green timber up to 50%		
Bronze, aluminum	481	7.7	Ash, white, red	40	0.62-0.65
Copper, cast, rolled	556	8.8-9.0	Cedar, white, red	22	0.32-0.38
Copper ore, pyrites	262	4.1-4.3	Chestnut	41	0.66
Gold, cast, hammered	1205	19.25-19.3	Cypress	30	0.48
Iron, cast, pig	450	7.2	Fir, Douglas spruce	32	0.51
Iron, wrought	485	7.6-7.9	Fir, eastern	25	0.40
Iron, spiegel-eisen	468	7.5	Elm, white	45	0.72
Iron, ferro-silicon	437	6.7-7.3	Hemlock	29	0.42-0.52
Iron ore, hematite	325	5.2	Hickory	49	0.74-0.84
Iron ore, hematite in bank	160-180	------	Locust	46	0.73
Iron ore, hematite loose	130-160	------	Maple, hard	43	0.68
Iron ore, limonite	237	3.6-4.0	Maple, white	33	0.53
Iron ore, magnetite	315	4.9-5.2	Oak, chestnut	54	0.86
Iron slag	172	2.5-3.0	Oak, live	59	0.95
Lead	710	11.37	Oak, red, black	41	0.65
Lead ore, galena	465	7.3-7.6	Oak, white	46	0.74
Magnesium, alloys	112	1.74-1.83	Pine, Oregon	32	0.51
Manganese	475	7.2-8.0	Pine, red	30	0.48
Manganese ore, pyrolusite	259	3.7-4.6	Pine, white	26	0.41
Mercury	849	13.6	Pine, yellow, long-leaf	44	0.70
Monel Metal	556	8.8-9.0	Pine, yellow, short-leaf	38	0.61
Nickel	565	8.9-9.2	Poplar	30	0.48
Platinum, cast, hammered	1330	21.1-21.5	Redwood, California	26	0.42
Silver, cast, hammered	656	10.4-10.6	Spruce, white, black	27	0.40-0.46
Steel, rolled	490	7.85	Walnut, black	38	0.61
Tin, cast, hammered	459	7.2-7.5	Walnut, white	26	0.41
Tin ore, cassiterite	418	6.4-7.0			
Zinc, cast, rolled	440	6.9-7.2			
Zinc ore, blende	253	3.9-4.2	**VARIOUS LIQUIDS**		
			Alcohol, 100%	49	0.79
			Acids, muriatic 40%	75	1.20
			Acids, nitric 91%	94	1.50
VARIOUS SOLIDS			Acids, sulphuric 87%	112	1.80
			Lye, soda 66%	106	1.70
Cereals, oats...........bulk	32	------	Oils, vegetable	58	0.91-0.94
Cereals, barley..........bulk	39	------	Oils, mineral, lubricants	57	0.90-0.93
Cereals, corn, rye........bulk	48	------	Water, 4°C. max. density	62.428	1.0
Cereals, wheat..........bulk	48	------	Water, 100°C.	59.830	0.9584
Hay and Straw.........bales	20	------	Water, ice	56	0.88-0.9
Cotton, Flax, Hemp	93	1.47-1.50	Water, snow, fresh fallen	8	.125
Fats	58	0.90-0.97	Water, sea water	64	1.02-1.03
Flour, loose	28	0.40-0.50			
Flour, pressed	47	0.70-0.80			
Glass, common	156	2.40-2.60	**GASES**		
Glass, plate or crown	161	2.45-2.72			
Glass, crystal	184	2.90-3.00	Air, 0°C. 760 mm.	.08071	1.0
Leather	59	0.86-1.02	Ammonia	.0478	0.5920
Paper	58	0.70-1.15	Carbon dioxide	.1234	1.5291
Potatoes, piled	42	------	Carbon monoxide	.0781	0.9673
Rubber, caoutchouc	59	0.92-0.96	Gas, illuminating	.028-.036	0.35-0.4
Rubber goods	94	1.0-2.0	Gas, natural	.038-.039	0.47-0.4
Salt, granulated, piled	48	------	Hydrogen	.00559	0.0693
Saltpeter	67	------	Nitrogen	.0784	0.9714
Starch	96	1.53	Oxygen	.0892	1.1056
Sulphur	125	1.93-2.07			
Wool	82	1.32			

The specific gravities of solids and liquids refer to water at 4°C., those of gases to air at 0°C. and 760 mm. pressure. The weights per cubic foot are derived from average specific gravities, except where stated that weights are for bulk, heaped or loose material, etc.

WEIGHTS AND SPECIFIC GRAVITIES

Substance	Weight Lb. per Cu. Ft.	Specific Gravity	Substance	Weight Lb. per Cu. Ft.	Specific Gravity
ASHLAR MASONRY			**MINERALS**		
Granite, syenite, gneiss	165	2.3-3.0	Asbestos	153	2.1-2.8
Limestone, marble	160	2.3-2.8	Barytes	281	4.50
Sandstone, bluestone	140	2.1-2.4	Basalt	184	2.7-3.2
			Bauxite	159	2.55
MORTAR RUBBLE			Borax	109	1.7-1.8
MASONRY			Chalk	137	1.8-2.6
Granite, syenite, gneiss	155	2.2-2.8	Clay, marl	137	1.8-2.6
Limestone, marble	150	2.2-2.6	Dolomite	181	2.9
Sandstone, bluestone	130	2.0-2.2	Feldspar, orthoclase	159	2.5-2.6
			Gneiss, serpentine	159	2.4-2.7
DRY RUBBLE MASONRY			Granite, syenite	175	2.5-3.1
Granite, syenite, gneiss	130	1.9-2.3	Greenstone, trap	187	2.8-3.2
Limestone, marble	125	1.9-2.1	Gypsum, alabaster	159	2.3-2.8
Sandstone, bluestone	110	1.8-1.9	Hornblende	187	3.0
			Limestone, marble	165	2.5-2.8
BRICK MASONRY			Magnesite	187	3.0
Pressed brick	140	2.2-2.3	Phosphate rock, apatite	200	3.2
Common brick	120	1.8-2.0	Porphyry	172	2.6-2.9
Soft brick	100	1.5-1.7	Pumice, natural	40	0.37-0.90
			Quartz, flint	165	2.5-2.8
CONCRETE MASONRY			Sandstone, bluestone	147	2.2-2.5
Cement, stone, sand	144	2.2-2.4	Shale, slate	175	2.7-2.9
Cement, slag, etc	130	1.9-2.3	Soapstone, talc	169	2.6-2.8
Cement, cinder, etc	100	1.5-1.7			
VARIOUS BUILDING			**STONE, QUARRIED, PILED**		
MATERIALS			Basalt, granite, gneiss	96	....
Ashes, cinders	40-45	....	Limestone, marble, quartz	95	....
Cement, portland, loose	90	....	Sandstone	82	....
Cement, portland, set	183	2.7-3.2	Shale	92	....
Lime, gypsum, loose	53-64	....	Greenstone, hornblende	107	....
Mortar, set	103	1.4-1.9			
Slags, bank slag	67-72	....			
Slags, bank screenings	98-117	....	**BITUMINOUS SUBSTANCES**		
Slags, machine slag	96	....	Asphaltum	81	1.1-1.5
Slags, slag sand	49-55	....	Coal, anthracite	97	1.4-1.7
			Coal, bituminous	84	1.2-1.5
EARTH, ETC., EXCAVATED			Coal, lignite	78	1.1-1.4
Clay, dry	63	....	Coal, peat, turf, dry	47	0.65-0.85
Clay, damp, plastic	110	....	Coal, charcoal, pine	23	0.28-0.44
Clay and gravel, dry	100	....	Coal, charcoal, oak	33	0.47-0.57
Earth, dry, loose	76	....	Coal, coke	75	1.0-1.4
Earth, dry, packed	95	....	Graphite	131	1.9-2.3
Earth, moist, loose	78	....	Paraffine	56	0.87-0.91
Earth, moist, packed	96	....	Petroleum	54	0.87
Earth, mud, flowing	108	....	Petroleum, refined	50	0.79-0.82
Earth, mud, packed	115	....	Petroleum, benzine	46	0.73-0.75
Riprap, limestone	80-85	....	Petroleum, gasoline	42	0.66-0.69
Riprap, sandstone	90	....	Pitch	69	1.07-1.15
Riprap, shale	105	....	Tar, bituminous	75	1.20
Sand, gravel, dry, loose	90-105	....			
Sand, gravel, dry, packed	100-120	....			
Sand, gravel, wet	118-120	....			
			COAL AND COKE, PILED		
EXCAVATIONS IN WATER			Coal, anthracite	47-58	....
Sand or gravel	60	....	Coal, bituminous, lignite	40-54	....
Sand or gravel and clay	65	....	Coal, peat, turf	20-26	....
Clay	80	....	Coal, charcoal	10-14	....
River mud	90	....	Coal, coke	23-32	....
Soil	70	....			
Stone riprap	65	....			

The specific gravities of solids and liquids refer to water at 4°C., those of gases to air at 0°C. and 760 mm. pressure. The weights per cubic foot are derived from average specific gravities, except where stated that weights are for bulk, heaped or loose material, etc.

WEIGHTS OF BUILDING MATERIALS

Materials	Weight Lb. per Sq. Ft.	Materials	Weight Lb. per Sq. Ft.
CEILINGS		**PARTITIONS**	
Channel suspended		Clay Tile	
system	1	3 in.	17
Lathing and plastering	See Partitions	4 in.	18
Acoustical fiber tile	1	6 in.	28
		8 in.	34
		10 in.	40
FLOORS		Gypsum Block	
Steel Deck	See	2 in.	9½
	Manufacturer	3 in.	10½
Concrete-Reinforced 1 in.		4 in.	12½
Stone	12½	5 in.	14
Slag	11½	6 in.	18½
Lightweight	6 to 10	Wood Studs 2 × 4	
		12–16 in. o.c.	2
Concrete-Plain 1 in.		Steel partitions	4
Stone	12	Plaster 1 inch	
Slag	11	Cement	10
Lightweight	3 to 9	Gypsum	5
		Lathing	
Fills 1 inch		Metal	½
Gypsum	6	Gypsum Board ½ in.	2
Sand	8		
Cinders	4		
		WALLS	
Finishes		Brick	
Terrazzo 1 in.	13	4 in.	40
Ceramic or Quarry Tile ¾		8 in.	80
in.	10	12 in.	120
Linoleum ¼ in.	1	Hollow Concrete Block	
Mastic ¾ in.	9	(Heavy Aggregate)	
Hardwood ⅞ in.	4	4 in.	30
Softwood ¾ in.	2½	6 in.	43
		8 in.	55
		12½ in.	80
ROOFS		Hollow Concrete Block	
Copper or tin	1	(Light Aggregate)	
Corrugated steel	See page 6 - 5	4 in.	21
3-ply ready roofing	1	6 in.	30
3-ply felt and gravel	5½	8 in.	38
5-ply felt and gravel	6	12 in.	55
		Clay tile	
Shingles		(Load Bearing)	
Wood	2	4 in.	25
Asphalt	3	6 in.	30
Clay tile	9 to 14	8 in.	33
Slate ¼	10	12 in.	45
		Stone 4 in.	55
Sheathing		Glass Block 4 in.	18
Wood ¾ in.	3	Windows, Glass, Frame	8
Gypsum 1 in.	4	& Sash	
		Curtain Walls	See
Insulation 1 in.			Manufactur
Loose	½	Structural Glass 1 in.	15
Poured in place	2	Corrugated Cement As-	
Rigid	1½	bestos ¼ in.	3

For weights of other materials used in building construction, see pages 6 - 14 and 6 - 15.

AMERICAN INSTITUTE OF STEEL CONSTRUCTION

WEIGHTS AND MEASURES

United States System

LINEAR MEASURE

Inches	Feet	Yards	Rods	Furlongs	Miles
1.0 =	.08333 =	.02778 =	.0050505 =	.00012626 =	.00001578
12.0 =	1.0 =	.33333 =	.0606061 =	.00151515 =	.00018939
36.0 =	3.0 =	1.0 =	.1818182 =	.00454545 =	.00056818
198.0 =	16.5 =	5.5 =	1.0 =	.025 =	.003125
7920.0 =	660.0 =	220.0 =	40.0 =	1.0 =	.125
63360.0 =	5280.0 =	1760.0 =	320.0 =	8.0 =	1.0

SQUARE AND LAND MEASURE

Sq. Inches	Square Feet	Square Yards	Sq. Rods	Acres	Sq. Miles
1.0 =	.006944 =	.000772			
144.0 =	1.0 =	.111111			
1296.0 =	9.0 =	1.0 =	.03306 =	.000207	
39204.0 =	272.25 =	30.25 =	1.0 =	.00625 =	.0000098
	43560.0 =	4840.0 =	160.0 =	1.0 =	.0015625
		3097600.0 =	102400.0 =	640.0 =	1.0

AVOIRDUPOIS WEIGHTS

Grains	Drams	Ounces	Pounds	Tons
1.0 =	.03657 =	.002286 =	.000143 =	.0000000714
27.34375 =	1.0 =	.0625 =	.003906 =	.00000195
437.5 =	16.0 =	1.0 =	.0625 =	.00003125
7000.0 =	256.0 =	16.0 =	1.0 =	.0005
14000000.0 =	512000.0 =	32000.0 =	2000.0 =	1.0

DRY MEASURE

Pints	Quarts	Pecks	Cubic Feet	Bushels
1.0 =	.5 =	.0625 =	.01945 =	.01563
2.0 =	1.0 =	.125 =	.03891 =	.03125
16.0 =	8.0 =	1.0 =	.31112 =	.25
51.42627 =	25.71314 =	3.21414 =	1.0 =	.80354
64.0 =	32.0 =	4.0 =	1.2445 =	1.0

LIQUID MEASURE

Gills	Pints	Quarts	U. S. Gallons	Cubic Feet
1.0 =	.25 =	.125 =	.03125 =	.00418
4.0 =	1.0 =	.5 =	.125 =	.01671
8.0 =	2.0 =	1.0 =	.250 =	.03342
32.0 =	8.0 =	4.0 =	1.0 =	.1337
			7.48052 =	1.0

Metric System

UNITS

Length—Meter : Mass—Gram : Capacity—Liter

for pure water at 4°C. (39.2°F.)

1 cubic decimeter or 1 liter = 1 kilogram

$$1000 \; \text{Milli} \begin{cases} meters \;(mm) \\ grams \;(mg) \\ liters \;(ml) \end{cases} = 100 \; \text{Centi} \begin{cases} meters \;(cm) \\ grams \;(cg) \\ liters \;(cl) \end{cases} = 10 \; \text{Deci} \begin{cases} meters \;(dm) \\ grams \;(dg) \\ liters \;(dl) \end{cases} = 1 \begin{cases} meter \\ gram \\ liter \end{cases}$$

$$1000 \begin{cases} meters \\ grams \\ liters \end{cases} = 100 \; \text{Deka} \begin{cases} meters \;(dkm) \\ grams \;(dkg) \\ liters \;(dkl) \end{cases} = 10 \; \text{Hecto} \begin{cases} meters \;(hm) \\ grams \;(hg) \\ liters \;(hl) \end{cases} = 1 \; \text{Kilo} \begin{cases} meter \;(km) \\ gram \;(kg) \\ liter \;(kl) \end{cases}$$

1 Metric Ton	= 1000 Kilograms
100 Square Meters	= 1 Are
100 Ares	= 1 Hectare
100 Hectares	= 1 Square Kilometer

ENGINEERING CONVERSION FACTORS

(For conversion factors meeting the standards of the SI metric system, refer to ASTM E380-72.)

Multiply	by	to obtain
acres	.404687	hectares
"	4.04687×10^{-3}	square kilometers
ares	1076.39	square feet
board feet	144 sq. in. $\times$ 1 in.	cubic inches
" "	.0833	cubic feet
centimeters	3.28083×10^{-2}	feet
"	.3937	inches
cubic centimeters	3.53145×10^{-5}	cubic feet
" "	6.102×10^{-2}	cubic inches
cubic feet	2.8317×10^{4}	cubic centimeters
" "	2.8317×10^{-2}	cubic meters
" "	6.22905	gallons, British Imperial
" "	28.3170	liters
" "	2.38095×10^{-2}	tons, British Shipping
" "	.025	tons, U. S. Shipping
cubic inches	16.38716	cubic centimeters
cubic meters	35.3145	cubic feet
" "	1.30794	cubic yards
cubic yards	.764559	cubic meters
degrees, angular	.0174533	radians
degrees, Fahrenheit (less 32 F.)	.5556	degrees, Centigrade
" Centigrade	1.8	degrees, Fahrenheit (less 32 F.)
foot pounds	.13826	kilogram meters
feet	30.4801	centimeters
"	.304801	meters
"	304.801	millimeters
"	1.64468×10^{-4}	miles, nautical
gallons, British Imperial	.160538	cubic feet
" " "	1.20091	gallons, U. S.
" " "	4.54596	liters
gallons, U. S.	.832702	gallons, British Imperial
" "	.13368	cubic feet
" "	231.	cubic inches
" "	3.78543	liters
grams, metric	2.20462×10^{-3}	pounds, avoirdupois
hectares	2.47104	acres
"	1.076387×10^{5}	square feet
"	3.86101×10^{-3}	square miles
horse-power, metric	.98632	horse-power, U. S.
horse-power, U. S.	1.01387	horse-power, metric
inches	2.54001	centimeters
"	2.54001×10^{-2}	meters
"	25.4001	millimeters
kilograms	2.20462	pounds
"	9.84206×10^{-4}	long tons
"	1.10231×10^{-3}	short tons
kilogram meters	7.233	foot pounds
kilograms per meter	.671972	pounds per foot
kilograms per square centimeter	14.2234	pounds per square inch
kilograms per square meter	.204817	pounds per square foot
" " " "	9.14362×10^{-5}	long tons per square foot
kilograms per square millimeter	1422.34	pounds per square inch
" " " "	.634973	long tons per square inch
kilograms per cubic meter	6.24283×10^{-2}	pounds per cubic foot
kilometers	.62137	miles, statute
"	.53959	miles, nautical

AMERICAN INSTITUTE OF STEEL CONSTRUCTION

ENGINEERING CONVERSION FACTORS

(For conversion factors meeting the standards of the SI metric system, refer to ASTM E380-72.)

Multiply	by	to obtain
liters	.219975	gallons, British Imperial
"	.26417	gallons, U. S.
"	3.53145×10^{-2}	cubic feet
meters	3.28083	feet
"	39.37	inches
"	1.09361	yards
miles, statute	1.60935	kilometer
" "	.8684	miles, nautical
miles, nautical	6080.204	feet
" "	1.85325	kilometers
" "	1.1516	miles, statute
millimeters	3.28083×10^{-3}	feet
"	3.937×10^{-2}	inches
pounds, avoirdupois	453.592	grams, metric
" "	.453592	kilograms
" "	4.464×10^{-4}	tons, long
" "	4.53592×10^{-4}	tons. metric
pounds per foot	1.48816	kilograms per meter
pounds per square foot	4.88241	kilograms per square meter
pounds per square inch	7.031×10^{-2}	kilograms per square centimeter
" " "	7.031×10^{-4}	kilograms per square millimeter
pounds per cubic foot	16.0184	kilograms per cubic meter
radians	57.29578	degrees, angular
square centimeters	.1550	square inches
square feet	9.29034×10^{-4}	ares
" "	9.29034×10^{-6}	hectares
" "	.0929034	square meters
square inches	6.45163	square centimeters
" "	645.163	square millimeters
square kilometers	247.104	acres
" "	.3861	square miles
square meters	10.7639	square feet
" "	1.19599	square yards
square miles	259.0	hectares
" "	2.590	square kilometers
square millimeters	1.550×10^{-3}	square inches
square yards	.83613	square meters
tons, long	1016.05	kilograms
" "	2240.	pounds
" "	1.01605	tons, metric
" "	1.120	tons, short
tons, long, per square foot	1.09366×10^{4}	kilograms per square meter
tons, long, per square inch	1.57464	kilograms per square millimeter
tons, metric	2204.62	pounds
" "	.98421	tons, long
" "	1.10231	tons, short
tons, short	907.185	kilograms
" "	.892857	tons, long
" "	.907185	tons, metric
tons, British Shipping	42.00	cubic feet
" " "	1.050	tons, U. S. Shipping
tons, U. S. Shipping	40.00	cubic feet
" " "	.952381	tons, British Shipping
yards	.914402	meters

BRACING FORMULAS

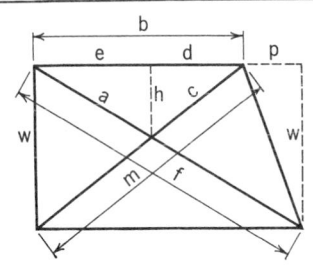 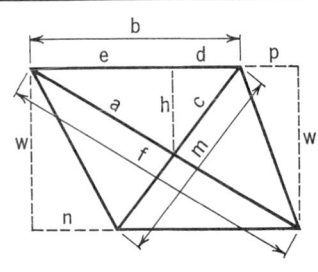

Given	To Find	Formula
bpw	f	$\sqrt{(b+p)^2 + w^2}$
bw	m	$\sqrt{b^2 + w^2}$
bp	d	$b^2 \div (2b + p)$
bp	e	$b(b+p) \div (2b+p)$
bfp	a	$bf \div (2b+p)$
bmp	c	$bm \div (2b+p)$
bpw	h	$bw \div (2b+p)$
afw	h	$aw \div f$
cmw	h	$cw \div m$

Given	To Find	Formula
bpw	f	$\sqrt{(b+p)^2 + w^2}$
bnw	m	$\sqrt{(b-n)^2 + w^2}$
bnp	d	$b(b-n) \div (2b+p-n)$
bnp	e	$b(b+p) \div (2b+p-n)$
bfnp	a	$bf \div (2b+p-n)$
bmnp	c	$bm \div (2b+p-n)$
bnpw	h	$bw \div (2b+p-n)$
afw	h	$aw \div f$
cmw	h	$cw \div m$

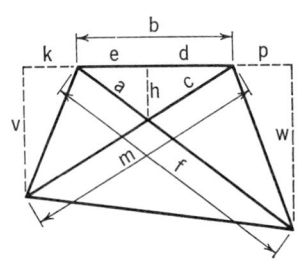

Given	To Find	Formula
bpw	f	$\sqrt{(b+p)^2 + w^2}$
bkv	m	$\sqrt{(b+k)^2 + v^2}$
bkpvw	d	$bw(b+k) \div [v(b+p) + w(b+k)]$
bkpvw	e	$bv(b+p) \div [v(b+p) + w(b+k)]$
bfkpvw	a	$fbv \div [v(b+p) + w(b+k)]$
bkmpvw	c	$bmw \div [v(b+p) + w(b+k)]$
bkpvw	h	$bvw \div [v(b+p) + w(b+k)]$
afw	h	$aw \div f$
cmv	h	$cv \div m$

PARALLEL BRACING

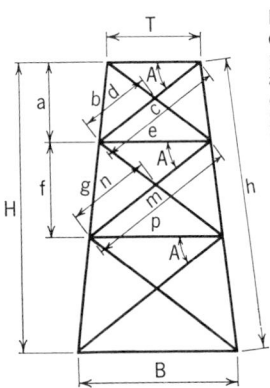

$k = (\log B - \log T) \div \text{no of panels.}$ Constant k plus the logarithm of any line equals the log of the corresponding line in the next panel below.

$a = TH \div (T + e + p)$

$b = Th \div (T + e + p)$

$c = \sqrt{(\tfrac{1}{2}T + \tfrac{1}{2}e)^2 + a}$

$d = ce \div (T + e)$

$\log e = k + \log T$

$\log f = k + \log$

$\log g = k + \log$

$\log m = k + \log$

$\log n = k + \log$

$\log p = k + \log$

The above method can be used for any number of panels.
In the formulas for "a" and "b" the sum in parenthesis, which in the case shown is (T + e + p), is always composed of all the horizontal distances except the base.

PROPERTIES OF PARABOLA AND ELLIPSE

PARABOLA	ELLIPSE

PARABOLA

When $H \div B = 0.1$ or less, approximate
$\frac{1}{2}$ perimeter $= \sqrt{B^2 + 4/3 H^2}$
or use formulas for circular arcs

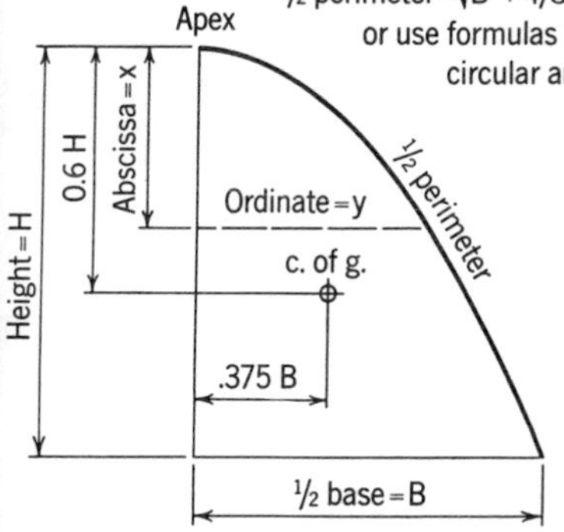

Apex

Abscissa $= x$

0.6 H

Ordinate $= y$

c. of g.

Height $= H$

.375 B

½ perimeter

½ base $= B$

Parameter $P = B^2 \div H$ Area $= \frac{2}{3} HB$
$x = y^2 \div P$
$y = \sqrt{xP}$

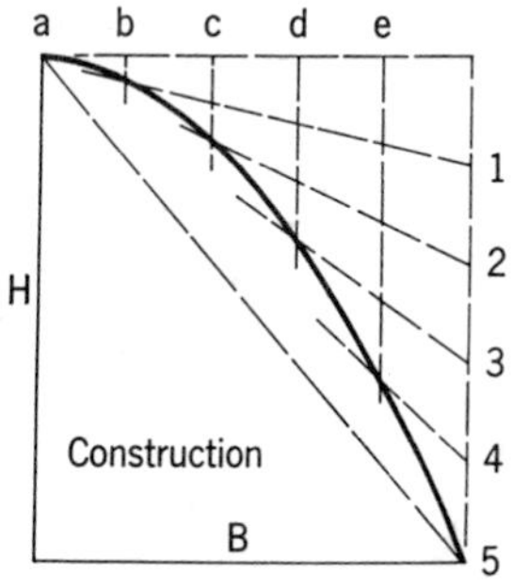

a b c d e

1
2
3
H
4
Construction
B
5

ELLIPSE

$(x^2 \div H^2) + (y^2 \div B^2) = 1$

$x = (H \div B)\sqrt{B^2 - y^2}$
$y = (B \div H)\sqrt{H^2 - x^2}$

Approximate ¼ perimeter $=$
$\frac{\pi}{4}\sqrt{2\,(H^2 + B^2)}$

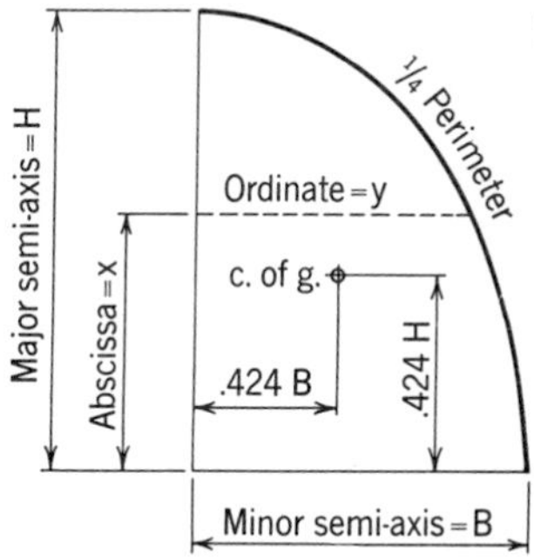

¼ perimeter

Major semi-axis $= H$

Ordinate $= y$

Abscissa $= x$

c. of g.

.424 B

.424 H

Minor semi-axis $= B$

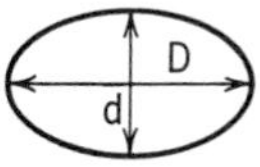

D
d

Area $= .7854\ Dd$

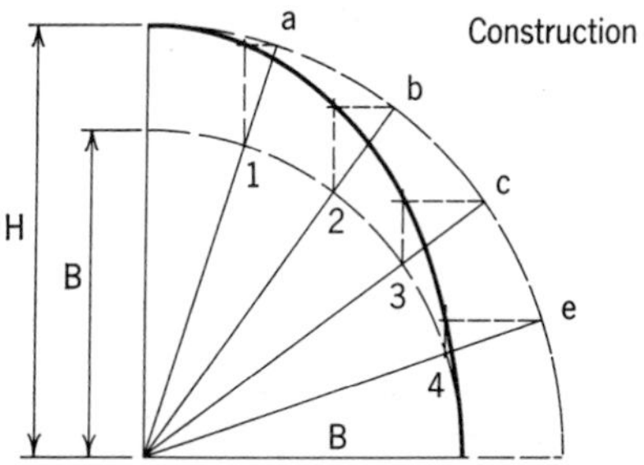

Construction

a
b
1
2
c
H
B
3
e
4
B

AREA BETWEEN PARABOLIC CURVE AND SECANT

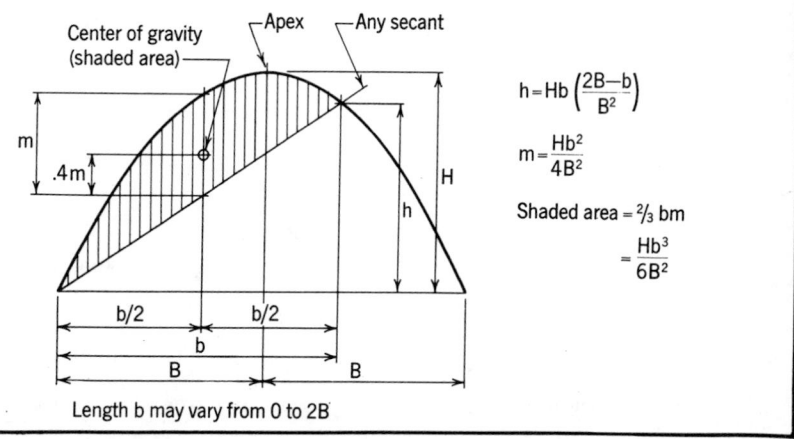

Center of gravity
(shaded area)

Apex   Any secant

m

.4m

H

h

b/2   b/2

b

B   B

Length b may vary from 0 to 2B

$h = Hb\left(\dfrac{2B - b}{B^2}\right)$

$m = \dfrac{Hb^2}{4B^2}$

Shaded area $= \frac{2}{3}\, bm$

$= \dfrac{Hb^3}{6B^2}$

PROPERTIES OF THE CIRCLE

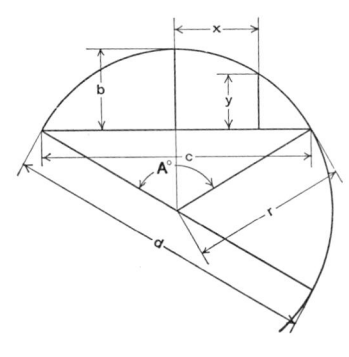

Circumference $= 6.28318\ r = 3.14159\ d$
Diameter $= 0.31831$ circumference
Area $= 3.14159\ r^2$

Arc $\quad a = \dfrac{\pi r\ A^\circ}{180^\circ} = 0.017453\ r\ A^\circ$

Angle $\quad A^\circ = \dfrac{180^\circ\ a}{\pi r} = 57.29578\ \dfrac{a}{r}$

Radius $r = \dfrac{4\ b^2 + c^2}{8\ b}$

Chord $\quad c = 2\sqrt{2\ br - b^2} = 2\ r \sin \dfrac{A}{2}$

Rise $\quad b = r - \frac{1}{2}\sqrt{4\ r^2 - c^2} = \dfrac{c}{2}\tan \dfrac{A}{4}$

$\qquad = 2\ r \sin^2 \dfrac{A}{4} = r + y - \sqrt{r^2 - x^2}$

$\quad y = b - r + \sqrt{r^2 - x^2}$

$\quad x = \sqrt{r^2 - (r + y - b)^2}$

Diameter of circle of equal periphery as square = 1.27324 side of square
Side of square of equal periphery as circle = 0.78540 diameter of circle
Diameter of circle circumscribed about square = 1.41421 side of square
Side of square inscribed in circle = 0.70711 diameter of circle

CIRCULAR SECTOR

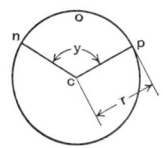

r = radius of circle $\quad y$ = angle ncp in degrees

Area of Sector ncpo = ½ (length of arc nop × r)

$\qquad = $ Area of Circle $\times \dfrac{y}{360}$

$\qquad = 0.0087266 \times r^2 \times y$

CIRCULAR SEGMENT

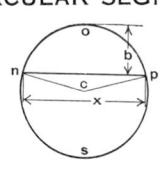

r = radius of circle $\quad x$ = chord $\quad b$ = rise

Area of Segment nop = Area of Sector ncpo — Area of triangle ncp

$\qquad = \dfrac{(\text{Length of arc nop} \times r) - x\ (r - b)}{2}$

Area of Segment nsp = Area of Circle — Area of Segment nop

VALUES FOR FUNCTIONS OF π

$\pi = 3.14159265359,\quad \log = 0.4971499$

$\pi^2 = 9.8696044,\ \log = 0.9942997 \quad \dfrac{1}{\pi} = 0.3183099,\ \log = \overline{1}.5028501 \quad \sqrt{\dfrac{1}{\pi}} = 0.5641896,\ \log = \overline{1}.7514251$

$\pi^3 = 31.0062767,\ \log = 1.4914496 \quad \dfrac{1}{\pi^2} = 0.1013212,\ \log = \overline{1}.0057003 \quad \dfrac{\pi}{180} = 0.0174533,\ \log = \overline{2}.2418774$

$\sqrt{\pi} = 1.7724539,\ \log = 0.2485749 \quad \dfrac{1}{\pi^3} = 0.0322515,\ \log = \overline{2}.5085504 \quad \dfrac{180}{\pi} = 57.2957795,\ \log = 1.7581226$

Note: Logs of fractions such as $\overline{1}.5028501$ and $\overline{2}.5085500$ may also be written 9.5028501 — 10 and 8.5085500 — 10 respectively.

LENGTH OF CIRCULAR ARCS FOR UNIT RADIUS

By the use of this table, the length of any arc may be found if the length of the radius and the angle of the segment are known.

Example: Required the length of arc of segment 32° 15′ 27″ with radius of 24 feet 3 inches.
From table: Length of arc (Radius 1) for 32° = .5585054
15′ = .0043633
27″ = .0001309
.5629996

.5629996 × 24.25 (length of radius) = 13.65 feet

DEGREES						MINUTES		SECONDS	
1	.017 4533	61	1.064 6508	121	2.111 8484	1	.000 2909	1	.000 0048
2	.034 9066	62	1.082 1041	122	2.129 3017	2	.000 5818	2	.000 0097
3	.052 3599	63	1.099 5574	123	2.146 7550	3	.000 8727	3	.000 0145
4	.069 8132	64	1.117 0107	124	2.164 2083	4	.001 1636	4	.000 0194
5	.087 2665	65	1.134 4640	125	2.181 6616	5	.001 4544	5	.000 0242
6	.104 7198	66	1.151 9173	126	2.199 1149	6	.001 7453	6	.000 0291
7	.122 1730	67	1.169 3706	127	2.216 5682	7	.002 0362	7	.000 0339
8	.139 6263	68	1.186 8239	128	2.234 0214	8	.002 3271	8	.000 0388
9	.157 0796	69	1.204 2772	129	2.251 4747	9	.002 6180	9	.000 0436
10	.174 5329	70	1 221 7305	130	2.268 9280	10	.002 9089	10	.000 0485
11	.191 9862	71	1.239 1838	131	2.286 3813	11	.003 1998	11	.000 0533
12	.209 4395	72	1.256 6371	132	2.303 8346	12	.003 4907	12	.000 0582
13	.226 8928	73	1.274 0904	133	2.321 2879	13	.003 7815	13	.000 0630
14	.244 3461	74	1.291 5436	134	2.338 7412	14	.004 0724	14	.000 0679
15	.261 7994	75	1.308 9969	135	2.356 1945	15	.004 3633	15	.000 0727
16	.279 2527	76	1.326 4502	136	2.373 6478	16	.004 6542	16	.000 0776
17	.296 7060	77	1.343 9035	137	2.391 1011	17	.004 9451	17	.000 0824
18	.314 1593	78	1.361 3568	138	2.408 5544	18	.005 2360	18	.000 0873
19	.331 6126	79	1.378 8101	139	2.426 0077	19	.005 5269	19	.000 0921
20	.349 0659	80	1.396 2634	140	2.443 4610	20	.005 8178	20	.000 0970
21	.366 5191	81	1.413 7167	141	2.460 9142	21	.006 1087	21	.000 1018
22	.383 9724	82	1.431 1700	142	2.478 3675	22	.006 3995	22	.000 1067
23	.401 4257	83	1.448 6233	143	2.495 8208	23	.006 6904	23	.000 1115
24	.418 8790	84	1.466 0766	144	2.513 2741	24	.006 9813	24	.000 1164
25	.436 3323	85	1.483 5299	145	2.530 7274	25	.007 2722	25	.000 1212
26	.453 7856	86	1.500 9832	146	2.548 1807	26	.007 5631	26	.000 1261
27	.471 2389	87	1.518 4364	147	2.565 6340	27	.007 8540	27	.000 1309
28	.488 6922	88	1.535 8897	148	2.583 0873	28	.008 1449	28	.000 1357
29	.506 1455	89	1.553 3430	149	2.600 5406	29	.008 4358	29	.000 1406
30	.523 5988	90	1.570 7963	150	2.617 9939	30	.008 7266	30	.000 1454
31	·541 0521	91	1.588 2496	151	2.635 4472	31	.009 0175	31	.000 1503
32	.558 5054	92	1.605 7029	152	2.652 9005	32	.009 3084	32	.000 1551
33	.575 9587	93	1.623 1562	153	2.670 3538	33	.009 5993	33	.000 1600
34	.593 4119	94	1.640 6095	154	2.687 8070	34	.009 8902	34	.000 1648
35	.610 8652	95	1.658 0628	155	2.705 2603	35	.010 1811	35	.000 1697
36	.628 3185	96	1.675 5161	156	2.722 7136	36	.010 4720	36	.000 1745
37	.645 7718	97	1.692 9694	157	2.740 1669	37	.010 7629	37	.000 1794
38	.663 2251	98	1.710 4227	158	2.757 6202	38	.011 0538	38	.000 1842
39	.680 6784	99	1.727 8760	159	2.775 0735	39	.011 3446	39	.000 1891
40	.698 1317	100	1.745 3293	160	2.792 5268	40	.011 6355	40	.000 1939
41	.715 5850	101	1.762 7825	161	2.809 9801	41	.011 9264	41	.000 1988
42	.733 0383	102	1.780 2358	162	2.827 4334	42	.012 2173	42	.000 2036
43	.750 4916	103	1.797 6891	163	2.844 8867	43	.012 5082	43	.000 2085
44	.767 9449	104	1.815 1424	164	2.862 3400	44	.012 7991	44	.000 2133
45	.785 3982	105	1.832 5957	165	2.879 7933	45	.013 0900	45	.000 2182
46	.802 8515	106	1.850 0490	166	2.897 2466	46	.013 3809	46	.000 2230
47	.820 3047	107	1.867 5023	167	2.914 6999	47	.013 6717	47	.000 2279
48	.837 7580	108	1.884 9556	168	2.932 1531	48	.013 9626	48	.000 2327
49	.855 2113	109	1.902 4089	169	2.949 6064	49	.014 2535	49	.000 2376
50	.872 6646	110	1.919 8622	170	2.967 0597	50	.014 5444	50	.000 2424
51	.890 1179	111	1.937 3155	171	2.984 5130	51	.014 8353	51	.000 2473
52	.907 5712	112	1.954 7688	172	3.001 9663	52	.015 1262	52	.000 2521
53	.925 0245	113	1.972 2221	173	3.019 4196	53	.015 4171	53	.000 2570
54	.942 4778	114	1.989 6753	174	3.036 8729	54	.015 7080	54	.000 2618
55	.959 9311	115	2.007 1286	175	3.054 3262	55	.015 9989	55	.000 2666
56	.977 3844	116	2.024 5819	176	3.071 7795	56	.016 2897	56	.000 2715
57	.994 8377	117	2.042 0352	177	3.089 2328	57	.016 5806	57	.000 2763
58	1.012 2910	118	2.059 4885	178	3.106 6861	58	.016 8715	58	.000 2812
59	1.029 7443	119	2.076 9418	179	3.124 1394	59	.017 1624	59	.000 2860
60	1.047 1976	120	2.094 3951	180	3.141 5927	60	.017 4533	60	.000 2909

PROPERTIES OF GEOMETRIC SECTIONS

SQUARE

Axis of moments through center

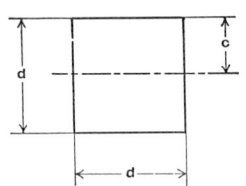

$A = d^2$

$c = \dfrac{d}{2}$

$I = \dfrac{d^4}{12}$

$S = \dfrac{d^3}{6}$

$r = \dfrac{d}{\sqrt{12}} = .288675\,d$

$Z = \dfrac{d^3}{4}$

SQUARE

Axis of moments on base

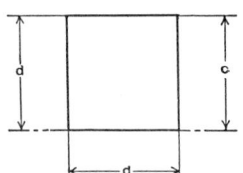

$A = d^2$

$c = d$

$I = \dfrac{d^4}{3}$

$S = \dfrac{d^3}{3}$

$r = \dfrac{d}{\sqrt{3}} = .577350\,d$

SQUARE

Axis of moments on diagonal

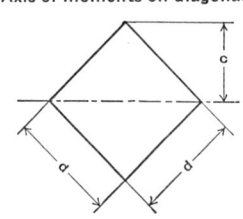

$A = d^2$

$c = \dfrac{d}{\sqrt{2}} = .707107\,d$

$I = \dfrac{d^4}{12}$

$S = \dfrac{d^3}{6\sqrt{2}} = .117851\,d^3$

$r = \dfrac{d}{\sqrt{12}} = .288675\,d$

$Z = \dfrac{2c^3}{3} = \dfrac{d^3}{3\sqrt{2}} = .235702d^3$

RECTANGLE

Axis of moments through center

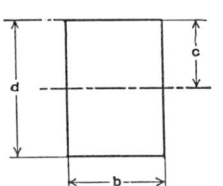

$A = bd$

$c = \dfrac{d}{2}$

$I = \dfrac{bd^3}{12}$

$S = \dfrac{bd^2}{6}$

$r = \dfrac{d}{\sqrt{12}} = .288675\,d$

$Z = \dfrac{bd^2}{4}$

PROPERTIES OF GEOMETRIC SECTIONS

RECTANGLE

Axis of moments on base

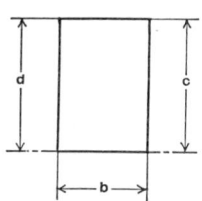

$$A = bd$$

$$c = d$$

$$I = \frac{bd^3}{3}$$

$$S = \frac{bd^2}{3}$$

$$r = \frac{d}{\sqrt{3}} = .577350\ d$$

RECTANGLE

Axis of moments on diagonal

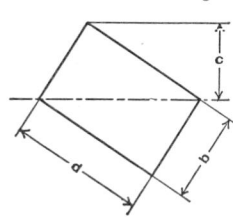

$$A = bd$$

$$c = \frac{bd}{\sqrt{b^2 + d^2}}$$

$$I = \frac{b^3 d^3}{6\,(b^2 + d^2)}$$

$$S = \frac{b^2 d^2}{6\sqrt{b^2 + d^2}}$$

$$= \frac{bd}{\sqrt{6\,(b^2 + d^2)}}$$

RECTANGLE

Axis of moments any line
through center of gravity

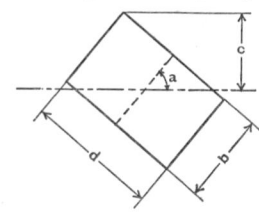

$$A = bd$$

$$c = \frac{b \sin a + d \cos a}{2}$$

$$I = \frac{bd\,(b^2 \sin^2 a + d^2 \cos^2 a)}{12}$$

$$S = \frac{bd\,(b^2 \sin^2 a + d^2 \cos^2 a)}{6\,(b \sin a + d \cos a)}$$

$$r = \sqrt{\frac{b^2 \sin^2 a + d^2 \cos^2 a}{12}}$$

HOLLOW RECTANGLE

Axis of moments through center

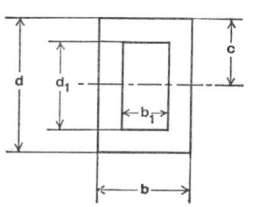

$$A = bd - b_1 d_1$$

$$c = \frac{d}{2}$$

$$I = \frac{bd^3 - b_1 d_1^3}{12}$$

$$S = \frac{bd^3 - b_1 d_1^3}{6d}$$

$$r = \sqrt{\frac{bd^3 - b_1 d_1^3}{12\,A}}$$

$$Z = \frac{bd^2}{4} - \frac{b_1 d_1^2}{4}$$

PROPERTIES OF GEOMETRIC SECTIONS

EQUAL RECTANGLES

Axis of moments through
center of gravity

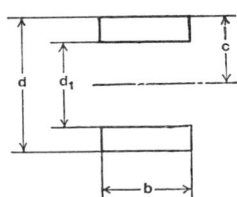

$$A = b(d - d_1)$$

$$c = \frac{d}{2}$$

$$I = \frac{b(d^3 - d_1^3)}{12}$$

$$S = \frac{b(d^3 - d_1^3)}{6d}$$

$$r = \sqrt{\frac{d^3 - d_1^3}{12(d - d_1)}}$$

$$Z = \frac{b}{4}(d^2 - d_1^2)$$

UNEQUAL RECTANGLES

Axis of moments through
center of gravity

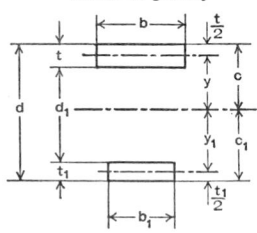

$$A = bt + b_1 t_1$$

$$c = \frac{\frac{1}{2} bt^2 + b_1 t_1 (d - \frac{1}{2} t_1)}{A}$$

$$I = \frac{bt^3}{12} + bty^2 + \frac{b_1 t_1^3}{12} + b_1 t_1 y_1^2$$

$$S = \frac{I}{c} \qquad S_1 = \frac{I}{c_1}$$

$$r = \sqrt{\frac{I}{A}}$$

$$Z = \frac{A}{2} \left[d - \left(\frac{t + t_1}{2} \right) \right]$$

TRIANGLE

Axis of moments through
center of gravity

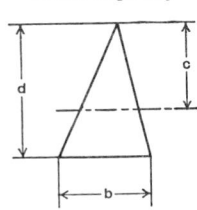

$$A = \frac{bd}{2}$$

$$c = \frac{2d}{3}$$

$$I = \frac{bd^3}{36}$$

$$S = \frac{bd^2}{24}$$

$$r = \frac{d}{\sqrt{18}} = .235702\, d$$

TRIANGLE

Axis of moments on base

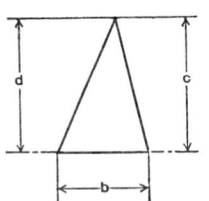

$$A = \frac{bd}{2}$$

$$c = d$$

$$I = \frac{bd^3}{12}$$

$$S = \frac{bd^2}{12}$$

$$r = \frac{d}{\sqrt{6}} = .408248\, d$$

PROPERTIES OF GEOMETRIC SECTIONS

TRAPEZOID

Axis of moments through center of gravity

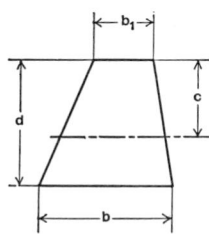

$$A = \frac{d(b + b_1)}{2}$$

$$c = \frac{d(2b + b_1)}{3(b + b_1)}$$

$$I = \frac{d^3 (b^2 + 4 bb_1 + b_1{}^2)}{36 (b + b_1)}$$

$$S = \frac{d^2 (b^2 + 4 bb_1 + b_1{}^2)}{12 (2b + b_1)}$$

$$r = \frac{d}{6(b + b_1)} \sqrt{2 (b^2 + 4 bb_1 + b_1{}^2)}$$

CIRCLE

Axis of moments through center

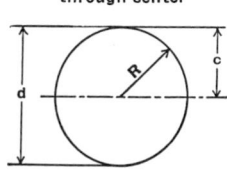

$$A = \frac{\pi d^2}{4} = \pi R^2 = .785398\, d^2 = 3.141593\, R^2$$

$$c = \frac{d}{2} = R$$

$$I = \frac{\pi d^4}{64} = \frac{\pi R^4}{4} = .049087\, d^4 = .785398\, R^4$$

$$S = \frac{\pi d^3}{32} = \frac{\pi R^3}{4} = .098175\, d^3 = .785398\, R^3$$

$$r = \frac{d}{4} = \frac{R}{2}$$

$$Z = \frac{d^3}{6}$$

HOLLOW CIRCLE

Axis of moments through center

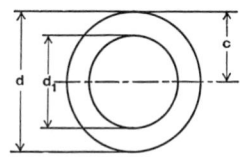

$$A = \frac{\pi(d^2 - d_1{}^2)}{4} = .785398\, (d^2 - d_1{}^2)$$

$$c = \frac{d}{2}$$

$$I = \frac{\pi(d^4 - d_1{}^4)}{64} = .049087\, (d^4 - d_1{}^4)$$

$$S = \frac{\pi(d^4 - d_1{}^4)}{32d} = .098175 \frac{d^4 - d_1{}^4}{d}$$

$$r = \frac{\sqrt{d^2 + d_1{}^2}}{4}$$

$$Z = \frac{d^3}{6} - \frac{d_1{}^3}{6}$$

HALF CIRCLE

Axis of moments through center of gravity

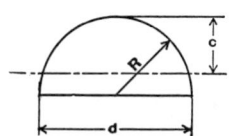

$$A = \frac{\pi R^2}{2} = 1.570796\, R^2$$

$$c = R \left(1 - \frac{4}{3\pi} \right) = .575587\, R$$

$$I = R^4 \left(\frac{\pi}{8} - \frac{8}{9\pi} \right) = .109757\, R^4$$

$$S = \frac{R^3}{24} \frac{(9\pi^2 - 64)}{(3\pi - 4)} = .190687\, R^3$$

$$r = R \frac{\sqrt{9\pi^2 - 64}}{6\pi} = .264336\, R$$

PROPERTIES OF GEOMETRIC SECTIONS

PARABOLA

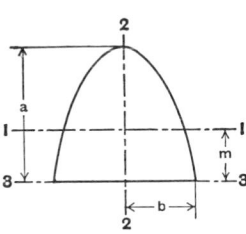

$$A = \frac{4}{3} ab$$

$$m = \frac{2}{5} a$$

$$I_1 = \frac{16}{175} a^3 b$$

$$I_2 = \frac{4}{15} ab^3$$

$$I_3 = \frac{32}{105} a^3 b$$

HALF PARABOLA

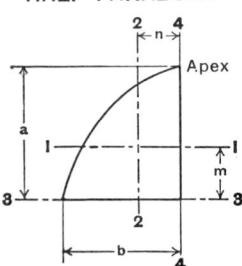

$$A = \frac{2}{3} ab$$

$$m = \frac{2}{5} a$$

$$n = \frac{3}{8} b$$

$$I_1 = \frac{8}{175} a^3 b$$

$$I_2 = \frac{19}{480} ab^3$$

$$I_3 = \frac{16}{105} a^3 b$$

$$I_4 = \frac{2}{15} ab^3$$

COMPLEMENT OF HALF PARABOLA

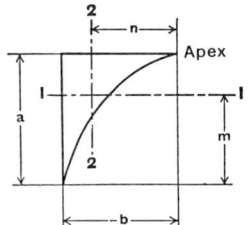

$$A = \frac{1}{3} ab$$

$$m = \frac{7}{10} a$$

$$n = \frac{3}{4} b$$

$$I_1 = \frac{37}{2100} a^3 b$$

$$I_2 = \frac{1}{80} ab^3$$

PARABOLIC FILLET IN RIGHT ANGLE

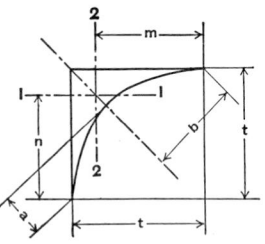

$$a = \frac{t}{2\sqrt{2}}$$

$$b = \frac{t}{\sqrt{2}}$$

$$A = \frac{1}{6} t^2$$

$$m = n = \frac{4}{5} t$$

$$I_1 = I_2 = \frac{11}{2100} t^4$$

PROPERTIES OF GEOMETRIC SECTIONS

* HALF ELLIPSE

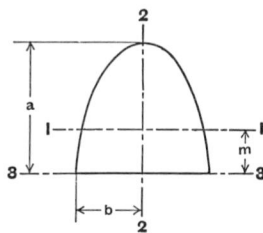

$$A = \frac{1}{2}\pi ab$$

$$m = \frac{4a}{3\pi}$$

$$I_1 = a^3b\left(\frac{\pi}{8} - \frac{8}{9\pi}\right)$$

$$I_2 = \frac{1}{8}\pi ab^3$$

$$I_3 = \frac{1}{8}\pi a^3b$$

* QUARTER ELLIPSE

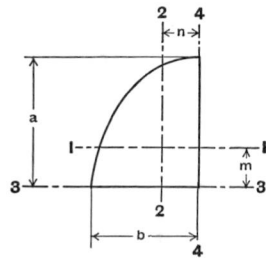

$$A = \frac{1}{4}\pi ab$$

$$m = \frac{4a}{3\pi}$$

$$n = \frac{4b}{3\pi}$$

$$I_1 = a^3b\left(\frac{\pi}{16} - \frac{4}{9\pi}\right)$$

$$I_2 = ab^3\left(\frac{\pi}{16} - \frac{4}{9\pi}\right)$$

$$I_3 = \frac{1}{16}\pi a^3b$$

$$I_4 = \frac{1}{16}\pi ab^3$$

* ELLIPTIC COMPLEMENT

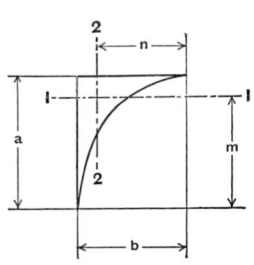

$$A = ab\left(1 - \frac{\pi}{4}\right)$$

$$m = \frac{a}{6\left(1 - \frac{\pi}{4}\right)}$$

$$n = \frac{b}{6\left(1 - \frac{\pi}{4}\right)}$$

$$I_1 = a^3b\left(\frac{1}{3} - \frac{\pi}{16} - \frac{1}{36\left(1 - \frac{\pi}{4}\right)}\right)$$

$$I_2 = ab^3\left(\frac{1}{3} - \frac{\pi}{16} - \frac{1}{36\left(1 - \frac{\pi}{4}\right)}\right)$$

* To obtain properties of half circle, quarter circle and circular complement substitute a = b = R.

AMERICAN INSTITUTE OF STEEL CONSTRUCTION

PROPERTIES OF GEOMETRIC SECTIONS
AND STRUCTURAL SHAPES

REGULAR POLYGON

Axis of moments
through center

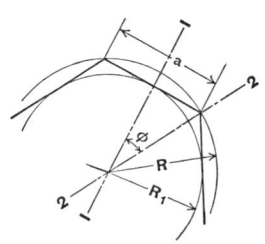

$n = $ Number of sides

$\phi = \dfrac{180°}{n}$

$a = 2\sqrt{R^2 - R_1^2}$

$R = \dfrac{a}{2\sin\phi}$

$R_1 = \dfrac{a}{2\tan\phi}$

$A = \dfrac{1}{4}na^2\cot\phi = \dfrac{1}{2}nR^2\sin 2\phi = nR_1^2\tan\phi$

$I_1 = I_2 = \dfrac{A(6R^2 - a^2)}{24} = \dfrac{A(12R_1^2 + a^2)}{48}$

$r_1 = r_2 = \sqrt{\dfrac{6R^2 - a^2}{24}} = \sqrt{\dfrac{12R_1^2 + a^2}{48}}$

ANGLE

Axis of moments through
center of gravity

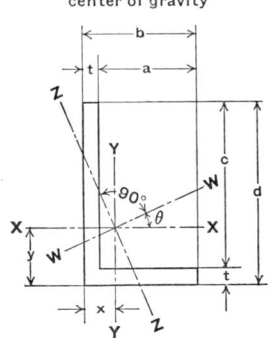

Z-Z is axis of minimum I

$\tan 2\theta = \dfrac{2K}{I_Y - I_X}$

$A = t(b + c) \quad x = \dfrac{b^2 + ct}{2(b + c)} \quad y = \dfrac{d^2 + at}{2(b + c)}$

$K = $ Product of Inertia about X-X & Y-Y

$\quad = \pm\dfrac{abcdt}{4(b + c)}$

$I_X = \dfrac{1}{3}\left(t(d - y)^3 + by^3 - a(y - t)^3 \right)$

$I_Y = \dfrac{1}{3}\left(t(b - x)^3 + dx^3 - c(x - t)^3 \right)$

$I_Z = I_X\sin^2\theta + I_Y\cos^2\theta + K\sin 2\theta$

$I_W = I_X\cos^2\theta + I_Y\sin^2\theta - K\sin 2\theta$

K is negative when heel of angle, with respect
to c. g., is in 1st or 3rd quadrant, positive
when in 2nd or 4th quadrant.

BEAMS AND CHANNELS

Transverse force oblique
through center of gravity

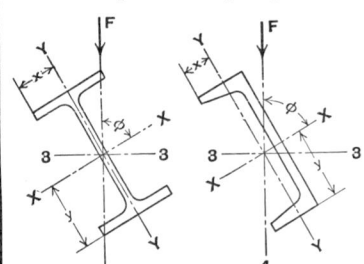

$I_3 = I_X\sin^2\phi + I_Y\cos^2\phi$

$I_4 = I_X\cos^2\phi + I_Y\sin^2\phi$

$f_b = M\left(\dfrac{y}{I_X}\sin\phi + \dfrac{x}{I_Y}\cos\phi \right)$

where M is bending moment due to force F.

TRIGONOMETRIC FORMULAS

TRIGONOMETRIC FUNCTIONS

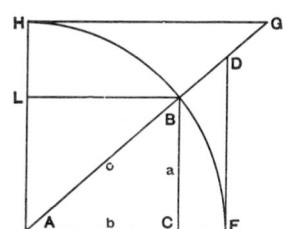

Radius AF $= 1$
$= \sin^2 A + \cos^2 A = \sin A \operatorname{cosec} A$
$= \cos A \sec A = \tan A \cot A$

Sine A $= \dfrac{\cos A}{\cot A} = \dfrac{1}{\operatorname{cosec} A} = \cos A \tan A = \sqrt{1-\cos^2 A} = BC$

Cosine A $= \dfrac{\sin A}{\tan A} = \dfrac{1}{\sec A} = \sin A \cot A = \sqrt{1-\sin^2 A} = AC$

Tangent A $= \dfrac{\sin A}{\cos A} = \dfrac{1}{\cot A} = \sin A \sec A = FD$

Cotangent A $= \dfrac{\cos A}{\sin A} = \dfrac{1}{\tan A} = \cos A \operatorname{cosec} A = HG$

Secant A $= \dfrac{\tan A}{\sin A} = \dfrac{1}{\cos A} = AD$

Cosecant A $= \dfrac{\cot A}{\cos A} = \dfrac{1}{\sin A} = AG$

RIGHT ANGLED TRIANGLES

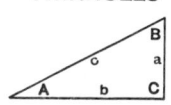

$$a^2 = c^2 - b^2$$
$$b^2 = c^2 - a^2$$
$$c^2 = a^2 + b^2$$

Known	Required					
	A	B	a	b	c	Area
a, b	$\tan A = \dfrac{a}{b}$	$\tan B = \dfrac{b}{a}$			$\sqrt{a^2+b^2}$	$\dfrac{ab}{2}$
a, c	$\sin A = \dfrac{a}{c}$	$\cos B = \dfrac{a}{c}$		$\sqrt{c^2-a^2}$		$\dfrac{a\sqrt{c^2-a^2}}{2}$
A, a		$90° - A$		$a \cot A$	$\dfrac{a}{\sin A}$	$\dfrac{a^2 \cot A}{2}$
A, b		$90° - A$	$b \tan A$		$\dfrac{b}{\cos A}$	$\dfrac{b^2 \tan A}{2}$
A, c		$90° - A$	$c \sin A$	$c \cos A$		$\dfrac{c^2 \sin 2A}{4}$

OBLIQUE ANGLED TRIANGLES

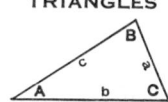

$$s = \dfrac{a+b+c}{2}$$
$$K = \sqrt{\dfrac{(s-a)(s-b)(s-c)}{s}}$$

$$a^2 = b^2 + c^2 - 2bc \cos A$$
$$b^2 = a^2 + c^2 - 2ac \cos B$$
$$c^2 = a^2 + b^2 - 2ab \cos C$$

Known	Required					
	A	B	C	b	c	Area
a, b, c	$\tan \dfrac{1}{2} A = \dfrac{K}{s-a}$	$\tan \dfrac{1}{2} B = \dfrac{K}{s-b}$	$\tan \dfrac{1}{2} C = \dfrac{K}{s-c}$			$\sqrt{s(s-a)(s-b)(s-c)}$
a, A, B			$180° - (A+B)$	$\dfrac{a \sin B}{\sin A}$	$\dfrac{a \sin C}{\sin A}$	
a, b, A		$\sin B = \dfrac{b \sin A}{a}$			$\dfrac{b \sin C}{\sin B}$	
a, b, C	$\tan A = \dfrac{a \sin C}{b - a \cos C}$				$\sqrt{a^2+b^2-2ab \cos C}$	$\dfrac{ab \sin C}{2}$

AMERICAN INSTITUTE OF STEEL CONSTRUCTION

NATURAL SINES

Angle	0'	10'	20'	30'	40'	50'	60'	
0°	0.00000	0.00291	0.00582	0.00873	0.01164	0.01454	0.01745	89°
1	0.01745	0.02036	0.02327	0.02618	0.02908	0.03199	0.03490	88
2	0.03490	0.03781	0.04071	0.04362	0.04653	0.04943	0.05234	87
3	0.05234	0.05524	0.05814	0.06105	0.06395	0.06685	0.06976	86
4	0.06976	0.07266	0.07556	0.07846	0.08136	0.08426	0.08716	85
5	0.08716	0.09005	0.09295	0.09585	0.09874	0.10164	0.10453	84
6	0.10453	0.10742	0.11031	0.11320	0.11609	0.11898	0.12187	83
7	0.12187	0.12476	0.12764	0.13053	0.13341	0.13629	0.13917	82
8	0.13917	0.14205	0.14493	0.14781	0.15069	0.15356	0.15643	81
9	0.15643	0.15931	0.16218	0.16505	0.16792	0.17078	0.17365	80
10	0.17365	0.17651	0.17937	0.18224	0.18509	0.18795	0.19081	79
11	0.19081	0.19366	0.19652	0.19937	0.20222	0.20507	0.20791	78
12	0.20791	0.21076	0.21360	0.21644	0.21928	0.22212	0.22495	77
13	0.22495	0.22778	0.23062	0.23345	0.23627	0.23910	0.24192	76
14	0.24192	0.24474	0.24756	0.25038	0.25320	0.25601	0.25882	75
15	0.25882	0.26163	0.26443	0.26724	0.27004	0.27284	0.27564	74
16	0.27564	0.27843	0.28123	0.28402	0.28680	0.28959	0.29237	73
17	0.29237	0.29515	0.29793	0.30071	0.30348	0.30625	0.30902	72
18	0.30902	0.31178	0.31454	0.31730	0.32006	0.32282	0.32557	71
19	0.32557	0.32832	0.33106	0.33381	0.33655	0.33929	0.34202	70
20	0.34202	0.34475	0.34748	0.35021	0.35293	0.35565	0.35837	69
21	0.35837	0.36108	0.36379	0.36650	0.36921	0.37191	0.37461	68
22	0.37461	0.37730	0.37999	0.38268	0.38537	0.38805	0.39073	67
23	0.39073	0.39341	0.39608	0.39875	0.40141	0.40408	0.40674	66
24	0.40674	0.40939	0.41204	0.41469	0.41734	0.41998	0.42262	65
25	0.42262	0.42525	0.42788	0.43051	0.43313	0.43575	0.43837	64
26	0.43837	0.44098	0.44359	0.44620	0.44880	0.45140	0.45399	63
27	0.45399	0.45658	0.45917	0.46175	0.46433	0.46690	0.46947	62
28	0.46947	0.47204	0.47460	0.47716	0.47971	0.48226	0.48481	61
29	0.48481	0.48735	0.48989	0.49242	0.49495	0.49748	0.50000	60
30	0.50000	0.50252	0.50503	0.50754	0.51004	0.51254	0.51504	59
31	0.51504	0.51753	0.52002	0.52250	0.52498	0.52745	0.52992	58
32	0.52992	0.53238	0.53484	0.53730	0.53975	0.54220	0.54464	57
33	0.54464	0.54708	0.54951	0.55194	0.55436	0.55678	0.55919	56
34	0.55919	0.56160	0.56401	0.56641	0.56880	0.57119	0.57358	55
35	0.57358	0.57596	0.57833	0.58070	0.58307	0.58543	0.58779	54
36	0.58779	0.59014	0.59248	0.59482	0.59716	0.59949	0.60182	53
37	0.60182	0.60414	0.60645	0.60876	0.61107	0.61337	0.61566	52
38	0.61566	0.61795	0.62024	0.62251	0.62479	0.62706	0.62932	51
39	0.62932	0.63158	0.63383	0.63608	0.63832	0.64056	0.64279	50
40	0.64279	0.64501	0.64723	0.64945	0.65166	0.65386	0.65606	49
41	0.65606	0.65825	0.66044	0.66262	0.66480	0.66697	0.66913	48
42	0.66913	0.67129	0.67344	0.67559	0.67773	0.67987	0.68200	47
43	0.68200	0.68412	0.68624	0.68835	0.69046	0.69256	0.69466	46
44°	0.69466	0.69675	0.69883	0.70091	0.70298	0.70505	0.70711	45°
	60'	50'	40'	30'	20'	10'	0'	Angle

NATURAL COSINES

NATURAL SINES

Angle	0′	10′	20′	30′	40′	50′	60′	
45°	0.70711	0.70916	0.71121	0.71325	0.71529	0.71732	0.71934	44°
46	0.71934	0.72136	0.72337	0.72537	0.72737	0.72937	0.73135	43
47	0.73135	0.73333	0.73531	0.73728	0.73924	0.74120	0.74314	42
48	0.74314	0.74509	0.74703	0.74896	0.75088	0.75280	0.75471	41
49	0.75471	0.75661	0.75851	0.76041	0.76229	0.76417	0.76604	40
50	0.76604	0.76791	0.76977	0.77162	0.77347	0.77531	0.77715	39
51	0.77715	0.77897	0.78079	0.78261	0.78442	0.78622	0.78801	38
52	0.78801	0.78980	0.79158	0.79335	0.79512	0.79688	0.79864	37
53	0.79864	0.80038	0.80212	0.80386	0.80558	0.80730	0.80902	36
54	0.80902	0.81072	0.81242	0.81412	0.81580	0.81748	0.81915	35
55	0.81915	0.82082	0.82248	0.82413	0.82577	0.82741	0.82904	34
56	0.82904	0.83066	0.83228	0.83389	0.83549	0.83708	0.83867	33
57	0.83867	0.84025	0.84182	0.84339	0.84495	0.84650	0.84805	32
58	0.84805	0.84959	0.85112	0.85264	0.85416	0.85567	0.85717	31
59	0.85717	0.85866	0.86015	0.86163	0.86310	0.86457	0.86603	30
60	0.86603	0.86748	0.86892	0.87036	0.87178	0.87321	0.87462	29
61	0.87462	0.87603	0.87743	0.87882	0.88020	0.88158	0.88295	28
62	0.88295	0.88431	0.88566	0.88701	0.88835	0.88968	0.89101	27
63	0.89101	0.89232	0.89363	0.89493	0.89623	0.89752	0.89879	26
64	0.89879	0.90007	0.90133	0.90259	0.90383	0.90507	0.90631	25
65	0.90631	0.90753	0.90875	0.90996	0.91116	0.91236	0.91355	24
66	0.91355	0.91472	0.91590	0.91706	0.91822	0.91936	0.92050	23
67	0.92050	0.92164	0.92276	0.92388	0.92499	0.92609	0.92718	22
68	0.92718	0.92827	0.92935	0.93042	0.93148	0.93253	0.93358	21
69	0.93358	0.93462	0.93565	0.93667	0.93769	0.93869	0.93969	20
70	0.93969	0.94068	0.94167	0.94264	0.94361	0.94457	0.94552	19
71	0.94552	0.94646	0.94740	0.94832	0.94924	0.95015	0.95106	18
72	0.95106	0.95195	0.95284	0.95372	0.95459	0.95545	0.95630	17
73	0.95630	0.95715	0.95799	0.95882	0.95964	0.96046	0.96126	16
74	0.96126	0.96206	0.96285	0.96363	0.96440	0.96517	0.96593	15
75	0.96593	0.96667	0.96742	0.96815	0.96887	0.96959	0.97030	14
76	0.97030	0.97100	0.97169	0.97237	0.97304	0.97371	0.97437	13
77	0.97437	0.97502	0.97566	0.97630	0.97692	0.97754	0.97815	12
78	0.97815	0.97875	0.97934	0.97992	0.98050	0.98107	0.98163	11
79	0.98163	0.98218	0.98272	0.98325	0.98378	0.98430	0.98481	10
80	0.98481	0.98531	0.98580	0.98629	0.98676	0.98723	0.98769	9
81	0.98769	0.98814	0.98858	0.98902	0.98944	0.98986	0.99027	8
82	0.99027	0.99067	0.99106	0.99144	0.99182	0.99219	0.99255	7
83	0.99255	0.99290	0.99324	0.99357	0.99390	0.99421	0.99452	6
84	0.99452	0.99482	0.99511	0.99540	0.99567	0.99594	0.99619	5
85	0.99619	0.99644	0.99668	0.99692	0.99714	0.99736	0.99756	4
86	0.99756	0.99776	0.99795	0.99813	0.99831	0.99847	0.99863	3
87	0.99863	0.99878	0.99892	0.99905	0.99917	0.99929	0.99939	2
88	0.99939	0.99949	0.99958	0.99966	0.99973	0.99979	0.99985	1
89°	0.99985	0.99989	0.99993	0.99996	0.99998	1.00000	1.00000	0°
	60′	50′	40′	30′	20′	10′	0′	Angle

NATURAL COSINES

AMERICAN INSTITUTE OF STEEL CONSTRUCTION

NATURAL TANGENTS

Angle	0′	10′	20′	30′	40′	50′	60′	
0°	0.00000	0.00291	0.00582	0.00873	0.01164	0.01455	0.01746	89°
1	0.01746	0.02036	0.02328	0.02619	0.02910	0.03201	0.03492	88
2	0.03492	0.03783	0.04075	0.04366	0.04658	0.04949	0.05241	87
3	0.05241	0.05533	0.05824	0.06116	0.06408	0.06700	0.06993	86
4	0.06993	0.07285	0.07578	0.07870	0.08163	0.08456	0.08749	85
5	0.08749	0.09042	0.09335	0.09629	0.09923	0.10216	0.10510	84
6	0.10510	0.10805	0.11099	0.11394	0.11688	0.11983	0.12278	83
7	0.12278	0.12574	0.12869	0.13165	0.13461	0.13758	0.14054	82
8	0.14054	0.14351	0.14648	0.14945	0.15243	0.15540	0.15838	81
9	0.15838	0.16137	0.16435	0.16734	0.17033	0.17333	0.17633	80
10	0.17633	0.17933	0.18233	0.18534	0.18835	0.19136	0.19438	79
11	0.19438	0.19740	0.20042	0.20345	0.20648	0.20952	0.21256	78
12	0.21256	0.21560	0.21864	0.22169	0.22475	0.22781	0.23087	77
13	0.23087	0.23393	0.23700	0.24008	0.24316	0.24624	0.24933	76
14	0.24933	0.25242	0.25552	0.25862	0.26172	0.26483	0.26795	75
15	0.26795	0.27107	0.27419	0.27732	0.28046	0.28360	0.28675	74
16	0.28675	0.28990	0.29305	0.29621	0.29938	0.30255	0.30573	73
17	0.30573	0.30891	0.31210	0.31530	0.31850	0.32171	0.32492	72
18	0.32492	0.32814	0.33136	0.33460	0.33783	0.34108	0.34433	71
19	0.34433	0.34758	0.35085	0.35412	0.35740	0.36068	0.36397	70
20	0.36397	0.36727	0.37057	0.37388	0.37720	0.38053	0.38386	69
21	0.38386	0.38721	0.39055	0.39391	0.39727	0.40065	0.40403	68
22	0.40403	0.40741	0.41081	0.41421	0.41763	0.42105	0.42447	67
23	0.42447	0.42791	0.43136	0.43481	0.43828	0.44175	0.44523	66
24	0.44523	0.44872	0.45222	0.45573	0.45924	0.46277	0.46631	65
25	0.46631	0.46985	0.47341	0.47698	0.48055	0.48414	0.48773	64
26	0.48773	0.49134	0.49495	0.49858	0.50222	0.50587	0.50953	63
27	0.50953	0.51320	0.51688	0.52057	0.52427	0.52798	0.53171	62
28	0.53171	0.53545	0.53920	0.54296	0.54673	0.55051	0.55431	61
29	0.55431	0.55812	0.56194	0.56577	0.56962	0.57348	0.57735	60
30	0.57735	0.58124	0.58513	0.58905	0.59297	0.59691	0.60086	59
31	0.60086	0.60483	0.60881	0.61280	0.61681	0.62083	0.62487	58
32	0.62487	0.62892	0.63299	0.63707	0.64117	0.64528	0.64941	57
33	0.64941	0.65355	0.65771	0.66189	0.66608	0.67028	0.67451	56
34	0.67451	0.67875	0.68301	0.68728	0.69157	0.69588	0.70021	55
35	0.70021	0.70455	0.70891	0.71329	0.71769	0.72211	0.72654	54
36	0.72654	0.73100	0.73547	0.73996	0.74447	0.74900	0.75355	53
37	0.75355	0.75812	0.76272	0.76733	0.77196	0.77661	0.78129	52
38	0.78129	0.78598	0.79070	0.79544	0.80020	0.80498	0.80978	51
39	0.80978	0.81461	0.81946	0.82434	0.82923	0.83415	0.83910	50
40	0.83910	0.84407	0.84906	0.85408	0.85912	0.86419	0.86929	49
41	0.86929	0.87441	0.87955	0.88473	0.88992	0.89515	0.90040	48
42	0.90040	0.90569	0.91099	0.91633	0.92170	0.92709	0.93252	47
43	0.93252	0.93797	0.94345	0.94896	0.95451	0.96008	0.96569	46
44°	0.96569	0.97133	0.97700	0.98270	0 98843	0.99420	1.00000	45°
	60′	50′	40′	30′	20′	10′	0′	Angle

NATURAL COTANGENTS

NATURAL TANGENTS

Angle	0'	10'	20'	30'	40'	50'	60'	
45°	1.00000	1.00583	1.01170	1.01761	1.02355	1.02952	1.03553	44°
46	1.03553	1.04158	1.04766	1.05378	1.05994	1.06613	1.07237	43
47	1.07237	1.07864	1.08496	1.09131	1.09770	1.10414	1.11061	42
48	1.11061	1.11713	1.12369	1.13029	1.13694	1.14363	1.15037	41
49	1.15037	1.15715	1.16398	1.17085	1.17777	1.18474	1.19175	40
50	1.19175	1.19882	1.20593	1.21310	1.22031	1.22758	1.23490	39
51	1.23490	1.24227	1.24969	1.25717	1.26471	1.27230	1.27994	38
52	1.27994	1.28764	1.29541	1.30323	1.31110	1.31904	1.32704	37
53	1.32704	1.33511	1.34323	1.35142	1.35968	1.36800	1.37638	36
54	1.37638	1.38484	1.39336	1.40195	1.41061	1.41934	1.42815	35
55	1.42815	1.43703	1.44598	1.45501	1.46411	1.47330	1.48256	34
56	1.48256	1.49190	1.50133	1.51084	1.52043	1.53010	1.53987	33
57	1.53987	1.54972	1.55966	1.56969	1.57981	1.59002	1.60033	32
58	1.60033	1.61074	1.62125	1.63185	1.64256	1.65337	1.66428	31
59	1.66428	1.67530	1.68643	1.69766	1.70901	1.72047	1.73205	30
60	1.73205	1.74375	1.75556	1.76749	1.77955	1.79174	1.80405	29
61	1.80405	1.81649	1.82906	1.84177	1.85462	1.86760	1.88073	28
62	1.88073	1.89400	1.90741	1.92098	1.93470	1.94858	1.96261	27
63	1.96261	1.97681	1.99116	2.00569	2.02039	2.03526	2.05030	26
64	2.05030	2.06553	2.08094	2.09654	2.11233	2.12832	2.14451	25
65	2.14451	2.16090	2.17749	2.19430	2.21132	2.22857	2.24604	24
66	2.24604	2.26374	2.28167	2.29984	2.31826	2.33693	2.35585	23
67	2.35585	2.37504	2.39449	2.41421	2.43422	2.45451	2.47509	22
68	2.47509	2.49597	2.51715	2.53865	2.56046	2.58261	2.60509	21
69	2.60509	2.62791	2.65109	2.67462	2.69853	2.72281	2.74748	20
70	2.74748	2.77254	2.79802	2.82391	2.85023	2.87700	2.90421	19
71	2.90421	2.93189	2.96004	2.98869	3.01783	3.04749	3.07768	18
72	3.07768	3.10842	3.13972	3.17159	3.20406	3.23714	3.27085	17
73	3.27085	3.30521	3.34023	3.37594	3.41236	3.44951	3.48741	16
74	3.48741	3.52609	3.56557	3.60588	3.64705	3.68909	3.73205	15
75	3.73205	3.77595	3.82083	3.86671	3.91364	3.96165	4.01078	14
76	4.01078	4.06107	4.11256	4.16530	4.21933	4.27471	4.33148	13
77	4.33148	4.38969	4.44942	4.51071	4.57363	4.63825	4.70463	12
78	4.70463	4.77286	4.84300	4.91516	4.98940	5.06584	5.14455	11
79	5.14455	5.22566	5.30928	5.39552	5.48451	5.57638	5.67128	10
80	5.67128	5.76937	5.87080	5.97576	6.08444	6.19703	6.31375	9
81	6.31375	6.43484	6.56055	6.69116	6.82694	6.96823	7.11537	8
82	7.11537	7.26873	7.42871	7.59575	7.77035	7.95302	8.14435	7
83	8.14435	8.34496	8.55555	8.77689	9.00983	9.25530	9.51436	6
84	9.51436	9.78817	10.07803	10.38540	10.71191	11.05943	11.43005	5
85	11.43005	11.82617	12.25051	12.70621	13.19688	13.72674	14.30067	4
86	14.30067	14.92442	15.60478	16.34986	17.16934	18.07498	19.08114	3
87	19.08114	20.20555	21.47040	22.90377	24.54176	26.43160	28.63625	2
88	28.63625	31.24158	34.36777	38.18846	42.96408	49.10388	57.28996	1
89°	57.28996	68.75009	85.93979	114.58865	171.88540	343.77371	Infinite.	0°
	60'	50'	40'	30'	20'	10'	0'	Angle

NATURAL COTANGENTS

NATURAL SECANTS

Angle	0′	10′	20′	30′	40′	50′	60′	
0°	1.00000	1.00001	1.00002	1.00004	1.00007	1.00011	1.00015	89°
1	1.00015	1.00021	1.00027	1.00034	1.00042	1.00051	1.00061	88
2	1.00061	1.00072	1.00083	1.00095	1.00108	1.00122	1.00137	87
3	1.00137	1.00153	1.00169	1.00187	1.00205	1.00224	1.00244	86
4	1.00244	1.00265	1.00287	1.00309	1.00333	1.00357	1.00382	85
5	1.00382	1.00408	1.00435	1.00463	1.00491	1.00521	1.00551	84
6	1.00551	1.00582	1.00614	1.00647	1.00681	1.00715	1.00751	83
7	1.00751	1.00787	1.00825	1.00863	1.00902	1.00942	1.00983	82
8	1.00983	1.01024	1.01067	1.01111	1.01155	1.01200	1.01247	81
9	1.01247	1.01294	1.01342	1.01391	1.01440	1.01491	1.01543	80
10	1.01543	1.01595	1.01649	1.01703	1.01758	1.01815	1.01872	79
11	1.01872	1.01930	1.01989	1.02049	1.02110	1.02171	1.02234	78
12	1.02234	1.02298	1.02362	1.02428	1.02494	1.02562	1.02630	77
13	1.02630	1.02700	1.02770	1.02842	1.02914	1.02987	1.03061	76
14	1.03061	1.03137	1.03213	1.03290	1.03368	1.03447	1.03528	75
15	1.03528	1.03609	1.03691	1.03774	1.03858	1.03944	1.04030	74
16	1.04030	1.04117	1.04206	1.04295	1.04385	1.04477	1.04569	73
17	1.04569	1.04663	1.04757	1.04853	1.04950	1.05047	1.05146	72
18	1.05146	1.05246	1.05347	1.05449	1.05552	1.05657	1.05762	71
19	1.05762	1.05869	1.05976	1.06085	1.06195	1.06306	1.06418	70
20	1.06418	1.06531	1.06645	1.06761	1.06878	1.06995	1.07115	69
21	1.07115	1.07235	1.07356	1.07479	1.07602	1.07727	1.07853	68
22	1.07853	1.07981	1.08109	1.08239	1.08370	1.08503	1.08636	67
23	1.08636	1.08771	1.08907	1.09044	1.09183	1.09323	1.09464	66
24	1.09464	1.09606	1.09750	1.09895	1.10041	1.10189	1.10338	65
25	1.10338	1.10488	1.10640	1.10793	1.10947	1.11103	1.11260	64
26	1.11260	1.11419	1.11579	1.11740	1.11903	1.12067	1.12233	63
27	1.12233	1.12400	1.12568	1.12738	1.12910	1.13083	1.13257	62
28	1.13257	1.13433	1.13610	1.13789	1.13970	1.14152	1.14335	61
29	1.14335	1.14521	1.14707	1.14896	1.15085	1.15277	1.15470	60
30	1.15470	1.15665	1.15861	1.16059	1.16259	1.16460	1.16663	59
31	1.16663	1.16868	1.17075	1.17283	1.17493	1.17704	1.17918	58
32	1.17918	1.18133	1.18350	1.18569	1.18790	1.19012	1.19236	57
33	1.19236	1.19463	1.19691	1.19920	1.20152	1.20386	1.20622	56
34	1.20622	1.20859	1.21099	1.21341	1.21584	1.21830	1.22077	55
35	1.22077	1.22327	1.22579	1.22833	1.23089	1.23347	1.23607	54
36	1.23607	1.23869	1.24134	1.24400	1.24669	1.24940	1.25214	53
37	1.25214	1.25489	1.25767	1.26047	1.26330	1.26615	1.26902	52
38	1.26902	1.27191	1.27483	1.27778	1.28075	1.28374	1.28676	51
39	1.28676	1.28980	1.29287	1.29597	1.29909	1.30223	1.30541	50
40	1.30541	1.30861	1.31183	1.31509	1.31837	1.32168	1.32501	49
41	1.32501	1.32838	1.33177	1.33519	1.33864	1.34212	1.34563	48
42	1.34563	1.34917	1.35274	1.35634	1.35997	1.36363	1.36733	47
43	1.36733	1.37105	1.37481	1.37860	1.38242	1.38628	1.39016	46
44°	1.39016	1.39409	1.39804	1.40203	1.40606	1.41012	1.41421	45°
	60′	50′	40′	30′	20′	10′	0′	Angl

NATURAL COSECANTS

AMERICAN INSTITUTE OF STEEL CONSTRUCTION

NATURAL SECANTS

Angle	0′	10′	20′	30′	40′	50′	60′	
45°	1.41421	1.41835	1.42251	1.42672	1.43096	1.43524	1.43956	44°
46	1.43956	1.44391	1.44831	1.45274	1.45721	1.46173	1.46628	43
47	1.46628	1.47087	1.47551	1.48019	1.48491	1.48967	1.49448	42
48	1.49448	1.49933	1.50422	1.50916	1.51415	1.51918	1.52425	41
49	1.52425	1.52938	1.53455	1.53977	1.54504	1.55036	1.55572	40
50	1.55572	1.56114	1.56661	1.57213	1.57771	1.58333	1.58902	39
51	1.58902	1.59475	1.60054	1.60639	1.61229	1.61825	1.62427	38
52	1.62427	1.63035	1.63648	1.64268	1.64894	1.65526	1.66164	37
53	1.66164	1.66809	1.67460	1.68117	1.68782	1.69452	1.70130	36
54	1.70130	1.70815	1.71506	1.72205	1.72911	1.73624	1.74345	35
55	1.74345	1.75073	1.75808	1.76552	1.77303	1.78062	1.78829	34
56	1.78829	1.79604	1.80388	1.81180	1.81981	1.82790	1.83608	33
57	1.83608	1.84435	1.85271	1.86116	1.86970	1.87834	1.88708	32
58	1.88708	1.89591	1.90485	1.91388	1.92302	1.93226	1.94160	31
59	1.94160	1.95106	1.96062	1.97029	1.98008	1.98998	2.00000	30
60	2.00000	2.01014	2.02039	2.03077	2.04128	2.05191	2.06267	29
61	2.06267	2.07356	2.08458	2.09574	2.10704	2.11847	2.13005	28
62	2.13005	2.14178	2.15366	2.16568	2.17786	2.19019	2.20269	27
63	2.20269	2.21535	2.22817	2.24116	2.25432	2.26766	2.28117	26
64	2.28117	2.29487	2.30875	2.32282	2.33708	2.35154	2.36620	25
65	2.36620	2.38107	2.39614	2.41142	2.42692	2.44264	2.45859	24
66	2.45859	2.47477	2.49119	2.50784	2.52474	2.54190	2.55930	23
67	2.55930	2.57698	2.59491	2.61313	2.63162	2.65040	2.66947	22
68	2.66947	2.68884	2.70851	2.72850	2.74881	2.76945	2.79043	21
69	2.79043	2.81175	2.83342	2.85545	2.87785	2.90063	2.92380	20
70	2.92380	2.94737	2.97135	2.99574	3.02057	3.04584	3.07155	19
71	3.07155	3.09774	3.12440	3.15155	3.17920	3.20737	3.23607	18
72	3.23607	3.26531	3.29512	3.32551	3.35649	3.38808	3.42030	17
73	3.42030	3.45317	3.48671	3.52094	3.55587	3.59154	3.62796	16
74	3.62796	3.66515	3.70315	3.74198	3.78166	3.82223	3.86370	15
75	3.86370	3.90613	3.94952	3.99393	4.03938	4.08591	4.13357	14
76	4.13357	4.18238	4.23239	4.28366	4.33622	4.39012	4.44541	13
77	4.44541	4.50216	4.56041	4.62023	4.68167	4.74482	4.80973	12
78	4.80973	4.87649	4.94517	5.01585	5.08863	5.16359	5.24084	11
79	5.24084	5.32049	5.40263	5.48740	5.57493	5.66533	5.75877	10
80	5.75877	5.85539	5.95536	6.05886	6.16607	6.27719	6.39245	9
81	6.39245	6.51208	6.63633	6.76547	6.89979	7.03962	7.18530	8
82	7.18530	7.33719	7.49571	7.66130	7.83443	8.01565	8.20551	7
83	8.20551	8.40466	8.61379	8.83367	9.06515	9.30917	9.56677	6
84	9.56677	9.83912	10.12752	10.43343	10.75849	11.10455	11.47371	5
85	11.47371	11.86837	12.29125	12.74550	13.23472	13.76312	14.33559	4
86	14.33559	14.95788	15.63679	16.38041	17.19843	18.10262	19.10732	3
87	19.10732	20.23028	21.49368	22.92559	24.56212	26.45051	28.65371	2
88	28.65371	31.25758	34.38232	38.20155	42.97571	49.11406	57.29869	1
89°	57.29869	68.75736	85.94561	114.59301	171.88831	343.77516	Infinite.	0°
	60′	50′	40′	30′	20′	10′	0′	Angle

NATURAL COSECANTS

AMERICAN INSTITUTE OF STEEL CONSTRUCTION

FUNCTIONS OF NUMBERS

.01
.49

No.	Square	Cube	Square Root	Cube Root	Logarithm	1000 × Reciprocal	No. = Diameter Circum.	No. = Diameter Area
.01	.0001	.000001	0.1000	0.2154	2̄.00000	100000.000	.03142	.000079
.02	.0004	.000008	0.1414	0.2714	2̄.30103	50000.000	.06283	.000314
.03	.0009	.000027	0.1732	0.3107	2̄.47712	33333.333	.09425	.000707
.04	.0016	.000064	0.2000	0.3420	2̄.60206	25000.000	.12566	.001257
.05	.0025	.000125	0.2236	0.3684	2̄.69897	20000.000	.15708	.001964
.06	.0036	.000216	0.2449	0.3915	2̄.77815	16666.667	.18850	.002827
.07	.0049	.000343	0.2646	0.4121	2̄.84510	14285.714	.21991	.003849
.08	.0064	.000512	0.2828	0.4309	2̄.90309	12500.000	.25133	.005027
.09	.0081	.000729	0.3000	0.4481	2̄.95424	11111.111	.28274	.006362
.10	.0100	.001000	0.3162	0.4642	1̄.00000	10000.000	.31416	.007854
.11	.0121	.001331	0.3317	0.4791	1̄.04139	9090.909	.34558	.009503
.12	.0144	.001728	0.3464	0.4932	1̄.07918	8333.333	.37699	.011310
.13	.0169	.002197	0.3606	0.5066	1̄.11394	7692.308	.40841	.013273
.14	.0196	.002744	0.3742	0.5192	1̄.14613	7142.857	.43982	.015394
.15	.0225	.003375	0.3873	0.5313	1̄.17609	6666.667	.47124	.017672
.16	.0256	.004096	0.4000	0.5429	1̄.20412	6250.000	.50265	.020106
.17	.0289	.004913	0.4123	0.5540	1̄.23045	5882.353	.53407	.022698
.18	.0324	.005832	0.4243	0.5646	1̄.25527	5555.556	.56549	.025447
.19	.0361	.006859	0.4359	0.5749	1̄.27875	5263.158	.59690	.028353
.20	.0400	.008000	0.4472	0.5848	1̄.30103	5000.000	.62832	.031416
.21	.0441	.009261	0.4583	0.5944	1̄.32222	4761.905	.65973	.034636
.22	.0484	.010648	0.4690	0.6037	1̄.34242	4545.455	.69115	.038013
.23	.0529	.012167	0.4796	0.6127	1̄.36173	4347.826	.72257	.041548
.24	.0576	.013824	0.4899	0.6214	1̄.38021	4166.667	.75398	.045239
.25	.0625	.015625	0.5000	0.6300	1̄.39794	4000.000	.78540	.049087
.26	.0676	.017576	0.5099	0.6383	1̄.41497	3846.154	.81681	.053093
.27	.0729	.019683	0.5196	0.6463	1̄.43136	3703.704	.84823	.057256
.28	.0784	.021952	0.5292	0.6542	1̄.44716	3571.429	.87965	.061575
.29	.0841	.024389	0.5385	0.6619	1̄.46240	3448.276	.91106	.066052
.30	.0900	.027000	0.5477	0.6694	1̄.47712	3333.333	.94248	.070686
.31	.0961	.029791	0.5568	0.6768	1̄.49136	3225.807	.97389	.075477
.32	.1024	.032768	0.5657	0.6840	1̄.50515	3125.000	1.00531	.080425
.33	.1089	.035937	0.5745	0.6910	1̄.51851	3030.303	1.03673	.085530
.34	.1156	.039304	0.5831	0.6980	1̄.53148	2941.177	1.06814	.090792
.35	.1225	.042875	0.5916	0.7047	1̄.54407	2857.143	1.09956	.096211
.36	.1296	.046656	0.6000	0.7114	1̄.55630	2777.778	1.13097	.101788
.37	.1369	.050653	0.6083	0.7179	1̄.56820	2702.703	1.16239	.107521
.38	.1444	.054872	0.6164	0.7243	1̄.57978	2631.579	1.19381	.113411
.39	.1521	.059319	0.6245	0.7306	1̄.59106	2564.103	1.22522	.119459
.40	.1600	.064000	0.6325	0.7368	1̄.60206	2500.000	1.2566	.125664
.41	.1681	.068921	0.6403	0.7429	1̄.61278	2439.024	1.2881	.132025
.42	.1764	.074088	0.6481	0.7489	1̄.62325	2380.952	1.3195	.138544
.43	.1849	.079507	0.6557	0.7548	1̄.63347	2325.581	1.3509	.145220
.44	.1936	.085184	0.6633	0.7606	1̄.64345	2272.727	1.3823	.152053
.45	.2025	.091125	0.6708	0.7663	1̄.65321	2222.222	1.4137	.159043
.46	.2116	.097336	0.6782	0.7719	1̄.66276	2173.913	1.4451	.166190
.47	.2209	.103823	0.6856	0.7775	1̄.67210	2127.660	1.4765	.173494
.48	.2304	.110592	0.6928	0.7830	1̄.68124	2083.333	1.5080	.180956
.49	.2401	.117649	0.7000	0.7884	1̄.69020	2040.816	1.5394	.188574

FUNCTIONS OF NUMBERS

No.	Square	Cube	Square Root	Cube Root	Logarithm	1000 × Reciprocal	No. = Diameter Circum.	No. = Diameter Area
.50	.2500	.125000	0.7071	0.7937	$\overline{1}$.69897	2000.000	1.5708	.19635
.51	.2601	.132651	0.7141	0.7990	$\overline{1}$.70757	1960.784	1.6022	.20428
.52	.2704	.140608	0.7211	0.8041	$\overline{1}$.71600	1923.077	1.6336	.21237
.53	.2809	.148877	0.7280	0.8093	$\overline{1}$.72428	1886.793	1.6650	.22062
.54	.2916	.157464	0.7348	0.8143	$\overline{1}$.73239	1851.852	1.6965	.22902
.55	.3025	.166375	0.7416	0.8193	$\overline{1}$.74036	1818.182	1.7279	.23758
.56	.3136	.175616	0.7483	0.8243	$\overline{1}$.74819	1785.714	1.7593	.24630
.57	.3249	.185193	0.7550	0.8291	$\overline{1}$.75587	1754.386	1.7907	.25518
.58	.3364	.195112	0.7616	0.8340	$\overline{1}$.76343	1724.138	1.8221	.26421
.59	.3481	.205379	0.7681	0.8387	$\overline{1}$.77085	1694.915	1.8535	.27340
.60	.3600	.216000	0.7746	0.8434	$\overline{1}$.77815	1666.667	1.8850	.28274
.61	.3721	.226981	0.7810	0.8481	$\overline{1}$.78533	1639.344	1.9164	.29225
.62	.3844	.238328	0.7874	0.8527	$\overline{1}$.79239	1612.903	1.9478	.30191
.63	.3969	.250047	0.7937	0.8573	$\overline{1}$.79934	1587.302	1.9792	.31173
.64	.4096	.262144	0.8000	0.8618	$\overline{1}$.80618	1562.500	2.0106	.32170
.65	.4225	.274625	0.8062	0.8662	$\overline{1}$.81291	1538.462	2.0420	.33183
.66	.4356	.287496	0.8124	0.8707	$\overline{1}$.81954	1515.152	2.0735	.34212
.67	.4489	.300763	0.8185	0.8750	$\overline{1}$.82607	1492.537	2.1049	.35257
.68	.4624	.314432	0.8246	0.8794	$\overline{1}$.83251	1470.588	2.1363	.36317
.69	.4761	.328509	0.8307	0.8837	$\overline{1}$.83885	1449.275	2.1677	.37393
.70	.4900	.343000	0.8367	0.8879	$\overline{1}$.84510	1428.571	2.1991	.38485
.71	.5041	.357911	0.8426	0.8921	$\overline{1}$.85126	1408.451	2.2305	.39592
.72	.5184	.373248	0.8485	0.8963	$\overline{1}$.85733	1388.889	2.2620	.40715
.73	.5329	.389017	0.8544	0.9004	$\overline{1}$.86332	1369.863	2.2934	.41854
.74	.5476	.405224	0.8602	0.9045	$\overline{1}$.86923	1351.351	2.3248	.43008
.75	.5625	.421875	0.8660	0.9086	$\overline{1}$.87506	1333.333	2.3562	.44179
.76	.5776	.438976	0.8718	0.9126	$\overline{1}$.88081	1315.790	2.3876	.45365
.77	.5929	.456533	0.8775	0.9166	$\overline{1}$.88649	1298.701	2.4190	.46566
.78	.6084	.474552	0.8832	0.9205	$\overline{1}$.89209	1282.051	2.4504	.47784
.79	.6241	.493039	0.8888	0.9244	$\overline{1}$.89763	1265.823	2.4819	.49017
.80	.6400	.512000	0.8944	0.9283	$\overline{1}$.90309	1250.000	2.5133	.50266
.81	.6561	.531441	0.9000	0.9322	$\overline{1}$.90849	1234.568	2.5447	.51530
.82	.6724	.551368	0.9055	0.9360	$\overline{1}$.91381	1219.512	2.5761	.52810
.83	.6889	.571787	0.9110	0.9398	$\overline{1}$.91908	1204.819	2.6075	.54106
.84	.7056	.592704	0.9165	0.9435	$\overline{1}$.92428	1190.476	2.6389	.55418
.85	.7225	.614125	0.9220	0.9473	$\overline{1}$.92942	1176.471	2.6704	.56745
.86	.7396	.636056	0.9274	0.9510	$\overline{1}$.93450	1162.791	2.7018	.58088
.87	.7569	.658503	0.9327	0.9546	$\overline{1}$.93952	1149.425	2.7332	.59447
.88	.7744	.681472	0.9381	0.9583	$\overline{1}$.94448	1136.364	2.7646	.60821
.89	.7921	.704969	0.9434	0.9619	$\overline{1}$.94939	1123.596	2.7960	.62211
.90	.8100	.729000	0.9487	0.9655	$\overline{1}$.95424	1111.111	2.8274	.63617
.91	.8281	.753571	0.9539	0.9691	$\overline{1}$.95904	1098.901	2.8589	.65039
.92	.8464	.778688	0.9592	0.9726	$\overline{1}$.96379	1086.957	2.8903	.66476
.93	.8649	.804357	0.9644	0.9761	$\overline{1}$.96848	1075.269	2.9217	.67929
.94	.8836	.830584	0.9695	0.9796	$\overline{1}$.97313	1063.830	2.9531	.69398
.95	.9025	.857375	0.9747	0.9830	$\overline{1}$.97772	1052.632	2.9845	.70882
.96	.9216	.884736	0.9798	0.9865	$\overline{1}$.98227	1041.667	3.0159	.72382
.97	.9409	.912673	0.9849	0.9899	$\overline{1}$.98677	1030.928	3.0473	.73898
.98	.9604	.941192	0.9899	0.9933	$\overline{1}$.99123	1020.408	3.0788	.75430
.99	.9801	.970299	0.9950	0.9967	$\overline{1}$.99564	1010.101	3.1102	.76977

AMERICAN INSTITUTE OF STEEL CONSTRUCTION

FUNCTIONS OF NUMBERS

1
49

No.	Square	Cube	Square Root	Cube Root	Logarithm	1000 × Reciprocal	No. = Diameter	
							Circum.	Area
1	1	1	1.0000	1.0000	0.00000	1000.000	3.142	0.7854
2	4	8	1.4142	1.2599	0.30103	500.000	6.283	3.1416
3	9	27	1.7321	1.4422	0.47712	333.333	9.425	7.0686
4	16	64	2.0000	1.5874	0.60206	250.000	12.566	12.5664
5	25	125	2.2361	1.7100	0.69897	200.000	15.708	19.6350
6	36	216	2.4495	1.8171	0.77815	166.667	18.850	28.2743
7	49	343	2.6458	1.9129	0.84510	142.857	21.991	38.4845
8	64	512	2.8284	2.0000	0.90309	125.000	25.133	50.2655
9	81	729	3.0000	2.0801	0.95424	111.111	28.274	63.6173
10	100	1000	3.1623	2.1544	1.00000	100.000	31.416	78.5398
11	121	1331	3.3166	2.2240	1.04139	90.9091	34.558	95.0332
12	144	1728	3.4641	2.2894	1.07918	83.3333	37.699	113.097
13	169	2197	3.6056	2.3513	1.11394	76.9231	40.841	132.732
14	196	2744	3.7417	2.4101	1.14613	71.4286	43.982	153.938
15	225	3375	3.8730	2.4662	1.17609	66.6667	47.124	176.715
16	256	4096	4.0000	2.5198	1.20412	62.5000	50.265	201.062
17	289	4913	4.1231	2.5713	1.23045	58.8235	53.407	226.980
18	324	5832	4.2426	2.6207	1.25527	55.5556	56.549	254.469
19	361	6859	4.3589	2.6684	1.27875	52.6316	59.690	283.529
20	400	8000	4.4721	2.7144	1.30103	50.0000	62.832	314.159
21	441	9261	4.5826	2.7589	1.32222	47.6190	65.973	346.361
22	484	10648	4.6904	2.8020	1.34242	45.4545	69.115	380.133
23	529	12167	4.7958	2.8439	1.36173	43.4783	72.257	415.476
24	576	13824	4.8990	2.8845	1.38021	41.6667	75.398	452.389
25	625	15625	5.0000	2.9240	1.39794	40.0000	78.540	490.874
26	676	17576	5.0990	2.9625	1.41497	38.4615	81.681	530.929
27	729	19683	5.1962	3.0000	1.43136	37.0370	84.823	572.555
28	784	21952	5.2915	3.0366	1.44716	35.7143	87.965	615.752
29	841	24389	5.3852	3.0723	1.46240	34.4828	91.106	660.520
30	900	27000	5.4772	3.1072	1.47712	33.3333	94.248	706.858
31	961	29791	5.5678	3.1414	1.49136	32.2581	97.389	754.768
32	1024	32768	5.6569	3.1748	1.50515	31.2500	100.531	804.248
33	1089	35937	5.7446	3.2075	1.51851	30.3030	103.673	855.299
34	1156	39304	5.8310	3.2396	1.53148	29.4118	106.814	907.920
35	1225	42875	5.9161	3.2711	1.54407	28.5714	109.956	962.113
36	1296	46656	6.0000	3.3019	1.55630	27.7778	113.097	1017.88
37	1369	50653	6.0828	3.3322	1.56820	27.0270	116.239	1075.21
38	1444	54872	6.1644	3.3620	1.57978	26.3158	119.381	1134.11
39	1521	59319	6.2450	3.3912	1.59106	25.6410	122.522	1194.59
40	1600	64000	6.3246	3.4200	1.60206	25.0000	125.66	1256.64
41	1681	68921	6.4031	3.4482	1.61278	24.3902	128.81	1320.25
42	1764	74088	6.4807	3.4760	1.62325	23.8095	131.95	1385.44
43	1849	79507	6.5574	3.5034	1.63347	23.2558	135.09	1452.20
44	1936	85184	6.6332	3.5303	1.64345	22.7273	138.23	1520.53
45	2025	91125	6.7082	3.5569	1.65321	22.2222	141.37	1590.43
46	2116	97336	6.7823	3.5830	1.66276	21.7391	144.51	1661.90
47	2209	103823	6.8557	3.6088	1.67210	21.2766	147.65	1734.94
48	2304	110592	6.9282	3.6342	1.68124	20.8333	150.80	1809.56
49	2401	117649	7.0000	3.6593	1.69020	20.4082	153.94	1885.74

FUNCTIONS OF NUMBERS

No.	Square	Cube	Square Root	Cube Root	Logarithm	1000 × Reciprocal	No. = Diameter	
							Circum.	Area
50	2500	125000	7.0711	3.6840	1.69897	20.0000	157.08	1963.50
51	2601	132651	7.1414	3.7084	1.70757	19.6078	160.22	2042.82
52	2704	140608	7.2111	3.7325	1.71600	19.2308	163.36	2123.72
53	2809	148877	7.2801	3.7563	1.72428	18.8679	166.50	2206.18
54	2916	157464	7.3485	3.7798	1.73239	18.5185	169.65	2290.22
55	3025	166375	7.4162	3.8030	1.74036	18.1818	172.79	2375.83
56	3136	175616	7.4833	3.8259	1.74819	17.8571	175.93	2463.01
57	3249	185193	7.5498	3.8485	1.75587	17.5439	179.07	2551.76
58	3364	195112	7.6158	3.8709	1.76343	17.2414	182.21	2642.08
59	3481	205379	7.6811	3.8930	1.77085	16.9492	185.35	2733.97
60	3600	216000	7.7460	3.9149	1.77815	16.6667	188.50	2827.43
61	3721	226981	7.8102	3.9365	1.78533	16.3934	191.64	2922.47
62	3844	238328	7.8740	3.9579	1.79239	16.1290	194.78	3019.07
63	3969	250047	7.9373	3.9791	1.79934	15.8730	197.92	3117.25
64	4096	262144	8.0000	4.0000	1.80618	15.6250	201.06	3216.99
65	4225	274625	8.0623	4.0207	1.81291	15.3846	204.20	3318.31
66	4356	287496	8.1240	4.0412	1.81954	15.1515	207.35	3421.19
67	4489	300763	8.1854	4.0615	1.82607	14.9254	210.49	3525.65
68	4624	314432	8.2462	4.0817	1.83251	14.7059	213.63	3631.68
69	4761	328509	8.3066	4.1016	1.83885	14.4928	216.77	3739.28
70	4900	343000	8.3666	4.1213	1.84510	14.2857	219.91	3848.45
71	5041	357911	8.4261	4.1408	1.85126	14.0845	223.05	3959.19
72	5184	373248	8.4853	4.1602	1.85733	13.8889	226.19	4071.50
73	5329	389017	8.5440	4.1793	1.86332	13.6986	229.34	4185.39
74	5476	405224	8.6023	4.1983	1.86923	13.5135	232.48	4300.84
75	5625	421875	8.6603	4.2172	1.87506	13.3333	235.62	4417.86
76	5776	438976	8.7178	4.2358	1.88081	13.1579	238.76	4536.46
77	5929	456533	8.7750	4.2543	1.88649	12.9870	241.90	4656.63
78	6084	474552	8.8318	4.2727	1.89209	12.8205	245.04	4778.36
79	6241	493039	8.8882	4.2908	1.89763	12.6582	248.19	4901.67
80	6400	512000	8.9443	4.3089	1.90309	12.5000	251.33	5026.55
81	6561	531441	9.0000	4.3267	1.90849	12.3457	254.47	5153.00
82	6724	551368	9.0554	4.3445	1.91381	12.1951	257.61	5281.02
83	6889	571787	9.1104	4.3621	1.91908	12.0482	260.75	5410.61
84	7056	592704	9.1652	4.3795	1.92428	11.9048	263.89	5541.77
85	7225	614125	9.2195	4.3968	1.92942	11.7647	267.04	5674.50
86	7396	636056	9.2736	4.4140	1.93450	11.6279	270.18	5808.80
87	7569	658503	9.3274	4.4310	1.93952	11.4943	273.32	5944.68
88	7744	681472	9.3808	4.4480	1.94448	11.3636	276.46	6082.12
89	7921	704969	9.4340	4.4647	1.94939	11.2360	279.60	6221.14
90	8100	729000	9.4868	4.4814	1.95424	11.1111	282.74	6361.73
91	8281	753571	9.5394	4.4979	1.95904	10.9890	285.88	6503.88
92	8464	778688	9.5917	4.5144	1.96379	10.8696	289.03	6647.61
93	8649	804357	9.6437	4.5307	1.96848	10.7527	292.17	6792.91
94	8836	830584	9.6954	4.5468	1.97313	10.6383	295.31	6939.78
95	9025	857375	9.7468	4.5629	1.97772	10.5263	298.45	7088.22
96	9216	884736	9.7980	4.5789	1.98227	10.4167	301.59	7238.23
97	9409	912673	9.8489	4.5947	1.98677	10.3093	304.73	7389.81
98	9604	941192	9.8995	4.6104	1.99123	10.2041	307.88	7542.96
99	9801	970299	9.9499	4.6261	1.99564	10.1010	311.02	7697.69

FUNCTIONS OF NUMBERS

100
149

No.	Square	Cube	Square Root	Cube Root	Logarithm	1000 × Reciprocal	No. = Diameter Circum.	No. = Diameter Area
100	10000	1000000	10.0000	4.6416	2.00000	10.0000	314.16	7853.98
101	10201	1030301	10.0499	4.6570	2.00432	9.90099	317.30	8011.85
102	10404	1061208	10.0995	4.6723	2.00860	9.80392	320.44	8171.28
103	10609	1092727	10.1489	4.6875	2.01284	9.70874	323.58	8332.29
104	10816	1124864	10.1980	4.7027	2.01703	9.61538	326.73	8494.87
105	11025	1157625	10.2470	4.7177	2.02119	9.52381	329.87	8659.01
106	11236	1191016	10.2956	4.7326	2.02531	9.43396	333.01	8824.73
107	11449	1225043	10.3441	4.7475	2.02938	9.34579	336.15	8992.02
108	11664	1259712	10.3923	4.7622	2.03342	9.25926	339.29	9160.88
109	11881	1295029	10.4403	4.7769	2.03743	9.17431	342.43	9331.32
110	12100	1331000	10.4881	4.7914	2.04139	9.09091	345.58	9503.32
111	12321	1367631	10.5357	4.8059	2.04532	9.00901	348.72	9676.89
112	12544	1404928	10.5830	4.8203	2.04922	8.92857	351.86	9852.03
113	12769	1442897	10.6301	4.8346	2.05308	8.84956	355.00	10028.7
114	12996	1481544	10.6771	4.8488	2.05690	8.77193	358.14	10207.0
115	13225	1520875	10.7238	4.8629	2.06070	8.69565	361.28	10386.9
116	13456	1560896	10.7703	4.8770	2.06446	8.62069	364.42	10568.3
117	13689	1601613	10.8167	4.8910	2.06819	8.54701	367.57	10751.3
118	13924	1643032	10.8628	4.9049	2.07188	8.47458	370.71	10935.9
119	14161	1685159	10.9087	4.9187	2.07555	8.40336	373.85	11122.0
120	14400	1728000	10.9545	4.9324	2.07918	8.33333	376.99	11309.7
121	14641	1771561	11.0000	4.9461	2.08279	8.26446	380.13	11499.0
122	14884	1815848	11.0454	4.9597	2.08636	8.19672	383.27	11689.9
123	15129	1860867	11.0905	4.9732	2.08991	8.13008	386.42	11882.3
124	15376	1906624	11.1355	4.9866	2.09342	8.06452	389.56	12076.3
125	15625	1953125	11.1803	5.0000	2.09691	8.00000	392.70	12271.8
126	15876	2000376	11.2250	5.0133	2.10037	7.93651	395.84	12469.0
127	16129	2048383	11.2694	5.0265	2.10380	7.87402	398.98	12667.7
128	16384	2097152	11.3137	5.0397	2.10721	7.81250	402.12	12868.0
129	16641	2146689	11.3578	5.0528	2.11059	7.75194	405.27	13069.8
130	16900	2197000	11.4018	5.0658	2.11394	7.69231	408.41	13273.2
131	17161	2248091	11.4455	5.0788	2.11727	7.63359	411.55	13478.2
132	17424	2299968	11.4891	5.0916	2.12057	7.57576	414.69	13684.8
133	17689	2352637	11.5326	5.1045	2.12385	7.51880	417.83	13892.9
134	17956	2406104	11.5758	5.1172	2.12710	7.46269	420.97	14102.6
135	18225	2460375	11.6190	5.1299	2.13033	7.40741	424.12	14313.9
136	18496	2515456	11.6619	5.1426	2.13354	7.35294	427.26	14526.7
137	18769	2571353	11.7047	5.1551	2.13672	7.29927	430.40	14741.1
138	19044	2628072	11.7473	5.1676	2.13988	7.24638	433.54	14957.1
139	19321	2685619	11.7898	5.1801	2.14301	7.19424	436.68	15174.7
140	19600	2744000	11.8322	5.1925	2.14613	7.14286	439.82	15393.8
141	19881	2803221	11.8743	5.2048	2.14922	7.09220	442.96	15614.5
142	20164	2863288	11.9164	5.2171	2.15229	7.04225	446.11	15836.8
143	20449	2924207	11.9583	5.2293	2.15534	6.99301	449.25	16060.6
144	20736	2985984	12.0000	5.2415	2.15836	6.94444	452.39	16286.0
145	21025	3048625	12.0416	5.2536	2.16137	6.89655	455.53	16513.0
146	21316	3112136	12.0830	5.2656	2.16435	6.84932	458.67	16741.5
147	21609	3176523	12.1244	5.2776	2.16732	6.80272	461.81	16971.7
148	21904	3241792	12.1655	5.2896	2.17026	6.75676	464.96	17203.4
149	22201	3307949	12.2066	5.3015	2.17319	6.71141	468.10	17436.6

FUNCTIONS OF NUMBERS

No.	Square	Cube	Square Root	Cube Root	Logarithm	1000 × Reciprocal	No. = Diameter	
							Circum.	Area
150	22500	3375000	12.2474	5.3133	2.17609	6.66667	471.24	17671.5
151	22801	3442951	12.2882	5.3251	2.17898	6.62252	474.38	17907.9
152	23104	3511808	12.3288	5.3368	2.18184	6.57895	477.52	18145.8
153	23409	3581577	12.3693	5.3485	2.18469	6.53595	480.66	18385.4
154	23716	3652264	12.4097	5.3601	2.18752	6.49351	483.81	18626.5
155	24025	3723875	12.4499	5.3717	2.19033	6.45161	486.95	18869.2
156	24336	3796416	12.4900	5.3832	2.19312	6.41026	490.09	19113.4
157	24649	3869893	12.5300	5.3947	2.19590	6.36943	493.23	19359.3
158	24964	3944312	12.5698	5.4061	2.19866	6.32911	496.37	19606.7
159	25281	4019679	12.6095	5.4175	2.20140	6.28931	499.51	19855.7
160	25600	4096000	12.6491	5.4288	2.20412	6.25000	502.65	20106.2
161	25921	4173281	12.6886	5.4401	2.20683	6.21118	505.80	20358.3
162	26244	4251528	12.7279	5.4514	2.20952	6.17284	508.94	20612.0
163	26569	4330747	12.7671	5.4626	2.21219	6.13497	512.08	20867.2
164	26896	4410944	12.8062	5.4737	2.21484	6.09756	515.22	21124.1
165	27225	4492125	12.8452	5.4848	2.21748	6.06061	518.36	21382.5
166	27556	4574296	12.8841	5.4959	2.22011	6.02410	521.50	21642.4
167	27889	4657463	12.9228	5.5069	2.22272	5.98802	524.65	21904.0
168	28224	4741632	12.9615	5.5178	2.22531	5.95238	527.79	22167.1
169	28561	4826809	13.0000	5.5288	2.22789	5.91716	530.93	22431.8
170	28900	4913000	13.0384	5.5397	2.23045	5.88235	534.07	22698.0
171	29241	5000211	13.0767	5.5505	2.23300	5.84795	537.21	22965.8
172	29584	5088448	13.1149	5.5613	2.23553	5.81395	540.35	23235.2
173	29929	5177717	13.1529	5.5721	2.23805	5.78035	543.50	23506.2
174	30276	5268024	13.1909	5.5828	2.24055	5.74713	546.64	23778.7
175	30625	5359375	13.2288	5.5934	2.24304	5.71429	549.78	24052.8
176	30976	5451776	13.2665	5.6041	2.24551	5.68182	552.92	24328.5
177	31329	5545233	13.3041	5.6147	2.24797	5.64972	556.06	24605.7
178	31684	5639752	13.3417	5.6252	2.25042	5.61798	559.20	24884.6
179	32041	5735339	13.3791	5.6357	2.25285	5.58659	562.35	25164.9
180	32400	5832000	13.4164	5.6462	2.25527	5.55556	565.49	25446.9
181	32761	5929741	13.4536	5.6567	2.25768	5.52486	568.63	25730.4
182	33124	6028568	13.4907	5.6671	2.26007	5.49451	571.77	26015.5
183	33489	6128487	13.5277	5.6774	2.26245	5.46448	574.91	26302.2
184	33856	6229504	13.5647	5.6877	2.26482	5.43478	578.05	26590.4
185	34225	6331625	13.6015	5.6980	2.26717	5.40541	581.19	26880.3
186	34596	6434856	13.6382	5.7083	2.26951	5.37634	584.34	27171.6
187	34969	6539203	13.6748	5.7185	2.27184	5.34759	587.48	27464.6
188	35344	6644672	13.7113	5.7287	2.27416	5.31915	590.62	27759.1
189	35721	6751269	13.7477	5.7388	2.27646	5.29101	593.76	28055.2
190	36100	6859000	13.7840	5.7489	2.27875	5.26316	596.90	28352.9
191	36481	6967871	13.8203	5.7590	2.28103	5.23560	600.04	28652.1
192	36864	7077888	13.8564	5.7690	2.28330	5.20833	603.19	28952.9
193	37249	7189057	13.8924	5.7790	2.28556	5.18135	606.33	29255.3
194	37636	7301384	13.9284	5.7890	2.28780	5.15464	609.47	29559.2
195	38025	7414875	13.9642	5.7989	2.29003	5.12821	612.61	29864.8
196	38416	7529536	14.0000	5.8088	2.29226	5.10204	615.75	30171.9
197	38809	7645373	14.0357	5.8186	2.29447	5.07614	618.89	30480.5
198	39204	7762392	14.0712	5.8285	2.29667	5.05051	622.04	30790.7
199	39601	7880599	14.1067	5.8383	2.29885	5.02513	625.18	31102.6

FUNCTIONS OF NUMBERS

No.	Square	Cube	Square Root	Cube Root	Logarithm	1000 × Reciprocal	No. = Diameter	
							Circum.	Area
200	40000	8000000	14.1421	5.8480	2.30103	5.00000	628.32	31415.9
201	40401	8120601	14.1774	5.8578	2.30320	4.97512	631.46	31730.9
202	40804	8242408	14.2127	5.8675	2.30535	4.95050	634.60	32047.4
203	41209	8365427	14.2478	5.8771	2.30750	4.92611	637.74	32365.5
204	41616	8489664	14.2829	5.8868	2.30963	4.90196	640.88	32685.1
205	42025	8615125	14.3178	5.8964	2.31175	4.87805	644.03	33006.4
206	42436	8741816	14.3527	5.9059	2.31387	4.85437	647.17	33329.2
207	42849	8869743	14.3875	5.9155	2.31597	4.83092	650.31	33653.5
208	43264	8998912	14.4222	5.9250	2.31806	4.80769	653.45	33979.5
209	43681	9129329	14.4568	5.9345	2.32015	4.78469	656.59	34307.0
210	44100	9261000	14.4914	5.9439	2.32222	4.76190	659.73	34636.1
211	44521	9393931	14.5258	5.9533	2.32428	4.73934	662.88	34966.7
212	44944	9528128	14.5602	5.9627	2.32634	4.71698	666.02	35298.9
213	45369	9663597	14.5945	5.9721	2.32838	4.69484	669.16	35632.7
214	45796	9800344	14.6287	5.9814	2.33041	4.67290	672.30	35968.1
215	46225	9938375	14.6629	5.9907	2.33244	4.65116	675.44	36305.0
216	46656	10077696	14.6969	6.0000	2.33445	4.62963	678.58	36643.5
217	47089	10218313	14.7309	6.0092	2.33646	4.60829	681.73	36983.6
218	47524	10360232	14.7648	6.0185	2.33846	4.58716	684.87	37325.3
219	47961	10503459	14.7986	6.0277	2.34044	4.56621	688.01	37668.5
220	48400	10648000	14.8324	6.0368	2.34242	4.54545	691.15	38013.3
221	48841	10793861	14.8661	6.0459	2.34439	4.52489	694.29	38359.6
222	49284	10941048	14.8997	6.0550	2.34635	4.50450	697.43	38707.6
223	49729	11089567	14.9332	6.0641	2.34830	4.48430	700.58	39057.1
224	50176	11239424	14.9666	6.0732	2.35025	4.46429	703.72	39408.1
225	50625	11390625	15.0000	6.0822	2.35218	4.44444	706.86	39760.8
226	51076	11543176	15.0333	6.0912	2.35411	4.42478	710.00	40115.0
227	51529	11697083	15.0665	6.1002	2.35603	4.40529	713.14	40470.8
228	51984	11852352	15.0997	6.1091	2.35793	4.38596	716.28	40828.1
229	52441	12008989	15.1327	6.1180	2.35984	4.36681	719.42	41187.1
230	52900	12167000	15.1658	6.1269	2.36173	4.34783	722.57	41547.6
231	53361	12326391	15.1987	6.1358	2.36361	4.32900	725.71	41909.6
232	53824	12487168	15.2315	6.1446	2.36549	4.31034	728.85	42273.3
233	54289	12649337	15.2643	6.1534	2.36736	4.29185	731.99	42638.5
234	54756	12812904	15.2971	6.1622	2.36922	4.27350	735.13	43005.3
235	55225	12977875	15.3297	6.1710	2.37107	4.25532	738.27	43373.6
236	55696	13144256	15.3623	6.1797	2.37291	4.23729	741.42	43743.5
237	56169	13312053	15.3948	6.1885	2.37475	4.21941	744.56	44115.0
238	56644	13481272	15.4272	6.1972	2.37658	4.20168	747.70	44488.1
239	57121	13651919	15.4596	6.2058	2.37840	4.18410	750.84	44862.7
240	57600	13824000	15.4919	6.2145	2.38021	4.16667	753.98	45238.9
241	58081	13997521	15.5242	6.2231	2.38202	4.14938	757.12	45616.7
242	58564	14172488	15.5563	6.2317	2.38382	4.13223	760.27	45996.1
243	59049	14348907	15.5885	6.2403	2.38561	4.11523	763.41	46377.0
244	59536	14526784	15.6205	6.2488	2.38739	4.09836	766.55	46759.5
245	60025	14706125	15.6525	6.2573	2.38917	4.08163	769.69	47143.5
246	60516	14886936	15.6844	6.2658	2.39094	4.06504	772.83	47529.2
247	61009	15069223	15.7162	6.2743	2.39270	4.04858	775.97	47916.4
248	61504	15252992	15.7480	6.2828	2.39445	4.03226	779.12	48305.1
249	62001	15438249	15.7797	6.2912	2.39620	4.01606	782.26	48695.5

FUNCTIONS OF NUMBERS

No.	Square	Cube	Square Root	Cube Root	Logarithm	1000 × Reciprocal	No. = Diameter	
							Circum.	Area
250	62500	15625000	15.8114	6.2996	2.39794	4.00000	785.40	49087.4
251	63001	15813251	15.8430	6.3080	2.39967	3.98406	788.54	49480.9
252	63504	16003008	15.8745	6.3164	2.40140	3.96825	791.68	49875.9
253	64009	16194277	15.9060	6.3247	2.40312	3.95257	794.82	50272.6
254	64516	16387064	15.9374	6.3330	2.40483	3.93701	797.96	50670.7
255	65025	16581375	15.9687	6.3413	2.40654	3.92157	801.11	51070.5
256	65536	16777216	16.0000	6.3496	2.40824	3.90625	804.25	51471.9
257	66049	16974593	16.0312	6.3579	2.40993	3.89105	807.39	51874.8
258	66564	17173512	16.0624	6.3661	2.41162	3.87597	810.53	52279.2
259	67081	17373979	16.0935	6.3743	2.41330	3.86100	813.67	52685.3
260	67600	17576000	16.1245	6.3825	2.41497	3.84615	816.81	53092.9
261	68121	17779581	16.1555	6.3907	2.41664	3.83142	819.96	53502.1
262	68644	17984728	16.1864	6.3988	2.41830	3.81679	823.10	53912.9
263	69169	18191447	16.2173	6.4070	2.41996	3.80228	826.24	54325.2
264	69696	18399744	16.2481	6.4151	2.42160	3.78788	829.38	54739.1
265	70225	18609625	16.2788	6.4232	2.42325	3.77358	832.52	55154.6
266	70756	18821096	16.3095	6.4312	2.42488	3.75940	835.66	55571.6
267	71289	19034163	16.3401	6.4393	2.42651	3.74532	838.81	55990.2
268	71824	19248832	16.3707	6.4473	2.42813	3.73134	841.95	56410.4
269	72361	19465109	16.4012	6.4553	2.42975	3.71747	845.09	56832.2
270	72900	19683000	16.4317	6.4633	2.43136	3.70370	848.23	57255.5
271	73441	19902511	16.4621	6.4713	2.43297	3.69004	851.37	57680.4
272	73984	20123648	16.4924	6.4792	2.43457	3.67647	854.51	58106.9
273	74529	20346417	16.5227	6.4872	2.43616	3.66300	857.65	58534.9
274	75076	20570824	16.5529	6.4951	2.43775	3.64964	860.80	58964.6
275	75625	20796875	16.5831	6.5030	2.43933	3.63636	863.94	59395.7
276	76176	21024576	16.6132	6.5108	2.44091	3.62319	867.08	59828.5
277	76729	21253933	16.6433	6.5187	2.44248	3.61011	870.22	60262.8
278	77284	21484952	16.6733	6.5265	2.44404	3.59712	873.36	60698.7
279	77841	21717639	16.7033	6.5343	2.44560	3.58423	876.50	61136.2
280	78400	21952000	16.7332	6.5421	2.44716	3.57143	879.65	61575.2
281	78961	22188041	16.7631	6.5499	2.44871	3.55872	882.79	62015.8
282	79524	22425768	16.7929	6.5577	2.45025	3.54610	885.93	62458.0
283	80089	22665187	16.8226	6.5654	2.45179	3.53357	889.07	62901.8
284	80656	22906304	16.8523	6.5731	2.45332	3.52113	892.21	63347.1
285	81225	23149125	16.8819	6.5808	2.45484	3.50877	895.35	63794.0
286	81796	23393656	16.9115	6.5885	2.45637	3.49650	898.50	64242.4
287	82369	23639903	16.9411	6.5962	2.45788	3.48432	901.64	64692.5
288	82944	23887872	16.9706	6.6039	2.45939	3.47222	904.78	65144.1
289	83521	24137569	17.0000	6.6115	2.46090	3.46021	907.92	65597.2
290	84100	24389000	17.0294	6.6191	2.46240	3.44828	911.06	66052.0
291	84681	24642171	17.0587	6.6267	2.46389	3.43643	914.20	66508.3
292	85264	24897088	17.0880	6.6343	2.46538	3.42466	917.35	66966.2
293	85849	25153757	17.1172	6.6419	2.46687	3.41297	920.49	67425.6
294	86436	25412184	17.1464	6.6494	2.46835	3.40136	923.63	67886.7
295	87025	25672375	17.1756	6.6569	2.46982	3.38983	926.77	68349.3
296	87616	25934336	17.2047	6.6644	2.47129	3.37838	929.91	68813.4
297	88209	26198073	17.2337	6.6719	2.47276	3.36700	933.05	69279.2
298	88804	26463592	17.2627	6.6794	2.47422	3.35570	936.19	69746.5
299	89401	26730899	17.2916	6.6869	2.47567	3.34448	939.34	70215.4

300
349

FUNCTIONS OF NUMBERS

No.	Square	Cube	Square Root	Cube Root	Logarithm	1000 × Reciprocal	No. = Diameter Circum.	No. = Diameter Area
300	90000	27000000	17.3205	6.6943	2.47712	3.33333	942.48	70685.8
301	90601	27270901	17.3494	6.7018	2.47857	3.32226	945.62	71157.9
302	91204	27543608	17.3781	6.7092	2.48001	3.31126	948.76	71631.5
303	91809	27818127	17.4069	6.7166	2.48144	3.30033	951.90	72106.6
304	92416	28094464	17.4356	6.7240	2.48287	3.28947	955.04	72583.4
305	93025	28372625	17.4642	6.7313	2.48430	3.27869	958.19	73061.7
306	93636	28652616	17.4929	6.7387	2.48572	3.26797	961.33	73541.5
307	94249	28934443	17.5214	6.7460	2.48714	3.25733	964.47	74023.0
308	94864	29218112	17.5499	6.7533	2.48855	3.24675	967.61	74506.0
309	95481	29503629	17.5784	6.7606	2.48996	3.23625	970.75	74990.6
310	96100	29791000	17.6068	6.7679	2.49136	3.22581	973.89	75476.8
311	96721	30080231	17.6352	6.7752	2.49276	3.21543	977.04	75964.5
312	97344	30371328	17.6635	6.7824	2.49415	3.20513	980.18	76453.8
313	97969	30664297	17.6918	6.7897	2.49554	3.19489	983.32	76944.7
314	98596	30959144	17.7200	6.7969	2.49693	3.18471	986.46	77437.1
315	99225	31255875	17.7482	6.8041	2.49831	3.17460	989.60	77931.1
316	99856	31554496	17.7764	6.8113	2.49969	3.16456	992.74	78426.7
317	100489	31855013	17.8045	6.8185	2.50106	3.15457	995.88	78923.9
318	101124	32157432	17.8326	6.8256	2.50243	3.14465	999.03	79422.6
319	101761	32461759	17.8606	6.8328	2.50379	3.13480	1002.2	79922.9
320	102400	32768000	17.8885	6.8399	2.50515	3.12500	1005.3	80424.8
321	103041	33076161	17.9165	6.8470	2.50651	3.11526	1008.5	80928.2
322	103684	33386248	17.9444	6.8541	2.50786	3.10559	1011.6	81433.2
323	104329	33698267	17.9722	6.8612	2.50920	3.09598	1014.7	81939.8
324	104976	34012224	18.0000	6.8683	2.51055	3.08642	1017.9	82448.0
325	105625	34328125	18.0278	6.8753	2.51188	3.07692	1021.0	82957.7
326	106276	34645976	18.0555	6.8824	2.51322	3.06749	1024.2	83469.0
327	106929	34965783	18.0831	6.8894	2.51455	3.05810	1027.3	83981.8
328	107584	35287552	18.1108	6.8964	2.51587	3.04878	1030.4	84496.3
329	108241	35611289	18.1384	6.9034	2.51720	3.03951	1033.6	85012.3
330	108900	35937000	18.1659	6.9104	2.51851	3.03030	1036.7	85529.9
331	109561	36264691	18.1934	6.9174	2.51983	3.02115	1039.9	86049.0
332	110224	36594368	18.2209	6.9244	2.52114	3.01205	1043.0	86569.7
333	110889	36926037	18.2483	6.9313	2.52244	3.00300	1046.2	87092.0
334	111556	37259704	18.2757	6.9382	2.52375	2.99401	1049.3	87615.9
335	112225	37595375	18.3030	6.9451	2.52504	2.98507	1052.4	88141.3
336	112896	37933056	18.3303	6.9521	2.52634	2.97619	1055.6	88668.3
337	113569	38272753	18.3576	6.9589	2.52763	2.96736	1058.7	89196.9
338	114244	38614472	18.3848	6.9658	2.52892	2.95858	1061.9	89727.0
339	114921	38958219	18.4120	6.9727	2.53020	2.94985	1065.0	90258.7
340	115600	39304000	18.4391	6.9795	2.53148	2.94118	1068.1	90792.0
341	116281	39651821	18.4662	6.9864	2.53275	2.93255	1071.3	91326.9
342	116964	40001688	18.4932	6.9932	2.53403	2.92398	1074.4	91863.3
343	117649	40353607	18.5203	7.0000	2.53529	2.91545	1077.6	92401.3
344	118336	40707584	18.5472	7.0068	2.53656	2.90698	1080.7	92940.9
345	119025	41063625	18.5742	7.0136	2.53782	2.89855	1083.8	93482.0
346	119716	41421736	18.6011	7.0203	2.53908	2.89017	1087.0	94024.7
347	120409	41781923	18.6279	7.0271	2.54033	2.88184	1090.1	94569.0
348	121104	42144192	18.6548	7.0338	2.54158	2.87356	1093.3	95114.9
349	121801	42508549	18.6815	7.0406	2.54283	2.86533	1096.4	95662.3

FUNCTIONS OF NUMBERS

No.	Square	Cube	Square Root	Cube Root	Logarithm	1000 × Reciprocal	No. = Diameter	
							Circum.	Area
350	122500	42875000	18.7083	7.0473	2.54407	2.85714	1099.6	96211.3
351	123201	43243551	18.7350	7.0540	2.54531	2.84900	1102.7	96761.8
352	123904	43614208	18.7617	7.0607	2.54654	2.84091	1105.8	97314.0
353	124609	43986977	18.7883	7.0674	2.54777	2.83286	1109.0	97867.7
354	125316	44361864	18.8149	7.0740	2.54900	2.82486	1112.1	98423.0
355	126025	44738875	18.8414	7.0807	2.55023	2.81690	1115.3	98979.8
356	126736	45118016	18.8680	7.0873	2.55145	2.80899	1118.4	99538.2
357	127449	45499293	18.8944	7.0940	2.55267	2.80112	1121.5	100098
358	128164	45882712	18.9209	7.1006	2.55388	2.79330	1124.7	100660
359	128881	46268279	18.9473	7.1072	2.55509	2.78552	1127.8	101223
360	129600	46656000	18.9737	7.1138	2.55630	2.77778	1131.0	101788
361	130321	47045881	19.0000	7.1204	2.55751	2.77008	1134.1	102354
362	131044	47437928	19.0263	7.1269	2.55871	2.76243	1137.3	102922
363	131769	47832147	19.0526	7.1335	2.55991	2.75482	1140.4	103491
364	132496	48228544	19.0788	7.1400	2.56110	2.74725	1143.5	104062
365	133225	48627125	19.1050	7.1466	2.56229	2.73973	1146.7	104635
366	133956	49027896	19.1311	7.1531	2.56348	2.73224	1149.8	105209
367	134689	49430863	19.1572	7.1596	2.56467	2.72480	1153.0	105785
368	135424	49836032	19.1833	7.1661	2.56585	2.71739	1156.1	106362
369	136161	50243409	19.2094	7.1726	2.56703	2.71003	1159.2	106941
370	136900	50653000	19.2354	7.1791	2.56820	2.70270	1162.4	107521
371	137641	51064811	19.2614	7.1855	2.56937	2.69542	1165.5	108103
372	138384	51478848	19.2873	7.1920	2.57054	2.68817	1168.7	108687
373	139129	51895117	19.3132	7.1984	2.57171	2.68097	1171.8	109272
374	139876	52313624	19.3391	7.2048	2.57287	2.67380	1175.0	109858
375	140625	52734375	19.3649	7.2112	2.57403	2.66676	1178.1	110447
376	141376	53157376	19.3907	7.2177	2.57519	2.65957	1181.2	111036
377	142129	53582633	19.4165	7.2240	2.57634	2.65252	1184.4	111628
378	142884	54010152	19.4422	7.2304	2.57749	2.64550	1187.5	112221
379	143641	54439939	19.4679	7.2368	2.57864	2.63852	1190.7	112815
380	144400	54872000	19.4936	7.2432	2.57978	2.63158	1193.8	113411
381	145161	55306341	19.5192	7.2495	2.58093	2.62467	1196.9	114009
382	145924	55742968	19.5448	7.2558	2.58206	2.61780	1200.1	114608
383	146689	56181887	19.5704	7.2622	2.58320	2.61097	1203.2	115209
384	147456	56623104	19.5959	7.2685	2.58433	2.60417	1206.4	115812
385	148225	57066625	19.6214	7.2748	2.58546	2.59740	1209.5	116416
386	148996	57512456	19.6469	7.2811	2.58659	2.59067	1212.7	117021
387	149769	57960603	19.6723	7.2874	2.58771	2.58398	1215.8	117628
388	150544	58411072	19.6977	7.2936	2.58883	2.57732	1218.9	118237
389	151321	58863869	19.7231	7.2999	2.58995	2.57069	1222.1	118847
390	152100	59319000	19.7484	7.3061	2.59106	2.56410	1225.2	119459
391	152881	59776471	19.7737	7.3124	2.59218	2.55754	1228.4	120072
392	153664	60236288	19.7990	7.3186	2.59329	2.55102	1231.5	120687
393	154449	60698457	19.8242	7.3248	2.59439	2.54453	1234.6	121304
394	155236	61162984	19.8494	7.3310	2.59550	2.53807	1237.8	121922
395	156025	61629875	19.8746	7.3372	2.59660	2.53165	1240.9	122542
396	156816	62099136	19.8997	7.3434	2.59770	2.52525	1244.1	123163
397	157609	62570773	19.9249	7.3496	2.59879	2.51889	1247.2	123786
398	158404	63044792	19.9499	7.3558	2.59988	2.51256	1250.4	124410
399	159201	63521199	19.9750	7.3619	2.60097	2.50627	1253.5	125036

400
449

FUNCTIONS OF NUMBERS

No.	Square	Cube	Square Root	Cube Root	Logarithm	1000 × Reciprocal	No. = Diameter	
							Circum.	Area
400	160000	64000000	20.0000	7.3681	2.60206	2.50000	1256.6	125664
401	160801	64481201	20.0250	7.3742	2.60314	2.49377	1259.8	126293
402	161604	64964808	20.0499	7.3803	2.60423	2.48756	1262.9	126923
403	162409	65450827	20.0749	7.3864	2.60531	2.48139	1266.1	127556
404	163216	65939264	20.0998	7.3925	2.60638	2.47525	1269.2	128190
405	164025	66430125	20.1246	7.3986	2.60746	2.46914	1272.3	128825
406	164836	66923416	20.1494	7.4047	2.60853	2.46305	1275.5	129462
407	165649	67419143	20.1742	7.4108	2.60959	2.45700	1278.6	130100
408	166464	67917312	20.1990	7.4169	2.61066	2.45098	1281.8	130741
409	167281	68417929	20.2237	7.4229	2.61172	2.44499	1284.9	131382
410	168100	68921000	20.2485	7.4290	2.61278	2.43902	1288.1	132025
411	168921	69426531	20.2731	7.4350	2.61384	2.43309	1291.2	132670
412	169744	69934528	20.2978	7.4410	2.61490	2.42718	1294.3	133317
413	170569	70444997	20.3224	7.4470	2.61595	2.42131	1297.5	133965
414	171396	70957944	20.3470	7.4530	2.61700	2.41546	1300.6	134614
415	172225	71473375	20.3715	7.4590	2.61805	2.40964	1303.8	135265
416	173056	71991296	20.3961	7.4650	2.61909	2.40385	1306.9	135918
417	173889	72511713	20.4206	7.4710	2.62014	2.39808	1310.0	136572
418	174724	73034632	20.4450	7.4770	2.62118	2.39234	1313.2	137228
419	175561	73560059	20.4695	7.4829	2.62221	2.38663	1316.3	137885
420	176400	74088000	20.4939	7.4889	2.62325	2.38095	1319.5	138544
421	177241	74618461	20.5183	7.4948	2.62428	2.37530	1322.6	139205
422	178084	75151448	20.5426	7.5007	2.62531	2.36967	1325.8	139867
423	178929	75686967	20.5670	7.5067	2.62634	2.36407	1328.9	140531
424	179776	76225024	20.5913	7.5126	2.62737	2.35849	1332.0	141196
425	180625	76765625	20.6155	7.5185	2.62839	2.35294	1335.2	141863
426	181476	77308776	20.6398	7.5244	2.62941	2.34742	1338.3	142531
427	182329	77854483	20.6640	7.5302	2.63043	2.34192	1341.5	143201
428	183184	78402752	20.6882	7.5361	2.63144	2.33645	1344.6	143872
429	184041	78953589	20.7123	7.5420	2.63246	2.33100	1347.7	144545
430	184900	79507000	20.7364	7.5478	2.63347	2.32558	1350.9	145220
431	185761	80062991	20.7605	7.5537	2.63448	2.32019	1354.0	145896
432	186624	80621568	20.7846	7.5595	2.63548	2.31481	1357.2	146574
433	187489	81182737	20.8087	7.5654	2.63649	2.30947	1360.3	147254
434	188356	81746504	20.8327	7.5712	2.63749	2.30415	1363.5	147934
435	189225	82312875	20.8567	7.5770	2.63849	2.29885	1366.6	148617
436	190096	82881856	20.8806	7.5828	2.63949	2.29358	1369.7	149301
437	190969	83453453	20.9045	7.5886	2.64048	2.28833	1372.9	149987
438	191844	84027672	20.9284	7.5944	2.64147	2.28311	1376.0	150674
439	192721	84604519	20.9523	7.6001	2.64246	2.27790	1379.2	151363
440	193600	85184000	20.9762	7.6059	2.64345	2.27273	1382.3	152053
441	194481	85766121	21.0000	7.6117	2.64444	2.26757	1385.4	152745
442	195364	86350888	21.0238	7.6174	2.64542	2.26244	1388.6	153439
443	196249	86938307	21.0476	7.6232	2.64640	2.25734	1391.7	154134
444	197136	87528384	21.0713	7.6289	2.64738	2.25225	1394.9	154830
445	198025	88121125	21.0950	7.6346	2.64836	2.24719	1398.0	155528
446	198916	88716536	21.1187	7.6403	2.64933	2.24215	1401.2	156228
447	199809	89314623	21.1424	7.6460	2.65031	2.23714	1404.3	156930
448	200704	89915392	21.1660	7.6517	2.65128	2.23214	1407.4	157633
449	201601	90518849	21.1896	7.6574	2.65225	2.22717	1410.6	158337

FUNCTIONS OF NUMBERS

No.	Square	Cube	Square Root	Cube Root	Logarithm	1000 × Reciprocal	No. = Diameter	
							Circum.	Area
450	202500	91125000	21.2132	7.6631	2.65321	2.22222	1413.7	159043
451	203401	91733851	21.2368	7.6688	2.65418	2.21729	1416.9	159751
452	204304	92345408	21.2603	7.6744	2.65514	2.21239	1420.0	160460
453	205209	92959677	21.2838	7.6801	2.65610	2.20751	1423.1	161171
454	206116	93576664	21.3073	7.6857	2.65706	2.20264	1426.3	161883
455	207025	94196375	21.3307	7.6914	2.65801	2.19780	1429.4	162597
456	207936	94818816	21.3542	7.6970	2.65896	2.19298	1432.6	163313
457	208849	95443993	21.3776	7.7026	2.65992	2.18818	1435.7	164030
458	209764	96071912	21.4009	7.7082	2.66087	2.18341	1438.8	164748
459	210681	96702579	21.4243	7.7138	2.66181	2.17865	1442.0	165468
460	211600	97336000	21.4476	7.7194	2.66276	2.17391	1445.1	166190
461	212521	97972181	21.4709	7.7250	2.66370	2.16920	1448.3	166914
462	213444	98611128	21.4942	7.7306	2.66464	2.16450	1451.4	167639
463	214369	99252847	21.5174	7.7362	2.66558	2.15983	1454.6	168365
464	215296	99897344	21.5407	7.7418	2.66652	2.15517	1457.7	169093
465	216225	100544625	21.5639	7.7473	2.66745	2.15054	1460.8	169823
466	217156	101194696	21.5870	7.7529	2.66839	2.14592	1464.0	170554
467	218089	101847563	21.6102	7.7584	2.66932	2.14133	1467.1	171287
468	219024	102503232	21.6333	7.7639	2.67025	2.13675	1470.3	172021
469	219961	103161709	21.6564	7.7695	2.67117	2.13220	1473.4	172757
470	220900	103823000	21.6795	7.7750	2.67210	2.12766	1476.5	173494
471	221841	104487111	21.7025	7.7805	2.67302	2.12314	1479.7	174234
472	222784	105154048	21.7256	7.7860	2.67394	2.11864	1482.8	174974
473	223729	105823817	21.7486	7.7915	2.67486	2.11416	1486.0	175716
474	224676	106496424	21.7715	7.7970	2.67578	2.10970	1489.1	176460
475	225625	107171875	21.7945	7.8025	2.67669	2.10526	1492.3	177205
476	226576	107850176	21.8174	7.8079	2.67761	2.10084	1495.4	177952
477	227529	108531333	21.8403	7.8134	2.67852	2.09644	1498.5	178701
478	228484	109215352	21.8632	7.8188	2.67943	2.09205	1501.7	179451
479	229441	109902239	21.8861	7.8243	2.68034	2.08768	1504.8	180203
480	230400	110592000	21.9089	7.8297	2.68124	2.08333	1508.0	180956
481	231361	111284641	21.9317	7.8352	2.68215	2.07900	1511.1	181711
482	232324	111980168	21.9545	7.8406	2.68305	2.07469	1514.2	182467
483	233289	112678587	21.9773	7.8460	2.68395	2.07039	1517.4	183225
484	234256	113379904	22.0000	7.8514	2.68485	2.06612	1520.5	183984
485	235225	114084125	22.0227	7.8568	2.68574	2.06186	1523.7	184745
486	236196	114791256	22.0454	7.8622	2.68664	2.05761	1526.8	185508
487	237169	115501303	22.0681	7.8676	2.68753	2.05339	1530.0	186272
488	238144	116214272	22.0907	7.8730	2.68842	2.04918	1533.1	187038
489	239121	116930169	22.1133	7.8784	2.68931	2.04499	1536.2	187805
490	240100	117649000	22.1359	7.8837	2.69020	2.04082	1539.4	188574
491	241081	118370771	22.1585	7.8891	2.69108	2.03666	1542.5	189345
492	242064	119095488	22.1811	7.8944	2.69197	2.03252	1545.7	190117
493	243049	119823157	22.2036	7.8998	2.69285	2.02840	1548.8	190890
494	244036	120553784	22.2261	7.9051	2.69373	2.02429	1551.9	191665
495	245025	121287375	22.2486	7.9105	2.69461	2.02020	1555.1	192442
496	246016	122023936	22.2711	7.9158	2.69548	2.01613	1558.2	193221
497	247009	122763473	22.2935	7.9211	2.69636	2.01207	1561.4	194000
498	248004	123505992	22.3159	7.9264	2.69723	2.00803	1564.5	194782
499	249001	124251499	22.3383	7.9317	2.69810	2.00401	1567.7	195565

500 549

FUNCTIONS OF NUMBERS

No.	Square	Cube	Square Root	Cube Root	Logarithm	1000 × Reciprocal	Circum.	Area
							No. = Diameter	
500	250000	125000000	22.3607	7.9370	2.69897	2.00000	1570.8	196350
501	251001	125751501	22.3830	7.9423	2.69984	1.99601	1573.9	197136
502	252004	126506008	22.4054	7.9476	2.70070	1.99203	1577.1	197923
503	253009	127263527	22.4277	7.9528	2.70157	1.98807	1580.2	198713
504	254016	128024064	22.4499	7.9581	2.70243	1.98413	1583.4	199504
505	255025	128787625	22.4722	7.9634	2.70329	1.98020	1586.5	200296
506	256036	129554216	22.4944	7.9686	2.70415	1.97628	1589.6	201090
507	257049	130323843	22.5167	7.9739	2.70501	1.97239	1592.8	201886
508	258064	131096512	22.5389	7.9791	2.70586	1.96850	1595.9	202683
509	259081	131872229	22.5610	7.9843	2.70672	1.96464	1599.1	203482
510	260100	132651000	22.5832	7.9896	2.70757	1.96078	1602.2	204282
511	261121	133432831	22.6053	7.9948	2.70842	1.95695	1605.4	205084
512	262144	134217728	22.6274	8.0000	2.70927	1.95312	1608.5	205887
513	263169	135005697	22.6495	8.0052	2.71012	1.94932	1611.6	206692
514	264196	135796744	22.6716	8.0104	2.71096	1.94553	1614.8	207499
515	265225	136590875	22.6936	8.0156	2.71181	1.94175	1617.9	208307
516	266256	137388096	22.7156	8.0208	2.71265	1.93798	1621.1	209117
517	267289	138188413	22.7376	8.0260	2.71349	1.93424	1624.2	209928
518	268324	138991832	22.7596	8.0311	2.71433	1.93050	1627.3	210741
519	269361	139798359	22.7816	8.0363	2.71517	1.92678	1630.5	211556
520	270400	140608000	22.8035	8.0415	2.71600	1.92308	1633.6	212372
521	271441	141420761	22.8254	8.0466	2.71684	1.91939	1636.8	213189
522	272484	142236648	22.8473	8.0517	2.71767	1.91571	1639.9	214008
523	273529	143055667	22.8692	8.0569	2.71850	1.91205	1643.1	214829
524	274576	143877824	22.8910	8.0620	2.71933	1.90840	1646.2	215651
525	275625	144703125	22.9129	8.0671	2.72016	1.90476	1649.3	216475
526	276676	145531576	22.9347	8.0723	2.72099	1.90114	1652.5	217301
527	277729	146363183	22.9565	8.0774	2.72181	1.89753	1655.6	218128
528	278784	147197952	22.9783	8.0825	2.72263	1.89394	1658.8	218956
529	279841	148035889	23.0000	8.0876	2.72346	1.89036	1661.9	219787
530	280900	148877000	23.0217	8.0927	2.72428	1.88679	1665.0	220618
531	281961	149721291	23.0434	8.0978	2.72509	1.88324	1668.2	221452
532	283024	150568768	23.0651	8.1028	2.72591	1.87970	1671.3	222287
533	284089	151419437	23.0868	8.1079	2.72673	1.87617	1674.5	223123
534	285156	152273304	23.1084	8.1130	2.72754	1.87266	1677.6	223961
535	286225	153130375	23.1301	8.1180	2.72835	1.86916	1680.8	224801
536	287296	153990656	23.1517	8.1231	2.72916	1.86567	1683.9	225642
537	288369	154854153	23.1733	8.1281	2.72997	1.86220	1687.0	226484
538	289444	155720872	23.1948	8.1332	2.73078	1.85874	1690.2	227329
539	290521	156590819	23.2164	8.1382	2.73159	1.85529	1693.3	228175
540	291600	157464000	23.2379	8.1433	2.73239	1.85185	1696.5	229022
541	292681	158340421	23.2594	8.1483	2.73320	1.84843	1699.6	229871
542	293764	159220088	23.2809	8.1533	2.73400	1.84502	1702.7	230722
543	294849	160103007	23.3024	8.1583	2.73480	1.84162	1705.9	231574
544	295936	160989184	23.3238	8.1633	2.73560	1.83824	1709.0	232428
545	297025	161878625	23.3452	8.1683	2.73640	1.83486	1712.2	233283
546	298116	162771336	23.3666	8.1733	2.73719	1.83150	1715.3	234140
547	299209	163667323	23.3880	8.1783	2.73799	1.82815	1718.5	234998
548	300304	164566592	23.4094	8.1833	2.73878	1.82482	1721.6	235858
549	301401	165469149	23.4307	8.1882	2.73957	1.82149	1724.7	236720

FUNCTIONS OF NUMBERS

No.	Square	Cube	Square Root	Cube Root	Logarithm	1000 × Reciprocal	No. = Diameter	
							Circum.	Area
550	302500	166375000	23.4521	8.1932	2.74036	1.81818	1727.9	237583
551	303601	167284151	23.4734	8.1982	2.74115	1.81488	1731.0	238448
552	304704	168196608	23.4947	8.2031	2.74194	1.81159	1734.2	239314
553	305809	169112377	23.5160	8.2081	2.74273	1.80832	1737.3	240182
554	306916	170031464	23.5372	8.2130	2.74351	1.80505	1740.4	241051
555	308025	170953875	23.5584	8.2180	2.74429	1.80180	1743.6	241922
556	309136	171879616	23.5797	8.2229	2.74507	1.79856	1746.7	242795
557	310249	172808693	23.6008	8.2278	2.74586	1.79533	1749.9	243669
558	311364	173741112	23.6220	8.2327	2.74663	1.79211	1753.0	244545
559	312481	174676879	23.6432	8.2377	2.74741	1.78891	1756.2	245422
560	313600	175616000	23.6643	8.2426	2.74819	1.78571	1759.3	246301
561	314721	176558481	23.6854	8.2475	2.74896	1.78253	1762.4	247181
562	315844	177504328	23.7065	8.2524	2.74974	1.77936	1765.6	248063
563	316969	178453547	23.7276	8.2573	2.75051	1.77620	1768.7	248947
564	318096	179406144	23.7487	8.2621	2.75128	1.77305	1771.9	249832
565	319225	180362125	23.7697	8.2670	2.75205	1.76991	1775.0	250719
566	320356	181321496	23.7908	8.2719	2.75282	1.76678	1778.1	251607
567	321489	182284263	23.8118	8.2768	2.75358	1.76367	1781.3	252497
568	322624	183250432	23.8328	8.2816	2.75435	1.76056	1784.4	253388
569	323761	184220009	23.8537	8.2865	2.75511	1.75747	1787.6	254281
570	324900	185193000	23.8747	8.2913	2.75587	1.75439	1790.7	255176
571	326041	186169411	23.8956	8.2962	2.75664	1.75131	1793.8	256072
572	327184	187149248	23.9165	8.3010	2.75740	1.74825	1797.0	256970
573	328329	188132517	23.9374	8.3059	2.75815	1.74520	1800.1	257869
574	329476	189119224	23.9583	8.3107	2.75891	1.74216	1803.3	258770
575	330625	190109375	23.9792	8.3155	2.75967	1.73913	1806.4	259672
576	331776	191102976	24.0000	8.3203	2.76042	1.73611	1809.6	260576
577	332929	192100033	24.0208	8.3251	2.76118	1.73310	1812.7	261482
578	334084	193100552	24.0416	8.3300	2.76193	1.73010	1815.8	262389
579	335241	194104539	24.0624	8.3348	2.76268	1.72712	1819.0	263298
580	336400	195112000	24.0832	8.3396	2.76343	1.72414	1822.1	264208
581	337561	196122941	24.1039	8.3443	2.76418	1.72117	1825.3	265120
582	338724	197137368	24.1247	8.3491	2.76492	1.71821	1828.4	266033
583	339889	198155287	24.1454	8.3539	2.76567	1.71527	1831.6	266948
584	341056	199176704	24.1661	8.3587	2.76641	1.71233	1834.7	267865
585	342225	200201625	24.1868	8.3634	2.76716	1.70940	1837.8	268783
586	343396	201230056	24.2074	8.3682	2.76790	1.70648	1841.0	269703
587	344569	202262003	24.2281	8.3730	2.76864	1.70358	1844.1	270624
588	345744	203297472	24.2487	8.3777	2.76938	1.70068	1847.3	271547
589	346921	204336469	24.2693	8.3825	2.77012	1.69779	1850.4	272471
590	348100	205379000	24.2899	8.3872	2.77085	1.69492	1853.5	273397
591	349281	206425071	24.3105	8.3919	2.77159	1.69205	1856.7	274325
592	350464	207474688	24.3311	8.3967	2.77232	1.68919	1859.8	275254
593	351649	208527857	24.3516	8.4014	2.77305	1.68634	1863.0	276184
594	352836	209584584	24.3721	8.4061	2.77379	1.68350	1866.1	277117
595	354025	210644875	24.3926	8.4108	2.77452	1.68067	1869.2	278051
596	355216	211708736	24.4131	8.4155	2.77525	1.67785	1872.4	278986
597	356409	212776173	24.4336	8.4202	2.77597	1.67504	1875.5	279923
598	357604	213847192	24.4540	8.4249	2.77670	1.67224	1878.7	280862
599	358801	214921799	24.4745	8.4296	2.77743	1.66945	1881.8	281802

600
649
FUNCTIONS OF NUMBERS

No.	Square	Cube	Square Root	Cube Root	Logarithm	1000 × Reciprocal	No. = Diameter Circum.	No. = Diameter Area
600	360000	216000000	24.4949	8.4343	2.77815	1.66667	1885.0	282743
601	361201	217081801	24.5153	8.4390	2.77887	1.66389	1888.1	283687
602	362404	218167208	24.5357	8.4437	2.77960	1.66113	1891.2	284631
603	363609	219256227	24.5561	8.4484	2.78032	1.65837	1894.4	285578
604	364816	220348864	24.5764	8.4530	2.78104	1.65563	1897.5	286526
605	366025	221445125	24.5967	8.4577	2.78176	1.65289	1900.7	287475
606	367236	222545016	24.6171	8.4623	2.78247	1.65017	1903.8	288426
607	368449	223648543	24.6374	8.4670	2.78319	1.64745	1906.9	289379
608	369664	224755712	24.6577	8.4716	2.78390	1.64474	1910.1	290333
609	370881	225866529	24.6779	8.4763	2.78462	1.64204	1913.2	291289
610	372100	226981000	24.6982	8.4809	2.78533	1.63934	1916.4	292247
611	373321	228099131	24.7184	8.4856	2.78604	1.63666	1919.5	293206
612	374544	229220928	24.7386	8.4902	2.78675	1.63399	1922.7	294166
613	375769	230346397	24.7588	8.4948	2.78746	1.63132	1925.8	295128
614	376996	231475544	24.7790	8.4994	2.78817	1.62866	1928.9	296092
615	378225	232608375	24.7992	8.5040	2.78888	1.62602	1932.1	297057
616	379456	233744896	24.8193	8.5086	2.78958	1.62338	1935.2	298024
617	380689	234885113	24.8395	8.5132	2.79029	1.62075	1938.4	298992
618	381924	236029032	24.8596	8.5178	2.79099	1.61812	1941.5	299962
619	383161	237176659	24.8797	8.5224	2.79169	1.61551	1944.6	300934
620	384400	238328000	24.8998	8.5270	2.79239	1.61290	1947.8	301907
621	385641	239483061	24.9199	8.5316	2.79309	1.61031	1950.9	302882
622	386884	240641848	24.9399	8.5362	2.79379	1.60772	1954.1	303858
623	388129	241804367	24.9600	8.5408	2.79449	1.60514	1957.2	304836
624	389376	242970624	24.9800	8.5453	2.79518	1.60256	1960.4	305815
625	390625	244140625	25.0000	8.5499	2.79588	1.60000	1963.5	306796
626	391876	245314376	25.0200	8.5544	2.79657	1.59744	1966.6	307779
627	393129	246491883	25.0400	8.5590	2.79727	1.59490	1969.8	308763
628	394384	247673152	25.0599	8.5635	2.79796	1.59236	1972.9	309748
629	395641	248858189	25.0799	8.5681	2.79865	1.58983	1976.1	310736
630	396900	250047000	25.0998	8.5726	2.79934	1.58730	1979.2	311725
631	398161	251239591	25.1197	8.5772	2.80003	1.58479	1982.3	312715
632	399424	252435968	25.1396	8.5817	2.80072	1.58228	1985.5	313707
633	400689	253636137	25.1595	8.5862	2.80140	1.57978	1988.6	314700
634	401956	254840104	25.1794	8.5907	2.80209	1.57729	1991.8	315696
635	403225	256047875	25.1992	8.5952	2.80277	1.57480	1994.9	316692
636	404496	257259456	25.2190	8.5997	2.80346	1.57233	1998.1	317690
637	405769	258474853	25.2389	8.6043	2.80414	1.56986	2001.2	318690
638	407044	259694072	25.2587	8.6088	2.80482	1.56740	2004.3	319692
639	408321	260917119	25.2784	8.6132	2.80550	1.56495	2007.5	320695
640	409600	262144000	25.2982	8.6177	2.80618	1.56250	2010.6	321699
641	410881	263374721	25.3180	8.6222	2.80686	1.56006	2013.8	322705
642	412164	264609288	25.3377	8.6267	2.80754	1.55763	2016.9	323713
643	413449	265847707	25.3574	8.6312	2.80821	1.55521	2020.0	324722
644	414736	267089984	25.3772	8.6357	2.80889	1.55280	2023.2	325733
645	416025	268336125	25.3969	8.6401	2.80956	1.55039	2026.3	326745
646	417316	269586136	25.4165	8.6446	2.81023	1.54799	2029.5	327759
647	418609	270840023	25.4362	8.6490	2.81090	1.54560	2032.6	328775
648	419904	272097792	25.4558	8.6535	2.81158	1.54321	2035.8	329792
649	421201	273359449	25.4755	8.6579	2.81224	1.54083	2038.9	330810

FUNCTIONS OF NUMBERS

No.	Square	Cube	Square Root	Cube Root	Logarithm	1000 × Reciprocal	No. = Diameter	
							Circum.	Area
650	422500	274625000	25.4951	8.6624	2.81291	1.53846	2042.0	331831
651	423801	275894451	25.5147	8.6668	2.81358	1.53610	2045.2	332853
652	425104	277167808	25.5343	8.6713	2.81425	1.53374	2048.3	333876
653	426409	278445077	25.5539	8.6757	2.81491	1.53139	2051.5	334901
654	427716	279726264	25.5734	8.6801	2.81558	1.52905	2054.6	335927
655	429025	281011375	25.5930	8.6845	2.81624	1.52672	2057.7	336955
656	430336	282300416	25.6125	8.6890	2.81690	1.52439	2060.9	337985
657	431649	283593393	25.6320	8.6934	2.81757	1.52207	2064.0	339016
658	432964	284890312	25.6515	8.6978	2.81823	1.51976	2067.2	340049
659	434281	286191179	25.6710	8.7022	2.81889	1.51745	2070.3	341084
660	435600	287496000	25.6905	8.7066	2.81954	1.51515	2073.5	342119
661	436921	288804781	25.7099	8.7110	2.82020	1.51286	2076.6	343157
662	438244	290117528	25.7294	8.7154	2.82086	1.51057	2079.7	344196
663	439569	291434247	25.7488	8.7198	2.82151	1.50830	2082.9	345237
664	440896	292754944	25.7682	8.7241	2.82217	1.50602	2086.0	346279
665	442225	294079625	25.7876	8.7285	2.82282	1.50376	2089.2	347323
666	443556	295408296	25.8070	8.7329	2.82347	1.50150	2092.3	348368
667	444889	296740963	25.8263	8.7373	2.82413	1.49925	2095.4	349415
668	446224	298077632	25.8457	8.7416	2.82478	1.49701	2098.6	350464
669	447561	299418309	25.8650	8.7460	2.82543	1.49477	2101.7	351514
670	448900	300763000	25.8844	8.7503	2.82607	1.49254	2104.9	352565
671	450241	302111711	25.9037	8.7547	2.82672	1.49031	2108.0	353618
672	451584	303464448	25.9230	8.7590	2.82737	1.48810	2111.2	354673
673	452929	304821217	25.9422	8.7634	2.82802	1.48588	2114.3	355730
674	454276	306182024	25.9615	8.7677	2.82866	1.48368	2117.4	356788
675	455625	307546875	25.9808	8.7721	2.82930	1.48148	2120.6	357847
676	456976	308915776	26.0000	8.7764	2.82995	1.47929	2123.7	358908
677	458329	310288733	26.0192	8.7807	2.83059	1.47710	2126.9	359971
678	459684	311665752	26.0384	8.7850	2.83123	1.47493	2130.0	361035
679	461041	313046839	26.0576	8.7893	2.83187	1.47275	2133.1	362101
680	462400	314432000	26.0768	8.7937	2.83251	1.47059	2136.3	363168
681	463761	315821241	26.0960	8.7980	2.83315	1.46843	2139.4	364237
682	465124	317214568	26.1151	8.8023	2.83378	1.46628	2142.6	365308
683	466489	318611987	26.1343	8.8066	2.83442	1.46413	2145.7	366380
684	467856	320013504	26.1534	8.8109	2.83506	1.46199	2148.8	367453
685	469225	321419125	26.1725	8.8152	2.83569	1.45985	2152.0	368528
686	470596	322828856	26.1916	8.8194	2.83632	1.45773	2155.1	369605
687	471969	324242703	26.2107	8.8237	2.83696	1.45560	2158.3	370684
688	473344	325660672	26.2298	8.8280	2.83759	1.45349	2161.4	371764
689	474721	327082769	26.2488	8.8323	2.83822	1.45138	2164.6	372845
690	476100	328509000	26.2679	8.8366	2.83885	1.44928	2167.7	373928
691	477481	329939371	26.2869	8.8408	2.83948	1.44718	2170.8	375013
692	478864	331373888	26.3059	8.8451	2.84011	1.44509	2174.0	376099
693	480249	332812557	26.3249	8.8493	2.84073	1.44300	2177.1	377187
694	481636	334255384	26.3439	8.8536	2.84136	1.44092	2180.3	378276
695	483025	335702375	26.3629	8.8578	2.84198	1.43885	2183.4	379367
696	484416	337153536	26.3818	8.8621	2.84261	1.43678	2186.5	380459
697	485809	338608873	26.4008	8.8663	2.84323	1.43472	2189.7	381553
698	487204	340068392	26.4197	8.8706	2.84386	1.43266	2192.8	382649
699	488601	341532099	26.4386	8.8748	2.84448	1.43062	2196.0	383746

700
749

FUNCTIONS OF NUMBERS

No.	Square	Cube	Square Root	Cube Root	Logarithm	1000 × Reciprocal	Circum.	Area
700	490000	343000000	26.4575	8.8790	2.84510	1.42857	2199.1	384845
701	491401	344472101	26.4764	8.8833	2.84572	1.42653	2202.3	385945
702	492804	345948408	26.4953	8.8875	2.84634	1.42450	2205.4	387047
703	494209	347428927	26.5141	8.8917	2.84696	1.42248	2208.5	388151
704	495616	348913664	26.5330	8.8959	2.84757	1.42045	2211.7	389256
705	497025	350402625	26.5518	8.9001	2.84819	1.41844	2214.8	390363
706	498436	351895816	26.5707	8.9043	2.84880	1.41643	2218.0	391471
707	499849	353393243	26.5895	8.9085	2.84942	1.41443	2221.1	392580
708	501264	354894912	26.6083	8.9127	2.85003	1.41243	2224.2	393692
709	502681	356400829	26.6271	8.9169	2.85065	1.41044	2227.4	394805
710	504100	357911000	26.6458	8.9211	2.85126	1.40845	2230.5	395919
711	505521	359425431	26.6646	8.9253	2.85187	1.40647	2233.7	397035
712	506944	360944128	26.6833	8.9295	2.85248	1.40449	2236.8	398153
713	508369	362467097	26.7021	8.9337	2.85309	1.40252	2240.0	399272
714	509796	363994344	26.7208	8.9378	2.85370	1.40056	2243.1	400393
715	511225	365525875	26.7395	8.9420	2.85431	1.39860	2246.2	401515
716	512656	367061696	26.7582	8.9462	2.85491	1.39665	2249.4	402639
717	514089	368601813	26.7769	8.9503	2.85552	1.39470	2252.5	403765
718	515524	370146232	26.7955	8.9545	2.85612	1.39276	2255.7	404892
719	516961	371694959	26.8142	8.9587	2.85673	1.39082	2258.8	406020
720	518400	373248000	26.8328	8.9628	2.85733	1.38889	2261.9	407150
721	519841	374805361	26.8514	8.9670	2.85794	1.38696	2265.1	408282
722	521284	376367048	26.8701	8.9711	2.85854	1.38504	2268.2	409415
723	522729	377933067	26.8887	8.9752	2.85914	1.38313	2271.4	410550
724	524176	379503424	26.9072	8.9794	2.85974	1.38122	2274.5	411687
725	525625	381078125	26.9258	8.9835	2.86034	1.37931	2277.7	412825
726	527076	382657176	26.9444	8.9876	2.86094	1.37741	2280.8	413965
727	528529	384240583	26.9629	8.9918	2.86153	1.37552	2283.9	415106
728	529984	385828352	26.9815	8.9959	2.86213	1.37363	2287.1	416248
729	531441	387420489	27.0000	9.0000	2.86273	1.37174	2290.2	417393
730	532900	389017000	27.0185	9.0041	2.86332	1.36986	2293.4	418539
731	534361	390617891	27.0370	9.0082	2.86392	1.36799	2296.5	419686
732	535824	392223168	27.0555	9.0123	2.86451	1.36612	2299.6	420835
733	537289	393832837	27.0740	9.0164	2.86510	1.36426	2302.8	421986
734	538756	395446904	27.0924	9.0205	2.86570	1.36240	2305.9	423138
735	540225	397065375	27.1109	9.0246	2.86629	1.36054	2309.1	424293
736	541696	398688256	27.1293	9.0287	2.86688	1.35870	2312.2	425447
737	543169	400315553	27.1477	9.0328	2.86747	1.35685	2315.4	426604
738	544644	401947272	27.1662	9.0369	2.86806	1.35501	2318.5	427762
739	546121	403583419	27.1846	9.0410	2.86864	1.35318	2321.6	428922
740	547600	405224000	27.2029	9.0450	2.86923	1.35135	2324.8	430084
741	549081	406869021	27.2213	9.0491	2.86982	1.34953	2327.9	431247
742	550564	408518488	27.2397	9.0532	2.87040	1.34771	2331.1	432412
743	552049	410172407	27.2580	9.0572	2.87099	1.34590	2334.2	433578
744	553536	411830784	27.2764	9.0613	2.87157	1.34409	2337.3	434746
745	555025	413493625	27.2947	9.0654	2.87216	1.34228	2340.5	435916
746	556516	415160936	27.3130	9.0694	2.87274	1.34048	2343.6	437087
747	558009	416832723	27.3313	9.0735	2.87332	1.33869	2346.8	438259
748	559504	418508992	27.3496	9.0775	2.87390	1.33690	2349.9	439433
749	561001	420189749	27.3679	9.0816	2.87448	1.33511	2353.1	440609

AMERICAN INSTITUTE OF STEEL CONSTRUCTION

FUNCTIONS OF NUMBERS

No.	Square	Cube	Square Root	Cube Root	Logarithm	1000 × Reciprocal	No. = Diameter Circum.	No. = Diameter Area
750	562500	421875000	27.3861	9.0856	2.87506	1.33333	2356.2	441786
751	564001	423564751	27.4044	9.0896	2.87564	1.33156	2359.3	442965
752	565504	425259008	27.4226	9.0937	2.87622	1.32979	2362.5	444146
753	567009	426957777	27.4408	9.0977	2.87680	1.32802	2365.6	445328
754	568516	428661064	27.4591	9.1017	2.87737	1.32626	2368.8	446511
755	570025	430368875	27.4773	9.1057	2.87795	1.32450	2371.9	447697
756	571536	432081216	27.4955	9.1098	2.87852	1.32275	2375.0	448883
757	573049	433798093	27.5136	9.1138	2.87910	1.32100	2378.2	450072
758	574564	435519512	27.5318	9.1178	2.87967	1.31926	2381.3	451262
759	576081	437245479	27.5500	9.1218	2.88024	1.31752	2384.5	452453
760	577600	438976000	27.5681	9.1258	2.88081	1.31579	2387.6	453646
761	579121	440711081	27.5862	9.1298	2.88138	1.31406	2390.8	454841
762	580644	442450728	27.6043	9.1338	2.88196	1.31234	2393.9	456037
763	582169	444194947	27.6225	9.1378	2.88252	1.31062	2397.0	457234
764	583696	445943744	27.6405	9.1418	2.88309	1.30890	2400.2	458434
765	585225	447697125	27.6586	9.1458	2.88366	1.30719	2403.3	459635
766	586756	449455096	27.6767	9.1498	2.88423	1.30548	2406.5	460837
767	588289	451217663	27.6948	9.1537	2.88480	1.30378	2409.6	462041
768	589824	452984832	27.7128	9.1577	2.88536	1.30208	2412.7	463247
769	591361	454756609	27.7308	9.1617	2.88593	1.30039	2415.9	464454
770	592900	456533000	27.7489	9.1657	2.88649	1.29870	2419.0	465663
771	594441	458314011	27.7669	9.1696	2.88705	1.29702	2422.2	466873
772	595984	460099648	27.7849	9.1736	2.88762	1.29534	2425.3	468085
773	597529	461889917	27.8029	9.1775	2.88818	1.29366	2428.5	469298
774	599076	463684824	27.8209	9.1815	2.88874	1.29199	2431.6	470513
775	600625	465484375	27.8388	9.1855	2.88930	1.29032	2434.7	471730
776	602176	467288576	27.8568	9.1894	2.88986	1.28866	2437.9	472948
777	603729	469097433	27.8747	9.1933	2.89042	1.28700	2441.0	474168
778	605284	470910952	27.8927	9.1973	2.89098	1.28535	2444.2	475389
779	606841	472729139	27.9106	9.2012	2.89154	1.28370	2447.3	476612
780	608400	474552000	27.9285	9.2052	2.89209	1.28205	2450.4	477836
781	609961	476379541	27.9464	9.2091	2.89265	1.28041	2453.6	479062
782	611524	478211768	27.9643	9.2130	2.89321	1.27877	2456.7	480290
783	613089	480048687	27.9821	9.2170	2.89376	1.27714	2459.9	481519
784	614656	481890304	28.0000	9.2209	2.89432	1.27551	2463.0	482750
785	616225	483736625	28.0179	9.2248	2.89487	1.27389	2466.2	483982
786	617796	485587656	28.0357	9.2287	2.89542	1.27226	2469.3	485216
787	619369	487443403	28.0535	9.2326	2.89597	1.27065	2472.4	486451
788	620944	489303872	28.0713	9.2365	2.89653	1.26904	2475.6	487688
789	622521	491169069	28.0891	9.2404	2.89708	1.26743	2478.7	488927
790	624100	493039000	28.1069	9.2443	2.89763	1.26582	2481.9	490167
791	625681	494913671	28.1247	9.2482	2.89818	1.26422	2485.0	491409
792	627264	496793088	28.1425	9.2521	2.89873	1.26263	2488.1	492652
793	628849	498677257	28.1603	9.2560	2.89927	1.26103	2491.3	493897
794	630436	500566184	28.1780	9.2599	2.89982	1.25945	2494.4	495143
795	632025	502459875	28.1957	9.2638	2.90037	1.25786	2497.6	496391
796	633616	504358336	28.2135	9.2677	2.90091	1.25628	2500.7	497641
797	635209	506261573	28.2312	9.2716	2.90146	1.25471	2503.8	498892
798	636804	508169592	28.2489	9.2754	2.90200	1.25313	2507.0	500145
799	638401	510082399	28.2666	9.2793	2.90255	1.25156	2510.1	501399

FUNCTIONS OF NUMBERS

800
849

No.	Square	Cube	Square Root	Cube Root	Logarithm	1000 × Reciprocal	No. = Diameter Circum.	No. = Diameter Area
800	640000	512000000	28.2843	9.2832	2.90309	1.25000	2513.3	502655
801	641601	513922401	28.3019	9.2870	2.90363	1.24844	2516.4	503912
802	643204	515849608	28.3196	9.2909	2.90417	1.24688	2519.6	505171
803	644809	517781627	28.3373	9.2948	2.90472	1.24533	2522.7	506432
804	646416	519718464	28.3549	9.2986	2.90526	1.24378	2525.8	507694
805	648025	521660125	28.3725	9.3025	2.90580	1.24224	2529.0	508958
806	649636	523606616	28.3901	9.3063	2.90634	1.24069	2532.1	510223
807	651249	525557943	28.4077	9.3102	2.90687	1.23916	2535.3	511490
808	652864	527514112	28.4253	9.3140	2.90741	1.23762	2538.4	512758
809	654481	529475129	28.4429	9.3179	2.90795	1.23609	2541.5	514028
810	656100	531441000	28.4605	9.3217	2.90849	1.23457	2544.7	515300
811	657721	533411731	28.4781	9.3255	2.90902	1.23305	2547.8	516573
812	659344	535387328	28.4956	9.3294	2.90956	1.23153	2551.0	517848
813	660969	537367797	28.5132	9.3332	2.91009	1.23001	2554.1	519124
814	662596	539353144	28.5307	9.3370	2.91062	1.22850	2557.3	520402
815	664225	541343375	28.5482	9.3408	2.91116	1.22699	2560.4	521681
816	665856	543338496	28.5657	9.3447	2.91169	1.22549	2563.5	522962
817	667489	545338513	28.5832	9.3485	2.91222	1.22399	2566.7	524245
818	669124	547343432	28.6007	9.3523	2.91275	1.22249	2569.8	525529
819	670761	549353259	28.6182	9.3561	2.91328	1.22100	2573.0	526814
820	672400	551368000	28.6356	9.3599	2.91381	1.21951	2576.1	528102
821	674041	553387661	28.6531	9.3637	2.91434	1.21803	2579.2	529391
822	675684	555412248	28.6705	9.3675	2.91487	1.21655	2582.4	530681
823	677329	557441767	28.6880	9.3713	2.91540	1.21507	2585.5	531973
824	678976	559476224	28.7054	9.3751	2.91593	1.21359	2588.7	533267
825	680625	561515625	28.7228	9.3789	2.91645	1.21212	2591.8	534562
826	682276	563559976	28.7402	9.3827	2.91698	1.21065	2595.0	535858
827	683929	565609283	28.7576	9.3865	2.91751	1.20919	2598.1	537157
828	685584	567663552	28.7750	9.3902	2.91803	1.20773	2601.2	538456
829	687241	569722789	28.7924	9.3940	2.91855	1.20627	2604.4	539758
830	688900	571787000	28.8097	9.3978	2.91908	1.20482	2607.5	541061
831	690561	573856191	28.8271	9.4016	2.91960	1.20337	2610.7	542365
832	692224	575930368	28.8444	9.4053	2.92012	1.20192	2613.8	543671
833	693889	578009537	28.8617	9.4091	2.92065	1.20048	2616.9	544979
834	695556	580093704	28.8791	9.4129	2.92117	1.19904	2620.1	546288
835	697225	582182875	28.8964	9.4166	2.92169	1.19760	2623.2	547599
836	698896	584277056	28.9137	9.4204	2.92221	1.19617	2626.4	548912
837	700569	586376253	28.9310	9.4241	2.92273	1.19474	2629.5	550226
838	702244	588480472	28.9482	9.4279	2.92324	1.19332	2632.7	551541
839	703921	590589719	28.9655	9.4316	2.92376	1.19190	2635.8	552858
840	705600	592704000	28.9828	9.4354	2.92428	1.19048	2638.9	554177
841	707281	594823321	29.0000	9.4391	2.92480	1.18906	2642.1	555497
842	708964	596947688	29.0172	9.4429	2.92531	1.18765	2645.2	556819
843	710649	599077107	29.0345	9.4466	2.92583	1.18624	2648.4	558142
844	712336	601211584	29.0517	9.4503	2.92634	1.18483	2651.5	559467
845	714025	603351125	29.0689	9.4541	2.92686	1.18343	2654.6	560794
846	715716	605495736	29.0861	9.4578	2.92737	1.18203	2657.8	562122
847	717409	607645423	29.1033	9.4615	2.92788	1.18064	2660.9	563452
848	719104	609800192	29.1204	9.4652	2.92840	1.17925	2664.1	564783
849	720801	611960049	29.1376	9.4690	2.92891	1.17786	2667.2	566116

FUNCTIONS OF NUMBERS

No.	Square	Cube	Square Root	Cube Root	Logarithm	1000 × Reciprocal	No. = Diameter	
							Circum.	Area
850	722500	614125000	29.1548	9.4727	2.92942	1.17647	2670.4	567450
851	724201	616295051	29.1719	9.4764	2.92993	1.17509	2673.5	568786
852	725904	618470208	29.1890	9.4801	2.93044	1.17371	2676.6	570124
853	727609	620650477	29.2062	9.4838	2.93095	1.17233	2679.8	571463
854	729316	622835864	29.2233	9.4875	2.93146	1.17096	2682.9	572803
855	731025	625026375	29.2404	9.4912	2.93197	1.16959	2686.1	574146
856	732736	627222016	29.2575	9.4949	2.93247	1.16822	2689.2	575490
857	734449	629422793	29.2746	9.4986	2.93298	1.16686	2692.3	576835
858	736164	631628712	29.2916	9.5023	2.93349	1.16550	2695.5	578182
859	737881	633839779	29.3087	9.5060	2.93399	1.16414	2698.6	579530
860	739600	636056000	29.3258	9.5097	2.93450	1.16279	2701.8	580880
861	741321	638277381	29.3428	9.5134	2.93500	1.16144	2704.9	582232
862	743044	640503928	29.3598	9.5171	2.93551	1.16009	2708.1	583585
863	744769	642735647	29.3769	9.5207	2.93601	1.15875	2711.2	584940
864	746496	644972544	29.3939	9.5244	2.93651	1.15741	2714.3	586297
865	748225	647214625	29.4109	9.5281	2.93702	1.15607	2717.5	587655
866	749956	649461896	29.4279	9.5317	2.93752	1.15473	2720.6	589014
867	751689	651714363	29.4449	9.5354	2.93802	1.15340	2723.8	590375
868	753424	653972032	29.4618	9.5391	2.93852	1.15207	2726.9	591738
869	755161	656234909	29.4788	9.5427	2.93902	1.15075	2730.0	583102
870	756900	658503000	29.4958	9.5464	2.93952	1.14943	2733.2	594468
871	758641	660776311	29.5127	9.5501	2.94002	1.14811	2736.3	595835
872	760384	663054848	29.5296	9.5537	2.94052	1.14679	2739.5	597204
873	762129	665338617	29.5466	9.5574	2.94101	1.14548	2742.6	598575
874	763876	667627624	29.5635	9.5610	2.94151	1.14416	2745.8	599947
875	765625	669921875	29.5804	9.5647	2.94201	1.14286	2748.9	601320
876	767376	672221376	29.5973	9.5683	2.94250	1.14155	2752.0	602696
877	769129	674526133	29.6142	9.5719	2.94300	1.14025	2755.2	604073
878	770884	676836152	29.6311	9.5756	2.94349	1.13895	2758.3	605451
879	772641	679151439	29.6479	9.5792	2.94399	1.13766	2761.5	606831
880	774400	681472000	29.6648	9.5828	2.94448	1.13636	2764.6	608212
881	776161	683797841	29.6816	9.5865	2.94498	1.13507	2767.7	609595
882	777924	686128968	29.6985	9.5901	2.94547	1.13379	2770.9	610980
883	779689	688465387	29.7153	9.5937	2.94596	1.13250	2774.0	612366
884	781456	690807104	29.7321	9.5973	2.94645	1.13122	2777.2	613754
885	783225	693154125	29.7489	9.6010	2.94694	1.12994	2780.3	615143
886	784996	695506456	29.7658	9.6046	2.94743	1.12867	2783.5	616534
887	786769	697864103	29.7825	9.6082	2.94792	1.12740	2786.6	617927
888	788544	700227072	29.7993	9.6118	2.94841	1.12613	2789.7	619321
889	790321	702595369	29.8161	9.6154	2.94890	1.12486	2792.9	620717
890	792100	704969000	29.8329	9.6190	2.94939	1.12360	2796.0	622114
891	793881	707347971	29.8496	9.6226	2.94988	1.12233	2799.2	623513
892	795664	709732288	29.8664	9.6262	2.95036	1.12108	2802.3	624913
893	797449	712121957	29.8831	9.6298	2.95085	1.11982	2805.4	626315
894	799236	714516984	29.8998	9.6334	2.95134	1.11857	2808.6	627718
895	801025	716917375	29.9166	9.6370	2.95182	1.11732	2811.7	629124
896	802816	719323136	29.9333	9.6406	2.95231	1.11607	2814.9	630530
897	804609	721734273	29.9500	9.6442	2.95279	1.11483	2818.0	631938
898	806404	724150792	29.9666	9.6477	2.95328	1.11359	2821.2	633348
899	808201	726572699	29.9833	9.6513	2.95376	1.11235	2824.3	634760

FUNCTIONS OF NUMBERS

900
949

No.	Square	Cube	Square Root	Cube Root	Logarithm	1000 × Reciprocal	No. = Diameter Circum.	No. = Diameter Area
900	810000	729000000	30.0000	9.6549	2.95424	1.11111	2827.4	636173
901	811801	731432701	30.0167	9.6585	2.95472	1.10988	2830.6	637587
902	813604	733870808	30.0333	9.6620	2.95521	1.10865	2833.7	639003
903	815409	736314327	30.0500	9.6656	2.95569	1.10742	2836.9	640421
904	817216	738763264	30.0666	9.6692	2.95617	1.10619	2840.0	641840
905	819025	741217625	30.0832	9.6727	2.95665	1.10497	2843.1	643261
906	820836	743677416	30.0998	9.6763	2.95713	1.10375	2846.3	644683
907	822649	746142643	30.1164	9.6799	2.95761	1.10254	2849.4	646107
908	824464	748613312	30.1330	9.6834	2.95809	1.10132	2852.6	647533
909	826281	751089429	30.1496	9.6870	2.95856	1.10011	2855.7	648960
910	828100	753571000	30.1662	9.6905	2.95904	1.09890	2858.8	650388
911	829921	756058031	30.1828	9.6941	2.95952	1.09769	2862.0	651818
912	831744	758550528	30.1993	9.6976	2.95999	1.09649	2865.1	653250
913	833569	761048497	30.2159	9.7012	2.96047	1.09529	2868.3	654684
914	835396	763551944	30.2324	9.7047	2.96095	1.09409	2871.4	656118
915	837225	766060875	30.2490	9.7082	2.96142	1.09290	2874.6	657555
916	839056	768575296	30.2655	9.7118	2.96190	1.09170	2877.7	658993
917	840889	771095213	30.2820	9.7153	2.96237	1.09051	2880.8	660433
918	842724	773620632	30.2985	9.7188	2.96284	1.08932	2884.0	661874
919	844561	776151559	30.3150	9.7224	2.96332	1.08814	2887.1	663317
920	846400	778688000	30.3315	9.7259	2.96379	1.08696	2890.3	664761
921	848241	781229961	30.3480	9.7294	2.96426	1.08578	2893.4	666207
922	850084	783777448	30.3645	9.7329	2.96473	1.08460	2896.5	667654
923	851929	786330467	30.3809	9.7364	2.96520	1.08342	2899.7	669103
924	853776	788889024	30.3974	9.7400	2.96567	1.08225	2902.8	670554
925	855625	791453125	30.4138	9.7435	2.96614	1.08108	2906.0	672006
926	857476	794022776	30.4302	9.7470	2.96661	1.07991	2909.1	673460
927	859329	796597983	30.4467	9.7505	2.96708	1.07875	2912.3	674915
928	861184	799178752	30.4631	9.7540	2.96755	1.07759	2915.4	676372
929	863041	801765089	30.4795	9.7575	2.96802	1.07643	2918.5	677831
930	864900	804357000	30.4959	9.7610	2.96848	1.07527	2921.7	679291
931	866761	806954491	30.5123	9.7645	2.96895	1.07411	2924.8	680752
932	868624	809557568	30.5287	9.7680	2.96942	1.07296	2928.0	682216
933	870489	812166237	30.5450	9.7715	2.96988	1.07181	2931.1	683680
934	872356	814780504	30.5614	9.7750	2.97035	1.07066	2934.2	685147
935	874225	817400375	30.5778	9.7785	2.97081	1.06952	2937.4	686615
936	876096	820025856	30.5941	9.7819	2.97128	1.06838	2940.5	688084
937	877969	822656953	30.6105	9.7854	2.97174	1.06724	2943.7	689555
938	879844	825293672	30.6268	9.7889	2.97220	1.06610	2946.8	691028
939	881721	827936019	30.6431	9.7924	2.97267	1.06496	2950.0	692502
940	883600	830584000	30.6594	9.7959	2.97313	1.06383	2953.1	693978
941	885481	833237621	30.6757	9.7993	2.97359	1.06270	2956.2	695455
942	887364	835896888	30.6920	9.8028	2.97405	1.06157	2959.4	696934
943	889249	838561807	30.7083	9.8063	2.97451	1.06045	2962.5	698415
944	891136	841232384	30.7246	9.8097	2.97497	1.05932	2965.7	699897
945	893025	843908625	30.7409	9.8132	2.97543	1.05820	2968.8	701380
946	894916	846590536	30.7571	9.8167	2.97589	1.05708	2971.9	702865
947	896809	849278123	30.7734	9.8201	2.97635	1.05597	2975.1	704352
948	898704	851971392	30.7896	9.8236	2.97681	1.05485	2978.2	705840
949	900601	854670349	30.8058	9.8270	2.97727	1.05374	2981.4	707330

FUNCTIONS OF NUMBERS

No.	Square	Cube	Square Root	Cube Root	Logarithm	1000 × Reciprocal	No. = Diameter Circum.	No. = Diameter Area
950	902500	857375000	30.8221	9.8305	2.97772	1.05263	2984.5	708822
951	904401	860085351	30.8383	9.8339	2.97818	1.05152	2987.7	710315
952	906304	862801408	30.8545	9.8374	2.97864	1.05042	2990.8	711809
953	908209	865523177	30.8707	9.8408	2.97909	1.04932	2993.9	713306
954	910116	868250664	30.8869	9.8443	2.97955	1.04822	2997.1	714803
955	912025	870983875	30.9031	9.8477	2.98000	1.04712	3000.2	716303
956	913936	873722816	30.9192	9.8511	2.98046	1.04603	3003.4	717804
957	915849	876467493	30.9354	9.8546	2.98091	1.04493	3006.5	719306
958	917764	879217912	30.9516	9.8580	2.98137	1.04384	3009.6	720810
959	919681	881974079	30.9677	9.8614	2.98182	1.04275	3012.8	722316
960	921600	884736000	30.9839	9.8648	2.98227	1.04167	3015.9	723823
961	923521	887503681	31.0000	9.8683	2.98272	1.04058	3019.1	725332
962	925444	890277128	31.0161	9.8717	2.98318	1.03950	3022.2	726842
963	927369	893056347	31.0322	9.8751	2.98363	1.03842	3025.4	728354
964	929296	895841344	31.0483	9.8785	2.98408	1.03734	3028.5	729867
965	931225	898632125	31.0644	9.8819	2.98453	1.03627	3031.6	731382
966	933156	901428696	31.0805	9.8854	2.98498	1.03520	3034.8	732899
967	935089	904231063	31.0966	9.8888	2.98543	1.03413	3037.9	734417
968	937024	907039232	31.1127	9.8922	2.98588	1.03306	3041.1	735937
969	938961	909853209	31.1288	9.8956	2.98632	1.03199	3044.2	737458
970	940900	912673000	31.1448	9.8990	2.98677	1.03093	3047.3	738981
971	942841	915498611	31.1609	9.9024	2.98722	1.02987	3050.5	740506
972	944784	918330048	31.1769	9.9058	2.98767	1.02881	3053.6	742032
973	946729	921167317	31.1929	9.9092	2.98811	1.02775	3056.8	743559
974	948676	924010424	31.2090	9.9126	2.98856	1.02669	3059.9	745088
975	950625	926859375	31.2250	9.9160	2.98900	1.02564	3063.1	746619
976	952576	929714176	31.2410	9.9194	2.98945	1.02459	3066.2	748151
977	954529	932574833	31.2570	9.9227	2.98989	1.02354	3069.3	749685
978	956484	935441352	31.2730	9.9261	2.99034	1.02249	3072.5	751221
979	958441	938313739	31.2890	9.9295	2.99078	1.02145	3075.6	752758
980	960400	941192000	31.3050	9.9329	2.99123	1.02041	3078.8	754296
981	962361	944076141	31.3209	9.9363	2.99167	1.01937	3081.9	755837
982	964324	946966168	31.3369	9.9396	2.99211	1.01833	3085.0	757378
983	966289	949862087	31.3528	9.9430	2.99255	1.01729	3088.2	758922
984	968256	952763904	31.3688	9.9464	2.99300	1.01626	3091.3	760466
985	970225	955671625	31.3847	9.9497	2.99344	1.01523	3094.5	762013
986	972196	958585256	31.4006	9.9531	2.99388	1.01420	3097.6	763561
987	974169	961504803	31.4166	9.9565	2.99432	1.01317	3100.8	765111
988	976144	964430272	31.4325	9.9598	2.99476	1.01215	3103.9	766662
989	978121	967361669	31.4484	9.9632	2.99520	1.01112	3107.0	768214
990	980100	970299000	31.4643	9.9666	2.99564	1.01010	3110.2	769769
991	982081	973242271	31.4802	9.9699	2.99607	1.00908	3113.3	771325
992	984064	976191488	31.4960	9.9733	2.99651	1.00806	3116.5	772882
993	986049	979146657	31.5119	9.9766	2.99695	1.00705	3119.6	774441
994	988036	982107784	31.5278	9.9800	2.99739	1.00604	3122.7	776002
995	990025	985074875	31.5436	9.9833	2.99782	1.00503	3125.9	777564
996	992016	988047936	31.5595	9.9866	2.99826	1.00402	3129.0	779128
997	994009	991026973	31.5753	9.9900	2.99870	1.00301	3132.2	780693
998	996004	994011992	31.5911	9.9933	2.99913	1.00200	3135.3	782260
999	998001	997002999	31.6070	9.9967	2.99957	1.00100	3138.5	783828

DECIMALS OF A FOOT
For each 32nd of an inch

Inch	0	1	2	3	4	5
0	0	.0833	.1667	.2500	.3333	.4167
1/32	.0026	.0859	.1693	.2526	.3359	.4193
1/16	.0052	.0885	.1719	.2552	.3385	.4219
3/32	.0078	.0911	.1745	.2578	.3411	.4245
1/8	.0104	.0938	.1771	.2604	.3438	.4271
5/32	.0130	.0964	.1797	.2630	.3464	.4297
3/16	.0156	.0990	.1823	.2656	.3490	.4323
7/32	.0182	.1016	.1849	.2682	.3516	.4349
1/4	.0208	.1042	.1875	.2708	.3542	.4375
9/32	.0234	.1068	.1901	.2734	.3568	.4401
5/16	.0260	.1094	.1927	.2760	.3594	.4427
11/32	.0286	.1120	.1953	.2786	.3620	.4453
3/8	.0313	.1146	.1979	.2812	.3646	.4479
13/32	.0339	.1172	.2005	.2839	.3672	.4505
7/16	.0365	.1198	.2031	.2865	.3698	.4531
15/32	.0391	.1224	.2057	.2891	.3724	.4557
1/2	.0417	.1250	.2083	.2917	.3750	.4583
17/32	.0443	.1276	.2109	.2943	.3776	.4609
9/16	.0469	.1302	.2135	.2969	.3802	.4635
19/32	.0495	.1328	.2161	.2995	.3828	.4661
5/8	.0521	.1354	.2188	.3021	.3854	.4688
21/32	.0547	.1380	.2214	.3047	.3880	.4714
11/16	.0573	.1406	.2240	.3073	.3906	.4740
23/32	.0599	.1432	.2266	.3099	.3932	.4766
3/4	.0625	.1458	.2292	.3125	.3958	.4792
25/32	.0651	.1484	.2318	.3151	.3984	.4818
13/16	.0677	.1510	.2344	.3177	.4010	.4844
27/32	.0703	.1536	.2370	.3203	.4036	.4870
7/8	.0729	.1563	.2396	.3229	.4063	.4896
29/32	.0755	.1589	.2422	.3255	.4089	.4922
15/16	.0781	.1615	.2448	.3281	.4115	.4948
31/32	.0807	.1641	.2474	.3307	.4141	.4974

AMERICAN INSTITUTE OF STEEL CONSTRUCTION

DECIMALS OF A FOOT
For each 32nd of an inch

Inch	6	7	8	9	10	11
0	.5000	.5833	.6667	.7500	.8333	.9167
1/32	.5026	.5859	.6693	.7526	.8359	.9193
1/16	.5052	.5885	.6719	.7552	.8385	.9219
3/32	.5078	.5911	.6745	.7578	.8411	.9245
1/8	.5104	.5938	.6771	.7604	.8438	.9271
5/32	.5130	.5964	.6797	.7630	.8464	.9297
3/16	.5156	.5990	.6823	.7656	.8490	.9323
7/32	.5182	.6016	.6849	.7682	.8516	.9349
1/4	.5208	.6042	.6875	.7708	.8542	.9375
9/32	.5234	.6068	.6901	.7734	.8568	.9401
5/16	.5260	.6094	.6927	.7760	.8594	.9427
11/32	.5286	.6120	.6953	.7786	.8620	.9453
3/8	.5313	.6146	.6979	.7813	.8646	.9479
13/32	.5339	.6172	.7005	.7839	.8672	.9505
7/16	.5365	.6198	.7031	.7865	.8698	.9531
15/32	.5391	.6224	.7057	.7891	.8724	.9557
1/2	.5417	.6250	.7083	.7917	.8750	.9583
17/32	.5443	.6276	.7109	.7943	.8776	.9609
9/16	.5469	.6302	.7135	.7969	.8802	.9635
19/32	.5495	.6328	.7161	.7995	.8828	.9661
5/8	.5521	.6354	.7188	.8021	.8854	.9688
21/32	.5547	.6380	.7214	.8047	.8880	.9714
11/16	.5573	.6406	.7240	.8073	.8906	.9740
23/32	.5599	.6432	.7266	.8099	.8932	.9766
3/4	.5625	.6458	.7292	.8125	.8958	.9792
25/32	.5651	.6484	.7318	.8151	.8984	.9818
13/16	.5677	.6510	.7344	.8177	.9010	.9844
27/32	.5703	.6536	.7370	.8203	.9036	.9870
7/8	.5729	.6563	.7396	.8229	.9063	.9896
29/32	.5755	.6589	.7422	.8255	.9089	.9922
15/16	.5781	.6615	.7448	.8281	.9115	.9948
31/32	.5807	.6641	.7474	.8307	.9141	.9974

DECIMALS OF AN INCH
For each 64th of an inch
With Millimeter Equivalents

Fraction	1/64ths	Decimal	Millimeters (Approx.)	Fraction	1/64ths	Decimal	Millimeters (Approx.)
...	1	.015625	0.397	...	33	.515625	13.097
1/32	2	.03125	0.794	17/32	34	.53125	13.494
...	3	.046875	1.191	...	35	.546875	13.891
1/16	4	.0625	1.588	9/16	36	.5625	14.288
...	5	.078125	1.984	...	37	.578125	14.684
3/32	6	.09375	2.381	19/32	38	.59375	15.081
...	7	.109375	2.778	...	39	.609375	15.478
1/8	8	.125	3.175	5/8	40	.625	15.875
...	9	.140625	3.572	...	41	.640625	16.272
5/32	10	.15625	3.969	21/32	42	.65625	16.669
...	11	.171875	4.366	...	43	.671875	17.066
3/16	12	.1875	4.763	11/16	44	.6875	17.463
...	13	.203125	5.159	...	45	.703125	17.859
7/32	14	.21875	5.556	23/32	46	.71875	18.256
...	15	.234375	5.953	...	47	.734375	18.653
1/4	16	.250	6.350	3/4	48	.750	19.050
...	17	.265625	6.747	...	49	.765625	19.447
9/32	18	.28125	7.144	25/32	50	.78125	19.844
...	19	.296875	7.541	...	51	.796875	20.241
5/16	20	.3125	7.938	13/16	52	.8125	20.638
...	21	.328125	8.334	...	53	.828125	21.034
11/32	22	.34375	8.731	27/32	54	.84375	21.431
...	23	.359375	9.128	...	55	.859375	21.828
3/8	24	.375	9.525	7/8	56	.875	22.225
...	25	.390625	9.922	...	57	.890625	22.622
13/32	26	.40625	10.319	29/32	58	.90625	23.019
...	27	.421875	10.716	...	59	.921875	23.416
7/16	28	.4375	11.113	15/16	60	.9375	23.813
...	29	.453125	11.509	...	61	.953125	24.209
15/32	30	.46875	11.906	31/32	62	.96875	24.606
...	31	.484375	12.303	...	63	.984375	25.003
1/2	32	.500	12.700	1	64	1.000	25.400

AMERICAN INSTITUTE OF STEEL CONSTRUCTION

Notes

PART 7
Index

AMERICAN INSTITUTE OF STEEL CONSTRUCTION

INDEX

AMERICAN INSTITUTE OF STEEL CONSTRUCTION

AMERICAN INSTITUTE OF STEEL CONSTRUCTION

AMERICAN INSTITUTE OF STEEL CONSTRUCTION

AMERICAN INSTITUTE OF STEEL CONSTRUCTION

AMERICAN INSTITUTE OF STEEL CONSTRUCTION

Notes

Notes

Notes

Notes

Notes

Notes

Notes

Notes

Notes